Speech and Language Processing

*An Introduction to Natural Language
Processing, Computational Linguistics,
and Speech Recognition*

Second Edition

D1296639

Daniel Jurafsky
James H. Martin

PEARSON

Authorized adaptation from the United States edition, entitled *Speech and Language Processing: An Introduction to Natural Language Processing, Computational Linguistics, and Speech Recognition, Second Edition,* ISBN 9780131873216, by Daniel Jurafsky and James H. Martin, published by Pearson Education Inc.© 2009, Pearson Education Inc.

Indian Subcontinent Version
© 2014 Dorling Kindersley (India) Pvt. Ltd

ISBN 978-93-325-1841-4

First Impression, 2014
Fourth Impression, 2015
Fifth Impression, 2016

Published by Pearson India Education Services Pvt.Ltd,CIN:U72200TN2005PTC057128.
Formerly known as TutorVista Global Pvt Ltd, licensees of Pearson Education in South Asia

Head Office: 7th Floor, knowledge Boulevard, A-8(A) Sector-62, Noida (U.P) 201309, India

Registered Office: Module G4, Ground Floor, Elnet Software City, TS -140,Block 2 & 9
Rajiv Gandhi Salai, Taramani, Chennai, Tamil Nadu 600113.,Fax: 080-30461003,
Phone: 080-30461060, www.pearson.co.in email id: companysecretary.india@pearson.com

Printed in India by HT Media Ltd., Noida

Table of Contents

Chapter 1

Introduction

> *Dave Bowman: Open the pod bay doors, HAL.*
> *HAL: I'm sorry Dave, I'm afraid I can't do that.*
> Stanley Kubrick and Arthur C. Clarke,
> screenplay of *2001: A Space Odyssey*

The idea of giving computers the ability to process human language is as old as the idea of computers themselves. This book is about the implementation and implications of that exciting idea. We introduce a vibrant interdisciplinary field with many names corresponding to its many facets, names like **speech and language processing**, **human language technology**, **natural language processing**, **computational linguistics**, and **speech recognition and synthesis**. The goal of this new field is to get computers to perform useful tasks involving human language, tasks like enabling human-machine communication, improving human-human communication, or simply doing useful processing of text or speech.

Conversational agent

One example of a useful such task is a **conversational agent**. The HAL 9000 computer in Stanley Kubrick's film *2001: A Space Odyssey* is one of the most recognizable characters in 20th century cinema. HAL is an artificial agent capable of such advanced language behavior as speaking and understanding English, and at a crucial moment in the plot, even reading lips. It is now clear that HAL's creator, Arthur C. Clarke, was a little optimistic in predicting when an artificial agent such as HAL would be available. But just how far off was he? What would it take to create at least the language-related parts of HAL? We call programs like HAL that converse with humans in natural

Dialogue system

language **conversational agents** or **dialogue systems**. In this text we study the various components that make up modern conversational agents, including language input (**automatic speech recognition** and **natural language understanding**) and language output (dialogue and response planning and **speech synthesis**).

Let's turn to another useful language-related task, that of making available to non-English-speaking readers the vast amount of scientific information on the Web in English. Or translating for English speakers the hundreds of millions of Web pages written

Machine translation

in other languages like Chinese. The goal of **machine translation** is to automatically translate a document from one language to another. We introduce the algorithms and mathematical tools needed to understand how modern machine translation works. Machine translation is far from a solved problem; we cover the algorithms currently used in the field, as well as important component tasks.

Question answering

Many other language processing tasks are also related to the Web. Another such task is **Web-based question answering**. This is a generalization of simple Web search, where instead of just typing keywords, a user might ask complete questions, ranging from easy to hard, like the following:

- What does "divergent" mean?
- What year was Abraham Lincoln born?
- How many states were in the United States that year?

From Chapter 1 of *Speech and Language Processing*, Second Edition. Daniel Jurafsky, James H. Martin.

- How much Chinese silk was exported to England by the end of the 18th century?
- What do scientists think about the ethics of human cloning?

Some of these, such as **definition** questions, or simple **factoid** questions like dates and locations, can already be answered by search engines. But answering more complicated questions might require extracting information that is embedded in other text on a Web page, doing **inference** (drawing conclusions based on known facts), or synthesizing and summarizing information from multiple sources or Web pages. In this text we study the various components that make up modern understanding systems of this kind, including **information extraction**, **word sense disambiguation**, and so on.

Although the subfields and problems we've described above are all very far from completely solved, these are all very active research areas and many technologies are already available commercially. In the rest of this chapter, we briefly summarize the kinds of knowledge that are necessary for these tasks (and others like **spelling correction**, **grammar checking**, and so on), as well as the mathematical models that are introduced throughout the book.

1.1   Knowledge in Speech and Language Processing

What distinguishes language processing applications from other data processing systems is their use of *knowledge of language*. Consider the Unix wc program, which counts the total number of bytes, words, and lines in a text file. When used to count bytes and lines, wc is an ordinary data processing application. However, when it is used to count the words in a file, it requires *knowledge about what it means to be a word* and thus becomes a language processing system.

Of course, wc is an extremely simple system with an extremely limited and impoverished knowledge of language. Sophisticated conversational agents like HAL, machine translation systems, or robust question-answering systems require much broader and deeper knowledge of language. To get a feeling for the scope and kind of required knowledge, consider some of what HAL would need to know to engage in the dialogue that begins this chapter, or for a question-answering system to answer one of the questions above.

HAL must be able to recognize words from an audio signal and to generate an audio signal from a sequence of words. These tasks of **speech recognition** and **speech synthesis** require knowledge about **phonetics and phonology**: how words are pronounced in terms of sequences of sounds and how each of these sounds is realized acoustically.

Note also that unlike Commander Data in "Star Trek", HAL is capable of producing contractions like *I'm* and *can't*. Producing and recognizing these and other variations of individual words (e.g., recognizing that *doors* is plural) requires knowledge about **morphology**, the way words break down into component parts that carry meanings like *singular* versus *plural*.

Moving beyond individual words, HAL must use structural knowledge to properly string together the words that constitute its response. For example, HAL must know that the following sequence of words will not make sense to Dave, despite the fact that it contains precisely the same set of words as the original.

(1.1) I'm I do, sorry that afraid Dave I'm can't.

The knowledge needed to order and group words comes under the heading of **syntax**.

Now consider a question-answering system dealing with the following question:

(1.2) How much Chinese silk was exported to Western Europe by the end of the 18th century?

To answer this question, we need to know something about **lexical semantics**, the meaning of all the words (*export* or *silk*) as well as **compositional semantics** (what exactly constitutes *Western Europe* as opposed to Eastern or Southern Europe, what does *end* mean when combined with *the 18th century*. We also need to know something about the relationship of the words to the syntactic structure. For example, we need to know that *by the end of the 18th century* is a temporal end-point and not a description of the agent, as the by-phrase is in the following sentence:

(1.3) How much Chinese silk was exported to Western Europe by southern merchants?

We also need the kind of knowledge that lets HAL determine that Dave's utterance is a request for action, as opposed to a simple statement about the world or a question about the door, as in the following variations of his original statement.

REQUEST:	*HAL, open the pod bay door.*
STATEMENT:	*HAL, the pod bay door is open.*
INFORMATION QUESTION:	*HAL, is the pod bay door open?*

Next, despite its bad behavior, HAL knows enough to be polite to Dave. It could, for example, have simply replied *No* or *No, I won't open the door*. Instead, it first embellishes its response with the phrases *I'm sorry* and *I'm afraid*, and then only indirectly signals its refusal by saying *I can't*, rather than the more direct (and truthful) *I won't*.[1] This knowledge about the kind of actions that speakers intend by their use of sentences is **pragmatic** or **dialogue** knowledge.

Another kind of pragmatic or **discourse** knowledge is required to answer the question

(1.4) How many states were in the United States *that year*?

What year is *that year*? To interpret words like *that year*, a question-answering system needs to examine the earlier questions that were asked; in this case, the previous question talked about the year that Lincoln was born. Thus, this task of **coreference resolution** makes use of knowledge about how words like *that* or pronouns like *it* or *she* refer to previous parts of the **discourse**.

To summarize, engaging in complex language behavior requires various kinds of knowledge of language:

- Phonetics and Phonology — knowledge about linguistic sounds

---

[1] For those unfamiliar with HAL, it is neither sorry nor afraid, nor is it incapable of opening the door. It has simply decided in a fit of paranoia to kill its crew.

- Morphology — knowledge of the meaningful components of words
- Syntax — knowledge of the structural relationships between words
- Semantics — knowledge of meaning
- Pragmatics — knowledge of the relationship of meaning to the goals and intentions of the speaker
- Discourse — knowledge about linguistic units larger than a single utterance

1.2   Ambiguity

Ambiguity
Ambiguous

A perhaps surprising fact about these categories of linguistic knowledge is that most tasks in speech and language processing can be viewed as resolving **ambiguity** at one of these levels. We say some input is **ambiguous** if multiple, alternative linguistic structures can be built for it. Consider the spoken sentence *I made her duck.* Here are five different meanings this sentence could have (see if you can think of some more), each of which exemplifies an ambiguity at some level:

(1.5) I cooked waterfowl for her.

(1.6) I cooked waterfowl belonging to her.

(1.7) I created the (plaster?) duck she owns.

(1.8) I caused her to quickly lower her head or body.

(1.9) I waved my magic wand and turned her into undifferentiated waterfowl.

These different meanings are caused by a number of ambiguities. First, the words *duck* and *her* are morphologically or syntactically ambiguous in their part-of-speech. *Duck* can be a verb or a noun, while *her* can be a dative pronoun or a possessive pronoun. Second, the word *make* is semantically ambiguous; it can mean *create* or *cook*. Finally, the verb *make* is syntactically ambiguous in a different way. *Make* can be transitive, that is, taking a single direct object (1.6), or it can be ditransitive, that is, taking two objects (1.9), meaning that the first object (*her*) was made into the second object (*duck*). Finally, *make* can take a direct object and a verb (1.8), meaning that the object (*her*) was caused to perform the verbal action (*duck*). Furthermore, in a spoken sentence, there is an even deeper kind of ambiguity; the first word could have been *eye* or the second word *maid*.

We often introduce the models and algorithms we present throughout the book as ways to **resolve** or **disambiguate** these ambiguities. For example, deciding whether *duck* is a verb or a noun can be solved by **part-of-speech tagging**. Deciding whether *make* means "create" or "cook" can be solved by **word sense disambiguation**. Resolution of part-of-speech and word sense ambiguities are two important kinds of **lexical disambiguation**. A wide variety of tasks can be framed as lexical disambiguation problems. For example, a text-to-speech synthesis system reading the word *lead* needs to decide whether it should be pronounced as in *lead pipe* or as in *lead me on*. By contrast, deciding whether *her* and *duck* are part of the same entity (as in (1.5) or (1.8)) or are different entities (as in (1.6)) is an example of **syntactic disambiguation** and can be addressed by **probabilistic parsing**. We also consider ambiguities that don't arise in this particular example, such as determining whether a sentence is a statement or a question (which can be resolved by **speech act interpretation**).

1.3   Models and Algorithms

One of the key insights of the last 50 years of research in language processing is that the various kinds of knowledge described in the last sections can be captured through the use of a small number of formal models or theories. Fortunately, these models and theories are all drawn from the standard toolkits of computer science, mathematics, and linguistics and should be generally familiar to those trained in those fields. Among the most important models are **state machines**, **rule systems**, **logic**, **probabilistic models**, and **vector-space models**. These models, in turn, lend themselves to a small number of algorithms, among the most important of which are **state space search** algorithms, such as **dynamic programming**, and machine learning algorithms, such as **classifiers** and Expectation-Maximization (**EM**) and other learning algorithms.

In their simplest formulation, state machines are formal models that consist of states, transitions among states, and an input representation. Some of the variations of this basic model that we will consider are **deterministic** and **non-deterministic finite-state automata** and **finite-state transducers**.

Closely related to these models are their declarative counterparts: formal rule systems. Among the more important ones we consider (in both probabilistic and non-probabilistic formulations) are **regular grammars** and **regular relations**, **context-free grammars**, and **feature-augmented grammars**. State machines and formal rule systems are the main tools used when dealing with knowledge of phonology, morphology, and syntax.

A third class of models that plays a critical role in capturing knowledge of language are models based on logic. We discuss **first-order logic**, also known as the **predicate calculus**, as well as such related formalisms as lambda-calculus, feature structures, and semantic primitives. These logical representations have traditionally been used for modeling semantics and pragmatics, although more recent work has tended to focus on potentially more robust techniques drawn from non-logical lexical semantics.

Probabilistic models are crucial for capturing every kind of linguistic knowledge. Each of the other models (state machines, formal rule systems, and logic) can be augmented with probabilities. For example, the state machine can be augmented with probabilities to become the **weighted automaton**, or **Markov model**. We spend a significant amount of time on **hidden Markov models** or **HMMs**, which are used everywhere in the field, in part-of-speech tagging, speech recognition, dialogue understanding, text-to-speech, and machine translation. The key advantage of probabilistic models is their ability to solve the many kinds of ambiguity problems that we discussed earlier; almost any speech and language processing problem can be recast as "given N choices for some ambiguous input, choose the most probable one".

Finally, vector-space models, based on linear algebra, underlie information retrieval and many treatments of word meanings.

Processing language with any of these models typically involves a search through a space of states representing hypotheses about an input. In speech recognition, we search through a space of phone sequences for the correct word. In parsing, we search through a space of trees for the syntactic parse of an input sentence. In machine translation, we search through a space of translation hypotheses for the correct translation of a sentence into another language. For non-probabilistic tasks, such as tasks involving state machines, we use well-known graph algorithms such as **depth-first search**. For probabilistic tasks, we use heuristic variants such as **best-first** and **A* search** and rely on dynamic programming algorithms for computational tractability.

Machine learning tools such as **classifiers** and **sequence models** play a significant role in many language processing tasks. Based on attributes describing each object, a classifier attempts to assign a single object to a single class while a sequence model attempts to jointly classify a sequence of objects into a sequence of classes.

For example, in the task of deciding whether a word is spelled correctly, classifiers such as **decision trees**, **support vector machines**, **Gaussian mixture models**, and **logistic regression** could be used to make a binary decision (correct or incorrect) for one word at a time. Sequence models such as **hidden Markov models**, **maximum entropy Markov models**, and conditional random fields could be used to assign correct/incorrect labels to all the words in a sentence at once.

Finally, researchers in language processing use many of the same methodological tools that are used in machine learning research—the use of distinct training and test sets, statistical techniques like **cross-validation**, and careful evaluation of trained systems.

1.4   Language, Thought, and Understanding

To many, the ability of computers to process language as skillfully as we humans do will signal the arrival of truly intelligent machines. The basis of this belief is the fact that the effective use of language is intertwined with our general cognitive abilities. Among the first to consider the computational implications of this intimate connection was Alan Turing (1950). In this famous paper, Turing introduced what has come to be known as the **Turing test**. Turing began with the thesis that the question of what it would mean for a machine to think was essentially unanswerable because of the inherent imprecision in the terms *machine* and *think*. Instead, he suggested an empirical test, a game, in which a computer's use of language would form the basis for determining if the machine could think. If the machine could win the game, it would be judged intelligent.

Turing test

In Turing's game, there are three participants: two people and a computer. One of the people is a contestant who plays the role of an interrogator. To win, the interrogator must determine which of the other two participants is the machine by asking a series of questions via a teletype. The task of the machine is to fool the interrogator into believing it is a person by responding as a person would to the interrogator's questions. The task of the second human participant is to convince the interrogator that the other participant is the machine and that she is human.

The following interaction from Turing's paper illustrates the kind of interactions he had in mind. Clearly, a convincing simulation of humanity doesn't require being an expert in all domains:

> Q: Please write me a sonnet on the topic of the Forth Bridge.
> A: Count me out on this one. I never could write poetry.
> Q: Add 34957 to 70764.
> A: (Pause about 30 seconds and then give answer as) 105621.

Turing predicted that roughly by the end of the 20th century a machine with 10 gigabytes of memory would have around a 30% chance of fooling a human interrogator after five minutes of questioning. Given the fact that you can fool some of the people all the time, it is not clear how rigorous this particular standard is. Nevertheless, the critical issue for Turing was that using language as humans do is sufficient, by itself, as an operational test for intelligence.

ELIZA   Surprisingly, many of the issues raised by Turing became relevant as early as 1966 in the context of the **ELIZA** program (Weizenbaum, 1966). ELIZA was an early natural language processing system capable of carrying on a limited form of conversation with a user. Consider the following session with a version of ELIZA that imitated the responses of a Rogerian psychotherapist.

> User$_1$:   You are like my father in some ways.
> ELIZA$_1$: WHAT RESEMBLANCE DO YOU SEE
> User$_2$:   You are not very aggressive but I think you don't want me to notice that.
> ELIZA$_2$: WHAT MAKES YOU THINK I AM NOT AGGRESSIVE
> User$_3$:   You don't argue with me.
> ELIZA$_3$: WHY DO YOU THINK I DON'T ARGUE WITH YOU
> User$_4$:   You are afraid of me.
> ELIZA$_4$: DOES IT PLEASE YOU TO BELIEVE I AM AFRAID OF YOU

As we discuss in more detail in Chapter 2, ELIZA is a remarkably simple program that uses pattern matching to process the input and translate it into suitable outputs. This simple technique succeeds in this domain because ELIZA doesn't actually need to *know* anything to mimic a Rogerian psychotherapist. As Weizenbaum notes, this is one of the few dialogue genres where listeners can act as if they know nothing of the world.

ELIZA's deep relevance to Turing's ideas is that many people who interacted with ELIZA came to believe that it really *understood* them and their problems. Indeed, Weizenbaum (1976) notes that many of these people continued to believe in ELIZA's abilities even after the program's operation was explained to them. In more recent years, Weizenbaum's informal tests have been repeated in a somewhat more controlled setting. Since 1991, an event known as the Loebner Prize competition has attempted to put various computer programs to the Turing test. Although these contests seem to have little scientific interest, a consistent result over the years has been that even the crudest programs can fool some of the judges some of the time (Shieber, 1994a). Not surprisingly, these results have done nothing to quell the ongoing debate over the suitability of the Turing test as a test for intelligence among philosophers and AI researchers (Searle, 1980).

Fortunately, for the purposes of this book, the relevance of these results does not hinge on whether computers will ever be intelligent or will ever understand natural language. Far more important is recent related research in the social sciences that has confirmed another of Turing's predictions from the same paper.

> Nevertheless I believe that at the end of the century the use of words and educated opinion will have altered so much that we will be able to speak of machines thinking without expecting to be contradicted.

It is now clear that regardless of what people believe or know about the inner workings of computers, they talk about them and interact with them as social entities. People act toward computers as if they were people; they are polite to them, treat them as team members, and expect, among other things, that computers should be able to understand their needs and be capable of interacting with them naturally. For example, Reeves and Nass (1996) found that when a computer asked a human to evaluate how well the computer had been doing, the human gives more positive responses than when a different computer asks the same questions. People seemed to be afraid of being impolite. In a different experiment, Reeves and Nass found that people also give computers higher performance ratings if the computer has recently said something flattering to the human. Given these predispositions, speech- and language-based systems may provide many users with the most natural interface for many applications. This fact has led to a long-term focus in the field on the design of **conversational agents**, artificial entities that communicate conversationally.

1.5   The State of the Art

We can only see a short distance ahead, but we can see plenty there that needs to be done.

Alan Turing

This is an exciting time for the field of speech and language processing. The startling increase in computing resources available to the average computer user, the rise of the Web as a massive source of information, and the increasing availability of wireless mobile access have all placed speech- and language-processing applications in the technology spotlight. The following are examples of some currently deployed systems that reflect this trend:

- Travelers calling Amtrak, United Airlines, and other travel providers interact with conversational agents that guide them through the process of making reservations and getting arrival and departure information.
- Car makers provide automatic speech recognition and text-to-speech systems that allow drivers to control their environmental, entertainment, and navigational systems by voice. A similar spoken dialogue system has been deployed by astronauts on the International Space Station.
- Video search companies provide search services for millions of hours of video on the Web by using speech recognition technology to capture the words in the sound track.
- Google provides cross-language information retrieval and translation services whereby users can supply queries in their native language to search collections

in another language. Google translates the query, finds the most relevant pages, and then automatically translates them back to the user's native language.

- Large educational publishers such as Pearson and testing services like ETS use automated systems to analyze thousands of student essays, grading and assessing them in a manner that is indistinguishable from human graders.

- Interactive virtual agents, based on lifelike animated characters, serve as tutors for children learning to read (Wise et al., 2007).

- Text analysis companies provide marketing intelligence based on automated measurements of user opinions, preferences, attitudes as expressed in weblogs, discussion forums, and user groups.

1.6   Some Brief History

Historically, speech and language processing has been treated very differently in computer science, electrical engineering, linguistics, and psychology/cognitive science. Because of this diversity, speech and language processing encompasses a number of different but overlapping fields in these different departments: **computational linguistics** in linguistics, **natural language processing** in computer science, **speech recognition** in electrical engineering, **computational psycholinguistics** in psychology. This section summarizes the different historical threads that have given rise to the field of speech and language processing. This section provides only a sketch, but many of the topics listed here are covered in more detail in subsequent chapters.

1.6.1   Foundational Insights: 1940s and 1950s

The earliest roots of the field date to the intellectually fertile period just after World War II that gave rise to the computer itself. This period from the 1940s through the end of the 1950s saw intense work on two foundational paradigms: the **automaton** and **probabilistic** or **information-theoretic models**.

The automaton arose in the 1950s out of Turing's (1936) model of algorithmic computation, considered by many to be the foundation of modern computer science. Turing's work led first to the **McCulloch-Pitts neuron** (McCulloch and Pitts, 1943), a simplified model of the neuron as a kind of computing element that could be described in terms of propositional logic, and then to the work of Kleene (1951) and (1956) on finite automata and regular expressions. Shannon (1948) applied probabilistic models of discrete Markov processes to automata for language. Drawing on the idea of a finite-state Markov process from Shannon's work, Chomsky (1956) first considered finite-state machines as a way to characterize a grammar and defined a finite-state language as a language generated by a finite-state grammar. These early models led to the field of **formal language theory**, which used algebra and set theory to define formal languages as sequences of symbols. This includes the context-free grammar, first defined by Chomsky (1956) for natural languages but independently discovered by Backus (1959) and Naur et al. (1960) in their descriptions of the ALGOL programming language.

The second foundational insight of this period was the development of probabilistic algorithms for speech and language processing, which dates to Shannon's other contribution: the metaphor of the **noisy channel** and **decoding** for the transmission of language through media such as communication channels and speech acoustics. Shannon also borrowed the concept of **entropy** from thermodynamics as a way of measuring the information capacity of a channel, or the information content of a language, and performed the first measure of the entropy of English by using probabilistic tech•iques.

It was also during this early period that the sound spectrograph was developed (Koenig et al., 1946), and foundational research was done in instrumental phonetics that laid the groundwork for later work in speech recognition. This led to the first machine speech recognizers in the early 1950s. In 1952, researchers at Bell Labs built a statistical system that could recognize any of the 10 digits from a single speaker (Davis et al., 1952). The system had 10 speaker-dependent stored patterns roughly representing the first two vowel formants in the digits. They achieved 97%–99% accuracy by choosing the pattern that had the highest relative correlation coefficient with the input.

1.6.2   The Two Camps: 1957–1970

By the end of the 1950s and the early 1960s, speech and language processing had split very cleanly into two paradigms: symbolic and stochastic.

The symbolic paradigm took off from two lines of research. The first was the work of Chomsky and others on formal language theory and generative syntax throughout the late 1950s and early to mid 1960s, and the work of many linguistics and computer scientists on parsing algorithms, initially top-down and bottom-up and then with dynamic programming. One of the earliest complete parsing systems was Zelig Harris's Transformations and Discourse Analysis Project (TDAP), which was implemented between June 1958 and July 1959 at the University of Pennsylvania (Harris, 1962).[2] The second line of research was the new field of artificial intelligence. In the summer of 1956 John McCarthy, Marvin Minsky, Claude Shannon, and Nathaniel Rochester brought together a group of researchers for a two-month workshop on what they decided to call artificial intelligence (AI). Although AI always included a minority of researchers focusing on stochastic and statistical algorithms (including probabilistic models and neural nets), the major focus of the new field was the work on reasoning and logic typified by Newell and Simon's work on the Logic Theorist and the General Problem Solver. At this point, early natural language understanding systems were built. These simple systems worked in single domains mainly by a combination of pattern matching and keyword search with simple heuristics for reasoning and question-answering. By the late 1960s, more formal logical systems were developed.

The stochastic paradigm took hold mainly in departments of statistics and of electrical engineering. By the late 1950s, the Bayesian method was beginning to be applied to the problem of optical character recognition. Bledsoe and Browning (1959) built a Bayesian text-recognition that used a large dictionary and computed the likelihood of each observed letter sequence given each word in the dictionary by multiplying the

---

2 This system was reimplemented recently and is described by Joshi and Hopely (1999) and Karttunen (1999), who note that the parser was essentially implemented as a cascade of finite-state transducers.

likelihoods for each letter. Mosteller and Wallace (1964) applied Bayesian methods to the problem of authorship attribution on *The Federalist* papers.

The 1960s also saw the rise of the first serious testable psychological models of human language processing based on transformational grammar, as well as the first on-line corpora: the Brown corpus of American English, a one-million-word collection of samples from 500 written texts from different genres (newspaper, novels, non-fiction, academic, etc.), which was assembled at Brown University in 1963–64 (Kučera and Francis, 1967; Francis, 1979; Francis and Kučera, 1982), and William S. Y. Wang's 1967 DOC (Dictionary on Computer), an on-line Chinese dialect dictionary.

1.6.3   Four Paradigms: 1970–1983

The next period saw an explosion in research in speech and language processing and the development of a number of research paradigms that still dominate the field.

The **stochastic** paradigm played a huge role in the development of speech recognition algorithms in this period, particularly the use of the hidden Markov model (HMM) and the metaphors of the noisy channel and decoding, developed independently by Jelinek, Bahl, Mercer, and colleagues at IBM's Thomas J. Watson Research Center, and by Baker at Carnegie Mellon University, who was influenced by the work of Baum and colleagues at the Institute for Defense Analyses in Princeton. AT&T's Bell Laboratories was another key center for work on speech recognition and synthesis; see Rabiner and Juang (1993) for descriptions of the wide range of this work.

The **logic-based** paradigm was begun by the work of Colmerauer and his colleagues on Q-systems and metamorphosis grammars (Colmerauer, 1970, 1975), the forerunners of Prolog, and Definite Clause Grammars (Pereira and Warren, 1980). Independently, Kay's (1979) work on functional grammar and shortly later, Bresnan and Kaplan's (1982) work on Lexical Functional Grammar (LFG), established the importance of feature structure unification.

The **natural language understanding** field took off during this period, beginning with Winograd's SHRDLU system, which simulated a robot embedded in a world of toy blocks (Winograd, 1972a). The program was able to accept natural-language text commands *(Move the red block on top of the smaller green one)* of a hitherto unseen complexity and sophistication. His system was also the first to attempt to build an extensive (for the time) grammar of English, based on Halliday's systemic grammar. Winograd's model made it clear that the problem of parsing was well enough understood to begin to focus on semantics and discourse. Roger Schank and his colleagues and students (in what was often referred to as the *Yale School*) built a series of language-understanding programs that focused on conceptual knowledge such as scripts, plans, and goals, and human memory organization (Schank and Abelson, 1977; Schank and Riesbeck, 1981; Cullingford, 1981; Wilensky, 1983; Lehnert, 1977). This work often used network-based semantics (Quillian, 1968; Norman and Rumelhart, 1975; Schank, 1972; Wilks, 1975c, 1975b; Kintsch, 1974) and began to incorporate Fillmore's notion of case roles (Fillmore, 1968) into their representations (Simmons, 1973).

The logic-based and natural-language-understanding paradigms were unified in systems that used predicate logic as a semantic representation, such as the LUNAR question-answering system (Woods, 1967, 1973).

The **discourse modeling** paradigm focused on four key areas in discourse. Grosz and her colleagues introduced the study of substructure in discourse, and of discourse focus (Grosz, 1977a; Sidner, 1983); a number of researchers began to work on automatic reference resolution (Hobbs, 1978); and the **BDI** (Belief-Desire-Intention) framework for logic-based work on speech acts was developed (Perrault and Allen, 1980; Cohen and Perrault, 1979).

1.6.4   Empiricism and Finite-State Models Redux: 1983–1993

This next decade saw the return of two classes of models that had lost popularity in the late 1950s and early 1960s, partially due to theoretical arguments against them such as Chomsky's influential review of Skinner's *Verbal Behavior* (Chomsky, 1959b). The first class was finite-state models, which began to receive attention again after work on finite-state phonology and morphology by Kaplan and Kay (1981) and finite-state models of syntax by Church (1980). A large body of work on finite-state models is described throughout the book.

The second trend in this period was what has been called the "return of empiricism"; most notable here was the rise of probabilistic models throughout speech and language processing, influenced strongly by the work at the IBM Thomas J. Watson Research Center on probabilistic models of speech recognition. These probabilistic methods and other such data-driven approaches spread from speech into part-of-speech tagging, parsing and attachment ambiguities, and semantics. This empirical direction was also accompanied by a new focus on model evaluation, based on using held-out data, developing quantitative metrics for evaluation, and emphasizing the comparison of performance on these metrics with previous published research.

This period also saw considerable work on natural language generation.

1.6.5   The Field Comes Together: 1994–1999

By the last five years of the millennium it was clear that the field was undergoing major changes. First, probabilistic and data-driven models had become quite standard throughout natural language processing. Algorithms for parsing, part-of-speech tagging, reference resolution, and discourse processing all began to incorporate probabilities and to employ evaluation methodologies borrowed from speech recognition and information retrieval. Second, the increases in the speed and memory of computers had allowed commercial exploitation of a number of subareas of speech and language processing, in particular, speech recognition, and spelling and grammar correction. Speech and language processing algorithms began to be applied to Augmentative and Alternative Communication (AAC). Finally, the rise of the Web emphasized the need for language-based information retrieval and information extraction.

1.6.6   The Rise of Machine Learning: 2000–2008

The empiricist trends begun in the latter part of the 1990s accelerated at an astounding pace in the new century. This acceleration was largely driven by three synergistic trends.

First, large amounts of spoken and written material became widely available through the auspices of the Linguistic Data Consortium (LDC) and other similar organizations. Importantly, included among these materials were annotated collections such as the Penn Treebank (Marcus et al., 1993), Prague Dependency Treebank (Hajič, 1998), PropBank (Palmer et al., 2005), Penn Discourse Treebank (Miltsakaki et al., 2004b), RSTBank (Carlson et al., 2001) and TimeBank (Pustejovsky et al., 2003b), all of which layered standard text sources with various forms of syntactic, semantic, and pragmatic annotations. The existence of these resources promoted the trend of casting more complex traditional problems, such as parsing and semantic analysis, as problems in supervised machine learning. These resources also promoted the establishment of additional competitive evaluations for parsing (Dejean and Tjong Kim Sang, 2001), information extraction (NIST, 2007a; Tjong Kim Sang, 2002; Tjong Kim Sang and De Meulder, 2003), word sense disambiguation (Palmer et al., 2001; Kilgarriff and Palmer, 2000), question answering (Voorhees and Tice, 1999), and summarization (Dang, 2006).

Second, this increased focus on learning led to a more serious interplay with the statistical machine learning community. Techniques such as support vector machines (Boser et al., 1992; Vapnik, 1995), maximum entropy techniques and their equivalent formulation as multinomial logistic regression (Berger et al., 1996), and graphical Bayesian models (Pearl, 1988) became standard practice in computational linguistics.

Third, the widespread availability of high-performance computing systems facilitated the training and deployment of systems that could not have been imagined a decade earlier.

Finally, near the end of this period, largely unsupervised statistical approaches began to receive renewed attention. Progress on statistical approaches to machine translation (Brown et al., 1990; Och and Ney, 2003) and topic modeling (Blei et al., 2003) demonstrated that effective applications could be constructed from systems trained on unannotated data alone. In addition, the widespread cost and difficulty of producing reliably annotated corpora became a limiting factor in the use of supervised approaches for many problems. This trend toward the use of unsupervised techniques will likely increase.

1.6.7   On Multiple Discoveries

Even in this brief historical overview, we have mentioned a number of cases of multiple independent discoveries of the same idea. Just a few of the "multiples" to be discussed in this book include the application of dynamic programming to sequence comparison by Viterbi, Vintsyuk, Needleman and Wunsch, Sakoe and Chiba, Sankoff, Reichert et al., and Wagner and Fischer (Chapters 3, 5, and 6); the HMM/noisy channel model of speech recognition by Baker and by Jelinek, Bahl, and Mercer (Chapters 6, 9, and 10); the development of context-free grammars by Chomsky and by Backus and Naur (Chapter 12); the proof that Swiss-German has a non-context-free syntax by Huybregts and by Shieber (Chapter 16); the application of unification to language processing by Colmerauer et al. and by Kay (Chapter 15).

Are these multiples to be considered astonishing coincidences? A well-known hypothesis by sociologist of science Robert K. Merton (1961) argues, quite the contrary, that all scientific discoveries are in principle multiples, including those that on the surface appear to be singletons.

Of course, there are many well-known cases of multiple discovery or invention; just a few examples from an extensive list in Ogburn and Thomas (1922) include the multiple invention of the calculus by Leibnitz and by Newton, the multiple development of the theory of natural selection by Wallace and by Darwin, and the multiple invention of the telephone by Gray and Bell.[3] But Merton gives a further array of evidence for the hypothesis that multiple discovery is the rule rather than the exception, including many cases of putative singletons that turn out be a rediscovery of previously unpublished or perhaps inaccessible work. An even stronger piece of evidence is his ethnomethodological point that scientists themselves act under the assumption that multiple invention is the norm. Thus many aspects of scientific life are designed to help scientists avoid being "scooped": submission dates on journal articles, careful dates in research records, circulation of preliminary or technical reports.

1.6.8   A Final Brief Note on Psychology

Many of the chapters in this book include short summaries of psychological research on human processing. Of course, understanding human language processing is an important scientific goal in its own right and is part of the general field of cognitive science. However, an understanding of human language processing can often be helpful in building better machine models of language. This seems contrary to the popular wisdom, which holds that direct mimicry of nature's algorithms is rarely useful in engineering applications. For example, the argument is often made that if we copied nature exactly, airplanes would flap their wings; yet airplanes with fixed wings are a more successful engineering solution. But language is not aeronautics. Cribbing from nature is sometimes useful for aeronautics (after all, airplanes do have wings), but it is particularly useful when we are trying to solve human-centered tasks. Airplane flight has different goals from bird flight; but the goal of speech recognition systems, for example, is to perform exactly the task that human court reporters perform every day: transcribe spoken dialog. Since people already do this well, we can learn from nature's previous solution. Furthermore, since an important application of speech and language processing systems is for human-computer interaction, it makes sense to copy a solution that behaves the way people are accustomed to.

1.7   Summary

This chapter introduces the field of speech and language processing. The following are some of the highlights of this chapter.

---

[3] Ogburn and Thomas are generally credited with noticing that the prevalence of multiple inventions suggests that the cultural milieu and not individual genius is the deciding causal factor in scientific discovery. In an amusing bit of recursion, however, Merton notes that even this idea has been multiply discovered, citing sources from the 19th century and earlier!

- A good way to understand the concerns of speech and language processing research is to consider what it would take to create an intelligent agent like HAL from *2001: A Space Odyssey*, or build a Web-based question answerer, or a machine translation engine.

- Speech and language technology relies on formal models, or representations, of knowledge of language at the levels of phonology and phonetics, morphology, syntax, semantics, pragmatics and discourse. A number of formal models including state machines, formal rule systems, logic, and probabilistic models are used to capture this knowledge.

- The foundations of speech and language technology lie in computer science, linguistics, mathematics, electrical engineering, and psychology. A small number of algorithms from standard frameworks are used throughout speech and language processing.

- The critical connection between language and thought has placed speech and language processing technology at the center of debate over intelligent machines. Furthermore, research on how people interact with complex media indicates that speech and language processing technology will be critical in the development of future technologies.

- Revolutionary applications of speech and language processing are currently in use around the world. The creation of the Web, as well as significant recent improvements in speech recognition and synthesis, will lead to many more applications.

Bibliographical and Historical Notes

Research in the various subareas of speech and language processing is spread across a wide number of conference proceedings and journals. The conferences and journals most centrally concerned with natural language processing and computational linguistics are associated with the Association for Computational Linguistics (ACL), its European counterpart (EACL), and the International Conference on Computational Linguistics (COLING). The annual proceedings of ACL, NAACL, and EACL, and the biennial COLING conference are the primary forums for work in this area. Related conferences include various proceedings of ACL Special Interest Groups (SIGs) such as the Conference on Natural Language Learning (CoNLL), as well as the conference on Empirical Methods in Natural Language Processing (EMNLP).

Research on speech recognition, understanding, and synthesis is presented at the annual INTERSPEECH conference, which is called the International Conference on Spoken Language Processing (ICSLP), and the European Conference on Speech Communication and Technology (EUROSPEECH) in alternating years, or the annual IEEE International Conference on Acoustics, Speech, and Signal Processing (IEEE ICASSP). Spoken language dialogue research is presented at these or at workshops like SIGDial.

Journals include *Computational Linguistics*, *Natural Language Engineering*, *Computer Speech and Language*, *Speech Communication*, the *IEEE Transactions on Audio,*

Speech & Language Processing, the *ACM Transactions on Speech and Language Processing*, and *Linguistic Issues in Language Technology*.

Many of these papers, including those from the *Computational Linguistics* journal and the *ACL*, *COLING*, and related conferences are available for free online at the *ACL Anthology* (`http://www.aclweb.org/anthology-index/`).

Work on language processing from an Artificial Intelligence perspective can be found in the annual meetings of the American Association for Artificial Intelligence (AAAI), as well as the biennial International Joint Conference on Artificial Intelligence (IJCAI) meetings. Artificial intelligence journals that periodically feature work on speech and language processing include *Machine Learning*, *Journal of Machine Learning Research*, and the *Journal of Artificial Intelligence Research*.

A fair number of textbooks covering various aspects of speech and language processing are available. Manning and Schütze (1999) (*Foundations of Statistical Language Processing*) focuses on statistical models of tagging, parsing, disambiguation, collocations, and other areas. Charniak (1993) (*Statistical Language Learning*) is an accessible, though older and less-extensive, introduction to similar material. Manning et al. (2008) focuses on information retrieval, text classification, and clustering. NLTK, the Natural Language Toolkit (Bird and Loper, 2004), is a suite of Python modules and data for natural language processing, together with a Natural Language Processing book based on the NLTK suite. Allen (1995) (*Natural Language Understanding*) provides extensive coverage of language processing from the AI perspective. Gazdar and Mellish (1989) (*Natural Language Processing in Lisp/Prolog/Pop11*) covers especially automata, parsing, features, and unification and is available free online. Pereira and Shieber (1987) gives a Prolog-based introduction to parsing and interpretation. Russell and Norvig (2002) introduce artificial intelligence with chapters on natural language processing. Partee et al. (1990) broadly cover mathematical linguistics. A historically significant collection of foundational papers can be found in Grosz et al. (1986) (*Readings in Natural Language Processing*).

There are many places to acquire corpora of speech and text. One of the largest is the Linguistic Data Consortium, a non-profit consortium that creates and distributes corpora (`http://www.ldc.upenn.edu/`). See the textbook web page for pointers to others such as CHILDES (`http://childes.psy.cmu.edu/`), the British National Corpus (`http://www.natcorp.ox.ac.uk/`), the International Corpus of English (`http://www.ucl.ac.uk/english-usage/ice/index.htm`), and Project Gutenberg (`http://www.gutenberg.org/`).

Chapter 2

Regular Expressions and Automata

User₁:	*Men are all alike.*

User₁: *Men are all alike.*
ELIZA₁: *IN WHAT WAY*
User₂: *They're always bugging us about something or other.*
ELIZA₂: *CAN YOU THINK OF A SPECIFIC EXAMPLE*
User₃: *Well, my boyfriend made me come here.*
ELIZA₃: *YOUR BOYFRIEND MADE YOU COME HERE*
User₄: *He says I'm depressed much of the time.*
ELIZA₄: *I AM SORRY TO HEAR YOU ARE DEPRESSED*

Weizenbaum (1966)

Imagine that you have become a passionate fan of woodchucks and have recently learned that *groundhog* and *woodchuck* are different names for the same animal. Since you are writing a term paper on woodchucks, you now need to search through your paper for every occurrence of the term *woodchuck* and replace *woodchucks* with *woodchucks (groundhogs)*. But you also need to replace singular *woodchuck* with *woodchuck (groundhog)*. Instead of having to do this search twice, you would prefer to perform a single command for something like *woodchuck with an optional final s*. Or perhaps you might want to search for all the prices in some document; you might want to see all strings that look like *$199* or *$25* or *$24.99* in order to automatically extract a table of prices. In this chapter we introduce the **regular expression**, the standard notation for characterizing text sequences. The regular expression is used for specifying text strings in all sorts of text processing and information extraction applications.

After we have defined regular expressions, we show how they can be implemented with the **finite-state automaton**. The finite-state automaton is not only the mathematical device used to implement regular expressions but also one of the most significant tools of computational linguistics. Variations of automata such as finite-state transducers, hidden Markov models, and *N*-gram grammars are important components of applications that we introduce in later chapters, including speech recognition and synthesis, machine translation, spell-checking, and information extraction.

2.1 Regular Expressions

SIR ANDREW: *Her C's, her U's and her T's: why that?*

Shakespeare, *Twelfth Night*

Regular expression   One of the unsung successes in standardization in computer science has been the **regular expression** (**RE**), a language for specifying text search strings. The regular expression languages used for searching texts in Unix tools like grep and Emacs, in Perl, Python, Ruby, Java, and .NET, and also in Microsoft Word are very similar, and many RE features exist in Web search engines. Besides this practical use, the regular expression is an important theoretical tool throughout computer science and linguistics.

Strings

A regular expression (first developed by Kleene (1956) but see the Historical Notes section for more details) is a formula in a special language that specifies simple classes of **strings**. A string is a sequence of symbols; for most text-based search techniques, a string is any sequence of alphanumeric characters (letters, numbers, spaces, tabs, and punctuation). For these purposes a space is just a character like any other, and we represent it with the symbol ␣.

Formally, a regular expression is an algebraic notation for characterizing a set of strings. Thus, they can specify search strings as well as define a language in a formal way. We begin by talking about regular expressions as a way of specifying searches in texts and proceed to other uses. Section 2.3 shows that the use of just three regular expression operators is sufficient to characterize strings, but we use the more convenient and commonly used regular expression syntax of the Perl language throughout this section. Since common text-processing programs agree on most of the syntax of regular expressions, most of what we say extends to all UNIX and Microsoft Word regular expressions.

Corpus

Regular expression search requires a **pattern** that we want to search for and a **corpus** of texts to search through. A regular expression search function will search through the corpus, returning all texts that match the pattern. In an information retrieval (IR) system such as a Web search engine, the texts might be entire documents or Web pages. In a word processor, the texts might be individual words or lines of a document. In the rest of this chapter, we use this last paradigm. Thus, when we give a search pattern, we assume that the search engine returns the *line of the document* returned. This is what the Unix `grep` command does. We underline the exact part of the pattern that matches the regular expression. A search can be designed to return all matches to a regular expression or only the first match. We show only the first match.

2.1.1   Basic Regular Expression Patterns

The simplest kind of regular expression is a sequence of simple characters. For example, to search for *woodchuck*, we type `/woodchuck/`. So the regular expression `/Buttercup/` matches any string containing the substring *Buttercup*, for example, the line *I'm called little Buttercup* (recall that we are assuming a search application that returns entire lines).

From here on we put slashes around each regular expression to make it clear what is a regular expression and what is a pattern. We use the slash since this is the notation used by Perl, but the slashes are *not* part of the regular expressions.

The search string can consist of a single character (like `/!/`) or a sequence of characters (like `/urgl/`). The *first* instance of each match to the regular expression is underlined below (although a given application might choose to return more than just the first instance):

RE	Example Patterns Matched
/woodchucks/	"interesting links to woodchucks and lemurs"
/a/	"Mary Ann stopped by Mona's"
/Claire_says,/	" "Dagmar, my gift please," Claire says,"
/DOROTHY/	"SURRENDER DOROTHY"
/!/	"You've left the burglar behind again!" said Nori

Regular expressions are **case sensitive**; lower case /s/ is distinct from upper case /S/ (/s/ matches a lower case *s* but not an uppercase *S*). This means that the pattern /woodchucks/ will not match the string *Woodchucks*. We can solve this problem with the use of the square braces [and]. The string of characters inside the braces specify a **disjunction** of characters to match. For example, Fig. 2.1 shows that the pattern /[wW]/ matches patterns containing either *w* or *W*.

RE	Match	Example Patterns
/[wW]oodchuck/	Woodchuck or woodchuck	"Woodchuck"
/[abc]/	'a', 'b', *or* 'c'	"In uomini, in soldati"
/[1234567890]/	any digit	"plenty of 7 to 5"

Figure 2.1   The use of the brackets [ ] to specify a disjunction of characters.

The regular expression /[1234567890]/ specified any single digit. While such classes of characters as digits or letters are important building blocks in expressions, they can get awkward (e.g., it's inconvenient to specify

/[ABCDEFGHIJKLMNOPQRSTUVWXYZ]/

Range   to mean "any capital letter"). In these cases the brackets can be used with the dash (–) to specify any one character in a **range**. The pattern /[2-5]/ specifies any one of the characters 2, 3, 4, or 5. The pattern /[b-g]/ specifies one of the characters *b*, *c*, *d*, *e*, *f*, or *g*. Some other examples are shown in Fig. 2.2.

RE	Match	Example Patterns Matched
/[A-Z]/	an upper case letter	"we should call it 'Drenched Blossoms' "
/[a-z]/	a lower case letter	"my beans were impatient to be hoed!"
/[0-9]/	a single digit	"Chapter 1: Down the Rabbit Hole"

Figure 2.2   The use of the brackets [ ] plus the dash – to specify a range.

The square braces can also be used to specify what a single character *cannot* be, by use of the caret ^. If the caret ^ is the first symbol after the open square brace [, the resulting pattern is negated. For example, the pattern /[^a]/ matches any single character (including special characters) except *a*. This is only true when the caret is the first symbol after the open square brace. If it occurs anywhere else, it usually stands for a caret; Fig. 2.3 shows some examples.

The use of square braces solves our capitalization problem for *woodchucks*. But we still haven't answered our original question; how do we specify both *woodchuck* and *woodchucks*? We can't use the square brackets, because while they allow us to say "s or S", they don't allow us to say "s or nothing". For this we use the question mark /?/, which means "the preceding character or nothing", as shown in Fig. 2.4.

RE	Match (single characters)	Example Patterns Matched
[^A-Z]	not an upper case letter	"<u>O</u>yfn pripetchik"
[^Ss]	neither 'S' nor 's'	"<u>I</u> have no exquisite reason for't"
[^\.]	not a period	"<u>o</u>ur resident Djinn"
[e^]	either 'e' or '^'	"look up <u>^</u> now"
a^b	the pattern 'a^b'	"look up <u>a^ b</u> now"

Figure 2.3   Uses of the caret ^ for negation or just to mean ^. We discuss below the need to escape the period by a backslash.

RE	Match	Example Patterns Matched
woodchucks?	woodchuck or woodchucks	"<u>woodchuck</u>"
colou?r	color or colour	"<u>colour</u>"

Figure 2.4   The question mark ? marks optionality of the previous expression.

We can think of the question mark as meaning "zero or one instances of the previous character". That is, it's a way of specifying how many of something that we want. So far we haven't needed to specify that we want more than one of something. But sometimes we need regular expressions that allow repetitions. For example, consider the language of (certain) sheep, which consists of strings that look like the following:

baa!
baaa!
baaaa!
baaaaa!
...

This language consists of strings with a *b*, followed by at least two *a*'s, followed by an exclamation point. The set of operators that allows us to say things like "some number of *a*'s" are based on the asterisk or *, commonly called the **Kleene *** (pronounced "cleany star"). The Kleene star means "zero or more occurrences of the immediately previous character or regular expression". So /a*/ means "any string of zero or more *a*s". This will match *a* or *aaaaaa*, but it will also match *Off Minor* since the string *Off Minor* has zero *a*'s. So the regular expression for matching one or more *a* is /aa*/, meaning one *a* followed by zero or more *a*s. More complex patterns can also be repeated. So /[ab]*/ means "zero or more *a*'s or *b*'s" (not "zero or more right square braces"). This will match strings like *aaaa* or *ababab* or *bbbb*.

*Kleene **

We now know enough to specify part of our regular expression for prices: multiple digits. Recall that the regular expression for an individual digit was /[0-9]/. So the regular expression for an integer (a string of digits) is /[0-9][0-9]*/. (Why isn't it just /[0-9]*/?)

Sometimes it's annoying to have to write the regular expression for digits twice, so there is a shorter way to specify "at least one" of some character. This is the **Kleene +**, which means "one or more of the previous character". Thus, the expression /[0-9]+/ is the normal way to specify "a sequence of digits". There are thus two ways to specify the sheep language: /baaa*!/ or /baa+!/.

Kleene +

One very important special character is the period (/./), a **wildcard** expression that matches any single character (*except* a carriage return), as shown in Fig. 2.5.

RE	Match	Example Patterns
`/beg.n/`	any character between *beg* and *n*	beg<u>i</u>n, beg'n, beg<u>u</u>n

Figure 2.5   The use of the period . to specify any character.

The wildcard is often used together with the Kleene star to mean "any string of characters". For example, suppose we want to find any line in which a particular word, for example, *aardvark*, appears twice. We can specify this with the regular expression `/aardvark.*aardvark/`.

Anchors   **Anchors** are special characters that anchor regular expressions to particular places in a string. The most common anchors are the caret ˆ and the dollar sign $. The caret ˆ matches the start of a line. The pattern `/ˆThe/` matches the word *The* only at the start of a line. Thus, the caret ˆ has three uses: to match the start of a line, to indicate a negation inside of square brackets, and just to mean a caret. (What are the contexts that allow Perl to know which function a given caret is supposed to have?) The dollar sign $ matches the end of a line. So the pattern ␣$ is a useful pattern for matching a space at the end of a line, and `/ˆThe dog\.$/` matches a line that contains only the phrase *The dog*. (We have to use the backslash here since we want the . to mean "period" and not the wildcard.)

There are also two other anchors: `\b` matches a word boundary, and `\B` matches a non-boundary. Thus, `/\bthe\b/` matches the word *the* but not the word *other*. More technically, Perl defines a word as any sequence of digits, underscores, or letters; this is based on the definition of "words" in programming languages like Perl or C. For example, `/\b99\b/` will match the string *99* in *There are 99 bottles of beer on the wall* (because 99 follows a space) but not *99* in *There are 299 bottles of beer on the wall* (since 99 follows a number). But it will match *99* in *$99* (since *99* follows a dollar sign ($), which is not a digit, underscore, or letter).

2.1.2   Disjunction, Grouping, and Precedence

Suppose we need to search for texts about pets; perhaps we are particularly interested in cats and dogs. In such a case, we might want to search for either the string *cat* or the string *dog*. Since we can't use the square brackets to search for "cat or dog" (why *Disjunction*   not?), we need a new operator, the **disjunction** operator, also called the **pipe** symbol `|`. The pattern `/cat|dog/` matches either the string `cat` or the string `dog`.

Sometimes we need to use this disjunction operator in the midst of a larger sequence. For example, suppose I want to search for information about pet fish for my cousin David. How can I specify both *guppy* and *guppies*? We cannot simply say `/guppy|ies/`, because that would match only the strings *guppy* and *ies*. This is be- *Precedence*   cause sequences like `guppy` take **precedence** over the disjunction operator `|`. To make the disjunction operator apply only to a specific pattern, we need to use the parenthesis operators (and). Enclosing a pattern in parentheses makes it act like a single character for the purposes of neighboring operators like the pipe `|` and the Kleene`*`. So the pattern `/gupp(y|ies)/` would specify that we meant the disjunction only to apply to the suffixes y and ies.

The parenthesis operator (is also useful when we are using counters like the Kleene∗. Unlike the | operator, the Kleene∗ operator applies by default only to a single character, not to a whole sequence. Suppose we want to match repeated instances of a string. Perhaps we have a line that has column labels of the form *Column 1 Column 2 Column 3*. The expression /Column␣[0-9]+␣∗/ will not match any number of columns; instead, it will match a single column followed by any number of spaces! The star here applies only to the space ␣ that precedes it, not to the whole sequence. With the parentheses, we could write the expression /(Column␣[0-9]+␣∗)∗/ to match the word *Column*, followed by a number and optional spaces, the whole pattern repeated any number of times.

Operator precedence

This idea that one operator may take precedence over another, requiring us to sometimes use parentheses to specify what we mean, is formalized by the **operator precedence hierarchy** for regular expressions. The following table gives the order of RE operator precedence, from highest precedence to lowest precedence.

Parenthesis	( )
Counters	∗ + ? {}
Sequences and anchors	the ^my end$
Disjunction	|

Thus, because counters have a higher precedence than sequences, /the∗/ matches *theeeee* but not *thethe*. Because sequences have a higher precedence than disjunction, /the|any/ matches *the* or *any* but not *theny*.

Patterns can be ambiguous in another way. Consider the expression /[a-z]∗/ when matching against the text *once upon a time*. Since /[a-z]∗/ matches zero or more letters, this expression could match nothing, or just the first letter *o*, *on*, *onc*, or *once*. In these cases regular expressions always match the *largest* string they can; we

Greedy

say that patterns are **greedy**, expanding to cover as much of a string as they can.

2.1.3   A Simple Example

Suppose we wanted to write a RE to find cases of the English article *the*. A simple (but incorrect) pattern might be:

/the/

One problem is that this pattern will miss the word when it begins a sentence and hence is capitalized (i.e., *The*). This might lead us to the following pattern:

/[tT]he/

But we will still incorrectly return texts with the embedded in other words (e.g., *other* or *theology*). So we need to specify that we want instances with a word boundary on both sides:

/\b[tT]he\b/

Suppose we wanted to do this without the use of /\b/. We might want this since /\b/ won't treat underscores and numbers as word boundaries; but we might want to find *the* in some context where it might also have underlines or numbers nearby (*the_* or *the25*). We need to specify that we want instances in which there are no alphabetic letters on either side of the *the*:

```
/[^a-zA-Z][tT]he[^a-zA-Z]/
```

But there is still one more problem with this pattern: it won't find the word *the* when it begins a line. This is because the regular expression [^a-zA-Z], which we used to avoid embedded instances of *the*, implies that there must be some single (although non-alphabetic) character before the *the*. We can avoid this by specifying that before the *the* we require *either* the beginning-of-line or a non-alphabetic character, and the same at the end of the line:

```
/(^|[^a-zA-Z])[tT]he([^a-zA-Z]|$)/
```

The process we just went through was based on fixing two kinds of errors: **false positives**, strings that we incorrectly matched like *other* or *there*, and **false negatives**, strings that we incorrectly missed, like *The*. Addressing these two kinds of errors comes up again and again in implementing speech and language processing systems. Reducing the error rate for an application thus involves two antagonistic efforts:

False positive
False negative

- Increasing **accuracy** (minimizing false positives)
- Increasing **coverage** (minimizing false negatives)

2.1.4   A More Complex Example

Let's try out a more significant example of the power of REs. Suppose we want to build an application to help a user buy a computer on the Web. The user might want "any PC with more than 6 GHz and 256 GB of disk space for less than $1000". To do this kind of retrieval, we first need to be able to look for expressions like *6 GHz* or *256 GB* or *Dell* or *Mac* or *$999.99*. In the rest of this section we'll work out some simple regular expressions for this task.

First, let's complete our regular expression for prices. Here's a regular expression for a dollar sign followed by a string of digits. Note that Perl is smart enough to realize that $ here doesn't mean end-of-line; how might it know that?

```
/$[0-9]+/
```

Now we just need to deal with fractions of dollars. We'll add a decimal point and two digits afterwards:

```
/$[0-9]+\.[0-9][0-9]/
```

This pattern only allows *$199.99* but not *$199*. We need to make the cents optional and to make sure we're at a word boundary:

```
/\b$[0-9]+(\.[0-9][0-9])?\b/
```

How about specifications for processor speed (in megahertz = MHz or gigahertz = GHz)? Here's a pattern for that:

```
/\b[0-9]+␣*(MHz|[Mm]egahertz|GHz|[Gg]igahertz)\b/
```

Note that we use /␣*/ to mean "zero or more spaces" since there might always be extra spaces lying around. Dealing with disk space or memory size (in GB = gigabytes), we need to allow for optional fractions again (*5.5 GB*). Note the use of ? for making the final s optional:

```
/\b[0-9]+(\.[0-9]+)?␣*(GB|[Gg]igabytes?)\b/
```

Finally, we might want some simple patterns to specify operating systems:

```
/\b(Windows␣*(Vista|XP)?)\b/
/\b(Mac|Macintosh|Apple|OS␣X)\b/
```

2.1.5 Advanced Operators

There are also some useful advanced regular expression operators. Figure 2.6 shows some aliases for common ranges, which can be used mainly to save typing. Besides the Kleene * and Kleene + we can also use explicit numbers as counters, by enclosing them in curly brackets. The regular expression /{3}/ means "exactly 3 occurrences of the previous character or expression". So /a\.{24}z/ will match *a* followed by 24 dots followed by *z* (but not *a* followed by 23 or 25 dots followed by a *z*).

RE	Expansion	Match	Examples
\d	[0-9]	any digit	Party␣of␣5
\D	[^0-9]	any non-digit	Blue␣moon
\w	[a-zA-Z0-9_]	any alphanumeric/underscore	Daiyu
\W	[^\w]	a non-alphanumeric	!!!!
\s	[␣\r\t\n\f]	whitespace (space, tab)	
\S	[^\s]	Non-whitespace	in␣Concord

Figure 2.6 Aliases for common sets of characters.

A range of numbers can also be specified. So /{n,m}/ specifies from *n* to *m* occurrences of the previous char or expression, and /{n,}/ means at least *n* occurrences of the previous expression. REs for counting are summarized in Fig. 2.7.

RE	Match
*	zero or more occurrences of the previous char or expression
+	one or more occurrences of the previous char or expression
?	exactly zero or one occurrence of the previous char or expression
{n}	*n* occurrences of the previous char or expression
{n,m}	from *n* to *m* occurrences of the previous char or expression
{n,}	at least *n* occurrences of the previous char or expression

Figure 2.7 Regular expression operators for counting.

Newline

Finally, certain special characters are referred to by special notation based on the backslash (\) (see Fig. 2.8). The most common of these are the **newline** character \n and the **tab** character \t. To refer to characters that are special themselves (like ., *, [, and \), precede them with a backslash, (i.e., /\./, /*/, /\[/, and /\\/).

RE	Match	Example Patterns Matched
*	an asterisk "*"	"K*A*P*L*A*N"
\.	a period "."	"Dr_. Livingston, I presume"
\?	a question mark	"Why don't they come and lend a hand_?"
\n	a newline	
\t	a tab	

Figure 2.8   Some characters that need to be backslashed.

2.1.6   Regular Expression Substitution, Memory, and ELIZA

Substitution   An important use of regular expressions is in **substitutions**. For example, the Perl substitution operator s/regexp1/pattern/ allows a string characterized by a regular expression to be replaced by another string:

s/colour/color/

It is often useful to be able to refer to a particular subpart of the string matching the first pattern. For example, suppose we wanted to put angle brackets around all integers in a text, for example, changing *the 35 boxes* to *the <35> boxes*. We'd like a way to refer to the integer we've found so that we can easily add the brackets. To do this, we put parentheses (and) around the first pattern and use the **number** operator \1 in the second pattern to refer back. Here's how it looks:

s/([0-9]+)/<\1>/

The parenthesis and number operators can also specify that a certain string or expression must occur twice in the text. For example, suppose we are looking for the pattern "the Xer they were, the Xer they will be", where we want to constrain the two X's to be the same string. We do this by surrounding the first X with the parenthesis operator, and replacing the second X with the number operator \1, as follows:

/the (.*)er they were, the \1er they will be/

Here the \1 will be replaced by whatever string matched the first item in parentheses. So this will match *The bigger they were, the bigger they will be* but not *The bigger they were, the faster they will be*.

The number operator can be used with other numbers. If you match two different sets of parenthesis, \2 means whatever matched the *second* set. For example,

/the (.*)er they (.*), the \1er we \2/

Register   will match *The faster they ran, the faster we ran* but not *The faster they ran, the faster we ate*. These numbered memories are called **registers** (e.g., register 1, register 2, register 3). This memory feature is not part of every regular expression language and is often considered an "extended" feature of regular expressions.

Substitutions using memory are useful in implementing simple natural-language-understanding programs like ELIZA (Weizenbaum, 1966). Recall that ELIZA simulates a Rogerian psychologist by carrying on conversations like the following:

User₁:	Men are all alike.

User₁: Men are all alike.
ELIZA₁: IN WHAT WAY
User₂: They're always bugging us about something or other.
ELIZA₂: CAN YOU THINK OF A SPECIFIC EXAMPLE
User₃: Well, my boyfriend made me come here.
ELIZA₃: YOUR BOYFRIEND MADE YOU COME HERE
User₄: He says I'm depressed much of the time.
ELIZA₄: I AM SORRY TO HEAR YOU ARE DEPRESSED

ELIZA works by having a cascade of regular expression substitutions that each match some part of the input lines and changes them. The first substitutions change all instances of *my* to *YOUR*, and *I'm* to *YOU ARE*, and so on. The next set of substitutions matches and replaces other patterns in the input. Here are some examples:

```
s/.* YOU ARE (depressed|sad) .*/I AM SORRY TO HEAR YOU ARE \1/
s/.* YOU ARE (depressed|sad) .*/WHY DO YOU THINK YOU ARE \1/
s/.* all .*/IN WHAT WAY/
s/.* always .*/CAN YOU THINK OF A SPECIFIC EXAMPLE/
```

Since multiple substitutions can apply to a given input, substitutions are assigned a rank and applied in order. Creating patterns is the topic of Exercise 2.2.

2.2   Finite-State Automata

Finite-state automaton
FSA

The regular expression is more than just a convenient metalanguage for text searching. First, a regular expression is one way of describing a **finite-state automaton (FSA)**. Finite-state automata are the theoretical foundation of a good deal of the computational work we describe in this book. Any regular expression can be implemented as a finite-state automaton (except regular expressions that use the memory feature; more on this later). Symmetrically, any finite-state automaton can be described with a regular expression. Second, a regular expression is one way of characterizing a particular kind of formal language called a **regular language**. Both regular expressions and finite-state automata can be used to describe regular languages. A third equivalent method of characterizing the regular languages, the **regular grammar**, is introduced in Chapter 16. The relation among these theoretical constructions is sketched in Fig. 2.9.

Regular language

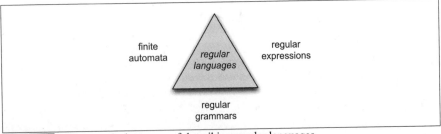

Figure 2.9   Three equivalent ways of describing regular languages.

This section begins by introducing finite-state automata for some of the regular expressions from the last section and then suggests how the mapping from regular expressions to automata proceeds in general. Although we begin with their use for implementing regular expressions, FSAs have a wide variety of other uses that we explore in this chapter and the next.

2.2.1   Use of an FSA to Recognize Sheeptalk

After a while, with the parrot's help, the Doctor got to learn the language of the animals so well that he could talk to them himself and understand everything they said.

Hugh Lofting, *The Story of Doctor Dolittle*

Let's begin with the "sheep language" we discussed previously. Recall that we defined the sheep language as any string from the following (infinite) set:

baa!
baaa!
baaaa!
baaaaa!
...

Automaton

The regular expression for this kind of "sheeptalk" is /baa+!/. Figure 2.10 shows an **automaton** for modeling this regular expression. The automaton (i.e., machine, also called **finite automaton**, **finite-state automaton**, or **FSA**) recognizes a set of strings, in this case the strings characterizing sheep talk in the same way that a regular expression does. We represent the automaton as a directed graph: a finite set of vertices (also called nodes), together with a set of directed links between pairs of vertices called arcs. We'll represent vertices with circles and arcs with arrows. The automaton has five

State

Start state

states, which are represented by nodes in the graph. State 0 is the **start state**. In our examples, state 0 will generally be the start state; to mark another state as the start state, we can add an incoming arrow to the start state. State 4 is the **final state** or **accepting state**, which we represent by the double circle. It also has five **transitions**, which we represent by arcs in the graph.

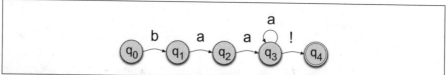

Figure 2.10   A finite-state automaton for talking sheep.

The FSA can be used for recognizing (we also say **accepting**) strings in the following way. First, think of the input as being written on a long tape broken up into cells, with one symbol written in each cell of the tape, as in Fig. 2.11.

The machine starts in the start state (q_0) and iterates the following process: Check the next letter of the input. If it matches the symbol on an arc leaving the current state, then cross that arc, move to the next state, and also advance one symbol in the input. If we are in the accepting state (q_4) when we run out of input, the machine has

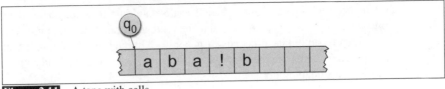

Figure 2.11   A tape with cells.

successfully recognized an instance of sheeptalk. If the machine never gets to the final state, either because it runs out of input or it gets some input that doesn't match an arc (as in Fig. 2.11), or if it just happens to get stuck in some non-final state, we say the

Rejecting   machine **rejects** or fails to accept an input.

State-transition   We can also represent an automaton with a **state-transition table**. As in the graph
table   notation, the state-transition table represents the start state, the ac-

	Input		
State	b	a	!
0	1	$\emptyset$	$\emptyset$
1	$\emptyset$	2	$\emptyset$
2	$\emptyset$	3	$\emptyset$
3	$\emptyset$	3	4
4:	$\emptyset$	$\emptyset$	$\emptyset$

cepting states, and what transitions leave each state with which symbols. On the right is the state-transition table for the FSA of Fig. 2.10. We've marked state 4 with a colon to indicate that it's a final state (you can have as many final states as you want), and the $\emptyset$ indicates an illegal or missing transition. We can read the first row as "if we're in state 0 and we see the input **b** we must go to state 1. If we're in state 0 and we see the input **a** or **!**, we fail".

More formally, a finite automaton is defined by the following five parameters:

$Q = q_0 q_1 q_2 \ldots q_{N-1}$	a finite set of N **states**
Σ	a finite **input alphabet** of symbols
q_0	the **start state**
F	the set of **final states**, $F \subseteq Q$
$\delta(q,i)$	the **transition function** or transition matrix between states. Given a state $q \in Q$ and an input symbol $i \in \Sigma$, $\delta(q,i)$ returns a new state $q' \in Q$. δ is thus a relation from $Q \times \Sigma$ to Q;

For the sheeptalk automaton in Fig. 2.10, $Q = \{q_0, q_1, q_2, q_3, q_4\}$, $\Sigma = \{a, b, !\}$, $F = \{q_4\}$, and $\delta(q,i)$ is defined by the transition table above.

Figure 2.12 presents an algorithm for recognizing a string using a state-transition table. The algorithm is called D-RECOGNIZE for "deterministic recognizer". A **deter-**

Deterministic   **ministic** algorithm is one that has no choice points; the algorithm always knows what to do for any input. The next section introduces non-deterministic automata that must make decisions about which states to move to.

D-RECOGNIZE takes as input a tape and an automaton. It returns *accept* if the string it is pointing to on the tape is accepted by the automaton, and *reject* otherwise. Note that since D-RECOGNIZE assumes it is already pointing at the string to be checked, its task is only a subpart of the general problem that we often use regular expressions for, finding a string in a corpus. (The general problem is left as Exercise 2.9 for the reader.)

D-RECOGNIZE begins by setting the variable *index* to the beginning of the tape, and *current-state* to the machine's initial state. D-RECOGNIZE then enters a loop that drives

function D-RECOGNIZE(*tape, machine*) **returns** accept or reject

   index ← Beginning of tape
   current-state ← Initial state of machine
  loop
    if End of input has been reached **then**
     if current-state is an accept state **then**
      return accept
    else
      return reject
    elsif *transition-table[current-state,tape[index]]* is empty **then**
     return reject
    else
     current-state ← *transition-table[current-state,tape[index]]*
     index ← *index* + 1
  end

Figure 2.12   An algorithm for deterministic recognition of FSAs. This algorithm returns *accept* if the entire string it is pointing at is in the language defined by the FSA, and *reject* if the string is not in the language.

the algorithm. It first checks whether it has reached the end of its input. If so, it either accepts the input (if the current state is an accept state) or rejects the input (if not).

If there is input left on the tape, D-RECOGNIZE looks at the transition table to decide which state to move to. The variable *current-state* indicates which row of the table to consult, and the current symbol on the tape indicates which column of the table to consult. The resulting transition-table cell is used to update the variable *current-state* and *index* is incremented to move forward on the tape. If the transition-table cell is empty, then the machine has nowhere to go and must reject the input.

Figure 2.13 traces the execution of this algorithm on the sheep language FSA given the sample input string *baaa!*.

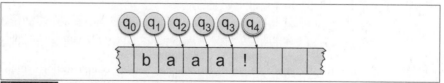

Figure 2.13   Tracing the execution of FSA #1 on some sheeptalk.

Before examining the beginning of the tape, the machine is in state q_0. Finding a *b* on input tape, it changes to state q_1 as indicated by the contents of *transition-table*$[q_0,b]$ on page 28. It then finds an *a* and switches to state q_2, another *a* puts it in state q_3, a third *a* leaves it in state q_3, where it reads the *!* and switches to state q_4. Since there is no more input, the end of input condition at the beginning of the loop is satisfied for the first time and the machine halts in q_4. State q_4 is an accepting state, so the machine has accepted the string *baaa!* as a sentence in the sheep language.

The algorithm fails whenever there is no legal transition for a given combination of state and input. The input *abc* will fail to be recognized since there is no legal transition out of state q_0 on the input a (i.e., this entry of the transition table on page 28 has a ∅). Even if the automaton had allowed an initial *a*, it would have certainly failed on *c* since *c* isn't even in the sheeptalk alphabet! We can think of these "empty" elements in the table as if they all pointed at one "empty" state, which we might call the **fail state** or **sink state**. In a sense then, we could view any machine with empty transitions *as if* we had augmented it with a fail state and had drawn in all the extra arcs so that we always had somewhere to go from any state on any possible input. Just for completeness, Fig. 2.14 shows the FSA from Fig. 2.10 with the fail state q_F filled in.

Fail state

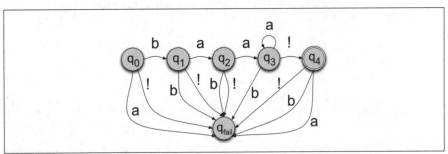

Figure 2.14   Adding a fail state to Fig. 2.10.

2.2.2   Formal Languages

We can use the same graph in Fig. 2.10 as an automaton for GENERATING sheeptalk. If we do, we would say that the automaton starts at state q_0 and crosses arcs to new states, printing out the symbols that label each arc it follows. When the automaton gets to the final state it stops. Notice that at state q_3, the automaton has to choose between printing a **!** and going to state q_4, or printing an **a** and returning to state q_3. Let's say for now that we don't care how the machine makes this decision; maybe it flips a coin. For now, we don't care which exact string of sheeptalk we generate, as long as it's a string captured by the regular expression for sheeptalk above.

> **Formal Language:** A model that can both generate and recognize all and only the strings of a formal language acts as a *definition* of the formal language.

Formal language

Alphabet

A **formal language** is a set of strings, each string composed of symbols from a finite symbol set called an **alphabet** (the same alphabet used above for defining an automaton). The alphabet for the sheep language is the set $\Sigma = a, b, !$. Given a model *m* (such as a particular FSA), we can use $L(m)$ to mean "the formal language characterized by *m*". So the formal language defined by our sheeptalk automaton *m* in Fig. 2.10 (and the transition table on page 28) is the infinite set

$$L(m) = baa!, baaa!, baaaa!, baaaaa!, baaaaaa!, \ldots \qquad (2.1)$$

The usefulness of an automaton for defining a language is that it can express an infinite set (such as the one above) in a closed form. Formal languages are not the same

Natural language   as **natural languages**, which are the languages that real people speak. In fact, a formal language may bear no resemblance at all to a real language (e.g., a formal language can be used to model the different states of a soda machine). But we often use a formal language to model part of a natural language, such as parts of the phonology, morphology, or syntax. The term **generative grammar** is sometimes used in linguistics to mean a grammar of a formal language; the origin of the term is this use of an automaton to define a language by generating all possible strings.

2.2.3   Another Example

In the previous examples, our formal alphabet consisted of letters; but we can also have a higher-level alphabet consisting of words. In this way we can write finite-state automata that model facts about word combinations. For example, suppose we wanted to build an FSA that modeled the subpart of English dealing with amounts of money. Such a formal language would model the subset of English consisting of phrases like *ten cents*, *three dollars*, *one dollar thirty-five cents*, and so on.

We might break this down by first building just the automaton to account for the numbers from 1 to 99, since we'll need them to deal with cents. Figure 2.15 shows this.

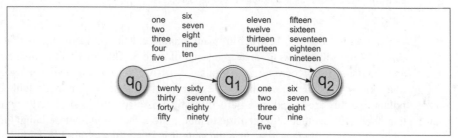

Figure 2.15   An FSA for the words for English numbers 1–99.

We could now add *cents* and *dollars* to our automaton. Figure 2.16 shows a simple version of this, where we just made two copies of the automaton in Fig. 2.15 with minor changes, and appended the words *cents* and *dollars*.

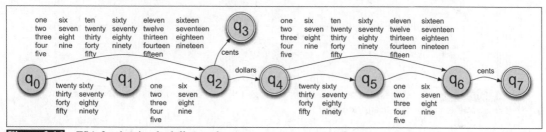

Figure 2.16   FSA for the simple dollars and cents.

We would now need to add in the grammar for different amounts of dollars; including higher numbers like *hundred*, *thousand*. We'd also need to make sure that the nouns like *cents* and *dollars* are singular when appropriate (*one cent*, *one dollar*), and plural when appropriate (*ten cents*, *two dollars*). This is left as an exercise for the reader (Exercise 2.3). We can think of the FSAs in Fig. 2.15 and Fig. 2.16 as simple grammars of parts of English. We return to grammar-building in Part III of this book, particularly in Chapter 12.

2.2.4   Non-Deterministic FSAs

Let's extend our discussion now to another class of FSAs: **non-deterministic FSAs** (or **NFSAs**). Consider the sheeptalk automaton in Fig. 2.17, which is much like our first automaton in Fig. 2.10.

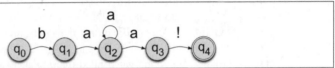

Figure 2.17   A non-deterministic finite-state automaton for talking sheep (NFSA #1). Compare with the deterministic automaton in Fig. 2.10.

Non-deterministic

NFSA

DFSA

ϵ-transition

The only difference between this automaton and the previous one is that here in Fig. 2.17 the self-loop is on state 2 instead of state 3. Consider using this network as an automaton for recognizing sheeptalk. When we get to state 2, if we see an **a** we don't know whether to remain in state 2 or go on to state 3. Automata with decision points like this are called **non-deterministic FSAs** (or **NFSAs**). Recall by contrast that Fig. 2.10 specified a **deterministic** automaton, that is one whose behavior during recognition is fully *determined* by the state it is in and the symbol it is looking at. A deterministic automaton can be referred to as a **DFSA**. That is not true for the machine in Fig. 2.17 (NFSA #1).

Another common type of non-determinism is one caused by arcs that have no symbols on them (called ϵ-**transitions**). The automaton in Fig. 2.18 defines exactly the same language as the last one and our first one, but it does it with an ϵ-transition.

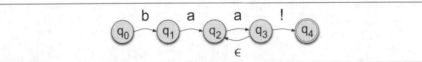

Figure 2.18   Another NFSA for the sheep language (NFSA #2). It differs from NFSA #1 in Fig. 2.17 in having an ϵ-transition.

We interpret this new arc as follows: If we are in state q_3, we are allowed to move to state q_2 *without* looking at the input or advancing our input pointer. So this introduces another kind of non-determinism—we might not know whether to follow the ϵ-transition or the **!** arc.

2.2.5   Use of an NFSA to Accept Strings

If we want to know whether a string is an instance of sheeptalk and if we use a non-deterministic machine to recognize it, we might follow the wrong arc and reject it when we should have accepted it. That is, since there is more than one choice at some point, we might take the wrong choice. This problem of choice in non-deterministic models will come up again and again as we build computational models, particularly for parsing. There are three standard **solutions to the problem of non-determinism**:

Backup

- **Backup:** Whenever we come to a choice point, we could put a *marker* to mark where we were in the input and what state the automaton was in. Then if it turns out that we took the wrong choice, we could back up and try another path.

Look-ahead

- **Look-ahead:** We could look ahead in the input to help us decide which path to take.

Parallelism

- **Parallelism:** Whenever we come to a choice point, we could look at every alternative path in parallel.

We focus here on the backup approach and defer discussion of the look-ahead and parallelism approaches to later chapters.

The backup approach suggests that we should blithely make choices that might lead to dead ends, knowing that we can always return to the unexplored alternatives. There are two keys to this approach: we need to remember all the alternatives for each choice point, and we need to store sufficient information about each alternative so that we can return to it when necessary. When a backup algorithm reaches a point in its processing where no progress can be made (because it runs out of input or has no legal transitions), it returns to a previous choice point, selects one of the unexplored alternatives, and continues from there. Applying this notion to our non-deterministic recognizer, we need only remember two things for each choice point: the state, or node, of the machine that we can go to and the corresponding position on the tape. We

Search-state

will call the combination of the node and position the **search-state** of the recognition algorithm. To avoid confusion, we will refer to the state of the automaton (as opposed to the state of the search) as a **node** or a **machine-state**.

Before going on to describe the main part of this algorithm, we should note two changes to the transition table that drives it. First, to represent nodes that have outgoing ϵ-transitions, we add a new ϵ-**column** to the transition table. If a node has an ϵ-transition, we list the destination node in the ϵ-column for that node's row. The second addition is needed to account for multiple transitions to different nodes from the same input symbol. We let each cell entry consist of a list of destination nodes

State	Input			
	b	a	!	ϵ
0	1	0	0	0
1	0	2	0	0
2	0	2,3	0	0
3	0	0	4	0
4:	0	0	0	0

rather than a single node. On the right we show the transition table for the machine in Fig. 2.17 (NFSA #1). While it has no ϵ-transitions, it does show that in machine-state q_2, the input a can lead back to q_2 or on to q_3.

Figure 2.19 shows the algorithm for using a non-deterministic FSA to recognize an input string. The function ND-RECOGNIZE uses the variable *agenda* to keep track of all the currently unexplored choices generated during the course of processing. Each choice (search-state) is a tuple consisting of a node (state) of the machine and a position on the tape. The variable *current-search-state* represents the branch choice being currently explored.

ND-RECOGNIZE begins by creating an initial search-state and placing it on the agenda. For now we don't specify in what order the search-states are placed on the agenda. This search-state consists of the initial machine-state of the machine and a pointer to the beginning of the tape. The function NEXT is then called to retrieve an item from the agenda and assign it to the variable *current-search-state*.

As with D-RECOGNIZE, the first task of the main loop is to determine if the entire contents of the tape have been successfully recognized. This is done by a call to ACCEPT-STATE?, which returns *accept* if the current search-state contains both an accepting machine-state and a pointer to the end of the tape. If we're not done, the machine generates a set of possible next steps by calling GENERATE-NEW-STATES, which creates search-states for any ϵ-transitions and any normal input-symbol transitions from the transition table. All of these search-state tuples are then added to the current agenda.

Finally, we attempt to get a new search-state to process from the agenda. If the agenda is empty, we've run out of options and have to reject the input. Otherwise, an unexplored option is selected and the loop continues.

It is important to understand why ND-RECOGNIZE returns a value of reject only when the agenda is found to be empty. Unlike D-RECOGNIZE, it does not return reject when it reaches the end of the tape in a non-accept machine-state or when it finds itself unable to advance the tape from some machine-state. This is because, in the nondeterministic case, such roadblocks indicate failure only down a given path, not overall failure. We can only be sure we can reject a string when all possible choices have been examined and found lacking.

Figure 2.20 illustrates the progress of ND-RECOGNIZE as it attempts to handle the input baaa!. Each strip illustrates the state of the algorithm at a given point in its processing. The *current-search-state* variable is captured by the solid bubbles representing the machine-state along with the arrow representing progress on the tape. Each strip lower down in the figure represents progress from one *current-search-state* to the next.

Little of interest happens until the algorithm finds itself in state q_2 while looking at the second a on the tape. An examination of the entry for transition-table$[q_2,a]$ returns both q_2 and q_3. Search states are created for each of these choices and placed on the agenda. Unfortunately, our algorithm chooses to move to state q_3, a move that results in neither an accept state nor any new states since the entry for transition-table$[q_3, a]$ is empty. At this point, the algorithm simply asks the agenda for a new state to pursue. Since the choice of returning to q_2 from q_2 is the only unexamined choice on the agenda, it is returned with the tape pointer advanced to the next a. Somewhat diabolically, ND-RECOGNIZE finds itself faced with the same choice. The entry for transition-table$[q_2,a]$ still indicates that looping back to q_2 or advancing to q_3 are valid choices. As before, states representing both are placed on the agenda. These search states are not the same as the previous ones since their tape index values have advanced. This time the agenda provides the move to q_3 as the next move. The move to q_4, and success, is then uniquely determined by the tape and the transition table.

---

function ND-RECOGNIZE(*tape, machine*) **returns** accept or reject

   agenda ← (Initial state of machine, beginning of tape)
   current-search-state ← NEXT(*agenda*)
   loop
     if ACCEPT-STATE?(*current-search-state*) returns true **then**
       return accept
     else
       agenda ← *agenda* ∪ GENERATE-NEW-STATES(*current-search-state*)
     if *agenda* is empty **then**
       return reject
     else
       current-search-state ← NEXT(*agenda*)
   end

function GENERATE-NEW-STATES(*current-state*) **returns** a set of search-states

   current-node ← the node the current search-state is in
   index ← the point on the tape the current search-state is looking at
   return a list of search states from transition table as follows:
     (*transition-table[current-node,ϵ], index*)
     ∪
     (*transition-table[current-node, tape[index]], index + 1*)

function ACCEPT-STATE?(*search-state*) **returns** true or false

   current-node ← the node search-state is in
   index ← the point on the tape search-state is looking at
   if *index* is at the end of the tape **and** *current-node* is an accept state of machine
   then
     return true
   else
     return false

Figure 2.19   An algorithm for NFSA recognition. The word *node* means a state of the FSA, and *state* or *search-state* means "the state of the search process", i.e., a combination of *node* and *tape position.*

2.2.6   Recognition as Search

ND-RECOGNIZE accomplishes the task of recognizing strings in a regular language by providing a way to systematically explore all the possible paths through a machine. If this exploration yields a path ending in an accept state, ND-RECOGNIZE accepts the string; otherwise, it rejects the string. This systematic exploration is made possible by the agenda mechanism, which on each iteration selects a partial path to explore and keeps track of any remaining, as yet unexplored, partial paths.

    Algorithms, such as ND-RECOGNIZE, which operate by systematically searching *State-space search* for solutions, are known as **state-space search** algorithms. In such algorithms, the problem definition creates a space of possible solutions; the goal is to explore this space, returning an answer when one is found or rejecting the input when the space

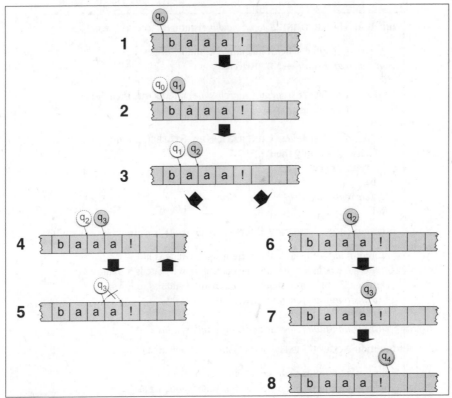

Figure 2.20 Tracing the execution of NFSA #1 (Fig. 2.17) on some sheeptalk.

has been exhaustively explored. In ND-RECOGNIZE, search states consist of pairings of machine-states with positions on the input tape. The state-space consists of all the pairings of machine-state and tape positions that are possible given the machine in question. The goal of the search is to navigate through this space from one state to another, looking for a pairing of an accept state with an end of tape position.

The key to the effectiveness of such programs is often the *order* in which the states in the space are considered. A poor ordering of states may lead to the examination of a large number of unfruitful states before a successful solution is discovered. Unfortunately, it is typically not possible to tell a good choice from a bad one, and often the best we can do is to ensure that each possible solution is eventually considered.

Careful readers may have noticed that the ordering of states in ND-RECOGNIZE has been left unspecified. We know only that unexplored states are added to the agenda as they are created and that the (undefined) function NEXT returns an unexplored state from the agenda when asked. How should the function NEXT be defined? Consider an ordering strategy by which the states that are considered next are the most recently created ones. We can implement such a policy by placing newly created states at the front of the agenda and having NEXT return the state at the front of the agenda when called. Thus, the agenda is implemented by a **stack**. This is commonly referred to as a *Depth-first* **depth-first search** or **last in first out** (**LIFO**) strategy.

Such a strategy dives into the search space following newly developed leads as they are generated. It will only return to consider earlier options when progress along a current lead has been blocked. The trace of the execution of ND-RECOGNIZE on the string baaa! as shown in Fig. 2.20 illustrates a depth-first search. The algorithm hits the first choice point after seeing ba when it has to decide whether to stay in q_2 or advance to state q_3. At this point, it chooses one alternative and follows it until sure the choice was wrong. The algorithm then backs up and tries another older alternative.

Depth-first strategies have one major pitfall: under certain circumstances they can enter an infinite loop. This is possible either if the search space happens to be set up in such a way that a search-state can be accidentally revisited, or if there are an infinite number of search states. We revisit this question when we turn to more complicated search problems in parsing in Chapter 13.

The second way to order the states in the search space is to consider states in the order in which they are created. We can implement such a policy by placing newly created states at the back of the agenda and still have NEXT return the state at the front of the agenda. Thus, the agenda is implemented via a **queue**. This is commonly *Breadth-first* referred to as a **breadth-first search** or **first in first out** (**FIFO**) strategy. Consider a different trace of the execution of ND-RECOGNIZE on the string baaa! as shown in Fig. 2.21. Again, the algorithm hits its first choice point after seeing ba when it had to decide whether to stay in q_2 or advance to state q_3. But now rather than picking one choice and following it up, we imagine examining all possible choices, expanding one ply of the search tree at a time.

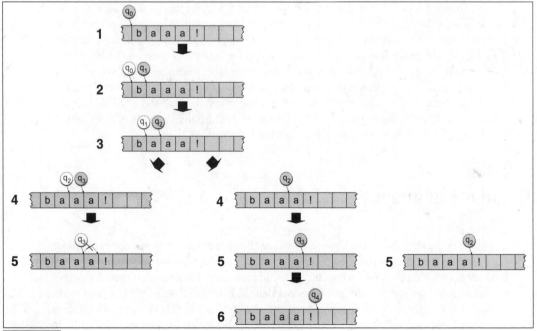

Figure 2.21   A breadth-first trace of FSA #1 on some sheeptalk.

Like depth-first search, breadth-first search has its pitfalls. As with depth-first, if the state-space is infinite, the search may never terminate. More importantly, due to growth in the size of the agenda if the state-space is even moderately large, the search may require an impractically large amount of memory. For small problems, either depth-first or breadth-first search strategies may be adequate, although depth-first is normally preferred for its more efficient use of memory. For larger problems, more complex search techniques such as **dynamic programming** or **A*** must be used, as we discuss in Chapters 6 and 13.

2.2.7   Relation of Deterministic and Non-Deterministic Automata

It may seem that allowing NFSAs to have non-deterministic features like ϵ-transitions would make them more powerful than DFSAs. In fact, this is not the case; for any NFSA, there is an exactly equivalent DFSA. There is a simple algorithm for converting an NFSA to an equivalent DFSA, although the number of states in this equivalent deterministic automaton may be much larger. See Lewis and Papadimitriou (1988) or Hopcroft and Ullman (1979) for the proof of the correspondence. The basic intuition of the proof is worth mentioning, however, and builds on the way NFSAs parse their input. Recall that the difference between NFSAs and DFSAs is that in an NFSA a state q_i may have more than one possible next state given an input i (e.g., q_a and q_b). The algorithm in Fig. 2.19 dealt with this problem by choosing either q_a or q_b and then *backtracking* if the choice turned out to be wrong. We mentioned that a parallel version of the algorithm would follow both paths (toward q_a and q_b) simultaneously.

The algorithm for converting an NFSA to a DFSA is like this parallel algorithm; we build an automaton that has a deterministic path for every path our parallel recognizer might have followed in the search space. We imagine following both paths simultaneously, and group into an equivalence class all the states we reach on the same input symbol (i.e., q_a and q_b). We now give a new state label to this new equivalence class state (e.g., q_{ab}). We continue doing this for every possible input for every possible group of states. The resulting DFSA can have as many states as there are distinct sets of the N states in the original NFSA. The number of different subsets of a set with N elements is 2^N; hence, the new DFSA can have as many as 2^N states.

2.3   Regular Languages and FSAs

As we suggested above, the class of languages that are definable by regular expressions is exactly the same as the class of languages that are characterizable by finite-state automata (whether deterministic or non-deterministic). We therefore call these languages

Regular language   the **regular languages**. To give a formal definition of the class of regular languages, we need to refer to two earlier concepts: the alphabet Σ, which is the set of all symbols in the language, and the *empty string* ϵ, which is conventionally not included in Σ. In addition, we refer to the *empty set* $\emptyset$ (which is distinct from ϵ). The class of regular languages (or **regular sets**) over Σ is then formally defined as follows: [1]

1. $\emptyset$ is a regular language
2. $\forall a \in \Sigma \cup \epsilon, \quad a$ is a regular language
3. If L_1 and L_2 are regular languages, then so are:
   - (a) $L_1 \cdot L_2 = \{ xy \mid x \in L_1, y \in L_2 \}$, the **concatenation** of L_1 and L_2
   - (b) $L_1 \cup L_2$, the **union** or **disjunction** of L_1 and L_2
   - (c) L_1^*, the **Kleene closure** of L_1

Only languages that meet the above properties are regular languages. Since the regular languages are the languages characterizable by regular expressions, all the regular expression operators introduced in this chapter (except memory) can be implemented by the three operations that define regular languages: concatenation, disjunction/union (also called "|"), and Kleene closure. For example, all the counters (`*`,`+`, `{n,m}`) are just a special case of repetition plus Kleene `*`. All the anchors can be thought of as individual special symbols. The square braces `[ ]` are a kind of disjunction (i.e., `[ab]` means "a or b", or the disjunction of a and b). Thus, it is true that any regular expression can be turned into a (perhaps larger) expression that only makes use of the three primitive operations.

Regular languages are also closed under the following operations (Σ^* means the infinite set of all possible strings formed from the alphabet Σ):

intersection	if L_1 and L_2 are regular languages, then so is $L_1 \cap L_2$, the language consisting of the set of strings that are in both L_1 and L_2.
difference	if L_1 and L_2 are regular languages, then so is $L_1 - L_2$, the language consisting of the set of strings that are in L_1 but not L_2.
complementation	If L_1 is a regular language, then so is $\Sigma^* - L_1$, the set of all possible strings that aren't in L_1.
reversal	If L_1 is a regular language, then so is L_1^R, the language consisting of the set of reversals of all the strings in L_1.

The proof that regular expressions are equivalent to finite-state automata can be found in Hopcroft and Ullman (1979); the proof has two parts: showing that an automaton can be built for each regular language and, conversely, that a regular language can be built for each automaton.

We won't give the proof, but we give the intuition by showing how to do the first part: build an automaton from any regular expression. The intuition is inductive on the number of operators: for the base case, we build an automaton to correspond to the regular expressions with no operators, that is, the regular expressions $\emptyset$, ϵ, or any single symbol $a \in \Sigma$. Figure 2.22 shows the automata for these three base cases.

Now for the inductive step, we show that each of the primitive operations of a regular expression (concatenation, union, closure) can be imitated by an automaton.

---

[1] Following van Santen and Sproat (1998), Kaplan and Kay (1994), and Lewis and Papadimitriou (1988).

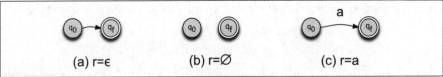

Figure 2.22   Automata for the base case (no operators) for the induction showing that any regular expression can be turned into an equivalent automaton.

- **concatenation**: As shown in Fig. 2.23, we just string two FSAs next to each other by connecting all the final states of FSA$_1$ to the initial state of FSA$_2$ by an ϵ-transition.

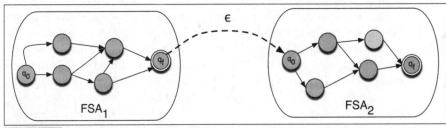

Figure 2.23   The concatenation of two FSAs.

- **closure**: As shown in Fig. 2.24, we create a new final and initial state, connect the original final states of the FSA back to the initial states by ϵ-transitions (this implements the repetition part of the Kleene *), and then put direct links between the new initial and final states by ϵ-transitions (this implements the possibility of having *zero* occurrences). We'd omit this last part to implement Kleene + instead.

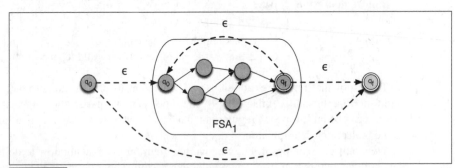

Figure 2.24   The closure (Kleene *) of an FSA.

- **union**: Finally, as shown in Fig. 2.25, we add a single new initial state q_0', and add new ϵ-transitions from it to the former initial states of the two machines to be joined.

We return to regular languages and regular grammars in Chapter 16.

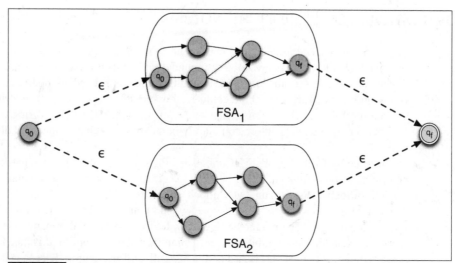

Figure 2.25   The union ( ) of two FSAs.

2.4   Summary

This chapter introduced the most important fundamental concept in language processing, the **finite automaton**, and the practical tool based on automaton, the **regular expression**. Here's a summary of the main points we covered about these ideas:

- The **regular expression** language is a powerful tool for pattern-matching.
- Basic operations in regular expressions include **concatenation** of symbols, **dis-
junction** of symbols ([ ], |, and .), **counters** (*, +, and {n,m}), **anchors** (^,
$) and precedence operators ((,)).
- Any regular expression can be realized as a **finite-state automaton** (**FSA**).
- Memory (\1 together with ( )) is an advanced operation that is often considered
part of regular expressions but that cannot be realized as a finite automaton.
- An automaton implicitly defines a **formal language** as the set of strings the
automaton **accepts** over any vocabulary (set of symbols).
- The behavior of a **deterministic** automaton (**DFSA**) is fully determined by the
state it is in.
- A **non-deterministic** automaton (**NFSA**) sometimes has to choose between multiple paths to take given the same current state and next input.
- Any **NFSA** can be converted to a **DFSA**.
- The order in which an **NFSA** chooses the next state to explore on the agenda defines its **search strategy**. The **depth-first search** or **LIFO** strategy corresponds
to the agenda-as-stack; the **breadth-first search** or **FIFO** strategy corresponds
to the agenda-as-queue.
- Any regular expression can automatically be compiled into a **NFSA** and hence
into a **FSA**.

Bibliographical and Historical Notes

Finite automata arose in the 1950s out of Turing's (1936) model of algorithmic computation, considered by many to be the foundation of modern computer science. The Turing machine was an abstract machine with a finite control and an input/output tape. In one move, the Turing machine could read a symbol on the tape, write a different symbol on the tape, change state, and move left or right. Thus, the Turing machine differs from a finite-state automaton mainly in its ability to change the symbols on its tape.

McCulloch-Pitts neuron

Inspired by Turing's work, McCulloch and Pitts built an automata-like model of the neuron (see von Neumann, 1963, p. 319). Their model, which is now usually called the **McCulloch-Pitts neuron** (McCulloch and Pitts, 1943), was a simplified model of the neuron as a kind of "computing element" that could be described in terms of propositional logic. The model was a binary device, at any point either active or not, that took excitatory and inhibitory input from other neurons and fired if its activation passed some fixed threshold. Based on the McCulloch-Pitts neuron, Kleene (1951) and (1956) defined the finite automaton and regular expressions and proved their equivalence. Non-deterministic automata were introduced by Rabin and Scott (1959), who also proved them equivalent to deterministic ones.

Ken Thompson was one of the first to build regular expressions compilers into editors for text searching (Thompson, 1968). His editor *ed* included a command "g/regular expression/p", or Global Regular Expression Print, which later became the Unix `grep` utility.

There are many general-purpose introductions to the mathematics underlying automata theory, such as Hopcroft and Ullman (1979) and Lewis and Papadimitriou (1988). These cover the mathematical foundations of the simple automata of this chapter, as well as the finite-state transducers of Chapter 3, the context-free grammars of Chapter 12, and the Chomsky hierarchy of Chapter 16. Friedl (1997) is a useful comprehensive guide to the advanced use of regular expressions.

The metaphor of problem-solving as search is basic to Artificial Intelligence (AI); more details on search can be found in any AI textbook such as Russell and Norvig (2002).

Exercises

2.1 Write regular expressions for the following languages. You may use either Perl/Python notation or the minimal "algebraic" notation of Section 2.3, but make sure to say which one you are using. By "word", we mean an alphabetic string separated from other words by whitespace, any relevant punctuation, line breaks, and so forth.

1. the set of all alphabetic strings;
2. the set of all lower case alphabetic strings ending in a *b*;

3. the set of all strings with two consecutive repeated words (e.g., "Humbert Humbert" and "the the" but not "the bug" or "the big bug");

4. the set of all strings from the alphabet a, b such that each a is immediately preceded by and immediately followed by a b;

5. all strings that start at the beginning of the line with an integer and that end at the end of the line with a word;

6. all strings that have both the word *grotto* and the word *raven* in them (but not, e.g., words like *grottos* that merely *contain* the word *grotto*);

7. write a pattern that places the first word of an English sentence in a register. Deal with punctuation.

2.2 Implement an ELIZA-like program, using substitutions such as those described on page 26. You may choose a different domain than a Rogerian psychologist, if you wish, although keep in mind that you would need a domain in which your program can legitimately engage in a lot of simple repetition.

2.3 Complete the FSA for English money expressions in Fig. 2.15 as suggested in the text following the figure. You should handle amounts up to $100,000, and make sure that "cent" and "dollar" have the proper plural endings when appropriate.

2.4 Design an FSA that recognizes simple date expressions like *March 15*, *the 22nd of November*, *Christmas*. You should try to include all such "absolute" dates (e.g., not "deictic" ones relative to the current day, like *the day before yesterday*). Each edge of the graph should have a word or a set of words on it. You should use some sort of shorthand for classes of words to avoid drawing too many arcs (e.g., furniture → desk, chair, table).

2.5 Now extend your date FSA to handle deictic expressions like *yesterday*, *tomorrow*, *a week from tomorrow*, *the day before yesterday*, *Sunday*, *next Monday*, *three weeks from Saturday*.

2.6 Write an FSA for time-of-day expressions like *eleven o'clock*, *twelve-thirty*, *midnight*, or *a quarter to ten*, and others.

2.7 (Thanks to Pauline Welby; this problem probably requires the ability to knit.) Write a regular expression (or draw an FSA) that matches all knitting patterns for scarves with the following specification: *32 stitches wide, K1P1 ribbing on both ends, stockinette stitch body, exactly two raised stripes.* All knitting patterns must include a cast-on row (to put the correct number of stitches on the needle) and a bind-off row (to end the pattern and prevent unraveling). Here's a sample pattern for one possible scarf matching the above description:[2]

---

[2] *Knit* and *purl* are two different types of stitches. The notation Kn means do n knit stitches. Similarly for purl stitches. Ribbing has a striped texture—most sweaters have ribbing at the sleeves, bottom, and neck. Stockinette stitch is a series of knit and purl rows that produces a plain pattern—socks or stockings are knit with this basic pattern, hence the name.

1. Cast on 32 stitches.	*cast on; puts stitches on needle*
2. K1 P1 across row (i.e., do (K1 P1) 16 times).	*K1P1 ribbing*
3. Repeat instruction 2 seven more times.	*adds length*
4. K32, P32.	*stockinette stitch*
5. Repeat instruction 4 an additional 13 times.	*adds length*
6. P32, P32.	*raised stripe stitch*
7. K32, P32.	*stockinette stitch*
8. Repeat instruction 7 an additional 251 times.	*adds length*
9. P32, P32.	*raised stripe stitch*
10. K32, P32.	*stockinette stitch*
11. Repeat instruction 10 an additional 13 times.	*adds length*
12. K1 P1 across row.	*K1P1 ribbing*
13. Repeat instruction 12 an additional 7 times.	*adds length*
14. Bind off 32 stitches.	*binds off row: ends pattern*

2.8   Write a regular expression for the language accepted by the NFSA in Fig. 2.26.

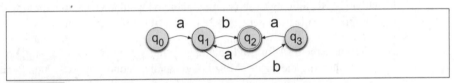

Figure 2.26   A mystery language.

2.9   Currently the function D-RECOGNIZE in Fig. 2.12 solves only a subpart of the important problem of finding a string in some text. Extend the algorithm to solve the following two deficiencies: (1) D-RECOGNIZE currently assumes that it is already pointing at the string to be checked, and (2) D-RECOGNIZE fails if the string it is pointing to includes as a proper substring a legal string for the FSA. That is, D-RECOGNIZE fails if there is an extra character at the end of the string.

2.10   Give an algorithm for negating a deterministic FSA. The negation of an FSA accepts exactly the set of strings that the original FSA rejects (over the same alphabet) and rejects all the strings that the original FSA accepts.

2.11   Why doesn't your previous algorithm work with NFSAs? Now extend your algorithm to negate an NFSA.

Chapter 3

Words and Transducers

How can there be any sin in sincere?
Where is the good in goodbye?
Meredith Willson, *The Music Man*

Chapter 2 introduced the regular expression, showing, for example, how a single search string could help us find both *woodchuck* and *woodchucks*. Hunting for singular or plural woodchucks was easy; the plural just tacks an *s* on to the end. But suppose we were looking for another fascinating woodland creatures; let's say a *fox*, a *fish*, that surly *peccary*, and perhaps a Canadian *wild goose*. Hunting for the plurals of these animals takes more than just tacking on an *s*. The plural of *fox* is *foxes*; of *peccary*, *peccaries*; and of *goose*, *geese*. To confuse matters further, fish don't usually change their form when they are plural.[1]

It takes two kinds of knowledge to correctly search for singulars and plurals of these forms. **Orthographic rules** tell us that we pluralize English words ending in *-y* by changing the *-y* to *-i-* and adding an *-es*. **Morphological rules** tell us that *fish* has a null plural and that the plural of *goose* is formed by a vowel change.

The problem of recognizing that a word (like *foxes*) breaks down into component morphemes (*fox* and *-es*) and building a structured representation of this fact is called **morphological parsing**.

Morphological parsing
Parsing

Parsing means taking an input and producing some sort of linguistic structure for it. We use the term parsing very broadly throughout this book to include many kinds of structures that might be produced; morphological, syntactic, semantic, discourse; in the form of a string, a tree, or a network. Morphological parsing or stemming applies to many affixes other than plurals; for example, we might need to take any English verb form ending in *-ing* (*going*, *talking*, *congratulating*) and parse it into its verbal stem plus the *-ing* morpheme. So given the **surface** or **input form** *going*, we might want to produce the parsed form VERB-go + GERUND-ing.

Surface form

Morphological parsing is important throughout speech and language processing. It plays a crucial role in Web search for morphologically complex languages like Russian or German; in Russian the word *Moscow* has different endings in the phrases *Moscow*, *of Moscow*, *from Moscow*, and so on. We want to be able to automatically search for the inflected forms of the word even if the user only typed in the base form. Morphological parsing also plays a crucial role in part-of-speech tagging for these morphologically complex languages, as we show in Chapter 5. It is important for producing the large dictionaries that are necessary for robust spell-checking. We need it in machine translation to realize, for example, that the French words *va* and *aller* should both translate to forms of the English verb *go*.

To solve the morphological parsing problem, why couldn't we just store all the plural forms of English nouns and *-ing* forms of English verbs in a dictionary and do parsing by lookup? Sometimes we can do this, and, for example, for English speech

---

[1] See, for example, Seuss (1960).

Productive

recognition this is exactly what we do. But for many NLP applications this isn't possible because *-ing* is a **productive** suffix; by this we mean that it applies to every verb. Similarly *-s* applies to almost every noun. Productive suffixes even apply to new words; thus, the new word *fax* can automatically be used in the *-ing* form: *faxing*. Since new words (particularly acronyms and proper nouns) are created every day, the class of nouns in English increases constantly and we need to be able to add the plural morpheme *-s* to each of these. Additionally, the plural form of these new nouns depends on the spelling/pronunciation of the singular form; for example, if the noun ends in *-z*, then the plural form is *-es* rather than *-s*. We'll need to encode these rules somewhere.

Finally, we certainly cannot list all the morphological variants of every word in morphologically complex languages like Turkish, which has words like these:

(3.1) uygarlaştıramadıklarımızdanmışsınızcasına

> *uygar* +*laş* +*tır* +*ama* +*dık* +*lar* +*ımız* +*dan* +*mış* +*sınız* +*casına*
> civilized +BEC +CAUS +NABL +PART +PL +P1PL +ABL +PAST +2PL +AsIf

"(behaving) as if you are among those whom we could not civilize"

The various pieces of this word (the **morphemes**) have these meanings:

+BEC	"become"
+CAUS	the causative verb marker ('cause to X')
+NABL	"not able"
+PART	past participle form
+P1PL	1st person pl possessive agreement
+2PL	2nd person pl
+ABL	ablative (from/among) case marker
+AsIf	derivationally forms an adverb from a finite verb

Not all Turkish words look like this; the average Turkish word has about three morphemes. But such long words do exist; indeed, Kemal Oflazer, who came up with this example, notes (p.c.) that verbs in Turkish have 40,000 possible forms, not counting derivational suffixes. Adding derivational suffixes, such as causatives, allows a theoretically infinite number of words, since causativization can be repeated in a single word (*You cause X to cause Y to ... do W*). Thus, we cannot store all possible Turkish words in advance and must do morphological parsing dynamically.

In the next section, we survey morphological knowledge for English and some other languages. We then introduce the key algorithm for morphological parsing, the **finite-state transducer**. Finite-state transducers are a crucial technology throughout speech and language processing, so we return to them again in later chapters.

After describing morphological parsing, we introduce some related algorithms in this chapter. In some applications we don't need to parse a word, but we do need to map from the word to its root or stem. For example, in information retrieval (IR) and web search, we might want to map from *foxes* to *fox*, but might not need to also know that *foxes* is plural. Just stripping off such word endings is called **stemming** in IR. We describe a simple stemming algorithm called the **Porter stemmer**.

Stemming

For other speech and language processing tasks, we need to know that two words have a similar root, despite their surface differences. For example, the words *sang*, *sung*, and *sings* are all forms of the verb *sing*. The word *sing* is sometimes called

the common *lemma* of these words, and mapping from all of these to *sing* is called
Lemmatization   **lemmatization**.[2]
Tokenization   Next, we introduce another task related to morphological parsing. **Tokenization**
or **word segmentation** is the task of separating out (tokenizing) words from running
text. In English, words are often separated from each other by blanks (whitespace), but
whitespace is not always sufficient; we'll need to notice that *New York* and *rock 'n' roll*
are individual words despite the fact that they contain spaces, but for many applications
we'll need to separate *I'm* into the two words *I* and *am*.

Finally, for many applications we need to know how similar two words are orthographically. Morphological parsing is one method for computing this similarity;
another is to use the **minimum edit distance** algorithm to compare the letters in the
two words. We introduce this important NLP algorithm and also show how it can be
used in spelling correction.

3.1   Survey of (Mostly) English Morphology

Morpheme   Morphology is the study of the way words are built up from smaller meaning-bearing
units, **morphemes**. A morpheme is often defined as the minimal meaning-bearing unit
in a language. So, for example, the word *fox* consists of one morpheme (the morpheme
fox) and the word *cats* consists of two: the morpheme *cat* and the morpheme *-s*.

As this example suggests, it is often useful to distinguish two broad classes of
Stem   morphemes: **stems** and **affixes**. The exact details of the distinction vary from language
Affix   to language, but intuitively, the stem is the "main" morpheme of the word, supplying
the main meaning, and the affixes add "additional" meanings of various kinds.

Affixes are further divided into **prefixes**, **suffixes**, **infixes**, and **circumfixes**. Prefixes precede the stem, suffixes follow the stem, circumfixes do both, and infixes are
inserted inside the stem. For example, the word *eats* is composed of a stem *eat* and the
suffix *-s*. The word *unbuckle* is composed of a stem *buckle* and the prefix *un-*. English
doesn't really have circumfixes, but many other languages do. In German, for example, the past participle of some verbs is formed by adding *ge-* to the beginning of the
stem and *-t* to the end; so the past participle of the verb *sagen* (to say) is *gesagt* (said).
Infixes, in which a morpheme is inserted in the middle of a word, occur commonly,
for example, in the Philipine language Tagalog. For example, the affix *um*, which
marks the agent of an action, is infixed to the Tagalog stem *hingi* "borrow" to produce
humingi. There is one infix that occurs in some dialects of English in which the taboo
morphemes "f**king" or "bl**dy" or others like them are inserted in the middle of
other words ("Man-f**king-hattan", "abso-bl**dy-lutely"[3]) (McCawley, 1978).

A word can have more than one affix. For example, the word *rewrites* has the prefix
re-, the stem *write*, and the suffix *-s*. The word *unbelievably* has a stem (*believe*) plus
three affixes (*un-*, *-able*, and *-ly*). While English doesn't tend to stack more than four

---

[2] Lemmatization is actually more complex, since it sometimes involves deciding on which sense of a word
is present. We return to this issue in Chapter 20.

[3] Alan Jay Lerner, the lyricist of My Fair Lady, bowdlerized the latter to *abso-bloomin'lutely* in the lyric to
"Wouldn't It Be Lovely?" (Lerner, 1978, p. 60).

or five affixes, languages like Turkish can have words with nine or ten affixes, as we saw above. Languages that tend to string affixes together as Turkish does are called **agglutinative** languages.

There are many ways to combine morphemes to create words. Four of these methods are common and play important roles in speech and language processing: **inflection**, **derivation**, **compounding**, and **cliticization**.

Inflection

Derivation

Compounding

Cliticization

Inflection is the combination of a word stem with a grammatical morpheme, usually resulting in a word of the same class as the original stem and usually filling some syntactic function like agreement. For example, English has the inflectional morpheme -*s* for marking the **plural** on nouns and the inflectional morpheme -*ed* for marking the past tense on verbs. **Derivation** is the combination of a word stem with a grammatical morpheme, usually resulting in a word of a *different* class, often with a meaning hard to predict exactly. For example, the verb *computerize* can take the derivational suffix -*ation* to produce the noun *computerization*. **Compounding** is the combination of multiple word stems together. For example, the noun *doghouse* is the concatenation of the morpheme *dog* with the morpheme *house*. Finally, **cliticization** is the combination

Clitic

of a word stem with a **clitic**. A clitic is a morpheme that acts syntactically like a word but is reduced in form and attached (phonologically and sometimes orthographically) to another word. For example the English morpheme '*ve* in the word *I've* is a clitic, as is the French definite article *l'* in the word *l'opera*. In the following sections we give more details on these processes.

3.1.1 Inflectional Morphology

English has a relatively simple inflectional system; only nouns, verbs, and some adjectives can be inflected, and the number of possible inflectional affixes is quite small.

Plural

English nouns have only two kinds of inflection: an affix that marks **plural** and an

Singular

affix that marks **possessive**. For example, many (but not all) English nouns can either appear in the bare stem or **singular** form or take a plural suffix. Here are examples of the regular plural suffix -*s* (also spelled -*es*), and irregular plurals.

	Regular Nouns		**Irregular Nouns**	
Singular	cat	thrush	mouse	ox
Plural	cats	thrushes	mice	oxen

While the regular plural is spelled -*s* after most nouns, it is spelled -*es* after words ending in -*s* (*ibis/ibises*), -*z* (*waltz/waltzes*), -*sh* (*thrush/thrushes*), -*ch* (*finch/finches*), and sometimes -*x* (*box/boxes*). Nouns ending in -*y* preceded by a consonant change the -*y* to -*i* (*butterfly/butterflies*).

The possessive suffix is realized by apostrophe + -*s* for regular singular nouns (*llama's*) and plural nouns not ending in -*s* (*children's*) and often by a lone apostrophe after regular plural nouns (*llamas'*) and some names ending in -*s* or -*z* (*Euripides' comedies*).

English verbal inflection is more complicated than nominal inflection. First, English has three kinds of verbs; **main verbs**, (*eat, sleep, impeach*), **modal verbs** (*can, will, should*), and **primary verbs** (*be, have, do*) (using the terms of Quirk et al., 1985).

Regular verb

In this chapter, we are mostly concerned with the main and primary verbs because these have inflectional endings. Of these verbs a large class are **regular**, that is, all verbs of this class have the same endings marking the same functions. These regular verbs (e.g., *walk* or *inspect*) have four morphological forms, as follows:

Morphological Class	Regularly Inflected Verbs			
stem	walk	merge	try	map
-s form	walks	merges	tries	maps
-ing participle	walking	merging	trying	mapping
Past form or *-ed* participle	walked	merged	tried	mapped

These verbs are called regular because just by knowing the stem we can predict the other forms by adding one of three predictable endings and making some regular spelling changes (and as we show in Chapter 7, regular pronunciation changes). These regular verbs and forms are significant in the morphology of English: first, because they cover a majority of the verbs; and second, because the regular class is **productive**. As discussed earlier, a productive class is one that automatically includes any new words that enter the language. For example, the recently created verb *fax* (*My mom faxed me the note from cousin Everett*) takes the regular endings *-ed*, *-ing*, *-es*. (Note that the *-s* form is spelled *faxes* rather than *faxs*; we will discuss spelling rules below).

Irregular verb

The **irregular verbs** are those that have some more or less idiosyncratic forms of inflection. Irregular verbs in English often have five different forms but can have as many as eight (e.g., the verb *be*) or as few as three (e.g., *cut* or *hit*). While irregular verbs constitute a much smaller class of verbs (Quirk et al. (1985) estimate there are only about 250 irregular verbs, not counting auxiliaries), this class includes most of the very frequent verbs of the language.[4] The table below shows some sample irregular

Preterite

forms. Note that an irregular verb can inflect in the past form (also called the **preterite**) by changing its vowel (*eat/ate*), its vowel and some consonants (*catch/caught*), or with no change at all (*cut/cut*).

Morphological Class	Irregularly Inflected Verbs		
stem	eat	catch	cut
-s form	eats	catches	cuts
-ing participle	eating	catching	cutting
preterite	ate	caught	cut
past participle	eaten	caught	cut

The way these forms are used in a sentence is discussed in the syntax and semantics chapters but is worth a brief mention here. The *-s* form is used in the "habitual present" form to distinguish the third-person singular ending (*She jogs every Tuesday*) from the other choices of person and number (*I/you/we/they jog every Tuesday*). The stem form is used in the infinitive form and also after certain other verbs (*I'd rather walk home, I want to walk home*). The *-ing* participle is used in the **progressive** construction to

Progressive

---

[4] In general, the more frequent a word form, the more likely it is to have idiosyncratic properties; this is due to a fact about language change: very frequent words tend to preserve their form even if other words around them are changing so as to become more regular.

Gerund

Perfect

mark present or ongoing activity (*It is raining*) or when the verb is treated as a noun; this latter kind of nominal use of a verb is called a **gerund**: *Fishing is fine if you live near water*. The *-ed/-en* participle is used in the **perfect** construction (*He's eaten lunch already*) or the passive construction (*The verdict was overturned yesterday*).

In addition to noting which suffixes can be attached to which stems, we need to capture the fact that a number of regular spelling changes occur at these morpheme boundaries. For example, a single consonant letter is doubled before the *-ing* and *-ed* suffixes (*beg/begging/begged*) is added. If the final letter is "c", the doubling is spelled "ck" (*picnic/picnicking/picnicked*). If the base ends in a silent *-e*, it is deleted before *-ing* and *-ed* (*merge/merging/merged*) are added. Just as for nouns, the *-s* ending is spelled *-es* after verb stems ending in *-s* (*toss/tosses*), *-z* (*waltz/waltzes*), *-sh* (*wash/washes*) *-ch* (*catch/catches*), and sometimes *-x* (*tax/taxes*). Also like nouns, verbs ending in *-y* preceded by a consonant change the *-y* to *-i* (*try/tries*).

The English verbal system is much simpler than for example the European Spanish system, which has as many as 50 distinct verb forms for each regular verb. Figure 3.1 shows just a few of the examples for the verb *amar*, "to love". Other languages can have even more forms than this Spanish example.

	Present Indicative	Imperfect Indicative	Future	Preterite	Present Subjunctive	Conditional	Imperfect Subjunctive	Future Subjunctive
1SG	amo	amaba	amaré	amé	ame	amaría	amara	amare
2SG	amas	amabas	amarás	amaste	ames	amarías	amaras	amares
3SG	ama	amaba	amará	amó	ame	amaría	amara	amáreme
1PL	amamos	amábamos	amaremos	amamos	amemos	amaríamos	amáramos	amáremos
2PL	amáis	amabais	amaréis	amasteis	améis	amaríais	amarais	amareis
3PL	aman	amaban	amarán	amaron	amen	amarían	amaran	amaren

Figure 3.1   "To love" in Spanish. Some of the inflected forms of the verb *amar* in European Spanish. *1SG* stands for "first-person singular", 3PL for "third-person plural", and so on.

3.1.2   Derivational Morphology

While English inflection is relatively simple compared to other languages, derivation in English is quite complex. Recall that derivation is the combination of a word stem with a grammatical morpheme, usually resulting in a word of a *different* class, often with a meaning hard to predict exactly.

Nominalization

A common kind of derivation in English is the formation of new nouns, often from verbs or adjectives. This process is called **nominalization**. For example, the suffix *-ation* produces nouns from verbs ending often in the suffix *-ize* (*computerize → computerization*). Here are examples of some productive English nominalizing suffixes.

Suffix	Base Verb/Adjective	Derived Noun
-ation	computerize (V)	computerization
-ee	appoint (V)	appointee
-er	kill (V)	killer
-ness	fuzzy (A)	fuzziness

Adjectives can also be derived from nouns and verbs. Here are examples of a few suffixes deriving adjectives from nouns or verbs.

Suffix	Base Noun/Verb	Derived Adjective
-al	computation (N)	computational
-able	embrace (V)	embraceable
-less	clue (N)	clueless

Derivation in English is more complex than inflection for a number of reasons. One is that it is generally less productive; even a nominalizing suffix like *-ation*, which can be added to almost any verb ending in *-ize*, cannot be added to absolutely every verb. Thus, we can't say **eatation* or **spellation* (we use an asterisk (*) to mark "non-examples" of English). Another is that there are subtle and complex meaning differences among nominalizing suffixes. For example, *sincerity* has a subtle difference in meaning from *sincereness*.

3.1.3   Cliticization

Proclitic

Enclitic

Recall that a clitic is a unit whose status lies between that of an affix and a word. The phonological behavior of clitics is like affixes; they tend to be short and unaccented (we talk more about phonology in Chapter 8). Their syntactic behavior is more like words, often acting as pronouns, articles, conjunctions, or verbs. Clitics preceding a word are called **proclitics**, and those following are **enclitics**.

English clitics include these auxiliary verbal forms:

Full Form	Clitic	Full Form	Clitic
am	'm	have	've
are	're	has	's
is	's	had	'd
will	'll	would	'd

Note that the clitics in English are ambiguous; Thus *she's* can mean *she is* or *she has*. Except for a few such ambiguities, however, correctly segmenting clitics in English is simplified by the presence of the apostrophe. Clitics can be harder to parse in other languages. In Arabic and Hebrew, for example, the definite article (*the*; *Al* in Arabic, *ha* in Hebrew) is cliticized on to the front of nouns. It must be segmented in order to do part-of-speech tagging, parsing, or other tasks. Other Arabic proclitics include prepositions like *b* 'by/with' and conjunctions like *w* 'and'. Arabic also has *enclitics* marking certain pronouns. For example, the word *and by their virtues* has clitics meaning *and*, *by*, and *their*, a stem *virtue*, and a plural affix. Note that since Arabic is read right to left, these would actually appear ordered from right to left in an Arabic word.

	Proclitic	Proclitic	Stem	Affix	Enclitic
Arabic	w	b	Hsn	At	hm
Gloss	and	by	virtue	s	their

3.1.4   Non-Concatenative Morphology

Concatenative morphology

The kind of morphology we have discussed so far, in which a word is composed of a string of concatenated morphemes is often called **concatenative morphology**. A number of languages have extensive **non-concatenative morphology**, in which morphemes are combined in more complex ways. The Tagalog infixation example above is one example of non-concatenative morphology since two morphemes (*hingi* and *um*) are intermingled.

Another kind of non-concatenative morphology is called **templatic morphology** or **root-and-pattern** morphology. This is common in Arabic, Hebrew, and other Semitic languages. In Hebrew, for example, a verb (as well as other parts-of-speech) is constructed from two components: a root, consisting usually of three consonants (CCC) and carrying the basic meaning; and a template, which gives the ordering of consonants and vowels and specifies more semantic information about the resulting verb, such as the semantic voice (e.g., active, passive, middle). For example, the Hebrew tri-consonantal root *lmd*, meaning 'learn' or 'study', can be combined with the active voice CaCaC template to produce the word *lamad*, 'he studied', or the intensive CiCeC template to produce the word *limed*, 'he taught', or the intensive passive template CuCaC to produce the word *lumad*, 'he was taught'. Arabic and Hebrew combine this templatic morphology with concatenative morphology (like the cliticization example shown in the previous section).

3.1.5   Agreement

Agreement

Gender

Noun class

We introduced the plural morpheme above and noted that plural is marked on both nouns and verbs in English. We say that the subject noun and the main verb in English have to **agree** in number, meaning that the two must either be both singular or both plural. There are other kinds of agreement processes. For example, nouns, adjectives, and sometimes verbs in many languages are marked for **gender**. A gender is a kind of equivalence class that is used by the language to categorize the nouns; each noun falls into one class. Many languages (e.g., Romance languages like French, Spanish, or Italian) have 2 genders, which are referred to as masculine and feminine. Other languages (like most Germanic and Slavic languages) have three (masculine, feminine, neuter). Some languages, for example, the Bantu languages of Africa, have as many as 20 genders. When the number of classes is very large, we often refer to them as **noun classes** instead of genders.

Gender is sometimes marked explicitly on a noun; for example, Spanish masculine words often end in *-o* and feminine words in *-a*. But in many cases the gender is not marked in the letters or phones of the noun itself. Instead, it is a property of the word that must be stored in a lexicon. We see an example of this in Fig. 3.2.

3.2   Finite-State Morphological Parsing

Let's now proceed to the problem of parsing morphology. Our goal is to take input forms like those in the first and third columns of Fig. 3.2 and produce output forms like those in the second and fourth column.

Feature

The second column contains the stem of each word as well as assorted morphological **features**. These features specify additional information about the stem. For

	English		Spanish		
Input	**Morphological Parse**	**Input**	**Morphological Parse**	**Gloss**	
cats	cat +N +PL	pavos	pavo +N +Masc +Pl	'ducks'	
cat	cat +N +SG	pavo	pavo +N +Masc +Sg	'duck'	
cities	city +N +Pl	bebo	beber +V +PInd +1P +Sg	'I drink'	
geese	goose +N +Pl	canto	cantar +V +PInd +1P +Sg	'I sing'	
goose	goose +N +Sg	canto	canto +N +Masc +Sg	'song'	
goose	goose +V	puse	poner +V +Perf +1P +Sg	'I was able'	
gooses	goose +V +3P +Sg	vino	venir +V +Perf +3P +Sg	'he/she came'	
merging	merge +V +PresPart	vino	vino +N +Masc +Sg	'wine'	
caught	catch +V +PastPart	lugar	lugar +N +Masc +Sg	'place'	
caught	catch +V +Past				

Figure 3.2   Output of a morphological parse for some English and Spanish words. Spanish output modified from the Xerox XRCE finite-state language tools.

example, the feature +N means that the word is a noun; +Sg means it is singular; +Pl that it is plural. Morphological features are referred to again in Chapter 5 and in more detail in Chapter 15; for now, consider +Sg to be a primitive unit that means "singular". Spanish has some features that don't occur in English; for example, the nouns *lugar* and *pavo* are marked +Masc (masculine). Because Spanish nouns agree in gender with adjectives, knowing the gender of a noun will be important for tagging and parsing.

Note that some of the input forms (like *caught*, *goose*, *canto*, or *vino*) are ambiguous between different morphological parses. For now, we will consider the goal of morphological parsing merely to list all possible parses. We return to the task of disambiguating among morphological parses in Chapter 5.

To build a morphological parser, we'll need at least the following:

Lexicon

1. **Lexicon:** the list of stems and affixes, together with basic information about them (whether a stem is a noun stem or a verb stem, etc.).

Morphotactics

2. **Morphotactics:** the model of morpheme ordering that explains which classes of morphemes can follow other classes of morphemes inside a word. For example, the fact that the English plural morpheme follows the noun rather than preceding it is a morphotactic fact.

Orthographic rules

3. **Orthographic rules:** these **spelling rules** are used to model the changes that occur in a word, usually when two morphemes combine (e.g., the $y \rightarrow ie$ spelling rule discussed above that changes *city + -s* to *cities* rather than *citys*).

The next section discusses how to represent a simple version of the lexicon just for the sub-problem of morphological recognition, including how to use FSAs to model morphotactic knowledge.

In following sections we then introduce the finite-state transducer (FST) as a way of modeling morphological features in the lexicon and addressing morphological parsing. Finally, we show how to use FSTs to model orthographic rules.

3.3   Construction of a Finite-State Lexicon

A lexicon is a repository for words. The simplest possible lexicon would consist of an explicit list of every word of the language (*every* word, i.e., including abbreviations ("AAA") and proper names ("Jane" or "Beijing")) as follows:

   a, AAA, AA, Aachen, aardvark, aardwolf, aba, abaca, aback, ...

Since it will often be inconvenient or impossible, for the various reasons we discussed above, to list every word in the language, computational lexicons are usually structured with a list of each of the stems and affixes of the language together with a representation of the morphotactics that tells us how they can fit together. There are many ways to model morphotactics; one of the most common is the finite-state automaton. A very simple finite-state model for English nominal inflection might look like Fig. 3.3.

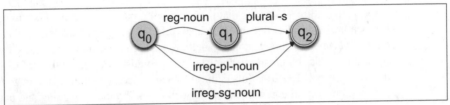

Figure 3.3   A finite-state automaton for English nominal inflection.

The FSA in Fig. 3.3 assumes that the lexicon includes regular nouns (**reg-noun**) that take the regular -*s* plural (e.g., *cat, dog, fox, aardvark*). These are the vast majority of English nouns since for now we will ignore the fact that the plural of words like *fox* have an inserted *e*: *foxes*. The lexicon also includes irregular noun forms that don't take -*s*, both singular **irreg-sg-noun** (*goose, mouse*) and plural **irreg-pl-noun** (*geese, mice*).

reg-noun	irreg-pl-noun	irreg-sg-noun	plural
fox	geese	goose	-s
cat	sheep	sheep	
aardvark	mice	mouse	

A similar model for English verbal inflection might look like Fig. 3.4.

This lexicon has three stem classes (**reg-verb-stem**, **irreg-verb-stem**, and **irreg-past-verb-form**), plus four more affix classes (-*ed* past, -*ed* participle, -*ing* participle, and third singular -*s*):

reg-verb-stem	irreg-verb-stem	irreg-past-stem	past	past-part	pres-part	3sg
walk	cut	caught	-ed	-ed	-ing	-s
fry	speak	ate				
talk	sing	eaten				
impeach		sang				

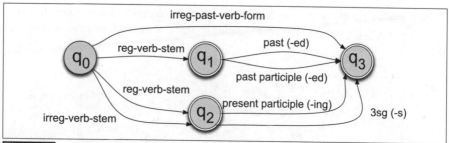

Figure 3.4   A finite-state automaton for English verbal inflection.

English derivational morphology is significantly more complex than English inflectional morphology, and so automata for modeling English derivation tend to be quite complex. Some models of English derivation, in fact, are based on the more complex context-free grammars of Chapter 12 (see also (Sproat, 1993)).

Consider a relatively simpler case of derivation: the morphotactics of English adjectives. Here are some examples from Antworth (1990):

big, bigger, biggest,	cool, cooler, coolest, coolly
happy, happier, happiest, happily	red, redder, reddest
unhappy, unhappier, unhappiest, unhappily	real, unreal, really
clear, clearer, clearest, clearly, unclear, unclearly	

An initial hypothesis might be that adjectives can have an optional prefix (*un-*), an obligatory root (*big, cool*, etc.), and an optional suffix (*-er, -est,* or *-ly*). This might suggest the FSA in Fig. 3.5.

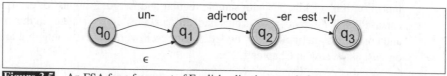

Figure 3.5   An FSA for a fragment of English adjective morphology: Antworth's Proposal #1.

Alas, while this FSA will recognize all the adjectives in the table above, it will also recognize ungrammatical forms like *unbig, unfast, oranger,* or *smally*. We need to set up classes of roots and specify their possible suffixes. Thus, **adj-root$_1$** would include adjectives that can occur with *un-* and *-ly* (*clear, happy,* and *real*), and **adj-root$_2$** will include adjectives that can't (*big, small*), and so on.

This gives an idea of the complexity to be expected from English derivation. As a further example, we give in Fig. 3.6 another fragment of an FSA for English nominal and verbal derivational morphology, based on Sproat (1993), Bauer (1983), and Porter (1980). This FSA models a number of derivational facts, such as the well-known generalization that any verb ending in *-ize* can be followed by the nominalizing suffix *-ation* (Bauer, 1983; Sproat, 1993). Thus, since there is a word *fossilize*, we can predict the word *fossilization* by following states q_0, q_1, and q_2. Similarly, adjectives ending in *-al* or *-able* at q_5 (*equal, formal, realizable*) can take the suffix *-ity*, or sometimes the suffix *-ness* to state q_6 (*naturalness, casualness*). We leave it as an exercise for the reader (Exercise 3.1) to discover some of the individual exceptions to many of these constraints and also to give examples of some of the various noun and verb classes.

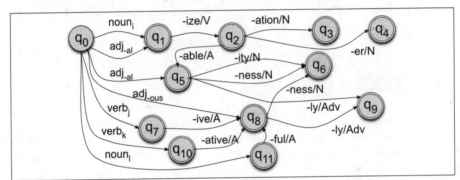

Figure 3.6   An FSA for another fragment of English derivational morphology.

We can now use these FSAs to solve the problem of **morphological recognition**; that is, of determining whether an input string of letters makes up a legitimate English word. We do this by taking the morphotactic FSAs and plugging each "sub-lexicon" into the FSA. That is, we expand each arc (e.g., the **reg-noun-stem** arc) with all the morphemes that make up the set of **reg-noun-stem**. The resulting FSA can then be defined at the level of the individual letter.

Figure 3.7 shows the noun-recognition FSA produced by expanding the nominal inflection FSA of Fig. 3.3 with sample regular and irregular nouns for each class. We can use Fig. 3.7 to recognize strings like *aardvarks* by simply starting at the initial state and comparing the input letter by letter with each word on each outgoing arc, and so on, just as we saw in Chapter 2.

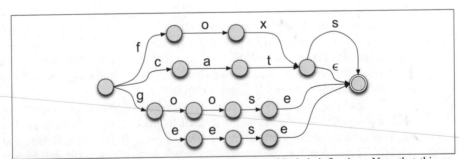

Figure 3.7   Expanded FSA for a few English nouns with their inflection. Note that this automaton will incorrectly accept the input *foxs*. We see, beginning on page 62, how to correctly deal with the inserted *e* in *foxes*.

3.4   Finite-State Transducers

We've now seen that FSAs can represent the morphotactic structure of a lexicon and can be used for word recognition. In this section, we introduce the finite-state transducer. The next section shows how transducers can be applied to morphological parsing.

A transducer maps between one representation and another: a **finite-state trans-**
FST   **ducer**, or **FST**, is a type of finite automaton which maps between two sets of symbols. We can visualize an FST as a two-tape automaton that recognizes or generates *pairs* of strings. Intuitively, we can do this by labeling each arc in the finite-state machine with two symbol strings, one from each tape. Figure 3.8 shows an example of an FST where each arc is labeled by an input and output string, separated by a colon.

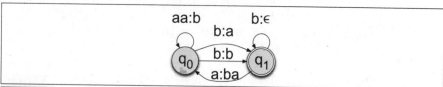

Figure 3.8   A finite-state transducer.

The FST thus has a more general function than an FSA; where an FSA defines a formal language by defining a set of strings, an FST defines a *relation* between sets of strings. Another way of looking at an FST is as a machine that reads one string and generates another. Here's a summary of this fourfold way of thinking about transducers:

- **FST as recognizer:** a transducer that takes a pair of strings as input and outputs; *accept* if the string-pair is in the string-pair language, and *reject* if it is not.

- **FST as generator:** a machine that outputs pairs of strings of the language. Thus, the output is a yes or no, and a pair of output strings.

- **FST as translator:** a machine that reads a string and outputs another string.

- **FST as set relater:** a machine that computes relations between sets.

All of these have applications in speech and language processing. For morphological parsing (and for many other NLP applications), we apply the FST as translator metaphor, taking as input a string of letters and producing as output a string of morphemes.

Let's begin with a formal definition. An FST can be formally defined with seven parameters:

Q	a finite set of N states $q_0, q_1, \ldots, q_{N-1}$
Σ	a finite set corresponding to the input alphabet
Δ	a finite set corresponding to the output alphabet
$q_0 \in Q$	the start state
$F \subseteq Q$	the set of final states
$\delta(q,w)$	the transition function or transition matrix between states. Given a state $q \in Q$ and a string $w \in \Sigma^*$, $\delta(q,w)$, returns a set of new states $Q' \in Q$. δ is thus a function from $Q \quad \Sigma^*$ to 2^Q (because there are 2^Q possible subsets of Q). δ returns a set of states rather than a single state because a given input may be ambiguous as to which state it maps to.
$\sigma(q,w)$	the output function giving the set of possible output strings for each state and input. Given a state $q \in Q$ and a string $w \in \Sigma^*$, $\sigma(q,w)$ gives a set of output strings, each a string $o \in \Delta^*$. σ is thus a function from $Q \quad \Sigma^*$ to 2^{Δ^*}.

Whereas FSAs are isomorphic to regular languages, FSTs are isomorphic to **regu-**

Regular relation   **lar relations**. Regular relations are sets of pairs of strings, a natural extension of the regular languages, which are sets of strings. Like FSAs and regular languages, FSTs and regular relations are closed under union, although in general they are not closed un-

Intersection   der difference, complementation, and **intersection** (although some useful subclasses of FSTs *are* closed under these operations; in general, FSTs that are not augmented with the ϵ are more likely to have such closure properties). Besides union, FSTs have two additional closure properties that turn out to be extremely useful:

Inversion   **Inversion**: The inversion of a transducer T (T^{-1}) simply switches the input and output labels. Thus, if T maps from the input alphabet I to the output alphabet O, T^{-1} maps from O to I.

Composition   **Composition**: If T_1 is a transducer from I_1 to O_1 and T_2 a transducer from O_1 to O_2, then $T_1 \circ T_2$ maps from I_1 to O_2.

Inversion is useful because it makes it easy to convert an FST-as-parser into an FST-as-generator.

Composition is useful because it allows us to replace two transducers that run in series with one, more complex, transducer. Composition works as in algebra; apply-ing $T_1 \circ T_2$ to an input sequence S is identical to applying T_1 to S and then T_2 to the result; thus, $T_1 \circ T_2(S) = T_2(T_1(S))$. Figure 3.9 shows, for example, the composition of [a:b]+ with [b:c]+ to produce [a:c]+.

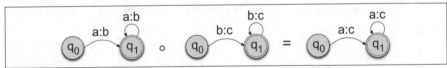

Figure 3.9   The composition of [a:b]+ with [b:c]+ to produce [a:c]+.

Projection   The **projection** of an FST is the FSA that is produced by extracting only one side

of the relation. We can refer to the projection to the left or upper side of the relation as the **upper** or **first** projection and the projection to the lower or right side of the relation as the **lower** or **second** projection.

3.4.1   Sequential Transducers and Determinism

Transducers as we have described them may be nondeterministic, in that a given input may translate to many possible output symbols. Thus, using general FSTs requires the kinds of search algorithms discussed in Chapter 2, making FSTs quite slow in the general case. This suggests that it would nice to have an algorithm to convert a non-deterministic FST to a deterministic one. But while every non-deterministic FSA is equivalent to some deterministic FSA, not all finite-state transducers can be determinized.

Sequential transducers

Sequential transducers, by contrast, are a subtype of transducers that are deterministic on their input. At any state of a sequential transducer, each given symbol of the input alphabet Σ can label at most one transition out of that state. Figure 3.10 gives an example of a sequential transducer from Mohri (1997); note that here, unlike the transducer in Fig. 3.8, the transitions out of each state are deterministic, based on the state and the input symbol. Sequential transducers can have epsilon symbols in the output string, but not on the input.

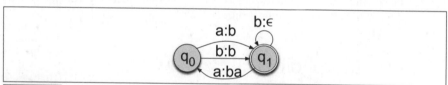

Figure 3.10   A sequential finite-state transducer, from Mohri (1997).

Sequential transducers are not necessarily sequential on their output. Mohri's transducer in Fig. 3.10 is not, for example, since two distinct transitions leaving state 0 have the same output (b). Since the inverse of a sequential transducer may thus not be sequential, we always need to specify the direction of the transduction when discussing sequentiality. Formally, the definition of sequential transducers modifies the δ and σ functions slightly; δ becomes a function from $Q \times \Sigma^*$ to Q (rather than to 2^Q), and σ becomes a function from $Q \times \Sigma^*$ to Δ^* (rather than to 2^{Δ^*}).

Subsequential transducer

A generalization of sequential transducers, the **subsequential transducer**, generates an additional output string at the final states, concatenating it onto the output produced so far (Schützenberger, 1977). What makes sequential and subsequential transducers important is their efficiency; because they are deterministic on input, they can be processed in time proportional to the number of symbols in the input (they are linear in their input length) rather than proportional to some much larger number that is a function of the number of states. Another advantage of subsequential transducers is that there exist efficient algorithms for their determinization (Mohri, 1997) and minimization (Mohri, 2000), extending the algorithms for determinization and minimization of finite-state automata that we saw in Chapter 2.

While both sequential and subsequential transducers are deterministic and efficient, neither of them can handle ambiguity, since they transduce each input string to exactly one possible output string. Since ambiguity is a crucial property of natural language, it will be useful to have an extension of subsequential transducers that can deal with ambiguity but still retain the efficiency and other useful properties of sequential transducers. One such generalization of subsequential transducers is the *p*-**subsequential** transducer. A *p*-**subsequential** transducer allows for $p(p \geq 1)$ final output strings to be associated with each final state (Mohri, 1996). They can thus handle a finite amount of ambiguity, which is useful for many NLP tasks. Figure 3.11 shows an example of a 2-subsequential FST.

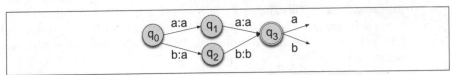

Figure 3.11   A 2-subsequential finite-state transducer, from Mohri (1997).

Mohri (1996, 1997) shows a number of tasks whose ambiguity can be limited in this way, including the representation of dictionaries, the compilation of morphological and phonological rules, and local syntactic constraints. For each of these kinds of problems, he and others have shown that they are **p-subsequentializable** and thus can be determinized and minimized. This class of transducers includes many, although not necessarily all, morphological rules.

3.5   FSTs for Morphological Parsing

Let's now turn to the task of morphological parsing. Given the input *cats*, for instance, we'd like to output *cat +N +Pl*, telling us that *cat* is a plural noun. Given the Spanish input *bebo* ("I drink"), we'd like *beber +V +PInd +1P +Sg*, telling us that *bebo* is the present indicative first person singular form of the Spanish verb *beber*, "to drink".

In the **finite-state morphology** paradigm that we use, we represent a word as a correspondence between a **lexical level**, which represents a concatenation of morphemes making up a word, and the **surface level**, which represents the concatenation of letters making up the actual spelling of the word. Figure 3.12 shows these two levels for (English) *cats*.

Surface level

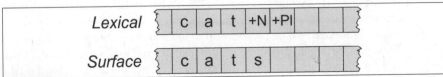

Figure 3.12   Schematic examples of the lexical and surface tapes; the actual transducers involve intermediate tapes as well.

For finite-state morphology, it's convenient to view an FST as having two tapes. The **upper** or **lexical tape** is composed from characters from one alphabet Σ. The

Lexical tape

lower or **surface tape** is composed of characters from another alphabet Δ. In the **two-level morphology** of Koskenniemi (1983), each arc is allowed to have a single symbol from each alphabet. We can then combine the two symbol alphabets Σ and Δ to create a new alphabet, Σ′, which makes the relationship to FSAs quite clear. Σ′ is a finite alphabet of complex symbols. Each complex symbol is composed of an input-output pair $i : o$, that has one symbol i from the input alphabet Σ, and one symbol o from an output alphabet Δ; thus, Σ′ ⊆ Σ   Δ. Σ and Δ may each also include the epsilon symbol ϵ. Thus, whereas an FSA accepts a language stated over a finite alphabet of single symbols, such as the alphabet of our sheep language:

$$\Sigma = \ b, a, ! \tag{3.2}$$

an FST defined this way accepts a language stated over *pairs* of symbols, as in

$$\Sigma' = \ a : a, \ b : b, \ ! : !, \ a : !, \ a : \epsilon, \ \epsilon : ! \tag{3.3}$$

Feasible pair   In two-level morphology, the pairs of symbols in Σ′ are also called **feasible pairs**. Thus, each feasible pair symbol $a : b$ in the transducer alphabet Σ′ expresses how the symbol a from one tape is mapped to the symbol b on the other tape. For example, $a : \epsilon$ means that an a on the upper tape will correspond to *nothing* on the lower tape. Just as for an FSA, we can write regular expressions in the complex alphabet Σ′. Since it's most common for symbols to map to themselves, in two-level morphology we call

Default pair   pairs like $a : a$ **default pairs** and just refer to them by the single letter a.

We are now ready to build an FST morphological parser out of our earlier morphotactic FSAs and lexica by adding an extra "lexical" tape and the appropriate morphological features. Figure 3.13 shows an augmentation of Fig. 3.3 with the nominal morphological features (+Sg and +Pl) that correspond to each morpheme. The sym-

Morpheme boundary bol ˆ indicates a **morpheme boundary**, and the symbol # indicates a **word boundary**.

#

Word boundary The morphological features map to the empty string ϵ or the boundary symbols since no segment on the output tape corresponds to them.

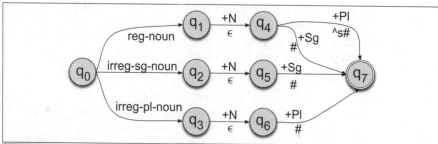

Figure 3.13   A schematic transducer for English nominal number inflection T_{num}. The symbols above each arc represent elements of the morphological parse in the lexical tape; the symbols below each arc represent the surface tape (or the intermediate tape, described later), using the morpheme-boundary symbol ˆ and word-boundary marker #. The labels on the arcs leaving q_0 are schematic and must be expanded by individual words in the lexicon.

In order for us to use Fig. 3.13 as a morphological noun parser, it needs to be expanded with all the individual regular and irregular noun stems, replacing the labels

reg-noun, etc. To do this, we need to update the lexicon for this transducer so that irregular plurals like *geese* will parse into the correct stem `goose +N +Pl`. We do this by allowing the lexicon to also have two levels. Since surface *geese* maps to lexical `goose`, the new lexical entry will be "`g:g o:e o:e s:s e:e`". Regular forms are simpler; the two-level entry for *fox* will now be "`f:f o:o x:x`", but by relying on the orthographic convention that `f` stands for `f:f` and so on, we can simply refer to it as `fox` and the form for *geese* as "`g o:e o:e s e`". Thus, the lexicon looks only slightly more complex:

reg-noun	irreg-pl-noun	irreg-sg-noun
fox	g o:e o:e s e	goose
cat	sheep	sheep
aardvark	m o:i u:ε s:c e	mouse

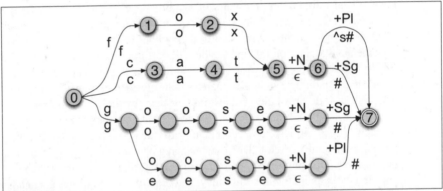

Figure 3.14   A fleshed-out English nominal inflection FST T_{lex}, expanded from T_{num} by replacing the three arcs with individual word stems (only a few sample word stems are shown).

The resulting transducer, shown in Fig. 3.14, will map plural nouns into the stem plus the morphological marker `+Pl`, and singular nouns into the stem plus the morphological marker `+Sg`. Thus, a surface *cats* will map to `cat +N +Pl`. This can be viewed in feasible-pair format as follows:

    `c:c a:a t:t +N:ε +Pl:^s#`

Since the output symbols include the morpheme- and word-boundary markers ^ and #, the lower labels in Fig. 3.14 do not correspond exactly to the surface level. Hence, we refer to tapes with these morpheme boundary markers in Fig. 3.15 as **intermediate** tapes; the next section shows how the boundary marker is removed.

3.6   Transducers and Orthographic Rules

The method described in the previous section will successfully recognize words like *aardvarks* and *mice*. But just concatenating the morphemes won't work for cases in

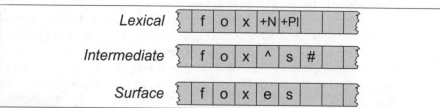

Figure 3.15   A schematic view of the lexical and intermediate tapes.

Spelling rule

which there is a spelling change; it would incorrectly reject an input like *foxes* and accept an input like *foxs*. We need to deal with the fact that English often requires spelling changes at morpheme boundaries by introducing **spelling rules** (or **orthographic rules**) This section introduces a number of notations for writing such rules and shows how to implement the rules as transducers. In general, the ability to implement rules as a transducer turns out to be useful throughout speech and language processing. Here are some spelling rules:

Name	Description of Rule	Example
Consonant doubling	1-letter consonant doubled before *-ing/-ed*	beg/begging
E deletion	silent e dropped before *-ing* and *-ed*	make/making
E insertion	e added after *-s,-z,-x,-ch*, *-sh* before *-s*	watch/watches
Y replacement	*-y* changes to *-ie* before *-s*, *-i* before *-ed*	try/tries
K insertion	verbs ending with *vowel* + *-c* add *-k*	panic/panicked

We can think of these spelling changes as taking as input a simple concatenation of morphemes (the "intermediate output" of the lexical transducer in Fig. 3.14) and producing as output a slightly modified (correctly spelled) concatenation of morphemes. Figure 3.16 shows in schematic form the three levels we are talking about: lexical, intermediate, and surface. So, for example, we could write an E-insertion rule that performs the mapping from the intermediate to surface levels shown in Fig. 3.16.

Figure 3.16   An example of the lexical, intermediate, and surface tapes. Between each pair of tapes is a two-level transducer; the lexical transducer of Fig. 3.14 between the lexical and intermediate levels, and the E-insertion spelling rule between the intermediate and surface levels. The E-insertion spelling rule inserts an *e* on the surface tape when the intermediate tape has a morpheme boundary ˆ followed by the morpheme *-s*.

Such a rule might say something like "insert an *e* on the surface tape just when the lexical tape has a morpheme ending in *x* (or *z*, etc.) and the next morpheme is *-s*". Here's a formalization of the rule:

$$\epsilon \rightarrow e \,/\, \left\{ \begin{array}{c} x \\ s \\ z \end{array} \right\} \hat{\ }\underline{\quad} s\# \qquad\qquad (3.4)$$

This is the rule notation of Chomsky and Halle (1968); a rule of the form $a \rightarrow$ $b\,/\,c\underline{\quad}d$ means "rewrite a as b when it occurs between c and d". Since the symbol ϵ means an empty transition, replacing it means inserting something. Recall that the symbol $\hat{\ }$ indicates a morpheme boundary. These boundaries are deleted by inclusion of the symbol $\hat{\ }$:ϵ in the default pairs for the transducer; thus, morpheme boundary markers are deleted on the surface level by default. The # symbol is a special symbol that marks a word boundary. Thus (3.4) means "insert an e after a morpheme-final x, s, or z, and before the morpheme s". Figure 3.17 shows an automaton that corresponds to this rule.

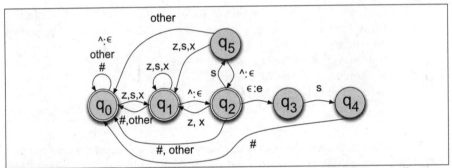

Figure 3.17   The transducer for the E-insertion rule of (3.4), extended from a similar transducer in Antworth (1990). We additionally need to delete the # symbol from the surface string; we can do this either by interpreting the symbol # as the pair #:ϵ or by postprocessing the output to remove word boundaries.

The idea in building a transducer for a particular rule is to express only the constraints necessary for that rule, allowing any other string of symbols to pass through unchanged. This rule ensures that we can only see the ϵ:e pair if we are in the proper context. So state q_0, which models having seen only default pairs unrelated to the rule, is an accepting state, as is q_1, which models having seen a z, s, or x. q_2 models having seen the morpheme boundary after the z, s, or x, and again is an accepting state. State q_3 models having just seen the E-insertion; it is not an accepting state, since the insertion is allowed only if it is followed by the s morpheme and then the end-of-word symbol #.

The *other* symbol is used in Fig. 3.17 to safely pass through any parts of words that don't play a role in the E-insertion rule; *other* means "any feasible pair that is not in this transducer". So, for example, when leaving state q_0, we go to q_1 on the z, s, or x symbols, rather than following the *other* arc and staying in q_0. The semantics of *other* depends on what symbols are on other arcs; since # is mentioned on some arcs, it is (by definition) not included in *other* and thus, for example, is explicitly mentioned on the arc from q_2 to q_0.

A transducer needs to correctly reject a string that applies the rule when it shouldn't. One possible bad string would have the correct environment for the E-insertion but have no insertion. State q_5 is used to ensure that the e is always inserted whenever the environment is appropriate; the transducer reaches q_5 only when it has seen an s after an appropriate morpheme boundary. If the machine is in state q_5 and the next symbol is #, the machine rejects the string (because there is no legal transition on # from q_5). Figure 3.18 shows the transition table for the rule that makes the illegal transitions explicit with the "–" symbol. The next section shows a trace of this E-insertion transducer running on a sample input string.

State \ Input	s:s	x:x	z:z	^:ε	ε:e	#	other
q_0:	1	1	1	0	-	0	0
q_1:	1	1	1	2	-	0	0
q_2:	5	1	1	0	3	0	0
q_3	4	-	-	-	-	-	-
q_4	-	-	-	-	-	0	-
q_5	1	1	1	2	-	-	0

Figure 3.18   The state-transition table for the E-insertion rule of Fig. 3.17, extended from a similar transducer in Antworth (1990).

3.7   The Combination of an FST Lexicon and Rules

We are now ready to combine our lexicon and rule transducers for parsing and generating. Figure 3.19 shows the architecture of a two-level morphology system, whether used for parsing or generating. The lexicon transducer maps between the lexical level, with its stems and morphological features and an intermediate level that represents a simple concatenation of morphemes. Then a host of transducers, each representing a single spelling rule constraint, all run in parallel to map between this intermediate level and the surface level. (We could instead have chosen to run all the spelling rules in series (as a long cascade) if we slightly changed each rule.)

Cascade   The architecture in Fig. 3.19 is a two-level **cascade** of transducers. Cascading two automata means running them in series with the output of the first feeding the input to the second. Cascades can be of arbitrary depth, and each level might be built out of many individual transducers. The cascade in Fig. 3.19 has two transducers in series: the transducer mapping from the lexical to the intermediate levels and the collection of parallel transducers mapping from the intermediate to the surface level. The cascade can be run top-down to generate a string, or bottom-up to parse it; Fig. 3.20 shows a trace of the system *accepting* the mapping from fox +N +PL to *foxes*.

The power of finite-state transducers is that exactly the same cascade with the same state sequences is used when the machine is generating the surface tape from the lexical tape or when it is parsing the lexical tape from the surface tape. For example, for generation, imagine leaving the Intermediate and Surface tapes blank. Now if we run the lexicon transducer, given fox +N +PL, it will produce *fox^s#* on the Intermediate

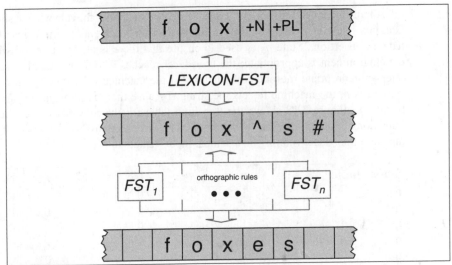

Figure 3.19   Generating or parsing with FST lexicon and rules.

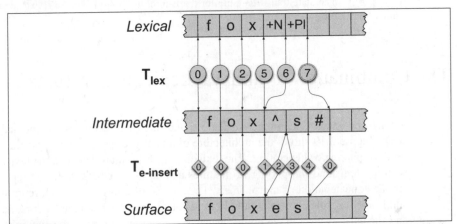

Figure 3.20   Accepting *foxes*: The lexicon transducer T_{lex} from Fig. 3.14 cascaded with the E-insertion transducer in Fig. 3.17.

tape via the same states that it accepted the Lexical and Intermediate tapes in our earlier example. If we then allow all possible orthographic transducers to run in parallel, we will produce the same surface tape.

Parsing can be slightly more complicated than generation because of the problem of **ambiguity**. For example, *foxes* can also be a verb (albeit a rare one, meaning "to baffle or confuse"), and hence the lexical parse for *foxes* could be fox +V +3Sg as well as fox +N +PL. How are we to know which one is the proper parse? In fact, for ambiguous cases of this sort, the transducer is not capable of deciding. **Disambiguating** will require some external evidence such as the surrounding words. Thus, *foxes* is likely to be a noun in the sequence *I saw two foxes yesterday*, but a verb in the sequence *That trickster foxes me every time!*. We discuss such disambiguation algorithms

Ambiguity

Disambiguating

in Chapter 5 and Chapter 20. Barring such external evidence, the best our transducer can do is just enumerate the possible choices so we can transduce *fox^s#* into both `fox +V +3SG` and `fox +N +PL`.

There is a kind of ambiguity that we do need to handle: local ambiguity that occurs during the process of parsing. For example, imagine parsing the input verb *assess*. After seeing *ass*, our E-insertion transducer may propose that the *e* that follows is inserted by the spelling rule (e.g., as far as the transducer is concerned, we might have been parsing the word *asses*). It is not until we don't see the # after *asses*, but rather run into another *s*, that we realize we have gone down an incorrect path.

Because of this non-determinism, FST-parsing algorithms need to incorporate some sort of search algorithm. Exercise 3.7 asks the reader to modify the algorithm for non-deterministic FSA recognition in Fig. 2.19 in Chapter 2 to do FST parsing.

Note that many possible spurious segmentations of the input, such as parsing *assess* as *^a^s^ses^s* will be ruled out since no entry in the lexicon will match this string.

Running a cascade can be made more efficient by **composing** and **intersecting** the transducers. We've already seen how to compose a cascade of transducers in series into a single more complex transducer. The intersection of two transducers/relations F and G ($F \wedge G$) defines a relation R such that R(x,y) if and only if F(x,y) and G(x,y). While transducers in general are not closed under intersection, as discussed on page 58, transducers between strings of equal length (without ϵ) are, and two-level rules can be written this way by treating the ϵ symbol as an ordinary symbol in the rule system. The *Intersection* **intersection** algorithm takes the Cartesian product of the states, that is, for each state q_i in machine 1 and state q_j in machine 2, we create a new state q_{ij}. Then for any input symbol *a*, if machine 1 would transition to state q_n and machine 2 would transition to state q_m, we transition to state q_{nm}. Figure 3.21 sketches how this intersection ($\wedge$) and composition ($\circ$) process might be carried out.

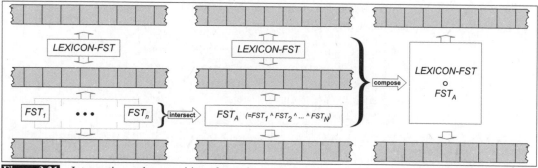

Figure 3.21   Intersection and composition of transducers.

Since there are a number of rule→FST compilers, it is almost never necessary in practice to write an FST by hand. Kaplan and Kay (1994) give the mathematics that define the mapping from rules to two-level relations, and Antworth (1990) gives details of the algorithms for rule compilation. Mohri (1997) gives algorithms for transducer minimization and determinization.

3.8   Lexicon-Free FSTs: The Porter Stemmer

Keyword

While building a transducer from a lexicon plus rules is the standard algorithm for morphological parsing, there are simpler algorithms that don't require the large on-line lexicon demanded by this algorithm. These are used especially in IR tasks like Web search (Chapter 23), in which a query such as a Boolean combination of relevant **key-words** or phrases, for example, (*marsupial OR kangaroo OR koala*) returns documents that have these words in them. Since a document with the word *marsupials* might not match the keyword *marsupial*, some IR systems first run a stemmer on the query and document words. Morphological information in IR is thus only used to determine that two words have the same stem; the suffixes are thrown away.

Stemming

Porter stemmer

One of the most widely used **stemming** algorithms is the simple and efficient Porter (1980) algorithm, which is based on a series of simple cascaded rewrite rules. Since cascaded rewrite rules are just the sort of thing that could be easily implemented as an FST, the Porter algorithm also can be viewed as a lexicon-free FST stemmer (this idea is developed further in the exercises (Exercise 3.6). The algorithm contains a series of rules like these:

$$\text{ATIONAL} \rightarrow \text{ATE} \quad (\text{e.g., relational} \rightarrow \text{relate})$$
$$\text{ING} \rightarrow \epsilon \quad \text{if stem contains vowel (e.g., motoring} \rightarrow \text{motor})$$
$$\text{SSES} \rightarrow \text{SS} \quad (\text{e.g., grasses} \rightarrow \text{grass})$$

Detailed rule lists for the Porter stemmer, as well as code (in Java, Python, etc.) can be found on Martin Porter's homepage; see also the original paper (Porter, 1980).

Stemming tends to improve the performance of information retrieval, especially with smaller documents (the larger the document, the higher the chance the keyword will occur in the exact form used in the query). But lexicon-free stemmers like the Porter algorithm, while simpler than full lexicon-based morphological parsers, commit errors like the following (Krovetz, 1993):

Errors of Commission		Errors of Omission	
organization	organ	European	Europe
doing	doe	analysis	analyzes
numerical	numerous	noise	noisy
policy	police	sparse	sparsity

Modern stemmers tend to be more complicated because, for example, we don't want to stem, say the word *Illustrator* to *illustrate*, since the capitalized form *Illustrator* tends to refer to the software package. We return to this issue in Chapter 23.

3.9   Word and Sentence Tokenization

We have focused so far in this chapter on a problem of segmentation: how words can be segmented into morphemes. We turn now to a brief discussion of the related problem

Tokenization   of segmenting running text into words and sentences. This task is called **tokenization**.

Word tokenization may seem simple in a language like English that separates words by a special 'space' character. As shown later, not every language does this (Chinese, Japanese, and Thai, for example, do not). But a closer examination will make it clear that whitespace is not sufficient by itself even for English. Consider the following sentences from *Wall Street Journal* and *New York Times* articles, respectively:

```
Mr.  Sherwood said reaction to Sea Containers' proposal
has been "very positive." In New York Stock Exchange
composite trading yesterday, Sea Containers closed at
$62.625, up 62.5 cents.


''I said, 'what're you?  Crazy?'  ''  said Sadowsky.  ''I
can't afford to do that.''
```

Segmenting purely on whitespace would produce words like these:

```
cents.        said,        positive."        Crazy?
```

We could address these errors by treating punctuation, in addition to whitespace, as a word boundary. But punctuation often occurs word internally, in examples like *m.p.h,*, *Ph.D.*, *AT&T*, *cap'n*, *01/02/06*, and *google.com*. Similarly, assuming that we want *62.5* to be a word, we'll need to avoid segmenting every period, since that will segment this number into 62 and 5. Number expressions introduce other complications as well; while commas normally appear at word boundaries, commas are used inside numbers in English, every three digits: *555,500.50*. Languages differ on punctuation styles for numbers; many continental European languages like Spanish, French, and German, by contrast, use a comma to mark the decimal point, and spaces (or sometimes periods) where English puts commas, for example, *555 500,50*.

A tokenizer can also be used to expand clitic contractions that are marked by apostrophes, for example, converting *what're* above to the two tokens *what are*, and *we're* to *we are*. This requires ambiguity resolution, since apostrophes are also used as genitive markers (as in *the book's over* or in *Containers'* above) or as quotative markers (as in *'what're you? Crazy?'* above). Such contractions occur in other alphabetic languages, including articles and pronouns in French (*j'ai*, *l'homme*). While these contractions tend to be clitics, not all clitics are marked this way with contraction. In general, then, segmenting and expanding clitics can be done as part of the process of morphological parsing presented earlier in the chapter.

Depending on the application, tokenization algorithms may also tokenize multiword expressions like *New York* or *rock 'n' roll*, which requires a multiword expression dictionary of some sort. This makes tokenization intimately tied up with the task of detecting names, dates, and organizations, a process called *named entity detection* which is discussed in Chapter 22.

Sentence segmentation   In addition to word segmentation, **sentence segmentation** is a crucial first step in text processing. Segmenting a text into sentences is generally based on punctuation. This is because certain kinds of punctuation (periods, question marks, exclamation points) tend to mark sentence boundaries. Question marks and exclamation points are relatively unambiguous markers of sentence boundaries. Periods, on the other hand, are more ambiguous. The period character "." is ambiguous between a sentence boundary marker and a marker of abbreviations like *Mr.* or *Inc.* The previous sentence that you just read showed an even more complex case of this ambiguity, in which the final period of *Inc.* marked both an abbreviation and the sentence boundary marker. For this reason, sentence tokenization and word tokenization tend to be addressed jointly.

In general, sentence tokenization methods work by building a binary classifier (based on a sequence of rules or on machine learning) that decides if a period is part of the word or is a sentence-boundary marker. In making this decision, it helps to know if the period is attached to a commonly used abbreviation; thus, an abbreviation dictionary is useful.

State-of-the-art methods for sentence tokenization are based on machine learning and are introduced in later chapters. But a useful first step can still be taken through a sequence of regular expressions. We introduce here the first part; a word tokenization algorithm. Figure 3.22 gives a simple Perl word tokenization algorithm based on Grefenstette (1999). The algorithm is quite minimal, designed mainly to clarify many of the segmentation issues we discussed in previous paragraphs.

The algorithm consists of a sequence of regular expression substitution rules. The first rule separates unambiguous punctuation like question marks and parentheses. The next rule segments commas unless they are inside numbers. We then disambiguate apostrophes and pull off word-final clitics. Finally, we deal with periods, using a (toy) abbreviation dictionary and some heuristics for detecting other abbreviations.

The fact that a simple tokenizer can be build with such simple regular expression patterns suggest that tokenizers like the one in Fig. 3.22 can be easily implemented in FSTs. This is indeed the case, and Karttunen et al. (1996) and Beesley and Karttunen (2003) describe such FST-based tokenizers.

3.9.1   Segmentation in Chinese

We mentioned above that some languages, including Chinese, Japanese, and Thai, do not use spaces to mark potential word-boundaries. Alternative segmentation methods are used for these languages.

In Chinese, for example, words are composed of characters known as *hanzi*. Each character generally represents a single morpheme and is pronounceable as a single syllable. Words on average are about 2.4 characters long. A simple algorithm that does remarkably well for segmenting Chinese, and often used as a baseline comparison for more advanced methods, is a version of greedy search called **maximum matching** or sometimes **maxmatch**. The algorithm requires a dictionary (wordlist) of the language.

Maximum matching

The maximum matching algorithm starts by pointing at the beginning of a string. It chooses the longest word in the dictionary that matches the input at the current position. The pointer is then advanced past each character in that word. If no word matches, the pointer is instead advanced one character (creating a one-character word). The algorithm is then iteratively applied again starting from the new pointer position. To help visualize this algorithm, Palmer (2000) gives an English analogy that approximates the Chinese situation by removing the spaces from the English sentence *the table down there* to produce *thetabledownthere*. The maximum match algorithm (given a long En-

```perl
#!/usr/bin/perl

$letternumber = "[A-Za-z0-9]";
$notletter = "[^A-Za-z0-9]";
$alwayssep = "[\\?!()\";/\\|'']";
$clitic = "('|:|-|'S|'D|'M|'LL|'RE|'VE|N'T|'s|'d|'m|'ll|'re|'ve|n't)";

$abbr{"Co."} = 1; $abbr{"Dr."} = 1; $abbr{"Jan."} = 1; $abbr{"Feb."} = 1;

while ($line = <>){ # read the next line from standard input

    # put whitespace around unambiguous separators
    $line =~ s/$alwayssep/ $& /g;

    # put whitespace around commas that aren't inside numbers
    $line =~ s/([^0-9]),/$1 , /g;
    $line =~ s/,([^0-9])/ , $1/g;

    # distinguish singlequotes from apostrophes by
    # segmenting off single quotes not preceded by letter
    $line =~ s/^'/$& /g;
    $line =~ s/($notletter)'/$1 '/g;

    # segment off unambiguous word-final clitics and punctuation
    $line =~ s/$clitic$/ $&/g;
    $line =~ s/$clitic($notletter)/ $1 $2/g;

    # now deal with periods.  For each possible word
    @possiblewords=split(/\s+/,$line);
    foreach $word (@possiblewords) {
        # if it ends in a period,
        if (($word =~ /$letternumber\./)
                 && !($abbr{$word})  # and isn't on the abbreviation list
                     # and isn't a sequence of letters and periods (U.S.)
                     # and doesn't resemble an abbreviation (no vowels: Inc.)
                 && !($word =~
                     /^([A-Za-z]\.([A-Za-z]\.)+|[A-Z][bcdfghj-nptvxz]+\.)$/)) {
            # then segment off the period
            $word =~ s/\.$/ \./;
        }
        # expand clitics
        $word =~s/'ve/have/;
        $word =~s/'m/am/;
        print $word," ";
    }
 print "\n";
}
```

Figure 3.22   A sample English tokenization script, adapted from Grefenstette (1999) and Palmer (2000). A real script would have a longer abbreviation dictionary.

glish dictionary) would first match the word *theta* in the input since that is the longest sequence of letters that matches a dictionary word. Starting from the end of *theta*, the longest matching dictionary word is *bled*, followed by *own* and then *there*, producing the incorrect sequence *theta bled own there*.

The algorithm seems to work better in Chinese (with such short words) than in languages like English with long words, as our failed example shows. Even in Chinese, however, maxmatch has a number of weakness, particularly with **unknown words** (words not in the dictionary) or **unknown genres** (genres which differ a lot from the assumptions made by the dictionary builder).

There is an annual competition (technically called a **bakeoff**) for Chinese segmentation algorithms. The most successful modern algorithms for Chinese word segmentation are based on machine learning from hand-segmented training sets. We return to these algorithms after we introduce probabilistic methods in Chapter 5.

3.10   Detection and Correction of Spelling Errors

> ALGERNON: *But my own sweet Cecily, I have never written you any letters.*
> CECILY: *You need hardly remind me of that, Ernest. I remember only too well that I was forced to write your letters for you. I wrote always three times a week, and sometimes oftener.*
> ALGERNON: *Oh, do let me read them, Cecily?*
> CECILY: *Oh, I couldn't possibly. They would make you far too conceited. The three you wrote me after I had broken off the engagement are so beautiful, and so badly spelled, that even now I can hardly read them without crying a little.*
>
> Oscar Wilde, *The Importance of Being Earnest*

Like Oscar Wilde's fabulous Cecily, a lot of people were thinking about spelling during the last turn of the century. Gilbert and Sullivan provide many examples. *The Gondoliers*' Giuseppe, for example, worries that his private secretary is "shaky in his spelling", while *Iolanthe*'s Phyllis can "spell every word that she uses". Thorstein Veblen's explanation (in his 1899 classic *The Theory of the Leisure Class*) was that a main purpose of the "archaic, cumbrous, and ineffective" English spelling system was to be difficult enough to provide a test of membership in the leisure class. Whatever the social role of spelling, we can certainly agree that many more of us are like Cecily than like Phyllis. Estimates for the frequency of spelling errors in human-typed text vary from 0.05% of the words in carefully edited newswire text to 38% in difficult applications like telephone directory lookup (Kukich, 1992).

In this section we introduce the problem of detecting and correcting spelling errors. Since the standard algorithm for spelling error correction is probabilistic, we continue our spell-checking discussion later in Chapter 5 after we define the probabilistic noisy channel model. The detection and correction of spelling errors is an integral part of modern word processors and search engines. It is also important in correcting errors in *OCR* **optical character recognition** (OCR), the automatic recognition of machine or hand-printed characters, and in **on-line handwriting recognition**, the recognition of human printed or cursive handwriting as the user is writing. Following Kukich (1992), we can distinguish three increasingly broader problems:

1. **Non-word error detection:** detecting spelling errors that result in non-words (like *graffe* for *giraffe*).

2. **Isolated-word error correction:** correcting spelling errors that result in non-words, for example, correcting *graffe* to *giraffe*, but looking only at the word in isolation.

3. **Context-dependent error detection and correction:** using the context to help detect and correct spelling errors even if they accidentally result in an actual word of English (**real-word errors**). This can happen from typographical errors (in-
Real-word errors sertion, deletion, transposition) that accidentally produce a real word (e.g., *there* for *three*), or because the writer substituted the wrong spelling of a homophone or near-homophone (e.g., *dessert* for *desert*, or *piece* for *peace*).

Detecting non-word errors is generally done by marking any word that is not found in a dictionary. For example, the misspelling *graffe* above would not occur in a dictionary. Some early research (Peterson, 1986) had suggested that such spelling dictionaries would need to be kept small because large dictionaries contain very rare words that resemble misspellings of other words. For example the rare words *wont* or *veery* are also common misspelling of *won't* and *very*. In practice, Damerau and Mays (1989) found that while some misspellings were hidden by real words in a larger dictionary, the larger dictionary proved more helpful than harmful by avoiding marking rare words as errors. This is especially true with probabilistic spell-correction algorithms that can use word frequency as a factor. Thus, modern spell-checking systems tend to be based on large dictionaries.

The finite-state morphological parsers described throughout this chapter provide a technology for implementing such large dictionaries. By giving a morphological parser for a word, an FST parser is inherently a word recognizer. Indeed, an FST morphological parser can be turned into an even more efficient FSA word recognizer by using the **projection** operation to extract the lower-side language graph. Such FST dictionaries also have the advantage of representing productive morphology like the English *-s* and *-ed* inflections. This is important for dealing with new legitimate combinations of stems and inflection. For example, a new stem can be easily added to the dictionary, and then all the inflected forms are easily recognized. This makes FST dictionaries especially powerful for spell-checking in morphologically rich languages in which a single stem can have tens or hundreds of possible surface forms.[5]

FST dictionaries can thus help with non-word error detection. But how about error correction? Algorithms for isolated-word error correction operate by finding words that are the likely source of the errorful form. For example, correcting the spelling error *graffe* requires searching through all possible words like *giraffe*, *graf*, *craft*, *grail*, etc., to pick the most likely source. To choose among these potential sources, we need a **distance metric** between the source and the surface error. Intuitively, *giraffe* is a more likely source than *grail* for *graffe* because *giraffe* is closer in spelling to *graffe* than *grail* is to *graffe*. The most powerful way to capture this similarity intuition requires the use of probability theory and is discussed in Chapter 5. The algorithm underlying this solution, however, is the non-probabilistic **minimum edit distance** algorithm that we introduce in the next section.

3.11   Minimum Edit Distance

String distance   Deciding which of two words is closer to some third word in spelling is a special case of the general problem of **string distance**. The distance between two strings is a measure of how alike two strings are to each other.

Many important algorithms for finding string distance rely on some version of the

---

[5] Early spell-checkers, by contrast, allowed any word to have any suffix; thus, early versions of Unix `spell` accepted bizarre prefixed words like *misclam* and *antiundoggingly* and suffixed words from *the*, like *thehood* and *theness*.

Minimum edit distance

minimum edit distance algorithm, named by Wagner and Fischer (1974) but independently discovered by many people (summarized later, in the Historical Notes section of Chapter 6). The minimum edit distance between two strings is the minimum number of editing operations (insertion, deletion, substitution) needed to transform one string into another. For example, the gap between the words *intention* and *execution* is five operations, shown in Fig. 3.23 as an **alignment** between the two strings. Given two sequences, an **alignment** is a correspondence between substrings of the two sequences. Thus, I aligns with the empty string, N with E, T with X, and so on. Beneath the aligned strings is another representation; a series of symbols expressing an **operation list** for converting the top string into the bottom string: d for deletion, s for substitution, i for insertion.

Alignment

```
        I N T E * N T I O N

        * E X E C U T I O N
        d s s   i s
```

Figure 3.23   Representing the minimum edit distance between two strings as an **alignment**. The final row gives the operation list for converting the top string into the bottom string: d for deletion, s for substitution, i for insertion.

We can also assign a particular cost or weight to each of these operations. The **Levenshtein** distance between two sequences is the simplest weighting factor in which each of the three operations has a cost of 1 (Levenshtein, 1966).[6] Thus, the Levenshtein distance between *intention* and *execution* is 5. Levenshtein also proposed an alternative version of his metric in which each insertion or deletion has a cost of 1 and substitutions are not allowed (equivalent to allowing substitution, but giving each substitution a cost of 2 since any substitution can be represented by one insertion and one deletion). Using this version, the Levenshtein distance between *intention* and *execution* is 8.

Dynamic programming

The minimum edit distance is computed by **dynamic programming**. Dynamic programming is the name for a class of algorithms, first introduced by Bellman (1957), that apply a table-driven method to solve problems by combining solutions to sub-problems. This class includes the most commonly used algorithms in speech and language processing; besides minimum edit distance, these include the **Viterbi** and **forward** algorithms (Chapter 6) and the **CKY** and **Earley** algorithm (Chapter 13).

The intuition of a dynamic programming problem is that a large problem can be solved by properly combining the solutions to various sub-problems. For example, consider the sequence or "path" of transformed words that comprise the minimum edit distance between the strings *intention* and *execution* shown in Fig. 3.24.

Imagine some string (perhaps it is *exention*) that is in this optimal path (whatever it is). The intuition of dynamic programming is that if *exention* is in the optimal operation list, then the optimal sequence must also include the optimal path from *intention* to *exention*. Why? If there were a shorter path from *intention* to *exention*, then we could

---

6 We assume that the substitution of a letter for itself, for example, substitution *t* for *t*, has zero cost.

```
i n t e n t i o n
                      ←— delete i
  n t e n t i o n
                      ←— substitute n by e
  e t e n t i o n
                      ←— substitute t by x
  e x e n t i o n
                      ←— insert u
  e x e n u t i o n
                      ←— substitute n by c
  e x e c u t i o n
```

Figure 3.24   Transformation list example of Kruskal (1983) from *intention* to *execution*.

use it instead, resulting in a shorter overall path, and the optimal sequence wouldn't be optimal, thus leading to a contradiction.

Dynamic programming algorithms for sequence comparison work by creating a distance matrix with one column for each symbol in the target sequence and one row for each symbol in the source sequence (i.e., target along the bottom, source along the side). For minimum edit distance, this matrix is the *edit-distance* matrix. Each cell *edit-distance*[*i,j*] contains the distance between the first *i* characters of the target and the first *j* characters of the source. Each cell can be computed as a simple function of the surrounding cells; thus, starting from the beginning of the matrix it is possible to fill in every entry. The value in each cell is computed by taking the minimum of the three possible paths through the matrix which arrive there:

$$distance[i,j] = \min \begin{cases} distance[i-1,j] + \text{ins-cost}(target_{i-1}) \\ distance[i-1,j-1] + \text{sub-cost}(source_{j-1}, target_{i-1}) \\ distance[i,j-1] + \text{del-cost}(source_{j-1})) \end{cases}$$

The algorithm itself is summarized in Fig. 3.25 and Fig. 3.26 shows the results of applying the algorithm to the distance between *intention* and *execution*, assuming the version of Levenshtein distance in which the insertions and deletions each have a cost of 1 (ins-cost( ) = del-cost( ) = 1), and substitutions have a cost of 2 (except that substitution of identical letters has zero cost).

Knowing the minimum edit distance is useful for algorithms like finding potential spelling error corrections. But the edit distance algorithm is important in another way; with a small change, it can also provide the minimum cost **alignment** between two strings. Aligning two strings is useful throughout speech and language processing. In speech recognition, minimum edit distance alignment is used to compute word error rate in speech recognition (Chapter 9). Alignment plays a role in machine translation, in which sentences in a parallel corpus (a corpus with a text in two languages) need to be matched to each other.

To extend the edit distance algorithm to produce an alignment, we can start by visualizing an alignment as a path through the edit distance matrix. Figure 3.27 shows this path with the boldfaced cell. Each boldfaced cell represents an alignment of a pair of letters in the two strings. If two boldfaced cells occur in the same row, there will be an insertion in going from the source to the target; two boldfaced cells in the same column indicates a deletion.

---

function MIN-EDIT-DISTANCE(*target, source*) **returns** *min-distance*

$n \leftarrow$ LENGTH(*target*)
$m \leftarrow$ LENGTH(*source*)
Create a distance matrix *distance[n+1,m+1]*
Initialize the zeroth row and column to be the distance from the empty string
  distance[0,0] = 0
  for each column i **from** 1 **to** n **do**
    distance[i,0] $\leftarrow$ *distance[i-1,0]* + *ins-cost(target[i])*
  for each row j **from** 1 **to** m **do**
    distance[0,j] $\leftarrow$ *distance[0,j-1]* + *del-cost(source[j])*
  for each column i **from** 1 **to** n **do**
    for each row j **from** 1 **to** m **do**
      distance[i,j] $\leftarrow$ MIN(*distance[i-1,j]* + *ins-cost(target$_{i-1}$)*,
                     distance[i-1,j-1] + *sub-cost(source$_{j-1}$,]target$_{i-1}$)*,
                     distance[i,j-1] + *del-cost(source$_{j-1}$))*
  return *distance*[n,m]

Figure 3.25   The minimum edit distance algorithm, an example of the class of dynamic programming algorithms. The various costs can either be fixed (e.g., $\forall x,$ ins-cost$(x) = 1$) or can be specific to the letter (to model the fact that some letters are more likely to be inserted than others). We assume that there is no cost for substituting a letter for itself (i.e., sub-cost$(x,x) = 0$).

n	9	8	9	10	11	12	11	10	9	8
o	8	7	8	9	10	11	10	9	8	9
i	7	6	7	8	9	10	9	8	9	10
t	6	5	6	7	8	9	8	9	10	11
n	5	4	5	6	7	8	9	10	11	10
e	4	3	4	5	6	7	8	9	10	9
t	3	4	5	6	7	8	7	8	9	8
n	2	3	4	5	6	7	8	7	8	7
i	1	2	3	4	5	6	7	6	7	8
#	0	1	2	3	4	5	6	7	8	9
	#	e	x	e	c	u	t	i	o	n

Figure 3.26   Computation of minimum edit distance between *intention* and *execution* with the algorithm of Fig. 3.25, using Levenshtein distance with cost of 1 for insertions or deletions, 2 for substitutions. In italics are the initial values representing the distance from the empty string.

Figure 3.27 also shows the intuition of how to compute this alignment path. The computation proceeds in two steps. In the first step, we augment the minimum edit distance algorithm to store backpointers in each cell. The backpointer from a cell points to the previous cell (or cells) that we came from in entering the current cell. We've shown a schematic of these backpointers in Fig. 3.27, after a similar diagram in Gusfield (1997). Some cells have multiple backpointers because the minimum extension could have come from multiple previous cells. In the second step, we perform a **backtrace**. In a backtrace, we start from the last cell (at the final row and column), and

Backtrace

follow the pointers back through the dynamic programming matrix. Each complete path between the final cell and the initial cell is a minimum distance alignment. Exercise 3.12 asks you to modify the minimum edit distance algorithm to store the pointers and compute the backtrace to output an alignment.

n	9	↓8	↙←↓9	↙←↓10	↙←↓11	↙←↓12	↓11	↓10	↓9	↙8
o	8	↓7	↙←↓8	↙←↓9	↙←↓10	↙←↓11	↓10	↓9	↙8	←9
i	7	↓6	↙←↓7	↙←↓8	↙←↓9	↙←↓10	↓9	↙8	←9	←10
t	6	↓5	↙←↓6	↙←↓7	↙←↓8	↙←↓9	↙8	←9	←10	←↓11
n	5	↓4	↙←↓5	↙←↓6	↙←↓7	↙←↓8	↙←↓9	↙←↓10	↙←↓11	↙↓10
e	4	↙3	←4	↙←5	←6	←7	←↓8	↙←↓9	↙←↓10	↓9
t	3	↙←↓4	↙←↓5	↙←↓6	↙←↓7	↙←↓8	↙7	←↓8	↙←↓9	↓8
n	2	↙←↓3	↙←↓4	↙←↓5	↙←↓6	↙←↓7	↙←↓8	↓7	↙←↓8	↙7
i	**1**	↙←↓2	↙←↓3	↙←↓4	↙←↓5	↙←↓6	↙←↓7	↙6	←7	←8
#	**0**	1	2	3	4	5	6	7	8	9
	#	e	x	e	c	u	t	i	o	n

Figure 3.27   When entering a value in each cell, we mark which of the three neighboring cells we came from with up to three arrows. After the table is full we compute an **alignment** (minimum edit path) by using a **backtrace**, starting at the **8** in the upper-right corner and following the arrows. The sequence of dark grey cells represents one possible minimum cost alignment between the two strings.

There are various publicly available packages to compute edit distance, including Unix `diff` and the NIST `sclite` program (NIST, 2005). Minimum edit distance can also be augmented in various ways. The Viterbi algorithm, for example, is an extension of minimum edit distance that uses probabilistic definitions of the operations. Instead of computing the "minimum edit distance" between two strings, Viterbi computes the "maximum probability alignment" of one string with another. The Viterbi algorithm is crucial in probabilistic tasks like speech recognition and part-of-speech tagging.

3.12   Human Morphological Processing

Full listing

Minimum redundancy

In this section we briefly survey psycholinguistic studies on how multimorphemic words are represented in the minds of speakers of English. Consider the word *walk* and its inflected forms *walks* and *walked*. Are all three in the human lexicon? Or merely *walk* along with *-ed* and *-s*? How about the word *happy* and its derived forms *happily* and *happiness*? We can imagine two ends of a spectrum of possible representations. The **full listing** hypothesis proposes that all words of a language are listed in the mental lexicon without any internal morphological structure. In this view, morphological structure is an epiphenomenon, and *walk*, *walks*, *walked*, *happy*, and *happily* are all separately listed in the lexicon. This hypothesis is untenable for morphologically complex languages like Turkish. The **minimum redundancy** hypothesis suggests that only the constituent morphemes are represented in the lexicon and when processing *walks*, (whether for reading, listening, or talking) we must always access both morphemes (*walk* and *-s*) and combine them. This view is probably too strict as well.

Some of the earliest evidence that the human lexicon represents at least some morphological structure comes from **speech errors**, also called **slips of the tongue**. In conversational speech, speakers often mix up the order of the words or sounds:

> if you <u>break</u> it it'll <u>drop</u>

In slips of the tongue collected by Fromkin and Ratner (1998) and Garrett (1975), inflectional and derivational affixes can appear separately from their stems. The ability of these affixes to be produced separately from their stem suggests that the mental lexicon contains some representation of morphological structure.

> it's not only us who have screw loose<u>s</u> (for "screws loose")
> word<u>s</u> of rule formation (for "rules of word formation")
> easy enough<u>ly</u> (for "easily enough")

More recent experimental evidence suggests that neither the full listing nor the minimum redundancy hypotheses may be completely true. Instead, it's possible that some but not all morphological relationships are mentally represented. Stanners et al. (1979), for example, found that some derived forms (*happiness*, *happily*) seem to be stored separately from their stem (*happy*) but that regularly inflected forms (*pouring*) are not distinct in the lexicon from their stems (*pour*). Stanners et al. did this by using a repetition priming experiment. In short, repetition priming takes advantage of *Priming* the fact that a word is recognized faster if it has been seen before (if it is **primed**). They found that *lifting* primed *lift*, and *burned* primed *burn*, but, for example, *selective* didn't prime *select*. Marslen-Wilson et al. (1994) found that *spoken* derived words can prime their stems, but only if the meaning of the derived form is closely related to the stem. For example, *government* primes *govern*, but *department* does not prime *depart*. A Marslen-Wilson et al. (1994) model compatible with their findings is shown in Fig. 3.28.

Figure 3.28   Marslen-Wilson et al. (1994) result: Derived words are linked to their stems only if semantically related.

In summary, these results suggest that (at least) productive morphology like inflection does play an online role in the human lexicon. More recent studies have shown effects of non-inflectional morphological structure on word reading time as well, such *Morphological* as the **morphological family size**. The morphological family size of a word is the *family size* number of other multimorphemic words and compounds in which it appears; the family for *fear*, for example, includes *fearful, fearfully, fearfulness, fearless, fearlessly, fearlessness, fearsome,* and *godfearing* (according to the CELEX database), for a total size of 9. Baayen and others (Baayen et al., 1997; De Jong et al., 2002; Moscoso del Prado Martín et al., 2004a) have shown that words with a larger morphological family size are recognized faster. Recent work has further shown that word recognition speed is affected by the total amount of **information** (or **entropy**) contained by the morphological paradigm (Moscoso del Prado Martín et al., 2004a); entropy will be introduced in the next chapter.

3.13   Summary

This chapter introduced **morphology**, the arena of language processing dealing with the subparts of words, and the **finite-state transducer**, the computational device that is important for morphology but that also plays a role in many other tasks in later chapters. We also introduced **stemming**, **word and sentence tokenization**, and **spelling error detection**. Here's a summary of the main points we covered about these ideas:

- **Morphological parsing** is the process of finding the constituent **morphemes** in a word (e.g., `cat +N +PL` for *cats*).

- English mainly uses **prefixes** and **suffixes** to express **inflectional** and **derivational** morphology.

- English **inflectional** morphology is relatively simple and includes person and number agreement (*-s*) and tense markings (*-ed* and *-ing*). English **derivational** morphology is more complex and includes suffixes like *-ation* and *-ness* and prefixes like *co-* and *re-*. Many constraints on the English **morphotactics** (allowable morpheme sequences) can be represented by finite automata.

- **Finite-state transducers** are an extension of finite-state automata that can generate output symbols. Important FST operations include **composition**, **projection**, and **intersection**.

- **Finite-state morphology** and **two-level morphology** are applications of finite-state transducers to morphological representation and parsing.

- Automatic transducer compilers can produce a transducer for any rewrite rule. The lexicon and spelling rules can be combined by **composing** and **intersecting** transducers.

- The **Porter algorithm** is a simple and efficient way to do **stemming**, stripping off affixes. It is not as accurate as a lexicon-based transducer model but is relevant for tasks like **information retrieval** in which exact morphological structure is not needed.

- **Word tokenization** can be done by simple regular expressions substitutions or by transducers.

- **Spelling error detection** is normally done by finding words that are not in a dictionary; an FST dictionary can be useful for this.

- The **minimum edit distance** between two strings is the minimum number of operations it takes to edit one into the other. Minimum edit distance can be computed by **dynamic programming**, which also results in an **alignment** of the two strings.

Bibliographical and Historical Notes

Despite the close mathematical similarity of finite-state transducers to finite-state automata, the two models grew out of somewhat different traditions. Chapter 2 described how the finite automaton grew out of Turing's (1936) model of algorithmic computation, and McCulloch and Pitts finite-state-like models of the neuron. The influence of the Turing machine on the transducer was somewhat more indirect. Huffman (1954) proposed what was essentially a state-transition table to model the behavior of sequential circuits, based on the work of Shannon (1938) on an algebraic model of relay circuits. Based on Turing and Shannon's work, and unaware of Huffman's work, Moore (1956) introduced the term **finite automaton** for a machine with a finite number of states with an alphabet of input symbols and an alphabet of output symbols. Mealy (1955) extended and synthesized the work of Moore and Huffman.

The finite automata in Moore's original paper and the extension by Mealy differed in an important way. In a Mealy machine, the input/output symbols are associated with the transitions between states. In a Moore machine, the input/output symbols are associated with the state. The two types of transducers are equivalent; any Moore machine can be converted into an equivalent Mealy machine, and vice versa. Further early work on finite-state transducers, sequential transducers, and so on, was conducted by Salomaa (1973) and by Schützenberger (1977).

Early algorithms for morphological parsing used either the **bottom-up** or **top-down** methods that we discuss when we turn to parsing in Chapter 13. An early bottom-up **affix-stripping** approach was Packard's (1973) parser for ancient Greek that iteratively stripped prefixes and suffixes off the input word, making note of them, and then looked up the remainder in a lexicon. It returned any root that was compatible with the stripped-off affixes. AMPLE (A Morphological Parser for Linguistic Exploration) (Weber and Mann, 1981; Weber et al., 1988; Hankamer and Black, 1991) is another early bottom-up morphological parser. Hankamer's (1986) keCi is an early top-down *generate-and-test* or *analysis-by-synthesis* morphological parser for Turkish, guided by a finite-state representation of Turkish morphemes. The program begins with a morpheme that might match the left edge of the word, applies every possible phonological rule to it, and checks each result against the input. If one of the outputs succeeds, the program then follows the finite-state morphotactics to the next morpheme and tries to continue matching the input.

The idea of modeling spelling rules as finite-state transducers is really based on Johnson's (1972) early idea that phonological rules (discussed in Chapter 7) have finite-state properties. Johnson's insight unfortunately did not attract the attention of the community and was independently discovered by Ronald Kaplan and Martin Kay, first in an unpublished talk (Kaplan and Kay, 1981) and then finally in print (Kaplan and Kay, 1994) (see page 13 for a discussion of multiple independent discoveries). Kaplan and Kay's work was followed up and most fully worked out by Koskenniemi (1983), who described finite-state morphological rules for Finnish. Karttunen (1983) built a program called KIMMO based on Koskenniemi's models. Antworth (1990) gives many details of two-level morphology and its application to English.

Besides Koskenniemi's work on Finnish and that of Antworth (1990) on English, two-level or other finite-state models of morphology have been worked out for many languages, such as Turkish (Oflazer, 1993) and Arabic (Beesley, 1996). Barton, Jr. et al. (1987) bring up some computational complexity problems with two-level models, which are responded to by Koskenniemi and Church (1988).

Readers with further interest in finite-state morphology should turn to Beesley and Karttunen (2003). Readers with further interest in computational models of Arabic and Semitic morphology should see Smrž (1998), Kiraz (2001), and Habash et al. (2005).

A number of practical implementations of sentence segmentation were available by the 1990s. Summaries of sentence segmentation history and various algorithms can be found in Palmer (2000), Grefenstette (1999), and Mikheev (2003). Word segmentation has been studied especially in Japanese and Chinese. While the max-match algorithm we describe is commonly used as a baseline or when a simple but reasonably accurate algorithm is required, more recent algorithms rely on stochastic and machine learning algorithms; see, for example, such algorithms as Sproat et al. (1996), Xue and Shen (2003), and Tseng et al. (2005a).

Gusfield (1997) is an excellent book covering everything you could want to know about string distance, minimum edit distance, and related areas.

Students interested in automata theory should see Hopcroft and Ullman (1979) or Lewis and Papadimitriou (1988). Roche and Schabes (1997b) is the definitive mathematical introduction to finite-state transducers for language applications, and together with Mohri (1997) and Mohri (2000), give many useful algorithms such as those for transducer minimization and determinization.

The CELEX dictionary is an extremely useful database for morphological analysis, containing full morphological parses of a large lexicon of English, German, and Dutch (Baayen et al., 1995). Roark and Sproat (2007) is a general introduction to computational issues in morphology and syntax. Sproat (1993) is an older general introduction to computational morphology.

Exercises

3.1 Give examples of each of the noun and verb classes in Fig. 3.6, and find some exceptions to the rules.

3.2 Extend the transducer in Fig. 3.17 to deal with `sh` and `ch`.

3.3 Write a transducer(s) for the K insertion spelling rule in English.

3.4 Write a transducer(s) for the consonant doubling spelling rule in English.

3.5 The Soundex algorithm (Knuth, 1973; Odell and Russell, 1922) is a method commonly used in libraries and older census records for representing people's names. It has the advantage that versions of the names that are slightly misspelled or otherwise modified (common, e.g., in hand-written census records) will still have the same representation as correctly spelled names. (e.g., Jurafsky, Jarofsky, Jarovsky, and Jarovski all map to J612).

1. Keep the first letter of the name, and drop all occurrences of non-initial a, e, h, i, o, u, w, y.

2. Replace the remaining letters with the following numbers:

   b, f, p, v → 1
   c, g, j, k, q, s, x, z → 2
   d, t → 3
   l → 4
   m, n → 5
   r → 6

3. Replace any sequences of identical numbers, only if they derive from two or more letters that were *adjacent* in the original name, with a single number (e.g., 666 → 6).

4. Convert to the form `Letter Digit Digit Digit` by dropping digits past the third (if necessary) or padding with trailing zeros (if necessary).

The exercise: write an FST to implement the Soundex algorithm.

3.6 Read Porter (1980) or see Martin Porter's official homepage on the Porter stemmer. Implement one of the steps of the Porter Stemmer as a transducer.

3.7 Write the algorithm for parsing a finite-state transducer, using the pseudocode introduced in Chapter 2. You should do this by modifying the algorithm ND-RECOGNIZE in Fig. 2.19 in Chapter 2.

3.8 Write a program that takes a word and, using an on-line dictionary, computes possible anagrams of the word, each of which is a legal word.

3.9 In Fig. 3.17, why is there a *z, s, x* arc from q_5 to q_1?

3.10 Computing minimum edit distances by hand, figure out whether *drive* is closer to *brief* or to *divers* and what the edit distance is. You may use any version of *distance* that you like.

3.11 Now implement a minimum edit distance algorithm and use your hand-computed results to check your code.

3.12 Augment the minimum edit distance algorithm to output an alignment; you will need to store pointers and add a stage to compute the backtrace.

Credit

Figs. 3.10 and 3.11 (© the authors; thanks to the Association of Computational Linguistics, the Journal of Computational Linguistics and its editor Robert Dale, and to Mehryar Mohri)

Chapter 4

N-Grams

But it must be recognized that the notion "probability of a sentence" is an entirely useless one, under any known interpretation of this term.

Noam Chomsky (1969, p. 57)

Anytime a linguist leaves the group the recognition rate goes up.

Fred Jelinek (then of the IBM speech group) (1988)[1]

Being able to predict the future is not always a good thing. Cassandra of Troy had the gift of foreseeing but was cursed by Apollo that her predictions would never be believed. Her warnings of the destruction of Troy were ignored and to simplify, let's just say that things just didn't go well for her later.

Predicting words seems somewhat less fraught, and in this chapter we take up this idea of word prediction. What word, for example, is likely to follow

Please turn your homework ...

Hopefully, most of you concluded that a very likely word is *in*, or possibly *over*, but probably not *the*. We formalize this idea of **word prediction** with probabilistic models called ***N*-gram models**, which predict the next word from the previous $N-1$ words. An *N*-gram is an *N*-token sequence of words: a 2-gram (more commonly called a **bigram**) is a two-word sequence of words like "please turn", "turn your", or "your homework", and a 3-gram (more commonly called a **trigram**) is a three-word sequence of words like "please turn your", or "turn your homework". An *N*-gram model, as we will explore in detail, is then a model which computes the last word of an *N*-gram from the previous ones.[2] Such statistical models of word sequences are also called **language models** or **LMs**. Computing the probability of the next word turns out to be closely related to computing the probability of a sequence of words. The following sequence, for example, has a non-zero probability of appearing in a text:

... all of a sudden I notice three guys standing on the sidewalk...

while this same set of words in a different order has a much much lower probability:

on guys all I of notice sidewalk three a sudden standing the

N-gram

Language model

LM

---

[1] This wording from his address is as recalled by Jelinek himself; the quotation didn't appear in the Proceedings (Palmer and Finin, 1990). Some remember a snappier version: *Every time I fire a linguist the performance of the recognizer improves.*

[2] In a bit of terminological ambiguity, we often drop the word "model", and thus the term *N*-gram is used to mean either the word sequence or the predictive model.

As we will see, estimators like *N*-grams that assign a conditional probability to possible next words can be used to assign a joint probability to an entire sentence. Whether estimating probabilities of next words or of whole sequences, the *N*-gram model is one of the most important tools in speech and language processing.

N-grams are essential in any task in which we have to identify words in noisy, ambiguous input. In **speech recognition**, for example, the input speech sounds are very confusable and many words sound extremely similar. Russell and Norvig (2002) give an intuition from **handwriting recognition** for how probabilities of word sequences can help. In the movie *Take the Money and Run*, Woody Allen tries to rob a bank with a sloppily written hold-up note that the teller incorrectly reads as "I have a gub". Any speech and language processing system could avoid making this mistake by using the knowledge that the sequence "I have a gun" is far more probable than the non-word "I have a gub" or even "I have a gull".

N-gram models are also essential in statistical **machine translation**. Suppose we are translating a Chinese source sentence 他向记者介绍了声明的主要内容 and as part of the process we have a set of potential rough English translations:

he briefed to reporters on the chief contents of the statement
he briefed reporters on the chief contents of the statement
he briefed to reporters on the main contents of the statement
he briefed reporters on the main contents of the statement

An *N*-gram grammar might tell us that, even after controlling for length, *briefed reporters* is more likely than *briefed to reporters*, and *main contents* is more likely than **chief contents**. This lets us select the boldfaced sentence above as the most fluent translation sentence, that is, the one that has the highest probability.

In **spelling correction**, we need to find and correct spelling errors like the following (from Kukich (1992)) that accidentally result in real English words:

They are leaving in about fifteen *minuets* to go to her house.
The design *an* construction of the system will take more than a year.

Since these errors have real words, we can't find them by just flagging words that aren't in the dictionary. But note that *in about fifteen minuets* is a much less probable sequence than *in about fifteen minutes*. A spellchecker can use a probability estimator both to detect these errors and to suggest higher-probability corrections.

Augmentative communication

Word prediction is also important for **augmentative communication** (Newell et al., 1998) systems that help people with disabilities. People, like the physicist Steven Hawking, who are unable to use speech or sign-language to communicate can communicate by using simple body movements to select words from a menu that are spoken by the system. Word prediction can be used to suggest likely words for the menu.

Besides these sample areas, *N*-grams are also crucial in NLP tasks like **part-of-speech tagging**, **natural language generation**, and **word similarity**, as well as in applications from **authorship identification** and **sentiment extraction** to **predictive text input** systems for cell phones.

4.1   Word Counting in Corpora

> [upon being asked if there weren't enough words in the English language for him]:
> *"Yes, there are enough, but they aren't the right ones."*
> James Joyce, reported in Bates (1997)

Corpus

Corpora

Probabilities are based on counting things. Before we talk about probabilities, we need to decide what we are going to count. Counting of things in natural language is based on a **corpus** (plural **corpora**), a computer-readable collection of text or speech. Let's look at two popular corpora, Brown and Switchboard. The Brown corpus is a million-word collection of samples from 500 written texts from different genres (newspaper, fiction, non-fiction, academic, etc.), assembled at Brown University in 1963–64 (Kučera and Francis, 1967; Francis, 1979; Francis and Kučera, 1982). How many words are in the following Brown sentence?

(4.1) He stepped out into the hall, was delighted to encounter a water brother.

Example (4.1) has 13 words if we don't count punctuation marks as words, 15 if we count punctuation. Whether we treat period ("."), comma (","), and so on as words depends on the task. Punctuation is critical for finding boundaries of things (commas, periods, colons) and for identifying some aspects of meaning (question marks, exclamation marks, quotation marks). For some tasks, like part-of-speech tagging or parsing or speech synthesis, we sometimes treat punctuation marks as if they were separate words.

The Switchboard corpus of telephone conversations between strangers was collected in the early 1990s; it contains 2430 conversations averaging 6 minutes each, totaling 240 hours of speech and about 3 million words (Godfrey et al., 1992). Such corpora of spoken language don't have punctuation but do introduce other complications with regard to defining words. Let's look at one utterance from Switchboard; an

Utterance

utterance is the spoken correlate of a sentence:

(4.2) I do uh main- mainly business data processing

Disfluency

Fragment

Filled pause

This utterance has two kinds of **disfluencies**. The broken-off word *main-* is called a **fragment**. Words like *uh* and *um* are called **fillers** or **filled pauses**. Should we consider these to be words? Again, it depends on the application. If we are building an automatic dictation system based on automatic speech recognition, we might want to eventually strip out the disfluencies.

But we also sometimes keep disfluencies around. How disfluent people are can be used to identify them or to detect whether they are stressed or confused. Disfluencies also often occur with particular syntactic structures, so they may help in parsing and word prediction. Stolcke and Shriberg (1996) found, for example, that treating *uh* as a word improves next-word prediction (why might this be?), and so most speech recognition systems treat *uh* and *um* as words.[3]

Are capitalized tokens like *They* and uncapitalized tokens like *they* the same word? These are lumped together in speech recognition, while for part-of-speech-tagging,

---

[3] Clark and Fox Tree (2002) showed that *uh* and *um* have different meanings. What do you think they are?

capitalization is retained as a separate feature. For the rest of this chapter we will assume our models are not case sensitive.

How about inflected forms like *cats* versus *cat*? These two words have the same **lemma** *cat* but are different wordforms. Recall from Chapter 3 that a lemma is a set of lexical forms having the same stem, the same major part-of-speech, and the same word sense. The **wordform** is the full inflected or derived form of the word. For morphologically complex languages like Arabic, we often need to deal with lemmatization. *N*-grams for speech recognition in English, however, and all the examples in this chapter, are based on wordforms.

Wordform

As we can see, *N*-gram models, and counting words in general, requires that we do the kind of tokenization or text normalization that we introduced in the previous chapter: separating out punctuation, dealing with abbreviations like *m.p.h.*, normalizing spelling, and so on.

How many words are there in English? To answer this question we need to distinguish **types**, the number of distinct words in a corpus or vocabulary size V, from **tokens**, the total number N of running words. The following Brown sentence has 16 tokens and 14 types (not counting punctuation):

Word type

Word token

(4.3) They picnicked by the pool, then lay back on the grass and looked at the stars.

The Switchboard corpus has about 20,000 wordform types (from about 3 million wordform tokens). Shakespeare's complete works have 29,066 wordform types (from 884,647 wordform tokens) (Kučera, 1992). The Brown corpus has 61,805 wordform types from 37,851 lemma types (from 1 million wordform tokens). Looking at a very large corpus of 583 million wordform tokens, Brown et al. (1992) found that it included 293,181 different wordform types. Dictionaries can help in giving lemma counts; dictionary entries or **boldface forms** are a very rough upper bound on the number of lemmas (since some lemmas have multiple boldface forms). The American Heritage Dictionary lists 200,000 boldface forms. It seems like the larger the corpora we look at, the more word types we find. In general, Gale and Church (1990) suggest that the vocabulary size (the number of types) grows with at least the square root of the number of tokens (i.e., $V > O(\sqrt{N})$.

In the rest of this chapter we continue to distinguish between types and tokens, using "types" to mean wordform types.

4.2   Simple (Unsmoothed) *N*-Grams

Let's start with some intuitive motivations for *N*-grams. We assume that the reader has acquired some basic background in probability theory. Our goal is to compute the probability of a word w given some history h, or $P(w\,h)$. Suppose the history h is "*its water is so transparent that*" and we want to know the probability that the next word is *the*:

$$P(the\ its\ water\ is\ so\ transparent\ that). \tag{4.4}$$

How can we compute this probability? One way is to estimate it from relative frequency counts. For example, we could take a very large corpus, count the number of times we see *the water is so transparent that*, and count the number of times this is followed by *the*. This would be answering the question "Out of the times we saw the history *h*, how many times was it followed by the word *w*", as follows:

$$P(\text{the its water is so transparent that}) =$$
$$\frac{C(\text{its water is so transparent that the})}{C(\text{its water is so transparent that})} \tag{4.5}$$

With a large enough corpus, such as the Web, we can compute these counts and estimate the probability from Eq. 4.5. You should pause now, go to the Web, and compute this estimate for yourself.

While this method of estimating probabilities directly from counts works fine in many cases, it turns out that even the Web isn't big enough to give us good estimates in most cases. This is because language is creative; new sentences are created all the time, and we won't always be able to count entire sentences. Even simple extensions of the example sentence may have counts of zero on the Web (such as "*Walden Pond's water is so transparent that the*").

Similarly, if we wanted to know the joint probability of an entire sequence of words like *its water is so transparent*, we could do it by asking "out of all possible sequences of five words, how many of them are *its water is so transparent*?" We would have to get the count of *its water is so transparent* and divide by the sum of the counts of all possible five word sequences. That seems rather a lot to estimate!

For this reason, we'll need to introduce cleverer ways of estimating the probability of a word *w* given a history *h*, or the probability of an entire word sequence *W*. Let's start with a little formalizing of notation. To represent the probability of a particular random variable X_i taking on the value "the", or $P(X_i = \text{"the"})$, we will use the simplification $P(\text{the})$. We'll represent a sequence of *N* words either as $w_1 \dots w_n$ or w_1^n. For the joint probability of each word in a sequence having a particular value $P(X = w_1, Y = w_2, Z = w_3, ..., W = w_n)$ we'll use $P(w_1, w_2, ..., w_n)$.

Now how can we compute probabilities of entire sequences like $P(w_1, w_2, ..., w_n)$? One thing we can do is decompose this probability using the **chain rule of probability**:

$$
\begin{aligned}
P(X_1...X_n) &= P(X_1)P(X_2\,X_1)P(X_3\,X_1^2)...P(X_n\,X_1^{n-1}) \\
&= \prod_{k=1}^{n} P(X_k\,X_1^{k-1})
\end{aligned} \tag{4.6}
$$

Applying the chain rule to words, we get

$$
\begin{aligned}
P(w_1^n) &= P(w_1)P(w_2\,w_1)P(w_3\,w_1^2)...P(w_n\,w_1^{n-1}) \\
&= \prod_{k=1}^{n} P(w_k\,w_1^{k-1})
\end{aligned} \tag{4.7}
$$

The chain rule shows the link between computing the joint probability of a sequence and computing the conditional probability of a word given previous words.

chain rule.

Equation 4.7 suggests that we could estimate the joint probability of an entire sequence of words by multiplying together a number of conditional probabilities. But using the chain rule doesn't really seem to help us! We don't know any way to compute the exact probability of a word given a long sequence of preceding words, $P(w_n w_1^{n-1})$. As we said above, we can't just estimate by counting the number of times every word occurs following every long string, because language is creative and any particular context might have never occurred before!

The intuition of the *N*-gram model is that instead of computing the probability of a word given its entire history, we can **approximate** the history by just the last few words.

Bigram

The **bigram** model, for example, approximates the probability of a word given all the previous words $P(w_n w_1^{n-1})$ by using only the conditional probability of the preceding word $P(w_n w_{n-1})$. In other words, instead of computing the probability

$$P(\text{the Walden Pond's water is so transparent that}) \tag{4.8}$$

we approximate it with the probability

$$P(\text{the that}) \tag{4.9}$$

When we use a bigram model to predict the conditional probability of the next word, we are thus making the following approximation:

$$P(w_n w_1^{n-1}) \approx P(w_n w_{n-1}) \tag{4.10}$$

Markov

This assumption that the probability of a word depends only on the previous word is called a **Markov** assumption. Markov models are the class of probabilistic models that assume we can predict the probability of some future unit without looking too far into the past. We can generalize the bigram (which looks one word into the past) to the trigram (which looks two words into the past) and thus to the *N*-**gram** (which looks $N-1$ words into the past).

N-gram

Thus, the general equation for this *N*-gram approximation to the conditional probability of the next word in a sequence is

$$P(w_n w_1^{n-1}) \approx P(w_n w_{n-N+1}^{n-1}) \tag{4.11}$$

Given the bigram assumption for the probability of an individual word, we can compute the probability of a complete word sequence by substituting Eq. 4.10 into Eq. 4.7:

$$P(w_1^n) \approx \prod_{k=1}^{n} P(w_k w_{k-1}) \tag{4.12}$$

Maximum likelihood estimation

How do we estimate these bigram or *N*-gram probabilities? The simplest and most intuitive way to estimate probabilities is called **maximum likelihood estimation** or **MLE**. We get the MLE estimate for the parameters of an *N*-gram model by normalizing counts from a corpus, and **normalize** them so that they lie between 0 and 1.[4]

Normalize

For example, to compute a particular bigram probability of a word *y* given a previous word *x*, we'll compute the count of the bigram $C(xy)$ and normalize by the sum of all the bigrams that share the same first word *x*:

$$P(w_n \mid w_{n-1}) = \frac{C(w_{n-1}w_n)}{\sum_w C(w_{n-1}w)} \qquad (4.13)$$

We can simplify this equation, since the sum of all bigram counts that start with a given word w_{n-1} must be equal to the unigram count for that word w_{n-1} (the reader should take a moment to be convinced of this):

$$P(w_n \mid w_{n-1}) = \frac{C(w_{n-1}w_n)}{C(w_{n-1})} \qquad (4.14)$$

Let's work through an example using a mini-corpus of three sentences. We'll first need to augment each sentence with a special symbol <s> at the beginning of the sentence, to give us the bigram context of the first word. We'll also need a special end-symbol </s>[5]

```
<s> I am Sam </s>
<s> Sam I am </s>
<s> I do not like green eggs and ham </s>
```

Here are the calculations for some of the bigram probabilities from this corpus

$$P(\text{I}\,|\,\text{<s>}) = \tfrac{2}{3} = .67 \qquad P(\text{Sam}\,|\,\text{<s>}) = \tfrac{1}{3} = .33 \qquad P(\text{am}\,|\,\text{I}) = \tfrac{2}{3} = .67$$

$$P(\text{</s>}\,|\,\text{Sam}) = \tfrac{1}{2} = 0.5 \qquad P(\text{Sam}\,|\,\text{am}) = \tfrac{1}{2} = .5 \qquad P(\text{do}\,|\,\text{I}) = \tfrac{1}{3} = .33$$

For the general case of MLE *N*-gram parameter estimation:

$$P(w_n \mid w_{n-N+1}^{n-1}) = \frac{C(w_{n-N+1}^{n-1}w_n)}{C(w_{n-N+1}^{n-1})} \qquad (4.15)$$

Equation 4.15 (like Eq. 4.14) estimates the *N*-gram probability by dividing the observed frequency of a particular sequence by the observed frequency of a prefix. This ratio is called a **relative frequency**. We said above that this use of relative frequencies as a way to estimate probabilities is an example of maximum likelihood estimation or MLE. In MLE, the resulting parameter set maximizes the likelihood of the training set *T* given the model *M* (i.e., $P(T \mid M)$). For example, suppose the word *Chinese* occurs 400 times in a corpus of a million words like the Brown corpus. What is the probability that a random word selected from some other text of, say, a million words will be the word *Chinese*? The MLE of its probability is $\frac{400}{1000000}$ or .0004. Now .0004 is not the best possible estimate of the probability of *Chinese* occurring in all situations; it might turn out that in some other corpus or context *Chinese* is a very unlikely word. But it is the probability that makes it *most likely* that Chinese will occur 400 times in a

Relative frequency

---

4   For probabilistic models, normalizing means dividing by some total count so that the resulting probabilities fall legally between 0 and 1.

5   As Chen and Goodman (1998) point out, we need the end-symbol to make the bigram grammar a true probability distribution. Without an end-symbol, the sentence probabilities for all sentences of a given length would sum to one, and the probability of the whole language would be infinite.

million-word corpus. We present ways to modify the MLE estimates slightly to get better probability estimates in Section 4.5.

Let's move on to some examples from a slightly larger corpus than our 14-word example above. We'll use data from the now-defunct Berkeley Restaurant Project, a dialogue system from the last century that answered questions about a database of restaurants in Berkeley, California (Jurafsky et al., 1994). Here are some sample user queries, lower-cased and with no punctuation (a representative corpus of 9332 sentences is on the website):

> can you tell me about any good cantonese restaurants close by
> mid priced thai food is what i'm looking for
> tell me about chez panisse
> can you give me a listing of the kinds of food that are available
> i'm looking for a good place to eat breakfast
> when is caffe venezia open during the day

Figure 4.1 shows the bigram counts from a piece of a bigram grammar from the Berkeley Restaurant Project. Note that the majority of the values are zero. In fact, we have chosen the sample words to cohere with each other; a matrix selected from a random set of seven words would be even more sparse.

	i	want	to	eat	chinese	food	lunch	spend
i	5	827	0	9	0	0	0	2
want	2	0	608	1	6	6	5	1
to	2	0	4	686	2	0	6	211
eat	0	0	2	0	16	2	42	0
chinese	1	0	0	0	0	82	1	0
food	15	0	15	0	1	4	0	0
lunch	2	0	0	0	0	1	0	0
spend	1	0	1	0	0	0	0	0

Figure 4.1   Bigram counts for eight of the words (out of $V = 1446$) in the Berkeley Restaurant Project corpus of 9332 sentences. Zero counts are in gray.

Figure 4.2 shows the bigram probabilities after normalization (dividing each row by the following unigram counts):

i	want	to	eat	chinese	food	lunch	spend
2533	927	2417	746	158	1093	341	278

Here are a few other useful probabilities:

$P(\texttt{i}|\texttt{<s>}) = 0.25$ $P(\texttt{english}|\texttt{want}) = 0.0011$
$P(\texttt{food}|\texttt{english}) = 0.5$ $P(\texttt{</s>}|\texttt{food}) = 0.68$

Now we can compute the probability of sentences like *I want English food* or *I want Chinese food* by simply multiplying the appropriate bigram probabilities together, as follows:

	i	want	to	eat	chinese	food	lunch	spend
i	0.002	0.33	0	0.0036	0	0	0	0.00079
want	0.0022	0	0.66	0.0011	0.0065	0.0065	0.0054	0.0011
to	0.00083	0	0.0017	0.28	0.00083	0	0.0025	0.087
eat	0	0	0.0027	0	0.021	0.0027	0.056	0
chinese	0.0063	0	0	0	0	0.52	0.0063	0
food	0.014	0	0.014	0	0.00092	0.0037	0	0
lunch	0.0059	0	0	0	0	0.0029	0	0
spend	0.0036	0	0.0036	0	0	0	0	0

Figure 4.2   Bigram probabilities for eight words in the Berkeley Restaurant Project corpus of 9332 sentences. Zero probabilities are in gray.

$$P(\texttt{<s> i want english food </s>})$$
$$= P(\texttt{i}|\texttt{<s>})P(\texttt{want}|\texttt{i})P(\texttt{english}|\texttt{want})$$
$$P(\texttt{food}|\texttt{english})P(\texttt{</s>}|\texttt{food})$$
$$= .25 \quad .33 \quad .0011 \quad 0.5 \quad 0.68$$
$$= = .000031$$

We leave it as an exercise for the reader to compute the probability of *i want chinese food*. But that exercise does suggest that we'll want to think a bit about what kinds of linguistic phenomena are captured in bigrams. Some of the bigram probabilities above encode some facts that we think of as strictly syntactic in nature, like the fact that what comes after *eat* is usually a noun or an adjective, or that what comes after *to* is usually a verb. Others might be more cultural than linguistic, like the low probability of anyone asking for advice on finding English food.

Although we generally show bigram models in this chapter for pedagogical purposes, note that when there is sufficient training data, we are more likely to use **trigram** models, which condition on the previous two words rather than the previous word. To compute trigram probabilities at the very beginning of sentence, we can use two pseudo-words for the first trigram (i.e., $P(\texttt{I}|\texttt{<s><s>})$).

Trigram

4.3   Training and Test Sets

The *N*-gram model is a good example of the kind of statistical models that we see throughout speech and language processing. The probabilities of an *N*-gram model come from the corpus it is trained on. In general, the parameters of a statistical model are trained on some set of data, and then we apply the models to some new data in some task (such as speech recognition) and see how well they work. Of course this new data or task won't be exactly the same data we trained on.

We can formalize this idea of training on some data and testing on some other data by talking about these two data sets as a **training set** and a **test set** (or a **training corpus** and a **test corpus**). Thus, when using a statistical model of language given some corpus of relevant data, we start by dividing the data into training and test sets.

Training set

Test set

Evaluation

We train the statistical parameters of the model on the training set and then use this trained model to compute probabilities on the test set.

This training-and-testing paradigm can also be used to **evaluate** different *N*-gram architectures. Suppose we want to compare different language models (such as those based on *N*-grams of different orders *N* or those using the different **smoothing** algorithms to be introduced in Section 4.5). We can do this by dividing a corpus into a training set and a test set. Then we train the two different *N*-gram models on the training set and see which one better models the test set. But what does it mean to "model the test set"? There is a useful metric for how well a given statistical model matches a test corpus; that method is called **perplexity**, introduced on page 95. Perplexity is based on computing the probability of each sentence in the test set; intuitively, whichever model assigns a higher probability to the test set (hence more accurately predicts the test set) is a better model.

Since our evaluation metric is based on test set probability, it's important not to let the test sentences into the training set. Suppose we are trying to compute the probability of a particular "test" sentence. If our test sentence is part of the training corpus, we will mistakenly assign it an artificially high probability when it occurs in the test set. We call this situation **training on the test set**. Training on the test set introduces a bias that makes the probabilities all look too high and causes huge inaccuracies in perplexity.

Held-out set

In addition to training and test sets, other divisions of data are often useful. Sometimes we need an extra source of data to augment the training set. Such extra data is called a **held-out** set, because we hold it out from our training set when we train our *N*-gram counts. The held-out corpus is then used to set some other parameters; for example we show the use of held-out data to set interpolation weights in **interpolated** *N*-gram models in Section 4.6. Finally, sometimes we need to have multiple test sets. This happens because we might use a particular test set so often that we implicitly tune to its characteristics. We would then definitely need a fresh test set that is truly unseen.

Development test

In such cases, we call the initial test set the **development** test set or, **devset**. We discuss development test sets again in Chapter 5.

How do we divide our data into training, development, and test sets? There is a tradeoff since we want our test set to be as large as possible and a small test set may be accidentally unrepresentative. On the other hand, we want as much training data as possible. At the minimum, we would want to pick the smallest test set that gives us enough statistical power to measure a statistically significant difference between two potential models. In practice, we often just divide our data into 80% training, 10% development, and 10% test. Given a large corpus that we want to divide into training and test, test data can either be taken from some continuous sequence of text inside the corpus, or we can remove smaller "stripes" of text from randomly selected parts of our corpus and combine them into a test set.

4.3.1 *N*-Gram Sensitivity to the Training Corpus

The *N*-gram model, like many statistical models, is dependent on the training corpus. One implication of this is that the probabilities often encode specific facts about a given training corpus. Another implication is that *N*-grams do a better and better job of modeling the training corpus as we increase the value of *N*.

We can visualize both of these facts by borrowing the technique of Shannon (1951) and Miller and Selfridge (1950) of generating random sentences from different *N*-gram models. It's simplest to visualize how this works for the unigram case. Imagine all the words of English covering the probability space between 0 and 1, each word covering an interval equal to its frequency. We choose a random value between 0 and 1 and print the word whose interval includes the real value we have chosen. We continue choosing random numbers and generating words until we randomly generate the sentence-final token </s>. We can use the same technique to generate bigrams by first generating a random bigram that starts with <s> (according to its bigram probability), then choosing a random bigram to follow (again, according to its bigram probability), and so on.

To give an intuition for the increasing power of higher-order *N*-grams, Fig. 4.3 shows random sentences generated from unigram, bigram, trigram, and quadrigram models trained on Shakespeare's works.

Unigram
To him swallowed confess hear both. Which. Of save on trail for are ay device and rote life have
Every enter now severally so, let
Hill he late speaks; or! a more to leg less first you enter
Are where exeunt and sighs have rise excellency took of.. Sleep knave we. near; vile like
Bigram
What means, sir. I confess she? then all sorts, he is trim, captain.
Why dost stand forth thy canopy, forsooth; he is this palpable hit the King Henry. Live king. Follow.
What we, hath got so she that I rest and sent to scold and nature bankrupt, nor the first gentleman?
Trigram
Sweet prince, Falstaff shall die. Harry of Monmouth's grave.
This shall forbid it should be branded, if renown made it empty.
Indeed the duke; and had a very good friend.
Fly, and will rid me these news of price. Therefore the sadness of parting, as they say, 'tis done.
Quadrigram
King Henry. What! I will go seek the traitor Gloucester. Exeunt some of the watch. A great banquet serv'd in;
Will you not tell me who I am?
It cannot be but so.
Indeed the short and the long. Marry, 'tis a noble Lepidus.

Figure 4.3   Sentences randomly generated from four *N*-gram models computed from Shakespeare's works. All characters were mapped to lower case and punctuation marks were treated as words. Output was hand-corrected for capitalization to improve readability.

The longer the context on which we train the model, the more coherent the sentences. In the unigram sentences, there is no coherent relation between words or any sentence-final punctuation. The bigram sentences have some local word-to-word coherence (especially if we consider that punctuation counts as a word). The trigram and quadrigram sentences are beginning to look a lot like Shakespeare. Indeed, a careful investigation of the quadrigram sentences shows that they look a little too much like Shakespeare. The words *It cannot be but so* are directly from *King John*. This is because, not to put the knock on Shakespeare, his oeuvre is not very large as corpora go ($N = 884{,}647, V = 29{,}066$), and our *N*-gram probability matrices are ridiculously sparse. There are $V^2 = 844{,}000{,}000$ possible bigrams alone, and the number of possible quadrigrams is $V^4 = 7 \quad 10^{17}$. Thus, once the generator has chosen the first quadrigram (*It cannot be but*), there are only five possible continuations (*that, I, he, thou,* and *so*); indeed, for many quadrigrams, there is only one continuation.

To get an idea of the dependence of a grammar on its training set, let's look at an *N*-gram grammar trained on a completely different corpus: the *Wall Street Journal* (WSJ) newspaper. Shakespeare and the *Wall Street Journal* are both English, so we might expect some overlap between our *N*-grams for the two genres. To check whether this is true, we created Fig. 4.4, which shows sentences generated by unigram, bigram, and trigram grammars trained on 40 million words from WSJ.

Unigram

Months the my and issue of year foreign new exchange's september were recession exchange new endorsed a acquire to six executives

Bigram

Last December through the way to preserve the Hudson corporation N. B. E. C. Taylor would seem to complete the major central planners one point five percent of U. S. E. has already old M. X. corporation of living on information such as more frequently fishing to keep her

Trigram

They also point to ninety nine point six billion dollars from two hundred four oh six three percent of the rates of interest stores as Mexico and Brazil on market conditions

Figure 4.4   Sentences randomly generated from three *N*-gram models computed from 40 million words of the *Wall Street Journal*, lower-casing all characters and treating punctuation as words. Output was then hand-corrected for capitalization to improve readability.

Compare these examples to the pseudo-Shakespeare in Fig. 4.3. While superficially they both seem to model "English-like sentences", there is obviously no overlap whatsoever in possible sentences, and little if any overlap even in small phrases. This stark difference tells us that statistical models are likely to be pretty useless as predictors if the training sets and the test sets are as different as Shakespeare and WSJ.

How should we deal with this problem when we build *N*-gram models? In general, we need to be sure to use a training corpus that looks like our test corpus. We especially wouldn't choose training and tests from different **genres** of text like newspaper text, early English fiction, telephone conversations, and Web pages. Sometimes finding appropriate training text for a specific new task can be difficult; to build *N*-grams for text prediction in Short Message Service (SMS), we need a training corpus of SMS data. To build *N*-grams on business meetings, we would need to have corpora of transcribed business meetings.

For general research when we know we want written English but don't have a domain in mind, we can use a balanced training corpus that includes cross sections from different genres, such as the million-word Brown corpus of English (Francis and Kučera, 1982) or the 100-million-word British National Corpus (Leech et al., 1994).

Recent research has also studied ways to dynamically **adapt** language models to different genres; see Section 4.9.4.

4.3.2   Unknown Words: Open Versus Closed Vocabulary Tasks

Closed vocabulary

Sometimes we have a language task in which we know all the words that can occur, and hence we know the vocabulary size V in advance. The **closed vocabulary** assumption is the assumption that we have such a lexicon and that the test set can only contain words from this lexicon. The closed vocabulary task thus assumes there are no unknown words.

But of course this is a simplification; as we suggested earlier, the number of unseen words grows constantly, so we can't possibly know in advance exactly how many there are, and we'd like our model to do something reasonable with them. We call these

OOV

unseen events **unknown** words, or **out of vocabulary** (**OOV**) words. The percentage of OOV words that appear in the test set is called the **OOV rate**.

Open vocabulary

An **open vocabulary** system is one in which we model these potential unknown words in the test set by adding a pseudo-word called <UNK>. We can train the probabilities of the unknown word model <UNK> as follows:

1. **Choose a vocabulary** (word list) that is fixed in advance.
2. **Convert** in the training set any word that is not in this set (any OOV word) to the unknown word token <UNK> in a text normalization step.
3. **Estimate** the probabilities for <UNK> from its counts just like any other regular word in the training set.

An alternative that doesn't require choosing a vocabulary is to replace the first occurrence of every word type in the training data by <UNK>.

4.4   Evaluating *N*-Grams: Perplexity

Extrinsic evaluation

The best way to evaluate the performance of a language model is to embed it in an application and measure the total performance of the application. Such end-to-end evaluation is called **extrinsic evaluation**, and also sometimes called **in vivo** evaluation (Sparck Jones and Galliers, 1996). Extrinsic evaluation is the only way to know if a particular improvement in a component is really going to help the task at hand. Thus, for speech recognition, we can compare the performance of two language models by running the speech recognizer twice, once with each language model, and seeing which gives the more accurate transcription.

Intrinsic evaluation

Unfortunately, end-to-end evaluation is often very expensive; evaluating a large speech recognition test set, for example, takes hours or even days. Thus, we would like a metric that can be used to quickly evaluate potential improvements in a language model. An **intrinsic evaluation** metric is one that measures the quality of a model independent of any application. **Perplexity** is the most common intrinsic evaluation metric for *N*-gram language models. While an (intrinsic) improvement in perplexity does not guarantee an (extrinsic) improvement in speech recognition performance (or any other end-to-end metric), it often correlates with such improvements. Thus, it is commonly used as a quick check on an algorithm, and an improvement in perplexity can then be confirmed by an end-to-end evaluation.

The intuition of perplexity is that given two probabilistic models, the better model is the one that has a tighter fit to the test data or that better predicts the details of the test data. We can measure better prediction by looking at the probability the model assigns to the test data; the better model will assign a higher probability to the test data. More

Perplexity formally, the **perplexity** (sometimes called *PP* for short) of a language model on a test set is a function of the probability that the language model assigns to that test set. For a test set $W = w_1 w_2 \ldots w_N$, the perplexity is the probability of the test set, normalized by the number of words:

$$\text{PP}(W) = P(w_1 w_2 \ldots w_N)^{-\frac{1}{N}} \tag{4.16}$$

$$= \sqrt[N]{\frac{1}{P(w_1 w_2 \ldots w_N)}})$$

We can use the chain rule to expand the probability of W:

$$\text{PP}(W) = \sqrt[N]{\prod_{i=1}^{N} \frac{1}{P(w_i \ w_1 \ldots w_{i-1})}} \tag{4.17}$$

Thus, if we are computing the perplexity of W with a bigram language model, we get:

$$\text{PP}(W) = \sqrt[N]{\prod_{i=1}^{N} \frac{1}{P(w_i \ w_{i-1})}} \tag{4.18}$$

Note that because of the inverse in Eq. 4.17, the higher the conditional probability of the word sequence, the lower the perplexity. Thus, minimizing perplexity is equivalent to maximizing the test set probability according to the language model. What we generally use for word sequence in Eq. 4.17 or Eq. 4.18 is the entire sequence of words in some test set. Since of course this sequence will cross many sentence boundaries, we need to include the begin- and end-sentence markers <s> and </s> in the probability computation. We also need to include the end-of-sentence marker </s> (but not the beginning-of-sentence marker <s>) in the total count of word tokens N.

There is another way to think about perplexity: as the **weighted average branching factor** of a language. The branching factor of a language is the number of possible next words that can follow any word. Consider the task of recognizing the digits in English (zero, one, two,..., nine), given that each of the 10 digits occurs with equal probability $P = \frac{1}{10}$. The perplexity of this mini-language is in fact 10. To see that, imagine a string of digits of length N. By Eq. 4.17, the perplexity will be

$$\text{PP}(W) = P(w_1 w_2 \ldots w_N)^{-\frac{1}{N}}$$

$$= \left(\frac{1}{10}^N\right)^{-\frac{1}{N}}$$

$$= \frac{1}{10}^{-1}$$
$$= 10 \tag{4.19}$$

But suppose that the number zero is really frequent and occurs 10 times more often than other numbers. Now we should expect the perplexity to be lower since most of the time the next number will be zero. Thus, although the branching factor is still 10, the perplexity or weighted branching factor is smaller. We leave this calculation as an exercise to the reader.

We see in Section 4.10 that perplexity is also closely related to the information-theoretic notion of entropy.

Finally, let's look at an example of how perplexity can be used to compare different N-gram models. We trained unigram, bigram, and trigram grammars on 38 million words (including start-of-sentence tokens) from the *Wall Street Journal*, using a 19,979 word vocabulary.[6] We then computed the perplexity of each of these models on a test set of 1.5 million words with Eq. 4.18. The table below shows the perplexity of a 1.5 million word WSJ test set according to each of these grammars.

	Unigram	Bigram	Trigram
Perplexity	962	170	109

As we see above, the more information the N-gram gives us about the word sequence, the lower the perplexity (since as Eq. 4.17 showed, perplexity is related inversely to the likelihood of the test sequence according to the model).

Note that in computing perplexities, the N-gram model P must be constructed without any knowledge of the test set. Any kind of knowledge of the test set can cause the perplexity to be artificially low. For example, we defined above the **closed vocabulary** task, in which the vocabulary for the test set is specified in advance. This can greatly reduce the perplexity. As long as this knowledge is provided equally to each of the models we are comparing, the closed vocabulary perplexity can still be useful for comparing models, but care must be taken in interpreting the results. In general, the perplexity of two language models is only comparable if they use the same vocabulary.

4.5   Smoothing

Never do I ever want / to hear another word!
There isn't one, / I haven't heard!

Eliza Doolittle
in Alan Jay Lerner's
My Fair Lady

There is a major problem with the maximum likelihood estimation process we have seen for training the parameters of an N-gram model. This is the problem of **sparse**
Sparse data   **data** caused by the fact that our maximum likelihood estimate was based on a particular

---

[6] Katz backoff grammars with Good-Turing discounting trained on 38 million words from the WSJ0 corpus (LDC, 1993), open-vocabulary, using the <UNK> token; see later sections for definitions.

set of training data. For any *N*-gram that occurred a sufficient number of times, we might have a good estimate of its probability. But because any corpus is limited, some perfectly acceptable English word sequences are bound to be missing from it. This missing data means that the *N*-gram matrix for any given training corpus is bound to have a very large number of cases of putative "zero probability *N*-grams" that should really have some non-zero probability. Furthermore, the MLE method also produces poor estimates when the counts are non-zero but still small.

We need a method which can help get better estimates for these zero or low-frequency counts. Zero counts turn out to cause another huge problem. The **perplexity** metric defined above requires that we compute the probability of each test sentence. But if a test sentence has an *N*-gram that never appeared in the training set, the maximum likelihood estimate of the probability for this *N*-gram, and hence for the whole test sentence, will be zero! This means that in order to evaluate our language models, we need to modify the MLE method to assign some non-zero probability to any *N*-gram, even one that was never observed in training.

Smoothing

For these reasons, we'll want to modify the maximum likelihood estimates for computing *N*-gram probabilities, focusing on the *N*-gram events that we incorrectly assumed had zero probability. We use the term **smoothing** for such modifications that address the poor estimates that are due to variability in small data sets. The name comes from the fact that (looking ahead a bit) we will be shaving a little bit of probability mass from the higher counts and piling it instead on the zero counts, making the distribution a little less jagged.

In the next few sections we introduce some smoothing algorithms and show how they modify the Berkeley Restaurant bigram probabilities in Fig. 4.2.

4.5.1   Laplace Smoothing

Laplace smoothing

One simple way to do smoothing might be just to take our matrix of bigram counts, before we normalize them into probabilities, and add 1 to all the counts. This algorithm is called **Laplace smoothing**, or Laplace's Law (Lidstone, 1920; Johnson, 1932; Jeffreys, 1948). Laplace smoothing does not perform well enough to be used in modern *N*-gram models, but we begin with it because it introduces many of the concepts that we see in other smoothing algorithms and also gives us a useful baseline.

Let's start with the application of Laplace smoothing to unigram probabilities. Recall that the unsmoothed maximum likelihood estimate of the unigram probability of the word w_i is its count c_i normalized by the total number of word tokens N:

$$P(w_i) = \frac{c_i}{N}$$

Add-one

Laplace smoothing merely adds one to each count (hence its alternate name **add-one** smoothing). Since there are V words in the vocabulary and each one was incremented, we also need to adjust the denominator to take into account the extra V observations. (What happens to our P values if we don't increase the denominator?)

$$P_{\text{Laplace}}(w_i) = \frac{c_i + 1}{N + V} \qquad (4.20)$$

Instead of changing both the numerator and denominator, it is convenient to describe how a smoothing algorithm affects the numerator, by defining an **adjusted count** c^*. This adjusted count is easier to compare directly with the MLE counts and can be turned into a probability like an MLE count by normalizing by N. To define this count, since we are only changing the numerator in addition to adding 1 we'll also need to multiply by a normalization factor $\frac{N}{N+V}$:

$$c_i^* = (c_i + 1)\frac{N}{N + V} \qquad (4.21)$$

We can now turn c_i^* into a probability P_i^* by normalizing by N.

Discounting

A related way to view smoothing is as **discounting** (lowering) some non-zero counts in order to get the probability mass that will be assigned to the zero counts. Thus, instead of referring to the discounted counts c^*, we might describe a smoothing

Discount

algorithm in terms of a relative **discount** d_c, the ratio of the discounted counts to the original counts:

$$d_c = \frac{c^*}{c}$$

Now that we have the intuition for the unigram case, let's smooth our Berkeley Restaurant Project bigrams. Figure 4.5 shows the add-one smoothed counts for the bigrams in Fig. 4.1.

	i	want	to	eat	chinese	food	lunch	spend
i	6	828	1	10	1	1	1	3
want	3	1	609	2	7	7	6	2
to	3	1	5	687	3	1	7	212
eat	1	1	3	1	17	3	43	1
chinese	2	1	1	1	1	83	2	1
food	16	1	16	1	2	5	1	1
lunch	3	1	1	1	1	2	1	1
spend	2	1	2	1	1	1	1	1

Figure 4.5   Add-one smoothed bigram counts for eight of the words (out of $V = 1446$) in the Berkeley Restaurant Project corpus of 9332 sentences. Previously-zero counts are in gray.

Figure 4.6 shows the add-one smoothed probabilities for the bigrams in Fig. 4.2. Recall that normal bigram probabilities are computed by normalizing each row of counts by the unigram count:

$$P(w_n \; w_{n-1}) = \frac{C(w_{n-1}w_n)}{C(w_{n-1})} \qquad (4.22)$$

For add-one smoothed bigram counts, we need to augment the unigram count by the number of total word types in the vocabulary V:

$$P^*_{\text{Laplace}}(w_n \ w_{n-1}) = \frac{C(w_{n-1}w_n) + 1}{C(w_{n-1}) + V} \tag{4.23}$$

Thus, each of the unigram counts given in the previous section will need to be augmented by $V = 1446$. The result is the smoothed bigram probabilities in Fig. 4.6.

	i	want	to	eat	chinese	food	lunch	spend
i	0.0015	0.21	0.00025	0.0025	0.00025	0.00025	0.00025	0.00075
want	0.0013	0.00042	0.26	0.00084	0.0029	0.0029	0.0025	0.00084
to	0.00078	0.00026	0.0013	0.18	0.00078	0.00026	0.0018	0.055
eat	0.00046	0.00046	0.0014	0.00046	0.0078	0.0014	0.02	0.00046
chinese	0.0012	0.00062	0.00062	0.00062	0.00062	0.052	0.0012	0.00062
food	0.0063	0.00039	0.0063	0.00039	0.00079	0.002	0.00039	0.00039
lunch	0.0017	0.00056	0.00056	0.00056	0.00056	0.0011	0.00056	0.00056
spend	0.0012	0.00058	0.0012	0.00058	0.00058	0.00058	0.00058	0.00058

Figure 4.6   Add-one smoothed bigram probabilities for eight of the words (out of $V = 1446$) in the BeRP corpus of 9332 sentences. Previously-zero probabilities are in gray.

It is often convenient to reconstruct the count matrix so we can see how much a smoothing algorithm has changed the original counts. These adjusted counts can be computed by Eq. 4.24. Figure 4.7 shows the reconstructed counts.

$$c^*(w_{n-1}w_n) = \frac{[C(w_{n-1}w_n) + 1] \quad C(w_{n-1})}{C(w_{n-1}) + V} \tag{4.24}$$

	i	want	to	eat	chinese	food	lunch	spend
i	3.8	527	0.64	6.4	0.64	0.64	0.64	1.9
want	1.2	0.39	238	0.78	2.7	2.7	2.3	0.78
to	1.9	0.63	3.1	430	1.9	0.63	4.4	133
eat	0.34	0.34	1	0.34	5.8	1	15	0.34
chinese	0.2	0.098	0.098	0.098	0.098	8.2	0.2	0.098
food	6.9	0.43	6.9	0.43	0.86	2.2	0.43	0.43
lunch	0.57	0.19	0.19	0.19	0.19	0.38	0.19	0.19
spend	0.32	0.16	0.32	0.16	0.16	0.16	0.16	0.16

Figure 4.7   Add-one reconstituted counts for eight words (of $V = 1446$) in the BeRP corpus of 9332 sentences. Previously-zero counts are in gray.

Note that add-one smoothing has made a very big change to the counts. $C(want\ to)$ changed from 608 to 238! We can see this in probability space as well: $P(to\ want)$ decreases from .66 in the unsmoothed case to .26 in the smoothed case. Looking at the discount d (the ratio between new and old counts) shows us how strikingly the counts for each prefix word have been reduced; the discount for the bigram *want to* is .39, while the discount for *Chinese food* is .10, a factor of 10!

The sharp change in counts and probabilities occurs because too much probability mass is moved to all the zeros. We could move a bit less mass by adding a fractional count rather than 1 (add-δ smoothing; (Lidstone, 1920; Johnson, 1932; Jeffreys,

1948)), but this method requires a method for choosing δ dynamically, results in an inappropriate discount for many counts, and turns out to give counts with poor variances. For these and other reasons (Gale and Church, 1994), we'll need better smoothing methods for N-grams like the ones we show in the next section.

4.5.2   Good-Turing Discounting

Good-Turing

There are a number of much better discounting algorithms that are only slightly more complex than add-one smoothing. In this section we introduce one of them, known as **Good-Turing** smoothing. The Good-Turing algorithm was first described by Good (1953), who credits Turing with the original idea.

The intuition of a number of discounting algorithms (Good-Turing, **Witten-Bell discounting**, and **Kneser-Ney smoothing**) is to use the count of things you've seen *once* to help estimate the count of things you've *never seen*. A word or N-gram (or

Singleton

any event) that occurs once is called a **singleton**, or a **hapax legomenon**. The Good-Turing intuition is to use the frequency of singletons as a re-estimate of the frequency of zero-count bigrams.

Let's formalize the algorithm. The Good-Turing algorithm is based on computing N_c, the number of N-grams that occur c times. We refer to the number of N-grams that occur c times as the **frequency of frequency** c. So applying the idea to smoothing the joint probability of bigrams, N_0 is the number of bigrams with count 0, N_1 the number of bigrams with count 1 (singletons), and so on. We can think of each of the N_c as a bin that stores the number of different N-grams that occur in the training set with that frequency c. More formally:

$$N_c = \sum_{x:count(x)=c} 1 \qquad (4.25)$$

The MLE count for N_c is c. The Good-Turing intuition is to estimate the probability of things that occur c times in the training corpus by the MLE probability of things that occur $c+1$ times in the corpus. So the Good-Turing estimate replaces the MLE count c for N_c with a smoothed count c^* that is a function of N_{c+1}:

$$c^* = (c+1)\frac{N_{c+1}}{N_c} \qquad (4.26)$$

We can use Eq. 4.26 to replace the MLE counts for all the bins N_1, N_2, and so on. Instead of using this equation directly to re-estimate the smoothed count c^* for N_0, we use the following equation for the probability P_{GT}^* for things that had zero count N_0, or what we might call the **missing mass**:

$$P_{GT}^*(\text{things with frequency zero in training}) = \frac{N_1}{N} \qquad (4.27)$$

Here N_1 is the count of items in bin 1, that is, that were seen once in training, and N is the total number of items we have seen in training. Equation 4.27 thus gives the probability that the $N+1$st bigram we see will be one that we never saw in training. Showing that Eq. 4.27 follows from Eq. 4.26 is left as Exercise 4.8 for the reader.

The Good-Turing method was first proposed for estimating the populations of animal species. Let's consider an illustrative example from this domain created by Joshua Goodman and Stanley Chen. Suppose we are fishing in a lake with 8 species (bass, carp, catfish, eel, perch, salmon, trout, whitefish) and we have seen 6 species with the following counts: 10 carp, 3 perch, 2 whitefish, 1 trout, 1 salmon, and 1 eel (so we haven't yet seen the catfish or bass). What is the probability that the next fish we catch will be a new species, that is, one that had a zero frequency in our training set, in this case, either a catfish or a bass?

The MLE count c of a hitherto-unseen species (bass or catfish) is 0. But Eq. 4.27 tells us that the probability of a new fish being one of these unseen species is $\frac{3}{18}$ since N_1 is 3 and N is 18:

$$P^*_{GT}(\text{things with frequency zero in training}) = \frac{N_1}{N} = \frac{3}{18} \qquad (4.28)$$

What is the probability that the next fish will be another trout? The MLE count for trout is 1, so the MLE probability is $\frac{1}{18}$. But the Good-Turing estimate must be lower since we just stole $\frac{3}{18}$ of our probability mass to use on unseen events. We'll need to discount the MLE probabilities for trout, perch, carp, etc. In summary, the revised counts c^* and Good-Turing smoothed probabilities P^*_{GT} for species with count 0 (like bass or catfish) or count 1 (like trout, salmon, or eel) are as follows:

	Unseen (Bass or Catfish)	**Trout**
c	0	1
MLE p	$p = \frac{0}{18} = 0$	$\frac{1}{18}$
c*		$c^*(\text{trout}) = 2 \quad \frac{N_2}{N_1} = 2 \quad \frac{1}{3} = .67$
GT P^*_{GT}	$P^*_{GT}(\text{unseen}) = \frac{N_1}{N} = \frac{3}{18} = .17$	$P^*_{GT}(\text{trout}) = \frac{.67}{18} = \frac{1}{27} = .037$

Note that the revised count c^* for trout was discounted from $c = 1.0$ to $c^* = .67$ (thus leaving some probability mass $P^*_{GT}(\text{unseen}) = \frac{3}{18} = .17$ for the catfish and bass). And since we know there were 2 unknown species, the probability of the next fish being specifically a catfish is $P^*_{GT}(\text{catfish}) = \frac{1}{2} \quad \frac{3}{18} = .085$.

Figure 4.8 gives two examples of the application of Good-Turing discounting to bigram grammars, one on the BeRP corpus of 9332 sentences, and a larger example computed from 22 million words from the Associated Press (AP) newswire by Church and Gale (1991). For both examples, the first column shows the count c, that is, the number of observed instances of a bigram. The second column shows the number of bigrams that had this count. Thus, 449,721 of the AP bigrams have a count of 2. The third column shows c^*, the Good-Turing re-estimation of the count.

4.5.3   Some Advanced Issues in Good-Turing Estimation

Good-Turing estimation assumes that the distribution of each bigram is binomial (see Church et al., 1991) and assumes we know N_0, the number of bigrams we haven't seen. We know this because given a vocabulary size of V, the total number of bigrams is V^2; hence N_0 is V^2 minus all the bigrams we have seen.

AP Newswire			Berkeley Restaurant		
c (MLE)	N_c	c^* (GT)	c (MLE)	N_c	c^* (GT)
0	74,671,100,000	0.0000270	0	2,081,496	0.002553
1	2,018,046	0.446	1	5315	0.533960
2	449,721	1.26	2	1419	1.357294
3	188,933	2.24	3	642	2.373832
4	105,668	3.24	4	381	4.081365
5	68,379	4.22	5	311	3.781350
6	48,190	5.19	6	196	4.500000

Figure 4.8 Bigram "frequencies of frequencies" and Good-Turing re-estimations for the 22 million AP bigrams from Church and Gale (1991) and from the Berkeley Restaurant corpus of 9332 sentences.

There are a number of additional complexities in the use of Good-Turing. For example, we don't just use the raw N_c values in Eq. 4.26. This is because the re-estimate c^* for N_c depends on N_{c+1}; hence, Eq. 4.26 is undefined when $N_{c+1} = 0$. Such zeros occur quite often. In our sample problem above, for example, since $N_4 = 0$, how *Simple* can we compute N_3? One solution to this is called **Simple Good-Turing** (Gale and *Good-Turing* Sampson, 1995). In Simple Good-Turing, after we compute the bins N_c but before we compute Eq. 4.26 from them, we smooth the N_c counts to replace any zeros in the sequence. The simplest thing is just to replace the value N_c with a value computed from a linear regression that is fit to map N_c to c in log space (see Gale and Sampson (1995) for details):

$$\log(N_c) = a + b \, \log(c) \qquad (4.29)$$

In addition, in practice, the discounted estimate c^* is not used for all counts c. Large counts (where $c > k$ for some threshold k) are assumed to be reliable. Katz (1987) suggests setting k at 5. Thus, we define

$$c^* = c \ \text{ for } c > k \qquad (4.30)$$

The correct equation for c^* when some k is introduced (from Katz (1987)) is

$$c^* = \frac{(c+1)\frac{N_{c+1}}{N_c} - c\frac{(k+1)N_{k+1}}{N_1}}{1 - \frac{(k+1)N_{k+1}}{N_1}}, \ \text{ for } 1 \le c \le k. \qquad (4.31)$$

Finally, with Good-Turing and other discounting, it is usual to treat N-grams with low raw counts (especially counts of 1) as if the count were 0, that is, to apply Good-Turing discounting to these as if they were unseen, and then using smoothing.

Good-Turing discounting is not used by itself in discounting N-grams; it is only used in combination with the backoff and interpolation algorithms described in the next sections.

4.6   Interpolation

The discounting we have been discussing so far can help solve the problem of zero
frequency *N*-grams. But there is an additional source of knowledge we can draw on.
If we are trying to compute $P(w_n w_{n-2}w_{n-1})$ but we have no examples of a particular
trigram $w_{n-2}w_{n-1}w_n$, we can instead estimate its probability by using the bigram probability $P(w_n w_{n-1})$. Similarly, if we don't have counts to compute $P(w_n w_{n-1})$, we can
look to the unigram $P(w_n)$.

Backoff   There are two ways to use this *N*-gram "hierarchy": **backoff** and **interpolation**. In
Interpolation backoff, if we have non-zero trigram counts, we rely solely on the trigram counts. We
only "back off" to a lower-order *N*-gram if we have zero evidence for a higher-order
N-gram. By contrast, in interpolation, we always mix the probability estimates from
all the *N*-gram estimators, that is, we do a weighted interpolation of trigram, bigram,
and unigram counts.

In simple linear interpolation, we combine different order *N*-grams by linearly interpolating all the models. Thus, we estimate the trigram probability $P(w_n w_{n-2}w_{n-1})$
by mixing together the unigram, bigram, and trigram probabilities, each weighted by a
λ:

$$
\begin{aligned}
\hat{P}(w_n w_{n-2}w_{n-1}) \;=\; & \lambda_1 P(w_n w_{n-2}w_{n-1}) \\
& +\lambda_2 P(w_n w_{n-1}) \\
& +\lambda_3 P(w_n)
\end{aligned}
\tag{4.32}
$$

such that the λs sum to 1:

$$
\sum_i \lambda_i = 1 \tag{4.33}
$$

In a slightly more sophisticated version of linear interpolation, each λ weight is
computed in a more sophisticated way, by conditioning on the context. This way, if
we have particularly accurate counts for a particular bigram, we assume that the counts
of the trigrams based on this bigram will be more trustworthy, so we can make the λs
for those trigrams higher and thus give that trigram more weight in the interpolation.
Equation 4.34 shows the equation for interpolation with context-conditioned weights:

$$
\begin{aligned}
\hat{P}(w_n w_{n-2}w_{n-1}) \;=\; & \lambda_1(w_{n-2}^{n-1})P(w_n w_{n-2}w_{n-1}) \\
& +\lambda_2(w_{n-2}^{n-1})P(w_n w_{n-1}) \\
& +\lambda_3(w_{n-2}^{n-1})P(w_n)
\end{aligned}
\tag{4.34}
$$

Held-out   How are these λ values set? Both the simple interpolation and conditional interpolation λs are learned from a **held-out** corpus. Recall from Section 4.3 that a held-out
corpus is an additional training corpus that we use, not to set the *N*-gram counts but to
set other parameters. In this case, we can use such data to set the λ values. We can do
this by choosing the λ values that maximize the likelihood of the held-out corpus. That

is, we fix the N-gram probabilities and then search for the λ values that when plugged into Eq. 4.32 give us the highest probability of the held-out set. There are various ways to find this optimal set of λs. One way is to use the **EM** algorithm defined in Chapter 6, which is an iterative learning algorithm that converges on locally optimal λs (Baum, 1972; Dempster et al., 1977; Jelinek and Mercer, 1980).

4.7   Backoff

Katz backoff

While simple interpolation is indeed simple to understand and implement, it turns out that there are a number of better algorithms. One of these is backoff N-gram modeling. The version of backoff that we describe uses Good-Turing discounting as well. It was introduced by Katz (1987); hence, this kind of backoff with discounting is also called **Katz backoff**. In a Katz backoff N-gram model, if the N-gram we need has zero counts, we approximate it by backing off to the $(N$-1)-gram. We continue backing off until we reach a history that has some counts:

$$P_{\text{katz}}(w_n\, w_{n-N+1}^{n-1}) = \begin{cases} P^*(w_n\, w_{n-N+1}^{n-1}), & \text{if } C(w_{n-N+1}^n) > 0 \\ \alpha(w_{n-N+1}^{n-1})P_{\text{katz}}(w_n\, w_{n-N+2}^{n-1}), & \text{otherwise.} \end{cases} \quad (4.35)$$

Equation 4.35 shows that the Katz backoff probability for an N-gram just relies on the (discounted) probability P^* if we've seen this N-gram before (i.e., if we have non-zero counts). Otherwise, we recursively back off to the Katz probability for the shorter-history $(N$-1)-gram. We'll define the discounted probability P^*, the normalizing factor α, and other details about dealing with zero counts in Section 4.7.1. Based on these details, the trigram version of backoff might be represented as follows (where for pedagogical clarity, since it's easy to confuse the indices w_i, w_{i-1} and so on, we refer to the three words in a sequence as x, y, z in that order):

$$P_{\text{katz}}(z\, x, y) = \begin{cases} P^*(z\, x, y), & \text{if } C(x, y, z) > 0 \\ \alpha(x, y)P_{\text{katz}}(z\, y), & \text{else if } C(x, y) > 0 \\ P^*(z), & \text{otherwise.} \end{cases} \quad (4.36)$$

$$P_{\text{katz}}(z\, y) = \begin{cases} P^*(z\, y), & \text{if } C(y, z) > 0 \\ \alpha(y)P^*(z), & \text{otherwise.} \end{cases} \quad (4.37)$$

Katz backoff incorporates discounting as an integral part of the algorithm. Our previous discussions of discounting showed how a method like Good-Turing could be used to assign probability mass to unseen events. For simplicity, we assumed that these unseen events were all equally probable, and so the probability mass was distributed evenly among all unseen events. Katz backoff gives us a better way to distribute the probability mass among unseen trigram events by relying on information from unigrams and bigrams. We use discounting to tell us how much total probability mass to set aside for all the events we haven't seen and backoff to tell us how to distribute this probability.

Discounting is implemented by using discounted probabilities $P^*( )$ rather than MLE probabilities $P( )$ in Eq. 4.35 and Eq. 4.37.

Why do we need discounts and α values in Eq. 4.35 and Eq. 4.37? Why couldn't we just have three sets of MLE probabilities without weights? Because without discounts and α weights, the result of the equation would not be a true probability! The MLE estimates of $P(w_n\, w_{n-N+1}^{n-1})$ are true probabilities; if we sum the probability of all w_i over a given *N*-gram context, we should get 1:

$$\sum_i P(w_i\, w_j w_k) = 1 \qquad (4.38)$$

But if that is the case, if we use MLE probabilities but back off to a lower-order model when the MLE probability is zero, we would be adding extra probability mass into the equation and the total probability of a word would be greater than 1!

Thus any backoff language model must also be discounted. The P^* is used to discount the MLE probabilities to save some probability mass for the lower-order *N*-grams. The α is used to ensure that the probability mass from all the lower-order *N*-grams sums up to exactly the amount that we saved by discounting the higher-order *N*-grams. We define P^* as the discounted (c^*) estimate of the conditional probability of an *N*-gram (and save P for MLE probabilities):

$$P^*(w_n\, w_{n-N+1}^{n-1}) = \frac{c^*(w_{n-N+1}^n)}{c(w_{n-N+1}^{n-1})} \qquad (4.39)$$

Because on average the (discounted) c^* will be less than c, this probability P^* will be slightly less than the MLE estimate, which is

$$\frac{c(w_{n-N+1}^n)}{c(w_{n-N+1}^{n-1})}$$

This will leave some probability mass for the lower-order *N*-grams which is then distributed by the α weights; details of computing α are in Section 4.7.1. Figure 4.9 shows the Katz backoff bigram probabilities for our 8 sample words, computed from the BeRP corpus, using the SRILM toolkit.

	i	want	to	eat	chinese	food	lunch	spend
i	0.0014	0.326	0.00248	0.00355	0.000205	0.0017	0.00073	0.000489
want	0.00134	0.00152	0.656	0.000483	0.00455	0.00455	0.00384	0.000483
to	0.000512	0.00152	0.00165	0.284	0.000512	0.0017	0.00175	0.0873
eat	0.00101	0.00152	0.00166	0.00189	0.0214	0.00166	0.0563	0.000585
chinese	0.00283	0.00152	0.00248	0.00189	0.000205	0.519	0.00283	0.000585
food	0.0137	0.00152	0.0137	0.00189	0.000409	0.00366	0.00073	0.000585
lunch	0.00363	0.00152	0.00248	0.00189	0.000205	0.00131	0.00073	0.000585
spend	0.00161	0.00152	0.00161	0.00189	0.000205	0.0017	0.00073	0.000585

Figure 4.9   Good-Turing smoothed bigram probabilities for eight words (of $V = 1446$) in the BeRP corpus of 9332 sentences, computing by using SRILM, with $k = 5$ and counts of 1 replaced by 0.

4.7.1   Advanced: Details of Computing Katz Backoff α and P^*

In this section we give the remaining details of the computation of the discounted probability P^* and the backoff weights $\alpha(w)$.

We begin with α, which passes the leftover probability mass to the lower-order N-grams. Let's represent the total amount of leftover probability mass by the function β, a function of the $(N-1)$-gram context. For a given $(N-1)$-gram context, the total leftover probability mass can be computed by subtracting from 1 the total discounted probability mass for all N-grams starting with that context:

$$\beta(w_{n-N+1}^{n-1}) = 1 - \sum_{w_n:c(w_{n-N+1}^n)>0} P^*(w_n\, w_{n-N+1}^{n-1}) \tag{4.40}$$

This gives us the total probability mass that we are ready to distribute to all $(N-1)$-gram (e.g., bigrams if our original model was a trigram). Each individual $(N-1)$-gram (bigram) will only get a fraction of this mass, so we need to normalize β by the total probability of all the $(N-1)$-grams (bigrams) that begin some N-gram (trigram) that has zero count. The final equation for computing how much probability mass to distribute from an N-gram to an $(N-1)$-gram is represented by the function α:

$$
\begin{aligned}
\alpha(w_{n-N+1}^{n-1}) &= \frac{\beta(w_{n-N+1}^{n-1})}{\sum_{w_n:c(w_{n-N+1}^n)=0} P_{\text{katz}}(w_n\, w_{n-N+2}^{n-1})} \\
&= \frac{1 - \sum_{w_n:c(w_{n-N+1}^n)>0} P^*(w_n\, w_{n-N+1}^{n-1})}{1 - \sum_{w_n:c(w_{n-N+1}^n)>0} P^*(w_n\, w_{n-N+2}^{n-1})}
\end{aligned} \tag{4.41}
$$

Note that α is a function of the preceding word string, that is, of w_{n-N+1}^{n-1}; thus the amount by which we discount each trigram (d) and the mass that gets reassigned to lower-order N-grams (α) are recomputed for every $(N-1)$-gram that occurs in any N-gram.

We need to specify what to do when the counts of an $(N-1)$-gram context are 0, (i.e., when $c(w_{n-N+1}^{n-1}) = 0$) and our definition is complete:

$$P_{\text{katz}}(w_n\, w_{n-N+1}^{n-1}) = P_{\text{katz}}(w_n\, w_{n-N+2}^{n-1}) \qquad \text{if } c(w_{n-N+1}^{n-1}) = 0 \tag{4.42}$$

and

$$P^*(w_n\, w_{n-N+1}^{n-1}) = 0 \qquad \text{if } c(w_{n-N+1}^{n-1}) = 0 \tag{4.43}$$

and

$$\beta(w_{n-N+1}^{n-1}) = 1 \qquad \text{if } c(w_{n-N+1}^{n-1}) = 0 \tag{4.44}$$

4.8   Practical Issues: Toolkits and Data Formats

Let's now examine how *N*-gram language models are represented. We represent and compute language model probabilities in log format, to avoid underflow and also to speed up computation. Since probabilities are (by definition) less than 1, the more probabilities we multiply together, the smaller the product becomes. Multiplying enough *N*-grams together would result in numerical underflow. By using log probabilities instead of raw probabilities, we get numbers that are not as small. Adding in log space is equivalent to multiplying in linear space, so we combine log probabilities by adding them. Besides avoiding underflow, addition is faster to compute than multiplication. The result of doing all computation and storage in log space is that when we need to report probabilities we just take the exp of the logprob:

$$p_1 \quad p_2 \quad p_3 \quad p_4 = \exp(\log p_1 + \log p_2 + \log p_3 + \log p_4) \tag{4.45}$$

Backoff *N*-gram language models are generally stored in **ARPA format**. An *N*-gram in ARPA format is an ASCII file with a small header followed by a list of all the non-zero *N*-gram probabilities (all the unigrams, followed by bigrams, followed by trigrams, and so on). Each *N*-gram entry is stored with its discounted log probability (in $\log_{10}$ format) and its backoff weight α. Backoff weights are only necessary for *N*-grams that form a prefix of a longer *N*-gram, so no α is computed for the highest order *N*-gram (in this case, the trigram) or *N*-grams ending in the end-of-sequence token <s>. Thus, for a trigram grammar, the format of each *N*-gram is

$$
\begin{array}{llll}
\text{unigram:} & \log P^*(w_i) & w_i & \log \alpha(w_i) \\
\text{bigram:} & \log P^*(w_i\, w_{i-1}) & w_{i-1}w_i & \log \alpha(w_{i-1}w_i) \\
\text{trigram:} & \log P^*(w_i\, w_{i-2}, w_{i-1}) & w_{i-2}w_{i-1}w_i &
\end{array}
$$

Figure 4.10 shows an ARPA formatted LM file with selected *N*-grams from the BeRP corpus. Given one of these trigrams, the probability $P(z\,x,y)$ for the word sequence x, y, z can be computed as follows (repeated from (4.37)):

$$
P_{\text{katz}}(z\,x,y) = \begin{cases}
P^*(z\,x,y), & \text{if } C(x,y,z) > 0 \\
\alpha(x,y)P_{\text{katz}}(z\,y), & \text{else if } C(x,y) > 0 \\
P^*(z), & \text{otherwise.}
\end{cases} \tag{4.46}
$$

$$
P_{\text{katz}}(z\,y) = \begin{cases}
P^*(z\,y), & \text{if } C(y,z) > 0 \\
\alpha(y)P^*(z), & \text{otherwise.}
\end{cases} \tag{4.47}
$$

Toolkits: Two commonly used toolkits for building language models are the SRILM toolkit (Stolcke, 2002) and the Cambridge-CMU toolkit (Clarkson and Rosenfeld, 1997). Both are publicly available and have similar functionality. In training mode, each toolkit takes a raw text file, one sentence per line with words separated by whitespace, and various parameters such as the order *N*, the type of discounting (Good-Turing or Kneser-Ney, discussed in Section 4.9.1), and various thresholds. The output is a language model in ARPA format. In perplexity or decoding mode, the toolkits

```
\data\
ngram 1=1447
ngram 2=9420
ngram 3=5201

\1-grams:\
-0.8679678     </s>
-99            <s>                              -1.068532
-4.743076      chow-fun                         -0.1943932
-4.266155      fries                            -0.5432462
-3.175167      thursday                         -0.7510199
-1.776296      want                             -1.04292
...

\2-grams:\
-0.6077676     <s>     i                        -0.6257131
-0.4861297     i       want                     0.0425899
-2.832415      to      drink                    -0.06423882
-0.5469525     to      eat                      -0.008193135
-0.09403705    today   </s>
...

\3-grams:\
-2.579416      <s>     i        prefer
-1.148009      <s>     about    fifteen
-0.4120701     to      go       to
-0.3735807     me      a        list
-0.260361      at      jupiter  </s>
-0.260361      a       malaysian restaurant
...
\end\
```

Figure 4.10   ARPA format for N-grams, showing some sample N-grams. Each is represented by a *logprob*, the word sequence, $w_1...w_n$, followed by the log backoff weight α. Note that no α is computed for the highest-order N-gram or for N-grams ending in <s>.

take a language model in ARPA format and a sentence or corpus, and produce the probability and perplexity of the sentence or corpus. Both also implement many advanced features discussed later in this chapter and in following chapters, including skip N-grams, word lattices, confusion networks, and N-gram pruning.

4.9   Advanced Issues in Language Modeling

Because language models play such a broad role throughout speech and language processing, they have been extended and augmented in many ways. In this section we briefly introduce a few of these, including Kneser-Ney Smoothing, class-based language modeling, language model adaptation, topic-based language models, cache language models, variable-length N-grams.

4.9.1   Advanced Smoothing Methods: Kneser-Ney Smoothing

One of the most commonly used modern N-gram smoothing methods is the interpo-

Kneser-Ney   lated **Kneser-Ney** algorithm.

Kneser-Ney has its roots in a discounting method called **absolute discounting**. Absolute discounting is a much better method of computing a revised count $c*$ than the Good-Turing discount formula we saw in Eq. 4.26, based on frequencies of frequencies. To get the intuition, let's revisit the Good-Turing estimates of the bigram c^*

extended from Fig. 4.8 and reformatted below.

c (MLE)	**0**	**1**	**2**	**3**	**4**	**5**	**6**	**7**	**8**	**9**
c^* (GT)	0.0000270	0.446	1.26	2.24	3.24	4.22	5.19	6.21	7.24	8.25

Absolute
discounting

The astute reader may have noticed that except for the re-estimated counts for 0 and 1, all the other re-estimated counts c^* could be estimated pretty well by just subtracting 0.75 from the MLE count c! **Absolute discounting** formalizes this intuition by subtracting a fixed (absolute) discount d from each count. The intuition is that we have good estimates already for the high counts, and a small discount d won't affect them much. It will mainly modify the smaller counts, for which we don't necessarily trust the estimate anyway. The equation for absolute discounting applied to bigrams (assuming a proper coefficient α on the backoff to make everything sum to 1) is

$$P_{\text{absolute}}(w_i \mid w_{i-1}) = \begin{cases} \frac{C(w_{i-1}w_i) - \mathbf{D}}{C(w_{i-1})}, & \text{if } C(w_{i-1}w_i) > 0 \\ \alpha(w_i)P(w_i), & \text{otherwise.} \end{cases} \tag{4.48}$$

In practice, we might also want to keep distinct discount values D for the 0 and 1 counts.

Kneser-Ney discounting (Kneser and Ney, 1995) augments absolute discounting with a more sophisticated way to handle the backoff distribution. Consider the job of predicting the next word in this sentence, assuming we are backing off to a unigram model:

I can't see without my reading _____ .

The word *glasses* seems much more likely to follow here than the word *Francisco*. But *Francisco* is in fact more common, so a unigram model will prefer it to *glasses*. We would like to capture the intuition that although *Francisco* is frequent, it is only frequent after the word *San*, that is, in the phrase *San Francisco*. The word *glasses* has a much wider distribution.

Thus, instead of backing off to the unigram MLE count (the number of times the word w has been seen), we want to use a completely different backoff distribution. We want a heuristic that more accurately estimates the number of times we might expect to see word w in a new unseen context. The Kneser-Ney intuition is to base our estimate on the *number of different contexts word w has appeared in*. Words that have appeared in more contexts are more likely to appear in some new context as well. We can express this new backoff probability, the "continuation probability", as follows:

$$P_{\text{CONTINUATION}}(w_i) = \frac{w_{i-1} : C(w_{i-1}w_i) > 0}{\sum_{w_i} w_{i-1} : C(w_{i-1}w_i) > 0} \tag{4.49}$$

The Kneser-Ney backoff intuition can be formalized as follows (again assuming a proper coefficient α on the backoff to make everything sum to 1):

$$P_{\text{KN}}(w_i \mid w_{i-1}) = \begin{cases} \frac{C(w_{i-1}w_i) - \mathbf{D}}{C(w_{i-1})}, & \text{if } C(w_{i-1}w_i) > 0 \\ \alpha(w_i) \frac{w_{i-1} : C(w_{i-1}w_i) > 0}{\sum_{w_i} w_{i-1} : C(w_{i-1}w_i) > 0} & \text{otherwise.} \end{cases} \tag{4.50}$$

Finally, it turns out to be better to use an **interpolated** rather than a **backoff** form of Kneser-Ney. While simple *linear* interpolation is generally not as successful as Katz backoff, it turns out that more powerful interpolated models, such as interpolated Kneser-Ney, work better than their backoff version. **Interpolated Kneser-Ney** discounting can be computed with an equation like the following (omitting the computation of β):

Interpolated Kneser-Ney

$$P_{\text{KN}}(w_i\,w_{i-1}) = \frac{C(w_{i-1}w_i) - \mathbf{D}}{C(w_{i-1})} + \beta(w_i)\frac{w_{i-1} : C(w_{i-1}w_i) > 0}{\sum_{w_i}\ w_{i-1} : C(w_{i-1}w_i) > 0} \qquad (4.51)$$

A final practical note: it turns out that any interpolation model can be represented as a backoff model, hence stored in ARPA backoff format. We simply do the interpolation when we build the model, so the 'bigram' probability stored in the backoff format is really 'bigram already interpolated with unigram'.

4.9.2   Class-Based *N*-Grams

Class-based N-gram

Cluster N-gram

The **class-based N-gram**, or **cluster N-gram**, is a variant of the *N*-gram that uses information about word classes or clusters. Class-based *N*-grams can be useful for dealing with sparsity in the training data. Suppose for a flight reservation system we want to compute the probability of the bigram *to Shanghai*, but this bigram never occurs in the training set. Instead, our training data has *to London*, *to Beijing*, and *to Denver*. If we knew that these were all cities and assuming that *Shanghai* does appear in the training set in other contexts, we could predict the likelihood of a city following *from*.

IBM clustering

There are many variants of cluster *N*-grams. The simplest one is sometimes known as **IBM clustering**, after its originators (Brown et al., 1992). IBM clustering is a kind of **hard clustering**, in which each word can belong to only one class. The model estimates the conditional probability of a word w_i by multiplying two factors: the probability of the word's class c_i given the preceding classes (based on an *N*-gram of classes), and the probability of w_i given c_i. Here is the IBM model in bigram form:

$$P(w_i\,w_{i-1}) \approx P(c_i\,c_{i-1})\quad P(w_i\,c_i)$$

If we had a training corpus in which we knew the class for each word, the maximum likelihood estimate of the probability of the word given the class and the probability of the class given the previous class could be computed as follows:

$$P(w\,c) = \frac{C(w)}{C(c)}$$

$$P(c_i\,c_{i-1}) = \frac{C(c_{i-1}c_i)}{\sum_c C(c_{i-1}c)}$$

Cluster *N*-grams are generally used in two ways. In dialog systems we often hand-design domain-specific word classes. Thus for an airline information system, we might use classes like CITYNAME, AIRLINE, DAYOFWEEK, or MONTH, as we see in Chapter 24. In other cases, we can automatically induce the classes by clustering words in a corpus (Brown et al., 1992). Syntactic categories like part-of-speech tags don't seem to work well as classes (Niesler et al., 1998).

Whether automatically induced or hand-designed, cluster *N*-grams are generally mixed with regular word-based *N*-grams.

4.9.3   Language Model Adaptation and Web Use

Adaptation

One of the most exciting recent developments in language modeling is language model **adaptation**. This is relevant when we have only a small amount of in-domain training data but a large amount of data from some other domain. We can train on the larger out-of-domain dataset and adapt our models to the small in-domain set (Federico, 1996; Iyer and Ostendorf, 1997, 1999a, 1999b; Bacchiani and Roark, 2003; Bacchiani et al., 2004; Bellegarda, 2004).

A useful large data source for this type of adaptation is the Web. The simplest way to apply the Web to improve, say, trigram language models is to use search engines to get counts for $w_1 w_2 w_3$ and $w_1 w_2 w_3$, and then compute

$$\hat{p}_{web} = \frac{c_{web}(w_1 w_2 w_3)}{c_{web}(w_1 w_2)} \qquad (4.52)$$

We can then mix $\hat{p}_{web}$ with a conventional *N*-gram (Berger and Miller, 1998; Zhu and Rosenfeld, 2001). We can also use more sophisticated combination methods that make use of topic or class dependencies to find domain-relevant data on the Web data (Bulyko et al., 2003).

In practice, it is difficult or impossible to download every page from the Web in order to compute *N*-grams. For this reason, most uses of Web data rely on page counts from search engines. Page counts are only an approximation to actual counts for many reasons: a page may contain an *N*-gram multiple times, most search engines round off their counts, punctuation is deleted, and the counts themselves may be adjusted due to links and other information. It seems that this kind of noise does not hugely affect the results of using the Web as a corpus (Keller and Lapata, 2003; Nakov and Hearst, 2005), although it is possible to perform specific adjustments, such as fitting a regression to predict actual word counts from page counts (Zhu and Rosenfeld, 2001).

4.9.4   Using Longer-Distance Information: A Brief Summary

There are many methods for incorporating longer-distance context into *N*-gram modeling. While we have limited our discussion mainly to bigrams and trigrams, state-of-the-art speech recognition systems, for example, are based on longer-distance *N*-grams, especially 4-grams, but also 5-grams. Goodman (2006) showed that with 284 million words of training data, 5-grams do improve perplexity scores over 4-grams, but not by much. Goodman checked contexts up to 20-grams and found that after 6-grams, longer contexts weren't useful, at least not with 284 million words of training data.

Many models focus on more sophisticated ways to get longer-distance information. For example people tend to repeat words they have used before. Thus, if a word is

Cache

used once in a text, it will probably be used again. We can capture this fact by a **cache** language model (Kuhn and De Mori, 1990). For example, to use a unigram cache model to predict word i of a test corpus, we create a unigram grammar from the preceding part of the test corpus (words 1 to $i - 1$) and mix this with our conventional N-gram. We might use only a shorter window from the previous words, rather than the entire set. Cache language models are very powerful in any applications in which we have perfect knowledge of the words. Cache models work less well in domains in which the previous words are not known exactly. In speech applications, for example, unless there is some way for users to correct errors, cache models tend to "lock in" errors that the speech recognizer has made on earlier words.

Topic-based

The fact that words are often repeated in a text is a symptom of a more general fact about texts; texts tend to be **about** things. Documents that are about particular topics tend to use similar words. This suggests that we could train separate language models for different topics. In **topic-based** language models (Chen et al., 1998; Gildea and Hofmann, 1999), we try to take advantage of the fact that different topics will have different kinds of words. For example, we can train different language models for each topic t and then mix them, weighted by how likely each topic is given the history h:

$$p(w\,h) = \sum_t P(w\,t)P(t\,h) \qquad (4.53)$$

Latent semantic indexing

A similar class of models relies on the intuition that upcoming words are semantically similar to preceding words in the text. These models use a measure of semantic word association such as the **latent semantic indexing** (Coccaro and Jurafsky, 1998; Bellegarda, 1999, 2000, see also Chapter 20) or computer-readable dictionaries or thesauri (Demetriou et al., 1997) to compute a probability based on a word's similarity to preceding words, and then mix it with a conventional N-gram.

Trigger

There are also various ways to extend the N-gram model by having the previous (conditioning) word be something other than a fixed window of previous words. For example, we can choose as a predictor a word called a **trigger** that is not adjacent but is very related to (has high mutual information with) the word we are trying to predict (Rosenfeld, 1996; Niesler and Woodland, 1999; Zhou and Lua, 1998). Or we

Skip N-gram

can create **skip N-grams**, where the preceding context "skips over" some intermediate words, for example, computing a probability such as $P(w_i\,w_{i-1}, w_{i-3})$. We can also use extra previous context just in cases in which a longer phrase is particularly frequent

Variable-length N-gram

or predictive, producing a **variable-length** N-gram (Ney et al., 1994; Kneser, 1996; Niesler and Woodland, 1996).

In general, using very large and rich contexts can result in very large language models. Thus, these models are often pruned by removal of low-probability events. Pruning is also essential for language models that are used on small platforms such as cellphones (Stolcke, 1998; Church et al., 2007).

Finally, there is a wide body of research on integrating sophisticated linguistic structures into language modeling. Language models based on syntactic structure from probabilistic parsers are described in Chapter 14. Language models based on the current speech act in dialogue are described in Chapter 24.

4.10   Advanced: Information Theory Background

I got the horse right here
Frank Loesser, *Guys and Dolls*

We introduced perplexity in Section 4.4 as a way to evaluate *N*-gram models on a test set. A better *N*-gram model is one that assigns a higher probability to the test data, and perplexity is a normalized version of the probability of the test set. Another way to think about perplexity is based on the information-theoretic concept of cross-entropy. To give another intuition into perplexity as a metric, this section briefly reviews fundamental facts from **information theory**, including the concept of cross-entropy that underlies perplexity. The interested reader should consult a good information theory textbook like Cover and Thomas (1991).

Entropy   Perplexity is based on the information-theoretic notion of **cross-entropy**, which we now work toward defining. **Entropy** is a measure of information and is invaluable throughout speech and language processing. It can be used as a metric for how much information there is in a particular grammar, and for how well a given grammar matches a given language, for how predictive a given *N*-gram grammar is about what the next word could be. Given two grammars and a corpus, we can use entropy to tell us which grammar better matches the corpus. We can also use entropy to compare how difficult two speech recognition tasks are and also to measure how well a given probabilistic grammar matches human grammars.

Computing entropy requires that we establish a random variable X that ranges over whatever we are predicting (words, letters, parts of speech, the set of which we'll call χ) and that has a particular probability function, call it $p(x)$. The entropy of this random variable X is then

$$H(X) = -\sum_{x \in \chi} p(x) \log_2 p(x) \tag{4.54}$$

The log can, in principle, be computed in any base. If we use log base 2, the resulting value of entropy will be measured in **bits**.

The most intuitive way to define entropy for computer scientists is to think of the entropy as a lower bound on the number of bits it would take to encode a certain decision or piece of information in the optimal coding scheme.

Cover and Thomas (1991) suggest the following example. Imagine that we want to place a bet on a horse race but it is too far to go all the way to Yonkers Racetrack, so we'd like to send a short message to the bookie to tell him which horse to bet on. Suppose there are eight horses in this particular race.

One way to encode this message is just to use the binary representation of the horse's number as the code; thus, horse 1 would be 001, horse 2 010, horse 3 011, and so on, with horse 8 coded as 000. If we spend the whole day betting and each horse is coded with 3 bits, on average we would be sending 3 bits per race.

Can we do better? Suppose that the spread is the actual distribution of the bets placed and that we represent it as the prior probability of each horse as follows:

Horse 1	$\frac{1}{2}$	Horse 5	$\frac{1}{64}$
Horse 2	$\frac{1}{4}$	Horse 6	$\frac{1}{64}$
Horse 3	$\frac{1}{8}$	Horse 7	$\frac{1}{64}$
Horse 4	$\frac{1}{16}$	Horse 8	$\frac{1}{64}$

The entropy of the random variable X that ranges over horses gives us a lower bound on the number of bits and is

$$
\begin{aligned}
H(X) &= -\sum_{i=1}^{i=8} p(i) \log p(i) \\
&= -\tfrac{1}{2}\log\tfrac{1}{2} - \tfrac{1}{4}\log\tfrac{1}{4} - \tfrac{1}{8}\log\tfrac{1}{8} - \tfrac{1}{16}\log\tfrac{1}{16} - 4(\tfrac{1}{64}\log\tfrac{1}{64}) \\
&= 2 \text{ bits}
\end{aligned}
\tag{4.55}
$$

A code that averages 2 bits per race can be built with short encodings for more probable horses, and longer encodings for less probable horses. For example, we could encode the most likely horse with the code 0, and the remaining horses as 10, then 110, 1110, 111100, 111101, 111110, and 111111.

What if the horses are equally likely? We saw above that if we used an equal-length binary code for the horse numbers, each horse took 3 bits to code, so the average was 3. Is the entropy the same? In this case each horse would have a probability of $\frac{1}{8}$. The entropy of the choice of horses is then

$$
H(X) = -\sum_{i=1}^{i=8} \frac{1}{8} \log \frac{1}{8} = -\log \frac{1}{8} = 3 \text{ bits}
\tag{4.56}
$$

Until now we have been computing the entropy of a single variable. But most of what we will use entropy for involves *sequences*. For a grammar, for example, we will be computing the entropy of some sequence of words $W = w_0, w_1, w_2, \ldots, w_n$. One way to do this is to have a variable that ranges over sequences of words. For example we can compute the entropy of a random variable that ranges over all finite sequences of words of length n in some language L as follows:

$$
H(w_1, w_2, \ldots, w_n) = -\sum_{W_1^n \in L} p(W_1^n) \log p(W_1^n)
\tag{4.57}
$$

Entropy rate   We could define the **entropy rate** (we could also think of this as the **per-word entropy**) as the entropy of this sequence divided by the number of words:

$$
\frac{1}{n} H(W_1^n) = -\frac{1}{n} \sum_{W_1^n \in L} p(W_1^n) \log p(W_1^n)
\tag{4.58}
$$

But to measure the true entropy of a language, we need to consider sequences of infinite length. If we think of a language as a stochastic process L that produces a sequence of words, its entropy rate $H(L)$ is defined as

$$H(L) = -\lim_{n \to \infty} \frac{1}{n} H(w_1, w_2, \ldots, w_n)$$

$$= -\lim_{n \to \infty} \frac{1}{n} \sum_{W \in L} p(w_1, \ldots, w_n) \log p(w_1, \ldots, w_n) \qquad (4.59)$$

The Shannon-McMillan-Breiman theorem (Algoet and Cover, 1988; Cover and Thomas, 1991) states that if the language is regular in certain ways (to be exact, if it is both stationary and ergodic),

$$H(L) = \lim_{n \to \infty} -\frac{1}{n} \log p(w_1 w_2 \ldots w_n) \qquad (4.60)$$

That is, we can take a single sequence that is long enough instead of summing over all possible sequences. The intuition of the Shannon-McMillan-Breiman theorem is that a long-enough sequence of words will contain in it many other shorter sequences and that each of these shorter sequences will reoccur in the longer sequence according to their probabilities.

Stationary   A stochastic process is said to be **stationary** if the probabilities it assigns to a sequence are invariant with respect to shifts in the time index. In other words, the probability distribution for words at time t is the same as the probability distribution at time $t + 1$. Markov models, and hence N-grams, are stationary. For example, in a bigram, P_i is dependent only on P_{i-1}. So if we shift our time index by x, P_{i+x} is still dependent on P_{i+x-1}. But natural language is not stationary, since as we show in Chapter 12, the probability of upcoming words can be dependent on events that were arbitrarily distant and time dependent. Thus, our statistical models only give an approximation to the correct distributions and entropies of natural language.

To summarize, by making some incorrect but convenient simplifying assumptions, we can compute the entropy of some stochastic process by taking a very long sample of the output and computing its average log probability. In the next section, we talk about the why and how: *why* we would want to do this (i.e., what kinds of problems the entropy would be useful for), and *how* to compute the probability of a very long sequence.

4.10.1   Cross-Entropy for Comparing Models

Cross-entropy   In this section, we introduce **cross-entropy** and discuss its usefulness in comparing different probabilistic models. The cross-entropy is useful when we don't know the actual probability distribution p that generated some data. It allows us to use some m, which is a model of p (i.e., an approximation to p). The cross-entropy of m on p is defined by

$$H(p, m) = \lim_{n \to \infty} -\frac{1}{n} \sum_{W \in L} p(w_1, \ldots, w_n) \log m(w_1, \ldots, w_n) \qquad (4.61)$$

That is, we draw sequences according to the probability distribution p, but sum the log of their probabilities according to m.

Again, following the Shannon-McMillan-Breiman theorem, for a stationary ergodic process:

$$H(p,m) = \lim_{n \to \infty} -\frac{1}{n} \log m(w_1 w_2 \dots w_n) \tag{4.62}$$

This means that, as for entropy, we can estimate the cross-entropy of a model m on some distribution p by taking a single sequence that is long enough instead of summing over all possible sequences.

What makes the cross-entropy useful is that the cross-entropy $H(p,m)$ is an upper bound on the entropy $H(p)$. For any model m:

$$H(p) \leq H(p,m) \tag{4.63}$$

This means that we can use some simplified model m to help estimate the true entropy of a sequence of symbols drawn according to probability p. The more accurate m is, the closer the cross-entropy $H(p,m)$ will be to the true entropy $H(p)$. Thus, the difference between $H(p,m)$ and $H(p)$ is a measure of how accurate a model is. Between two models m_1 and m_2, the more accurate model will be the one with the lower cross-entropy. (The cross-entropy can never be lower than the true entropy, so a model cannot err by underestimating the true entropy.)

We are finally ready to see the relation between perplexity and cross-entropy as we saw it in Eq. 4.62. Cross-entropy is defined in the limit, as the length of the observed word sequence goes to infinity. We will need an approximation to cross-entropy, relying on a (sufficiently long) sequence of fixed length. This approximation to the cross-entropy of a model $M = P(w_i \, w_{i-N+1} \dots w_{i-1})$ on a sequence of words W is

$$H(W) = -\frac{1}{N} \log P(w_1 w_2 \dots w_N) \tag{4.64}$$

Perplexity   The **perplexity** of a model P on a sequence of words W is now formally defined as the exp of this cross-entropy:

$$
\begin{aligned}
\text{Perplexity}(W) &= 2^{H(W)} \\
&= P(w_1 w_2 \dots w_N)^{-\frac{1}{N}} \\
&= \sqrt[N]{\frac{1}{P(w_1 w_2 \dots w_N)}} \\
&= \sqrt[N]{\prod_{i=1}^{N} \frac{1}{P(w_i \, w_1 \dots w_{i-1})}}
\end{aligned}
\tag{4.65}
$$

4.11   Advanced: The Entropy of English and Entropy Rate Constancy

As we suggested in the previous section, the cross-entropy of some model *m* can be used as an upper bound on the true entropy of some process. We can use this method to get an estimate of the true entropy of English. Why should we care about the entropy of English?

One reason is that the true entropy of English would give us a solid lower bound for all of our future experiments on probabilistic grammars. Another is that we can use the entropy values for English to help understand what parts of a language provide the most information (e.g., is the predictability of English mainly based on word order, on semantics, on morphology, on constituency, or on pragmatic cues?) This can help us immensely in knowing where to focus our language-modeling efforts.

There are two common methods for computing the entropy of English. The first was employed by Shannon (1951) as part of his groundbreaking work in defining the field of information theory. His idea is to use human subjects and to construct a psychological experiment that requires them to guess strings of letters. By looking at how many guesses it takes them to guess letters correctly, we can estimate the probability of the letters and hence the entropy of the sequence.

The actual experiment is designed as follows: We present subjects with some English text and ask them to guess the next letter. The subjects will use their knowledge of the language to guess the most probable letter first, the next most probable next, and so on. We record the number of guesses it takes for a subject to guess correctly. Shannon's insight was that the entropy of the number-of-guesses sequence is the same as the entropy of English. (The intuition is that given the number-of-guesses sequence, we could reconstruct the original text by choosing the "*n*th most probable" letter whenever a subject took *n* guesses.) This methodology requires the use of letter guesses rather than word guesses (since the subject sometimes has to do an exhaustive search of all the possible letters!), so Shannon computed the **per-letter entropy** of English rather than the per-word entropy. He reported an entropy of 1.3 bits (for 27 characters (26 letters plus space)). Shannon's estimate is likely to be too low since it is based on a single text (*Jefferson the Virginian* by Dumas Malone). Shannon notes that his subjects had worse guesses (hence higher entropies) on other texts (newspaper writing, scientific work, and poetry). More recent variations on the Shannon experiments include the use of a gambling paradigm whereby the subjects get to bet on the next letter (Cover and King, 1978; Cover and Thomas, 1991).

The second method for computing the entropy of English helps avoid the single-text problem that confounds Shannon's results. This method is to train a very good stochastic model on a very large corpus and uses it to assign a log-probability to a very long sequence of English, using the Shannon-McMillan-Breiman theorem:

$$H(\text{English}) \leq \lim_{n \to \infty} -\frac{1}{n} \log m(w_1 w_2 \ldots w_n) \tag{4.66}$$

For example, Brown et al. (1992) trained a trigram language model on 583 million words of English (293,181 different types) and used it to compute the probability of the entire Brown corpus (1,014,312 tokens). The training data include newspapers, encyclopedias, novels, office correspondence, proceedings of the Canadian parliament, and other miscellaneous sources.

Brown et al. (1992) then computed the character entropy of the Brown corpus by using their word-trigram grammar to assign probabilities to the Brown corpus, considered as a sequence of individual letters. They obtained an entropy of 1.75 bits per character (where the set of characters included all the 95 printable ASCII characters).

The average length of English written words (including space) has been reported at 5.5 letters (Nádas, 1984). If this is correct, it means that the Shannon estimate of 1.3 bits per letter corresponds to a per-word perplexity of 142 for general English. The numbers we reported earlier for the WSJ experiments are significantly lower than this since the training and test set came from the same subsample of English. That is, those experiments underestimate the complexity of English (since the *Wall Street Journal* looks very little like Shakespeare, for example).

A number of scholars have independently made the intriguing suggestion that entropy rate plays a role in human communication in general (Lindblom, 1990; Van Son et al., 1998; Aylett, 1999; Genzel and Charniak, 2002; Van Son and Pols, 2003; Levy and Jaeger, 2007). The idea is that people speak so as to keep the rate of information being transmitted per second roughly constant, that is, transmitting a constant number of bits per second or maintaining a constant entropy rate. Since the most efficient way of transmitting information through a channel is at a constant rate, language may even have evolved for such communicative efficiency (Plotkin and Nowak, 2000). There is a wide variety of evidence for the constant entropy rate hypothesis. One class of evidence, for speech, shows that speakers shorten predictable words (i.e., they take less time to say predictable words) and lengthen unpredictable words (Aylett, 1999; Jurafsky et al., 2001a; Aylett and Turk, 2004; Pluymaekers et al., 2005). In another line of research, Genzel and Charniak (2002, 2003) show that entropy rate constancy makes predictions about the entropy of individual sentences from a text. In particular, they show that it predicts that local measures of sentence entropy which ignore previous discourse context (e.g., the N-gram probability of sentence) should increase with the sentence number, and they document this increase in corpora. Keller (2004) provides evidence that entropy rate plays a role for the addressee as well, showing a correlation between the entropy of a sentence and the processing effort it causes in comprehension, as measured by reading times in eye-tracking data.

4.12   Summary

This chapter introduced the N-gram, one of the oldest and most broadly useful practical tools in language processing.

- An N-gram probability is the conditional probability of a word given the previous $N - 1$ words. N-gram probabilities can be computed by simply counting in a corpus and normalizing (the **maximum likelihood estimate**), or they can be computed by more sophisticated algorithms. The advantage of *N*-grams is that they take advantage of lots of rich lexical knowledge. A disadvantage for some purposes is that they are very dependent on the corpus they were trained on.

- **Smoothing** algorithms provide a better way of estimating the probability of *N*-grams than maximum likelihood estimation. Commonly used smoothing algorithms for *N*-grams rely on lower-order *N*-gram counts through **backoff** or **interpolation**.

- Both backoff and interpolation require discounting such as **Kneser-Ney**, **Witten-Bell**, or **Good-Turing** discounting.

- *N*-gram **language models** are evaluated by separating the corpus into a **training set** and a **test set**, training the model on the training set, and evaluating on the test set. The **perplexity** 2^H of the language model on a test set is used to compare language models.

Bibliographical and Historical Notes

The underlying mathematics of the *N*-gram was first proposed by Markov (1913), who used what are now called **Markov chains** (bigrams and trigrams) to predict whether an upcoming letter in Pushkin's *Eugene Onegin* would be a vowel or a consonant. Markov classified 20,000 letters as V or C and computed the bigram and trigram probability that a given letter would be a vowel given the previous one or two letters. Shannon (1948) applied *N*-grams to compute approximations to English word sequences. Based on Shannon's work, Markov models were commonly used in engineering, linguistic, and psychological work on modeling word sequences by the 1950s.

In a series of extremely influential papers starting with Chomsky (1956) and including Chomsky (1957) and Miller and Chomsky (1963), Noam Chomsky argued that "finite-state Markov processes", while a possibly useful engineering heuristic, were incapable of being a complete cognitive model of human grammatical knowledge. These arguments led many linguists and computational linguists to ignore work in statistical modeling for decades.

The resurgence of *N*-gram models came from Jelinek, Mercer, Bahl, and colleagues at the IBM Thomas J. Watson Research Center, who were influenced by Shannon, and Baker at CMU, who was influenced by the work of Baum and colleagues. Independently these two labs successfully used *N*-grams in their speech recognition systems (Baker, 1990; Jelinek, 1976; Baker, 1975; Bahl et al., 1983; Jelinek, 1990). A trigram model was used in the IBM TANGORA speech recognition system in the 1970s, but the idea was not written up until later.

Add-one smoothing derives from Laplace's 1812 law of succession and was first applied as an engineering solution to the zero-frequency problem by Jeffreys (1948) based on an earlier Add-K suggestion by Johnson (1932). Problems with the add-one algorithm are summarized in Gale and Church (1994). The Good-Turing algorithm was first applied to the smoothing of *N*-gram grammars at IBM by Katz, as cited in Nádas (1984). Church and Gale (1991) give a good description of the Good-Turing method, as well as the proof. Sampson (1996) also has a useful discussion of Good-Turing.

Jelinek (1990) summarizes this and many other early language model innovations used in the IBM language models.

A wide variety of different language modeling and smoothing techniques were tested through the 1980s and 1990s, including Witten-Bell discounting (Witten and Bell, 1991), varieties of class-based models (Jelinek, 1990; Kneser and Ney, 1993; Heeman, 1999; Samuelsson and Reichl, 1999), and others (Gupta et al., 1992). In the late 1990s, Chen and Goodman produced a highly influential series of papers with a comparison of different language models (Chen and Goodman, 1996, 1998, 1999; Goodman, 2006). They performed a number of carefully controlled experiments comparing different discounting algorithms, cache models, class-based (cluster) models, and other language model parameters. They showed the advantages of Interpolated Kneser-Ney, which has since become one of the most popular current methods for language modeling. These papers influenced our discussion in this chapter and are recommended reading if you have further interest in language modeling.

Recent research in language modeling has focused on adaptation, on the use of sophisticated linguistic structures based on syntactic and dialogue structure, and on very large N-grams. For example in 2006 Google publicly released a very large set of N-grams that is a useful research resource, consisting of all the five-word sequences that appear at least 40 times from 1,024,908,267,229 words of running text; there are 1,176,470,663 five-word sequences using over 13 million unique words types (Franz and Brants, 2006). Large language models generally need to be pruned to be practical, by techniques such as Stolcke (1998) and Church et al. (2007).

Exercises

4.1 Write out the equation for trigram probability estimation (modifying Eq. 4.14).

4.2 Write a program to compute unsmoothed unigrams and bigrams.

4.3 Run your N-gram program on two different small corpora of your choice (you might use email text or newsgroups). Now compare the statistics of the two corpora. What are the differences in the most common unigrams between the two? How about interesting differences in bigrams?

4.4 Add an option to your program to generate random sentences.

4.5 Add an option to your program to do Good-Turing discounting.

4.6 Add an option to your program to implement Katz backoff.

4.7 Add an option to your program to compute the perplexity of a test set.

4.8 (Adapted from Michael Collins). Prove Eq. 4.27 given Eq. 4.26 and any necessary assumptions. That is, show that given a probability distribution defined by the GT formula in Eq. 4.26 for the N items seen in training, the probability of the next (i.e., $N + 1$st) item being unseen in training can be estimated by Eq. 4.27. You may make any necessary assumptions for the proof, including assuming that all N_c are non-zero.

Bag of words

4.9   (Advanced) Suppose someone took all the words in a sentence and reordered them randomly. Write a program that takes as input such a **bag of words** and produces as output a guess at the original order. You will need to use an *N*-gram grammar produced by your *N*-gram program (on some corpus), and you will need to use the Viterbi algorithm introduced in the next chapter. This task is sometimes called **bag generation**.

Bag generation

Authorship attribution

4.10   The field of **authorship attribution** is concerned with discovering the author of a particular text. Authorship attribution is important in many fields, including history, literature, and forensic linguistics. For example, Mosteller and Wallace (1964) applied authorship identification techniques to discover who wrote *The Federalist* papers. The Federalist papers were written in 1787–1788 by Alexander Hamilton, John Jay, and James Madison to persuade New York to ratify the United States Constitution. They were published anonymously, and as a result, although some of the 85 essays were clearly attributable to one author or another, the authorship of 12 were in dispute between Hamilton and Madison. Foster (1989) applied authorship identification techniques to suggest that W.S.'s *Funeral Elegy* for William Peter might have been written by William Shakespeare (he turned out to be wrong on this one) and that the anonymous author of *Primary Colors*, the roman à clef about the Clinton campaign for the American presidency, was journalist Joe Klein (Foster, 1996).

A standard technique for authorship attribution, first used by Mosteller and Wallace, is a Bayesian approach. For example, they trained a probabilistic model of the writing of Hamilton and another model on the writings of Madison, then computed the maximum-likelihood author for each of the disputed essays. Many complex factors go into these models, including vocabulary use, word length, syllable structure, rhyme, grammar; see Holmes (1994) for a summary. This approach can also be used for identifying which genre a text comes from.

One factor in many models is the use of rare words. As a simple approximation to this one factor, apply the Bayesian method to the attribution of any particular text. You will need three things: a text to test and two potential authors or genres, with a large computer-readable text sample of each. One of them should be the correct author. Train a unigram language model on each of the candidate authors. You are going to use only the **singleton** unigrams in each language model. You will compute $P(T \, A_1)$, the probability of the text given author or genre A_1, by (1) taking the language model from A_1, (2) multiplying together the probabilities of all the unigrams that occur only once in the "unknown" text, and (3) taking the geometric mean of these (i.e., the nth root, where n is the number of probabilities you multiplied). Do the same for A_2. Choose whichever is higher. Did it produce the correct candidate?

Chapter 5

Part-of-Speech Tagging

Conjunction Junction, what's your function?
Bob Dorough, *Schoolhouse Rock*, 1973

A gnostic was seated before a grammarian. The grammarian said, 'A word must be one of three things: either it is a noun, a verb, or a particle.' The gnostic tore his robe and cried, 'Alas! Twenty years of my life and striving and seeking have gone to the winds, for I laboured greatly in the hope that there was another word outside of this. Now you have destroyed my hope.' Though the gnostic had already attained the word which was his purpose, he spoke thus in order to arouse the grammarian.
Rumi (1207–1273), *The Discourses of Rumi*, Translated by A. J. Arberry

Dionysius Thrax of Alexandria (*c.* 100 B.C.), or perhaps someone else (exact authorship being understandably difficult to be sure of with texts of this vintage), wrote a grammatical sketch of Greek (a "*technē*") that summarized the linguistic knowledge of his day. This work is the direct source of an astonishing proportion of our modern linguistic vocabulary, including among many other words, *syntax*, *diphthong*, *clitic*, and *analogy*. Also included are a description of eight **parts-of-speech**: noun, verb, pronoun, preposition, adverb, conjunction, participle, and article. Although earlier scholars (including Aristotle as well as the Stoics) had their own lists of parts-of-speech, it was Thrax's set of eight that became the basis for practically all subsequent part-of-speech descriptions of Greek, Latin, and most European languages for the next 2000 years.

Parts-of-speech

Schoolhouse Rock was a popular series of 3-minute musical animated clips first aired on television in 1973. The series was designed to inspire kids to learn multiplication tables, grammar, basic science, and history. The Grammar Rock sequence, for example, included songs about parts-of-speech, thus bringing these categories into the realm of popular culture. As it happens, Grammar Rock was remarkably traditional in its grammatical notation, including exactly eight songs about parts-of-speech. Although the list was slightly modified from Thrax's original, substituting adjective and interjection for the original participle and article, the astonishing durability of the parts-of-speech through two millenia is an indicator of both the importance and the transparency of their role in human language.

Tagset

More recent lists of parts-of-speech (or **tagsets**) have many more word classes; 45 for the Penn Treebank (Marcus et al., 1993), 87 for the Brown corpus (Francis, 1979; Francis and Kučera, 1982), and 146 for the C7 tagset (Garside et al., 1997).

POS

The significance of parts-of-speech (also known as **POS**, **word classes**, **morphological classes**, or **lexical tags**) for language processing is the large amount of information they give about a word and its neighbors. This is clearly true for major categories,

From Chapter 5 of *Speech and Language Processing*, Second Edition. Daniel Jurafsky, James H. Martin.

(**verb** versus **noun**), but it is also true for the many finer distinctions. For example, these tagsets distinguish between possessive pronouns (*my, your, his, her, its*) and personal pronouns (*I, you, he, me*). Knowing whether a word is a possessive pronoun or a personal pronoun can tell us what words are likely to occur in its vicinity (possessive pronouns are likely to be followed by a noun, personal pronouns by a verb). This can be useful in a language model for speech recognition.

A word's part of speech can tell us something about how the word is pronounced. As Chapter 8 discusses, the word *content*, for example, can be a noun or an adjective. They are pronounced differently (the noun is pronounced *CONtent* and the adjective *conTENT*). Thus, knowing the part of speech can produce more natural pronunciations in a speech synthesis system and more accuracy in a speech recognition system. (Other pairs like this include *OBject* (noun) and *obJECT* (verb), *DIScount* (noun) and *disCOUNT* (verb); see Cutler (1986).)

Parts-of-speech can also be used in stemming for informational retrieval (IR), since knowing a word's part of speech can help tell us which morphological affixes it can take, as we saw in Chapter 3. They can also enhance an IR application by selecting nouns or other important words from a document. Automatic assignment of part of speech plays a role in parsing, in word sense disambiguation algorithms, and in shallow parsing of texts to quickly find names, times, dates, or other named entities for the information extraction applications discussed in Chapter 22. Finally, corpora that have been marked for parts-of-speech are useful for linguistic research. For example, they can help find instances or frequencies of particular constructions.

This chapter focuses on computational methods for assigning parts-of-speech to words (**part-of-speech tagging**). Many algorithms have been applied to this problem, including hand-written rules (**rule-based tagging**), statistical methods (**HMM tagging** and **maximum entropy tagging**), and other methods like **transformation-based tagging** and **memory-based tagging**. We introduce three of these algorithms in this chapter: rule-based tagging, HMM tagging, and transformation-based tagging. But before turning to the algorithms themselves, let's begin with a summary of English word classes and of various tagsets for formally coding these classes.

5.1   (Mostly) English Word Classes

Until now we have been using part-of-speech terms like **noun** and **verb** rather freely. In this section we give a more complete definition of these and other classes. Traditionally, the definition of parts-of-speech has been based on syntactic and morphological function; words that function similarly with respect to what can occur nearby (their "syntactic distributional properties") or with respect to the affixes they take (their morphological properties) are grouped into classes. While word classes do have tendencies toward semantic coherence (nouns do in fact often describe "people, places, or things", and adjectives often describe properties), this is not necessarily the case, and in general we don't use semantic coherence as a definitional criterion for parts-of-speech.

Closed class   Parts-of-speech can be divided into two broad supercategories: **closed class** types
Open class   and **open class** types. Closed classes are those that have relatively fixed membership.

For example, prepositions are a closed class because there is a fixed set of them in English; new prepositions are rarely coined. By contrast, nouns and verbs are open classes because new nouns and verbs are continually coined or borrowed from other languages (e.g., the new verb *to fax* or the borrowed noun *futon*). It is likely that any given speaker or corpus will have different open class words, but all speakers of a language, and corpora that are large enough, will likely share the set of closed class words.

Function word Closed class words are also generally **function words** like *of*, *it*, *and*, or *you*, which tend to be very short, occur frequently, and often have structuring uses in grammar.

Four major open classes occur in the languages of the world: **nouns**, **verbs**, **adjectives**, and **adverbs**. It turns out that English has all four of these, although not every language does.

Noun **Noun** is the name given to the syntactic class in which the words for most people, places, or things occur. But since syntactic classes like **noun** are defined syntactically and morphologically rather than semantically, some words for people, places, and things may not be nouns, and conversely, some nouns may not be words for people, places, or things. Thus, nouns include concrete terms like *ship* and *chair*, abstractions like *bandwidth* and *relationship*, and verb-like terms like *pacing* as in *His pacing to and fro became quite annoying*. What defines a noun in English, then, are things like its ability to occur with determiners (*a goat, its bandwidth, Plato's Republic*), to take possessives (*IBM's annual revenue*), and for most but not all nouns to occur in the plural form (*goats, abaci*).

Proper noun Nouns are traditionally grouped into **proper nouns** and **common nouns**. Proper
Common noun nouns, like *Regina*, *Colorado*, and *IBM*, are names of specific persons or entities. In English, they generally aren't preceded by articles (e.g., *the book is upstairs*, but *Regina is upstairs*). In written English, proper nouns are usually capitalized.

Count nouns In many languages, including English, common nouns are divided into **count nouns**
Mass noun and **mass nouns**. Count nouns are those that allow grammatical enumeration; that is, they can occur in both the singular and plural (*goat/goats, relationship/relationships*) and they can be counted (*one goat, two goats*). Mass nouns are used when something is conceptualized as a homogeneous group. So words like *snow, salt*, and *communism* are not counted (i.e., **two snows* or **two communisms*). Mass nouns can also appear without articles where singular count nouns cannot (*Snow is white* but not **Goat is white*).

Verb The **verb** class includes most of the words referring to actions and processes, including main verbs like *draw, provide, differ*, and *go*. As we saw in Chapter 3, English verbs have a number of morphological forms (non-third-person-sg (*eat*), third-person-sg (*eats*), progressive (*eating*), past participle (*eaten*)). A subclass of English verbs
Auxiliary called **auxiliaries** is discussed when we turn to closed class forms.

While many researchers believe that all human languages have the categories of noun and verb, others have argued that some languages, such as Riau Indonesian and Tongan, don't even make this distinction (Broschart, 1997; Evans, 2000; Gil, 2000).

Adjective The third open class English form is **adjectives**; semantically this class includes many terms that describe properties or qualities. Most languages have adjectives for the concepts of color (*white, black*), age (*old, young*), and value (*good, bad*), but there are languages without adjectives. In Korean, for example, the words corresponding

Adverb

to English adjectives act as a subclass of verbs, so what is in English an adjective "beautiful" acts in Korean like a verb meaning "to be beautiful" (Evans, 2000).

The final open class form, **adverbs**, is rather a hodge-podge, both semantically and formally. For example, Schachter (1985) points out that in a sentence like the following, all the italicized words are adverbs:

Unfortunately, John walked *home extremely slowly yesterday*

Locative

Degree

Manner

Temporal

What coherence the class has semantically may be solely that each of these words can be viewed as modifying something (often verbs, hence the name "adverb", but also other adverbs and entire verb phrases). **Directional adverbs** or **locative adverbs** (*home*, *here*, *downhill*) specify the direction or location of some action; **degree adverbs** (*extremely*, *very*, *somewhat*) specify the extent of some action, process, or property; **manner adverbs** (*slowly*, *slinkily*, *delicately*) describe the manner of some action or process; and **temporal adverbs** describe the time that some action or event took place (*yesterday*, *Monday*). Because of the heterogeneous nature of this class, some adverbs (e.g., temporal adverbs like *Monday*) are tagged in some tagging schemes as nouns.

The closed classes differ more from language to language than do the open classes. Here's a quick overview of some of the more important closed classes in English, with a few examples of each:

- **prepositions:** on, under, over, near, by, at, from, to, with
- **determiners:** a, an, the
- **pronouns:** she, who, I, others
- **conjunctions:** and, but, or, as, if, when
- **auxiliary verbs:** can, may, should, are
- **particles:** up, down, on, off, in, out, at, by
- **numerals:** one, two, three, first, second, third

Prepositions

Prepositions occur before noun phrases; semantically they are relational, often indicating spatial or temporal relations, whether literal (*on it*, *before then*, *by the house*) or metaphorical (*on time*, *with gusto*, *beside herself*). But they often indicate other relations as well (*Hamlet was written by Shakespeare*, and [from Shakespeare] "*And I did laugh sans intermission an hour by his dial*"). Figure 5.1 shows the prepositions of English according to the CELEX online dictionary (Baayen et al., 1995), sorted by their frequency in the COBUILD 16-million-word corpus of English. Figure 5.1 should not be considered a definitive list, since different dictionaries and tagsets label word classes differently. Furthermore, this list combines prepositions and particles.

Particle

A **particle** is a word that resembles a preposition or an adverb and is used in combination with a verb. Particles often have extended meanings that aren't quite the same as the prepositions they resemble:

He arose slowly and brushed himself *off*.
. . . she had turned the paper *over*.

Phrasal verb

When a verb and a particle behave as a single syntactic and/or semantic unit, we call the combination a **phrasal verb**. Phrasal verbs can behave as a semantic unit; thus, they often have a meaning that is not predictable from the separate meanings of the verb and the particle. Thus, *turn down* means something like 'reject', *rule out* means 'eliminate',

of	540,085	through	14,964	worth	1,563	pace	12
in	331,235	after	13,670	toward	1,390	nigh	9
for	142,421	between	13,275	plus	750	re	4
to	125,691	under	9,525	till	686	mid	3
with	124,965	per	6,515	amongst	525	o'er	2
on	109,129	among	5,090	via	351	but	0
at	100,169	within	5,030	amid	222	ere	0
by	77,794	towards	4,700	underneath	164	less	0
from	74,843	above	3,056	versus	113	midst	0
about	38,428	near	2,026	amidst	67	o'	0
than	20,210	off	1,695	sans	20	thru	0
over	18,071	past	1,575	circa	14	vice	0

Figure 5.1   Prepositions (and particles) of English from the CELEX online dictionary. Frequency counts are from the COBUILD 16-million-word corpus.

find out is 'discover', and *go on* is 'continue'; these are not meanings that could have been predicted from the meanings of the verb and the particle independently. Here are some examples of phrasal verbs from Thoreau:

So I *went on* for some days cutting and hewing timber. . .
Moral reform is the effort to *throw off* sleep. . .

We show in Fig. 5.2 a list of single-word particles from Quirk et al. (1985). Since it is extremely hard to automatically distinguish particles from prepositions, some tagsets (like the one used for CELEX) do not distinguish them, and even in corpora that do (like the Penn Treebank), the distinction is very difficult to make reliably in an automatic process, so we do not give counts.

aboard	aside	besides	forward(s)	opposite	through
about	astray	between	home	out	throughout
above	away	beyond	in	outside	together
across	back	by	inside	over	under
ahead	before	close	instead	overhead	underneath
alongside	behind	down	near	past	up
apart	below	east, etc.	off	round	within
around	beneath	eastward(s),etc.	on	since	without

Figure 5.2   English single-word particles from Quirk et al. (1985).

Determiner
Article
A closed class that occurs with nouns, often marking the beginning of a noun phrase, is the **determiners**. One small subtype of determiners is the **articles**: English has three articles: *a*, *an*, and *the*. Other determiners include *this* (as in *this chapter*) and *that* (as in *that page*). *A* and *an* mark a noun phrase as indefinite, while *the* can mark it as definite; definiteness is a discourse and semantic property that is discussed in Chapter 21. Articles are quite frequent in English; indeed, *the* is the most frequently occurring word in most corpora of written English. Here are COBUILD statistics, again out of 16 million words:

the: 1,071,676 a: 413,887 an: 59,359

Conjunctions
Conjunctions join two phrases, clauses, or sentences. Coordinating conjunctions like *and*, *or*, and *but*, join two elements of equal status. Subordinating conjunctions are

Complementizer

used when one of the elements is of some sort of embedded status. For example, *that* in *"I thought that you might like some milk"* is a subordinating conjunction that links the main clause *I thought* with the subordinate clause *you might like some milk*. This clause is called subordinate because this entire clause is the "content" of the main verb *thought*. Subordinating conjunctions like *that* which link a verb to its argument in this way are also called **complementizers**. Chapter 12 and Chapter 15 discuss complementation in more detail. Figure 5.3 lists English conjunctions.

and	514,946	yet	5,040	considering	174	forasmuch as	0
that	134,773	since	4,843	lest	131	however	0
but	96,889	where	3,952	albeit	104	immediately	0
or	76,563	nor	3,078	providing	96	in as far as	0
as	54,608	once	2,826	whereupon	85	in so far as	0
if	53,917	unless	2,205	seeing	63	inasmuch as	0
when	37,975	why	1,333	directly	26	insomuch as	0
because	23,626	now	1,290	ere	12	insomuch that	0
so	12,933	neither	1,120	notwithstanding	3	like	0
before	10,720	whenever	913	according as	0	neither nor	0
though	10,329	whereas	867	as if	0	now that	0
than	9,511	except	864	as long as	0	only	0
while	8,144	till	686	as though	0	provided that	0
after	7,042	provided	594	both and	0	providing that	0
whether	5,978	whilst	351	but that	0	seeing as	0
for	5,935	suppose	281	but then	0	seeing as how	0
although	5,424	cos	188	but then again	0	seeing that	0
until	5,072	supposing	185	either or	0	without	0

Figure 5.3   Coordinating and subordinating conjunctions of English from CELEX. Frequency counts are from COBUILD (16 million words).

Pronoun

Personal

Possessive

Wh

Pronouns are forms that often act as a kind of shorthand for referring to some noun phrase or entity or event. **Personal pronouns** refer to persons or entities (*you*, *she*, *I*, *it*, *me*, etc.). **Possessive pronouns** are forms of personal pronouns that indicate either actual possession or more often just an abstract relation between the person and some object (*my, your, his, her, its, one's, our, their*). **Wh-pronouns** (*what, who, whom, whoever*) are used in certain question forms, or may also act as complementizers (*Frida, who married Diego*...). Figure 5.4 shows English pronouns, again from CELEX.

Auxiliary

A closed class subtype of English verbs are the **auxiliary** verbs. Cross-linguistically, auxiliaries are words (usually verbs) that mark certain semantic features of a main verb, including whether an action takes place in the present, past, or future (tense), whether it is completed (aspect), whether it is negated (polarity), and whether an action is necessary, possible, suggested, desired, etc. (mood).

Copula

Modal

English auxiliaries include the **copula** verb *be*, the two verbs *do* and *have*, along with their inflected forms, as well as a class of **modal verbs**. *Be* is called a copula because it connects subjects with certain kinds of predicate nominals and adjectives (*He is a duck*). The verb *have* is used, for example, to mark the perfect tenses (*I have gone, I had gone*), and *be* is used as part of the passive (*We were robbed*) or progressive (*We are leaving*) constructions. The modals are used to mark the mood associated with the event or action depicted by the main verb. So *can* indicates ability or possibility, *may* indicates permission or possibility, *must* indicates necessity, and so on. In addition to the perfect *have* mentioned above, there is a modal verb *have* (e.g., *I have to go*), which is common in spoken English. Neither it nor the modal verb *dare*, which is

it	199,920	how	13,137	yourself	2,437	no one	106
I	198,139	another	12,551	why	2,220	wherein	58
he	158,366	where	11,857	little	2,089	double	39
you	128,688	same	11,841	none	1,992	thine	30
his	99,820	something	11,754	nobody	1,684	summat	22
they	88,416	each	11,320	further	1,666	suchlike	18
this	84,927	both	10,930	everybody	1,474	fewest	15
that	82,603	last	10,816	ourselves	1,428	thyself	14
she	73,966	every	9,788	mine	1,426	whomever	11
her	69,004	himself	9,113	somebody	1,322	whosoever	10
we	64,846	nothing	9,026	former	1,177	whomsoever	8
all	61,767	when	8,336	past	984	wherefore	6
which	61,399	one	7,423	plenty	940	whereat	5
their	51,922	much	7,237	either	848	whatsoever	4
what	50,116	anything	6,937	yours	826	whereon	2
my	46,791	next	6,047	neither	618	whoso	2
him	45,024	themselves	5,990	fewer	536	aught	1
me	43,071	most	5,115	hers	482	howsoever	1
who	42,881	itself	5,032	ours	458	thrice	1
them	42,099	myself	4,819	whoever	391	wheresoever	1
no	33,458	everything	4,662	least	386	you-all	1
some	32,863	several	4,306	twice	382	additional	0
other	29,391	less	4,278	theirs	303	anybody	0
your	28,923	herself	4,016	wherever	289	each other	0
its	27,783	whose	4,005	oneself	239	once	0
our	23,029	someone	3,755	thou	229	one another	0
these	22,697	certain	3,345	'un	227	overmuch	0
any	22,666	anyone	3,318	ye	192	such and such	0
more	21,873	whom	3,229	thy	191	whate'er	0
many	17,343	enough	3,197	whereby	176	whenever	0
such	16,880	half	3,065	thee	166	whereof	0
those	15,819	few	2,933	yourselves	148	whereto	0
own	15,741	everyone	2,812	latter	142	whereunto	0
us	15,724	whatever	2,571	whichever	121	whichsoever	0

Figure 5.4   Pronouns of English from the CELEX online dictionary. Frequency counts are from the COBUILD 16-million-word corpus.

can	70,930	might	5,580	shouldn't	858
will	69,206	couldn't	4,265	mustn't	332
may	25,802	shall	4,118	'll	175
would	18,448	wouldn't	3,548	needn't	148
should	17,760	won't	3,100	mightn't	68
must	16,520	'd	2,299	oughtn't	44
need	9,955	ought	1,845	mayn't	3
can't	6,375	will	862	dare, have	???

Figure 5.5   English modal verbs from the CELEX online dictionary. Frequency counts are from the COBUILD 16-million-word corpus.

rare, have frequency counts because the CELEX dictionary does not distinguish the main verb sense (*I have three oranges*, *He dared me to eat them*) from the modal sense (*There has to be some mistake*, *Dare I confront him?*), from the non-modal auxiliary verb sense (*I have never seen that*). Figure 5.5 lists English modal verbs.

English also has many words of more or less unique function, including **interjections** (*oh, ah, hey, man, alas, uh, um*), **negatives** (*no, not*), **politeness markers** (*please, thank you*), **greetings** (*hello, goodbye*), and the existential **there** (*there are two on the*

Interjection

Negative

131

table) among others. Whether these classes are assigned particular names or lumped together (as interjections or even adverbs) depends on the purpose of the labeling.

5.2   Tagsets for English

The previous section broadly described some syntactic classes for English words. This section fleshes out that sketch by describing the actual tagsets used in part-of-speech tagging, in preparation for introducing various tagging algorithms.

Most of the popular tagsets for English evolved from the 87-tag tagset used for the Brown corpus (Francis, 1979; Francis and Kučera, 1982). The Brown corpus is a million-word collection of samples from 500 written texts from different genres (newspaper, novels, non-fiction, academic, etc.), which was assembled at Brown University in 1963–1964 (Kučera and Francis, 1967; Francis, 1979; Francis and Kučera, 1982). This corpus was tagged with parts-of-speech first with the TAGGIT program and then by hand-correction of the tags.

Besides this original Brown tagset, shown in Figs. 5.7–5.8, two of the most commonly used tagsets are the small 45-tag Penn Treebank tagset (Marcus et al., 1993), shown in Fig. 5.6, and the medium-sized 61-tag C5 tagset, shown in Fig. 5.9, used by the Lancaster UCREL project's CLAWS (the Constituent Likelihood Automatic Word-tagging System) tagger to tag the British National Corpus (BNC) (Garside et al., 1997).

We focus our discussion on the widely used Penn Treebank set, shown in Fig. 5.6, which has been applied to the Brown corpus, the *Wall Street Journal* corpus, and the Switchboard corpus among others. We discuss difficult tagging decisions as well as some useful distinctions made in the larger tagsets. Here are some examples of tagged sentences from the Penn Treebank version of the Brown corpus (we represent a tagged word by placing the tag after each word, delimited by a slash):

(5.1) The/DT grand/JJ jury/NN commented/VBD on/IN a/DT number/NN of/IN other/JJ topics/NNS ./.

(5.2) **There/EX** are/VBP 70/CD children/NNS **there/RB**

(5.3) Although/IN preliminary/JJ findings/NNS were/VBD **reported/VBN** more/RBR than/IN a/DT year/NN ago/IN ,/, the/DT latest/JJS results/NNS appear/VBP in/IN today/NN **'s/POS** New/NNP England/NNP Journal/NNP of/IN Medicine/NNP ,/,

Example (5.1) shows phenomena that we discussed in the previous section; the determiners *the* and *a*, the adjectives *grand* and *other*, the common nouns *jury*, *number*, and *topics*, the past tense verb *commented*. Example (5.2) shows the use of the EX tag to mark the existential *there* construction in English, and, for comparison, another use of *there* which is tagged as an adverb (RB). Example (5.3) shows the segmentation of the possessive morpheme *'s* and shows an example of a passive construction, 'were reported', in which the verb *reported* is marked as a past participle (VBN), rather than a simple past (VBD). Note also that the proper noun *New England* is tagged NNP. Finally, note that since *New England Journal of Medicine* is a proper noun, the Tree-

Tag	Description	Example	Tag	Description	Example
CC	coordin. conjunction	*and, but, or*	SYM	symbol	*+,%, &*
CD	cardinal number	*one, two, three*	TO	"to"	*to*
DT	determiner	*a, the*	UH	interjection	*ah, oops*
EX	existential 'there'	*there*	VB	verb, base form	*eat*
FW	foreign word	*mea culpa*	VBD	verb, past tense	*ate*
IN	preposition/sub-conj	*of, in, by*	VBG	verb, gerund	*eating*
JJ	adjective	*yellow*	VBN	verb, past participle	*eaten*
JJR	adj., comparative	*bigger*	VBP	verb, non-3sg pres	*eat*
JJS	adj., superlative	*wildest*	VBZ	verb, 3sg pres	*eats*
LS	list item marker	*1, 2, One*	WDT	wh-determiner	*which, that*
MD	modal	*can, should*	WP	wh-pronoun	*what, who*
NN	noun, sing. or mass	*llama*	WP$	possessive wh-	*whose*
NNS	noun, plural	*llamas*	WRB	wh-adverb	*how, where*
NNP	proper noun, singular	*IBM*	$	dollar sign	*$*
NNPS	proper noun, plural	*Carolinas*	#	pound sign	*#*
PDT	predeterminer	*all, both*	"	left quote	*' or "*
POS	possessive ending	*'s*	"	right quote	*' or "*
PRP	personal pronoun	*I, you, he*	(	left parenthesis	*[, (, , <*
PRP$	possessive pronoun	*your, one's*	)	right parenthesis	*],), , >*
RB	adverb	*quickly, never*	,	comma	*,*
RBR	adverb, comparative	*faster*	.	sentence-final punc	*. ! ?*
RBS	adverb, superlative	*fastest*	:	mid-sentence punc	*: ; ... – -*
RP	particle	*up, off*			

Figure 5.6   Penn Treebank part-of-speech tags (including punctuation).

bank tagging chooses to mark each noun in it separately as NNP, including *journal* and *medicine*, which might otherwise be labeled as common nouns (NN).

Some tagging distinctions are quite hard for both humans and machines to make. For example, prepositions (IN), particles (RP), and adverbs (RB) can have a large overlap. Words like *around* can be all three:

(5.4)   Mrs./NNP Shaefer/NNP never/RB got/VBD **around/RP** to/TO joining/VBG

(5.5)   All/DT we/PRP gotta/VBN do/VB is/VBZ go/VB **around/IN** the/DT corner/NN

(5.6)   Chateau/NNP Petrus/NNP costs/VBZ **around/RB** 250/CD

Making these decisions requires sophisticated knowledge of syntax; tagging manuals (Santorini, 1990) give various heuristics that can help human coders make these decisions and that can also provide useful features for automatic taggers. For example, two heuristics from Santorini (1990) are that prepositions generally are associated with a following noun phrase (although they also may be followed by prepositional phrases) and that the word *around* is tagged as an adverb when it means "approximately". Furthermore, particles often can either precede or follow a noun phrase object, as in the following examples:

(5.7) She told off/RP her friends

(5.8) She told her friends off/RP.

Prepositions, on the other hand, cannot follow their noun phrase (* marks an ungrammatical sentence, a concept we return to in Chapter 12):

(5.9) She stepped off/IN the train

(5.10) *She stepped the train off/IN.

Another difficulty is labeling the words that can modify nouns. Sometimes the modifiers preceding nouns are common nouns like *cotton*, below; other times the Treebank tagging manual specifies that modifiers be tagged as adjectives (e.g., if the modifier is a hyphenated common noun like *income-tax*) and other times as proper nouns (for modifiers that are hyphenated proper nouns like *Gramm-Rudman*):

(5.11) cotton/NN sweater/NN

(5.12) income-tax/JJ return/NN

(5.13) the/DT Gramm-Rudman/NP Act/NP

Some words that can be adjectives, common nouns, or proper nouns are tagged in the Treebank as common nouns when acting as modifiers:

(5.14) Chinese/NN cooking/NN

(5.15) Pacific/NN waters/NNS

A third known difficulty in tagging is distinguishing past participles (VBN) from adjectives (JJ). A word like *married* is a past participle when it is being used in an eventive, verbal way, as in (5.16) below, and is an adjective when it is being used to express a property, as in (5.17):

(5.16) They were married/VBN by the Justice of the Peace yesterday at 5:00.

(5.17) At the time, she was already married/JJ.

Tagging manuals like Santorini (1990) give various helpful criteria for deciding how 'verb-like' or 'eventive' a particular word is in a specific context.

The Penn Treebank tagset was culled from the original 87-tag tagset for the Brown corpus. This reduced set leaves out information that can be recovered from the identity of the lexical item. For example the original Brown and C5 tagsets include a separate tag for each of the different forms of the verbs *do* (e.g., C5 tag VDD for *did* and VDG for *doing*), *be*, and *have*. These were omitted from the Treebank set.

Certain syntactic distinctions were not marked in the Penn Treebank tagset because Treebank sentences were parsed, not merely tagged, and so some syntactic information is represented in the phrase structure. For example, the single tag IN is used for both prepositions and subordinating conjunctions since the tree-structure of the sentence disambiguates them (subordinating conjunctions always precede clauses, prepositions precede noun phrases or prepositional phrases). Most tagging situations, however, do not involve parsed corpora; for this reason, the Penn Treebank set is not specific enough for many uses. The original Brown and C5 tagsets, for example, distinguish prepositions (IN) from subordinating conjunctions (CS), as in the following examples:

(5.18) **after/CS** spending/VBG a/AT day/NN at/IN the/AT Brown/NP Palace/NN

(5.19) **after/IN** a/AT wedding/NN trip/NN to/IN Corpus/NP Christi/NP ./.

The original Brown and C5 tagsets also have two tags for the word *to*; in Brown the infinitive use is tagged TO, and the prepositional use as IN:

(5.20) **to/TO** give/VB priority/NN **to/IN** teacher/NN pay/NN raises/NNS

Brown also has the tag NR for adverbial nouns like *home*, *west*, *Monday*, and *tomorrow*. Because the Treebank lacks this tag, it has a much less consistent policy for adverbial nouns; *Monday*, *Tuesday*, and other days of the week are marked NNP, *tomorrow*, *west*, and *home* are marked sometimes as NN, sometimes as RB. This makes the Treebank tagset less useful for high-level NLP tasks like the detection of time phrases.

Nonetheless, the Treebank tagset has been the most widely used in evaluating tagging algorithms, so many of the algorithms we describe below have been evaluated mainly on this tagset. Of course, whether a tagset is useful for a particular application depends on how much information the application needs.

5.3   Part-of-Speech Tagging

Tagging   Part-of-speech tagging (or just **tagging** for short) is the process of assigning a part of speech or other syntactic class marker to each word in a corpus. Because tags are generally also applied to punctuation, tagging requires that the punctuation marks (period, comma, etc) be separated from the words. Thus, **tokenization** of the sort described in Chapter 3 is usually performed before, or as part of, the tagging process, separating commas, quotation marks, etc., from words and disambiguating end-of-sentence punctuation (period, question mark, etc.) from part-of-word punctuation (such as in abbreviations like *e.g.* and *etc.*)

The input to a tagging algorithm is a string of words and a specified tagset of the kind described in the previous section. The output is a single best tag for each word. For example, here are some sample sentences from the ATIS corpus of dialogues about air-travel reservations that we discuss in Chapter 12. For each we have shown a potential tagged output using the Penn Treebank tagset defined in Fig. 5.6 on page 131:

(5.21) Book/VB that/DT flight/NN ./.

(5.22) Does/VBZ that/DT flight/NN serve/VB dinner/NN ?/.

Ambiguous   The previous section discussed some tagging decisions that are difficult to make for humans. Even in these simple examples, automatically assigning a tag to each word is not trivial. For example, *book* is **ambiguous**. That is, it has more than one possible usage and part-of-speech. It can be a verb (as in *book that flight* or *to book the suspect*) or a noun (as in *hand me that book* or *a book of matches*). Similarly, *that* can be a determiner (as in *Does that flight serve dinner*) or a complementizer (as in *I thought that your flight was earlier*). The problem of POS-tagging is to **resolve** these ambiguities, choosing the proper tag for the context. Part-of-speech tagging is thus one *Disambiguation* of the many **disambiguation** tasks we see in this book.

How hard is the tagging problem? The previous section described some difficult tagging decisions; how common is tag ambiguity? It turns out that most words in English are unambiguous; that is, they have only a single tag. But many of the most common words of English are ambiguous (for example, *can* can be an auxiliary ('to be able'), a noun ('a metal container'), or a verb ('to put something in such a metal container')). In fact, DeRose (1988) reports that while only 11.5% of English word types in the Brown corpus are ambiguous, over 40% of Brown tokens are ambiguous.

Tag	Description	Example
(	opening parenthesis	*(, [*
)	closing parenthesis	*),]*
*	negator	*not, n't*
,	comma	*,*
–	dash	*–*
.	sentence terminator	*. ; ? !*
:	colon	*:*
ABL	pre-qualifier	*quite, rather, such*
ABN	pre-quantifier	*half, all*
ABX	pre-quantifier, double conjunction	*both*
AP	post-determiner	*many, next, several, last*
AT	article	*a, the, an, no, a, every*
BE/BED/BEDZ/BEG/BEM/BEN/BER/BEZ		*be/were/was/being/am/been/are/is*
CC	coordinating conjunction	*and, or, but, either, neither*
CD	cardinal numeral	*two, 2, 1962, million*
CS	subordinating conjunction	*that, as, after, whether, before*
DO/DOD/DOZ		*do, did, does*
DT	singular determiner	*this, that*
DTI	singular or plural determiner	*some, any*
DTS	plural determiner	*these, those, them*
DTX	determiner, double conjunction	*either, neither*
EX	existential there	*there*
HV/HVD/HVG/HVN/HVZ		*have, had, having, had, has*
IN	preposition	*of, in, for, by, to, on, at*
JJ	adjective	
JJR	comparative adjective	*better, greater, higher, larger, lower*
JJS	semantically superlative adj.	*main, top, principal, chief, key, foremost*
JJT	morphologically superlative adj.	*best, greatest, highest, largest, latest, worst*
MD	modal auxiliary	*would, will, can, could, may, must, should*
NN	(common) singular or mass noun	*time, world, work, school, family, door*
NN$	possessive singular common noun	*father's, year's, city's, earth's*
NNS	plural common noun	*years, people, things, children, problems*
NNS$	possessive plural noun	*children's, artist's parent's years'*
NP	singular proper noun	*Kennedy, England, Rachel, Congress*
NP$	possessive singular proper noun	*Plato's Faulkner's Viola's*
NPS	plural proper noun	*Americans, Democrats, Chinese*
NPS$	possessive plural proper noun	*Yankees', Gershwins' Earthmen's*
NR	adverbial noun	*home, west, tomorrow, Friday, North*
NR$	possessive adverbial noun	*today's, yesterday's, Sunday's, South's*
NRS	plural adverbial noun	*Sundays, Fridays*
OD	ordinal numeral	*second, 2nd, twenty-first, mid-twentieth*
PN	nominal pronoun	*one, something, nothing, anyone, none*
PN$	possessive nominal pronoun	*one's, someone's, anyone's*
PP$	possessive personal pronoun	*his, their, her, its, my, our, your*
PP$$	second possessive personal pronoun	*mine, his, ours, yours, theirs*
PPL	singular reflexive personal pronoun	*myself, herself*
PPLS	plural reflexive pronoun	*ourselves, themselves*
PPO	objective personal pronoun	*me, us, him*
PPS	3rd. sg. nominative pronoun	*he, she, it*
PPSS	other nominative pronoun	*I, we, they*
QL	qualifier	*very, too, most, quite, almost, extremely*
QLP	post-qualifier	*enough, indeed*
RB	adverb	
RBR	comparative adverb	*later, more, better, longer, further*
RBT	superlative adverb	*best, most, highest, nearest*
RN	nominal adverb	*here, then*

Figure 5.7   First part of original 87-tag Brown corpus tagset (Francis and Kučera, 1982). Four special hyphenated tags are omitted from this list.

Tag	Description	Example
RP	adverb or particle	*across, off, up*
TO	infinitive marker	*to*
UH	interjection, exclamation	*well, oh, say, please, okay, uh, goodbye*
VB	verb, base form	*make, understand, try, determine, drop*
VBD	verb, past tense	*said, went, looked, brought, reached, kept*
VBG	verb, present participle, gerund	*getting, writing, increasing*
VBN	verb, past participle	*made, given, found, called, required*
VBZ	verb, 3rd singular present	*says, follows, requires, transcends*
WDT	wh- determiner	*what, which*
WP$	possessive wh- pronoun	*whose*
WPO	objective wh- pronoun	*whom, which, that*
WPS	nominative wh- pronoun	*who, which, that*
WQL	how	
WRB	wh- adverb	*how, when*

Figure 5.8   Rest of 87-tag Brown corpus tagset (Francis and Kučera, 1982).

Figure 5.10 shows the number of word types with different levels of part-of-speech ambiguity from the Brown corpus. We show these computations from two versions of the tagged Brown corpus, the original tagging done at Brown by Francis and Kučera (1982), and the Treebank-3 tagging done at the University of Pennsylvania. Note that despite having more coarse-grained tags, the 45-tag corpus unexpectedly has more ambiguity than the 87-tag corpus.

Luckily, it turns out that many of the 40% ambiguous tokens are easy to disambiguate. This is because the various tags associated with a word are not equally likely. For example, *a* can be a determiner or the letter *a* (perhaps as part of an acronym or an initial). But the determiner sense of *a* is much more likely.

Rule-based tagger   Most tagging algorithms fall into one of two classes: **rule-based taggers** and probabilistic or **stochastic taggers** taggers. Rule-based taggers generally involve a large database of hand-written disambiguation rules that specify, for example, that an ambiguous word is a noun rather than a verb if it follows a determiner. The next section describes a sample rule-based tagger, **EngCG**, based on the Constraint Grammar architecture of Karlsson et al. (1995).

HMM tagger   Stochastic taggers generally resolve tagging ambiguities by using a training corpus to compute the probability of a given word having a given tag in a given context. Section 5.5 describes the hidden Markov model, or **HMM tagger**.

Brill tagger   Finally, Section 5.6 describes an approach to tagging called the **transformation-based tagger**, or the **Brill tagger**, after Brill (1995). The Brill tagger shares features of both tagging architectures. Like the rule-based tagger, it is based on rules that determine when an ambiguous word should have a given tag. Like the stochastic taggers, it has a machine-learning component: the rules are automatically induced from a previously tagged training corpus.

5.4   Rule-Based Part-of-Speech Tagging

The earliest algorithms for automatically assigning part-of-speech were based on a two-stage architecture (Harris, 1962; Klein and Simmons, 1963; Greene and Rubin, 1971).

Tag	Description	Example
AJ0	adjective (unmarked)	*good, old*
AJC	comparative adjective	*better, older*
AJS	superlative adjective	*best, oldest*
AT0	article	*the, a, an*
AV0	adverb (unmarked)	*often, well, longer, furthest*
AVP	adverb particle	*up, off, out*
AVQ	wh-adverb	*when, how, why*
CJC	coordinating conjunction	*and, or*
CJS	subordinating conjunction	*although, when*
CJT	the conjunction *that*	
CRD	cardinal numeral (except *one*)	*3, twenty-five, 734*
DPS	possessive determiner	*your, their*
DT0	general determiner	*these, some*
DTQ	wh-determiner	*whose, which*
EX0	existential *there*	
ITJ	interjection or other isolate	*oh, yes, mhm*
NN0	noun (neutral for number)	*aircraft, data*
NN1	singular noun	*pencil, goose*
NN2	plural noun	*pencils, geese*
NP0	proper noun	*London, Michael, Mars*
ORD	ordinal	*sixth, 77th, last*
PNI	indefinite pronoun	*none, everything*
PNP	personal pronoun	*you, them, ours*
PNQ	wh-pronoun	*who, whoever*
PNX	reflexive pronoun	*itself, ourselves*
POS	possessive *'s* or *'*	
PRF	the preposition *of*	
PRP	preposition (except *of*)	*for, above, to*
PUL	punctuation – left bracket	*(or [*
PUN	punctuation – general mark	*. ! , : ; - ? ...*
PUQ	punctuation – quotation mark	*' ' "*
PUR	punctuation – right bracket	*) or]*
TO0	infinitive marker *to*	
UNC	unclassified items (not English)	
VBB	base forms of *be* (except infinitive)	*am, are*
VBD	past form of *be*	*was, were*
VBG	-ing form of *be*	*being*
VBI	infinitive of *be*	
VBN	past participle of *be*	*been*
VBZ	-s form of *be*	*is, 's*
VDB/D/G/I/N/Z form of *do*		*do, does, did, doing, to do*
VHB/D/G/I/N/Z form of *have*		*have, had, having, to have*
VM0	modal auxiliary verb	*can, could, will, 'll*
VVB	base form of lexical verb (except infin.)	*take, live*
VVD	past tense form of lexical verb	*took, lived*
VVG	-ing form of lexical verb	*taking, living*
VVI	infinitive of lexical verb	*take, live*
VVN	past participle form of lex. verb	*taken, lived*
VVZ	-s form of lexical verb	*takes, lives*
XX0	the negative *not* or *n't*	
ZZ0	alphabetical symbol	*A, B, c, d*

Figure 5.9   UCREL's C5 tagset for the British National Corpus (Garside et al., 1997).

The first stage used a dictionary to assign each word a list of potential parts-of-speech. The second stage used large lists of hand-written disambiguation rules to winnow down this list to a single part of speech for each word.

		87-tag Original Brown	45-tag Treebank Brown
Unambiguous (1 tag)		**44,019**	**38,857**
Ambiguous (2–7 tags)		**5,490**	**8844**
Details:	2 tags	4,967	6,731
	3 tags	411	1621
	4 tags	91	357
	5 tags	17	90
	6 tags	2 (*well, beat*)	32
	7 tags	2 (*still, down*)	6 (*well, set, round, open, fit, down*)
	8 tags		4 (*'s, half, back, a*)
	9 tags		3 (*that, more, in*)

Figure 5.10   The amount of tag ambiguity for word types in the Brown corpus, from the ICAME release of the original (87-tag) tagging and the Treebank-3 (45-tag) tagging. Numbers are not strictly comparable because only the Treebank segments *'s*. An earlier estimate of some of these numbers is reported in DeRose (1988).

Modern rule-based approaches to part-of-speech tagging have a similar architecture, although the dictionaries and the rulesets are vastly larger than in the 1960s. One of the most comprehensive rule-based approaches is the Constraint Grammar approach (Karlsson et al., 1995). In this section we describe a tagger based on this approach, the *EngCG* **EngCG** tagger (Voutilainen, 1995, 1999).

The EngCG ENGTWOL lexicon is based on the two-level morphology described in Chapter 3 and has about 56,000 entries for English word stems (Heikkilä, 1995), counting a word with multiple parts-of-speech (e.g., nominal and verbal senses of *hit*) as separate entries and not counting inflected and many derived forms. Each entry is annotated with a set of morphological and syntactic features. Figure 5.11 shows some selected words, together with a slightly simplified listing of their features, as used in rule writing.

Word	POS	Additional POS features
smaller	ADJ	COMPARATIVE
fast	ADV	SUPERLATIVE
that	DET	CENTRAL DEMONSTRATIVE SG
all	DET	PREDETERMINER SG/PL QUANTIFIER
dog's	N	GENITIVE SG
furniture	N	NOMINATIVE SG NOINDEFDETERMINER
one-third	NUM	SG
she	PRON	PERSONAL FEMININE NOMINATIVE SG3
show	V	PRESENT -SG3 VFIN
show	N	NOMINATIVE SG
shown	PCP2	SVOO SVO SV
occurred	PCP2	SV
occurred	V	PAST VFIN SV

Figure 5.11   Lexical entries in the ENGTWOL lexicon (Voutilainen, 1995; Heikkilä, 1995).

Most of the features in Fig. 5.11 are relatively self-explanatory; SG for singular, -SG3 for other than third-person singular. NOMINATIVE means non-genitive, and PCP2 means past participle. PRE, CENTRAL, and POST are ordering slots for determiners (predeterminers (*all*) come before determiners (*the*): *all the president's men*). NOINDEFDETERMINER means that words like *furniture* do not appear with the indefinite determiner *a*. SV, SVO, and SVOO specify the **subcategorization** or **complementation** pattern for the verb. Subcategorization is discussed in Chapter 12 and Chapter 15, but briefly SV means the verb appears solely with a subject (*nothing occurred*); SVO with a subject and an object (*I showed the film*); SVOO with a subject and two complements (*She showed her the ball*).

Subcategorization
Complementation

In the first stage of the tagger, each word is run through the two-level lexicon transducer and the entries for all possible parts-of-speech are returned. For example, the phrase *Pavlov had shown that salivation . . .* would return the following list (one line per possible tag, with the correct tag shown in boldface):

Pavlov	**PAVLOV N NOM SG PROPER**
had	**HAVE V PAST VFIN SVO**
	HAVE PCP2 SVO
shown	**SHOW PCP2 SVOO SVO SV**
that	ADV
	PRON DEM SG
	DET CENTRAL DEM SG
	CS
salivation	**N NOM SG**
. . .	

EngCG then applies a large set of constraints (as many as 3,744 constraints in the EngCG-2 system) to the input sentence to rule out incorrect parts-of-speech. The boldfaced entries in the table above show the desired result, in which the simple past tense tag (rather than the past participle tag) is applied to *had* and the complementizer (CS) tag is applied to *that*. The constraints are used in a negative way, to eliminate tags that are inconsistent with the context. For example, one constraint eliminates all readings of *that* except the ADV (adverbial intensifier) sense (this is the sense in the sentence *it isn't that odd*). Here's a simplified version of the constraint:

ADVERBIAL-THAT RULE
Given input: "that"
if
    (+1 A/ADV/QUANT); /* *if next word is adj, adverb, or quantifier* */
    (+2 SENT-LIM);   /* *and following which is a sentence boundary,* */
    (NOT -1 SVOC/A); /* *and the previous word is not a verb like* */
            /* *'consider' which allows adjs as object complements* */
then eliminate non-ADV tags
else eliminate ADV tag

The first two clauses of this rule check to see that the *that* directly precedes a sentence-final adjective, adverb, or quantifier. In all other cases, the adverb reading is eliminated. The last clause eliminates cases preceded by verbs like *consider* or *believe* that can take a noun and an adjective; this is to avoid tagging the following instance of *that* as an adverb:

    I consider that odd.

Another rule is used to express the constraint that the complementizer sense of *that* is most likely to be used if the previous word is a verb that expects a complement (like *believe*, *think*, or *show*), and if *that* is followed by the beginning of a noun phrase and a finite verb.

This description oversimplifies the EngCG architecture; the system also includes probabilistic constraints and also makes use of other syntactic information we haven't discussed. The interested reader should consult Karlsson et al. (1995) and Voutilainen (1999).

5.5   HMM Part-of-Speech Tagging

The use of probabilities in tags is quite old; probabilities in tagging were first used by Stolz et al. (1965), a complete probabilistic tagger with Viterbi decoding was sketched by Bahl and Mercer (1976), and various stochastic taggers were built in the 1980s (Marshall, 1983; Garside, 1987; Church, 1988; DeRose, 1988). This section describes a particular stochastic tagging algorithm generally known as the hidden Markov model or HMM tagger. Hidden Markov models themselves are more fully introduced and defined in Chapter 6. In this section, we prefigure Chapter 6 a bit by introducing the hidden Markov model as applied to part-of-speech tagging.

Bayesian
inference
Use of a hidden Markov model to do part-of-speech tagging, as we define it, is a special case of **Bayesian inference**, a paradigm that has been known since the work of Bayes (1763). Bayesian inference or Bayesian classification was applied successfully to language problems as early as the late 1950s, including the OCR work of Bledsoe in 1959 and the seminal work of Mosteller and Wallace (1964) on applying Bayesian inference to determine the authorship of the Federalist papers.

In a classification task, we are given some observation(s) and our job is to determine which of a set of classes it belongs to. Part-of-speech tagging is generally treated as a sequence classification task. So here the observation is a sequence of words (let's say a sentence), and it is our job to assign them a sequence of part-of-speech tags.

For example, say we are given a sentence like

(5.23) Secretariat is expected to **race** tomorrow.

What is the best sequence of tags that corresponds to this sequence of words? In Bayesian inference, we start by considering all possible sequences of classes—in this case, all possible sequences of tags. Out of this universe of tag sequences, we want to choose the tag sequence that is most probable given the observation sequence of n words w_1^n. In other words, we want, out of all sequences of n tags t_1^n the single tag sequence such that $P(t_1^n \ w_1^n)$ is highest. We use the hat notation ^ to mean "our estimate of the correct tag sequence".

$$\hat{t}_1^n = \operatorname*{argmax}_{t_1^n} P(t_1^n \ w_1^n) \qquad (5.24)$$

The function $\operatorname{argmax}_x f(x)$ means "the x such that $f(x)$ is maximized". Equation 5.24 thus means, that out of all tag sequences of length n, we want the particular tag sequence t_1^n that maximizes the right-hand side. While Eq. 5.24 is guaranteed to give us the optimal tag sequence, it is not clear how to make the equation operational; that is, for a given tag sequence t_1^n and word sequence w_1^n, we don't know how to directly compute $P(t_1^n\ w_1^n)$.

The intuition of Bayesian classification is to use Bayes' rule to transform Eq. 5.24 into a set of other probabilities, which turn out to be easier to compute. Bayes' rule is presented in Eq. 5.25; it gives us a way to break down any conditional probability $P(x\ y)$ into three other probabilities:

$$P(x\ y) = \frac{P(y\ x)P(x)}{P(y)} \tag{5.25}$$

We can then substitute Eq. 5.25 into Eq. 5.24 to get Eq. 5.26:

$$\hat{t}_1^n = \operatorname*{argmax}_{t_1^n} \frac{P(w_1^n\ t_1^n)P(t_1^n)}{P(w_1^n)} \tag{5.26}$$

We can conveniently simplify Eq. 5.26 by dropping the denominator $P(w_1^n)$. Why is that? Since we are choosing a tag sequence out of all tag sequences, we will be computing $\frac{P(w_1^n\ t_1^n)P(t_1^n)}{P(w_1^n)}$ for each tag sequence. But $P(w_1^n)$ doesn't change for each tag sequence; we are always asking about the most likely tag sequence for the same observation w_1^n, which must have the same probability $P(w_1^n)$. Thus, we can choose the tag sequence that maximizes this simpler formula:

$$\hat{t}_1^n = \operatorname*{argmax}_{t_1^n} P(w_1^n\ t_1^n)P(t_1^n) \tag{5.27}$$

To summarize, we compute the most probable tag sequence $\hat{t}_1^n$ given some word string w_1^n by multiplying two probabilities for each tag sequence and choosing the tag *Prior probability* sequence for which this product is greatest. The two terms are the **prior probability** *Likelihood* of the tag sequence $P(t_1^n)$ and the **likelihood** of the word string $P(w_1^n\ t_1^n)$:

$$\hat{t}_1^n = \operatorname*{argmax}_{t_1^n} \overbrace{P(w_1^n\ t_1^n)}^{\text{likelihood}}\ \overbrace{P(t_1^n)}^{\text{prior}} \tag{5.28}$$

Unfortunately, Eq. 5.28 is still too hard to compute directly. HMM taggers therefore make two simplifying assumptions. The first assumption is that the probability of a word appearing depends only on its own part-of-speech tag; that is, it is independent of other words around it and of the other tags around it:

$$P(w_1^n\ t_1^n) \approx \prod_{i=1}^{n} P(w_i\ t_i) \tag{5.29}$$

The second assumption is that the probability of a tag appearing is dependent only on the previous tag, rather than the entire tag sequence. This is the **bigram** assumption that we saw in Chapter 4:

$$P(t_1^n) \approx \prod_{i=1}^{n} P(t_i t_{i-1})$$ (5.30)

Plugging the simplifying assumptions Eq. 5.29 and Eq. 5.30 into Eq. 5.28 results in the following equation by which a bigram tagger estimates the most probable tag sequence:

$$\hat{t}_1^n = \operatorname*{argmax}_{t_1^n} P(t_1^n w_1^n) \approx \operatorname*{argmax}_{t_1^n} \prod_{i=1}^{n} P(w_i t_i) P(t_i t_{i-1})$$ (5.31)

Equation 5.31 contains two kinds of probabilities, tag transition probabilities and word likelihoods. Let's take a moment to see what these probabilities represent. The tag transition probabilities, $P(t_i t_{i-1})$, represent the probability of a tag given the previous tag. For example, determiners are very likely to precede adjectives and nouns, as in sequences like *that/DT flight/NN* and *the/DT yellow/JJ hat/NN*. Thus we would expect the probabilities $P(NN DT)$ and $P(JJ DT)$ to be high. But in English, adjectives don't tend to precede determiners, so the probability $P(DT JJ)$ ought to be low.

We can compute the maximum likelihood estimate of a tag transition probability $P(NN DT)$ by taking a corpus in which parts-of-speech are labeled and then counting, out of the times we see DT, how many of those times we see NN after the DT. That is, we compute the following ratio of counts:

$$P(t_i t_{i-1}) = \frac{C(t_{i-1}, t_i)}{C(t_{i-1})}$$ (5.32)

Let's choose a specific corpus to examine. For the examples in this chapter we'll use the Brown corpus, the million-word corpus of American English described earlier. The Brown corpus has been tagged twice, once in the 1960s with the 87-tag tagset, and again in the 1990s with the 45-tag Treebank tagset. This makes it useful for comparing tagsets, and is also widely available.

In the 45-tag Treebank Brown corpus, the tag DT occurs 116,454 times. Of these, DT is followed by NN 56,509 times (if we ignore the few cases of ambiguous tags). Thus, the MLE estimate of the transition probability is calculated as follows:

$$P(NN DT) = \frac{C(DT, NN)}{C(DT)} = \frac{56,509}{116,454} = .49$$ (5.33)

The probability of getting a common noun after a determiner, .49, is indeed quite high, as we suspected.

The word likelihood probabilities, $P(w_i t_i)$, represent the probability, given that we see a given tag, that it will be associated with a given word. For example, if we were to see the tag VBZ (third-person singular present verb) and guess the verb that is likely to have that tag, we might likely guess the verb *is* since the verb *to be* is so common in English.

We can compute the MLE of a word likelihood probability like $P(is VBZ)$ again by counting, out of the times we see VBZ in a corpus, how many of those times the VBZ is labeling the word *is*. That is, we compute the following ratio of counts:

$$P(w_i \, t_i) = \frac{C(t_i, w_i)}{C(t_i)} \tag{5.34}$$

In Treebank Brown corpus, the tag VBZ occurs 21,627 times, and VBZ is the tag for *is* 10,073 times. Thus:

$$P(is \, VBZ) = \frac{C(VBZ, is)}{C(VBZ)} = \frac{10,073}{21,627} = .47 \tag{5.35}$$

For those readers who are new to Bayesian modeling, note that this likelihood term is not asking "which is the most likely tag for the word *is*?" That is, the term is not $P(\text{VBZ is})$. Instead, we are computing $P(\text{is VBZ})$. The probability, slightly counterintuitively, answers the question "If we were expecting a third-person singular verb, how likely is it that this verb would be *is*?"

We have now defined HMM tagging as a task of choosing a tag-sequence with the maximum probability, derived the equations by which we will compute this probability, and shown how to compute the component probabilities. In fact, we have simplified the presentation of the probabilities in many ways; in later sections we return to these equations and introduce the deleted interpolation algorithm for smoothing these counts, the trigram model of tag history, and a model for unknown words.

But before turning to these augmentations, we need to introduce the decoding algorithm by which these probabilities are combined to choose the most likely tag sequence.

5.5.1   Computing the Most Likely Tag Sequence: An Example

The previous section showed that the HMM tagging algorithm chooses as the most likely tag sequence the one that maximizes the product of two terms: the probability of the sequence of tags and the probability of each tag generating a word. In this section we ground these equations in a specific example, showing for a particular sentence how the correct tag sequence achieves a higher probability than one of the many possible wrong sequences.

We focus on resolving the part-of-speech ambiguity of the word *race*, which can be a noun or verb in English, as we show in two examples modified from the Brown and Switchboard corpus. For this example, we will use the 87-tag Brown corpus tagset because it has a specific tag for *to*, TO, used only when *to* is an infinitive; prepositional uses of *to* are tagged as IN. This will come in handy in our example.[1]

In (5.36) *race* is a verb (VB) while in (5.37) *race* is a common noun (NN):

(5.36)   Secretariat/NNP is/BEZ expected/VBN to/TO **race**/VB tomorrow/NR

(5.37)   People/NNS continue/VB to/TO inquire/VB the/AT reason/NN for/IN the/AT **race**/NN for/IN outer/JJ space/NN

Let's look at how *race* can be correctly tagged as a VB instead of an NN in (5.36). HMM part-of-speech taggers resolve this ambiguity globally rather than locally, pick-

---

[1] The 45-tag Treebank-3 tagset does make this distinction in the Switchboard corpus but not, alas, in the Brown corpus. Recall that in the 45-tag tagset time adverbs like *tomorrow* are tagged as NN; in the 87-tag tagset they appear as NR.

ing the best tag sequence for the whole sentence. There are many hypothetically possible tag sequences for (5.36) since there are other ambiguities in the sentence (e.g., *expected* can be an adjective (JJ), a past tense/preterite (VBD), or a past participle (VBN)). But let's just consider two of the potential sequences, shown in Fig. 5.12. Note that these sequences differ in only one place: whether the tag chosen for *race* is VB or NN.

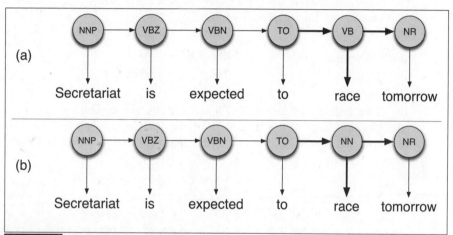

Figure 5.12   Two of the possible sequences of tags corresponding to the Secretariat sentence, one of them corresponding to the correct sequence, in which *race* is a VB. Each arc in these graphs would be associated with a probability. Note that the two graphs differ only in three arcs, hence in three probabilities.

Almost all the probabilities in these two sequences are identical; in Fig. 5.12 we have highlighted in boldface the three probabilities that differ. Let's consider two of these, corresponding to $P(t_i \, t_{i-1})$ and $P(w_i \, t_i)$. The probability $P(t_i \, t_{i-1})$ in Fig. 5.12a is $P(\text{VB TO})$, and in Fig. 5.12b the transition probability is $P(\text{NN TO})$.

The tag transition probabilities $P(\text{NN TO})$ and $P(\text{VB TO})$ give us the answer to the question "How likely are we to expect a verb (noun) given the previous tag?" As we saw in the previous section, the maximum likelihood estimate for these probabilities can be derived from corpus counts.

Since the (87-tag Brown tagset) tag TO is used only for the infinitive marker *to*, we expect that only a very small number of nouns can follow this marker (as an exercise, try to think of a sentence where a noun can follow the infinitive marker use of *to*). Sure enough, a look at the (87-tag) Brown corpus gives us the following probabilities, showing that verbs are about 500 times as likely as nouns to occur after TO:

$$P(\text{NN TO}) \;=\; .00047$$
$$P(\text{VB TO}) \;=\; .83$$

Let's now turn to $P(w_i \, t_i)$, the lexical likelihood of the word *race* given a part-of-speech tag. For the two possible tags VB and NN, these correspond to the probabilities

P(race VB) and P(race NN). Here are the lexical likelihoods from Brown:

$$P(\text{race NN}) = .00057$$
$$P(\text{race VB}) = .00012$$

Finally, we need to represent the tag sequence probability for the following tag (in this case the tag NR for *tomorrow*):

$$P(\text{NR VB}) = .0027$$
$$P(\text{NR NN}) = .0012$$

If we multiply the lexical likelihoods with the tag sequence probabilities, we see that the probability of the sequence with the VB tag is higher and the HMM tagger correctly tags *race* as a VB in Fig. 5.12 despite the fact that it is the less likely sense of *race*:

$$P(\text{VB TO})P(\text{NR VB})P(\text{race VB}) = .00000027$$
$$P(\text{NN TO})P(\text{NR NN})P(\text{race NN}) = .00000000032$$

5.5.2   Formalizing Hidden Markov Model Taggers

Now that we have seen the equations and some examples of choosing the most probable tag sequence, we show a brief formalization of this problem as a hidden Markov model (see Chapter 6 for the more complete formalization).

Weighted

The HMM is an extension of the finite automata of Chapter 3. Recall that a finite automaton is defined by a set of states and a set of transitions between states that are taken according to the input observations. A **weighted finite-state automaton** is a simple augmentation of the finite automaton in which each arc is associated with a probability, indicating how likely that path is to be taken. The probability on all the

Markov chain

arcs leaving a node must sum to 1. A **Markov chain** is a special case of a weighted automaton in which the input sequence uniquely determines which states the automaton will go through. Because it can't represent inherently ambiguous problems, a Markov chain is only useful for assigning probabilities to unambiguous sequences.

While the Markov chain is appropriate for situations in which we can see the actual conditioning events, it is not appropriate in part-of-speech tagging. This is because in part-of-speech tagging, while we observe the words in the input, we do *not* observe the part-of-speech tags. Thus, we can't condition any probabilities on, say, a previous part-of-speech tag, because we cannot be completely certain exactly which tag applied

Hidden Markov model

to the previous word. A **hidden Markov model** (HMM) allows us to talk both about *observed* events (like words that we see in the input) and about *hidden* events (like part-of-speech tags) that we think of as causal factors in our probabilistic model.

HMM

An **HMM** is specified by the following components:

$Q = q_1 q_2 \dots q_N$	a set of N **states**.
$A = a_{11} a_{12} \dots a_{n1} \dots a_{nn}$	a **transition probability matrix** A, each a_{ij} representing the probability of moving from state i to state j, s.t. $\sum_{j=1}^{n} a_{ij} = 1 \quad \forall i$.
$O = o_1 o_2 \dots o_T$	a sequence of T **observations**, each one drawn from a vocabulary $V = v_1, v_2, \dots, v_V$.
$B = b_i(o_t)$	A sequence of **observation likelihoods**, also called **emission probabilities**, each expressing the probability of an observation o_t being generated from a state i.
q_0, q_F	a special **start state** and **end (final) state** that are not associated with observations, together with transition probabilities $a_{01} a_{02} \dots a_{0n}$ out of the start state and $a_{1F} a_{2F} \dots a_{nF}$ into the end state.

An HMM thus has two kinds of probabilities: the A transition probabilities, and the B observation likelihoods, corresponding respectively to the **prior** and **likelihood** probabilities that we saw in Eq. 5.31. Figure 5.13 illustrates the prior probabilities in an HMM part-of-speech tagger, showing three sample states and some of the A transition probabilities between them. Figure 5.14 shows another view of an HMM part-of-speech tagger, focusing on the word likelihoods B. Each hidden state is associated with a vector of likelihoods for each observation word.

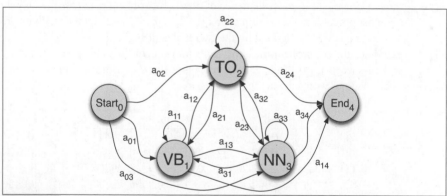

Figure 5.13   The Markov chain corresponding to the hidden states of the HMM. The A transition probabilities are used to compute the prior probability.

5.5.3   Using the Viterbi Algorithm for HMM Tagging

Decoding

Viterbi

For any model, such as an HMM, that contains hidden variables, the task of determining which sequence of variables is the underlying source of some sequence of observations is called the **decoding** task. The **Viterbi** algorithm is perhaps the most common decoding algorithm used for HMMs, whether for part-of-speech tagging or for speech recognition. The term **Viterbi** is common in speech and language processing, but this

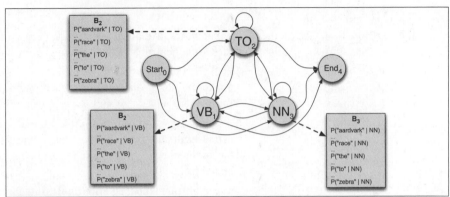

Figure 5.14   The B observation likelihoods for the HMM in the previous figure. Each state (except the non-emitting start and end states) is associated with a vector of probabilities, one likelihood for each possible observation word.

is really a standard application of the classic **dynamic programming** algorithm and looks a lot like the **minimum edit distance** algorithm of Chapter 3. The Viterbi algorithm was first applied to speech and language processing in the context of speech recognition by Vintsyuk (1968) but has what Kruskal (1983) calls a "remarkable history of multiple independent discovery and publication"; see the Historical Notes section at the end of Chapter 6 for more details.

The slightly simplified version of the Viterbi algorithm that we present takes as input a single HMM and a sequence of observed words $O = (o_1 o_2 o_3 \ldots o_T)$ and returns the most probable state/tag sequence $Q = (q_1 q_2 q_3 \ldots q_T)$, together with its probability.

Let the HMM be defined by the two tables in Fig. 5.15 and Fig. 5.16. Figure 5.15 expresses the a_{ij} probabilities, the *transition* probabilities between hidden states (i.e., part-of-speech tags). Figure 5.16 expresses the $b_i(o_t)$ probabilities, the *observation* likelihoods of words given tags.

	VB	TO	NN	PPSS
\<s\>	.019	.0043	.041	.067
VB	.0038	.035	.047	.0070
TO	.83	0	.00047	0
NN	.0040	.016	.087	.0045
PPSS	.23	.00079	.0012	.00014

Figure 5.15   Tag transition probabilities (the a array, $p(t_i \, t_{i-1})$) computed from the 87-tag Brown corpus without smoothing. The rows are labeled with the conditioning event; thus $P(PPSS \, VB)$ is .0070. The symbol \<s\> is the start-of-sentence symbol.

Figure 5.17 shows pseudocode for the Viterbi algorithm. The Viterbi algorithm sets up a probability matrix, with one column for each observation t and one row for each state in the state graph. Each column thus has a cell for each state q_i in the single combined automaton for the four words.

The algorithm first creates N or four state columns. The first column corresponds to the observation of the first word i, the second to the second word *want*, the third to

	I	want	to	race
VB	0	.0093	0	.00012
TO	0	0	.99	0
NN	0	.000054	0	.00057
PPSS	.37	0	0	0

Figure 5.16 Observation likelihoods (the *b* array) computed from the 87-tag Brown corpus without smoothing.

---

function VITERBI(*observations* of len *T*,*state-graph* of len *N*) **returns** *best-path*

create a path probability matrix *viterbi[N+2,T]*
for each state *s* **from** 1 **to** *N* **do**   ; initialization step
    $viterbi[s,1] \leftarrow a_{0,s} * b_s(o_1)$
    $backpointer[s,1] \leftarrow 0$
for each time step *t* **from** 2 **to** *T* **do**   ; recursion step
  for each state *s* **from** 1 **to** *N* **do**
    $viterbi[s,t] \leftarrow \max_{s'=1}^{N} viterbi[s',t-1] * a_{s',s} * b_s(o_t)$
    $backpointer[s,t] \leftarrow \operatorname{argmax}_{s'=1}^{N} viterbi[s',t-1] * a_{s',s}$
$viterbi[q_F,T] \leftarrow \max_{s=1}^{N} viterbi[s,T] * a_{s,q_F}$; termination step
$backpointer[q_F,T] \leftarrow \operatorname{argmax}_{s=1}^{N} viterbi[s,T] * a_{s,q_F}$; termination step
return the backtrace path by following backpointers to states back in time from $backpointer[q_F,T]$

Figure 5.17 Viterbi algorithm for finding optimal sequence of tags. Given an observation sequence and an HMM $\lambda = (A,B)$, the algorithm returns the state path through the HMM that assigns maximum likelihood to the observation sequence. Note that states 0 and q_F are non-emitting.

---

the third word *to*, and the fourth to the fourth word *race*. We begin in the first column by setting the Viterbi value in each cell to the product of the transition probability (into it from the start state) and the observation probability (of the first word); the reader should find this in Fig. 5.18.

Then we move on, column by column; for every state in column 1, we compute the probability of moving into each state in column 2, and so on. For each state q_j at time *t*, we compute the value $viterbi[s,t]$ by taking the maximum over the extensions of all the paths that lead to the current cell, using the following equation:

$$v_t(j) = \max_{i=1}^{N} v_{t-1}(i) \, a_{ij} \, b_j(o_t) \tag{5.38}$$

The three factors that are multiplied in Eq. 5.38 for extending the previous paths to compute the Viterbi probability at time *t* are

$v_{t-1}(i)$ the **previous Viterbi path probability** from the previous time step
a_{ij} the **transition probability** from previous state q_i to current state q_j
$b_j(o_t)$ the **state observation likelihood** of the observation symbol o_t given the current state j

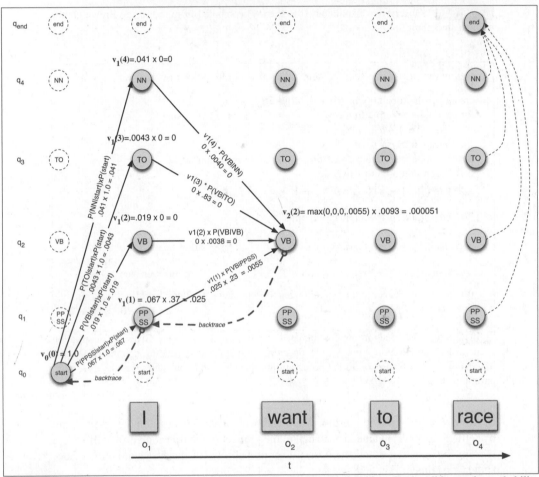

Figure 5.18   The entries in the individual state columns for the Viterbi algorithm. Each cell keeps the probability of the best path so far and a pointer to the previous cell along that path. We have only filled out columns 0 and 1 and one cell of column 2; the rest is left as an exercise for the reader. After the cells are filled in, backtracing from the *end* state, we should be able to reconstruct the correct state sequence PPSS VB TO VB.

In Fig. 5.18, each cell of the trellis in the column for the word *I* is computed by multiplying the previous probability at the start state (1.0), the transition probability from the start state to the tag for that cell, and the observation likelihood of the word *I* given the tag for that cell. As it turns out, three of the cells are zero (since the word *I* cannot be NN, TO, or VB). Next, each cell in the *want* column gets updated with the maximum probability path from the previous column. We have shown only the value for the VB cell. That cell gets the max of four values; as it happens in this case, three

150

of them are zero (since there were zero values in the previous column). The remaining value is multiplied by the relevant transition probability, and the (trivial) max is taken. In this case the final value, .000051, comes from the PPSS state at the previous column.

The reader should fill in the rest of the trellis in Fig. 5.18 and backtrace to reconstruct the correct state sequence PPSS VB TO VB.

5.5.4   Extending the HMM Algorithm to Trigrams

We mentioned earlier that HMM taggers in actual use have a number of sophistications not present in the simplified tagger as we have described it so far. One important missing feature has to do with the tag context. In the tagger described above, we assume that the probability of a tag appearing is dependent only on the previous tag:

$$P(t_1^n) \approx \prod_{i=1}^{n} P(t_i \, t_{i-1}) \tag{5.39}$$

Most modern HMM taggers actually use a little more of the history, letting the probability of a tag depend on the two previous tags:

$$P(t_1^n) \approx \prod_{i=1}^{n} P(t_i \, t_{i-1}, t_{i-2}) \tag{5.40}$$

In addition to increasing the window before a tagging decision, state-of-the-art HMM taggers like Brants (2000) let the tagger know the location of the end of the sentence by adding dependence on an end-of-sequence marker for t_{n+1}. This gives the following equation for part-of-speech tagging:

$$\hat{t}_1^n = \operatorname*{argmax}_{t_1^n} P(t_1^n \, w_1^n) \approx \operatorname*{argmax}_{t_1^n} \left[\prod_{i=1}^{n} P(w_i \, t_i) P(t_i \, t_{i-1}, t_{i-2}) \right] P(t_{n+1} \, t_n) \tag{5.41}$$

In tagging any sentence with Eq. 5.41, three of the tags used in the context will fall off the edge of the sentence, and hence will not match regular words. These tags, t_{-1}, t_0, and t_{n+1}, can all be set to be a single special 'sentence boundary' tag that is added to the tagset. This requires that sentences passed to the tagger have sentence boundaries demarcated, as discussed in Chapter 3.

There is one large problem with Eq. 5.41: data sparsity. Any particular sequence of tags t_{i-2}, t_{i-1}, t_i that occurs in the test set may simply never have occurred in the training set. That means we cannot compute the tag trigram probability just by the maximum likelihood estimate from counts, following Eq. 5.42:

$$P(t_i \, t_{i-1}, t_{i-2}) = \frac{C(t_{i-2}, t_{i-1}, t_i)}{C(t_{i-2}, t_{i-1})} \tag{5.42}$$

Why not? Because many of these counts will be zero in any training set, and we will incorrectly predict that a given tag sequence will never occur! What we need is a way to estimate $P(t_i \, t_{i-1}, t_{i-2})$ even if the sequence t_{i-2}, t_{i-1}, t_i never occurs in the training data.

The standard approach to solving this problem is to estimate the probability by combining more robust, but weaker estimators. For example, if we've never seen the tag sequence PRP VB TO, and so can't compute $P(\text{TO PRP,VB})$ from this frequency, we still could rely on the bigram probability $P(\text{TO VB})$, or even the unigram probability $P(\text{TO})$. The maximum likelihood estimation of each of these probabilities can be computed from a corpus with the following counts:

$$\text{Trigrams} \quad \hat{P}(t_i \, t_{i-1}, t_{i-2}) \;=\; \frac{C(t_{i-2}, t_{i-1}, t_i)}{C(t_{i-2}, t_{i-1})} \tag{5.43}$$

$$\text{Bigrams} \quad \hat{P}(t_i \, t_{i-1}) \;=\; \frac{C(t_{i-1}, t_i)}{C(t_{i-1})} \tag{5.44}$$

$$\text{Unigrams} \quad \hat{P}(t_i) \;=\; \frac{C(t_i)}{N} \tag{5.45}$$

How should these three estimators be combined in order to estimate the trigram probability $P(t_i \, t_{i-1}, t_{i-2})$? The simplest method of combination is linear interpolation. In linear interpolation, we estimate the probability $P(t_i \, t_{i-1} t_{i-2})$ by a weighted sum of the unigram, bigram, and trigram probabilities:

$$P(t_i \, t_{i-1} t_{i-2}) \;=\; \lambda_3 \hat{P}(t_i \, t_{i-1} t_{i-2}) + \lambda_2 \hat{P}(t_i \, t_{i-1}) + \lambda_1 \hat{P}(t_i) \tag{5.46}$$

Deleted interpolation

We require $\lambda_1 + \lambda_2 + \lambda_3 = 1$, ensuring that the resulting P is a probability distribution. How should these λs be set? One good way is **deleted interpolation**, developed by Jelinek and Mercer (1980). In deleted interpolation, we successively delete each trigram from the training corpus and choose the λs so as to maximize the likelihood of the rest of the corpus. The idea of the deletion is to set the λs in such a way as to generalize to unseen data and not overfit the training corpus. Figure 5.19 gives the Brants (2000) version of the deleted interpolation algorithm for tag trigrams.

Brants (2000) achieves an accuracy of 96.7% on the Penn Treebank with a trigram HMM tagger. Weischedel et al. (1993) and DeRose (1988) have also reported accuracies of above 96% for HMM tagging. Thede and Harper (1999) offer a number of augmentations of the trigram HMM model, including the idea of conditioning word likelihoods on neighboring words and tags.

The HMM taggers we have seen so far are trained on hand-tagged data. Kupiec (1992), Cutting et al. (1992a), and others show that it is also possible to train an HMM tagger on unlabeled data, using the EM algorithm that we introduce in Chapter 6. These taggers still start with a dictionary that lists which tags can be assigned to which words; the EM algorithm then learns the word likelihood function for each tag and the tag transition probabilities. An experiment by Merialdo (1994), however, indicates that with even a small amount of training data, a tagger trained on hand-tagged data worked better than one trained by EM. Thus, the EM-trained "pure HMM" tagger is probably best suited to cases for which no training data is available, for example, when tagging languages for which no data was previously hand-tagged.

---

function DELETED-INTERPOLATION(*corpus*) **returns** $\lambda_1, \lambda_2, \lambda_3$

$\quad \lambda_1 \leftarrow 0$
$\quad \lambda_2 \leftarrow 0$
$\quad \lambda_3 \leftarrow 0$
$\quad$ **foreach** trigram t_1, t_2, t_3 with $f(t_1, t_2, t_3) > 0$
$\quad\quad$ **depending** on the maximum of the following three values
$\quad\quad\quad$ **case** $\frac{C(t_1, t_2, t_3) - 1}{C(t_1, t_2) - 1}$: increment λ_3 by $C(t_1, t_2, t_3)$
$\quad\quad\quad$ **case** $\frac{C(t_2, t_3) - 1}{C(t_2) - 1}$: increment λ_2 by $C(t_1, t_2, t_3)$
$\quad\quad\quad$ **case** $\frac{C(t_3) - 1}{N - 1}$: increment λ_1 by $C(t_1, t_2, t_3)$
$\quad\quad$ **end**
$\quad$ **end**
$\quad$ normalize $\lambda_1, \lambda_2, \lambda_3$
$\quad$ **return** $\lambda_1, \lambda_2, \lambda_3$

Figure 5.19   The deleted interpolation algorithm for setting the weights for combining unigram, bigram, and trigram tag probabilities. If the denominator is 0 for any case, we define the result of that case to be 0. N is the total number of tokens in the corpus. After Brants (2000).

5.6   Transformation-Based Tagging

Transformation-based learning

Transformation-Based tagging, sometimes called Brill tagging, is an instance of the **transformation-based learning** (TBL) approach to machine learning (Brill, 1995). It draws inspiration from both the rule-based and stochastic taggers. Like the rule-based taggers, TBL is based on rules that specify what tags should be assigned to what words. But like the stochastic taggers, TBL is a machine learning technique, in which rules are automatically induced from the data. Like some but not all of the HMM taggers, TBL is a supervised learning technique; it assumes a pre-tagged training corpus.

Samuel et al. (1998) offer a useful analogy for understanding the TBL paradigm which they credit to Terry Harvey. Imagine an artist painting a picture of a white house with green trim against a blue sky. Suppose most of the picture was sky and hence most of the picture was blue. The artist might begin by using a very broad brush and painting the entire canvas blue. Next she might switch to a somewhat smaller white brush and paint the entire house white. She would just color in the whole house, not worrying about the brown roof or the blue windows or the green gables. Next she takes a smaller brown brush and colors over the roof. Now she takes up the blue paint on a small brush and paints in the blue windows on the house. Finally, she takes a very fine green brush and does the trim on the gables.

The painter starts with a broad brush that covers a lot of the canvas but colors a lot of areas that will have to be repainted. The next layer colors less of the canvas but also makes fewer "mistakes". Each new layer uses a finer brush that corrects less of the picture but makes fewer mistakes. TBL uses somewhat the same method as this painter. The TBL algorithm has a set of tagging rules. A corpus is first tagged according to the broadest rule, that is, the one that applies to the most cases. Then a slightly more specific rule is chosen, which changes some of the original tags. Next an even narrower rule changes a smaller number of tags (some of which might be previously changed tags).

5.6.1   How TBL Rules Are Applied

Let's look at one of the rules used by Brill's (1995) tagger. Before the rules apply, the tagger labels every word with its most likely tag. We get these most likely tags from a tagged corpus. For example, in the Brown corpus, *race* is most likely to be a noun:

$$P(\text{NN race}) = .98$$
$$P(\text{VB race}) = .02$$

This means that the two examples of *race* that we saw above will both be coded as NN. In the first case, this is a mistake since NN is the incorrect tag:

(5.47) is/VBZ expected/VBN to/TO race/**NN** tomorrow/NN

In the second case this *race* is correctly tagged as an NN:

(5.48) the/DT race/**NN** for/IN outer/JJ space/NN

After selecting the most likely tag, Brill's tagger applies its transformation rules. As it happens, Brill's tagger learned a rule that applies exactly to this mistagging of *race*:

> *Change* NN *to* VB *when the previous tag is* TO

This rule would change *race/NN* to *race/VB* in exactly the following situation since it is preceded by *to/TO*:

(5.49) expected/VBN to/TO race/NN → expected/VBN to/TO race/VB

5.6.2   How TBL Rules Are Learned

Brill's TBL algorithm has three major stages. It first labels every word with its most likely tag. It then examines every possible transformation and selects the one that results in the most improved tagging. Finally, it then re-tags the data according to this rule. TBL repeats the last two stages until it reaches some stopping criterion, such as insufficient improvement over the previous pass. Note that stage two requires that TBL knows the correct tag of each word; that is, TBL is a supervised learning algorithm.

Template   The output of the TBL process is an ordered list of transformations; these then constitute a "tagging procedure" that can be applied to a new corpus. In principle, the set of possible transformations is infinite since we could imagine transformations such as "transform NN to VB if the previous word was 'IBM' and the word "the" occurs between 17 and 158 words before that". But TBL needs to consider every possible transformation in order to pick the best one on each pass through the algorithm. Thus the algorithm needs a way to limit the set of transformations. This is done by a small set of **templates** (abstracted transformations). Every allowable transformation is an instantiation of one of the templates. Brill's set of templates is listed in Fig. 5.20. Figure 5.21 gives the details of this algorithm for learning transformations.

> The preceding (following) word is tagged **z**.
> The word two before (after) is tagged **z**.
> One of the two preceding (following) words is tagged **z**.
> One of the three preceding (following) words is tagged **z**.
> The preceding word is tagged **z** and the following word is tagged **w**.
> The preceding (following) word is tagged **z** and the word
>   two before (after) is tagged **w**.

Figure 5.20   Brill's (1995) templates. Each begins with *"Change tag **a** to tag **b** when: ..."*. The variables **a**, **b**, **z**, and **w** range over parts-of-speech.

At the heart of Fig. 5.21 are the two functions GET_BEST_TRANSFORMATION and GET_BEST_INSTANCE. GET_BEST_TRANSFORMATION is called with a list of potential templates; for each template, GET_BEST_TRANSFORMATION calls GET_BEST_INSTANCE. GET_BEST_INSTANCE iteratively tests every possible instantiation of each template by filling in specific values for the tag variables **a**, **b**, **z**, and **w**.

In practice, there are a number of ways to make the algorithm more efficient. For example, templates and instantiated transformations can be suggested in a data-driven manner; a transformation-instance might be suggested only if it would improve the tagging of some specific word. The search can also be made more efficient by pre-indexing the words in the training corpus by potential transformation. Roche and Schabes (1997a) show how the tagger can also be speeded up by converting each rule into a finite-state transducer and composing all the transducers.

Figure 5.22 shows a few of the rules learned by Brill's original tagger.

5.7   Evaluation and Error Analysis

The probabilities in a statistical model like an HMM POS-tagger come from the corpus it is trained on. We saw in Section 4.3 that in order to train statistical models like taggers or *N*-grams, we need to set aside a **training set**. The design of the training set or **training corpus** needs to be carefully considered. If the training corpus is too specific to the task or domain, the probabilities may be too narrow and not generalize well to tagging sentences in very different domains. But if the training corpus is too general, the probabilities may not do a sufficient job of reflecting the task or domain.

Development test set
Dev-test

For evaluating *N*-grams models, we said in Section 4.3 that we need to divide our corpus into a distinct training set, test set, and a second test set called a development test set. We train our tagger on the training set. Then we use the **development test set** (also called a **dev-test** set) to perhaps tune some parameters, and in general decide what the best model is. Once we come up with what we think is the best model, we run it on the (hitherto unseen) test set to see its performance. We might use 80% of our data for training and save 10% each for dev-test and test. Why do we need a development test set distinct from the final test set? Because if we used the final test set to compute performance for all our experiments during our development phase, we would be tuning the various changes and parameters to this set. Our final error rate on the test set would then be optimistic: it would underestimate the true error rate.

---

function TBL(*corpus*) **returns** *transforms-queue*
INITIALIZE-WITH-MOST-LIKELY-TAGS(*corpus*)
until end condition is met **do**
  templates ← GENERATE-POTENTIAL-RELEVANT-TEMPLATES
  best-transform ← GET-BEST-TRANSFORM(*corpus*, *templates*)
  APPLY-TRANSFORM(*best-transform*, *corpus*)
  ENQUEUE(*best-transform-rule*, *transforms-queue*)
end
return(*transforms-queue*)

---

function GET-BEST-TRANSFORM(*corpus*, *templates*) **returns** *transform*
  for each *template* in *templates*
    (*instance*, *score*) ← GET-BEST-INSTANCE(*corpus*, *template*)
    if (*score* > *best-transform.score*) **then** *best-transform* ← (*instance*, *score*)
  return(*best-transform*)

---

function GET-BEST-INSTANCE(*corpus*, template) **returns** *transform*
  for *from-tag* ← **from** tag_1 **to** tag_n **do**
   for *to-tag* ← **from** tag_1 **to** tag_n **do**
    for *pos* ← **from** 1 **to** *corpus-size* **do**
     if (*correct-tag(pos)* == *to-tag* && *current-tag(pos)* == *from-tag*)
      num-good-transforms(current-tag(pos−1))++
      elseif (*correct-tag(pos)*==*from-tag* && *current-tag(pos)*==*from-tag*)
       num-bad-transforms(current-tag(pos−1))++
    end
    best-Z ← ARGMAX$_t$(*num-good-transforms*(t) - *num-bad-transforms*(t))
    if(*num-good-transforms(best-Z)* - *num-bad-transforms(best-Z)*
       > *best-instance.score*) **then**
     best.rule ← "Change tag from *from-tag* to *to-tag* if prev tag is *best-Z*"
     best.score ← *num-good-transforms(best-Z)* - *num-bad-transforms(best-Z)*
  return(*best*)

---

procedure APPLY-TRANSFORM(*transform*, *corpus*)
for *pos* ← **from** 1 **to** *corpus-size* **do**
  if (*current-tag(pos)*==*best-rule-from*)
    && (*current-tag(pos*−1)==*best-rule-prev*))
  current-tag(pos) ← *best-rule-to*

Figure 5.21   The Brill (1995) TBL algorithm for learning to tag. GET_BEST_INSTANCE would change for transformation templates other than *"Change tag from X to Y if previous tag is Z"*.

The problem with having a fixed training set, devset, and test set is that in order to save lots of data for training, the test set might not be large enough to be representative. Thus, a better approach would be to somehow use **all** our data both for training and *Cross-validation* test. How is this possible? The idea is to use **cross-validation**. In cross-validation, we randomly choose a training and test set division of our data, train our tagger, and then compute the error rate on the test set. Then we repeat with a different randomly

#	Change tags From	To	Condition	Example
1	NN	VB	previous tag is TO	to/TO race/NN → VB
2	VBP	VB	one of the previous 3 tags is MD	might/MD vanish/VBP → VB
3	NN	VB	one of the previous 2 tags is MD	might/MD not reply/NN → VB
4	VB	NN	one of the previous 2 tags is DT	
5	VBD	VBN	one of the previous 3 tags is VBZ	

Figure 5.22   The first 20 non-lexicalized transformations from Brill (1995).

10-fold cross-validation

selected training set and test set. We do this sampling process 10 times and average these 10 runs to get an average error rate. This is called **10-fold cross-validation**.

The only problem with cross-validation is that because all the data is used for testing, we need the whole corpus to be blind; we can't examine any of the data to suggest possible features and in general see what's going on. But looking at the corpus is often important for designing the system. For this reason, it is common to create a fixed training set and test set, then do 10-fold cross-validation inside the training set, but compute error rate the normal way in the test set.

Once we have a test set, we evaluate taggers by comparing their labeling of the test set with a human-labeled **gold standard** test set, based on **accuracy**: the percentage of all tags in the test set where the tagger and the gold standard agree. Most current tagging algorithms have an accuracy of around 96%–97% for simple tagsets like the Penn Treebank set. These accuracies are for words and punctuation; the accuracy for words only would be lower.

Baseline
Ceiling

How good is 97%? Since tagsets and tasks differ, the performance of tags can be compared against a lower-bound **baseline** and an upper-bound **ceiling**. One way to set a ceiling is to see how well humans do on the task. Marcus et al. (1993), for example, found that human annotators agreed on about 96%–97% of the tags in the Penn Treebank version of the Brown corpus. This suggests that the gold standard may have a 3%-4% margin of error and that it is meaningless to get 100% accuracy (modeling the last 3% would just be modeling noise). Indeed, Ratnaparkhi (1996) showed that the tagging ambiguities that caused problems for his tagger were exactly the ones that humans had labeled inconsistently in the training set. Two experiments by Voutilainen (1995, p. 174), however, found that when humans were allowed to discuss tags, they reached consensus on 100% of the tags.

> **Human Ceiling:** When using a human Gold Standard to evaluate a classification algorithm, check the agreement rate of humans on the standard.

The standard **baseline**, suggested by Gale et al. (1992a) (in the slightly different context of word sense disambiguation), is to choose the **unigram most likely tag** for each ambiguous word. The most likely tag for each word can be computed from a hand-tagged corpus (which may be the same as the training corpus for the tagger being evaluated).

> **Most Frequent Class Baseline:** Always compare a classifier against a baseline at least as good as the most frequent class baseline (assigning each token to the class it occurred in most often in the training set).

Tagging algorithms since Harris (1962) incorporate this tag frequency intuition.

Charniak et al. (1993) showed that this baseline algorithm achieves an accuracy of 90%–91% on the 87-tag Brown tagset; Toutanova et al. (2003) showed that a more complex version, augmented with an unknown word model, achieved 93.69% on the 45-tag Treebank tagset.

When comparing models, it is important to use statistical tests (introduced in any statistics class or textbook for the social sciences) to determine if the difference between two models is significant. Cohen (1995) is a useful reference that focuses on statistical research methods for artificial intelligence. Dietterich (1998) focuses on statistical tests for comparing classifiers. When statistically comparing sequence models like part-of-speech taggers, it is important to use **paired tests** or **matched-pairs** tests. Commonly used paired tests for evaluating part-of-speech taggers include the **Wilcoxon signed-rank test**, **paired t-tests**, the **McNemar test**, and the Matched-Pair Sentence Segment Word Error (**MAPSSWE**) test, originally applied to word error rate in speech recognition.

Paired test

Wilcoxon signed-rank test

Paired t-test

McNemar test

MAPSSWE

5.7.1   Error Analysis

In order to improve any model, we need to understand where it went wrong. Analyzing the error in a classifier like a part-of-speech tagger is done with a **confusion matrix**, or **contingency table**. A confusion matrix for an N-way classification task is an N-by-N matrix, where the cell (x, y) contains the number of times an item with correct classification x was classified by the model as y. For example, the following table shows a portion of the confusion matrix from the HMM tagging experiments of Franz (1996). The row labels indicate correct tags, column labels indicate the tagger's hypothesized tags, and each cell indicates percentage of the overall tagging error. Thus, 4.4% of the total errors were caused by mistagging a VBD as a VBN. Common errors are highlighted.

	IN	JJ	NN	NNP	RB	VBD	VBN
IN	—	.2			.7		
JJ	.2	—	3.3	2.1	1.7	.2	2.7
NN		8.7	—				.2
NNP	.2	3.3	4.1	—	.2		
RB	2.2	2.0	.5		—		
VBD		.3	.5			—	4.4
VBN		2.8				2.6	—

The confusion matrix above and related error analyses in Franz (1996), Kupiec (1992), and Ratnaparkhi (1996) suggest some major problems facing taggers:

1. **NN versus NNP versus JJ:** These are hard to distinguish prenominally. Distinguishing proper nouns is especially important for information extraction and machine translation.

2. **RP versus RB versus IN:** All of these can appear in sequences of satellites immediately following the verb.

3. **VBD versus VBN versus JJ:** Distinguishing these is important for partial parsing (participles are used to find passives) and for correctly labeling the edges of noun phrases.

Error analysis like this is a crucial part of any computational linguistic application. Error analysis can help find bugs, find problems in the training data, and, most important, help in developing new kinds of knowledge or algorithms to use in solving problems.

5.8 Advanced Issues in Part-of-Speech Tagging

Many additional issues must be resolved in order to build a working tagger. In this section we introduce some of these, including preprocessing steps for text normalization, dealing with unknown words, and complications that result when tagging morphologically rich languages like Czech, Hungarian and Turkish.

5.8.1 Practical Issues: Tag Indeterminacy and Tokenization

Tag indeterminacy arises when a word is ambiguous between multiple tags and is impossible or very difficult to disambiguate. In this case, some taggers allow the use of multiple tags. This is the case in both the Penn Treebank and in the British National Corpus. Common tag indeterminacies include adjective versus preterite versus past participle (JJ/VBD/VBN) and adjective versus noun as prenominal modifier (JJ/NN). Given a corpus with these indeterminate tags, there are three ways to deal with tag indeterminacy when training and scoring part-of-speech taggers:

1. Somehow replace the indeterminate tags with only one tag.
2. In testing, count a tagger as having correctly tagged an indeterminate token if it gives either of the correct tags. In training, somehow choose only one of the tags for the word.
3. Treat the indeterminate tag as a single complex tag.

The second approach is perhaps the most sensible, although most previous published results seem to have used the third approach. This third approach applied to the Penn Treebank Brown corpus, for example, results in a much larger tagset of 85 tags instead of 45, but the additional 40 complex tags cover a total of only 121 word instances out of the million-word corpus.

Most tagging algorithms assume that a process of tokenization has been applied to the tags. Chapter 3 discussed the issue of tokenization of periods for distinguishing sentence-final periods from word-internal periods in words like *etc*. An additional role for tokenization is in word splitting. The Penn Treebank and the British National Corpus split contractions and the *'s*-genitive from their stems:

would/MD n't/RB
children/NNS 's/POS

Indeed, the special Treebank tag POS is used only for the morpheme *'s*, which must be segmented off during tokenization.

Another tokenization issue concerns multipart words. The Treebank tagset assumes that tokenization of words like *New York* is done at whitespace. The phrase *a New York City firm* is tagged in Treebank notation as five separate words: *a/DT New/NNP York/NNP City/NNP firm/NN*. The C5 tagset, by contrast, allow prepositions like "*in terms of*" to be treated as a single word by adding numbers to each tag, as in *in/II31 terms/II32 of/II33*.

5.8.2   Unknown Words

> *words people*
> *never use —*
> *could be*
> *only I*
> *know them*
> Ishikawa Takuboku 1885–1912

All the tagging algorithms we have discussed require a dictionary that lists the possible parts-of-speech of every word. But the largest dictionary will still not contain every possible word, as we see in Chapter 7. Proper names and acronyms are created very often, and even new common nouns and verbs enter the language at a surprising rate. Therefore, in order to build a complete tagger, we cannot always use a dictionary to give us $p(w_i \, t_i)$. We need some method for guessing the tag of an unknown word.

The simplest possible unknown-word algorithm is to pretend that each unknown word is ambiguous among all possible tags, with equal probability. Then the tagger must rely solely on the contextual POS-trigrams to suggest the proper tag. A slightly more complex algorithm is based on the idea that the probability distribution of tags over unknown words is similar to the distribution of tags over words that occurred only once in a training set, an idea that was suggested by both Baayen and Sproat (1996) and Dermatas and Kokkinakis (1995). These words that only occur once are known *Hapax legomena* as **hapax legomena** (singular **hapax legomenon**). For example, unknown words and hapax legomena are similar in that they are both most likely to be nouns, followed by verbs, but are very unlikely to be determiners or interjections. Thus, the likelihood $P(w_i \, t_i)$ for an unknown word is determined by the average of the distribution over all singleton words in the training set. This idea of using "things we've seen once" as an estimator for "things we've never seen" proved useful in the Good-Turing algorithm of Chapter 4.

Most unknown-word algorithms, however, make use of a much more powerful source of information: the morphology of the words. For example, words that end in *-s* are likely to be plural nouns (NNS), words ending with *-ed* tend to be past participles (VBN), words ending with *able* tend to be adjectives (JJ), and so on. Even if we've never seen a word, we can use facts about its morphological form to guess its part-of-speech. Besides morphological knowledge, orthographic information can be very helpful. For example, words starting with capital letters are likely to be proper nouns (NP). The presence of a hyphen is also a useful feature; hyphenated words in the Treebank version of Brown are most likely to be adjectives (JJ). This prevalence of JJs is caused by the labeling instructions for the Treebank, which specified that prenominal modifiers should be labeled as JJ if they contained a hyphen.

How are these features combined and used in part-of-speech taggers? One method is to train separate probability estimators for each feature, assume independence, and multiply the probabilities. Weischedel et al. (1993) built such a model, based on four specific kinds of morphological and orthographic features. They used 3 inflectional endings (*-ed, -s, -ing*), 32 derivational endings (such as *-ion, -al, -ive*, and *-ly*), 4 values of capitalization depending on whether a word is sentence-initial (+/- capitalization, +/-initial) and whether the word was hyphenated. For each feature, they trained maximum likelihood estimates of the probability of the feature given a tag from a labeled training set. They then combined the features to estimate the probability of an unknown word by assuming independence and multiplying:

$$P(w_i \ t_i) = p(\text{unknown-word} \ t_i) * p(\text{capital} \ t_i) * p(\text{endings/hyph} \ t_i) \qquad (5.50)$$

Another HMM-based approach, from Samuelsson (1993) and Brants (2000), generalizes this use of morphology in a data-driven way. In this approach, rather than pre-selecting certain suffixes by hand, they consider all final letter sequences of all words. They consider such suffixes of up to ten letters, computing for each suffix of length i the probability of the tag t_i given the suffix:

$$P(t_i \ l_{n-i+1} \ldots l_n) \qquad (5.51)$$

These probabilities are smoothed with successively shorter and shorter suffixes. Separate suffix tries are kept for capitalized and uncapitalized words.

In general, most unknown-word models try to capture the fact that unknown words are unlikely to be closed-class words like prepositions. Brants models this fact by computing suffix probabilities only from the training set for words whose frequency in the training set is ≤ 10. In the HMM tagging model of Thede and Harper (1999), this fact is modeled instead by training only on open-class words.

Note that Eq. 5.51 gives an estimate of $p(t_i \ w_i)$; since for the HMM tagging approach we need the likelihood $p(w_i \ t_i)$, we can derive this from Eq. 5.51 by using Bayesian inversion (i.e., using Bayes rule and computation of the two priors $P(t_i)$ and $P(t_i \ l_{n-i+1} \ldots l_n)$).

In addition to using capitalization information for unknown words, Brants (2000) also uses capitalization for known words by adding a capitalization feature to each tag. Thus, instead of computing $P(t_i \ t_{i-1}, t_{i-2})$ as in Eq. 5.44, he actually computes the probability $P(t_i, c_i \ t_{i-1}, c_{i-1}, t_{i-2}, c_{i-2})$. This is equivalent to having a capitalized and uncapitalized version of each tag, essentially doubling the size of the tagset.

A non-HMM based approach to unknown-word detection was that of Brill (1995), using the TBL algorithm, by which the allowable templates were defined orthographically (the first N letters of the words, the last N letters of the word, etc.).

Most recent approaches to unknown-word handling, however, combine these features in a third way: by using maximum entropy (**MaxEnt**) models such as the **maximum entropy Markov model** (**MEMM**) first introduced by Ratnaparkhi (1996) and McCallum et al. (2000); we study MEMMs in Chapter 6. The maximum entropy approach is one of a family of log-linear approaches to classification in which many features are computed for the word to be tagged and all the features are combined in a model based on multinomial logistic regression. The unknown-word model in the tagger of Toutanova et al. (2003) uses a feature set extended from Ratnaparkhi (1996), in which each feature represents a property of a word, including features like

> word contains a number
> word contains an upper-case letter
> word contains a hyphen
> word is all upper case
> word contains a particular prefix (from the set of all prefixes of length $\leq$ 4)
> word contains a particular suffix (from the set of all prefixes of length $\leq$ 4)
> word is upper case and has a digit and a dash (like *CFC-12*)
> word is upper case and followed within 3 words by Co., Inc., etc.

Toutanova et al. (2003) found this last feature, a simple company name detector looking for a nearby Co. or Inc., particularly useful. Note that the Ratnaparkhi (1996) model ignored all features with counts less than 10.

Log-linear models have also been applied to Chinese tagging (Tseng et al., 2005b). Chinese words are very short (around 2.4 characters per unknown word compared with 7.7 for English), but Tseng et al. (2005b) found that morphological features still improved tagging performance for unknown words. For example, for each character in an unknown word and each POS tag, they added a binary feature indicating whether that character ever occurred with that tag in any training set word. There is also an interesting distributional difference in unknown words between Chinese and English. While English unknown words tend to be proper nouns (41% of unknown words in WSJ are NP), in Chinese the majority of unknown words are common nouns and verbs (61% in the Chinese TreeBank 5.0). These ratios are similar to German and seem to be caused by the prevalence of compounding as a morphological device in Chinese and German.

5.8.3   Part-of-Speech Tagging for Other Languages

As the previous paragraph suggests, part-of-speech tagging algorithms have all been applied to many other languages as well. In some cases, the methods work well without large modifications; Brants (2000) showed exactly the same performance for tagging on the German NEGRA corpus (96.7%) as on the English Penn Treebank. But a number of augmentations and changes become necessary when dealing with highly inflected or agglutinative languages.

One problem with these languages is simply the large number of words when compared with English. Recall from Chapter 3 that agglutinative languages like Turkish (and to some extent mixed agglutinative-inflectional languages like Hungarian) are those in which words contain long strings of morphemes; and since each morpheme has relatively few surface forms, it is often possible to clearly see the morphemes in the surface text. For example, Megyesi (1999) gives the following typical example of a Hungarian word meaning "of their hits":

(5.52) találataiknak

> *talál* *-at*   *-a -i*   *-k* *-nak*
> hit/find nominalizer his poss.plur their dat/gen
>
> "of their hits"

Similarly, the following list, excerpted from Hakkani-Tür et al. (2002), shows a few of the words producible in Turkish from the root *uyu-*, 'sleep':

uyuyorum	'I am sleeping'	uyuyorsun	'you are sleeping'
uyuduk	'we slept'	uyumadan	'without sleeping'
uyuman	'your sleeping'	uyurken	'while (somebody) is sleeping'
uyutmak	'to cause someone to sleep'	uyutturmak	'to cause someone to cause another person to sleep'

These productive word-formation processes result in a large vocabulary for these languages. Oravecz and Dienes (2002), for example, show that a quarter-million-word corpus of English has about 19,000 different words (i.e., word types); the same size corpus of Hungarian has almost 50,000 different words. This problem continues even with much larger corpora; note in the table below on Turkish from Hakkani-Tür et al. (2002) that the vocabulary size of Turkish is far bigger than that of English and is growing faster than English even at 10 million words.

Corpus Size	Vocabulary Size	
	Turkish	English
1 million words	106,547	33,398
10 million words	417,775	97,734

The large vocabulary size seems to cause a significant degradation in tagging performance when the HMM algorithm is applied directly to agglutinative languages. For example, Oravecz and Dienes (2002) applied the same HMM software (called 'TnT') that Brants (2000) used to achieve 96.7% on both English and German, and achieved only 92.88% on Hungarian. The performance on known words (98.32%) was comparable to English results; the problem was the performance on unknown words: 67.07% on Hungarian, compared with around 84%–85% for unknown words with a comparable amount of English training data. Hajič (2000) notes the same problem in a wide variety of other languages (including Czech, Slovene, Estonian, and Romanian); the performance of these taggers is hugely improved by the addition of a dictionary that essentially gives a better model of unknown words. In summary, one difficulty in tagging highly inflected and agglutinative languages is the tagging of unknown words.

A second, related, issue with such languages is the vast amount of information that is coded in the morphology of the word. In English, lots of information about the syntactic function of a word is represented by word order, or neighboring function words. In highly inflectional languages, information such as the case (nominative, accusative, genitive) or gender (masculine, feminine) is marked on the words themselves, and word order plays less of a role in marking syntactic function. Since tagging is often used in a preprocessing step for other NLP algorithms such as parsing or information extraction, this morphological information is crucial to extract. This means that a part-of-speech tagging output for, say, Czech needs to include information about the case and gender of each word in order to be as useful as parts-of-speech without case or gender are in English.

For this reason, tagsets for agglutinative and highly inflectional languages are usually much larger than the 50–100 tags we have seen for English. Tags in such enriched tagsets are sequences of morphological tags rather than a single primitive tag. Assigning tags from such a tagset to words means that we are jointly solving the problems of part-of-speech tagging and morphological disambiguation. Hakkani-Tür et al. (2002) give the following example of tags from Turkish, in which the word *izin* has three possible morphological/part-of-speech tags (and meanings):

1. Yerdeki **izin** temizlenmesi gerek.   iz + Noun+A3sg+Pnon+Gen
   The trace on the floor should be cleaned.

2. Üzerinde parmak **izin** kalmış   iz + Noun+A3sg+P2sg+Nom
   Your finger **print** is left on (it).

3. İçeri girmek için **izin** alman gerekiyor.   izin + Noun+A3sg+Pnon+Nom
   You need a **permission** to enter.

Using a morphological parse sequence like `Noun+A3sg+Pnon+Gen` as the part-of-speech tag greatly increases the number of parts-of-speech, of course. We can see this clearly in the morphologically tagged MULTEXT-East corpora, in English, Czech, Estonian, Hungarian, Romanian, and Slovene (Dimitrova et al., 1998; Erjavec, 2004). Hajič (2000) gives the following tagset sizes for these corpora:

Language	Tagset Size
English	139
Czech	970
Estonian	476
Hungarian	401
Romanian	486
Slovene	1033

With such large tagsets, it is generally necessary to perform morphological analysis on each word to generate the list of possible morphological tag sequences (i.e., the list of possible part-of-speech tags) for the word. The role of the tagger is then to disambiguate among these tags. The morphological analysis can be done in various ways. The Hakkani-Tür et al. (2002) model of Turkish morphological analysis is based on the two-level morphology we introduced in Chapter 3. For Czech and the MULTEXT-East languages, Hajič (2000) and Hajič and Hladká (1998) use a fixed external dictionary for each language; the dictionary compiles out all the possible forms of each word and lists possible tags for each wordform. The morphological parse also crucially helps address the problem of unknown words since morphological parsers can accept unknown stems and still segment the affixes properly.

Given such a morphological parse, various methods for the tagging itself can be used. The Hakkani-Tür et al. (2002) model for Turkish uses a Markov model of tag sequences. The model assigns a probability to sequences of tags like

`izin+Noun+A3sg+Pnon+Nom`

by computing tag transition probabilities from a training set. Other models use similar techniques to those for English. Hajič (2000) and Hajič and Hladká (1998), for example, use a log-linear exponential tagger for the MULTEXT-East languages, Oravecz and Dienes (2002) and Džeroski et al. (2000) use the TnT HMM tagger (Brants, 2000), and so on.

5.8.4 Tagger Combination

The various part-of-speech tagging algorithms we have described can also be combined. The most common approach to tagger combination is to run multiple taggers in parallel on the same sentence and then combine their output, either by voting or by training another classifier to choose which tagger to trust in a given context. Brill and Wu (1998), for example, combined unigram, HMM, TBL, and maximum-entropy taggers by voting through a higher-order classifier, and showed a small gain over the best of the four classifiers. In general, this kind of combination is only useful if the taggers have complementary errors, and so research on combination often begins by checking to see if the errors are indeed different from different taggers. Another option is to combine taggers in series. Hajič et al. (2001) apply this option for Czech, using the rule-based approach to remove some of the impossible tag possibilities for each word and then using an HMM tagger to choose the best sequence from the remaining tags.

5.9 Advanced: The Noisy Channel Model for Spelling

The Bayesian inference model introduced in Section 5.5 for tagging has another interpretation: as an implementation of the **noisy channel** model, a crucial tool in speech recognition and machine translation.

In this section we introduce this noisy channel model and show how to apply it to the task of correcting spelling errors. The noisy channel model is used in Microsoft Word and in many search engines; in general it is the most widely used algorithm for correcting any kind of single-word spelling error, including **non-word spelling errors** and **real-word spelling errors**.

Recall that non-word spelling errors are those that are not English words (like *recieve* for *receive*) and that we can **detect** these by simply looking for any word not in a dictionary. We saw in Section 3.10 that candidate corrections for some spelling errors could be found by looking for words that had a small **edit distance** to the misspelled word.

The Bayesian models we have seen in this chapter and the noisy channel model, will give us a better way to find these corrections. Furthermore, we'll be able to use the noisy channel model for **contextual spell checking**, which is the task of correcting **real-word spelling errors** like the following:

> They are leaving in about fifteen *minuets* to go to her house.
> The study was conducted mainly *be* John Black.

Since these errors have real words, we can't find them by just flagging words not in the dictionary, and we can't correct them by just using edit distance alone. But note that words around the candidate correction *in about fifteen minutes* make it a much more probable word sequence than the original *in about fifteen minuets*. The noisy channel model implements this idea with *N*-gram models.

Noisy Channel   The intuition of the **noisy channel** model (see Fig. 5.23) is to treat the misspelled word as if a correctly spelled word had been "distorted" by being passed through a

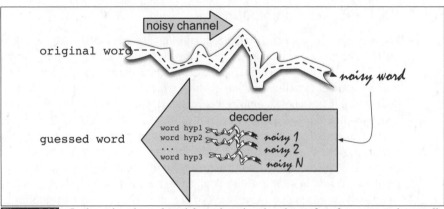

Figure 5.23   In the noisy channel model, we imagine that the surface form we see is actually a "distorted" form of an original word passed through a noisy channel. The decoder passes each hypothesis through a model of this channel and picks the word that best matches the surface noisy word.

noisy communication channel. This channel introduces "noise" in the form of substitutions or other changes to the letters, making it hard to recognize the "true" word. Our goal, then, is to build a model of the channel. Given this model, we then find the true word by passing every word of the language through our model of the noisy channel and seeing which one comes the closest to the misspelled word.

Bayesian

V

This noisy channel model, like the HMM tagging architecture we saw earlier, is a special case of **Bayesian inference**. We see an observation O (a misspelled word) and our job is to find the word w that generated this misspelled word. Out of all possible words in the vocabulary V we want to find the word w such that $P(w\ O)$ is highest, or:

$$\hat{w} = \operatorname*{argmax}_{w \in V} P(w\ O) \tag{5.53}$$

As we saw for part-of-speech tagging, we can use Bayes rule to turn the problem around (and note that, as for tagging, we can ignore the denominator):

$$\hat{w} = \operatorname*{argmax}_{w \in V} \frac{P(O\ w)P(w)}{P(O)} = \operatorname*{argmax}_{w \in V} P(O\ w)\, P(w) \tag{5.54}$$

To summarize, the noisy channel model says that we have some true underlying word w, and we have a noisy channel that modifies the word into some possible misspelled surface form. The probability of the noisy channel producing any particular observation sequence O is modeled by $P(O\ w)$. The probability distribution over possible hidden words is modeled by $P(w)$. We can compute the most probable word $\hat{w}$ given that we've seen some observed misspelling O by taking the product of the word prior $P(w)$ and the observation likelihood $P(O\ w)$ and choosing the word for which this product is greatest.

Let's apply the noisy channel approach to correcting non-word spelling errors. This approach was first suggested by Kernighan et al. (1990); their program, `correct`, takes words rejected by the Unix `spell` program, generates a list of potential correct words, ranks them according to Eq. 5.54, and picks the highest-ranked one. We'll apply the algorithm to the example misspelling *acress*. The algorithm has two stages: *proposing candidate corrections* and *scoring the candidates*.

To propose candidate corrections Kernighan et al. (1990) make the reasonable simplifying assumption (Damerau, 1964) that the correct word will differ from the misspelling by a single insertion, deletion, substitution, or transposition. The list of candidate words is generated from the typo by application of any single transformation that results in a word in a large online dictionary. Applying all possible transformations to *acress* yields the list of candidate words in Fig. 5.24.

		Transformation			
		Correct	Error	Position	
Error	Correction	Letter	Letter	(Letter #)	Type
acress	actress	t	–	2	deletion
acress	cress	–	a	0	insertion
acress	caress	ca	ac	0	transposition
acress	access	c	r	2	substitution
acress	across	o	e	3	substitution
acress	acres	–	2	5	insertion
acress	acres	–	2	4	insertion

Figure 5.24 Candidate corrections for the misspelling *acress* and the transformations that would have produced the error (after Kernighan et al. (1990)). "–" represents a null letter.

The second stage of the algorithm scores each correction by Eq. 5.54. Let t represent the typo (the misspelled word), and let c range over the set C of candidate corrections. The most likely correction is then

$$\hat{c} = \underset{c \in C}{\mathrm{argmax}} \quad \overbrace{P(t \mid c)}^{\text{likelihood}} \quad \overbrace{P(c)}^{\text{prior}} \tag{5.55}$$

The prior probability of each correction $P(c)$ is the language model probability of the word c in context; in this section for pedagogical reasons we'll make the simplifying assumption that this is the unigram probability $P(c)$, but in practice, in spelling correction this is extended to trigram or 4-gram probabilities. Let's use the corpus of Kernighan et al. (1990), which is the 1988 AP newswire corpus of 44 million words. Since in this corpus the word *actress* occurs 1343 times out of 44 million, the word *acres* 2879 times, and so on, the resulting unigram prior probabilities are as follows:

c	freq(c)	p(c)
actress	1343	.0000315
cress	0	.000000014
caress	4	.0000001
access	2280	.000058
across	8436	.00019
acres	2879	.000065

How can we estimate $P(t \mid c)$? It is difficult to model the actual channel perfectly (i.e., computing the exact probability that a word will be mistyped) because it would require knowing who the typist was, whether the typist was left-handed or right-handed, and many other factors. Luckily, it turns out we can get a pretty reasonable estimate of $p(t\ c)$ just by looking at simple local context factors. That's because the most important factors predicting an insertion, deletion, or transposition are the identity of the correct letter itself, how the letter was misspelled, and the surrounding context. For example, the letters m and n are often substituted for each other; this is partly a fact about their identity (these two letters are pronounced similarly and they are next to each other on the keyboard) and partly a fact about context (because they are pronounced similarly and they occur in similar contexts). Kernighan et al. (1990) used a simple model of this sort. They estimated, for example, $p(acress\ across)$ just using the number of times that the letter e was substituted for the letter o in some large corpus of errors.

Confusion matrix This is represented by a **confusion matrix**, a square 26 26 matrix that represents the number of times one letter was incorrectly used instead of another. For example, the cell labeled $[o,e]$ in a substitution confusion matrix would give the count of times that e was substituted for o. The cell labeled $[t,s]$ in an insertion confusion matrix would give the count of times that t was inserted after s. A confusion matrix can be computed by coding a collection of spelling errors with the correct spelling and then counting the number of times different errors occurred (Grudin, 1983). Kernighan et al. (1990) used four confusion matrices, one for each type of single error:

- del$[x,y]$ contains the number of times in the training set that the characters xy in the correct word were typed as x.
- ins$[x,y]$ contains the number of times in the training set that the character x in the correct word was typed as xy.
- sub$[x,y]$ the number of times that x was typed as y.
- trans$[x,y]$ the number of times that xy was typed as yx.

Note that Kernighan et al. (1990) chose to condition their insertion and deletion probabilities on the previous character; they could also have chosen to condition on the following character. Using these matrices, they estimated $p(t\ c)$ as follows (where c_p is the pth character of the word c):

$$P(t\ c) = \begin{cases} \dfrac{\text{del}_{[c_{p-1},c_p]}}{\text{count}_{[c_{p-1}c_p]}}, \text{ if deletion} \\[2mm] \dfrac{\text{ins}_{[c_{p-1},t_p]}}{\text{count}_{[c_{p-1}]}}, \text{ if insertion} \\[2mm] \dfrac{\text{sub}_{[t_p,c_p]}}{\text{count}_{[c_p]}}, \text{ if substitution} \\[2mm] \dfrac{\text{trans}_{[c_p,c_{p+1}]}}{\text{count}_{[c_pc_{p+1}]}}, \text{ if transposition} \end{cases} \qquad (5.56)$$

Figure 5.25 shows the final probabilities for each of the potential corrections; the unigram prior is multiplied by the likelihood (computed with Eq. 5.56 and the confusion matrices). The final column shows the "normalized percentage".

This implementation of the Bayesian algorithm predicts *acres* as the correct word (at a total normalized percentage of 45%) and *actress* as the second most likely word. Unfortunately, the algorithm was wrong here: The writer's intention becomes clear from the context: ...*was called a "stellar and versatile* **acress** *whose combination of*

c	freq(c)	p(c)	p(t c)	p(t c)p(c)	%
actress	1343	.0000315	.000117	3.69 10^{-9}	**37%**
cress	0	.000000014	.00000144	2.02 10^{-14}	**0%**
caress	4	.0000001	.00000164	1.64 10^{-13}	**0%**
access	2280	.000058	.000000209	1.21 10^{-11}	**0%**
across	8436	.00019	.0000093	1.77 10^{-9}	**18%**
acres	2879	.000065	.0000321	2.09 10^{-9}	**21%**
acres	2879	.000065	.0000342	2.22 10^{-9}	**23%**

Figure 5.25 Computation of the ranking for each candidate correction. Note that the highest ranked word is not *actress* but *acres* (the two lines at the bottom of the table) since *acres* can be generated in two ways. The *del*[], *ins*[], *sub*[], and *trans*[] confusion matrices are given in full in Kernighan et al. (1990).

sass and glamour has defined her...". The surrounding words make it clear that *actress* and not *acres* was the intended word. This is the reason that in practice we use trigram (or larger) language models in the noisy channel model, rather than unigrams. Seeing whether a **bigram** model of $P(c)$ correctly solves this problem is left as Exercise 5.10 for the reader.

The algorithm as we have described it requires hand-annotated data to train the confusion matrices. An alternative approach used by Kernighan et al. (1990) is to compute the matrices by iteratively using this very spelling error correction algorithm itself. The iterative algorithm first initializes the matrices with equal values; thus, any character is equally likely to be deleted, equally likely to be substituted for any other character, etc. Next, the spelling error correction algorithm is run on a set of spelling errors. Given the set of typos paired with their corrections, the confusion matrices can now be recomputed, the spelling algorithm run again, and so on. This clever method turns out to be an instance of the important **EM** algorithm (Dempster et al., 1977), which we discuss in Chapter 6.

5.9.1 Contextual Spelling Error Correction

Real-word error detection

As we mentioned above, the noisy channel approach can also be applied to detect and correct **real-word spelling errors**, errors that result in an actual word of English. This can happen from typographical errors (insertion, deletion, transposition) that accidentally produce a real word (e.g., *there* for *three*) or because the writer substituted the wrong spelling of a homophone or near-homophone (e.g., *dessert* for *desert*, or *piece* for *peace*). The task of correcting these errors is also called **context-sensitive spell**

Context-sensitive spell correction

correction. A number of studies suggest that between 25% and 40% of spelling errors are valid English words as in the following examples (Kukich, 1992):

They are leaving in about fifteen *minuets* to go to her house.
The design *an* construction of the system will take more than a year.
Can they *lave* him my messages?
The study was conducted mainly *be* John Black.

We can extend the noisy channel model to deal with real-word spelling errors by generating a *candidate spelling set* for every word in a sentence (Mays et al., 1991).

The candidate set includes the word itself, plus every English word that would be generated from the word either by typographical modifications (letter insertion, deletion, substitution), or from a homophone list. The algorithm then chooses the spelling for each word that gives the whole sentence the highest probability. That is, given a sentence $W = w_1, w_2, \ldots, w_k, \ldots, w_n$, where w_k has alternative spelling w_k', w_k'', etc., we choose from among these possible spellings the spelling that maximizes $P(W)$, by using the N-gram grammar to compute $P(W)$.

More recent research has focused on improving the channel model $P(t\ c)$, such as by incorporating phonetic information or allowing more complex errors (Brill and Moore, 2000; Toutanova and Moore, 2002). The most important improvement to the language model $P(c)$ is to use very large contexts, for example, by using the very large set of 5-grams publicly released by Google in 2006 (Franz and Brants, 2006). See Norvig (2007) for a nice explanation and a Python implementation of the noisy channel model; the end of the chapter has further pointers.

5.10   Summary

This chapter introduced the idea of **parts-of-speech** and **part-of-speech tagging**. The main ideas:

- Languages generally have a relatively small set of **closed class** words that are often highly frequent, generally act as **function words**, and can be ambiguous in their part-of-speech tags. Open-class words generally include various kinds of **nouns, verbs, adjectives**. There are a number of part-of-speech coding schemes, based on **tagsets** of between 40 and 200 tags.

- **Part-of-speech tagging** is the process of assigning a part-of-speech label to each of a sequence of words. Rule-based taggers use hand-written rules to distinguish tag ambiguity. HMM taggers choose the tag sequence that maximizes the product of word likelihood and tag sequence probability. Other machine learning models used for tagging include maximum entropy and other log-linear models, decision trees, memory-based learning, and transformation-based learning.

- The probabilities in HMM taggers are trained on hand-labeled training corpora, combine different N-gram levels by using deleted interpolation, and incorporate sophisticated unknown word models.

- Given an HMM and an input string, the Viterbi algorithm can decode the optimal tag sequence.

- Taggers are evaluated by comparison of their output from a test set to human labels for that test set. Error analysis can help pinpoint areas in which a tagger doesn't perform well.

Bibliographical and Historical Notes

The earliest implemented part-of-speech assignment algorithm may have been part of the parser in Zellig Harris's Transformations and Discourse Analysis Project (TDAP), which was implemented between June 1958 and July 1959 at the University of Pennsylvania (Harris, 1962). Previous natural language processing systems had used dictionaries with part-of-speech information for words but have not been described as performing part-of-speech disambiguation. As part of its parsing, TDAP did part-of-speech disambiguation with 14 hand-written rules, whose use of part-of-speech tag sequences prefigures all modern algorithms and whose run order was based on the relative frequency of tags for a word. The parser/tagger was reimplemented recently and is described by Joshi and Hopely (1999) and Karttunen (1999), who note that the parser was essentially implemented (in a modern way) as a cascade of finite-state transducers.

Soon after the TDAP parser was the Computational Grammar Coder (CGC) of Klein and Simmons (1963). The CGC had three components: a lexicon, a morphological analyzer, and a context disambiguator. The small 1500-word lexicon included exceptional words that could not be accounted for in the simple morphological analyzer, including function words as well as irregular nouns, verbs, and adjectives. The morphological analyzer used inflectional and derivational suffixes to assign part-of-speech classes. A word was run through the lexicon and morphological analyzer to produce a candidate set of parts-of-speech. A set of 500 context rules was then used to disambiguate this candidate set by relying on surrounding islands of unambiguous words. For example, one rule said that between an ARTICLE and a VERB, the only allowable sequences were ADJ-NOUN, NOUN-ADVERB, or NOUN-NOUN. The CGC algorithm reported 90% accuracy on applying a 30-tag tagset to articles from the *Scientific American* and a children's encyclopedia.

The TAGGIT tagger (Greene and Rubin, 1971) was based on the Klein and Simmons (1963) system, using the same architecture but increasing the size of the dictionary and the size of the tagset to 87 tags. For example, the following sample rule states that a word x is unlikely to be a plural noun (NNS) before a third person singular verb (VBZ):

$$x \text{ VBZ} \rightarrow not \text{ NNS}$$

TAGGIT was applied to the Brown corpus and, according to Francis and Kučera (1982, p. 9), "resulted in the accurate tagging of 77% of the corpus" (the remainder of the Brown corpus was tagged by hand).

In the 1970s, the Lancaster-Oslo/Bergen (LOB) corpus was compiled as a British English equivalent of the Brown corpus. It was tagged with the CLAWS tagger (Marshall, 1983, 1987; Garside, 1987), a probabilistic algorithm that can be viewed as an approximation to the HMM tagging approach. The algorithm used tag bigram probabilities, but instead of storing the word likelihood of each tag, the algorithm marked tags either as *rare* ($P(\text{tag word}) < .01$) *infrequent* ($P(\text{tag word}) < .10$) or *normally frequent* ($P(\text{tag word}) > .10$),

The probabilistic PARTS tagger of Church (1988) was close to a full HMM tagger. It extended the CLAWS idea to assign full lexical probabilities to each word/tag combination and used Viterbi decoding to find a tag sequence. Like the CLAWS tagger, however, it stored the probability of the tag, given the word

171

$$P(\text{tag word}) * P(\text{tag previous } n \text{ tags}) \qquad (5.57)$$

rather than using the probability of the word, given the tag, as an HMM tagger does:

$$P(\text{word tag}) * P(\text{tag previous } n \text{ tags}) \qquad (5.58)$$

Later taggers explicitly introduced the use of the hidden Markov model, often with the EM training algorithm (Kupiec, 1992; Merialdo, 1994; Weischedel et al., 1993), including the use of variable-length Markov models (Schütze and Singer, 1994).

Most recent tagging algorithms, like the HMM and TBL approaches we have discussed, are machine learning classifiers that estimate the best tag-sequence for a sentence, given various features such as the current word, neighboring parts-of-speech or words, and unknown word features such as orthographic and morphological features. Many kinds of classifiers have been used to combine these features, including decision trees (Jelinek et al., 1994; Magerman, 1995), maximum entropy models (Ratnaparkhi, 1996), other log-linear models (Franz, 1996), memory-based learning (Daelemans et al., 1996), and networks of linear separators (SNOW) (Roth and Zelenko, 1998).

Most machine learning models seem to achieve relatively similar performance given similar features, roughly 96%–97% on the Treebank 45-tag tagset on the *Wall Street Journal* corpus. As of the writing of this chapter, the highest-performing published model on this WSJ Treebank task is a log-linear tagger that uses information about neighboring words as well as tags and a sophisticated unknown-word model, achieving 97.24% accuracy (Toutanova et al., 2003). Most such models are supervised, although work is beginning on unsupervised models (Schütze, 1995; Brill, 1997; Clark, 2000; Banko and Moore, 2004; Goldwater and Griffiths, 2007).

Readers interested in the history of parts-of-speech should consult a history of linguistics such as Robins (1967) or Koerner and Asher (1995), particularly the article by Householder (1995) in the latter. Sampson (1987) and Garside et al. (1997) give a detailed summary of the provenance and makeup of the Brown and other tagsets. More information on part-of-speech tagging can be found in van Halteren (1999).

Algorithms for spelling error detection and correction have existed since at least Blair (1960). Most early algorithms were based on similarity keys like the Soundex algorithm discussed in the exercises on page 81 (Odell and Russell, 1922; Knuth, 1973). Damerau (1964) gave a dictionary-based algorithm for error detection; most error-detection algorithms since then have been based on dictionaries. Damerau also gave a correction algorithm that worked for single errors. Most algorithms since then have relied on dynamic programming, beginning with Wagner and Fischer (1974). Kukich (1992) wrote the definitive survey article on spelling error detection and correction. Modern algorithms are based on statistical or machine learning algorithm, following, for example, Kashyap and Oommen (1983) and Kernighan et al. (1990).

Recent approaches to spelling include extensions to the noisy channel model (Brill and Moore, 2000; Toutanova and Moore, 2002) as well as many other machine learning architectures such as Bayesian classifiers (Gale et al., 1993; Golding, 1997; Golding and Schabes, 1996), decision lists (Yarowsky, 1994), transformation-based learning (Mangu and Brill, 1997), latent semantic analysis (Jones and Martin, 1997), and Winnow (Golding and Roth, 1999). Hirst and Budanitsky (2005) explore the use of word relatedness; see Chapter 20. Noisy channel spelling correction is used in a number of commercial applications, including the Microsoft Word contextual spell checker.

Exercises

5.1 Find one tagging error in each of the following sentences that are tagged with the Penn Treebank tagset:

1. I/PRP need/VBP a/DT flight/NN from/IN Atlanta/NN
2. Does/VBZ this/DT flight/NN serve/VB dinner/NNS
3. I/PRP have/VB a/DT friend/NN living/VBG in/IN Denver/NNP
4. Can/VBP you/PRP list/VB the/DT nonstop/JJ afternoon/NN flights/NNS

5.2 Use the Penn Treebank tagset to tag each word in the following sentences from Damon Runyon's short stories. You may ignore punctuation. Some of these are quite difficult; do your best.

1. It is a nice night.
2. This crap game is over a garage in Fifty-second Street...
3. ...Nobody ever takes the newspapers she sells...
4. He is a tall, skinny guy with a long, sad, mean-looking kisser, and a mournful voice.
5. ...I am sitting in Mindy's restaurant putting on the gefillte fish, which is a dish I am very fond of, ...
6. When a guy and a doll get to taking peeks back and forth at each other, why there you are indeed.

5.3 Now compare your tags from the previous exercise with one or two friend's answers. On which words did you disagree the most? Why?

5.4 Now tag the sentences in Exercise 5.2; use the more detailed Brown tagset in Fig. 5.7.

5.5 Implement the TBL algorithm in Fig. 5.21. Create a small number of templates and train the tagger on any POS-tagged training set you can find.

5.6 Implement the "most likely tag" baseline. Find a POS-tagged training set, and use it to compute for each word the tag that maximizes $p(t w)$. You will need to implement a simple tokenizer to deal with sentence boundaries. Start by assuming that all unknown words are NN and compute your error rate on known and unknown words. Now write at least five rules to do a better job of tagging unknown words, and show the difference in error rates.

5.7 Recall that the Church (1988) tagger is not an HMM tagger since it incorporates the probability of the tag given the word:

$$P(\text{tag word}) * P(\text{tag previous } n \text{ tags}) \qquad (5.59)$$

rather than using the likelihood of the word given the tag, as an HMM tagger does:

$$P(\text{word tag}) * P(\text{tag previous } n \text{ tags}) \qquad (5.60)$$

Interestingly, this use of a kind of "reverse likelihood" has proven to be useful in the modern log-linear approach to machine translation (see page 903). As a gedanken-experiment, construct a sentence, a set of tag transition probabilities, and a set of lexical tag probabilities that demonstrate a way in which the HMM tagger can produce a better answer than the Church tagger, and create another example in which the Church tagger is better.

5.8 Build a bigram HMM tagger. You will need a part-of-speech-tagged corpus. First split the corpus into a training set and test set. From the labeled training set, train the transition and observation probabilities of the HMM tagger directly on the hand-tagged data. Then implement the Viterbi algorithm from this chapter and Chapter 6 so that you can decode (label) an arbitrary test sentence. Now run your algorithm on the test set. Report its error rate and compare its performance to the most frequent tag baseline.

5.9 Do an error analysis of your tagger. Build a confusion matrix and investigate the most frequent errors. Propose some features for improving the performance of your tagger on these errors.

5.10 Compute a bigram grammar on a large corpus and re-estimate the spelling correction probabilities shown in Fig. 5.25 given the correct sequence ... *was called a "stellar and versatile* **acress** *whose combination of sass and glamour has defined her...".* Does a bigram grammar prefer the correct word *actress*?

5.11 Read Norvig (2007) and implement one of the extensions he suggests to his Python noisy channel spellchecker.

Chapter 6

Hidden Markov and Maximum Entropy Models

Numquam ponenda est pluralitas sine necessitat
'Plurality should never be proposed unless needed'
William of Occam

Her sister was called Tatiana.
For the first time with such a name
the tender pages of a novel,
we'll whimsically grace.
Pushkin, *Eugene Onegin*, in the Nabokov translation

Alexander Pushkin's novel in verse, *Eugene Onegin*, serialized in the early 19th century, tells of the young dandy Onegin, his rejection of the love of young Tatiana, his duel with his friend Lenski, and his later regret for both mistakes. But the novel is mainly beloved for its style and structure rather than its plot. Among other interesting structural innovations, the novel is written in a form now known as the *Onegin stanza*, iambic tetrameter with an unusual rhyme scheme. These elements have caused complications and controversy in its translation into other languages. Many of the translations have been in verse, but Nabokov famously translated it strictly literally into English prose. The issue of its translation and the tension between literal and verse translations have inspired much commentary (see, for example, Hofstadter (1997)).

In 1913, A. A. Markov asked a less controversial question about Pushkin's text: could we use frequency counts from the text to help compute the probability that the next letter in sequence would be a vowel? In this chapter we introduce two important classes of statistical models for processing text and speech, both descendants of Markov's models. One of them is the **hidden Markov model** (**HMM**). The other is the **maximum entropy** model (**MaxEnt**), and particularly a Markov-related variant of MaxEnt called the **maximum entropy Markov model** (**MEMM**). All of these are **machine learning** models. We have already touched on some aspects of machine learning in Chapter 4, and we briefly introduced the hidden Markov model in the previous chapter. In this chapter, we introduce more completely and formally these two important models.

Sequence classifier

HMMs and MEMMs are both **sequence classifiers**. A sequence classifier or **sequence labeler** is a model whose job is to assign some label or class to each unit in a sequence. The finite-state transducer we studied in Chapter 3 is a kind of nonprobabilistic sequence classifier, for example, transducing from sequences of words to sequences of morphemes. The HMM and MEMM extend this notion by being probabilistic sequence classifiers; given a sequence of units (words, letters, morphemes, sentences, whatever), they compute a probability distribution over possible labels and choose the best label sequence.

We have already seen one important sequence classification task: part-of-speech tagging, whereby each word in a sequence must be assigned a part-of-speech tag. Sequence labeling tasks come up throughout speech and language processing, a fact that isn't too surprising if we consider that language consists of sequences at many representational levels. Besides part-of-speech tagging, in this book we apply sequence models to tasks like speech recognition (Chapter 9), sentence segmentation and grapheme-to-phoneme conversion (Chapter 8), partial parsing/chunking (Chapter 13), and named entity recognition and information extraction (Chapter 22).

This chapter is roughly divided into two sections: hidden Markov models followed by maximum entropy Markov models. Our discussion of the hidden Markov model extends what we said about HMM part-of-speech tagging. We begin in the next section by introducing the Markov chain, then give details of HMMs and the forward and Viterbi algorithms with more formalization, and finally introduce the important EM algorithm for unsupervised (or semi-supervised) learning of a hidden Markov model.

In the second half of the chapter, we gradually introduce maximum entropy Markov models, beginning with techniques that may already be familiar to you from statistics: linear regression and logistic regression. We next introduce MaxEnt. MaxEnt by itself is not a sequence classifier; it is used to assign a class to a single element. The name maximum entropy comes from the idea that the classifier finds the probabilistic model that follows Occam's Razor in being the simplest (least constrained; has the maximum entropy) yet still consistent with some specific constraints. The maximum entropy Markov model is the extension of MaxEnt to the sequence labeling task, adding components such as the Viterbi algorithm.

Although this chapter introduces MaxEnt, which is a classifier, we do not focus in general on non-sequential classification. Non-sequential classification is addressed in later chapters with the introduction of classifiers like the **Gaussian mixture model** in (Chapter 9) and the **naive Bayes** and **decision list** classifiers in (Chapter 20).

6.1   Markov Chains

The hidden Markov model is one of the most important machine learning models in speech and language processing. To define it properly, we need to first introduce the **Markov chain**, sometimes called the **observed Markov model**. Markov chains and hidden Markov models are both extensions of the finite automata of Chapter 2. Recall that a finite automaton is defined by a set of states and a set of transitions between states.

Weighted FSA   A **weighted finite-state automaton** is a simple augmentation of the finite automaton in which each arc is associated with a probability, indicating how likely that path is to be taken. The probability on all the arcs leaving a node must sum to 1.

Markov chain   A **Markov chain** is a special case of a weighted automaton in which the input sequence uniquely determines which states the automaton will go through. Because it can't represent inherently ambiguous problems, a Markov chain is only useful for assigning probabilities to unambiguous sequences.

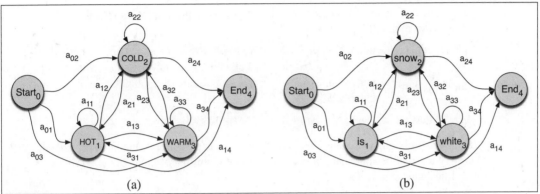

Figure 6.1 A Markov chain for weather (a) and one for words (b). A Markov chain is specified by the structure, the transition between states, and the start and end states.

Figure 6.1a shows a Markov chain for assigning a probability to a sequence of weather events, for which the vocabulary consists of HOT, COLD, and RAINY. Figure 6.1b shows another simple example of a Markov chain for assigning a probability to a sequence of words $w_1...w_n$. This Markov chain should be familiar; in fact, it represents a bigram language model. Given the two models in Fig. 6.1, we can assign a probability to any sequence from our vocabulary. We go over how to do this shortly.

First, let's be more formal and view a Markov chain as a kind of probabilistic **graphical model**: a way of representing probabilistic assumptions in a graph. A Markov chain is specified by the following components:

$Q = q_1 q_2 \ldots q_N$	a set of N **states**
$A = a_{01} a_{02} \ldots a_{n1} \ldots a_{nn}$	a **transition probability matrix** A, each a_{ij} representing the probability of moving from state i to state j, s.t. $\sum_{j=1}^{n} a_{ij} = 1 \quad \forall i$
q_0, q_F	a special **start state** and **end (final) state** that are not associated with observations

Figure 6.1 shows that we represent the states (including start and end states) as nodes in the graph, and the transitions as edges between nodes.

First-order Markov chain

A Markov chain embodies an important assumption about these probabilities. In a **first-order** Markov chain, the probability of a particular state depends only on the previous state:

$$\textbf{Markov Assumption:} \quad P(q_i \, q_1...q_{i-1}) = P(q_i \, q_{i-1}) \tag{6.1}$$

Note that because each a_{ij} expresses the probability $p(q_j \, q_i)$, the laws of probability require that the values of the outgoing arcs from a given state must sum to 1:

$$\sum_{j=1}^{n} a_{ij} = 1 \quad \forall i \tag{6.2}$$

An alternative representation that is sometimes used for Markov chains doesn't rely on a start or end state, instead representing the distribution over initial states and accepting states explicitly:

> $\pi = \pi_1, \pi_2, ..., \pi_N$ an **initial probability distribution** over states. π_i is the probability that the Markov chain will start in state i. Some states j may have $\pi_j = 0$, meaning that they cannot be initial states. Also, $\sum_{i=1}^{n} \pi_i = 1$
>
> $QA = q_x, q_y...$ a set $QA \subset Q$ of legal **accepting states**

Thus, the probability of state 1 being the first state can be represented either as a_{01} or as π_1. Note that because each π_i expresses the probability $p(q_i\ START)$, all the π probabilities must sum to 1:

$$\sum_{i=1}^{n} \pi_i = 1 \tag{6.3}$$

Before you go on, use the sample probabilities in Fig. 6.2b to compute the probability of each of the following sequences:

(6.4)   hot hot hot hot

(6.5)   cold hot cold hot

What does the difference in these probabilities tell you about a real-world weather fact encoded in Fig. 6.2b?

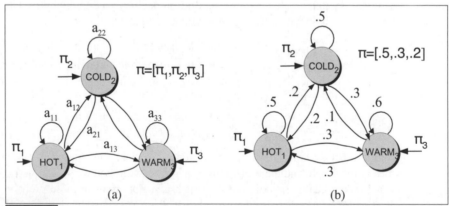

Figure 6.2   Another representation of the same Markov chain for weather shown in Fig. 6.1. Instead of using a special start state with a_{01} transition probabilities, we use the π vector, which represents the distribution over starting state probabilities. The figure in (b) shows sample probabilities.

6.2   The Hidden Markov Model

A Markov chain is useful when we need to compute a probability for a sequence of events that we can observe in the world. In many cases, however, the events we are interested in may not be directly observable in the world. For example, in part-of-speech tagging (Chapter 5) we didn't observe part-of-speech tags in the world; we saw words and had to infer the correct tags from the word sequence. We call the part-of-speech tags **hidden** because they are not observed. The same architecture comes up in speech recognition; in that case we see acoustic events in the world and have to infer the presence of "hidden" words that are the underlying causal source of the acoustics.

Hidden Markov model

A **hidden Markov model** (**HMM**) allows us to talk about both *observed* events (like words that we see in the input) and *hidden* events (like part-of-speech tags) that we think of as causal factors in our probabilistic model.

To exemplify these models, we'll use a task conceived of by Jason Eisner (2002b). Imagine that you are a climatologist in the year 2799 studying the history of global warming. You cannot find any records of the weather in Baltimore, Maryland, for the summer of 2007, but you do find Jason Eisner's diary, which lists how many ice creams Jason ate every day that summer. Our goal is to use these observations to estimate the temperature every day. We'll simplify this weather task by assuming there are only two kinds of days: cold (C) and hot (H). So the Eisner task is as follows:

> Given a sequence of observations O, each observation an integer corresponding to the number of ice creams eaten on a given day, figure out the correct 'hidden' sequence Q of weather states (H or C) which caused Jason to eat the ice cream.

Let's begin with a formal definition of a hidden Markov model, focusing on how it differs from a Markov chain. An HMM is specified by the following components:

$Q = q_1 q_2 \ldots q_N$	a set of N **states**
$A = a_{11} a_{12} \ldots a_{n1} \ldots a_{nn}$	a **transition probability matrix** A, each a_{ij} representing the probability of moving from state i to state j, s.t. $\sum_{j=1}^{n} a_{ij} = 1 \quad \forall i$
$O = o_1 o_2 \ldots o_T$	a sequence of T **observations**, each one drawn from a vocabulary $V = v_1, v_2, \ldots, v_V$
$B = b_i(o_t)$	a sequence of **observation likelihoods**, also called **emission probabilities**, each expressing the probability of an observation o_t being generated from a state i
q_0, q_F	a special **start state** and **end (final) state** that are not associated with observations, together with transition probabilities $a_{01} a_{02} \ldots a_{0n}$ out of the start state and $a_{1F} a_{2F} \ldots a_{nF}$ into the end state

As we noted for Markov chains, an alternative representation that is sometimes used for HMMs doesn't rely on a start or end state, instead representing the distribution over initial and accepting states explicitly. We don't use the π notation in this textbook, but you may see it in the literature:

$\pi = \pi_1, \pi_2, ..., \pi_N$ an **initial probability distribution** over states. π_i is the probability that the Markov chain will start in state i. Some states j may have $\pi_j = 0$, meaning that they cannot be initial states. Also, $\sum_{i=1}^{n} \pi_i = 1$

$QA = q_x, q_y...$ a set $QA \subset Q$ of legal **accepting states**

A first-order hidden Markov model instantiates two simplifying assumptions. First, as with a first-order Markov chain, the probability of a particular state depends only on the previous state:

$$\text{Markov Assumption:} \quad P(q_i \, q_1...q_{i-1}) = P(q_i \, q_{i-1}) \tag{6.6}$$

Second, the probability of an output observation o_i depends only on the state that produced the observation q_i and not on any other states or any other observations:

$$\textbf{Output Independence:} \quad P(o_i \, q_1 ... q_i, ..., q_T, o_1, ..., o_i, ..., o_T) = P(o_i \, q_i) \tag{6.7}$$

Figure 6.3 shows a sample HMM for the ice cream task. The two hidden states (H and C) correspond to hot and cold weather, and the observations (drawn from the alphabet $O = 1, 2, 3$) correspond to the number of ice creams eaten by Jason on a given day.

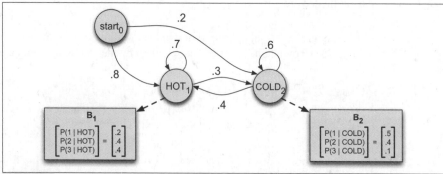

Figure 6.3   A hidden Markov model for relating numbers of ice creams eaten by Jason (the observations) to the weather (H or C, the hidden variables). For this example we are not using an end-state, instead allowing both states 1 and 2 to be a final (accepting) state.

Ergodic HMM

Bakis network

Notice that in the HMM in Fig. 6.3, there is a (non-zero) probability of transitioning between any two states. Such an HMM is called a **fully connected** or **ergodic HMM**. Sometimes, however, we have HMMs in which many of the transitions between states have zero probability. For example, in **left-to-right** (also called **Bakis**) HMMs, the state transitions proceed from left to right, as shown in Fig. 6.4. In a Bakis HMM, no transitions go from a higher-numbered state to a lower-numbered state (or, more accurately, any transitions from a higher-numbered state to a lower-numbered state have zero probability). Bakis HMMs are generally used to model temporal processes like speech; we show more of them in Chapter 9.

Now that we have seen the structure of an HMM, we turn to algorithms for computing things with them. An influential tutorial by Rabiner (1989), based on tutorials

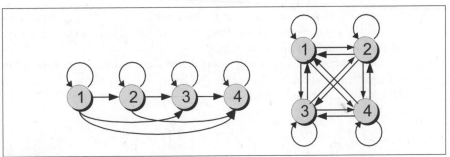

Figure 6.4   Two 4-state hidden Markov models; a left-to-right (Bakis) HMM on the left and a fully connected (ergodic) HMM on the right. In the Bakis model, all transitions not shown have zero probability.

by Jack Ferguson in the 1960s, introduced the idea that hidden Markov models should be characterized by **three fundamental problems**:

> **Problem 1 (Likelihood):**   Given an HMM $\lambda = (A,B)$ and an observation sequence O, determine the likelihood $P(O \lambda)$.
>
> **Problem 2 (Decoding):**   Given an observation sequence O and an HMM $\lambda = (A,B)$, discover the best hidden state sequence Q.
>
> **Problem 3 (Learning):**   Given an observation sequence O and the set of states in the HMM, learn the HMM parameters A and B.

We already saw an example of Problem 2 in Chapter 5. In the next three sections we introduce all three problems more formally.

6.3   Likelihood Computation: The Forward Algorithm

Our first problem is to compute the likelihood of a particular observation sequence. For example, given the HMM in Fig. 6.2b, what is the probability of the sequence *3 1 3*? More formally:

> **Computing Likelihood:** Given an HMM $\lambda = (A,B)$ and an observation sequence O, determine the likelihood $P(O \lambda)$.

For a Markov chain, where the surface observations are the same as the hidden events, we could compute the probability of *3 1 3* just by following the states labeled *3 1 3* and multiplying the probabilities along the arcs. For a hidden Markov model, things are not so simple. We want to determine the probability of an ice-cream observation sequence like *3 1 3*, but we don't know what the hidden state sequence is!

Let's start with a slightly simpler situation. Suppose we already knew the weather and wanted to predict how much ice cream Jason would eat. This is a useful part of many HMM tasks. For a given hidden state sequence (e.g., *hot hot cold*), we can easily compute the output likelihood of *3 1 3*.

Let's see how. First, recall that for hidden Markov models, each hidden state produces only a single observation. Thus, the sequence of hidden states and the sequence of observations have the same length.[1]

Given this one-to-one mapping and the Markov assumptions expressed in Eq. 6.6, for a particular hidden state sequence $Q = q_0, q_1, q_2, ..., q_T$ and an observation sequence $O = o_1, o_2, ..., o_T$, the likelihood of the observation sequence is

$$P(O \mid Q) = \prod_{i=1}^{T} P(o_i \mid q_i) \tag{6.8}$$

The computation of the forward probability for our ice-cream observation *3 1 3* from one possible hidden state sequence *hot hot cold* is shown in Eq. 6.9. Figure 6.5 shows a graphic representation of this computation.

$$P(3\ 1\ 3 \mid \text{hot hot cold}) = P(3 \mid \text{hot})\quad P(1 \mid \text{hot})\quad P(3 \mid \text{cold}) \tag{6.9}$$

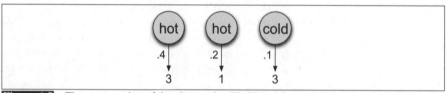

Figure 6.5   The computation of the observation likelihood for the ice-cream events *3 1 3* given the hidden state sequence *hot hot cold*.

But of course, we don't actually know what the hidden state (weather) sequence was. We'll need to compute the probability of ice-cream events *3 1 3* instead by summing over all possible weather sequences, weighted by their probability. First, let's compute the joint probability of being in a particular weather sequence Q and generating a particular sequence O of ice-cream events. In general, this is

$$P(O, Q) = P(O \mid Q)\quad P(Q) = \prod_{i=1}^{n} P(o_i \mid q_i)\ \prod_{i=1}^{n} P(q_i \mid q_{i-1}) \tag{6.10}$$

The computation of the joint probability of our ice-cream observation *3 1 3* and one possible hidden state sequence *hot hot cold* is shown in Eq. 6.11. Figure 6.6 shows a graphic representation of this computation.

$$\begin{aligned}
P(3\ 1\ 3, \text{hot hot cold}) &= P(\text{hot} \mid \text{start})\quad P(\text{hot} \mid \text{hot})\quad P(\text{cold} \mid \text{hot})\\
&\quad P(3 \mid \text{hot})\quad P(1 \mid \text{hot})\quad P(3 \mid \text{cold})
\end{aligned} \tag{6.11}$$

---

[1] In a variant of HMMs called **segmental HMMs** (in speech recognition) or **semi-HMMs** (in text processing) this one-to-one mapping between the length of the hidden state sequence and the length of the observation sequence does not hold.

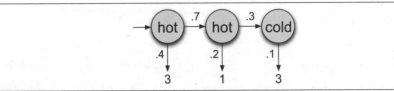

Figure 6.6   The computation of the joint probability of the ice-cream events *3 1 3* and the hidden state sequence *hot hot cold*.

Now that we know how to compute the joint probability of the observations with a particular hidden state sequence, we can compute the total probability of the observations just by summing over all possible hidden state sequences:

$$P(O) = \sum_Q P(O, Q) = \sum_Q P(O\ Q)P(Q) \qquad (6.12)$$

For our particular case, we would sum over the eight 3-event sequences *cold cold cold*, *cold cold hot*, that is,

$$P(3\ 1\ 3) = P(3\ 1\ 3, \text{cold cold cold}) + P(3\ 1\ 3, \text{cold cold hot}) + P(3\ 1\ 3, \text{hot hot cold}) + \dots$$

For an HMM with N hidden states and an observation sequence of T observations, there are N^T possible hidden sequences. For real tasks, where N and T are both large, N^T is a very large number, so we cannot compute the total observation likelihood by computing a separate observation likelihood for each hidden state sequence and then summing them.

Forward algorithm   Instead of using such an extremely exponential algorithm, we use an efficient $O(N^2T)$ algorithm called the **forward algorithm**. The forward algorithm is a kind of **dynamic programming** algorithm, that is, an algorithm that uses a table to store intermediate values as it builds up the probability of the observation sequence. The forward algorithm computes the observation probability by summing over the probabilities of all possible hidden state paths that could generate the observation sequence, but it does so efficiently by implicitly folding each of these paths into a single **forward trellis**.

Figure 6.7 shows an example of the forward trellis for computing the likelihood of *3 1 3* given the hidden state sequence *hot hot cold*.

Each cell of the forward algorithm trellis $\alpha_t(j)$ represents the probability of being in state j after seeing the first t observations, given the automaton λ. The value of each cell $\alpha_t(j)$ is computed by summing over the probabilities of every path that could lead us to this cell. Formally, each cell expresses the following probability:

$$\alpha_t(j) = P(o_1, o_2 \dots o_t, q_t = j \lambda) \qquad (6.13)$$

Here, $q_t = j$ means "the probability that the tth state in the sequence of states is state j". We compute this probability by summing over the extensions of all the paths that lead to the current cell. For a given state q_j at time t, the value $\alpha_t(j)$ is computed as

$$\alpha_t(j) = \sum_{i=1}^{N} \alpha_{t-1}(i) a_{ij} b_j(o_t) \qquad (6.14)$$

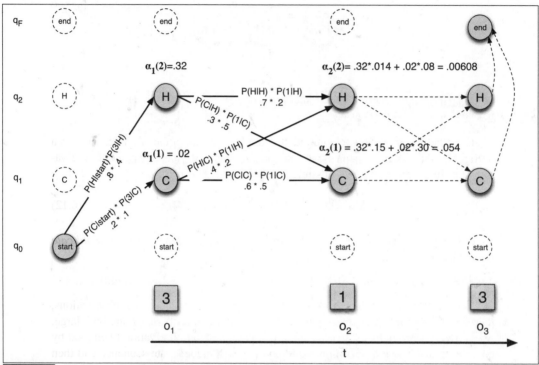

Figure 6.7   The forward trellis for computing the total observation likelihood for the ice-cream events *3 1 3*. Hidden states are in circles, observations in squares. White (unfilled) circles indicate illegal transitions. The figure shows the computation of $\alpha_t(j)$ for two states at two time steps. The computation in each cell follows Eq. 6.14: $\alpha_t(j) = \sum_{i=1}^{N} \alpha_{t-1}(i)a_{ij}b_j(o_t)$. The resulting probability expressed in each cell is Eq. 6.13: $\alpha_t(j) = P(o_1, o_2 \ldots o_t, q_t = j \, \lambda)$.

The three factors that are multiplied in Eq. 6.14 in extending the previous paths to compute the forward probability at time *t* are

> $\alpha_{t-1}(i)$ the **previous forward path probability** from the previous time step
>
> a_{ij} the **transition probability** from previous state q_i to current state q_j
>
> $b_j(o_t)$ the **state observation likelihood** of the observation symbol o_t given the current state j

Consider the computation in Fig. 6.7 of $\alpha_2(1)$, the forward probability of being at time step 2 in state 1 having generated the partial observation *3 1*. We compute by extending the α probabilities from time step 1, via two paths, each extension consisting of the three factors above: $\alpha_1(1)$ $P(H\,H)$ $P(1\,H)$ and $\alpha_1(2)$ $P(H\,C)$ $P(1\,H)$.

Figure 6.8 shows another visualization of this induction step for computing the value in one new cell of the trellis.

We give two formal definitions of the forward algorithm: the pseudocode in Fig. 6.9 and a statement of the definitional recursion here.

1. Initialization:

$$\alpha_1(j) \; = \; a_{0j}b_j(o_1) \; 1 \leq j \leq N \tag{6.15}$$

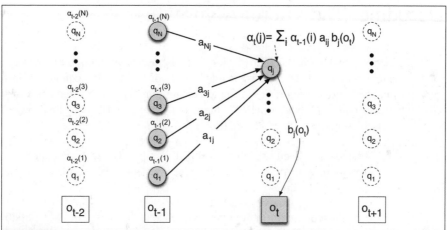

Figure 6.8   Visualizing the computation of a single element $\alpha_t(i)$ in the trellis by summing all the previous values α_{t-1}, weighted by their transition probabilities a, and multiplying by the observation probability $b_i(o_{t+1})$. For many applications of HMMs, many of the transition probabilities are 0, so not all previous states will contribute to the forward probability of the current state. Hidden states are in circles, observations in squares. Shaded nodes are included in the probability computation for $\alpha_t(i)$. Start and end states are not shown.

---

function FORWARD(*observations* of len T, *state-graph* of len N) **returns** *forward-prob*

create a probability matrix *forward[N+2,T]*
for each state s **from** 1 **to** N **do**   ; initialization step
    $forward[s,1] \leftarrow a_{0,s} * b_s(o_1)$
for each time step t **from** 2 **to** T **do**   ; recursion step
  for each state s **from** 1 **to** N **do**

$$forward[s,t] \leftarrow \sum_{s'=1}^{N} forward[s',t-1] * a_{s',s} * b_s(o_t)$$

$$forward[q_F,T] \leftarrow \sum_{s=1}^{N} forward[s,T] * a_{s,q_F}$$; termination step

return $forward[q_F,T]$

Figure 6.9   The forward algorithm. We've used the notation *forward[s,t]* to represent $\alpha_t(s)$.

2. Recursion (since states 0 and F are non-emitting):

$$\alpha_t(j) = \sum_{i=1}^{N} \alpha_{t-1}(i)a_{ij}b_j(o_t); \quad 1 \le j \le N, 1 < t \le T \qquad (6.16)$$

3. Termination:

$$P(O\ \lambda) = \alpha_T(q_F) = \sum_{i=1}^{N} \alpha_T(i)a_{iF} \qquad (6.17)$$

6.4   Decoding: The Viterbi Algorithm

Decoding

Decoder

For any model, such as an HMM, that contains hidden variables, the task of determining which sequence of variables is the underlying source of some sequence of observations is called the **decoding** task. In the ice-cream domain, given a sequence of ice-cream observations *3 1 3* and an HMM, the task of the **decoder** is to find the best hidden weather sequence (*H H H*). More formally,

> **Decoding**: Given as input an HMM $\lambda = (A, B)$ and a sequence of observations $O = o_1, o_2, ..., o_T$, find the most probable sequence of states $Q = q_1 q_2 q_3 ... q_T$.

We might propose to find the best sequence as follows: For each possible hidden state sequence (*HHH*, *HHC*, *HCH*, etc.), we could run the forward algorithm and compute the likelihood of the observation sequence given that hidden state sequence. Then we could choose the hidden state sequence with the maximum observation likelihood. It should be clear from the previous section that we cannot do this because there are an exponentially large number of state sequences.

Viterbi algorithm

Instead, the most common decoding algorithms for HMMs is the **Viterbi algorithm**. Like the forward algorithm, **Viterbi** is a kind of **dynamic programming** that makes uses of a dynamic programming trellis. Viterbi also strongly resembles another dynamic programming variant, the **minimum edit distance** algorithm of Chapter 3.

Figure 6.10 shows an example of the Viterbi trellis for computing the best hidden state sequence for the observation sequence *3 1 3*. The idea is to process the observation sequence left to right, filling out the trellis. Each cell of the trellis, $v_t(j)$, represents the probability that the HMM is in state j after seeing the first t observations and passing through the most probable state sequence $q_0, q_1, ..., q_{t-1}$, given the automaton λ. The value of each cell $v_t(j)$ is computed by recursively taking the most probable path that could lead us to this cell. Formally, each cell expresses the probability

$$v_t(j) = \max_{q_0, q_1, ..., q_{t-1}} P(q_0, q_1 ... q_{t-1}, o_1, o_2 ... o_t, q_t = j \lambda) \tag{6.18}$$

Note that we represent the most probable path by taking the maximum over all possible previous state sequences $\max_{q_0, q_1, ..., q_{t-1}}$. Like other dynamic programming algorithms, Viterbi fills each cell recursively. Given that we had already computed the probability of being in every state at time $t - 1$, we compute the Viterbi probability by taking the most probable of the extensions of the paths that lead to the current cell. For a given state q_j at time t, the value $v_t(j)$ is computed as

$$v_t(j) = \max_{i=1}^{N} v_{t-1}(i) \, a_{ij} \, b_j(o_t) \tag{6.19}$$

The three factors that are multiplied in Eq. 6.19 for extending the previous paths to compute the Viterbi probability at time t are

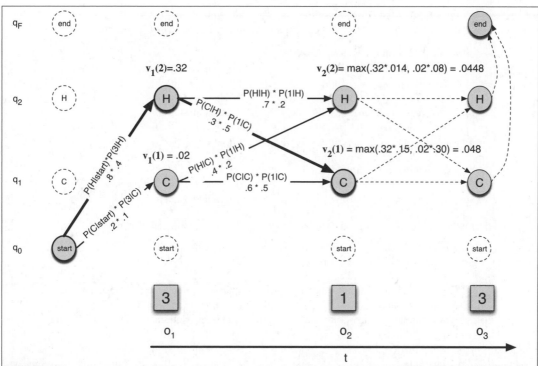

Figure 6.10   The Viterbi trellis for computing the best path through the hidden state space for the ice-cream eating events *3 1 3*. Hidden states are in circles, observations in squares. White (unfilled) circles indicate illegal transitions. The figure shows the computation of $v_t(j)$ for two states at two time steps. The computation in each cell follows Eq. 6.19: $v_t(j) = \max_{1 \leq i \leq N-1} v_{t-1}(i)\, a_{ij}\, b_j(o_t)$. The resulting probability expressed in each cell is Eq. 6.18: $v_t(j) = P(q_0, q_1, \ldots, q_{t-1}, o_1, o_2, \ldots, o_t, q_t = j\,\lambda)$.

$v_{t-1}(i)$	the **previous Viterbi path probability** from the previous time step
a_{ij}	the **transition probability** from previous state q_i to current state q_j
$b_j(o_t)$	the **state observation likelihood** of the observation symbol o_t given the current state j

Figure 6.11 shows pseudocode for the Viterbi algorithm. Note that the Viterbi algorithm is identical to the forward algorithm except that it takes the **max** over the previous path probabilities wheres the forward algorithm takes the **sum**. Note also that the Viterbi algorithm has one component that the forward algorithm doesn't have: **backpointers**. The reason is that while the forward algorithm needs to produce an observation likelihood, the Viterbi algorithm must produce a probability and also the most likely state sequence. We compute this best state sequence by keeping track of the path of hidden states that led to each state, as suggested in Fig. 6.12, and then at the end backtracing the best path to the beginning (the Viterbi **backtrace**).

Viterbi backtrace

Finally, we can give a formal definition of the Viterbi recursion as follows:

---

function VITERBI(*observations* of len *T*, *state-graph* of len *N*) **returns** *best-path*

create a path probability matrix *viterbi[N+2,T]*
for each state *s* **from** 1 **to** *N* **do**   ; initialization step
    viterbi[s,1] ← $a_{0,s} * b_s(o_1)$
    backpointer[s,1] ← 0
for each time step *t* **from** 2 **to** *T* **do**   ; recursion step
  for each state *s* **from** 1 **to** *N* **do**
    viterbi[s,t] ← $\max\limits_{s'=1}^{N}$ *viterbi[s',t−1]* $* a_{s',s} * b_s(o_t)$
    backpointer[s,t] ← $\underset{s'=1}{\operatorname{argmax}}^{N}$ *viterbi[s',t−1]* $* a_{s',s}$
  viterbi[q_F,T] ← $\max\limits_{s=1}^{N}$ *viterbi[s,T]* $* a_{s,q_F}$; termination step
  backpointer[q_F,T] ← $\underset{s=1}{\operatorname{argmax}}^{N}$ *viterbi[s,T]* $* a_{s,q_F}$; termination step
return the backtrace path by following backpointers to states back in
    time from *backpointer[q_F,T]*

Figure 6.11   Viterbi algorithm for finding optimal sequence of hidden states. Given an observation sequence and an HMM $\lambda = (A, B)$, the algorithm returns the state path through the HMM that assigns maximum likelihood to the observation sequence. Note that states 0 and q_F are non-emitting.

1. **Initialization:**

$$v_1(j) = a_{0j}b_j(o_1) \; 1 \leq j \leq N \tag{6.20}$$

$$bt_1(j) = 0 \tag{6.21}$$

2. **Recursion** (recall that states 0 and q_F are non-emitting):

$$v_t(j) = \max_{i=1}^{N} v_{t-1}(i)\, a_{ij} b_j(o_t); \quad 1 \leq j \leq N, 1 < t \leq T \tag{6.22}$$

$$bt_t(j) = \operatorname*{argmax}_{i=1}^{N} v_{t-1}(i)\, a_{ij} b_j(o_t); \quad 1 \leq j \leq N, 1 < t \leq T \tag{6.23}$$

3. **Termination:**

The best score: $P* = v_t(q_F) = \max\limits_{i=1}^{N} v_T(i) * a_{i,F}$ (6.24)

The start of backtrace: $q_T* = bt_T(q_F) = \operatorname*{argmax}\limits_{i=1}^{N} v_T(i) * a_{i,F}$ (6.25)

6.5   HMM Training: The Forward-Backward Algorithm

We turn to the third problem for HMMs: learning the parameters of an HMM, that is, the *A* and *B* matrices. Formally,

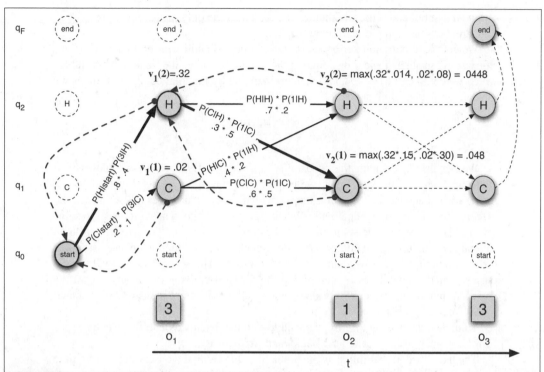

Figure 6.12   The Viterbi backtrace. As we extend each path to a new state account for the next observation, we keep a backpointer (shown with broken lines) to the best path that led us to this state.

> **Learning:** Given an observation sequence O and the set of possible states in the HMM, learn the HMM parameters A and B.

The input to such a learning algorithm would be an unlabeled sequence of observations O and a vocabulary of potential hidden states Q. Thus, for the ice cream task, we would start with a sequence of observations $O = 1,3,2,...$, and the set of hidden states H and C. For the part-of-speech tagging task, we would start with a sequence of observations $O = w_1, w_2, w_3 ...$ and a set of hidden states *NN, NNS, VBD, IN,...* and so on.

Forward-
backward
Baum-Welch
EM

The standard algorithm for HMM training is the **forward-backward**, or **Baum-Welch** algorithm (Baum, 1972), a special case of the **Expectation-Maximization** or **EM** algorithm (Dempster et al., 1977). The algorithm will let us train both the transition probabilities A and the emission probabilities B of the HMM.

Let us begin by considering the much simpler case of training a Markov chain rather than a hidden Markov model. Since the states in a Markov chain are observed, we can run the model on the observation sequence and directly see which path we took through the model and which state generated each observation symbol. A Markov chain of course has no emission probabilities B (alternatively, we could view a Markov chain as a degenerate hidden Markov model where all the b probabilities are 1.0 for the observed symbol and 0 for all other symbols). Thus, the only probabilities we need to train are the transition probability matrix A.

We get the maximum likelihood estimate of the probability a_{ij} of a particular transition between states i and j by counting the number of times the transition was taken, which we could call $C(i \rightarrow j)$, and then normalizing by the total count of all times we took any transition from state i:

$$a_{ij} = \frac{C(i \rightarrow j)}{\sum_{q \in Q} C(i \rightarrow q)} \tag{6.26}$$

We can directly compute this probability in a Markov chain because we know which states we were in. For an HMM, we cannot compute these counts directly from an observation sequence since we don't know which path of states was taken through the machine for a given input. The Baum-Welch algorithm uses two neat intuitions to solve this problem. The first idea is to *iteratively* estimate the counts. We will start with an estimate for the transition and observation probabilities and then use these estimated probabilities to derive better and better probabilities. The second idea is that we get our estimated probabilities by computing the forward probability for an observation and then dividing that probability mass among all the different paths that contributed to this forward probability.

To understand the algorithm, we need to define a useful probability related to the forward probability and called the **backward probability**.

Backward probability

The backward probability β is the probability of seeing the observations from time $t + 1$ to the end, given that we are in state i at time t (and given the automaton λ):

$$\beta_t(i) = P(o_{t+1}, o_{t+2} \ldots o_T \ q_t = i, \lambda) \tag{6.27}$$

It is computed inductively in a similar manner to the forward algorithm.

1. **Initialization:**

$$\beta_T(i) = a_{i,F}, \quad 1 \leq i \leq N \tag{6.28}$$

2. **Recursion** (again since states 0 and q_F are non-emitting):

$$\beta_t(i) = \sum_{j=1}^{N} a_{ij} \, b_j(o_{t+1}) \, \beta_{t+1}(j), \quad 1 \leq i \leq N, 1 \leq t < T \tag{6.29}$$

3. **Termination:**

$$P(O \ \lambda) = \alpha_T(q_F) = \beta_1(0) = \sum_{j=1}^{N} a_{0j} \, b_j(o_1) \, \beta_1(j) \tag{6.30}$$

Figure 6.13 illustrates the backward induction step.

We are now ready to understand how the forward and backward probabilities can help us compute the transition probability a_{ij} and observation probability $b_i(o_t)$ from

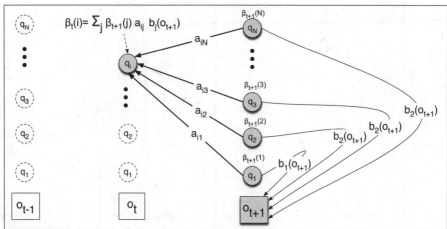

Figure 6.13   The computation of $\beta_t(i)$ by summing all the successive values $\beta_{t+1}(j)$ weighted by their transition probabilities a_{ij} and their observation probabilities $b_j(o_{t+1})$. Start and end states not shown.

an observation sequence, even though the actual path taken through the machine is hidden.

Let's begin by seeing how to estimate $\hat{a}_{ij}$ by a variant of Eq. 6.26:

$$\hat{a}_{ij} = \frac{\text{expected number of transitions from state } i \text{ to state } j}{\text{expected number of transitions from state } i} \tag{6.31}$$

How do we compute the numerator? Here's the intuition. Assume we had some estimate of the probability that a given transition $i \rightarrow j$ was taken at a particular point in time t in the observation sequence. If we knew this probability for each particular time t, we could sum over all times t to estimate the total count for the transition $i \rightarrow j$.

More formally, let's define the probability ξ_t as the probability of being in state i at time t and state j at time $t+1$, given the observation sequence and of course the model:

$$\xi_t(i,j) = P(q_t = i, q_{t+1} = j \, O, \lambda) \tag{6.32}$$

To compute ξ_t, we first compute a probability which is similar to ξ_t, but differs in including the probability of the observation; note the different conditioning of O from Eq. 6.32:

$$\text{not-quite-}\xi_t(i,j) = P(q_t = i, q_{t+1} = j, O \, \lambda) \tag{6.33}$$

Figure 6.14 shows the various probabilities that go into computing *not-quite-*ξ_t: the transition probability for the arc in question, the α probability before the arc, the β probability after the arc, and the observation probability for the symbol just after the arc. These four are multiplied together to produce *not-quite-*ξ_t as follows:

$$\text{not-quite-}\xi_t(i,j) = \alpha_t(i) \, a_{ij} b_j(o_{t+1}) \beta_{t+1}(j) \tag{6.34}$$

To compute ξ_t from *not-quite-*ξ_t, we follow the laws of probability and divide by $P(O \, \lambda)$, since

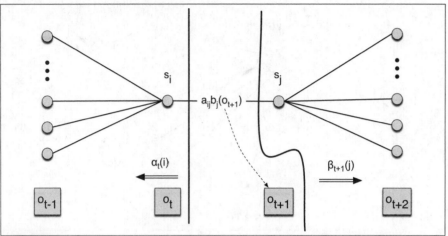

Figure 6.14   Computation of the joint probability of being in state i at time t and state j at time $t+1$. The figure shows the various probabilities that need to be combined to produce $P(q_t = i, q_{t+1} = j, O \lambda)$: the α and β probabilities, the transition probability a_{ij} and the observation probability $b_j(o_{t+1})$. After Rabiner (1989) which is ©1989 IEEE.

$$P(X\ Y, Z) = \frac{P(X, Y\ Z)}{P(Y\ Z)} \qquad (6.35)$$

The probability of the observation given the model is simply the forward probability of the whole utterance (or alternatively, the backward probability of the whole utterance), which can thus be computed in a number of ways:

$$P(O\ \lambda) = \alpha_T(N) = \beta_T(1) = \sum_{j=1}^{N} \alpha_t(j)\beta_t(j) \qquad (6.36)$$

So, the final equation for ξ_t is

$$\xi_t(i, j) = \frac{\alpha_t(i)\, a_{ij} b_j(o_{t+1}) \beta_{t+1}(j)}{\alpha_T(N)} \qquad (6.37)$$

The expected number of transitions from state i to state j is then the sum over all t of ξ. For our estimate of a_{ij} in Eq. 6.31, we just need one more thing: the total expected number of transitions from state i. We can get this by summing over all transitions out of state i. Here's the final formula for $\hat{a}_{ij}$:

$$\hat{a}_{ij} = \frac{\sum_{t=1}^{T-1} \xi_t(i, j)}{\sum_{t=1}^{T-1} \sum_{j=1}^{N} \xi_t(i, j)} \qquad (6.38)$$

We also need a formula for recomputing the observation probability. This is the probability of a given symbol v_k from the observation vocabulary V, given a state j: $\hat{b}_j(v_k)$. We will do this by trying to compute

$$\hat{b}_j(v_k) = \frac{\text{expected number of times in state } j \text{ and observing symbol } v_k}{\text{expected number of times in state } j} \qquad (6.39)$$

For this, we will need to know the probability of being in state j at time t, which we will call $\gamma_t(j)$:

$$\gamma_t(j) = P(q_t = j \, O, \lambda) \qquad (6.40)$$

Once again, we will compute this by including the observation sequence in the probability:

$$\gamma_t(j) = \frac{P(q_t = j, O \, \lambda)}{P(O \, \lambda)} \qquad (6.41)$$

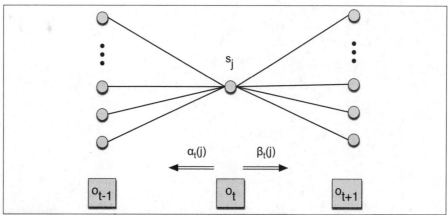

Figure 6.15   The computation of $\gamma_t(j)$, the probability of being in state j at time t. Note that γ is really a degenerate case of ξ and hence this figure is like a version of Fig. 6.14 with state i collapsed with state j. After Rabiner (1989) which is ©1989 IEEE.

As Fig. 6.15 shows, the numerator of Eq. 6.41 is just the product of the forward probability and the backward probability:

$$\gamma_t(j) = \frac{\alpha_t(j)\beta_t(j)}{P(O \, \lambda)} \qquad (6.42)$$

We are ready to compute b. For the numerator, we sum $\gamma_t(j)$ for all time steps t in which the observation o_t is the symbol v_k that we are interested in. For the denominator, we sum $\gamma_t(j)$ over all time steps t. The result is the percentage of the times that we were in state j and saw symbol v_k (the notation $\sum_{t=1 s.t. O_t = v_k}^{T}$ means "sum over all t for which the observation at time t was v_k"):

$$\hat{b}_j(v_k) = \frac{\sum_{t=1 s.t. O_t = v_k}^{T} \gamma_t(j)}{\sum_{t=1}^{T} \gamma_t(j)} \qquad (6.43)$$

We now have ways in Eq. 6.38 and Eq. 6.43 to *re-estimate* the transition A and observation B probabilities from an observation sequence O, assuming that we already have a previous estimate of A and B.

These re-estimations form the core of the iterative forward-backward algorithm. The forward-backward algorithm (Fig. 6.16) starts with some initial estimate of the HMM parameters $\lambda = (A, B)$. We then iteratively run two steps. Like other cases of the EM (expectation-maximization) algorithm, the forward-backward algorithm has two steps: the **expectation** step, or **E-step**, and the **maximization** step, or **M-step**.

E-step

M-step

In the E-step, we compute the expected state occupancy count γ and the expected state transition count ξ from the earlier A and B probabilities. In the M-step, we use γ and ξ to recompute new A and B probabilities.

---

function FORWARD-BACKWARD(*observations* of len T, *output vocabulary V, hidden state set Q*) **returns** *HMM=(A,B)*

initialize A and B
iterate until convergence
    E-step
$$\gamma_t(j) = \frac{\alpha_t(j)\beta_t(j)}{P(O \mid \lambda)} \quad \forall t \text{ and } j$$
$$\xi_t(i, j) = \frac{\alpha_t(i)\, a_{ij} b_j(o_{t+1})\beta_{t+1}(j)}{\alpha_T(N)} \quad \forall t,\ i, \text{ and } j$$
    M-step
$$\hat{a}_{ij} = \frac{\sum_{t=1}^{T-1} \xi_t(i, j)}{\sum_{t=1}^{T-1} \sum_{j=1}^{N} \xi_t(i, j)}$$
$$\hat{b}_j(v_k) = \frac{\sum_{t=1 \, s.t. \, O_t = v_k}^{T} \gamma_t(j)}{\sum_{t=1}^{T} \gamma_t(j)}$$

return A, B

Figure 6.16   The forward-backward algorithm.

Although in principle the forward-backward algorithm can do completely unsupervised learning of the A and B parameters, in practice the initial conditions are very important. For this reason the algorithm is often given extra information. For example, for speech recognition, in practice the HMM structure is often set by hand, and only the emission (B) and (non-zero) A transition probabilities are trained from a set of observation sequences O. Section 9.7 in Chapter 9 also discusses how initial A and B estimates are derived in speech recognition. We also show that for speech the forward-backward algorithm can be extended to inputs that are non-discrete ("continuous observation densities").

6.6   Maximum Entropy Models: Background

We turn now to a second probabilistic machine learning framework called **maximum entropy** modeling, **MaxEnt** for short. MaxEnt is more widely known as **multinomial logistic regression**.

Our goal in this chapter is to introduce the use of MaxEnt for sequence classification. Recall that the task of sequence classification or sequence labeling is to assign a label to each element in some sequence, such as assigning a part-of-speech tag to a word. The most common MaxEnt sequence classifier is the **maximum entropy Markov model** or **MEMM**, introduced in Section 6.8. But before we describe the use of MaxEnt as a sequence classifier, we need to introduce non-sequential classification.

The task of classification is to take a single observation, extract some useful features describing the observation, and then, based on these features, to **classify** the observation into one of a set of discrete classes. A **probabilistic** classifier does slightly more than this; in addition to assigning a label or class, it gives the **probability** of the observation being in that class; indeed, for a given observation, a probabilistic classifier gives a probability distribution over all classes.

Such non-sequential classification tasks occur throughout speech and language processing. For example, in **text classification** we might need to decide whether a particular email should be classified as spam. In **sentiment analysis** we have to determine whether a particular sentence or document expresses a positive or negative **opinion**. In many tasks, we'll need to know where the sentence boundaries are, and so we'll need to classify a period character ('.') as either a sentence boundary or not. We show more examples of the need for classification throughout this book.

Log-linear classifier   MaxEnt belongs to the family of classifiers known as the **exponential** or **log-linear** classifiers. MaxEnt works by extracting some set of features from the input, combining them **linearly** (meaning that each feature is multiplied by a weight and then added up), and then, for reasons discussed below, using this sum as an exponent.

Let's flesh out this intuition just a bit more. Assume that we have some input x (perhaps it is a word that needs to be tagged or a document that needs to be classified) from which we extract some features. A feature for tagging might be *this word ends in -ing* or *the previous word was 'the'*. For each such feature f_i, we have some weight w_i.

Given the features and weights, our goal is to choose a class (e.g., a part-of-speech tag) for the word. MaxEnt does this by choosing the most probable tag; the probability of a particular class c given the observation x is

$$p(c\,x) \;=\; \frac{1}{Z}\exp\Big(\sum_i w_i f_i\Big) \qquad (6.44)$$

Here Z is a normalizing factor, used to make the probabilities correctly sum to 1; and as usual $\exp(x) = e^x$. As we show later, this is a simplified equation in various ways; for example, in the actual MaxEnt model, the features f and weights w both depend on the class c (i.e., we'll have different features and weights for different classes). To explain the details of the MaxEnt classifier, including the definition of the normalizing term Z and the intuition of the exponential function, we must first understand both **linear regression**, which lays the groundwork for prediction by using features, and **logistic regression**, which is our introduction to exponential models. We cover these areas in the next two sections; readers with a background in regression may want to skip ahead. Then, in Section 6.7 we introduce the details of the MaxEnt classifier. Finally, in Section 6.8 we show how the MaxEnt classifier is used for sequence classification in the **maximum entropy Markov model** (**MEMM**).

6.6.1   Linear Regression

In statistics we use two different names for tasks that map some input features into some output value: we use the word **regression** when the output is real-valued and **classification** when the output is one of a discrete set of classes.

You may already be familiar with linear regression from a statistics class. The idea is that we are given a set of observations, each observation associated with some features, and we want to predict some real-valued outcome for each observation. Let's see an example from the domain of predicting housing prices. Levitt and Dubner (2005) showed that the words used in a real estate ad can be a good predictor of whether a house will sell for more or less than its asking price. They showed, for example, that houses whose real estate ads had words like *fantastic*, *cute*, or *charming*, tended to sell for lower prices, while houses whose ads had words like *maple* and *granite* tended to sell for higher prices. Their hypothesis was that real estate agents used vague positive words like *fantastic* to mask the lack of any specific positive qualities in the house. Just for pedagogical purposes, we created the fake data in Fig. 6.17.

# of Vague Adjectives	Amount House Sold Over Asking Price
4	0
3	$1000
2	$1500
2	$6000
1	$14000
0	$18000

Figure 6.17   Some made-up data on the number of vague adjectives (*fantastic*, *cute*, *charming*) in a real estate ad and the amount the house sold for over the asking price.

Regression line

Figure 6.18 shows a graph of these points, with the feature (# of adjectives) on the x-axis, and the price on the y-axis. We have also plotted a **regression line**, which is the line that best fits the observed data. The equation of any line is $y = mx + b$; as we show on the graph, the slope of this line is $m = -4900$, and the intercept is 16550. We can think of these two parameters of this line (slope m and intercept b) as a set of weights that we use to map from our features (in this case x, number of adjectives) to our output value y (in this case, price). We can represent this linear function by using w to refer to weights as follows:

$$\text{price} = w_0 + w_1 * \text{Num\_Adjectives} \tag{6.45}$$

Thus, Eq. 6.45 gives us a linear function that lets us estimate the sales price for any number of these adjectives. For example, how much would we expect a house whose

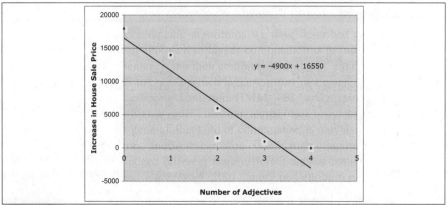

Figure 6.18 A plot of the (made-up) points in Fig. 6.17 and the regression line that best fits them, with the equation $y = -4900x + 16550$.

ad has five adjectives to sell for?

The true power of linear models comes when we use more than one feature (technically, we call this **multiple linear regression**). For example, the final house price probably depends on many factors, such as the current mortgage rate, the number of unsold houses on the market, etc. We could encode each of these as a variable, and the importance of each factor would be the weight on that variable, as follows:

$$\text{price} = w_0 + w_1 * \text{Num\_Adjectives} + w_2 * \text{Mortgage\_Rate} + w_3 * \text{Num\_Unsold\_Houses}$$

Feature

In speech and language processing, we often call each of these predictive factors, like the number of adjectives or the mortgage rate, a **feature**. We represent each observation (each house for sale) by a vector of these features. Suppose a house has one adjective in its ad and the mortgage rate was 6.5 and there were 10,000 unsold houses in the city. The feature vector for the house would be $\vec{f} = (1, 6.5, 10000)$. Suppose the weight vector that we had previously learned for this task was $\vec{w} = (w_0, w_1, w_2, w_3) = (18000, -5000, -3000, -1.8)$. Then the predicted value for this house would be computed by multiplying each feature by its weight:

$$\text{price} = w_0 + \sum_{i=1}^{N} w_i \ f_i \qquad (6.46)$$

In general, we will pretend that there is an extra feature, f_0, that has the value 1, an **intercept feature**, which make the equations simpler with regard to that pesky w_0, and so in general we can represent a linear regression for estimating the value of y as

$$\textbf{linear regression:} \qquad y = \sum_{i=0}^{N} w_i \ f_i \qquad (6.47)$$

Dot product

Taking two vectors and creating a scalar by multiplying each element in a pairwise fashion and summing the results is called the **dot product**. Recall that the dot product

197

$a \cdot b$ between two vectors a and b is defined as

dot product: $$a \cdot b = \sum_{i=1}^{N} a_i b_i = a_1 b_1 + a_2 b_2 + \cdots + a_n b_n \qquad (6.48)$$

Thus, Eq. 6.47 is equivalent to the dot product between the weights vector and the feature vector:

$$y = w \cdot f \qquad (6.49)$$

Vector dot products frequently occur in speech and language processing; we often rely on the dot product notation to avoid the messy summation signs.

Learning in Linear Regression

How do we learn the weights for linear regression? Intuitively, we'd like to choose weights that make the estimated values y as close as possible to the actual values that we saw in a training set.

Consider a particular instance $x^{(j)}$ from the training set that has an observed label in the training set $y_{obs}^{(j)}$ (we'll use superscripts in parentheses to represent training instances). Our linear regression model predicts a value for $y^{(j)}$ as follows:

$$y_{pred}^{(j)} = \sum_{i=0}^{N} w_i \cdot f_i^{(j)} \qquad (6.50)$$

We'd like to choose the whole set of weights W so as to minimize the difference between the predicted value $y_{pred}^{(j)}$ and the observed value $y_{obs}^{(j)}$, and we want this difference minimized over all the M examples in our training set. Actually, we want to minimize the absolute value of the difference since we don't want a negative distance in one example to cancel out a positive difference in another example, so for simplicity (and differentiability), we minimize the square of the difference. Thus, the total value *Sum-squared error* we want to minimize, which we call the **sum-squared error**, is this cost function of the current set of weights W:

$$\text{cost}(W) = \sum_{j=0}^{M} \left(y_{pred}^{(j)} - y_{obs}^{(j)} \right)^2 \qquad (6.51)$$

We don't give here the details of choosing the optimal set of weights to minimize the sum-squared error. But, briefly, it turns out that if we put the entire training set into a single matrix X with each row in the matrix consisting of the vector of features associated with each observation $x^{(i)}$ and put all the observed y values in a vector $\vec{y}$, there is a closed-form formula for the optimal weight values W that will minimize $\text{cost}(W)$:

$$W = (X^T X)^{-1} X^T \vec{y} \qquad (6.52)$$

Implementations of this equation are widely available in statistical packages like SPSS or R.

6.6.2 Logistic Regression

Linear regression is what we want when we are predicting a real-valued outcome. But often in speech and language processing we are doing **classification**, in which the output y we are trying to predict takes on one from a small set of discrete values.

Consider the simplest case of binary classification: classifying whether some observation x is in the class (true) or not in the class (false). In other words, y can only take on the values 1 (true) or 0 (false), and we'd like a classifier that can take features of x and return true or false. Furthermore, instead of just returning the 0 or 1 value, we'd like a model that can give us the **probability** that a particular observation is in class 0 or 1. This is important because in most real-world tasks we're passing the results of this classifier to some further classifier to accomplish some task. Since we are rarely completely certain about which class an observation falls in, we'd prefer not to make a hard decision at this stage, ruling out all other classes. Instead, we'd like to pass on to the later classifier as much information as possible: the entire set of classes, with the probability value that we assign to each class.

Could we modify our linear regression model to use it for this kind of probabilistic classification? Suppose we just tried to train a linear model to predict a probability as follows:

$$P(y = \text{true } x) = \sum_{i=0}^{N} w_i \quad f_i \tag{6.53}$$

$$= w \ f \tag{6.54}$$

We could train such a model by assigning each training observation the target value $y = 1$ if it was in the class (true) and the target value $y = 0$ if it was not (false). Each observation x would have a feature vector f, and we would train the weight vector w to minimize the predictive error from 1 (for observations in the class) or 0 (for observations not in the class). After training, we would compute the probability of a class given an observation by just taking the dot product of the weight vector with the features for that observation.

The problem with this model is that nothing forces the output to be a legal probability, that is, to lie between 0 and 1. The expression $\sum_{i=0}^{N} w_i \quad f_i$ produces values from $-\infty$ to ∞. How can we fix this problem? Suppose that we keep our linear predictor $w \ f$, but instead of having it predict a probability, we have it predict a *ratio* of two probabilities. Specifically, suppose we predict the ratio of the probability of being in the class to the probability of not being in the class. This ratio is called the **odds**. If an event has probability .75 of occurring and probability .25 of not occurring, we say the **odds** of occurring is $.75/.25 = 3$. We could use the linear model to predict the odds of y being true:

Odds

$$\frac{p(y = \text{true}) \ x}{1 - p(y = \text{true } x)} = w \ f \tag{6.55}$$

This last model is close: a ratio of probabilities can lie between 0 and ∞. But we need the left-hand side of the equation to lie between $-\infty$ and ∞. We can achieve this by taking the natural log of this probability:

$$\ln\left(\frac{p(y=\text{true } x)}{1-p(y=\text{true } x)}\right) = w \ f \tag{6.56}$$

Now both the left and right hand lie between $-\infty$ and ∞. This function on the left

Logit function (the log of the odds) is known as the **logit function**:

$$\text{logit}(p(x)) = \ln\left(\frac{p(x)}{1-p(x)}\right) \tag{6.57}$$

Logistic regression The model of regression in which we use a linear function to estimate the logit of the probability rather than the probability is known as **logistic regression**. If the linear function is estimating the logit, what is the actual formula in logistic regression for the probability $P(y=\text{true})$? You should stop here and with Eq. 6.56 apply some simple algebra to solve for the probability $P(y=\text{true})$.

Hopefully, when you solved for $P(y=\text{true})$, you came up with a derivation something like the following:

$$\ln\left(\frac{p(y=\text{true } x)}{1-p(y=\text{true } x)}\right) = w \ f$$

$$\frac{p(y=\text{true } x)}{1-p(y=\text{true } x)} = e^{w f} \tag{6.58}$$

$$p(y=\text{true } x) = (1-p(y=\text{true } x))e^{w f}$$

$$p(y=\text{true } x) = e^{w f} - p(y=\text{true } x)e^{w f}$$

$$p(y=\text{true } x) + p(y=\text{true } x)e^{w f} = e^{w f}$$

$$p(y=\text{true } x)(1+e^{w f}) = e^{w f}$$

$$p(y=\text{true } x) = \frac{e^{w f}}{1+e^{w f}} \tag{6.59}$$

Once we have this probability, it is easy to state the probability of the observation not belonging to the class, $p(y=\text{false } x)$, as the two must sum to 1:

$$p(y=\text{false } x) = \frac{1}{1+e^{w f}} \tag{6.60}$$

Here are the equations again in explicit summation notation:

$$p(y=\text{true } x) = \frac{\exp(\sum_{i=0}^{N} w_i f_i)}{1+\exp(\sum_{i=0}^{N} w_i f_i)} \tag{6.61}$$

$$p(y=\text{false } x) = \frac{1}{1+\exp(\sum_{i=0}^{N} w_i f_i)} \tag{6.62}$$

We can express the probability $P(y=\text{true } x)$ in a slightly different way, by dividing the numerator and denominator in (6.59) by $e^{-w f}$:

$$p(y=\text{true } x) = \frac{e^{w f}}{1+e^{w f}} \tag{6.63}$$

$$= \frac{1}{1+e^{-w\,f}} \tag{6.64}$$

Logistic function   The last equation is now in the form of what is called the **logistic function** (the function that gives logistic regression its name). The general form of the logistic function is

$$\frac{1}{1+e^{-x}} \tag{6.65}$$

The logistic function maps values from $-\infty$ and ∞ to lie between 0 and 1. Again, we can express $P(y=$ false $x)$ so as to make the probabilities sum to 1:

$$p(y= \text{false } x) \;=\; \frac{e^{-w\,f}}{1+e^{-w\,f}} \tag{6.66}$$

6.6.3   Logistic Regression: Classification

Classification   Given a particular observation, how do we decide which of the two classes ('true' or
Inference   'false') it belongs to? This is the task of **classification**, also called **inference**. Clearly, the correct class is the one with the higher probability. Thus, we can safely say that our observation should be labeled 'true' if

$$p(y= \text{true } x) > p(y= \text{false } x)$$
$$\frac{p(y= \text{true } x)}{p(y= \text{false } x)} > 1$$
$$\frac{p(y= \text{true } x)}{1 - p(y= \text{true } x)} > 1$$

and substituting from Eq. 6.58 for the odds ratio:

$$e^{w\,f} > 1$$
$$w\ f > 0 \tag{6.67}$$

or with the explicit sum notation:

$$\sum_{i=0}^{N} w_i f_i > 0 \tag{6.68}$$

Thus, to decide if an observation is a member of the class, we just need to compute the linear function and see if its value is positive; if so, the observation is in the class.

A more advanced point: the equation $\sum_{i=0}^{N} w_i f_i = 0$ is the equation of a **hyperplane** (a generalization of a line to N dimensions). The equation $\sum_{i=0}^{N} w_i f_i > 0$ is thus the part of N-dimensional space above this hyperplane. Thus, we can see the logistic regression function as learning a hyperplane which separates points in space that are in the class ('true') from points that are not in the class.

6.6.4   Advanced: Learning in Logistic Regression

Conditional maximum likelihood estimation

In linear regression, learning consisted of choosing the weights w that minimized the sum-squared error on the training set. In logistic regression we use **conditional maximum likelihood estimation**. What this means is that we choose the parameters w that make the probability of the observed y values in the training data to be the highest, given the observations x. In other words, for an individual training observation x, we want to choose the weights as follows:

$$\hat{w} = \operatorname*{argmax}_{w} P(y^{(i)} \, x^{(i)}) \tag{6.69}$$

And we'd like to choose the optimal weights for the entire training set:

$$\hat{w} = \operatorname*{argmax}_{w} \prod_{i} P(y^{(i)} \, x^{(i)}) \tag{6.70}$$

We generally work with the log likelihood:

$$\hat{w} = \operatorname*{argmax}_{w} \sum_{i} \log P(y^{(i)} \, x^{(i)}) \tag{6.71}$$

So, more explicitly:

$$\hat{w} = \operatorname*{argmax}_{w} \sum_{i} \log \begin{cases} P(y^{(i)} = 1 \, x^{(i)})) & \text{for } y^{(i)} = 1 \\ P(y^{(i)} = 0 \, x^{(i)})) & \text{for } y^{(i)} = 0 \end{cases} \tag{6.72}$$

This equation is unwieldy, so we usually apply a convenient representational trick. Note that if $y = 0$, the first term goes away, while if $y = 1$ the second term goes away:

$$\hat{w} = \operatorname*{argmax}_{w} \sum_{i} y^{(i)} \log P(y^{(i)} = 1 \, x^{(i)}) + (1 - y^{(i)}) \log P(y^{(i)} = 0 \, x^{(i)}) \tag{6.73}$$

Now if we substitute in Eq. 6.64 and Eq. 6.66, we get

$$\hat{w} = \operatorname*{argmax}_{w} \sum_{i} y^{(i)} \log \frac{1}{1 + e^{-w f}} + (1 - y^{(i)}) \log \frac{e^{-w f}}{1 + e^{-w f}} \tag{6.74}$$

Convex optimization

Finding the weights that result in the maximum log-likelihood according to Eq. 6.74 is a problem in the field known as **convex optimization**. Among the most commonly used algorithms are **quasi-Newton** methods like L-BFGS (Nocedal, 1980; Byrd et al., 1995), as well as gradient ascent, conjugate gradient, and various iterative scaling algorithms (Darroch and Ratcliff, 1972; Della Pietra et al., 1997; Malouf, 2002). These learning algorithms are available in MaxEnt modeling toolkits but are too complex to define here; interested readers should see the Historical Notes at the end of the chapter.

6.7   Maximum Entropy Modeling

Multinomial logistic regression

MaxEnt

We showed above how logistic regression can be used to classify an observation into one of two classes. But most of the time, the kinds of classification problems that come up in language processing involve larger numbers of classes (such as the set of part-of-speech classes). Logistic regression can also be defined for such functions with many discrete values. In such cases it is called **multinomial logistic regression**. As we mentioned above, multinomial logistic regression is called **MaxEnt** in speech and language processing (see Section 6.7.1 on the intuition behind the name "maximum entropy").

The equations for computing the class probabilities for a MaxEnt classifier are a generalization of Eqs. 6.61–6.62 above. Let's assume that the target value y is a random variable that can take on C different values corresponding to the classes $c_1, c_2,...,c_C$.

We said earlier in this chapter that in a MaxEnt model we estimate the probability that y is a particular class c as

$$p(c\ x) = \frac{1}{Z}\exp\sum_i w_i f_i \tag{6.75}$$

Let's now add some details to this schematic equation. First, we'll flesh out the normalization factor Z, specify the number of features as N, and make the value of the weight dependent on the class c. The final equation is

$$p(c\ x) = \frac{\exp\left(\sum_{i=0}^{N} w_{ci} f_i\right)}{\sum_{c'\in C}\exp\left(\sum_{i=0}^{N} w_{c'i} f_i\right)} \tag{6.76}$$

Note that the normalization factor Z is just used to make the exponential into a true probability:

$$Z = \sum_C p(c\ x) = \sum_{c'\in C}\exp\left(\sum_{i=0}^{N} w_{c'i} f_i\right) \tag{6.77}$$

Indicator function

We need to make one more change to see the final MaxEnt equation. So far we've been assuming that the features f_i are real-valued. It is more common in speech and language processing, however, to use binary-valued features. A feature that takes on only the values 0 and 1 is also called an **indicator function**. In general, the features we use are indicator functions of some property of the observation and the class we are considering assigning. Thus, in MaxEnt, instead of the notation f_i, we often use the notation $f_i(c,x)$, meaning a feature i for a particular class c for a given observation x.

The final equation for computing the probability of y being of class c given x in MaxEnt is

$$p(c\ x) = \frac{\exp\left(\displaystyle\sum_{i=0}^{N} w_{ci} f_i(c,x)\right)}{\displaystyle\sum_{c' \in C} \exp\left(\displaystyle\sum_{i=0}^{N} w_{c'i} f_i(c',x)\right)} \tag{6.78}$$

To get a clearer intuition of this use of binary features, let's look at some sample features for the task of part-of-speech tagging. Suppose we are assigning a part-of-speech tag to the word *race* in Eq. 6.79, repeated from Eq. 5.36:

(6.79) Secretariat/NNP is/BEZ expected/VBN to/TO **race**/?? tomorrow/

Again, for now we're just doing classification, not sequence classification, so let's consider just this single word. We discuss in Section 6.8 how to perform tagging for a whole sequence of words.

We would like to know whether to assign the class *VB* to *race* (or instead assign some other class like *NN*). One useful feature, we'll call it f_1, would be the fact that the current word is *race*. We can thus add a binary feature that is true if this is the case:

$$f_1(c,x) = \begin{cases} 1 & \text{if } word_i = \text{``race''} \ \& \ c = \text{NN} \\ 0 & \text{otherwise} \end{cases}$$

Another feature would be whether the previous word has the tag *TO*:

$$f_2(c,x) = \begin{cases} 1 & \text{if } t_{i-1} = \text{TO} \ \& \ c = \text{VB} \\ 0 & \text{otherwise} \end{cases}$$

Two more part-of-speech tagging features might focus on aspects of a word's spelling and case:

$$f_3(c,x) = \begin{cases} 1 & \text{if } \text{suffix}(word_i) = \text{``ing''} \ \& \ c = \text{VBG} \\ 0 & \text{otherwise} \end{cases}$$

$$f_4(c,x) = \begin{cases} 1 & \text{if } \text{is\_lower\_case}(word_i) \ \& \ c = \text{VB} \\ 0 & \text{otherwise} \end{cases}$$

Since each feature is dependent on both a property of the observation and the class being labeled, we would need to have a separate feature, for example, for the link between *race* and VB or the link between a previous TO and NN:

$$f_5(c,x) = \begin{cases} 1 & \text{if } word_i = \text{"race"} \ \& \ c = \text{VB} \\ 0 & \text{otherwise} \end{cases}$$

$$f_6(c,x) = \begin{cases} 1 & \text{if } t_{i-1} = \text{TO} \ \& \ c = \text{NN} \\ 0 & \text{otherwise} \end{cases}$$

Each of these features has a corresponding weight. Thus, the weight $w_1(c,x)$ would indicate how strong a cue the word *race* is for the tag VB, the weight $w_2(c,x)$ would indicate how strong a cue the previous tag *TO* is for the current word being a VB, and so on.

		f1	f2	f3	f4	f5	f6
VB	f	0	1	0	1	1	0
VB	w		.8		.01	.1	
NN	f	1	0	0	0	0	1
NN	w	.8					-1.3

Figure 6.19   Some sample feature values and weights for tagging the word *race* in Eq. 6.79.

Let's assume that the feature weights for the two classes VB and VN are as shown in Fig. 6.19. Let's call the current input observation (where the current word is *race*) x. We can now compute $P(NN\ x)$ and $P(VB\ x)$, using Eq. 6.78:

$$P(NN\ x) \;=\; \frac{e^{.8}e^{-1.3}}{e^{.8}e^{-1.3}+e^{.8}e^{.01}e^{.1}} = .20 \tag{6.80}$$

$$P(VB\ x) \;=\; \frac{e^{.8}e^{.01}e^{.1}}{e^{.8}e^{-1.3}+e^{.8}e^{.01}e^{.1}} = .80 \tag{6.81}$$

Notice that when we use MaxEnt to perform **classification**, MaxEnt naturally gives us a probability distribution over the classes. If we want to do a hard classification and choose the single-best class, we can choose the class that has the highest probability, that is,

$$\hat{c} = \operatorname*{argmax}_{c\in C} P(c\ x) \tag{6.82}$$

Classification in MaxEnt is thus a generalization of classification in (Boolean) logistic regression. In Boolean logistic regression, classification involves building one linear expression that separates the observations in the class from the observations not in the class. Classification in MaxEnt, by contrast, involves building a separate linear expression for each of C classes.

But as we show later in Section 6.8, we generally don't use MaxEnt for hard classification. We usually want to use MaxEnt as part of sequence classification, where we want not the best single class for one unit, but the best total sequence. For this task, it's useful to exploit the entire probability distribution for each individual unit, to help find the best sequence. Indeed, even in many non-sequence applications a probability distribution over the classes is more useful than a hard choice.

The features we have described so far express a single binary property of an observation. But it is often useful to create more complex features that express combinations of properties of a word. Some kinds of machine learning models, like Support Vector Machines (SVMs), can automatically model the interactions between primitive properties, but in MaxEnt any kind of complex feature has to be defined by hand. For example, a word starting with a capital letter (like the word *Day*) is more likely to be a proper noun (NNP) than a common noun (e.g., in the expression *United Nations Day*). But a word that is capitalized but that occurs at the beginning of the sentence (the previous word is <s>), as in *Day after day*...., is not more likely to be a proper noun. Even if each of these properties were already a primitive feature, MaxEnt would not model their combination, so this Boolean combination of properties would need to be encoded as a feature by hand:

$$f_{125}(c,x) = \begin{cases} 1 & \text{if } word_{i-1} = \text{<s> \& isupperfirst}(word_i) \text{ \& } c = \text{NNP} \\ 0 & \text{otherwise} \end{cases}$$

A key to successful use of MaxEnt is thus the design of appropriate features and feature combinations.

Learning Maximum Entropy Models

Learning a MaxEnt model can be done through a generalization of the logistic regression learning algorithms described in Section 6.6.4. As we saw in Eq. 6.71, we want to find the parameters w that maximize the log likelihood of the M training samples:

$$\hat{w} = \underset{w}{\text{argmax}} \sum_i \log P(y^{(i)} \, x^{(i)}) \tag{6.83}$$

As with binary logistic regression, we use some convex optimization algorithm to find the weights which maximize this function.

Regularization   A brief note: One important aspect of MaxEnt training is a kind of smoothing of the weights called **regularization**. The goal of regularization is to penalize large weights; it turns out that otherwise a MaxEnt model will learn very high weights that overfit the training data. We implement regularization in training by changing the likelihood function that is optimized. Instead of the optimization in Eq. 6.83, we optimize the following:

$$\hat{w} = \underset{w}{\text{argmax}} \sum_i \log P(y^{(i)} \, x^{(i)}) - \alpha R(w) \tag{6.84}$$

where $R(w)$ is a **regularization** term used to penalize large weights. It is common to make the regularization term $R(w)$ be a quadratic function of the weight values:

$$R(W) = \sum_{j=1}^{N} w_j^2 \tag{6.85}$$

Subtracting squares of the weights thus results in preferring smaller weights:

$$\hat{w} = \underset{w}{\text{argmax}} \sum_i \log P(y^{(i)} \, x^{(i)}) - \alpha \sum_{j=1}^{N} w_j^2 \tag{6.86}$$

It turns that this kind of regularization corresponds to assuming that weights are distributed according to a Gaussian distribution with mean $\mu = 0$. In a Gaussian or normal distribution, the further away a value is from the mean, the lower its probability (scaled by the variance σ). By using a Gaussian prior on the weights, we are saying that weights prefer to have the value 0. A Gaussian for a weight w_j is

$$\frac{1}{\sqrt{2\pi\sigma_j^2}} \exp\left(-\frac{(w_j - \mu_j)^2}{2\sigma_j^2}\right) \qquad (6.87)$$

If we multiply each weight by a Gaussian prior on the weight, we are thus maximizing the following constraint:

$$\hat{w} = \underset{w}{\operatorname{argmax}} \prod_{i}^{M} P(y^{(i)}\, x^{(i)}) \ \prod_{j=1}^{N} \frac{1}{\sqrt{2\pi\sigma_j^2}} \exp\left(-\frac{(w_j - \mu_j)^2}{2\sigma_j^2}\right) \qquad (6.88)$$

which in log space, with $\mu = 0$, corresponds to

$$\hat{w} = \underset{w}{\operatorname{argmax}} \sum_{i} \log P(y^{(i)}\, x^{(i)}) - \sum_{j=1}^{N} \frac{w_j^2}{2\sigma_j^2} \qquad (6.89)$$

which is in the same form as Eq. 6.86.

There is a vast literature on the details of learning in MaxEnt; see the end of the chapter for pointers to further details.

6.7.1   Why We Call It Maximum Entropy

Why do we refer to multinomial logistic regression models as MaxEnt or Maximum Entropy models? Let's give the intuition of this interpretation in the context of part-of-speech tagging. Suppose we want to assign a tag to the word *zzfish* (a word we made up for this example). What is the probabilistic tagging model (the distribution of part-of-speech tags across words) that makes the fewest assumptions, imposing no constraints at all? Intuitively it would be the equiprobable distribution:

NN	JJ	NNS	VB	NNP	IN	MD	UH	SYM	VBG	POS	PRP	CC	CD	...
$\frac{1}{45}$	$\frac{1}{45}$	$\frac{1}{45}$	$\frac{1}{45}$	$\frac{1}{45}$	$\frac{1}{45}$	$\frac{1}{45}$	$\frac{1}{45}$	$\frac{1}{45}$	$\frac{1}{45}$	$\frac{1}{45}$	$\frac{1}{45}$	$\frac{1}{45}$	$\frac{1}{45}$	...

Now suppose we had some training data labeled with part-of-speech tags, and from this data we learned only one fact: the set of possible tags for *zzfish* is NN, JJ, NNS, and VB (so *zzfish* is a word something like *fish* but can also be an adjective). What is the tagging model that relies on this constraint but makes no further assumptions at all? Since one of these must be the correct tag, we know that

$$P(NN) + P(JJ) + P(NNS) + P(VB) = 1 \qquad (6.90)$$

Since we have no further information, a model that makes no further assumptions beyond what we know would simply assign equal probability to each of these words:

NN	JJ	NNS	VB	NNP	IN	MD	UH	SYM	VBG	POS	PRP	CC	CD	...
$\frac{1}{4}$	$\frac{1}{4}$	$\frac{1}{4}$	$\frac{1}{4}$	0	0	0	0	0	0	0	0	0	0	...

In the first example, where we wanted an uninformed distribution over 45 parts-of-speech, and in this case, where we wanted an uninformed distribution over 4 parts-of-speech, it turns out that of all possible distributions, the equiprobable distribution has the **maximum entropy**. Recall from Section 4.10 that the entropy of the distribution of a random variable x is computed as

$$H(x) = -\sum_x P(x) \log_2 P(x) \tag{6.91}$$

An equiprobable distribution in which all values of the random variable have the same probability has a higher entropy than one in which there is more information. Thus, of all distributions over four variables, the distribution $\frac{1}{4}, \frac{1}{4}, \frac{1}{4}, \frac{1}{4}$ has the maximum entropy. (To have an intuition for this, use Eq. 6.91 to compute the entropy for a few other distributions, such as the distribution $\frac{1}{4}, \frac{1}{2}, \frac{1}{8}, \frac{1}{8}$, and make sure they are all lower than the equiprobable distribution.)

The intuition of MaxEnt modeling is that the probabilistic model we are building should follow whatever constraints we impose on it, but beyond these constraints it should follow Occam's Razor, that is, make the fewest possible assumptions.

Let's add some more constraints into our tagging example. Suppose we looked at our tagged training data and noticed that 8 times out of 10, *zzfish* was tagged as some sort of common noun, either NN or NNS. We can think of this as specifying the feature 'word is *zzfish* and t_i = NN or t_i = NNS'. We might now want to modify our distribution so that we give $\frac{8}{10}$ of our probability mass to nouns, that is, now we have two constraints

$$P(NN) + P(JJ) + P(NNS) + P(VB) = 1$$

$$P(\text{word is } \textit{zzfish} \text{ and } t_i = NN \text{ or } t_i = NNS) = \frac{8}{10}$$

but make no further assumptions (keep JJ and VB equiprobable and NN and NNS equiprobable).

NN	JJ	NNS	VB	NNP	...
$\frac{4}{10}$	$\frac{1}{10}$	$\frac{4}{10}$	$\frac{1}{10}$	0	...

Now suppose we have no more information about *zzfish*. But we notice in the training data that for all English words (not just *zzfish*), verbs (VB) occur as 1 word in 20. We can now add this constraint (corresponding to the feature $t_i = VB$):

$$P(NN) + P(JJ) + P(NNS) + P(VB) = 1$$

$$P(\text{word is } \textit{zzfish} \text{ and } t_i = NN \text{ or } t_i = NNS) = \frac{8}{10}$$

$$P(VB) = \frac{1}{20}$$

The resulting maximum entropy distribution is now as follows:

NN	JJ	NNS	VB
$\frac{4}{10}$	$\frac{3}{20}$	$\frac{4}{10}$	$\frac{1}{20}$

In summary, the intuition of maximum entropy is to build a distribution by continuously adding features. Each feature is an indicator function, which picks out a subset of the training observations. For each feature we add a constraint on our total distribution, specifying that our distribution for this subset should match the empirical distribution we saw in our training data. We then choose the maximum entropy distribution that otherwise accords with these constraints. Berger et al. (1996) pose the optimization problem of finding this distribution as follows:

> *"To select a model from a set c of allowed probability distributions, choose the model $p^* \in \mathscr{C}$ with maximum entropy $H(p)$":*

$$p^* = \underset{p \in \mathscr{C}}{\operatorname{argmax}} H(p) \qquad (6.92)$$

Now we come to the important conclusion. Berger et al. (1996) show that the solution to this optimization problem turns out to be exactly the probability distribution of a multinomial logistic regression model whose weights W maximize the likelihood of the training data! Thus, the exponential model for multinomial logistic regression, when trained according to the maximum likelihood criterion, also finds the maximum entropy distribution subject to the constraints from the feature functions.

6.8   Maximum Entropy Markov Models

We began our discussion of MaxEnt by pointing out that the basic MaxEnt model is not in itself a classifier for sequences. Instead, it is used to classify a single observation into one of a set of discrete classes, as in text classification (choosing between possible authors of an anonymous text or classifying an email as spam) or tasks like deciding whether a period marks the end of a sentence.

We turn in this section to the **maximum entropy Markov model** or **MEMM**, which is an augmentation of the basic MaxEnt classifier so that it can be applied to assign a class to each element in a sequence, just as we do with HMMs. Why would we want a sequence classifier built on MaxEnt? How might such a classifier be better than an HMM?

Consider the HMM approach to part-of-speech tagging. The HMM tagging model is based on probabilities of the form $P(\text{tag}|\text{tag})$ and $P(\text{word}|\text{tag})$. That means that if we want to include some source of knowledge into the tagging process, we must find a way to encode the knowledge into one of these two probabilities. But many knowledge sources are hard to fit into these models. For example, we saw in Section 5.8.2 that for tagging unknown words, useful features include capitalization, the presence of hyphens, word endings, and so on. There is no easy way to fit probabilities like $P(\text{capitalization}|\text{tag})$, $P(\text{hyphen}|\text{tag})$, $P(\text{suffix}|\text{tag})$, and so on into an HMM-style model.

We gave part of this intuition in the previous section, when we discussed applying MaxEnt to part-of-speech tagging. Part-of-speech tagging is definitely a sequence labeling task, but we only discussed assigning a part-of-speech tag to a single word.

How can we take this single local classifier and turn it into a general sequence classifier? When classifying each word, we can rely on features from the current word, features from surrounding words, as well as the output of the classifier from previous words. For example, the simplest method is to run our local classifier left to right, first making a hard classification of the first word in the sentence, then the second word, and so on. When classifying each word, we can rely on the output of the classifier from the previous word as a feature. For example, we saw in tagging the word *race* that a useful feature was the tag of the previous word; a previous TO is a good indication that *race* is a VB, whereas a previous DT is a good indication that *race* is an NN. Such a strict left-to-right sliding window approach has been shown to yield surprisingly good results across a wide range of applications.

While it is possible to perform part-of-speech tagging in this way, this simple left-to-right classifier has a flaw: it makes a hard decision on each word before moving on to the next word. This means that the classifier is unable to use information from later words to inform its earlier decisions. Recall that in hidden Markov models, by contrast, we didn't have to make a hard decision at each word; we used Viterbi decoding to find the sequence of part-of-speech tags that was optimal for the whole sentence.

The maximum entropy Markov model (or MEMM) allows us to achieve this same advantage by mating the Viterbi algorithm with MaxEnt. Let's see how it works, again looking at part-of-speech tagging. It is easiest to understand an MEMM when comparing it to an HMM. Remember that in using an HMM to model the most probable part-of-speech tag sequence, we rely on Bayes' rule, computing $P(W\ T)P(W)$ instead of directly computing $P(T\ W)$:

$$
\begin{aligned}
\hat{T} &= \operatorname*{argmax}_{T} P(T\ W) \\
&= \operatorname*{argmax}_{T} P(W\ T)P(T) \\
&= \operatorname*{argmax}_{T} \prod_{i} P(word_i\ tag_i) \prod_{i} P(tag_i\ tag_{i-1})
\end{aligned}
\tag{6.93}
$$

That is, an HMM as we've described it is a generative model that optimizes the likelihood $P(W\ T)$, and we estimate the posterior by combining the likelihood and the prior $P(T)$.

In an MEMM, by contrast, we compute the posterior $P(T\ W)$ directly. Because we train the model directly to discriminate among the possible tag sequences, we call an *Discriminative model* MEMM a **discriminative model** rather than a generative model. In an MEMM, we break down the probabilities as follows:

$$
\begin{aligned}
\hat{T} &= \operatorname*{argmax}_{T} P(T\ W) \\
&= \operatorname*{argmax}_{T} \prod_{i} P(tag_i\ word_i, tag_{i-1})
\end{aligned}
\tag{6.94}
$$

Thus, in an MEMM, instead of having a separate model for likelihoods and priors, we train a single probabilistic model to estimate $P(tag_i \mid word_i, tag_{i-1})$. We will use MaxEnt for this last piece, estimating the probability of each local tag given the previous tag, the observed word, and, as we show, any other features we want to include.

We can see the HMM versus MEMM intuitions of the POS tagging task in Fig. 6.20, which repeats the HMM model of Fig. 5.12a from Chapter 5 and adds a new model for the MEMM. Note that the HMM model includes distinct probability estimates for each transition and observation, whereas the MEMM gives one probability estimate per hidden state, which is the probability of the next tag given the previous tag and the observation.

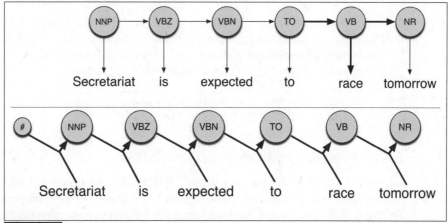

Figure 6.20   The HMM (top) and MEMM (bottom) representation of the probability computation for the correct sequence of tags for the Secretariat sentence. Each arc would be associated with a probability; the HMM computes two separate probabilities for the observation likelihood and the prior, while the MEMM computes a single probability function at each state, conditioned on the previous state and current observation.

Figure 6.21 emphasizes another advantage of MEMMs over HMMs not shown in Fig. 6.20: unlike the HMM, the MEMM can condition on any useful feature of the input observation. In the HMM this wasn't possible, because the HMM is likelihood based; hence it would have needed to compute the likelihood of each feature of the observation.

More formally, in the HMM we compute the probability of the state sequence given the observations as

$$P(Q \mid O) = \prod_{i=1}^{n} P(o_i \mid q_i) \quad \prod_{i=1}^{n} P(q_i \mid q_{i-1}) \tag{6.95}$$

In the MEMM, we compute the probability of the state sequence given the observations as

$$P(Q \mid O) = \prod_{i=1}^{n} P(q_i \mid q_{i-1}, o_i) \tag{6.96}$$

211

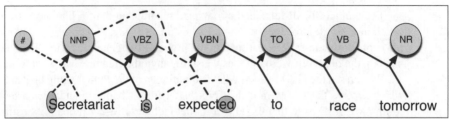

Figure 6.21   An MEMM for part-of-speech tagging, augmenting the description in Fig. 6.20 by showing that an MEMM can condition on many features of the input, such as capitalization, morphology (ending in *-s* or *-ed*), as well as earlier words or tags. We have shown some potential additional features for the first three decisions, using different line styles for each class.

In practice, however, an MEMM can also condition on many more features than the HMM, so, in general, we condition the right-hand side on many more factors.

To estimate the individual probability of a transition from a state q' to a state q producing an observation o, we build a MaxEnt model as follows:

$$P(q\,q',o) = \frac{1}{Z(o,q')} \exp\left(\sum_i w_i f_i(o,q)\right) \tag{6.97}$$

6.8.1   Decoding and Learning in MEMMs

Like HMMs, the MEMM uses the Viterbi algorithm to perform the task of decoding (inference). Concretely, this involves filling an $N\ T$ array with the appropriate values for $P(t_i\,t_{i-1}, word_i)$, maintaining backpointers as we proceed. As with HMM Viterbi, when the table is filled, we simply follow pointers back from the maximum value in the final column to retrieve the desired set of labels. The requisite changes from the HMM-style application of Viterbi have to do only with how we fill each cell. Recall from Eq. 6.22 that the recursive step of the Viterbi equation computes the Viterbi value of time t for state j as

$$v_t(j) = \max_{i=1}^{N} v_{t-1}(i)\, a_{ij} b_j(o_t); \quad 1 \le j \le N, 1 < t \le T \tag{6.98}$$

which is the HMM implementation of

$$v_t(j) = \max_{i=1}^{N} v_{t-1}(i)\, P(s_j\,s_i)\, P(o_t\,s_j) \quad 1 \le j \le N, 1 < t \le T \tag{6.99}$$

The MEMM requires only a slight change to this latter formula, replacing the a and b prior and likelihood probabilities with the direct posterior:

$$v_t(j) = \max_{i=1}^{N} v_{t-1}(i)\, P(s_j\,s_i, o_t) \quad 1 \le j \le N, 1 < t \le T \tag{6.100}$$

Figure 6.22 shows an example of the Viterbi trellis for an MEMM applied to the ice-cream task from Section 6.4. Recall that the task is figuring out the hidden weather (hot or cold) from observed numbers of ice creams eaten in Jason Eisner's diary. Figure 6.22 shows the abstract Viterbi probability calculation, assuming that we have a MaxEnt model which computes $P(s_i \, s_{i-1}, o_i)$ for us.

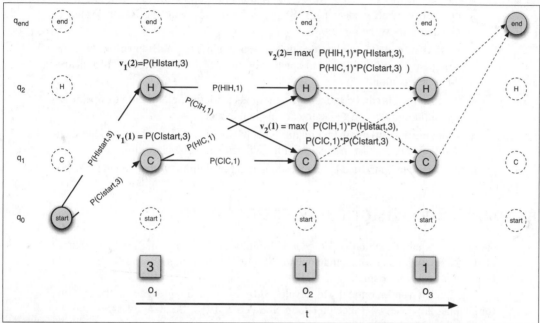

Figure 6.22   Inference from ice-cream eating computed by an MEMM instead of an HMM. The Viterbi trellis for computing the best path through the hidden state space for the ice-cream eating events *3 1 3*, modified from the HMM figure in Fig. 6.10.

Learning in MEMMs relies on the same supervised learning algorithms we presented for logistic regression and MaxEnt. Given a sequence of observations, feature functions, and corresponding hidden states, we train the weights so as maximize the log-likelihood of the training corpus. As with HMMs, it is also possible to train MEMMs in semi-supervised modes, for example, when the sequence of labels for the training data is missing or incomplete in some way: a version of the EM algorithm can be used for this purpose.

6.9   Summary

This chapter described two important models for probabilistic **sequence classification**: the **hidden Markov model** and the **maximum entropy Markov model**. Both models are widely used throughout speech and language processing.

- Hidden Markov models (**HMMs**) are a way of relating a sequence of **observations** to a sequence of **hidden classes** or **hidden states** that explain the observations.

- The process of discovering the sequence of hidden states, given the sequence of observations, is known as **decoding** or **inference**. The **Viterbi** algorithm is commonly used for decoding.

- The parameters of an HMM are the A transition probability matrix and the B observation likelihood matrix. Both can be trained with the **Baum-Welch** or **forward-backward** algorithm.

- A **MaxEnt** model is a classifier that assigns a **class** to an **observation** by computing a probability from an exponential function of a **weighted** set of **features** of the observation.

- MaxEnt models can be trained with methods from the field of **convex optimization**, although we don't give the details in this textbook.

- A **maximum Entropy Markov model** or **MEMM** is a sequence model augmentation of MaxEnt that makes use of the Viterbi decoding algorithm.

- MEMMs can be trained by augmenting MaxEnt training with a version of EM.

Bibliographical and Historical Notes

As we discussed at the end of Chapter 4, Markov chains were first used by Markov (1913, 2006), to predict whether an upcoming letter in Pushkin's *Eugene Onegin* would be a vowel or a consonant.

The hidden Markov model was developed by Baum and colleagues at the Institute for Defense Analyses in Princeton (Baum and Petrie, 1966; Baum and Eagon, 1967).

The **Viterbi** algorithm was first applied to speech and language processing in the context of speech recognition by Vintsyuk (1968) but has what Kruskal (1983) calls a "remarkable history of multiple independent discovery and publication".[2] Kruskal and others give at least the following independently-discovered variants of the algorithm published in four separate fields:

Citation	Field
Viterbi (1967)	information theory
Vintsyuk (1968)	speech processing
Needleman and Wunsch (1970)	molecular biology
Sakoe and Chiba (1971)	speech processing
Sankoff (1972)	molecular biology
Reichert et al. (1973)	molecular biology
Wagner and Fischer (1974)	computer science

The use of the term **Viterbi** is now standard for the application of dynamic programming to any kind of probabilistic maximization problem in speech and language processing. For non-probabilistic problems (such as for minimum edit distance), the plain term **dynamic programming** is often used. Forney, Jr. (1973) wrote an early survey paper that explores the origin of the Viterbi algorithm in the context of information and communications theory.

---

[2]   Seven is pretty remarkable, but see page 13 for a discussion of the prevalence of multiple discovery.

Our presentation of the idea that hidden Markov models should be characterized by three fundamental problems was modeled after an influential tutorial by Rabiner (1989), which was itself based on tutorials by Jack Ferguson of IDA in the 1960s. Jelinek (1997) and Rabiner and Juang (1993) give very complete descriptions of the forward-backward algorithm as applied to the speech recognition problem. Jelinek (1997) also shows the relationship between forward-backward and EM. See also the description of HMMs in other textbooks such as Manning and Schütze (1999). See Durbin et al. (1998) for the application of probabilistic models like HMMs to biological sequences of proteins and nucleic acids. Bilmes (1997) is a tutorial on EM.

While logistic regression and other log-linear models have been used in many fields since the middle of the 20th century, the use of maximum entropy/multinomial logistic regression in natural language processing dates from work in the early 1990s at IBM (Berger et al., 1996; Della Pietra et al., 1997). This early work introduced the maximum entropy formalism, proposed a learning algorithm (improved iterative scaling), and proposed the use of regularization. A number of applications of MaxEnt followed. For further discussion of regularization and smoothing for maximum entropy models, see (*inter alia*) Chen and Rosenfeld (2000), Goodman (2004), and Dudík and Schapire (2006). Our presentation in this chapter was influenced by lecture notes from Andrew Ng.

Although the second part of this chapter focused on MaxEnt-style classification, numerous other approaches to classification are used throughout speech and language processing. Naive Bayes (Duda et al., 2000) is often employed as a good baseline method (often yielding results that are sufficiently good for practical use); we cover naive Bayes in Chapter 20. Support Vector Machines (Vapnik, 1995) have been, successfully used in text classification and in a wide variety of sequence processing applications. Decision lists have been widely used in word sense discrimination, and decision trees (Breiman et al., 1984; Quinlan, 1986) have been used in many applications in speech processing. Good references to supervised machine learning approaches to classification include Duda et al. (2000), Hastie et al. (2001), and Witten and Frank (2005).

Maximum entropy Markov models (MEMMs) were introduced by Ratnaparkhi (1996) and McCallum et al. (2000).

Many sequence models augment the MEMM, such as the **conditional random field** (**CRF**) (Lafferty et al., 2001; Sutton and McCallum, 2006). In addition, there are various generalizations of **maximum margin** methods (the insights that underlie SVM classifiers) to sequence tasks.

Conditional random field
CRF

Exercises

6.1 Implement the Forward algorithm and run it with the HMM in Fig. 6.3 to compute the probability of the observation sequences *331122313* and *331123312*. Which is more likely?

6.2 Implement the Viterbi algorithm and run it with the HMM in Fig. 6.3 to compute the most likely weather sequences for each of the two observation sequences above, *331122313* and *331123312*.

6.3   Extend the HMM tagger you built in Exercise 5.8 by adding the ability to make use of some unlabeled data in addition to your labeled training corpus. First acquire a large unlabeled (i.e., no part-of-speech tags) corpus. Next, implement the forward-backward training algorithm. Now start with the HMM parameters you trained on the training corpus in Exercise 5.8; call this model M_0. Run the forward-backward algorithm with these HMM parameters to label the unsupervised corpus. Now you have a new model M_1. Test the performance of M_1 on some held-out labeled data.

6.4   As a generalization of the previous homework, implement Jason Eisner's HMM tagging homework available from his webpage. His homework includes a corpus of weather and ice-cream observations, a corpus of English part-of-speech tags, and a very hand spreadsheet with exact numbers for the forward-backward algorithm that you can compare against.

6.5   Train a MaxEnt classifier to decide if a movie review is a positive review (the critic liked the movie) or a negative review. Your task is to take the text of a movie review as input, and produce as output either 1 (positive) or 0 (negative). You don't need to implement the classifier itself, you can find various MaxEnt classifiers on the Web. You'll need training and test sets of documents from a labeled corpus (which you can get by scraping any web-based movie review site), and a set of useful features. For features, the simplest thing is just to create a binary feature for the 2500 most frequent words in your training set, indicating if the word was present in the document or not.

Sentiment analysis

Determining the polarity of a movie review is a kind of **sentiment analysis** task. For pointers to the rapidly growing body of work on extraction of sentiment, opinions, and subjectivity see the collected papers in Qu et al. (2005), and individual papers like Wiebe (2000), Pang et al. (2002), Turney (2002), Turney and Littman (2003), Wiebe and Mihalcea (2006), Thomas et al. (2006) and Wilson et al. (2006).

Credit

Figs. 6.14 and 6.15 (© IEEE and the authors; we thank Lawrence Rabiner)

Chapter 7

Phonetics

(Upon being asked by Director George Cukor to teach Rex Harrison, the star of the 1964 film *My Fair Lady*, how to behave like a phonetician:)

> *"My immediate answer was, 'I don't have a singing butler and three maids who sing, but I will tell you what I can as an assistant professor.'"*
>
> Peter Ladefoged, quoted in his obituary, *LA Times*, 2004

The debate between the "whole language" and "phonics" methods of teaching reading to children seems at first glance like a purely modern educational debate. Like many modern debates, however, this one recapitulates an important historical dialectic, in this case, in writing systems. The earliest independently invented writing systems (Sumerian, Chinese, Mayan) were mainly logographic: one symbol represented a whole word. But from the earliest stages we can find, most such systems contain elements of syllabic or phonemic writing systems, in which symbols represent the sounds that make up the words. Thus, the Sumerian symbol pronounced *ba* and meaning "ration" could also function purely as the sound /ba/. Even modern Chinese, which remains primarily logographic, uses sound-based characters to spell out foreign words. Purely sound-based writing systems, whether syllabic (like Japanese *hiragana* or *katakana*), alphabetic (like the Roman alphabet used in this book), or consonantal (like Semitic writing systems), can generally be traced back to these early logo-syllabic systems, often as two cultures came together. Thus, the Arabic, Aramaic, Hebrew, Greek, and Roman systems all derive from a West Semitic script that is presumed to have been modified by Western Semitic mercenaries from a cursive form of Egyptian hieroglyphs. The Japanese syllabaries were modified from a cursive form of a set of Chinese characters that represented sounds. These Chinese characters themselves were used in Chinese to phonetically represent the Sanskrit in the Buddhist scriptures that were brought to China in the Tang dynasty.

Whatever its origins, the idea implicit in a sound-based writing system—that the spoken word is composed of smaller units of speech—is the Ur-theory that underlies all our modern theories of **phonology**. This idea of decomposing speech and words into smaller units also underlies the modern algorithms for **speech recognition** (transcribing acoustic waveforms into strings of text words) and **speech synthesis** or **text-to-speech** (converting strings of text words into acoustic waveforms).

In this chapter we introduce **phonetics** from a computational perspective. Phonetics is the study of linguistic sounds, how they are produced by the articulators of the human vocal tract, how they are realized acoustically, and how this acoustic realization can be digitized and processed.

We begin with a key element of both speech recognition and text-to-speech systems: how words are pronounced in terms of individual speech units called **phones**.

From Chapter 7 of *Speech and Language Processing*, Second Edition. Daniel Jurafsky, James H. Martin.

A speech recognition system needs to have a pronunciation for every word it can recognize, and a text-to-speech system needs to have a pronunciation for every word it can say. The first section of this chapter introduces **phonetic alphabets** for describing these pronunciations. We then introduce the two main areas of phonetics, **articulatory phonetics**, the study of how speech sounds are produced by articulators in the mouth, and **acoustic phonetics**, the study of the acoustic analysis of speech sounds.

We also briefly touch on **phonology**, the area of linguistics that describes the systematic way that sounds are differently realized in different environments and how this system of sounds is related to the rest of the grammar. We focus on the crucial phenomenon of **variation**: phones are pronounced differently in different contexts. We return to computational aspects of phonology in Chapter 11.

7.1   Speech Sounds and Phonetic Transcription

Phonetics

The study of the pronunciation of words is part of the field of **phonetics**, the study of the speech sounds used in the languages of the world. We model the pronunciation of

Phone

a word as a string of symbols that represent **phones** or **segments**. A phone is a speech sound; phones are represented with phonetic symbols that bear some resemblance to a letter in an alphabetic language like English.

This section surveys the different phones of English, particularly American English, showing how they are produced and how they are represented symbolically. We use two different alphabets for describing phones. The **International Phonetic Alpha-**

IPA

bet (IPA) is an evolving standard originally developed by the International Phonetic Association in 1888 with the goal of transcribing the sounds of all human languages. The IPA is not just an alphabet but also a set of transcription principles, which differ according to the needs of the transcription, so the same utterance can be transcribed in different ways all according to the principles of the IPA.

The ARPAbet (Shoup, 1980) is another phonetic alphabet, but one that is specifically designed for American English and that uses ASCII symbols; it can be thought of as a convenient ASCII representation of an American-English subset of the IPA. ARPAbet symbols are often used in applications in which non-ASCII fonts are inconvenient, such as in pronunciation dictionaries for speech recognition and synthesis. Because the ARPAbet is common for computational representations of pronunciations, we rely on it rather than the IPA in the remainder of this book. Figures 7.1 and 7.2 show the ARPAbet symbols for transcribing consonants and vowels, respectively, together with their IPA equivalents.

Many of the IPA and ARPAbet symbols are equivalent to the Roman letters used in the orthography of English and many other languages. So, for example, the ARPAbet phone [p] represents the consonant sound at the beginning of *platypus*, *puma*, and *pachyderm*, the middle of *leopard*, or the end of *antelope*. In general, however, the mapping between the letters of English orthography and phones is relatively **opaque**; a single letter can represent very different sounds in different contexts. The English letter *c* corresponds to phone [k] in *cougar* [k uw g axr], but phone [s] in *cell* [s eh l]. Besides appearing as *c* and *k*, the phone [k] can appear as part of *x* (*fox* [f aa k s]), as

ARPAbet Symbol	IPA Symbol	Word	ARPAbet Transcription
[p]	[p]	parsley	[p aa r s l iy]
[t]	[t]	tea	[t iy]
[k]	[k]	cook	[k uh k]
[b]	[b]	bay	[b ey]
[d]	[d]	dill	[d ih l]
[g]	[g]	garlic	[g aa r l ix k]
[m]	[m]	mint	[m ih n t]
[n]	[n]	nutmeg	[n ah t m eh g]
[ng]	[ŋ]	baking	[b ey k ix ng]
[f]	[f]	flour	[f l aw axr]
[v]	[v]	clove	[k l ow v]
[th]	[θ]	thick	[th ih k]
[dh]	[ð]	those	[dh ow z]
[s]	[s]	soup	[s uw p]
[z]	[z]	eggs	[eh g z]
[sh]	[ʃ]	squash	[s k w aa sh]
[zh]	[ʒ]	ambrosia	[ae m b r ow zh ax]
[ch]	[tʃ]	cherry	[ch eh r iy]
[jh]	[dʒ]	jar	[jh aa r]
[l]	[l]	licorice	[l ih k axr ix sh]
[w]	[w]	kiwi	[k iy w iy]
[r]	[r]	rice	[r ay s]
[y]	[j]	yellow	[y eh l ow]
[h]	[h]	honey	[h ah n iy]
Less commonly used phones and allophones			
[q]	[ʔ]	uh-oh	[q ah q ow]
[dx]	[ɾ]	butter	[b ah dx axr]
[nx]	[ɾ̃]	winner	[w ih nx axr]
[el]	[l̩]	table	[t ey b el]

Figure 7.1   ARPAbet symbols for transcription of English consonants, with IPA equivalents. Note that some rarer symbols like the flap [dx], nasal flap [nx], glottal stop [q], and the syllabic consonants are used mainly for narrow transcriptions.

ck (*jackal* [jh ae k el]) and as *cc* (*raccoon* [r ae k uw n]). Many other languages, for example, Spanish, are much more **transparent** in their sound-orthography mapping than English.

7.2   Articulatory Phonetics

Articulatory phonetics

The list of ARPAbet phones is useless without an understanding of how each phone is produced. We thus turn to **articulatory phonetics**, the study of how phones are

ARPAbet Symbol	IPA Symbol	Word	ARPAbet Transcription
[iy]	[i]	lily	[l ih l iy]
[ih]	[ɪ]	lily	[l ih l iy]
[ey]	[eɪ]	daisy	[d ey z iy]
[eh]	[ɛ]	pen	[p eh n]
[ae]	[æ]	aster	[ae s t axr]
[aa]	[ɑ]	poppy	[p aa p iy]
[ao]	[ɔ]	orchid	[ao r k ix d]
[uh]	[ʊ]	wood	[w uh d]
[ow]	[oʊ]	lotus	[l ow dx ax s]
[uw]	[u]	tulip	[t uw l ix p]
[ah]	[ʌ]	buttercup	[b ah dx axr k ah p]
[er]	[ɝ]	bird	[b er d]
[ay]	[aɪ]	iris	[ay r ix s]
[aw]	[aʊ]	sunflower	[s ah n f l aw axr]
[oy]	[ɔɪ]	soil	[s oy l]
Reduced and uncommon phones			
[ax]	[ə]	lotus	[l ow dx ax s]
[axr]	[ɚ]	heather	[h eh dh axr]
[ix]	[ɨ]	tulip	[t uw l ix p]
[ux]	[ʉ]	dude[1]	[d ux d]

Figure 7.2   ARPAbet symbols for transcription of English vowels, with IPA equivalents. Note again the list of rarer phones and reduced vowels (see Section 7.2.5); for example [ax] is the reduced vowel schwa, [ix] is the reduced vowel corresponding to [ih], and [axr] is the reduced vowel corresponding to [er].

produced as the various organs in the mouth, throat, and nose modify the airflow from the lungs.

7.2.1   The Vocal Organs

Figure 7.3 shows the organs of speech. Sound is produced by the rapid movement of air. Humans produce most sounds in spoken languages by expelling air from the lungs through the windpipe (technically, the **trachea**) and then out the mouth or nose. As it passes through the trachea, the air passes through the **larynx**, commonly known as the Adam's apple or voice box. The larynx contains two small folds of muscle, the **vocal folds** (often referred to non-technically as the **vocal cords**), which can be moved

Glottis   together or apart. The space between these two folds is called the **glottis**. If the folds are close together (but not tightly closed), they will vibrate as air passes through them; if they are far apart, they won't vibrate. Sounds made with the vocal folds together and

---

[1] The phone [ux] is rare in general American English and not generally used in speech recognition/synthesis. It represents the fronted [uw] which appeared in (at least) Western and Northern Cities dialects of American English starting in the late 1970s (Labov, 1994). This fronting was first called to public attention by imitations and recordings of 'Valley Girls' speech by Moon Zappa (Zappa and Zappa, 1982). Nevertheless, for most speakers [uw] is still much more common than [ux] in words like *dude*.

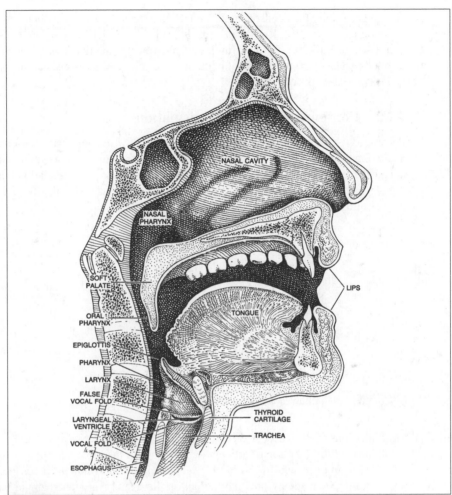

Figure 7.3   The vocal organs, shown in side view. Drawing by Laszlo Kubinyi from Sundberg (1977), ©Scientific American, used by permission.

Voiced sound
Unvoiced sound
Voiceless

vibrating are called **voiced**; sounds made without this vocal cord vibration are called **unvoiced** or **voiceless**. Voiced sounds include [b], [d], [g], [v], [z], and all the English vowels, among others. Unvoiced sounds include [p], [t], [k], [f], [s], and others.

The area above the trachea is called the **vocal tract**; it consists of the **oral tract** and the **nasal tract**. After the air leaves the trachea, it can exit the body through the mouth or the nose. Most sounds are made by air passing through the mouth. Sounds made by air passing through the nose are called **nasal sounds**; nasal sounds use both the oral and nasal tracts as resonating cavities; English nasal sounds include [m], [n], and [ng].

Nasal

Consonant
Vowel

Phones are divided into two main classes: **consonants** and **vowels**. Both kinds of sounds are formed by the motion of air through the mouth, throat or nose. Consonants are made by restriction or blocking of the airflow in some way, and can be voiced or unvoiced. Vowels have less obstruction, are usually voiced, and are generally louder and longer-lasting than consonants. The technical use of these terms is much like the common usage; [p], [b], [t], [d], [k], [g], [f], [v], [s], [z], [r], [l], etc., are consonants; [aa], [ae], [ao], [ih], [aw], [ow], [uw], etc., are vowels. **Semivowels** (such as [y] and [w]) have some of the properties of both; they are voiced like vowels, but they are short and less syllabic like consonants.

7.2.2   Consonants: Place of Articulation

Place of articulation

Because consonants are made by restricting the airflow in some way, consonants can be distinguished by where this restriction is made: the point of maximum restriction is called the **place of articulation** of a consonant. Places of articulation, shown in Fig. 7.4, are often used in automatic speech recognition as a useful way of grouping phones into equivalence classes, described below.

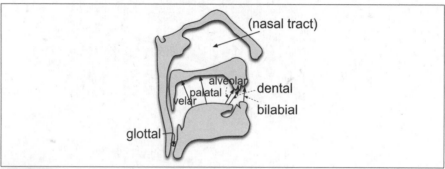

Figure 7.4   Major English places of articulation.

Labial

Labial: Consonants whose main restriction is formed by the two lips coming together have a **bilabial** place of articulation. In English these include [p] as in *possum*, [b] as in *bear*, and [m] as in *marmot*. The English **labiodental** consonants [v] and [f] are made by pressing the bottom lip against the upper row of teeth and letting the air flow through the space in the upper teeth.

Dental

Dental: Sounds that are made by placing the tongue against the teeth are dentals. The main dentals in English are the [th] of *thing* and the [dh] of *though*, which are made by placing the tongue behind the teeth with the tip slightly between the teeth.

Alveolar

Alveolar: The alveolar ridge is the portion of the roof of the mouth just behind the upper teeth. Most speakers of American English make the phones [s], [z], [t], and [d] by placing the tip of the tongue against the alveolar ridge. The word

Coronal

coronal is often used to refer to both dental and alveolar.

Palatal

Palate

Palatal: The roof of the mouth (the **palate**) rises sharply from the back of the alveolar ridge. The **palato-alveolar** sounds [sh] (*shrimp*), [ch] (*china*), [zh] (*Asian*), and [jh] (*jar*) are made with the blade of the tongue against the rising back of the alveolar ridge. The palatal sound [y] of *yak* is made by placing the front of the tongue up close to the palate.

Velar

Velum

Velar: The **velum**, or soft palate, is a movable muscular flap at the very back of the

Glottal

roof of the mouth. The sounds [k] (*cuckoo*), [g] (*goose*), and [ŋ] (*kingfisher*) are made by pressing the back of the tongue up against the velum.

Glottal: The glottal stop [q] (IPA [?]) is made by closing the glottis (by bringing the vocal folds together).

7.2.3   Consonants: Manner of Articulation

Manner of articulation

Consonants are also distinguished by *how* the restriction in airflow is made, for example, by a complete stoppage of air or by a partial blockage. This feature is called the **manner of articulation** of a consonant. The combination of place and manner of articulation is usually sufficient to uniquely identify a consonant. Following are the major manners of articulation for English consonants:

Stop

A **stop** is a consonant in which airflow is completely blocked for a short time. This blockage is followed by an explosive sound as the air is released. The period of blockage is called the **closure**, and the explosion is called the **release**. English has voiced stops like [b], [d], and [g] as well as unvoiced stops like [p], [t], and [k]. Stops are also called **plosives**. Some computational systems use a more narrow (detailed) transcription style that has separate labels for the closure and release parts of a stop. In one version of the ARPAbet, for example, the closure of a [p], [t], or [k] is represented as [pcl], [tcl], or [kcl], respectively, and the symbols [p], [t], and [k] mean only the release portion of the stop. In another version, the symbols [pd], [td], [kd], [bd], [dd], [gd] mean unreleased stops (stops at the end of words or phrases often are missing the explosive release), and [p], [t], [k], etc mean normal stops with a closure and a release. The IPA uses a special symbol to mark unreleased stops: [p˺], [t˺], or [k˺]. We do not use these narrow transcription styles in this chapter; we always use [p] to mean a full stop with both a closure and a release.

Nasal

The **nasal** sounds [n], [m], and [ng] are made by lowering the velum and allowing air to pass into the nasal cavity.

Fricative

In **fricatives**, airflow is constricted but not cut off completely. The turbulent airflow that results from the constriction produces a characteristic "hissing" sound. The English labiodental fricatives [f] and [v] are produced by pressing the lower lip against the upper teeth, allowing a restricted airflow between the upper teeth. The dental fricatives [th] and [dh] allow air to flow around the tongue between the teeth. The alveolar fricatives [s] and [z] are produced with the tongue against the alveolar ridge, forcing air over the edge of the teeth. In the palato-alveolar fricatives [sh] and [zh], the tongue is at the back of the alveolar ridge, forcing air through a groove formed in the tongue. The

Sibilant

higher-pitched fricatives (in English [s], [z], [sh] and [zh]) are called **sibilants**. Stops that are followed immediately by fricatives are called **affricates**; these include English [ch] (*chicken*) and [jh] (*giraffe*).

Approximant

In **approximants**, the two articulators are close together but not close enough to cause turbulent airflow. In English [y] (*yellow*), the tongue moves close to the roof of the mouth but not close enough to cause the turbulence that would characterize a fricative. In English [w] (*wood*), the back of the tongue comes close to the velum. American [r] can be formed in at least two ways; with just the tip of the tongue extended and close to the palate or with the whole tongue bunched up near the palate. [l] is formed with the tip of the tongue up against the alveolar ridge or the teeth, with one or both sides of the tongue lowered to allow air to flow over it. [l] is called a **lateral** sound because of the drop in the sides of the tongue.

Tap

Flap

A **tap** or **flap** [dx] (or IPA [ɾ]) is a quick motion of the tongue against the alveolar ridge. The consonant in the middle of the word *lotus* ([l ow dx ax s]) is a tap in most dialects of American English; speakers of many U.K. dialects would use a [t] instead of a tap in this word.

7.2.4   Vowels

Like consonants, vowels can be characterized by the position of the articulators as they are made. The three most relevant parameters for vowels are what is called vowel **height**, which correlates roughly with the height of the highest part of the tongue, vowel **frontness** or **backness**, indicating whether this high point is toward the front or back of the oral tract and whether the shape of the lips is **rounded** or not. Figure 7.5 shows the position of the tongue for different vowels.

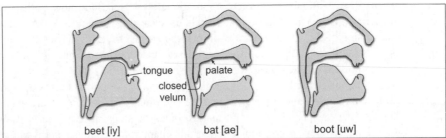

beet [iy]   bat [ae]   boot [uw]

Figure 7.5   Positions of the tongue for three English vowels: high front [iy], low front [ae] and high back [uw].

In the vowel [iy], for example, the highest point of the tongue is toward the front of the mouth. In the vowel [uw], by contrast, the high-point of the tongue is located toward the back of the mouth. Vowels in which the tongue is raised toward the front

Front vowel

Back vowel

are called **front vowels**; those in which the tongue is raised toward the back are called **back vowels**. Note that while both [ih] and [eh] are front vowels, the tongue is higher for [ih] than for [eh]. Vowels in which the highest point of the tongue is comparatively

High vowel

high are called **high vowels**; vowels with mid or low values of maximum tongue height are called **mid vowels** or **low vowels**, respectively.

Figure 7.6 shows a schematic characterization of the height of different vowels. It is schematic because the abstract property **height** correlates only roughly with actual tongue positions; it is, in fact, a more accurate reflection of acoustic facts. Note that the chart has two kinds of vowels: those in which tongue height is represented as a point and those in which it is represented as a path. A vowel in which the tongue

Diphthong

position changes markedly during the production of the vowel is a **diphthong**. English is particularly rich in diphthongs.

The second important articulatory dimension for vowels is the shape of the lips. Certain vowels are pronounced with the lips rounded (the same lip shape used for

Rounded vowel

whistling). These **rounded** vowels include [uw], [ao], and [ow].

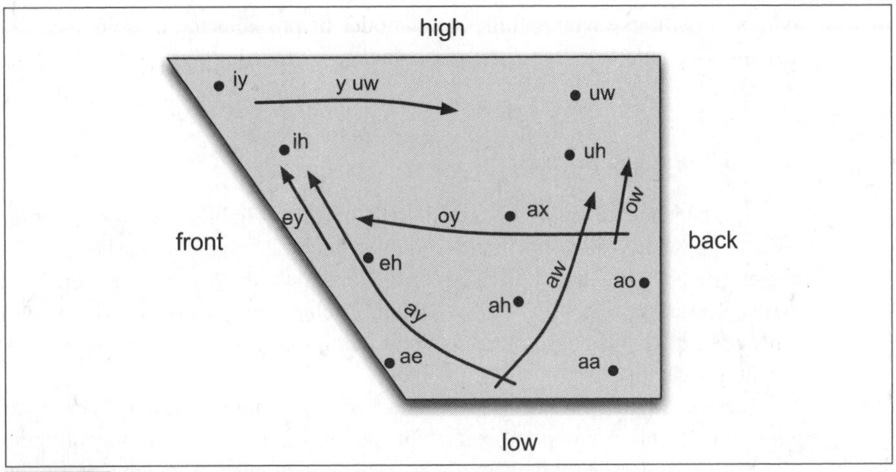

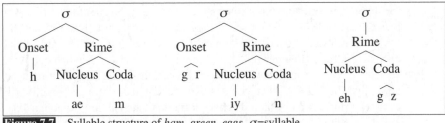

Figure 7.6   The schematic "vowel space" for English vowels.

7.2.5   Syllables

Syllable   Consonants and vowels combine to make a **syllable**. There is no completely agreed-upon definition of a syllable; roughly speaking, a syllable is a vowel-like (or **sonorant**) sound together with some of the surrounding consonants that are most closely associated with it. The word *dog* has one syllable, [d aa g]; the word *catnip* has two syllables, *Nucleus*   [k ae t] and [n ih p]. We call the vowel at the core of a syllable the **nucleus**. The *Onset*   optional initial consonant or set of consonants is called the **onset**. If the onset has more than one consonant (as in the word *strike* [s t r ay k]), we say it has a **complex onset**. *Coda*   The **coda** is the optional consonant or sequence of consonants following the nucleus. *Rime*   Thus [d] is the onset of *dog*, and [g] is the coda. The **rime**, or **rhyme**, is the nucleus plus coda. Figure 7.7 shows some sample syllable structures.

Figure 7.7   Syllable structure of *ham, green, eggs*. σ=syllable.

Syllabification   The task of automatically breaking up a word into syllables is called **syllabification**, and is discussed in Section 11.4.

Phonotactics   Syllable structure is also closely related to the **phonotactics** of a language. The term **phonotactics** means the constraints on which phones can follow each other in a language. For example, English has strong constraints on what kinds of consonants can appear together in an onset; the sequence [zdr], for example, cannot be a legal English syllable onset. Phonotactics can be represented by a list of constraints on fillers of

227

syllable positions or by a finite-state model of possible phone sequences. It is also possible to create a probabilistic phonotactics by training *N*-gram grammars on phone sequences.

Lexical Stress and Schwa

Pitch accent

In a natural sentence of American English, certain syllables are more **prominent** than others. These are called **accented** syllables, and the linguistic marker associated with this prominence is called a **pitch accent**. Words or syllables that are prominent are said to **bear** (be associated with) a pitch accent. Pitch accent is also sometimes referred to as **sentence stress**, although sentence stress can instead refer to only the most prominent accent in a sentence.

Accented syllables can be prominent by being louder, longer, associated with a pitch movement, or any combination of the above. Since accent plays important roles in meaning, understanding exactly why a speaker chooses to accent a particular syllable is very complex; we return to this in detail in Section 8.3.2. But one important factor in accent is often represented in pronunciation dictionaries. This factor is called **lexical**

Lexical stress

stress. The syllable that has lexical stress is the one that will be louder or longer if the word is accented. For example, the word *parsley* is stressed in its first syllable, not its second. Thus, if the word *parsley* receives a pitch accent in a sentence, it is the first syllable that will be stronger.

In IPA we write the symbol ['] before a syllable to indicate that it has lexical stress (e.g., ['par.sli]). This difference in lexical stress can affect the meaning of a word. For example the word *content* can be a noun or an adjective. When pronounced in isolation the two senses are pronounced differently since they have different stressed syllables (the noun is pronounced ['kɑn.tɛnt] and the adjective [kən.'tɛnt]).

Reduced vowel
Schwa

Vowels that are unstressed can be weakened even further to **reduced vowels**. The most common reduced vowel is **schwa** ([ax]). Reduced vowels in English don't have their full form; the articulatory gesture isn't as complete as for a full vowel. As a result, the shape of the mouth is somewhat neutral; the tongue is neither particularly high nor low. For example, the second vowel in *parakeet* is a schwa: [p ae r ax k iy t].

While schwa is the most common reduced vowel, it is not the only one, at least not in some dialects. Bolinger (1981) proposed that American English had three reduced vowels: a reduced mid vowel [ə], a reduced front vowel [ɨ], and a reduced rounded vowel [ɵ]. The full ARPAbet includes two of these, the schwa [ax] and [ix] ([ɨ]), as well as [axr], which is an r-colored schwa (often called **schwar**), although [ix] is generally dropped in computational applications (Miller, 1998), and [ax] and [ix] are falling together in many dialects of English (Wells, 1982, p. 167–168).

Not all unstressed vowels are reduced; any vowel, and diphthongs in particular, can retain its full quality even in unstressed position. For example, the vowel [iy] can appear in stressed position as in the word *eat* [iy t] or in unstressed position as in the word *carry* [k ae r iy].

Some computational ARPAbet lexicons explicitly mark reduced vowels like schwa. But in general, predicting reduction requires knowledge of things outside the lexicon (the prosodic context, rate of speech, etc., as we show in the next section). Thus, other ARPAbet versions mark stress but don't mark how stress affects reduction. The

CMU dictionary (CMU, 1993), for example, marks each vowel with the number 0 (unstressed), 1 (stressed), or 2 (secondary stress). Thus, the word *counter* is listed as [K AW1 N T ER0] and the word *table* as [T EY1 B AH0 L]. **Secondary stress** is defined as a level of stress lower than primary stress but higher than an unstressed vowel, as in the word *dictionary* [D IH1 K SH AH0 N EH2 R IY0].

Secondary stress

Prominence

We have mentioned a number of potential levels of **prominence**: accented, stressed, secondary stress, full vowel, and reduced vowel. It is still an open research question exactly how many levels are appropriate. Very few computational systems make use of all five of these levels, most using between one and three. We return to this discussion when we introduce prosody in more detail in Section 8.3.1.

7.3   Phonological Categories and Pronunciation Variation

> *'Scuse me, while I kiss the sky*
> Jimi Hendrix, "Purple Haze"
> *'Scuse me, while I kiss this guy*
> Common mis-hearing of same lyrics

If each word were pronounced with a fixed string of phones, each of which was pronounced the same in all contexts and by all speakers, the speech recognition and speech synthesis tasks would be really easy. Alas, the realization of words and phones varies massively depending on many factors. Figure 7.8 shows a sample of the wide variation in pronunciation in the words *because* and *about* from the hand-transcribed Switchboard corpus of American English telephone conversations (Greenberg et al., 1996).

because				about			
ARPAbet	**%**	**ARPAbet**	**%**	**ARPAbet**	**%**	**ARPAbet**	**%**
b iy k ah z	27%	k s	2%	ax b aw	32%	b ae	3%
b ix k ah z	14%	k ix z	2%	ax b aw t	16%	b aw t	3%
k ah z	7%	k ih z	2%	b aw	9%	ax b aw dx	3%
k ax z	5%	b iy k ah zh	2%	ix b aw	8%	ax b ae	3%
b ix k ax z	4%	b iy k ah s	2%	ix b aw t	5%	b aa	3%
b ih k ah z	3%	b iy k ah	2%	ix b ae	4%	b ae dx	3%
b ax k ah z	3%	b iy k aa z	2%	ax b ae dx	3%	ix b aw dx	2%
k uh z	2%	ax z	2%	b aw dx	3%	ix b aa t	2%

Figure 7.8   The 16 most common pronunciations of *because* and *about* from the hand-transcribed Switchboard corpus of American English conversational telephone speech (Godfrey et al., 1992; Greenberg et al., 1996).

How can we model and predict this extensive variation? One useful tool is the assumption that what is mentally represented in the speaker's mind are abstract categories rather than phones in all their gory phonetic detail. For example consider the different pronunciations of [t] in the words *tunafish* and *starfish*. The [t] of *tunafish* is **aspirated**. Aspiration is a period of voicelessness after a stop closure and before the onset of voicing of the following vowel. Since the vocal cords are not vibrating,

Aspirated

Unaspirated

aspiration sounds like a puff of air after the [t] and before the vowel. By contrast, a [t] following an initial [s] is **unaspirated**; thus, the [t] in *starfish* ([s t aa r f ih sh]) has no period of voicelessness after the [t] closure. This variation in the realization of [t] is predictable: whenever a [t] begins a word or unreduced syllable in English, it is aspirated. The same variation occurs for [k]; the [k] of *sky* is often mis-heard as [g] in Jimi Hendrix's lyrics because [k] and [g] are both unaspirated.[2]

There are other contextual variants of [t]. For example, when [t] occurs between two vowels, particularly when the first is stressed, it is often pronounced as a **tap**. Recall that a tap is a voiced sound in which the top of the tongue is curled up and back and struck quickly against the alveolar ridge. Thus, the word *buttercup* is usually pronounced [b ah dx axr k uh p] rather than [b ah t axr k uh p]. Another variant of [t] occurs before the dental consonant [th]. Here, the [t] becomes dentalized (IPA [t̪]). That is, instead of the tongue forming a closure against the alveolar ridge, the tongue touches the back of the teeth.

Phoneme

Allophone

In both linguistics and in speech processing, we use abstract classes to capture the similarity among all these [t]s. The simplest abstract class is called the **phoneme**, and its different surface realizations in different contexts are called **allophones**. We traditionally write phonemes inside slashes. So in the above examples, /t/ is a phoneme whose allophones include (in IPA) [tʰ], [ɾ], and [t̪]. Figure 7.9 summarizes a number of allophones of /t/. In speech synthesis and recognition, we use phonesets like the ARPAbet to approximate this idea of abstract phoneme units, and we represent pronunciation lexicons by using ARPAbet phones. For this reason, the allophones listed in Fig. 7.1 tend to be used for narrow transcriptions for analysis and less often used in speech recognition or synthesis systems.

IPA	ARPAbet	Description	Environment	Example
tʰ	[t]	aspirated	in initial position	*toucan*
t		unaspirated	after [s] or in reduced syllables	*starfish*
ʔ	[q]	glottal stop	word-finally or after vowel before [n]	*kitten*
ʔt	[qt]	glottal stop t	sometimes word-finally	*cat*
ɾ	[dx]	tap	between vowels	*butter*
t˺	[tcl]	unreleased t	before consonants or word-finally	*fruitcake*
t̪		dental t	before dental consonants ([θ])	*eighth*
		deleted t	sometimes word-finally	*past*

Figure 7.9   Some allophones of /t/ in General American English.

Variation is even more common than Fig. 7.9 suggests. One factor influencing variation is that the more natural and colloquial speech becomes, and the faster the speaker talks, the more the sounds are shortened and reduced and generally run together. This phenomena is known as **reduction** or **hypoarticulation**. For example, **assimilation** is the change in a segment to make it more like a neighboring segment. The dentalization of [t] to ([t̪]) before the dental consonant [θ] is an example of assimilation. A common type of assimilation cross-linguistically is **palatalization**, when the constriction for a segment moves closer to the palate than it normally would because the following

Reduction

Hypoarticulation

Assimilation

Palatalization

---

[2] The ARPAbet does not have a way of marking aspiration; in the IPA, aspiration is marked as [ʰ], so in IPA the word *tunafish* would be transcribed [tʰunəfɪʃ].

segment is palatal or alveolo-palatal. In the most common cases, /s/ becomes [sh], /z/ becomes [zh], /t/ becomes [ch], and /d/ becomes [jh], We saw one case of palatalization in Fig. 7.8 in the pronunciation of *because* as [b iy k ah zh] because the following word was *you've*. The lemma *you* (*you*, *your*, *you've*, and *you'd*) is extremely likely to cause palatalization in the Switchboard corpus.

Deletion   **Deletion** is quite common in English speech. We saw examples of deletion of final /t/ above in the words *about* and *it*. Deletion of final /t/ and /d/ has been extensively studied. /d/ is more likely to be deleted than /t/, and both are more likely to be deleted before a consonant (Labov, 1972). Figure 7.10 shows examples of palatalization and final t/d deletion from the Switchboard corpus.

Palatalization			Final t/d Deletion		
Phrase	**Lexical**	**Reduced**	**Phrase**	**Lexical**	**Reduced**
set your	s eh t y ow r	s eh ch er	find him	f ay n d h ih m	f ay n ix m
not yet	n aa t y eh t	n aa ch eh t	and we	ae n d w iy	eh n w iy
did you	d ih d y uw	d ih jh y ah	draft the	d r ae f t dh iy	d r ae f dh iy

Figure 7.10   Examples of palatalization and final t/d/ deletion from the Switchboard corpus. Some of the t/d examples may have glottalization instead of being completely deleted.

7.3.1   Phonetic Features

The phoneme gives us only a very gross way to model contextual effects. Many of the phonetic processes like assimilation and deletion are best modeled by more fine-grained articulatory facts about the neighboring context. Figure 7.10 showed that /t/ and /d/ were deleted before [h], [dh], and [w]; rather than list all the possible following phones that could influence deletion, we instead generalize that /t/ often deletes "before consonants". Similarly, flapping can be viewed as a kind of voicing assimilation in which unvoiced /t/ becomes a voiced tap [dx] between voiced vowels or glides. Rather than list every possible vowel or glide, we just say that flapping happens "near vowels or voiced segments". Finally, vowels that precede nasal sounds [n], [m], and [ng] often acquire some of the nasal quality of the following vowel. In each of these cases, a phone is influenced by the articulation of the neighboring phones (nasal, consonantal, voiced). The reason these changes happen is that the movement of the speech articulators (tongue, lips, velum) during speech production is continuous and is subject to physical constraints like momentum. Thus, an articulator may start moving during one phone to get into place in time for the next phone. When the realization of a phone is influenced by the articulatory movement of neighboring phones, we say it is influenced *Coarticulation*   by coarticulation. **Coarticulation** is the movement of articulators to anticipate the next sound or perseverating movement from the last sound.

Distinctive feature   We can capture generalizations about the different phones that cause coarticulation by using **distinctive features**. Features are (generally) binary variables that express some generalizations about groups of phonemes. For example, the feature [voice] is true of the voiced sounds (vowels, [n], [v], [b], etc.); we say they are [+voice] and unvoiced sounds are [-voice]. These articulatory features can draw on the articulatory ideas of **place** and **manner** that we described earlier. Common **place** features include [+labial] ([p, b, m]), [+coronal] ([ch d dh jh l n r s sh t th z zh]), and [+dorsal].

Manner features include [+consonantal] (or alternatively, [+vocalic]), [+continuant], [+sonorant]. For vowels, features include [+high], [+low], [+back], [+round] and so on. Distinctive features are used to represent each phoneme as a matrix of feature values. Many different sets of distinctive features exist; probably any of these are perfectly adequate for most computational purposes. Figure 7.11 shows the values for some phones from one partial set of features.

	syl	son	cons	strident	nasal	high	back	round	tense	voice	labial	coronal	dorsal
b	-	-	+	-	-	-	-	+	+	+	+	-	-
p	-	-	+	-	-	-	-	-	+	-	+	-	-
iy	+	+	-	-	-	+	-	-	-	+	-	-	-

Figure 7.11   Some partial feature matrices for phones; values simplified from Chomsky and Halle (1968). *Syl* is short for syllabic; *son* for sonorant, and *cons* for consonantal.

One main use of these distinctive features is in capturing natural articulatory classes of phones. In both synthesis and recognition, as we will see, we often need to build models of how a phone behaves in a certain context. But we rarely have enough data to model the interaction of every possible left and right context phone on the behavior of a phone. For this reason we can use the relevant feature ([voice], [nasal], etc.) as a useful model of the context; the feature functions as a kind of backoff model of the phone. Another use in speech recognition is building articulatory feature detectors and to use in phone detection; for example, Kirchhoff et al. (2002) built neural-net detectors for the following set of multivalued articulatory features and used them to improve the detection of phones in German speech recognition:

Feature	Values		Feature	Value
voicing	+voice, -voice, silence		**manner**	stop, vowel, lateral, nasal, fricative, silence
cplace	labial, coronal, palatal, velar		**vplace**	glottal, high, mid, low, silence
front-back	front, back, nil, silence		**rounding**	+round, -round, nil, silence

7.3.2   Predicting Phonetic Variation

For speech synthesis as well as recognition, we need to be able to represent the relation between the abstract category and its surface appearance and to predict the surface appearance from the abstract category and the context of the utterance. In early work in phonology, the relationship between a phoneme and its allophones was captured with a **phonological rule**. Here is the phonological rule for flapping in the traditional notation of Chomsky and Halle (1968):

$$\left/ \left\{ \begin{matrix} t \\ d \end{matrix} \right\} \right/ \rightarrow [\mathrm{dx}] \; / \; \acute{\mathrm{V}} \underline{\quad} \mathrm{V} \tag{7.1}$$

In this notation, the surface allophone appears to the right of the arrow, and the phonetic environment is indicated by the symbols surrounding the underbar (___). Simple rules like these are used in both speech recognition and synthesis when we want to generate many pronunciations for a word; in speech recognition, this rule is often used as a first step toward picking the most likely single pronunciation for a word (see Section 10.5.3).

In general, however, there are two reasons why these simple "Chomsky-Halle"-type rules don't do well at telling us **when** a given surface variant is likely to be used. First, variation is a stochastic process; flapping sometimes occurs, and sometimes doesn't, even in the same environment. Second, many factors that are not related to the phonetic environment are important to this prediction task. Thus, linguistic research and speech recognition/synthesis both rely on statistical tools to predict the surface form of a word by showing which factors cause, for example, a particular /t/ to flap in a particular context.

7.3.3   Factors Influencing Phonetic Variation

Rate of speech One important factor that influences phonetic variation is the **rate of speech**, generally measured in syllables per second. Rate of speech varies both across and within speakers. Many kinds of phonetic reduction processes are much more common in fast speech, including flapping, vowel reduction, and final /t/ and /d/ deletion (Wolfram, 1969). We can measure syllables per second (or words per second) with a transcription (by counting the number of words or syllables in the transcription of a region and dividing by the number of seconds), or with signal-processing metrics (Morgan and Fosler-Lussier, 1989).

Another factor affecting variation is word frequency or predictability. Final /t/ and /d/ deletion is particularly likely to happen in frequently used words like *and* and *just* (Labov, 1975; Neu, 1980). Deletion is also more likely when the two words surrounding the segment are a collocation (Bybee, 2000; Zwicky, 1972). The phone [t] is more likely to be palatalized in frequent words and phrases. Words with higher conditional probability are more likely to have reduced vowels or deleted consonants (Bell et al., 2003).

Other phonetic, phonological, and morphological factors affect variation as well. For example, /t/ is much more likely to flap than /d/; and interactions with syllable, foot, and word boundaries are complicated (Rhodes, 1992). As we discuss in Chapter 8, speech is broken up into units called **intonation phrases** or **breath groups**. Words at the beginning or end of intonation phrases are longer and less likely to be reduced. As for morphology, it turns out that deletion is less likely if the word-final /t/ or /d/ is the English past tense ending (Guy, 1980). For example, in Switchboard, deletion is more likely in the word *around* (73% /d/-deletion) than in the word *turned* (30% /d/-deletion) even though the two words have similar frequencies.

Variation is also affected by the speaker's state of mind. For example, the word *the* can be pronounced with a full vowel [dh iy] or reduced vowel [dh ax]. It is more likely to be pronounced with the full vowel [iy] when the speaker is disfluent and having "planning problems"; in general, speakers are more likely to use a full vowel than a reduced one if they don't know what they are going to say next (Fox Tree and Clark, 1997; Bell et al., 2003; Keating et al., 1994).

Sociolinguistic **Sociolinguistic** factors like gender, class, and **dialect** also affect pronunciation
Dialect variation. North American English is often divided into eight dialect regions (Northern, Southern, New England, New York/Mid-Atlantic, North Midlands, South Midlands, Western, Canadian). Southern dialect speakers use a monophthong or near-monophthong [aa] or [ae] instead of a diphthong in some words with the vowel [ay].

African-American Vernacular English

In these dialects *rice* is pronounced [r aa s]. **African-American Vernacular English** (AAVE) shares many vowels with Southern American English and also has individual words with specific pronunciations, such as [b ih d n ih s] for *business* and [ae k s] for *ask*. For older speakers or those not from the American West or Midwest, the words *caught* and *cot* have different vowels ([k ao t] and [k aa t], respectively). Young American speakers or those from the West pronounce the two words *cot* and *caught* the same; the vowels [ao] and [aa] are usually not distinguished in these dialects except before [r]. For speakers of some American and most non-American dialects of English (e.g., Australian English), the words *Mary* ([m ey r iy]), *marry* ([m ae r iy]), and *merry* ([m eh r iy]) are all pronounced differently. Many American speakers pronounce all three of these words identically as ([m eh r iy]).

Register

Style

Other sociolinguistic differences are due to **register** or **style**; a speaker might pronounce the same word differently depending on the social situation or the identity of the interlocutor. One of the most well-studied examples of style variation is the suffix *-ing* (as in *something*), which can be pronounced [ih ng] or [ih n] (this is often written *somethin'*). Most speakers use both forms; as Labov (1966) shows, they use [ih ng] when they are being more formal, and [ih n] when more casual. Wald and Shopen (1981) found that men are more likely to use the non-standard form [ih n] than women, that both men and women are more likely to use more of the standard form [ih ng] when the addressee is a women, and that men (but not women) tend to switch to [ih n] when they are talking with friends.

Many of these results on predicting variation rely on logistic regression on phonetically transcribed corpora, a technique with a long history in the analysis of phonetic variation (Cedergren and Sankoff, 1974), particularly with the VARBRUL and GOLD-VARB software (Rand and Sankoff, 1990).

Finally, the detailed acoustic realization of a particular phone is very strongly influenced by **coarticulation** with its neighboring phones. We return to these fine-grained phonetic details in the following chapters (Section 8.4 and Section 10.3) after we introduce acoustic phonetics.

7.4   Acoustic Phonetics and Signals

We begin with a brief introduction to the acoustic waveform and how it is digitized and summarize the idea of frequency analysis and spectra. This is an extremely brief overview; the interested reader is encouraged to consult the references at the end of the chapter.

7.4.1   Waves

Acoustic analysis is based on the sine and cosine functions. Figure 7.12 shows a plot of a sine wave, in particular the function

$$y = A * sin(2\pi ft) \tag{7.2}$$

where we have set the amplitude A to 1 and the frequency *f* to 10 cycles per second.

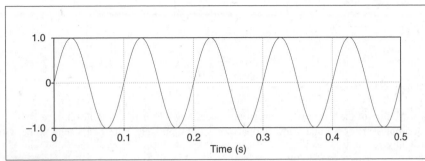

Figure 7.12   A sine wave with a frequency of 10 Hz and an amplitude of 1.

Frequency

Amplitude

Cycles per second

Hertz

Recall from basic mathematics that two important characteristics of a wave are its **frequency** and **amplitude**. The frequency is the number of times a second that a wave repeats itself, that is, the number of **cycles**. We usually measure frequency in **cycles per second**. The signal in Fig. 7.12 repeats itself 5 times in .5 seconds, hence 10 cycles per second. Cycles per second are usually called **hertz** (shortened to **Hz**), so the frequency in Fig. 7.12 would be described as 10 Hz. The **amplitude** A of a sine wave is the maximum value on the Y axis.

Period

The **period** T of the wave is defined as the time it takes for one cycle to complete, defined as

$$T = \frac{1}{f} \tag{7.3}$$

In Fig. 7.12 we can see that each cycle lasts a tenth of a second; hence $T = .1$ seconds.

7.4.2   Speech Sound Waves

Let's turn from hypothetical waves to sound waves. The input to a speech recognizer, like the input to the human ear, is a complex series of changes in air pressure. These changes in air pressure obviously originate with the speaker and are caused by the specific way that air passes through the glottis and out the oral or nasal cavities. We represent sound waves by plotting the change in air pressure over time. One metaphor which sometimes helps in understanding these graphs is that of a vertical plate blocking the air pressure waves (perhaps in a microphone in front of a speaker's mouth, or the eardrum in a hearer's ear). The graph measures the amount of **compression** or **rarefaction** (uncompression) of the air molecules at this plate. Figure 7.13 shows a short segment of a waveform taken from the Switchboard corpus of telephone speech of the vowel [iy] from someone saying "she just had a baby".

Let's explore how the digital representation of the sound wave shown in Fig. 7.13 would be constructed. The first step in processing speech is to convert the analog representations (first air pressure and then analog electric signals in a microphone) into a digital signal. This process of **analog-to-digital conversion** has two steps: **sampling** and **quantization**. To sample a signal, we measure its amplitude at a particular time; the **sampling rate** is the number of samples taken per second. To accurately measure a wave, we must have at least two samples in each cycle: one measuring the

Sampling

Sampling rate

235

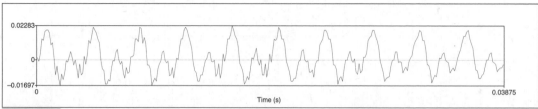

Figure 7.13   A waveform of the vowel [iy] from an utterance shown later in Fig. 7.17 on page 236. The *y*-axis shows the level of air pressure above and below normal atmospheric pressure. The *x*-axis shows time. Notice that the wave repeats regularly.

positive part of the wave and one measuring the negative part. More than two samples per cycle increases the amplitude accuracy, but fewer than two samples causes the frequency of the wave to be completely missed. Thus, the maximum frequency wave that can be measured is one whose frequency is half the sample rate (since every cycle needs two samples). This maximum frequency for a given sampling rate is called the *Nyquist frequency* **Nyquist frequency**. Most information in human speech is in frequencies below 10,000 Hz; thus, a 20,000 Hz sampling rate would be necessary for complete accuracy. But telephone speech is filtered by the switching network, and only frequencies less than 4,000 Hz are transmitted by telephones. Thus, an 8,000 Hz sampling rate is sufficient *Telephone bandwidth* for **telephone-bandwidth** speech like the Switchboard corpus. A 16,000 Hz sampling *Wideband* rate (sometimes called **wideband**) is often used for microphone speech.

Even an 8,000 Hz sampling rate requires 8000 amplitude measurements for each second of speech, so it is important to store amplitude measurements efficiently. They are usually stored as integers, either 8 bit (values from -128–127) or 16 bit (values from -32768–32767). This process of representing real-valued numbers as integers is *Quantization* called **quantization** because the difference between two integers acts as a minimum granularity (a quantum size) and all values that are closer together than this quantum size are represented identically.

Once data is quantized, it is stored in various formats. One parameter of these formats is the sample rate and sample size discussed above; telephone speech is often sampled at 8 kHz and stored as 8-bit samples, and microphone data is often sampled at 16 kHz and stored as 16-bit samples. Another parameter of these formats is the *Channel* number of **channels**. For stereo data or for two-party conversations, we can store both channels in the same file or we can store them in separate files. A final parameter is individual sample storage—linearly or compressed. One common compression format used for telephone speech is μ-law (often written u-law but still pronounced mu-law). The intuition of log compression algorithms like μ-law is that human hearing is more sensitive at small intensities than large ones; the log represents small values with more faithfulness at the expense of more error on large values. The linear (unlogged) values *PCM* are generally referred to as **linear PCM** values (PCM stands for pulse code modulation, but never mind that). Here's the equation for compressing a linear PCM sample value *x* to 8-bit μ-law, (where μ=255 for 8 bits):

$$F(x) = \frac{sgn(s)\log(1 + \mu \, s \,)}{\log(1 + \mu)} \tag{7.4}$$

There are a number of standard file formats for storing the resulting digitized wave-file, such as Microsoft's .wav, Apple's AIFF and Sun's AU, all of which have special headers; simple headerless "raw" files are also used. For example, the .wav format is a subset of Microsoft's RIFF format for multimedia files; RIFF is a general format that can represent a series of nested chunks of data and control information. Figure 7.14 shows a simple .wav file with a single data chunk together with its format chunk.

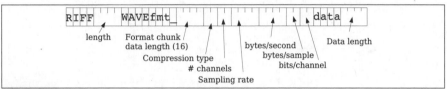

Figure 7.14   Microsoft wavefile header format, assuming simple file with one chunk. Following this 44-byte header would be the data chunk.

7.4.3   Frequency and Amplitude; Pitch and Loudness

Sound waves, like all waves, can be described in terms of frequency, amplitude, and the other characteristics that we introduced earlier for pure sine waves. In sound waves, these are not quite as simple to measure as they were for sine waves. Let's consider frequency. Note in Fig. 7.13 that although not exactly a sine, the wave is nonetheless periodic, repeating 10 times in the 38.75 milliseconds (.03875 seconds) captured in the figure. Thus, the frequency of this segment of the wave is 10/.03875 or 258 Hz.

Where does this periodic 258 Hz wave come from? It comes from the speed of vibration of the vocal folds; since the waveform in Fig. 7.13 is from the vowel [iy], it is voiced. Recall that voicing is caused by regular openings and closing of the vocal folds. When the vocal folds are open, air is pushing up through the lungs, creating a region of high pressure. When the folds are closed, there is no pressure from the lungs. Thus, when the vocal folds are vibrating, we expect to see regular peaks in amplitude of the kind we see in Fig. 7.13, each major peak corresponding to an opening of the vocal folds. The frequency of the vocal fold vibration, or the frequency of the complex

Fundamental frequency wave, is called the **fundamental frequency** of the waveform, often abbreviated **F0**.

F0 We can plot F0 over time in a **pitch track**. Figure 7.15 shows the pitch track of a short

Pitch track question, "Three o'clock?" represented below the waveform. Note the rise in F0 at the end of the question.

The vertical axis in Fig. 7.13 measures the amount of air pressure variation; pressure is force per unit area, measured in Pascals (Pa). A high value on the vertical axis (a high amplitude) indicates that there is more air pressure at that point in time, a zero value means there is normal (atmospheric) air pressure, and a negative value means there is lower than normal air pressure (rarefaction).

In addition to this value of the amplitude at any point in time, we also often need to know the average amplitude over some time range, to give us some idea of how great the average displacement of air pressure is. But we can't just take the average of the amplitude values over a range; the positive and negative values would (mostly) cancel out, leaving us with a number close to zero. Instead, we generally use the RMS

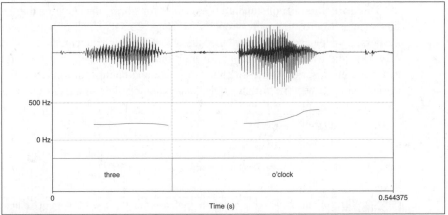

Figure 7.15 Pitch track of the question "Three o'clock?", shown below the wavefile. Note the rise in F0 at the end of the question. Note the lack of pitch trace during the very quiet part (the "o'" of "o'clock"; automatic pitch tracking is based on counting the pulses in the voiced regions, and doesn't work if there is no voicing (or insufficient sound).

(root-mean-square) amplitude, which squares each number before averaging (making it positive), and then takes the square root at the end.

$$\text{RMS amplitude}_{i=1}^{N} = \sqrt{\frac{1}{N}\sum_{i=1}^{N} x_i^2} \tag{7.5}$$

Power   The **power** of the signal is related to the square of the amplitude. If the number of samples of a sound is N, the power is

$$\text{Power} = \frac{1}{N}\sum_{i=1}^{N} x_i^2 \tag{7.6}$$

Intensity   Rather than power, we more often refer to the **intensity** of the sound, which normalizes the power to the human auditory threshold and is measured in dB. If P_0 is the auditory threshold pressure = 2 10^{-5} Pa, then intensity is defined as follows:

$$\text{Intensity} = 10\log_{10}\frac{1}{NP_0}\sum_{i=1}^{N} x_i^2 \tag{7.7}$$

Figure 7.16 shows an intensity plot for the sentence "Is it a long movie?" from the CallHome corpus, again shown below the waveform plot.

Two important perceptual properties, **pitch** and **loudness**, are related to frequency

Pitch   and intensity. The **pitch** of a sound is the mental sensation, or perceptual correlate, of fundamental frequency; in general, if a sound has a higher fundamental frequency we perceive it as having a higher pitch. We say "in general" because the relationship is not linear, since human hearing has different acuities for different frequencies. Roughly speaking, human pitch perception is most accurate between 100 Hz and 1000 Hz and

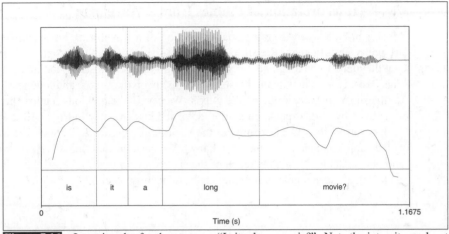

Figure 7.16   Intensity plot for the sentence "Is it a long movie?". Note the intensity peaks at each vowel and the especially high peak for the word *long*.

in this range pitch correlates linearly with frequency. Human hearing represents frequencies above 1000 Hz less accurately, and above this range, pitch correlates logarithmically with frequency. Logarithmic representation means that the differences between high frequencies are compressed and hence not as accurately perceived. There are various psychoacoustic models of pitch perception scales. One common model is the **mel** scale (Stevens et al., 1937; Stevens and Volkmann, 1940). A mel is a unit of pitch defined such that pairs of sounds which are perceptually equidistant in pitch are separated by an equal number of mels. The mel frequency m can be computed from the raw acoustic frequency as follows:

Mel

$$m = 1127 \ln(1 + \frac{f}{700}) \tag{7.8}$$

We return to the mel scale in Chapter 9 when we introduce the MFCC representation of speech used in speech recognition.

The **loudness** of a sound is the perceptual correlate of the **power**. So sounds with higher amplitudes are perceived as louder, but again the relationship is not linear. First of all, as we mentioned above when we defined μ-law compression, humans have greater resolution in the low-power range; the ear is more sensitive to small power differences. Second, it turns out that there is a complex relationship between power, frequency, and perceived loudness; sounds in certain frequency ranges are perceived as being louder than those in other frequency ranges.

Various algorithms exist for automatically extracting F0. In a slight abuse of terminology, these are called **pitch extraction** algorithms. The autocorrelation method of pitch extraction, for example, correlates the signal with itself at various offsets. The offset that gives the highest correlation gives the period of the signal. Other methods for pitch extraction are based on the cepstral features we introduce in Chapter 9. There are various publicly available pitch extraction toolkits; for example, an augmented autocorrelation pitch tracker is provided with Praat (Boersma and Weenink, 2005).

Pitch extraction

239

7.4.4   Interpretation of Phones from a Waveform

Much can be learned from a visual inspection of a waveform. For example, vowels are pretty easy to spot. Recall that vowels are voiced; another property of vowels is that they tend to be long and are relatively loud (as we can see in the intensity plot in Fig. 7.16). Length in time manifests itself directly on the x-axis, and loudness is related to (the square of) amplitude on the y-axis. We saw in the previous section that voicing is realized by regular peaks in amplitude of the kind we saw in Fig. 7.13, each major peak corresponding to an opening of the vocal folds. Figure 7.17 shows the waveform of the short sentence "she just had a baby". We have labeled this waveform with word and phone labels. Notice that each of the six vowels in Fig. 7.17, [iy], [ax], [ae], [ax], [ey], [iy], all have regular amplitude peaks indicating voicing.

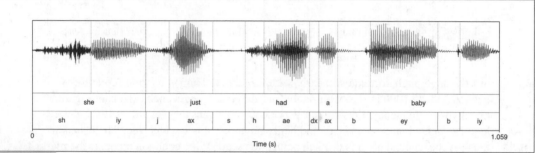

Figure 7.17   A waveform of the sentence "She just had a baby" from the Switchboard corpus (conversation 4325). The speaker is female, was 20 years old in 1991, which is approximately when the recording was made, and speaks the South Midlands dialect of American English.

For a stop consonant, which consists of a closure followed by a release, we can often see a period of silence or near silence followed by a slight burst of amplitude. We can see this for both of the [b]'s in *baby* in Fig. 7.17.

Another phone that is often quite recognizable in a waveform is a fricative. Recall that fricatives, especially very strident fricatives like [sh], are made when a narrow channel for airflow causes noisy, turbulent air. The resulting hissy sounds have a noisy, irregular waveform. This can be seen somewhat in Fig. 7.17; it's even clearer in Fig. 7.18, where we've magnified just the first word *she*.

7.4.5   Spectra and the Frequency Domain

While some broad phonetic features (such as energy, pitch, and the presence of voicing, stop closures, or fricatives) can be interpreted directly from the waveform, most computational applications such as speech recognition (as well as human auditory processing) are based on a different representation of the sound in terms of its component frequencies. The insight of **Fourier analysis** is that every complex wave can be represented as a sum of many sine waves of different frequencies. Consider the waveform in Fig. 7.19. This waveform was created (in Praat) by summing two sine waveforms, one of frequency 10 Hz and one of frequency 100 Hz.

Spectrum   We can represent these two component frequencies with a **spectrum**. The spectrum

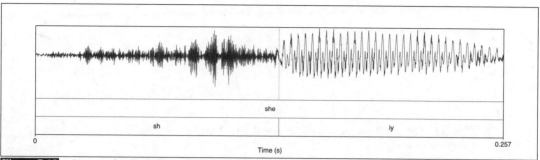

Figure 7.18   A more detailed view of the first word "she" extracted from the wavefile in Fig. 7.17. Notice the difference between the random noise of the fricative [sh] and the regular voicing of the vowel [iy].

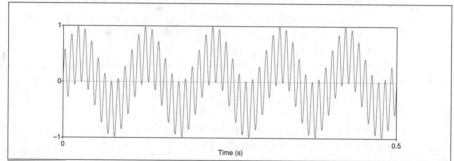

Figure 7.19   A waveform that is the sum of two sine waveforms, one of frequency 10 Hz (note five repetitions in the half-second window) and one of frequency 100 Hz, both of amplitude 1.

of a signal is a representation of each of its frequency components and their amplitudes. Figure 7.20 shows the spectrum of Fig. 7.19. Frequency in Hz is on the x-axis and amplitude on the y-axis. Note the two spikes in the figure, one at 10 Hz and one at 100 Hz. Thus, the spectrum is an alternative representation of the original waveform, and we use the spectrum as a tool to study the component frequencies of a sound wave at a particular time point.

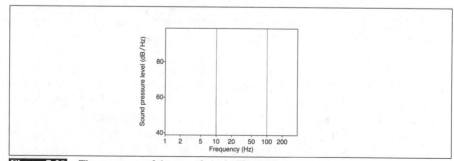

Figure 7.20   The spectrum of the waveform in Fig. 7.19.

Let's look now at the frequency components of a speech waveform. Figure 7.21 shows part of the waveform for the vowel [ae] of the word *had*, cut out from the sentence shown in Fig. 7.17.

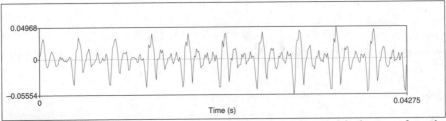

Figure 7.21   The waveform of part of the vowel [ae] from the word *had* cut out from the waveform shown in Fig. 7.17.

Note that there is a complex wave that repeats about ten times in the figure; but there is also a smaller repeated wave that repeats four times for every larger pattern (notice the four small peaks inside each repeated wave). The complex wave has a frequency of about 234 Hz (we can figure this out since it repeats roughly 10 times in .0427 seconds, and 10 cycles/.0427 seconds = 234 Hz).

The smaller wave then should have a frequency of roughly four times the frequency of the larger wave, or roughly 936 Hz. Then, if you look carefully, you can see two little waves on the peak of many of the 936 Hz waves. The frequency of this tiniest wave must be roughly twice that of the 936 Hz wave, hence 1872 Hz.

Figure 7.22 shows a smoothed spectrum for the waveform in Fig. 7.21, computed with a discrete Fourier transform (DFT).

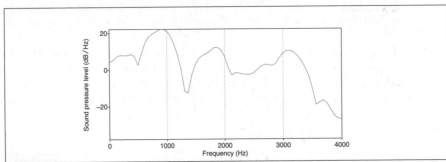

Figure 7.22   A spectrum for the vowel [ae] from the word *had* in the waveform of *She just had a baby* in Fig. 7.17.

The *x*-axis of a spectrum shows frequency, and the *y*-axis shows some measure of the magnitude of each frequency component (in decibels (dB), a logarithmic measure of amplitude that we saw earlier). Thus, Fig. 7.22 shows significant frequency components at around 930 Hz, 1860 Hz, and 3020 Hz, along with many other lower-magnitude frequency components. These first two components are just what we noticed in the time domain by looking at the wave in Fig. 7.21!

Why is a spectrum useful? It turns out that these spectral peaks that are easily visible in a spectrum are characteristic of different phones; phones have characteristic spectral "signatures". Just as chemical elements give off different wavelengths of light when they burn, allowing us to detect elements in stars by looking at the spectrum of the light, we can detect the characteristic signature of the different phones by looking at the

Cochlea

spectrum of a waveform. This use of spectral information is essential to both human and machine speech recognition. In human audition, the function of the **cochlea**, or **inner ear**, is to compute a spectrum of the incoming waveform. Similarly, the various kinds of acoustic features used in speech recognition as the HMM observation are all different representations of spectral information.

Spectrogram

Let's look at the spectrum of different vowels. Since some vowels change over time, we'll use a different kind of plot called a **spectrogram**. While a spectrum shows the frequency components of a wave at one point in time, a **spectrogram** is a way of envisioning how the different frequencies that make up a waveform change over time. The *x*-axis shows time, as it did for the waveform, but the *y*-axis now shows frequencies in hertz. The darkness of a point on a spectrogram corresponds to the amplitude of the frequency component. Very dark points have high amplitude, light points have low amplitude. Thus, the spectrogram is a useful way of visualizing the three dimensions (time x frequency x amplitude).

Figure 7.23 shows spectrograms of three American English vowels, [ih], [ae], and [ah]. Note that each vowel has a set of dark bars at various frequency bands, slightly different bands for each vowel. Each of these represents the same kind of spectral peak that we saw in Fig. 7.21.

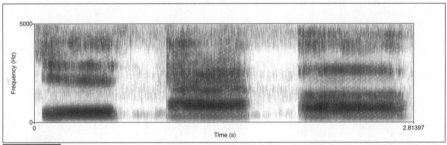

Figure 7.23   Spectrograms for three American English vowels, [ih], [ae], and [uh], spoken by the first author.

Formant

Each dark bar (or spectral peak) is called a **formant**. As we discuss below, a formant is a frequency band that is particularly amplified by the vocal tract. Since different vowels are produced with the vocal tract in different positions, they will produce different kinds of amplifications or resonances. Let's look at the first two formants, called F1 and F2. Note that F1, the dark bar closest to the bottom, is in a different position for the three vowels; it's low for [ih] (centered at about 470 Hz) and somewhat higher for [ae] and [ah] (somewhere around 800 Hz). By contrast, F2, the second dark bar from the bottom, is highest for [ih], in the middle for [ae], and lowest for [ah].

We can see the same formants in running speech, although the reduction and coarticulation processes make them somewhat harder to see. Figure 7.24 shows the spectrogram of "she just had a baby", whose waveform was shown in Fig. 7.17. F1 and F2 (and also F3) are pretty clear for the [ax] of *just*, the [ae] of *had*, and the [ey] of *baby*.

What specific clues can spectral representations give for phone identification? First, since different vowels have their formants at characteristic places, the spectrum can distinguish vowels from each other. We've seen that [ae] in the sample waveform had formants at 930 Hz, 1860 Hz, and 3020 Hz. Consider the vowel [iy] at the beginning

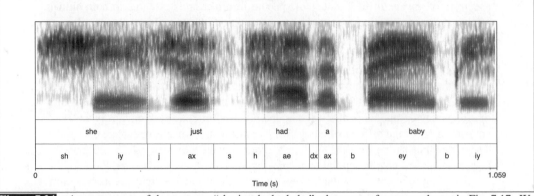

Figure 7.24   A spectrogram of the sentence "she just had a baby" whose waveform was shown in Fig. 7.17. We can think of a spectrogram as a collection of spectra (time slices), like Fig. 7.22 placed end to end.

of the utterance in Fig. 7.17. The spectrum for this vowel is shown in Fig. 7.25. The first formant of [iy] is 540 Hz, much lower than the first formant for [ae], and the second formant (2581 Hz) is much higher than the second formant for [ae]. If you look carefully, you can see these formants as dark bars in Fig. 7.24 just around 0.5 seconds.

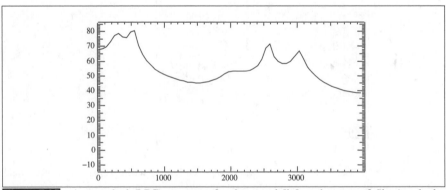

Figure 7.25   A smoothed (LPC) spectrum for the vowel [iy] at the start of *She just had a baby*. Note that the first formant (540 Hz) is much lower than the first formant for [ae] shown in Fig. 7.22, and the second formant (2581 Hz) is much higher than the second formant for [ae].

The location of the first two formants (called F1 and F2) plays a large role in determining vowel identity, although the formants still differ from speaker to speaker. Higher formants tend to be caused more by general characteristics of a speaker's vocal tract rather than by individual vowels. Formants also can be used to identify the nasal phones [n], [m], and [ng] and the liquids [l] and [r].

7.4.6   The Source-Filter Model

Source-filter model

Why do different vowels have different spectral signatures? As we briefly mentioned above, the formants are caused by the resonant cavities of the mouth. The **source-filter** model is a way of explaining the acoustics of a sound by modeling how the pulses produced by the glottis (the **source**) are shaped by the vocal tract (the **filter**).

Harmonic

Let's see how this works. Whenever we have a wave such as the vibration in air caused by the glottal pulse, the wave also has **harmonics**. A harmonic is another wave whose frequency is a multiple of the fundamental wave. Thus, for example, a 115 Hz glottal fold vibration leads to harmonics (other waves) of 230 Hz, 345 Hz, 460 Hz, and so on on. In general, each of these waves will be weaker, that is, will have much less amplitude than the wave at the fundamental frequency.

It turns out, however, that the vocal tract acts as a kind of filter or amplifier; indeed any cavity, such as a tube, causes waves of certain frequencies to be amplified and others to be damped. This amplification process is caused by the shape of the cavity; a given shape will cause sounds of a certain frequency to resonate and hence be amplified. Thus, by changing the shape of the cavity, we can cause different frequencies to be amplified.

When we produce particular vowels, we are essentially changing the shape of the vocal tract cavity by placing the tongue and the other articulators in particular positions. The result is that different vowels cause different harmonics to be amplified. So a wave of the same fundamental frequency passed through different vocal tract positions will result in different harmonics being amplified.

We can see the result of this amplification by looking at the relationship between the shape of the vocal tract and the corresponding spectrum. Figure 7.26 shows the vocal tract position for three vowels and a typical resulting spectrum. The formants are places in the spectrum where the vocal tract happens to amplify particular harmonic frequencies.

7.5   Phonetic Resources

Pronunciation dictionary

A wide variety of phonetic resources can be drawn on for computational work. One key set of resources are **pronunciation dictionaries**. Such on-line phonetic dictionaries give phonetic transcriptions for each word. Three commonly used on-line dictionaries for English are the CELEX, CMUdict, and PRONLEX lexicons; for other languages, the LDC has released pronunciation dictionaries for Egyptian Arabic, German, Japanese, Korean, Mandarin, and Spanish. All these dictionaries can be used for both speech recognition and synthesis work.

The CELEX dictionary (Baayen et al., 1995) is the most richly annotated of the dictionaries. It includes all the words in the 1974 Oxford Advanced Learner's Dictionary (41,000 lemmata) and the 1978 Longman Dictionary of Contemporary English (53,000 lemmata); in total it has pronunciations for 160,595 wordforms. Its (British rather than American) pronunciations are transcribed with an ASCII version of the IPA called SAM. In addition to basic phonetic information like phone strings, syllabification, and stress level for each syllable, each word is also annotated with morphological, part-of-speech, syntactic, and frequency information. CELEX (as well as CMU and PRONLEX) represent three levels of stress: primary stress, secondary stress, and no stress. For example, some of the CELEX information for the word *dictionary* includes

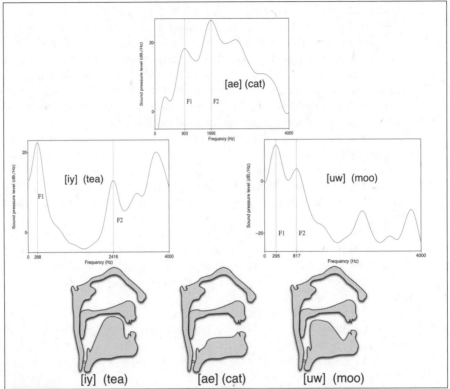

Figure 7.26   Visualizing the vocal tract position as a filter: the tongue positions for three English vowels and the resulting smoothed spectra showing F1 and F2.

multiple pronunciations ('dIk-S@n-rI and 'dIk-S@-n@-rI, corresponding to ARPAbet [d ih k sh ax n r ih] and [d ih k sh ax n ax r ih], respectively), together with the CV skelata for each one ([CVC][CVC][CV] and [CVC][CV][CV][CV]), the frequency of the word, the fact that it is a noun, and its morphological structure (diction+ary).

The free CMU Pronouncing Dictionary (CMU, 1993) has pronunciations for about 125,000 wordforms. It uses a 39-phone ARPAbet-derived phoneme set. Transcriptions are phonemic, and thus instead of marking any kind of surface reduction like flapping or reduced vowels, it marks each vowel with the number 0 (unstressed), 1 (stressed), or 2 (secondary stress). Thus, the word *tiger* is listed as [T AY1 G ER0], the word *table* as [T EY1 B AH0 L], and the word *dictionary* as [D IH1 K SH AH0 N EH2 R IY0]. The dictionary is not syllabified, although the nucleus is implicitly marked by the (numbered) vowel.

The PRONLEX dictionary (LDC, 1995) was designed for speech recognition and contains pronunciations for 90,694 wordforms. It covers all the words used in many years of the *Wall Street Journal*, as well as the Switchboard Corpus. PRONLEX has the advantage that it includes many proper names (20,000, whereas CELEX only has about 1000). Names are important for practical applications, and they are both frequent and difficult; we return to a discussion of deriving name pronunciations in Chapter 8.

Another useful resource is a **phonetically annotated corpus**, in which a collection of waveforms is hand-labeled with the corresponding string of phones. Three important phonetic corpora in English are the TIMIT corpus, the Switchboard corpus, and the Buckeye corpus.

The TIMIT corpus (NIST, 1990) was collected as a joint project between Texas Instruments (TI), MIT, and SRI. It is a corpus of 6300 read sentences, with 10 sentences each from 630 speakers. The 6300 sentences were drawn from a set of 2342 pre-designed sentences, some selected to have particular dialect shibboleths, others to maximize phonetic diphone coverage. Each sentence in the corpus was phonetically hand-labeled, the sequence of phones was automatically aligned with the sentence wavefile, and then the automatic phone boundaries were manually hand-corrected (Seneff and Zue, 1988). The result is a **time-aligned transcription**: a transcription in which each phone is associated with a start and end time in the waveform. We showed a graphical example of a time-aligned transcription in Fig. 7.17 on page 236.

Time-aligned transcription

The phoneset for TIMIT and for the Switchboard Transcription Project corpus below, is a more detailed one than the minimal phonemic version of the ARPAbet. In particular, these phonetic transcriptions make use of the various reduced and rare phones mentioned in Fig. 7.1 and Fig. 7.2: the flap [dx], glottal stop [q], reduced vowels [ax], [ix], [axr], voiced allophone of [h] ([hv]), and separate phones for stop closure ([dcl], [tcl], etc) and release ([d], [t], etc.). An example transcription is shown in Fig. 7.27.

she	had	your	dark	suit	in	greasy	wash	water	all	year
sh iy	hv ae dcl	jh axr	dcl d aa r kcl	s ux q	en	gcl g r iy s ix	w aa sh	q w aa dx axr q	aa l	y ix axr

Figure 7.27   Phonetic transcription from the TIMIT corpus. Note palatalization of [d] in *had*, unreleased final stop in *dark*, glottalization of final [t] in *suit* to [q], and flap of [t] in *water*. The TIMIT corpus also includes time-alignments for each phone (not shown).

Where TIMIT is based on read speech, the more recent Switchboard Transcription Project corpus is based on the Switchboard corpus of conversational speech. This phonetically annotated portion consists of approximately 3.5 hours of sentences extracted from various conversations (Greenberg et al., 1996). As with TIMIT, each annotated utterance contains a time-aligned transcription. The Switchboard transcripts are time aligned at the syllable level rather than at the phone level; thus, a transcript consists of a sequence of syllables with the start and end time of each syllables in the corresponding wavefile. Figure 7.28 shows an example from the Switchboard Transcription Project for the phrase *they're kind of in between right now*.

0.470	0.640	0.720	0.900	0.953	1.279	1.410	1.630
dh er	k aa	n ax	v ih m	b ix	t w iy n	r ay	n aw

Figure 7.28   Phonetic transcription of the Switchboard phrase *they're kind of in between right now*. Note vowel reduction in *they're* and *of*, coda deletion in *kind* and *right*, and resyllabification (the [v] of *of* attaches as the onset of *in*). Time is given in number of seconds from the beginning of sentence to the start of each syllable.

The Buckeye corpus (Pitt et al., 2007, 2005) is a more recent phonetically transcribed corpus of spontaneous American speech, containing about 300,000 words from 40 talkers. Phonetically transcribed corpora are also available for other languages; the

Kiel corpus of German is commonly used, as are various Mandarin corpora transcribed by the Chinese Academy of Social Sciences (Li et al., 2000).

In addition to resources like dictionaries and corpora, there are many useful phonetic software tools. One of the most versatile is the free Praat package (Boersma and Weenink, 2005), which includes spectrum and spectrogram analysis, pitch extraction and formant analysis, and an embedded scripting language for automation. It is available for Microsoft, Macintosh, and Unix environments.

7.6   Advanced: Articulatory and Gestural Phonology

We saw in Section 7.3.1 that we could use **distinctive features** to capture generalizations across phone class. These generalizations were mainly articulatory, although some, like [strident] and the vowel height features, are primarily acoustic.

Articulatory phonology
Gesture

This idea that articulation underlies phonetic production is used in a more sophisticated way in **articulatory phonology**, in which the **articulatory gesture** is the underlying phonological abstraction (Browman and Goldstein, 1992, 1995). Articulatory gestures are defined as parameterized **dynamical systems**. Since speech production requires the coordinated actions of tongue, lips, glottis, etc., articulatory phonology represents a speech utterances as a sequence of potentially overlapping articulatory

Gestural score

gestures. Figure 7.29 shows the sequence of gestures (or **gestural score**) required for the production of the word *pan* [p ae n]. The lips first close, then the glottis opens, then the tongue body moves down and back toward the pharynx wall for the vowel [ae], the velum drops for the nasal sounds, and finally the tongue tip closes against the alveolar ridge. The lines in the diagram indicate gestures that are phased with respect to each other. With such a gestural representation, the nasality in the [ae] vowel is explained by the timing of the gestures: the velum drops before the tongue tip has quite closed.

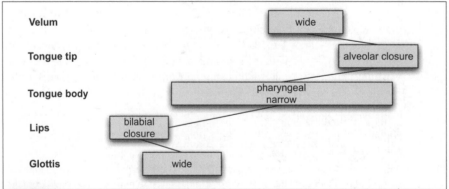

Figure 7.29   The Browman and Goldstein (1995) gestural score for the word *pan* as pronounced [p ae n].

The intuition behind articulatory phonology is that the gestural score is likely to be much better as a set of hidden states at capturing the continuous nature of speech than as a discrete sequence of phones. In addition, using articulatory gestures as a basic unit can help in modeling the fine-grained effects of coarticulation of neighboring gestures that we explore further when we introduce **diphones** (Section 8.4) and **triphones** (Section 10.3).

Computational implementations of articulatory phonology have recently appeared in speech recognition. These implementations use articulatory gestures rather than phones as the underlying representation or hidden variable. Since multiple articulators (tongue, lips, etc) can move simultaneously, using gestures as the hidden variable implies a multitier hidden representation. Figure 7.30 shows the articulatory feature set used in the work of Livescu and Glass (2004b) and Livescu (2005); Fig. 7.31 shows examples of how phones are mapped onto this feature set.

Feature	Description	Value = meaning
LIP-LOC	position of lips	LAB = labial (neutral position); PRO = protruded (rounded); DEN = dental
LIP-OPEN	degree of opening of lips	CL = closed; CR = critical (labial/labio-dental fricative); NA = narrow (e.g., [w], [uw]); WI = wide (all other sounds)
TT-LOC	location of tongue tip	DEN = inter-dental ([th], [dh]); ALV = alveolar ([t], [n]); P-A = palato-alveolar ([sh]); RET = retroflex ([r])
TT-OPEN	degree of opening of tongue tip	CL = closed (stop); CR = critical (fricative); NA = narrow ([r], alveolar glide); M-N = medium-narrow;MID = medium;WI = wide
TB-LOC	location of tongue body	PAL = palatal (e.g., [sh], [y]); VEL = velar (e.g., [k], [ng]); UVU = uvular (neutral position); PHA = pharyngeal (e.g., [aa])
TB-OPEN	degree of opening of tongue body	CL = closed (stop); CR = critical (e.g., fricated [g] in "legal"); NA = narrow (e.g., [y]); M-N = medium-narrow; MID = medium; WI = wide
VEL	state of the velum	CL = closed (non-nasal); OP = open (nasal)
GLOT	state of the glottis	CL = closed (glottal stop); CR = critical (voiced); OP = open (voiceless)

Figure 7.30   Articulatory-phonology-based feature set from Livescu (2005).

phone	LIP-LOC	LIP-OPEN	TT-LOC	TT-OPEN	TB-LOC	TB-OPEN	VEL	GLOT
aa	LAB	W	ALV	W	PHA	M-N	CL(.9),OP(.1)	CR
ae	LAB	W	ALV	W	VEL	W	CL(.9),OP(.1)	CR
b	LAB	CR	ALV	M	UVU	W	CL	CR
f	DEN	CR	ALV	M	VEL	M	CL	OP
n	LAB	W	ALV	CL	UVU	M	OP	CR
s	LAB	W	ALV	CR	UVU	M	CL	OP
uw	PRO	N	P-A	W	VEL	N	CL(.9),OP(.1)	CR

Figure 7.31   Livescu (2005): Sample of mapping from phones to underyling target articulatory feature values. Note that some values are probabilistic.

7.7   Summary

This chapter has introduced many of the important concepts of phonetics and computational phonetics.

- We can represent the pronunciation of words in terms of units called **phones**. The standard system for representing phones is the **International Phonetic Al-**

phabet or **IPA**. The most common computational system for transcription of English is the **ARPAbet**, which conveniently uses ASCII symbols.

- Phones can be described by how they are produced **articulatorily** by the vocal organs; consonants are defined in terms of their **place** and **manner** of articulation and **voicing**; vowels by their **height**, **backness**, and **roundness**.

- A **phoneme** is a generalization or abstraction over different phonetic realizations. **Allophonic rules** express how a phoneme is realized in a given context.

- Speech sounds can also be described **acoustically**. Sound waves can be described in terms of **frequency**, **amplitude**, or their perceptual correlates, **pitch** and **loudness**.

- The **spectrum** of a sound describes its different frequency components. While some phonetic properties are recognizable from the waveform, both humans and machines rely on spectral analysis for phone detection.

- A **spectrogram** is a plot of a spectrum over time. Vowels are described by characteristic harmonics called **formants**.

- **Pronunciation dictionaries** are widely available and used for both speech recognition and synthesis, including the CMU dictionary for English and CELEX dictionaries for English, German, and Dutch. Other dictionaries are available from the LDC.

- Phonetically transcribed corpora are a useful resource for building computational models of phone variation and reduction in natural speech.

Bibliographical and Historical Notes

The major insights of articulatory phonetics date to the linguists of 800–150 B.C. India. They invented the concepts of place and manner of articulation, worked out the glottal mechanism of voicing, and understood the concept of assimilation. European science did not catch up with the Indian phoneticians until over 2000 years later, in the late 19th century. The Greeks did have some rudimentary phonetic knowledge; by the time of Plato's *Theaetetus* and *Cratylus*, for example, they distinguished vowels from consonants, and stop consonants from continuants. The Stoics developed the idea of the syllable and were aware of phonotactic constraints on possible words. An unknown Icelandic scholar of the 12th century exploited the concept of the phoneme and proposed a phonemic writing system for Icelandic, including diacritics for length and nasality. But his text remained unpublished until 1818 and even then was largely unknown outside Scandinavia (Robins, 1967). The modern era of phonetics is usually said to have begun with Sweet, who proposed what is essentially the phoneme in his *Handbook of Phonetics* (1877). He also devised an alphabet for transcription and distinguished between *broad* and *narrow* transcription, proposing many ideas that were eventually incorporated into the IPA. Sweet was considered the best practicing phonetician of his time; he made the first scientific recordings of languages for phonetic purposes and advanced the state of the art of articulatory description. He was also infamously difficult to get along with, a trait that is well captured in Henry Higgins, the stage character that George Bernard Shaw modeled after him. The phoneme was first named by the Polish scholar Baudouin de Courtenay, who published his theories in 1894.

Students with further interest in transcription and articulatory phonetics should consult an introductory phonetics textbook such as Ladefoged (1993) or Clark and Yallop (1995). Pullum and Ladusaw (1996) is a comprehensive guide to each of the symbols and diacritics of the IPA. A good resource for details about reduction and other phonetic processes in spoken English is Shockey (2003). Wells (1982) is the definitive three-volume source on dialects of English.

Many of the classic insights in acoustic phonetics had been developed by the late 1950s or early 1960s; just a few highlights include techniques like the sound spectrograph (Koenig et al., 1946), theoretical insights like the working out of the source-filter theory and other issues in the mapping between articulation and acoustics (Fant, 1960; Stevens et al., 1953; Stevens and House, 1955; Heinz and Stevens, 1961; Stevens and House, 1961), the F1xF2 space of vowel formants (Peterson and Barney, 1952), the understanding of the phonetic nature of stress and the use of duration and intensity as cues (Fry, 1955), and a basic understanding of issues in phone perception (Miller and Nicely, 1955; Liberman et al., 1952). Lehiste (1967) is a collection of classic papers on acoustic phonetics. Many of the seminal papers of Gunnar Fant have been collected in Fant (2004).

Excellent textbooks on acoustic phonetics include Johnson (2003) and Ladefoged (1996). Coleman (2005) includes an introduction to computational processing of acoustics as well as other speech processing issues, from a linguistic perspective. Stevens (1998) lays out an influential theory of speech sound production. A wide variety of books address speech from a signal processing and electrical engineering perspective. The ones with the greatest coverage of computational phonetics issues include Huang et al. (2001), O'Shaughnessy (2000), and Gold and Morgan (1999). Excellent textbooks on digital signal processing are Lyons (2004) and Rabiner and Schafer (1978).

There are a number of software packages for acoustic phonetic analysis. Probably the most widely-used one is **Praat** (Boersma and Weenink, 2005).

Many phonetics papers of computational interest are to be found in the *Journal of the Acoustical Society of America (JASA)*, *Computer Speech and Language*, and *Speech Communication*.

Exercises

7.1 Find the mistakes in the ARPAbet transcriptions of the following words:

a. "three" [dh r i]   **d.** "study" [s t uh d i]   **g.** "slight" [s l iy t]
b. "sing" [s ih n g]   **e.** "though" [th ow]
c. "eyes" [ay s]   **f.** "planning" [p pl aa n ih ng]

7.2 Translate the pronunciations of the following color words from the IPA into the ARPAbet (and make a note if you think you pronounce them differently than this!):

a. [rɛd]	**e.** [blæk]	**i.** [pjus]
b. [blu]	**f.** [waɪt]	**j.** [toʊp]
c. [grin]	**g.** [ˈɔrɪndʒ]	
d. [ˈjɛloʊ]	**h.** [ˈpɝpl̩]	

7.3 Ira Gershwin's lyric for *Let's Call the Whole Thing Off* talks about two pronunciations (each) of the words "tomato", "potato", and "either". Transcribe into the ARPAbet both pronunciations of each of these three words.

7.4 Transcribe the following words in the ARPAbet:

1. dark
2. suit
3. greasy
4. wash
5. water

7.5 Take a wavefile of your choice. Some examples are on the textbook website. Download the Praat software, and use it to transcribe the wavefiles at the word level and into ARPAbet phones, using Praat to help you play pieces of each wavefile and to look at the wavefile and the spectrogram.

7.6 Record yourself saying five of the English vowels: [aa], [eh], [ae], [iy], [uw]. Find F1 and F2 for each of your vowels.

Credit

Fig. 7.3 (© Laszlo Kubinyi and *Scientific American*)

Chapter 8

Speech Synthesis

And computers are getting smarter all the time: Scientists tell us that soon they will be able to talk to us. (By 'they' I mean 'computers': I doubt scientists will ever be able to talk to us.)

Dave Barry

In Vienna in 1769, Wolfgang von Kempelen built for the Empress Maria Theresa the famous Mechanical Turk, a chess-playing automaton consisting of a wooden box filled with gears, behind which sat a robot mannequin who played chess by moving pieces with his mechanical arm. The Turk toured Europe and the Americas for decades, defeating Napolean Bonaparte and even playing Charles Babbage. The Mechanical Turk might have been one of the early successes of artificial intelligence were it not for the fact that it was, alas, a hoax, powered by a human chess player hidden inside the box.

What is less well known is that von Kempelen, an extraordinarily prolific inventor, also built between 1769 and 1790 what was definitely not a hoax: the first full-sentence speech synthesizer. His device consisted of a bellows to simulate the lungs, a rubber mouthpiece and a nose aperature, a reed to simulate the vocal folds, various whistles for the fricatives, and a small auxiliary bellows to provide the puff of air for plosives. By moving levers with both hands to open and close aperatures, and adjusting the flexible leather "vocal tract", an operator could produce different consonants and vowels.

More than two centuries later, we no longer build our synthesizers out of wood and leather, nor do we need human operators. The modern task of **speech synthesis**, also called **text-to-speech** or **TTS**, is to produce speech (acoustic waveforms) from text.

Speech synthesis
Text-to-speech
TTS

Modern speech synthesis has a wide variety of applications. Synthesizers are used in telephone-based conversational agents that conduct dialogues with people (Chapter 24). Synthesizers are also important in non-conversational applications that speak **to** people, such as in devices that read out loud for the blind or in video games or children's toys. Finally, speech synthesis can be used to speak **for** sufferers of neurological disorders, such as astrophysicist Steven Hawking who, having lost the use of his voice because of ALS, speaks by typing to a speech synthesizer and having the synthesizer speak the words. State of the art systems in speech synthesis can achieve remarkably natural speech for a very wide variety of input situations, although even the best systems still tend to sound wooden and are limited in the voices they use.

The task of speech synthesis is to map a text like the following:

(8.1) `PG&E will file schedules on April 20.`

to a waveform like the following:

From Chapter 8 of *Speech and Language Processing*, Second Edition. Daniel Jurafsky, James H. Martin.

Speech synthesis systems perform this mapping in two steps, first converting the input text into a **phonemic internal representation** and then converting this internal representation into a waveform. We will call the first step **text analysis**, and the second step **waveform synthesis** (although other names are also used for these steps).

Text analysis
Waveform
synthesis

A sample of the internal representation for this sentence is shown in Fig. 8.1. Note that the acronym PG&E is expanded into the words P G AND E, the number 20 is expanded into *twentieth*, a phone sequence is given for each of the words, and there is also prosodic and phrasing information (the *'s), which we define later.

P	G	AND	E*	WILL	FILE	SCHEDULES*	ON	APRIL	TWENTIETH*	L-L%
p iy	jh iy	ae n d	iy	w ih l	f ay l	s k eh jh ax l z	aa n	ey p r ih l	t w eh n t iy ax th	

Figure 8.1   Intermediate output for a unit selection synthesizer for the sentence *PG&E will file schedules on April 20.*. The numbers and acronyms have been expanded, words have been converted into phones, and prosodic features have been assigned.

While text analysis algorithms are relatively standard, there are three widely different paradigms for waveform synthesis: **concatenative synthesis**, **formant synthesis**, and **articulatory synthesis**. The architecture of most modern commercial TTS systems is based on concatenative synthesis, in which samples of speech are chopped up, stored in a database, and combined and reconfigured to create new sentences. Thus, we focus on concatenative synthesis for most of this chapter, although we briefly introduce formant and articulatory synthesis at the end of the chapter.

Figure 8.2 shows the TTS architecture for concatenative unit selection synthesis, using the two-step **hourglass metaphor** of Taylor (2008). In the following sections, we examine each of the components in this architecture.

Hourglass
metaphor

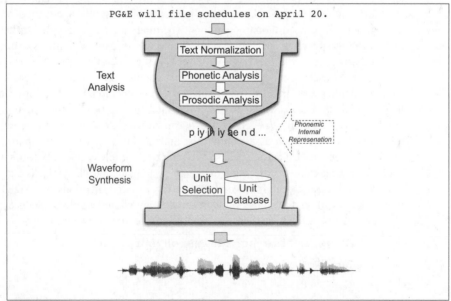

Figure 8.2   The TTS architecture for unit selection (concatenative) speech synthesis.

8.1   Text Normalization

Text normalization   To generate a phonemic internal representation, we must first preprocess or **normalize** the raw text in a variety of ways. We'll need to break the input text into sentences, deal with the idiosyncracies of abbreviations, numbers, and so on. Consider the difficulties in the following text drawn from the Enron corpus (Klimt and Yang, 2004):

> He said the increase in credit limits helped B.C. Hydro achieve record net income of about $1 billion during the year ending March 31. This figure does not include any write-downs that may occur if Powerex determines that any of its customer accounts are not collectible. Cousins, however, was insistent that all debts will be collected: "We continue to pursue monies owing and we expect to be paid for electricity we have sold."

Sentence tokenization   The first task in text normalization is **sentence tokenization**. To segment this paragraph into separate utterances for synthesis, we need to know that the first sentence ends at the period after *March 31*, not at the period of *B.C.* We also need to know that there is a sentence ending at the word *collected*, despite the punctuation being a colon rather than a period. The second normalization task is dealing with **non-standard words**. Non-standard words include numbers, acronyms, abbreviations, and so on. For example, *March 31* needs to be pronounced *March thirty-first*, not *March three one*; *$1 billion* needs to be pronounced *one billion dollars*, with the word *dollars* appearing after the word *billion*.

8.1.1   Sentence Tokenization

We saw two examples above where sentence tokenization is difficult because sentence boundaries are not always indicated by periods and can sometimes be indicated by punctuation like colons. An additional problem occurs when an abbreviation ends a sentence, in which case the abbreviation-final period is playing a dual role:

(8.2)   He said the increase in credit limits helped B.C. Hydro achieve record net income of about $1 billion during the year ending March 31.

(8.3)   Cousins, however, was insistent that all debts will be collected: "We continue to pursue monies owing and we expect to be paid for electricity we have sold."

(8.4)   The group included Dr. J. M. Freeman and T. Boone Pickens Jr.

A key part of sentence tokenization is thus period disambiguation; we've seen a simple Perl script for period disambiguation in Chapter 3. Most sentence tokenization algorithms are slightly more complex than this deterministic algorithm, and, in particular, are trained by machine learning methods rather than being hand-built. We do this training by first hand-labeling a training set with sentence boundaries and then applying any supervised machine learning method (decision trees, logistic regression, SVM, etc.) to train a classifier to mark the sentence boundary decisions.

More specifically, we could start by tokenizing the input text into tokens separated by whitespace and then select any token containing one of the three characters !, . or ? (or possibly also :). After hand-labeling a corpus of such tokens, we train a classifier to make a binary decision (EOS (end-of-sentence) versus not-EOS) on these potential sentence boundary characters inside these tokens.

The success of such a classifier depends on the features that are extracted for the classification. Let's consider some feature templates we might use to disambiguate these **candidate** sentence boundary characters, assuming we have a small amount of training data labeled for sentence boundaries:

- the prefix (the portion of the candidate token preceding the candidate)
- the suffix (the portion of the candidate token following the candidate)
- whether the prefix or suffix is an abbreviation (from a list)
- the word preceding the candidate
- the word following the candidate
- whether the word preceding the candidate is an abbreviation
- whether the word following the candidate is an abbreviation

Consider the following example:

(8.5) ANLP Corp. chairman Dr. Smith resigned.

Given these feature templates, the feature values for the period `.` in the word `Corp.` in (8.5) would be

```
PreviousWord = ANLP              NextWord = chairman
Prefix = Corp                    Suffix = NULL
PreviousWordAbbreviation = 1 NextWordAbbreviation = 0
```

If our training set is large enough, we can also look for lexical cues about sentence boundaries. For example, certain words may tend to occur sentence-initially or sentence-finally. We can thus add the following features:

- Probability[candidate occurs at end of sentence]
- Probability[word following candidate occurs at beginning of sentence]

Finally, while most of the above features are relatively language independent, we can use language-specific features. For example, in English, sentences usually begin with capital letters, suggesting features like the following:

- case of candidate: Upper, Lower, AllCap, Numbers
- case of word following candidate: Upper, Lower, AllCap, Numbers

Similarly, we can have specific subclasses of abbreviations, such as honorifics or titles (e.g., Dr., Mr., Gen.), corporate designators (e.g., Corp., Inc.), or month names (e.g., Jan., Feb.).

Any machine learning method can be applied to train EOS classifiers. Logistic regression (Section 6.6.2) and decision trees are two common methods; logistic regression may have somewhat higher accuracy, although we have instead shown a decision tree in Fig. 8.3 because it is easier to see how the features are used.

8.1.2   Non-Standard Words

Non-standard words

The second step in text normalization is normalizing **non-standard words** (NSWs). Non-standard words are tokens, like numbers or abbreviations, that need to be expanded into sequences of English words before they can be pronounced.

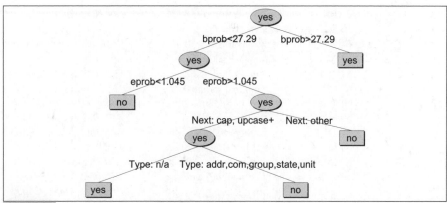

Figure 8.3 A decision tree from Richard Sproat for predicting whether a period "." is an end of sentence (YES) or not an end-of-sentence (NO). We use features like the log likelihood of the current word being the beginning of a sentence (`bprob`), the previous word being an end-of-sentence (`eprob`), the capitalization of the next word, and the abbreviation subclass (company, state, unit of measurement).

Non-standard words are difficult because they are often ambiguous. For example, the number *1750* can be spoken in at least four different ways, depending on the context:

```
seventeen fifty:   (in "The European economy in 1750")
one seven five zero:   (in "The password is 1750")
seventeen hundred and fifty:   (in "1750 dollars")
one thousand, seven hundred, and fifty:   (in "1750 dollars")
```

Similar ambiguities occur for Roman numerals like *IV* (which can be pronounced `four`, `fourth`, or as the letters `I V` (meaning "intravenous")), or *2/3*, which can be `two thirds` or `February third` or `March second` or `two slash three`.

Some non-standard words are composed of letters, such as **abbreviations**, **letter sequences**, and **acronyms**. Abbreviations are generally pronounced as if **expanded**; thus, *Wed* is pronounced `Wednesday`, and *Jan 1* is pronounced `January first`. **Letter sequences** like *UN, DVD, PC,* and *IBM* are pronounced letter by letter in a sequence; IBM is thus pronounced [ay b iy eh m]. **Acronyms** like *IKEA, MoMA, NASA,* and *UNICEF* are pronounced as if they were words; *MoMA* is pronounced [m ow m ax]. Ambiguity occurs here as well; should *Jan* be read as a word (the name `Jan`) or expanded as the month `January`? Different types of numeric and alphabetic non-standard words are summarized in Fig. 8.4.

Paired digits

Serial digits

Each of the types has a particular realization (or realizations). For example, a year (NYER) is generally read in the **paired** method, in which each pair of digits is pronounced as an integer (e.g., `seventeen fifty` for 1750), while a U.S. zip code (NZIP) is generally read in the **serial** method, as a sequence of single digits (e.g., `nine four one one zero` for *94110*). The type BMONEY deals with the idiosyncrasies of expressions like *$3.2 billion*, which must be read out with the word `dollars` at the end, as `three point two billion dollars`. For the alphabetic NSWs, we have the class EXPN for abbreviations like *N.Y.* that are expanded,

ALPHA	EXPN	abbreviation	*adv, N.Y., mph, gov't*
	LSEQ	letter sequence	*DVD, D.C., PC, UN, IBM,*
	ASWD	read as word	*IKEA,* unknown words/names
NUMBERS	NUM	number (cardinal)	*12, 45, 1/2, 0.6*
	NORD	number (ordinal)	*May 7, 3rd, Bill Gates III*
	NTEL	telephone (or part of)	*212-555-4523*
	NDIG	number as digits	*Room 101*
	NIDE	identifier	*747, 386, I5, pc110, 3A*
	NADDR	number as street address	*747, 386, I5, pc110, 3A*
	NZIP	zip code or PO Box	91020
	NTIME	a (compound) time	*3.20, 11:45*
	NDATE	a (compound) date	*2/28/05, 28/02/05*
	NYER	year(s)	*1998, 80s, 1900s, 2008*
	MONEY	money (US or other)	*$3.45, HK$300, Y20,200, $200K*
	BMONEY	money tr/m/billions	*$3.45 billion*
	PRCT	percentage	*75% 3.4%*

Figure 8.4   Some types of non-standard words in text normalization, selected from Table 1 of Sproat et al. (2001); not listed are types for URLs, emails, and some complex uses of punctuation.

LSEQ for acronyms pronounced as letter sequences, and ASWD for acronyms pronounced as if they were words.

Dealing with non-standard words requires at least three steps: **tokenization** to separate and identify potential non-standard words, **classification** to label them with a type from Fig. 8.4, and **expansion** to convert each type into a string of standard words.

In the tokenization step, we can tokenize the input by whitespace and then assume that any word not in the pronunciation dictionary is a non-standard word. More sophisticated tokenization algorithms would also deal with the fact that some dictionaries already contain some abbreviations. The CMU dictionary, for example, contains abbreviated (and hence incorrect) pronunciations for *st, mr, mrs*, as well as day and month abbreviations like *mon, tues, nov, dec*, etc. Thus, in addition to unseen words, we also need to label any of these acronyms and also single-character tokens as potential non-standard words. Tokenization algorithms also need to split words that are combinations of two tokens, like *2-car* or *RVing*. Words can be split by simple heuristics, such as splitting at dashes, or at changes from lower case to upper case.

The next step is assigning an NSW type; many types can be detected with simple regular expressions. For example, NYER could be detected by the following regular expression:

/(1[89][0-9][0-9]) (20[0-9][0-9]/

Other classes might be harder to write rules for, so a more powerful option is to use a machine learning classifier with many features.

To distinguish between the alphabetic ASWD, LSEQ and EXPN classes, for example we might want features over the component letters. Thus short, all-capital words (*IBM, US*) might be LSEQ, longer all-lowercase words with a single-quote (*gov't, cap'n*) might be EXPN, and all-capital words with multiple vowels (*NASA, IKEA*) might be more likely to be ASWD.

Another useful feature is the identity of neighboring words. Consider ambiguous strings like *3/4*, which can be a NUM (`three-fourths`) or an NDATE (`march third`). NDATE might be preceded by the word *on*, followed by the word *of*, or have the word *Monday* somewhere in the surrounding words. By contrast, NUM examples might be preceded by another number or followed by words like *mile* and *inch*. Similarly, Roman numerals like *VII* tend to be NORD (*seven*) when preceded by *Chapter*, *part*, or *Act*, but NUM (*seventh*) when the words *king* or *Pope* occur in the neighborhood. These context words can be chosen as features by hand or can be learned by machine learning techniques like the **decision list** algorithm of Chapter 20.

We can achieve the most power by building a single machine learning classifier that combines all the above ideas. For example, the NSW classifier of Sproat et al. (2001) uses 136 features, including letter-based features like *'all-upper-case'*, *'has-two-vowels'*, *'contains-slash'*, and *'token-length'*, as well as binary features for the presence of certain words like *Chapter*, *on*, or *king* in the surrounding context. Sproat et al. (2001) also included a rough-draft, rule-based classifier, which used hand-written regular expression to classify many of the number NSWs. The output of this rough-draft classifier was used as just another feature in the main classifier.

To build such a main classifier, we need a hand-labeled training set in which each token has been labeled with its NSW category; one such hand-labeled database was produced by Sproat et al. (2001). Given the labeled training set, we can apply any supervised machine learning algorithm, such as the logistic regression or decision tree algorithms discussed earlier. For each observed token o_i we extract the features discussed above. Then we train the classifier to use these features to try to predict the hand-labeled NSW category from Fig. 8.4.

The third step in dealing with NSWs is expansion into ordinary words. One NSW type, EXPN, is quite difficult to expand. The type includes abbreviations and acronyms like *NY*. Generally these must be expanded with the help of an abbreviation dictionary, and any ambiguities can be dealt with by the homonym disambiguation algorithms discussed in the next section.

Expansion of the other NSW types is generally deterministic. Many expansions are trivial; for example, LSEQ expands to a sequence of words, one for each letter, ASWD expands to itself, NUM expands to a sequence of words representing the cardinal number, NORD expands to a sequence of words representing the ordinal number, and NDIG and NZIP both expand to a sequence of words, one for each digit.

Other types are slightly more complex; NYER expands to two pairs of digits, unless the year ends in *00*, in which case the four years are pronounced as a cardinal number (*2000* as `two thousand`) or in the **hundreds** method (e.g., 1800 as `eighteen hundred`). NTEL can be expanded just as a sequence of digits; alternatively, the last four digits can be read as **paired digits**, in which each pair is read as an integer. It is also possible to read them in a form known as **trailing unit**, in which the digits are read serially until the last non-zero digit, which is pronounced followed by the appropriate unit (e.g., *876-5000* as `eight seven six five thousand`). The expansions of NDATE, MONEY, and NTIME are left as Exercises 8.1–8.4 for the reader.

Hundreds digits

Trailing unit digits

Of course, many of these expansions are dialect-specific. In Australian English, the sequence *33* in a telephone number is generally read `double three`. Other languages also present additional difficulties in non-standard word normalization. In

French or German, for example, in addition to the above issues, normalization may depend on morphological properties. In French, the phrase *1 fille* ('one girl') is normalized to `une fille`, but *1 garçon* ('one boy') is normalized to `un garçon`. Similarly, in German, *Heinrich IV* ('Henry IV') can be normalized to `Heinrich der Vierte`, `Heinrich des Vierten`, `Heinrich dem Vierten`, or `Heinrich den Vierten` depending on the grammatical case of the noun (Demberg, 2006).

8.1.3   Homograph Disambiguation

Homograph

The goal of our NSW algorithms in the previous section was to determine which sequence of standard words to pronounce for each NSW. But sometimes determining how to pronounce even standard words is difficult. This is particularly true for **homographs**, which are words with the same spelling but different pronunciations. Here are some examples of the English homographs *use*, *live*, and *bass*:

(8.6) It's no use (/y uw s/) to ask to use (/y uw z/) the telephone.

(8.7) Do you live (/l ih v/) near a zoo with live (/l ay v/) animals?

(8.8) I prefer bass (/b ae s/) fishing to playing the bass (/b ey s/) guitar.

French homographs include *fils* (which has two pronunciations [fis] 'son' versus [fil] 'thread']), or the multiple pronunciations for *fier* ('proud' or 'to trust'), and *est* ('is' or 'East') (Divay and Vitale, 1997).

Luckily for the task of homograph disambiguation, the two forms of homographs in English (as well as in similar languages like French and German) tend to have different parts of speech. For example, the two forms of *use* above are (respectively) a noun and a verb, while the two forms of *live* are (respectively) a verb and a noun. Figure 8.5 shows some interesting systematic relations between the pronunciation of some noun-verb and adj-verb homographs. Indeed, Liberman and Church (1992) showed that many of the most frequent homographs in 44 million words of AP newswire are disambiguatable just by using part of speech (the most frequent 15 homographs in order are *use*, *increase*, *close*, *record*, *house*, *contract*, *lead*, *live*, *lives*, *protest*, *survey*, *project*, *separate*, *present*, *read*).

Final voicing		Stress shift			-ate final vowel	
N (/s/)	**V** (/z/)	**N** (init. stress)	**V** (fin. stress)		**N/A** (final /ax/)	**V** (final /ey/)
use y uw s	y uw z	record r eh1 k axr0 d	r ix0 k ao1 r d	estimate	eh s t ih m ax t	eh s t ih m ey t
close k l ow s	k l ow z	insult ih1 n s ax0 l t	ix0 n s ah1 l t	separate	s eh p ax r ax t	s eh p ax r ey t
house h aw s	h aw z	object aa1 b j eh0 k t	ax0 b j eh1 k t	moderate	m aa d ax r ax t	m aa d ax r ey t

Figure 8.5   Some systematic relationships between homographs: final consonant (noun /s/ versus verb /z/), stress shift (noun initial stress versus verb final stress), and final vowel weakening in *-ate* noun/adjs.

Because knowledge of part of speech is sufficient to disambiguate many homographs, in practice we perform homograph disambiguation by storing distinct pronunciations for these homographs labeled by part of speech and then running a part-of-speech tagger to choose the pronunciation for a given homograph in context.

There are a number of homographs, however, for which both pronunciations have the same part of speech. We saw two pronunciations for *bass* (fish versus instrument) above. Other examples of these include *lead* (because there are two noun pronunciations, /l iy d/ (a leash or restraint) and /l eh d/ (a metal)). We can also think of the task of disambiguating certain abbreviations (mentioned earlier as NSW disambiguation) as homograph disambiguation. For example, *Dr.* is ambiguous between `doctor` and `drive`, and *St.* between `Saint` or `street`. Finally, there are some words that differ in capitalizations like *polish/Polish*, which are homographs only in situations like sentence beginnings or all-capitalized text.

In practice, these latter classes of homographs that cannot be resolved by part of speech are often ignored in TTS systems. Alternatively, we can attempt to resolve them by using the word sense disambiguation algorithms, like the **decision-list** algorithm of Yarowsky (1997), which we will introduce in Chapter 20.

8.2   Phonetic Analysis

The next stage in synthesis is to produce a pronunciation for each word in the normalized word strings from text analysis. The most important component here is a large pronunciation dictionary. Dictionaries alone turn out to be insufficient, however, since running text always contains words that don't appear in the dictionary. For example Black et al. (1998) used a British English dictionary, the OALD lexicon on the first section of the Penn Wall Street Journal Treebank. Of the 39,923 words (tokens) in this section, 1775 word tokens (4.6%) were not in the dictionary, of which 943 are unique (i.e., 943 types). The distributions of these unseen word tokens was as follows:

Names	Unknown	Typos and other
1360	351	64
76.6%	19.8%	3.6%

Thus, the two main areas in which dictionaries need to be augmented are in dealing with names and with other unknown words. The next three sections discuss each of these in order: dictionaries, names, and grapheme-to-phoneme rules for other unknown words.

8.2.1   Dictionary Lookup

Phonetic dictionaries were introduced in Section 7.5. One of the most widely used for TTS is the freely available CMU Pronouncing Dictionary (CMU, 1993), which has pronunciations for about 120,000 words. The pronunciations are roughly phonemic, from a 39-phone ARPAbet-derived phoneme set. Phonemic transcriptions means that instead of marking surface reductions like the reduced vowels [ax] or [ix], CMUdict marks each vowel with a stress tag: 0 (unstressed), 1 (primary stress), or 2 (secondary stress). Thus, (non-diphthong) vowels with 0 stress generally correspond to [ax] or [ix]. Most of the words have only a single pronunciation, but about 8,000 of them have two or even three pronunciations and some kinds of phonetic reductions are marked in these pronunciations. The dictionary is not syllabified, although the nucleus is implicitly marked by the (numbered) vowel. Figure 8.6 shows some sample pronunciations.

ANTECEDENTS	AE2 N T IH0 S IY1 D AH0 N T S	*PAKISTANI*	P AE2 K IH0 S T AE1 N IY0
CHANG	CH AE1 NG	*TABLE*	T EY1 B AH0 L
DICTIONARY	D IH1 K SH AH0 N EH2 R IY0	*TROTSKY*	T R AA1 T S K IY2
DINNER	D IH1 N ER0	*WALTER*	W AO1 L T ER0
LUNCH	L AH1 N CH	*WALTZING*	W AO1 L T S IH0 NG
MCFARLAND	M AH0 K F AA1 R L AH0 N D	*WALTZING(2)*	W AO1 L S IH0 NG

Figure 8.6   Some sample pronunciations from the CMU Pronouncing Dictionary.

The CMU dictionary was designed for speech recognition rather than synthesis uses; thus, it does not specify which of the multiple pronunciations to use for synthesis, does not mark syllable boundaries, and because it capitalizes the dictionary headwords, does not distinguish between, for example, *US* and *us* (the form *US* has the two pronunciations [AH1 S] and [Y UW1 EH1 S]).

The 110,000 word UNISYN dictionary, freely available for research purposes, resolves many of these issues as it was designed specifically for synthesis (Fitt, 2002). UNISYN gives syllabifications, stress, and some morphological boundaries. Furthermore, pronunciations in UNISYN can also be read off in any of dozens of dialects of English, including General American, RP British, Australia, and so on. The UNISYN uses a slightly different phone set; here are some examples:

```
going:       { g * ou }.> i ng >
antecedents: { * a n . t^ i . s ~ ii . d n! t }> s >
dictionary:  { d * i k . sh @ . n ~ e . r ii }
```

8.2.2   Names

The distribution of unknown words discussed on page 257 above indicated the importance of names, including for example personal names (first names and surnames), geographical names (city, street, and other place names), and commercial names (company and product names). Considering only personal names, Spiegel (2003) estimates that there are about two million different surnames and 100,000 first names just for the United States. Two million is a very large number: an order of magnitude more than the entire size of the CMU dictionary. For this reason, most large-scale TTS systems include a large name-pronunciation dictionary. As we saw in Fig. 8.6 the CMU dictionary itself contains a wide variety of names; in particular, it includes the pronunciations of the most frequent 50,000 surnames from an old Bell Lab estimate of US personal name frequency, as well as 6,000 first names.

How many names are sufficient? Liberman and Church (1992) found that a dictionary of 50,000 names covered 70% of the name tokens in 44 million words of AP newswire. Interestingly, many of the remaining names (up to 97.43% of the tokens in their corpus) could be accounted for by simple modifications of these 50,000 names, such as adding stress-neutral suffixes to names like *Walter* or *Lucas* to produce *Walters* or *Lucasville*. Other pronunciations might be created by rhyme analogy. If we have the pronunciation for the name *Trotsky*, but not the name *Plotsky*, we can replace the initial /tr/ from *Trotsky* with initial /pl/ to derive a pronunciation for *Plotsky*.

Techniques such as this, including morphological decomposition, analogical formation, and mapping of unseen names to spelling variants already in the dictionary

(Fackrell and Skut, 2004), have achieved some success in name pronunciation. In general, however, name pronunciation is still difficult. Many modern systems deal with unknown names via the grapheme-to-phoneme methods described in the next section, often by building two predictive systems, one for names and one for non-names. Spiegel (2003, 2002) summarizes many more issues in proper name pronunciation.

8.2.3   Grapheme-to-Phoneme Conversion

Grapheme-to-phoneme

Letter-to-sound

Once we have expanded non-standard words and looked them all up in a pronunciation dictionary, we need to pronounce the remaining, unknown words. The process of converting a sequence of letters into a sequence of phones is called **grapheme-to-phoneme** conversion, sometimes shortened **g2p**. The job of a grapheme-to-phoneme algorithm is thus to convert a letter string like *cake* into a phone string like [K EY K].

The earliest such algorithms were rules written by hand in the Chomsky-Halle rewrite rule format of Eq. 7.1 in Chapter 7. These are often called **letter-to-sound** or LTS rules, and they are sometimes still used. LTS rules are applied in order, with later (default) rules applying only if the context for earlier rules is not applicable. A simple pair of rules for pronouncing the letter *c* might be as follows:

$$c \rightarrow [k] / \underline{\quad} \text{ a,o V} \qquad \text{; context dependent} \qquad (8.9)$$

$$c \rightarrow [s] \qquad\qquad\qquad\qquad \text{; context independent} \qquad (8.10)$$

Actual rules must be much more complicated (for example *c* can also be pronounced [ch] in *cello* or *concerto*). Even more complex are rules for assigning stress, which are famously difficult for English. Consider just one of the many stress rules from Allen et al. (1987), whereby the symbol *X* represents all possible syllable onsets:

$$V \rightarrow [+\text{stress}] / X \underline{\quad} C^* \ V_{\text{short}} \ C \ C? \ V \quad V_{\text{short}} \ C^* \ V \qquad (8.11)$$

This rule represents the following two situations:

1. Assign 1-stress to the vowel in a syllable followed by a weak syllable followed by a morpheme-final syllable with a short vowel and 0 or more consonants (e.g., *difficult*).

2. Assign 1-stress to the vowel in a syllable preceding a weak syllable followed by a vowel that is morpheme-final (e.g., *oregano*).

While some modern systems still use such complex hand-written rules, most systems achieve higher accuracy by relying instead on automatic or semi-automatic methods based on machine learning. This modern probabilistic grapheme-to-phoneme problem was first formalized by Lucassen and Mercer (1984). Given a letter sequence *L*, we are searching for the most probable phone sequence *P*:

$$\hat{P} = \operatorname*{argmax}_{P} P(P \ L) \qquad (8.12)$$

The probabilistic method assumes a training set and a test set; both sets are lists of words from a dictionary, with a spelling and a pronunciation for each word. The next subsections show how a classifier can be trained to estimate this probability $P(P \ L)$ and applied to produce the pronunciation for an unseen word.

Finding a Letter-to-Phone Alignment for the Training Set

Most letter-to-phone algorithms assume that we have an **alignment** that tells us which phones align with each letter. We'll need this alignment for each word in the training set. A letter can align to multiple phones (e.g., *x* often aligns to k s), or to no phones at all, like the final letter of *cake* in the following alignment:

L: c   a   k   e

P: K EY K ϵ

One method for finding such a letter-to-phone alignment is the semi-automatic method of Black et al. (1998). Their algorithm is semi-automatic because it relies on a hand-written list of the **allowable** phones that can realize each letter. Here are allowables lists for the letters *c* and *e*:

c: k ch s sh t-s ϵ
e: ih iy er ax ah eh ey uw ay ow y-uw oy aa ϵ

To produce an alignment for each word in the training set, we take this allowables list for all the letters, and for each word in the training set, we find all alignments between the pronunciation and the spelling that conform to the allowables list. From this large list of alignments, we compute, by summing over all alignments for all words, the total count for each letter being aligned to each phone (or multi-phone or ϵ). From these counts we can normalize to get for each phone p_i and letter l_j a probability $P(p_i l_j)$:

$$P(p_i l_j) = \frac{\text{count}(p_i, l_j)}{\text{count}(l_j)} \qquad (8.13)$$

We can now take these probabilities and realign the letters to the phones, using the Viterbi algorithm to produce the best (Viterbi) alignment for each word, where the probability of each alignment is just the product of all the individual phone/letter alignments. The result is a single good alignment A for each training pair (P, L).

Choosing the Best Phone String for the Test Set

Given a new word w, we now need to map its letters into a phone string. We'll train a machine learning classifier on the aligned training set. The classifier will look at a letter of the word and generate the most probable phone. Obviously, we can do a better job of predicting the phone if we look at a window of surrounding letters; for example, consider the letter *a*. In the word *cat*, the *a* is pronounced AE. But in our word *cake*, *a* is pronounced EY because *cake* has a final *e*; thus, knowing whether there is a final *e* is a useful feature. Typically, we look at the k previous letters and the k following letters.

Another useful feature would be the correct identity of the previous phone. Knowing this would allow us to get some phonotactic information into our probability model. Of course, we can't know the true identity of the previous phone, but we can approximate this by looking at the previous phone that was predicted by our model. To do this, we can run our classifier left to right, generating phones one by one.

In summary, in the most common classifier model, the probability of each phone p_i is estimated from a window of k previous and k following letters, as well as the most recent k phones that were previously produced.

Figure 8.7 shows a sketch of this left-to-right process, indicating the features that the classifier would use to choose a phone for the letter *s* in the word *Jurafsky*. We can integrate stress prediction into phone prediction by augmenting our set of phones with stress information, for example having two copies of each vowel (e.g., AE and AE1) or even the three levels of stress AE0, AE1, and AE2 used in the CMU lexicon. Other useful features include the part-of-speech tag of the word (most part-of-speech taggers provide an estimate of the part-of-speech tag even for unknown words) and facts such as whether the previous vowel was stressed or even using classes of letters (corresponding roughly to consonants, vowels, liquids, and so on).

Liaison   For some languages, we also need to know features about the following word. For example, French has a phenomenon called **liaison**, in which the realization of the final phone of some words depends on whether there is a next word and whether that word starts with a consonant or a vowel. For example, the French word *six* can be pronounced [sis] (in *j'en veux six* 'I want six'), [siz] (*six enfants* 'six children'), [si] (*six filles* 'six girls').

Finally, most synthesis systems build two separate grapheme-to-phoneme classifiers, one for unknown personal names, and one for other unknown words. For pronouncing personal names it turns out to be helpful to use additional features that indicate which foreign language the names originally came from. Such features could be the output of a foreign-language classifier based on letter sequences (different languages have characteristic letter *N*-gram sequences).

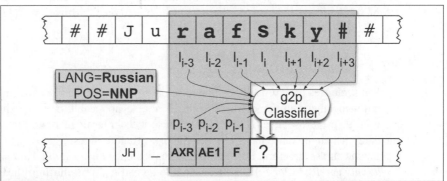

Figure 8.7   The left-to-right process of converting graphemes to phonemes, showing the decision for the letter *s*. The features are shown in shading, using a context window $k = 3$; real TTS systems use window sizes of 5 or larger.

Decision trees and logistic regression are conditional classifiers, computing the phoneme string that has the highest conditional probability given the grapheme sequence. More recent grapheme-to-phoneme conversion makes use of a joint classifier in which the hidden state is a combination of phone and grapheme called a **graphone**; see the Historical Notes section at the end of the chapter for references.

8.3   Prosodic Analysis

Prosody

The final stage of linguistic analysis is prosodic analysis. In poetry, the word **prosody** refers to the study of the metrical structure of verse. In linguistics and language processing, however, we use the term **prosody** to mean the study of the intonational and rhythmic aspects of language. More technically, prosody has been defined by Ladd (1996) as the "use of suprasegmental features to convey sentence-level pragmatic meanings". The term **suprasegmental** means above and beyond the level of the segment or phone. The term refers especially to the uses of acoustic features like **F0**, **duration**, and **energy** independently of the phone string.

Suprasegmental

By **sentence-level pragmatic meaning**, Ladd is referring to a number of kinds of meaning that have to do with the relation between a sentence and its discourse or external context. For example, prosody can be used to mark **discourse structure or function**, like the difference between statements and questions, or the way that a conversation is structured into segments or subdialogs. Prosody is also used to mark **saliency**, such as indicating that a particular word or phrase is important or salient. Finally, prosody is heavily used for affective and emotional meaning, such as expressing happiness, surprise, or anger.

In the next sections we introduce the three aspects of prosody, each of which is important for speech synthesis: **prosodic structure**, **prosodic prominence**, and **tune**. Prosodic analysis generally proceeds in two parts. First, we compute an abstract representation of the prosodic structure, prominence, and tune of the text. For unit selection synthesis, this is all we need to do in the text analysis component. For diphone and HMM synthesis, we have one further step, which is to predict **duration** and **F0** values from these prosodic structures.

8.3.1   Prosodic Structure

Spoken sentences have prosodic structure in the sense that some words seem to group naturally together and some words seem to have a noticeable break or disjuncture between them. Prosodic structure is often described in terms of **prosodic phrasing**, meaning that an utterance has a prosodic phrase structure in a similar way to it having a syntactic phrase structure. For example, in the sentence *I wanted to go to London, but could only get tickets for France* there seem to be two main **intonation phrases**, their boundary occurring at the comma. Furthermore, in the first phrase, there seems to be another set of lesser prosodic phrase boundaries (often called **intermediate phrase**s) that split up the words as *I wanted   to go   to London.*

Prosodic phrasing

Intonation phrase

Intermediate phrase

Prosodic phrasing has many implications for speech synthesis; the final vowel of a phrase is longer than usual, we often insert a pause after an intonation phrases, and, as we discuss in Section 8.3.6, there is often a slight drop in F0 from the beginning of an intonation phrase to its end, and F0 then resets at the beginning of a new intonation phrase.

Practical phrase boundary prediction is generally treated as a binary classification task, where we are given a word and we have to decide whether to put a prosodic boundary after it. A simple model for boundary prediction can be based on deterministic rules. A very high precision rule is the one we saw for sentence segmentation: insert a boundary after punctuation. Another commonly used rule inserts a phrase boundary before a function word following a content word.

More sophisticated models are based on machine learning classifiers. To create a training set for classifiers, we first choose a corpus and then mark every prosodic boundary in the corpus. One way to do this prosodic boundary labeling is to use an intonational model like ToBI or Tilt (see Section 8.3.4) and have human labelers listen to speech and label the transcript with the boundary events defined by the theory. Because prosodic labeling is extremely time-consuming, however, a text-only alternative is often used. In this method, a human labeler looks only at the text of the training corpus, ignoring the speech. The labeler marks any juncture between words at which a prosodic boundary might legitimately occur if the utterance were spoken.

Given a labeled training corpus, we can train a classifier to make a binary (boundary vs. no boundary) decision at every juncture between words (Wang and Hirschberg, 1992; Ostendorf and Veilleux, 1994; Taylor and Black, 1998).

Features that are commonly used in classification include the following:

- **Length features**: Phrases tend to be of roughly equal length, so we can use various features that hint at phrase length (Bachenko and Fitzpatrick, 1990; Grosjean et al., 1979; Gee and Grosjean, 1983).
  - The total number of words and syllables in utterance
  - The distance of the juncture from the beginning and end of the sentence (in words or syllables)
  - The distance in words from the last punctuation mark

- **Neighboring part of speech and punctuation**:
  - The part-of-speech tags for a window of words around the juncture. Generally, the two words before and after the juncture are used.
  - The type of following punctuation

There is also a correlation between prosodic structure and **syntactic structure** (Price et al., 1991). Thus, robust parsers like Collins (1997) can be used to label the sentence with rough syntactic information, from which we can extract syntactic features such as the size of the biggest syntactic phrase that ends with this word (Ostendorf and Veilleux, 1994; Koehn et al., 2000). We will introduce syntactic structure and parsing in Chapters 12–14.

8.3.2   Prosodic Prominence

Prominence

In any spoken utterance, some words sound more **prominent** than others. Prominent words are perceptually more salient to the listener; speakers make a word more salient in English by saying it louder, saying it slower (so it has a longer duration), or by varying F0 during the word, making it higher or more variable.

Pitch accent

We generally capture the core notion of prominence by associating a linguistic marker with prominent words, a marker called **pitch accent**. Words that are prominent are said to **bear** (be associated with) a pitch accent. Pitch accent is thus part of the phonological description of a word in context in a spoken utterance.

Pitch accent is related to **stress**, which we discussed in Chapter 7. The stressed syllable of a word is where pitch accent is realized. In other words, if a speaker decides to highlight a word by giving it a pitch accent, the accent will appear on the stressed syllable of the word. The following example shows accented words in capital letters, with the stressed syllable bearing the accent (the louder, longer syllable) in boldface:

(8.14) I'm a little SUR**PRISED** to hear it **CHAR**ACTERIZED as UP**BEAT**.

We generally need more fine-grained distinctions than just a binary distinction between accented and unaccented words. For example, the last accent in a phrase generally is perceived as being more prominent than the other accents. This prominent last accent is called the **nuclear accent**. Emphatic accents are generally used for semantic purposes, for example, to indicate that a word is the **semantic focus** of the sentence (see Chapter 21) or that a word is contrastive or otherwise important in some way. Such emphatic words are often written IN CAPITAL LETTERS or with **stars** around them in SMS or email or *Alice in Wonderland*; here's an example from the latter:

Nuclear accent

(8.15) "I know SOMETHING interesting is sure to happen," she said to herself.

Some words can also be **less** prominent than usual, such as function words, which are often phonetically very **reduced** (see Chapter 7). Accents can also differ according to the **tune** associated with them. Accents with particularly high pitch, for example, have different functions than those with particularly low pitch; we show how this is modeled in the ToBI model in Section 8.3.4.

Ignoring tune for the moment, we can summarize by saying that speech synthesis systems can use as many as four levels of prominence: **emphatic accent**, **pitch accent**, **unaccented**, and **reduced**. In practice, however, many implemented systems make do with a subset of only two or three of these levels.

With two levels, pitch accent prediction is a binary classification task, for which we must decide whether a given word is accented or not. Since in general, informative words (content words, and especially those that are new or unexpected) tend to bear accent (Ladd, 1996; Bolinger, 1972), the simplest accent prediction system is to just accent all content words and no function words.

Better models might seem to require sophisticated semantic knowledge, for example, to understand if a word is new or old in the discourse, whether it is being used contrastively, and exactly how much new information a word contains, and such information was indeed used in early systems (Hirschberg, 1993). But Hirschberg and others showed better prediction by using simple, robust features that correlate with these sophisticated semantics.

For example, the fact that new or unpredictable information tends to be accented can be modeled with robust features like N-grams or tf-idf (Pan and Hirschberg, 2000; Pan and McKeown, 1999). The unigram probability of a word $P(w_i)$ and its bigram probability $P(w_i\,w_{i-1})$ both correlate with accent; the more probable a word, the less likely it is to be accented. Similarly, an information-retrieval measure known as **tf-idf** (Term-Frequency/Inverse-Document Frequency; see Chapter 23) is a useful accent predictor. Tf-idf captures the semantic importance of a word in a particular document d, by downgrading words that appear in many different documents in a large N-document background corpus. One of the many versions of tf-idf can be expressed formally as

tf-idf

follows, assuming $tf_{i,j}$ is the frequency of w_i in the document d_j and n_i is the total number of documents in the corpus that contain w_i:

$$idf_i = \log\left(\frac{N}{n_i}\right)$$
$$\text{tf-idf}_{i,j} == \text{tf}_{i,j} \quad \text{idf}_i \tag{8.16}$$

Accent ratio   For words that have been seen enough times in a training set, we can use the **accent ratio** feature, which models a word's individual probability of being accented. The accent ratio of a word is just the probability of the word being accented (if this probability is significantly different from 0.5, and is 0.5 otherwise). More formally,

$$AccentRatio(w) = \begin{cases} \frac{k}{N} & \text{if } B(k,N,0.5) \le 0.05 \\ 0.5 & \texttt{otherwise} \end{cases}$$

where N is the total number of times the word w occurred in the training set, k is the number of times it was accented, and $B(k,n,0.5)$ is the probability (under a binomial distribution) that there are k successes in n trials if the probability of success and failure is equal (Nenkova et al., 2007; Yuan et al., 2005).

Features like part of speech, N-grams, tf-idf, and accent ratio can then be combined in a classifier to predict accents. While these robust features work relatively well, a number of problems in accent prediction still remain the subject of research.

For example, it is difficult to predict which of the two words should be accented in adjective-noun or noun-noun compounds. Some regularities do exist; for example, adjective-noun combinations like *new truck* are likely to have accent on the right word (*new TRUCK*), while noun-noun compounds like *TREE surgeon* are likely to have accent on the left. But exceptions to these rules make accent prediction in noun compounds quite complex. For example, the noun-noun compound *APPLE cake* has the accent on the first word, while the noun-noun compound *apple PIE* or *city HALL* both have the accent on the second word (Liberman and Sproat, 1992; Sproat, 1994, 1998a).

Clash
Lapse   Another complication has to do with rhythm; in general, speakers avoid putting accents too close together (a phenomenon known as **clash**) or too far apart (**lapse**). Thus, *city HALL* and *PARKING lot* combine as *CITY hall PARKING lot* with the accent on *HALL* shifting forward to *CITY* to avoid the clash with the accent on *PARKING* (Liberman and Prince, 1977),

Some of these rhythmic constraints can be captured by using sequence modeling methods such as the sequence classifier shown in Fig. 8.7, in which we run a classifier left to right through a sentence, using the output of the previous word as a feature. We can also use more sophisticated machine learning models like MEMMs (Chapter 6) or conditional random fields (CRFs) (Gregory and Altun, 2004).

8.3.3   Tune

Tune   Two utterances with the same prominence and phrasing patterns can still differ prosodically by having different **tunes**. The **tune** of an utterance is the rise and fall of its F0 over time. A very obvious example of tune is the difference between statements

271

and yes-no questions in English. The same sentence can be said with a final rise in F0 to indicate a yes-no question, or a final fall in F0 to indicate a declarative intonation. Figure 8.8 shows the F0 track of the same words spoken as a question or a statement. *Question rise* Note that the question rises at the end; this is often called a **question rise**. The falling *Final fall* intonation of the statement is called a **final fall**.

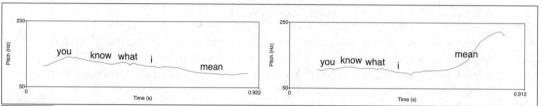

Figure 8.8   The same text read as the statement *You know what I mean* (on the left) and as a question *You know what I mean?* (on the right). Notice that yes-no question intonation in English has a sharp final rise in F0.

It turns out that English makes wide use of tune to express meaning. Besides this well-known rise for yes-no questions, an English phrase containing a list of nouns separated by commas often has a short rise called a **continuation rise** after each noun. *Continuation rise* Other examples include the characteristic English contours for expressing **contradiction** and expressing **surprise**.

The mapping between meaning and tune in English is extremely complex, and linguistic theories of intonation like ToBI have only begun to develop sophisticated models of this mapping. In practice, therefore, most synthesis systems just distinguish two or three tunes, such as the **continuation rise** (at commas), the **question rise** (at question mark if the question is a yes-no question), and a **final fall** otherwise.

8.3.4   More Sophisticated Models: ToBI

While current synthesis systems generally use simple models of prosody like the ones discussed above, recent research focuses on the development of much more sophisticated models. We briefly discuss the **ToBI** and **Tilt** models here.

ToBI

ToBI One of the most widely used linguistic models of prosody is the **ToBI** (Tone and Break Indices) model (Silverman et al., 1992; Beckman and Hirschberg, 1994; Pierrehumbert, 1980; Pitrelli et al., 1994). ToBI is a phonological theory of intonation that models prominence, tune, and boundaries. ToBI's model of prominence and tunes is based on the five **pitch accents** and four **boundary tones** shown in Fig. 8.9.

An utterance in ToBI consists of a sequence of intonational phrases, each of which *Boundary tone* ends in one of the four **boundary tones**. The boundary tones represent the utterance final aspects of tune discussed in Section 8.3.3. Each word in the utterances can optionally be associated with one of the five types of pitch accents.

Each intonational phrase consists of one or more **intermediate phrase**. These phrases can also be marked with kinds of boundary tone, including the **%H** high initial boundary tone, which marks a phrase that is particularly high in the speaker's pitch range, as well as final phrase accents **H-** and **L-**.

	Pitch Accents		Boundary Tones	
H*	peak accent	**L-L%**	"final fall": "declarative contour" of American English	
L*	low accent	**L-H%**	continuation rise	
L*+H	scooped accent	**H-H%**	"question rise": cantonical yes-no question contour	
L+H*	rising peak accent	**H-L%**	final level plateau (plateau because H- causes "upstep" of following)	
H+!H*	step down			

Figure 8.9   The accent and boundary tones labels from the ToBI transcription system for American English intonation (Beckman and Ayers, 1997; Beckman and Hirschberg, 1994).

In addition to accents and boundary tones, ToBI distinguishes four levels of phrasing, labeled on a separate **break index** tier. The largest phrasal breaks are the intonational phrase (break index **4**) and the intermediate phrase (break index **3**), discussed above. Break index **2** is used to mark a disjuncture or pause between words that is smaller than an intermediate phrase, and **1** is used for normal phrase-medial word boundaries.

Break index

Figure 8.10 shows the tone, orthographic, and phrasing **tiers** of a ToBI transcription, using the Praat program. The same sentence is read with two different tunes. In (a), the word *Marianna* is spoken with a high H* accent, and the sentence has the declarative boundary tone L-L%. In (b), the word *Marianna* is spoken with a low L* accent and the yes-no question boundary tone H-H%. One goal of ToBI is to express different meanings to the different type of accents. Here, the L* accent adds a meaning of *surprise* to the sentence (i.e., with a connotation like 'Are you really saying it was Marianna?') (Hirschberg and Pierrehumbert, 1986; Steedman, 2007).

Tier

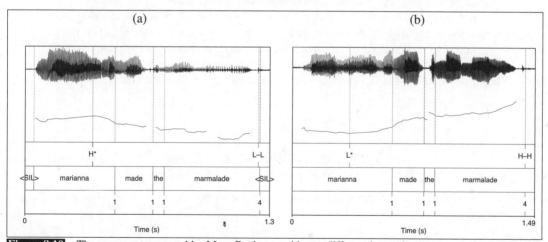

Figure 8.10   The same sentence read by Mary Beckman with two different intonation patterns and transcribed in ToBI. (a) Shows an H* accent and the typical American English declarative final fall L-L%. (b) Shows the L* accent, with the typical American English yes-no question rise H-H%.

ToBI models have been proposed for many languages (Jun, 2005), such as the J_TOBI system for Japanese (Venditti, 2005).

Other Intonation models

Tilt   The **Tilt** model (Taylor, 2000) resembles ToBI in that it uses sequences of intonational events like accents and boundary tones. But Tilt does not use ToBI-style discrete phonemic classes for accents. Instead, each event is modeled by continuous parameters that represent the F0 shape of the accent. Instead of giving each event a category label, as in ToBI, each Tilt prosodic event is characterized by a set of three acoustic parameters: the duration, the amplitude, and the **tilt** parameter. These acoustic parameters are trained on a corpus that has been hand-labeled for pitch accents (**a**) and boundary tones (**b**). The human labeling specifies the syllable that bears the accent or tone; the acoustic parameters are then trained automatically from the wavefile. Figure 8.11 shows a sample of a Tilt representation.

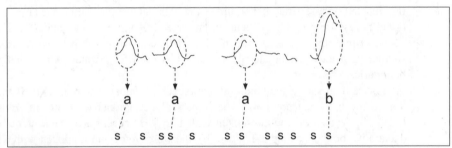

Figure 8.11   Schematic view of events in the Tilt model (Taylor, 2000). Each pitch accent (*a*) and boundary tone (*b*) is aligned with a syllable nucleus *s*.

Each accent in Tilt is viewed as having a (possibly zero) **rise component** up to peak, followed by a (possible zero) **fall component**. An automatic accent detector finds the start, peak, and end-point of each accent in the wavefile, all of which determine the duration and amplitude of the rise and fall components. The tilt parameter is an abstract description of the F0 slope of an event, calculated by comparison of the relative sizes of the rise and fall for an event. A tilt value of 1.0 indicates a rise, tilt of -1.0 a fall, 0 equal rise and fall, -0.5 is an accent with a rise and a larger fall, and so on:

$$\text{tilt} \;=\; \frac{\text{tilt}_\text{amp} + \text{tilt}_\text{dur}}{2}$$

$$=\; \frac{A_\text{rise} - A_\text{fall}}{A_\text{rise} + A_\text{fall}} + \frac{D_\text{rise} - D_\text{fall}}{D_\text{rise} + D_\text{fall}} \tag{8.17}$$

See the Historical Notes section at the end of the chapter for pointers to other intonational models.

8.3.5   Computing Duration from Prosodic Labels

The results of the text analysis processes described so far is a string of phonemes, annotated with words with pitch accent marked on relevant words, and appropriate boundary tones marked. For the **unit selection** synthesis approaches that we describe in Section 8.5, this is a sufficient output from the text analysis component.

For **diphone** synthesis, as well as other approaches like formant synthesis, we also need to specify the **duration** and the **F0** values of each segment.

Phones vary quite a bit in duration. Some of the duration is inherent to the identity of the phone itself. Vowels, for example, are generally much longer than consonants; in the Switchboard corpus of telephone speech, the phone [aa] averages 118 milliseconds, and [d] averages 68 milliseconds. But phone duration is also affected by a wide variety of contextual factors, which can be modeled by rule-based or statistical methods.

The most well-known of the rule-based methods is the method of Klatt (1979), which uses rules to model how the average or 'context-neutral' duration of a phone $\bar{d}$ is lengthened or shortened by context, while staying above a minimum duration d_{min}. Each Klatt rule is associated with a duration multiplicative factor; some examples:

Prepasual lengthening:	the vowel or syllabic consonant in the syllable before a pause is lengthened by 1.4.
Non-phrase-final shortening:	segments not phrase-final are shortened by 0.6. Phrase-final postvocalic liquids and nasals are lengthened by 1.4.
Unstressed shortening:	unstressed segments are more compressible, so their minimum duration d_{min} is halved, and they are shortened by .7 for most phone types.
Lengthening for accent:	a vowel which bears accent is lengthened by 1.4.
Shortening in clusters:	a consonant followed by a consonant is shortened by 0.5.
Pre-voiceless shortening:	vowels are shortened before a voiceless plosive by 0.7.

Given the N factor weights f, the Klatt formula for the duration of a phone is

$$d = d_{min} + \prod_{i=1}^{N} f_i \quad (\bar{d} - d_{min}) \tag{8.18}$$

More recent machine learning systems use the Klatt hand-written rules as the basis for defining features, for example, using features such as the following:

- identity of the left and right context phone
- lexical stress and accent values of current phone
- position in syllable, word, phrase
- following pause

Sum-of-products

We can then train machine learning classifiers like decision trees or the **sum-of-products** model (van Santen, 1994, 1997, 1998), to combine the features to predict the final duration of the segment.

8.3.6   Computing F0 from Prosodic Labels

Target point

For diphone, articulatory, HMM, and formant synthesis we also need to specify the F0 values of each segment. For the tone sequence models like ToBI or Tilt, we can do F0 generation in two stages. We first specify F0 **target points** for each pitch accent and boundary tone and then create the F0 contour for the whole sentence by interpolating among these targets (Anderson et al., 1984).

To specify a target point we must first describe what it is (the F0 value) and when it occurs (the exact time at which this peak or trough occurs in the syllable). The F0

Pitch range

Baseline

Topline

Reference line

values of the target points are generally not specified in absolute terms of hertz. Instead, they are defined relative to **pitch range**. A speaker's **pitch range** is the range between the lowest frequency in a particular utterance (the **baseline frequency**) and the highest frequency in the utterance (the **topline**). In some models, target points are specified relative to a line in between called the **reference line**.

For example, we might write a rule specifying that the very beginning of an utterance have a target point of 50% (halfway between the baseline and the topline). In the rule-based system of Jilka et al. (1999), the target point for an H* accent is at 100% (the topline) and for an L* accent at 0% (at the baseline). L+H* accents have two target points, at 20% and 100%. Final boundary tones H-H% and L-L% are extra high and extra low at 120% and -20% respectively.

Alignment

Second, we must also specify exactly where in the accented syllable the targets apply; this is known as accent **alignment**. In the rule-based system of Jilka et al. (1999), again, H* accents are aligned 60% of the way through the voiced part of the accent syllable (although IP-initial accents are aligned somewhat later in the syllable, and IP-final accents are aligned somewhat earlier).

An alternative to writing these rules by hand is to automatically learn the mapping from pitch accent sequence to F0 value. Black and Hunt (1996), for example, used linear regression to assign target values to each syllable. For each syllable with a pitch accent or boundary tone, they predicted three target values, at the beginning, middle, and end of the syllable. They trained three separate linear regression models, one for each of the three positions in the syllable. Features included the following:

- accent type on the current syllable, two previous and two following syllables
- lexical stress of this syllable and surrounding syllables
- number of syllables to start of phrase and to end of phrase
- number of accented syllables to end of phrase

Such machine learning models require a training set that is labeled for accent; a number of such prosodically labeled corpora exist, although it is not clear how well these models generalize to unseen corpora.

Declination

Finally, F0 computation models must model the fact that pitch tends to decline through a sentence; this subtle drop in pitch across an utterance is called **declination**; an example is shown in Fig. 8.12.

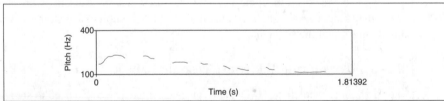

Figure 8.12   F0 declination in the sentence "I was pretty goofy for about 24 hours afterwards".

Downstep

The exact nature of declination is a subject of much research; some models treat it by allowing the baseline (or both baseline and topline) to decrease slowly over the utterance. In ToBI-like models, this downdrift in F0 is modeled by two separate components; in addition to declination, certain high tones are marked as carrying **downstep**.

Each downstepped high accent causes the pitch range to be compressed, resulting in a lowered topline for each such accent.

8.3.7   Final Result of Text Analysis: Internal Representation

The final output of text analysis is the **internal representation** of the input text sentence. For unit selection synthesis, the internal representation can be as simple as a phone string together with indications of prosodic boundaries and prominent syllables, as shown in Fig. 8.1 on page 250. For diphone synthesis as well as non-concatenative synthesis algorithms, the internal representation must also include a duration and an F0 value for each phone.

Figure 8.13 shows some sample TTS output from the Festival (Black et al., 1999) diphone speech synthesis system for the sentence "*Do you really want to see all of it?*". This output, together with the F0 values shown in Fig. 8.14 would be the input to the **waveform synthesis** component described in Section 8.4. The durations here are computed by a CART-style decision tree (Riley, 1992).

do		you		H* really				want				to		see		L* all		L- H% of		it	
d	uw	y	uw	r	ih	l	iy	w	aa	n	t	t	ax	s	iy	ao	l	ah	v	ih	t
110	110	50	50	75	64	57	82	57	50	72	41	43	47	54	130	76	90	44	62	46	220

Figure 8.13   Output of the Festival (Black et al., 1999) generator for the sentence "*Do you really want to see all of it?*", together with the F0 contour shown in Fig. 8.14. (Figure thanks to Paul Taylor.)

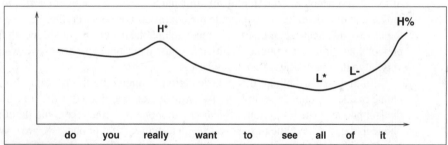

Figure 8.14   The F0 contour for the sample sentence generated by the Festival synthesis system in Fig. 8.13, thanks to Paul Taylor.

As was suggested above, determining the proper prosodic pattern for a sentence is difficult, because we need real-world knowledge and semantic information to know which syllables to accent and which tune to apply. This sort of information is difficult to extract from the text; hence, prosody modules often aim to produce a "neutral declarative" version of the input text and assume the sentence should be spoken in a default way with no reference to discourse history or real-world events. This is one of the main reasons why intonation in TTS often sounds wooden.

8.4   Diphone Waveform Synthesis

We are now ready to see how the internal representation can be turned into a waveform. We present two kinds of **concatentative** synthesis: **diphone synthesis** in this section, and **unit selection synthesis** in the next section.

Recall that for diphone synthesis, our internal representation is as shown in Fig. 8.13 and Fig. 8.14 and consists of a list of phones, each phone associated with a duration and a set of F0 targets.

Diphone

The diphone concatenative synthesis model generates a waveform from a sequence of phones by selecting and concatenating units from a prerecorded database of **diphones**. A diphone is a phone-like unit going from roughly the middle of one phone to the middle of the following phone. Diphone concatenative synthesis can be characterized by the following steps:

Training:

1. Record a single speaker saying an example of each diphone.
2. Cut each diphone from the speech and store all diphones in a database.

Synthesis:

1. Take from the database a sequence of diphones that corresponds to the desired phone sequence.
2. Concatenate the diphones, with slight signal processing at the boundaries.
3. Use signal processing to change the prosody (f0, duration) of the diphone sequence to the desired prosody.

Coarticulation

We tend to use diphones rather than phones for concatenative synthesis because of the phenomenon of **coarticulation**. In Chapter 7 we defined **coarticulation** as the movement of articulators to anticipate the next sound or perseverating movement from the last sound. Because of coarticulation, each phone differs slightly depending on the previous and following phone. Thus if we just concatenated phones we would have very large discontinuities at the boundaries.

In a diphone, we model this coarticulation by including the transition to the next phone inside the unit. The diphone [w-eh], for example, includes the transition from the [w] phone to the [eh] phone. Because a diphone is defined from the middle of one phone to the middle of the next, when we concatenate the diphones, we are concatenating the middle of phones, and the middle of phones tends to be less influenced by the context. Figure 8.15 shows the intuition that the beginning and end of the vowel [eh] have much more movement than the center.

8.4.1   Steps for Building a Diphone Database

Building a diphone database requires six steps:

1. Create a **diphone inventory**.
2. Recruit a speaker.
3. Create a text for the speaker to read for each diphone.

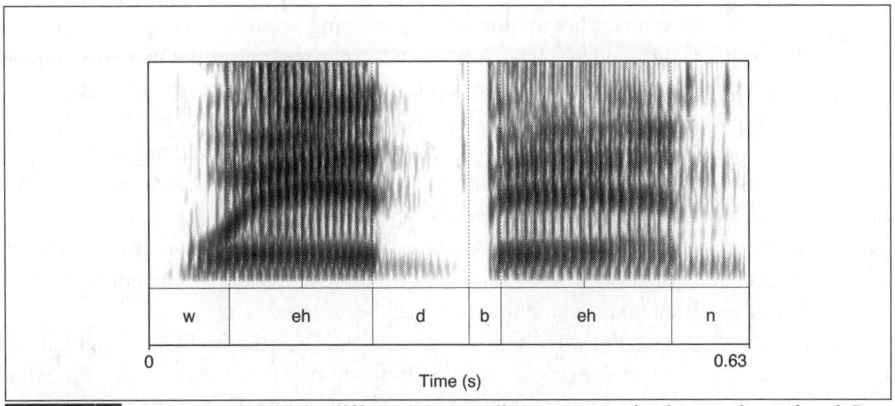

Figure 8.15   The vowel [eh] in different surrounding contexts, in the words *wed* and *Ben*. Notice the differences in the second formants (F2) at the beginning and end of the [eh], but the relatively steady state portion in the middle at the center mark.

4. Record the speaker reading each diphone.

5. Segment, label, and pitch-mark the diphones.

6. Excise the diphones.

What is the inventory of diphones that we need for a system? If we have 43 phones (like the AT&T system of Olive et al. (1998)), there are $43^2 = 1849$ hypothetically possible diphone combinations. Not all of these diphones can actually occur. For example, English **phonotactic** constraints rule out some combinations; phones like [h], [y], and [w] can only occur before vowels. In addition, some diphone systems don't bother storing diphones if there is no possible coarticulation between the phones, such as across the silence between successive voiceless stops. The 43-phone system of Olive et al. (1998) thus has only 1162 diphones rather than the 1849 hypothetically possible set.

Voice talent   Next, we recruit our speaker, often called a **voice talent**. The database of diphones
Voice   for this speaker is called a **voice**; commercial systems often have multiple voices, such as one male and one female voice.

We'll now create a text for the voice talent to say, and record each diphone. The most important thing in recording diphones is to keep them as consistent as possible; if possible, they should have constant pitch, energy, and duration, so that they are easy to paste together without noticeable breaks. We promote consistency by enclosing
Carrier phrase   each diphone to be recorded in a **carrier phrase**. By surrounding the diphone with other phones, we keep utterance-final lengthening or initial phone effects from making any diphone louder or quieter than the others. We'll need different carrier phrases for consonant-vowel, vowel-consonant, phone-silence, and silence-phone sequences. For example, a consonant vowel sequence like [b aa] or [b ae] could be embedded between the syllables [t aa] and [m aa]:

pause t aa b aa m aa pause
pause t aa b ae m aa pause
pause t aa b eh m aa pause

...

If we have an earlier synthesizer voice lying around, we can use that voice to read the prompts out loud and have our voice talent repeat after the prompts. This is another way to keep the pronunciation of each diphone consistent. It is also important to use a high-quality microphone and a quiet room or, better, a sound booth.

Once we have recorded the speech, we need to label and segment the two phones that make up each diphone, usually by running a speech recognizer in **Forced align-**
Forced alignment   **ment** mode. In forced alignment mode, a speech recognition is told exactly what the phone sequence is; its job is just to find the exact phone boundaries in the waveform. Speech recognizers are not completely accurate at finding phone boundaries, so usually the automatic phone segmentation is hand-corrected.

We now have the two phones (for example, [b aa]) with hand-corrected boundaries. There are two ways we can create the /b-aa/ diphone for the database. One method is to use rules to decide how far into the phone to place the diphone boundary. For example, for stops, we place the diphone boundary 30% of the way into the phone. For most other phones, we place the diphone boundary 50% into the phone.

A more sophisticated way to find diphone boundaries is to store all of both phones and wait to excise the diphones until we are know what phone we are about to con-
Optimal coupling   catenate with. In this method, known as **optimal coupling**, we take the two (complete, uncut) diphones we need to concatenate and check every possible cutting point for each diphones, choosing the two cutting points that would make the final frame of the first diphone acoustically most similar to the end frame of the next diphone (Taylor and Isard, 1991; Conkie and Isard, 1996). Acoustic similarity can be measured by **cepstral similarity**, as defined in Section 9.3.

8.4.2   Diphone Concatenation and TD-PSOLA for Prosody

We are now ready to see the remaining steps for synthesizing an individual utterance. Assume that we have completed text analysis for the utterance, have arrived at a sequence of diphones and prosodic targets, and have also grabbed the appropriate sequence of diphones from the diphone database. Next, we need to concatenate the diphones and then adjust the prosody (pitch, energy, and duration) of the diphone sequence to match the prosodic requirements from the intermediate representation.

Given two diphones, what do we need to do to concatenate them successfully? If the waveforms of the two diphones edges across the juncture are very different, a
Click   perceptible **click** will result. Thus, we need to apply a windowing function to the edge of both diphones so that the samples at the juncture have low or zero amplitude. Furthermore, if both diphones are voiced, we need to ensure that the two diphones are
Pitch-synchronous   joined **pitch-synchronously**. This means that the pitch periods at the end of the first diphone must line up with the pitch periods at the beginning of the second diphone; otherwise, the resulting single irregular pitch period at the juncture is perceptible as well.

Now given our sequence of concatenated diphones, how do we modify the pitch and duration to meet our prosodic requirements? It turns out there is a simple algorithm
TD-PSOLA   for doing this, called **TD-PSOLA (Time-Domain Pitch-Synchronous OverLap-and-Add)**.

As we just said, a **pitch-synchronous** algorithm is one in which we do something at each pitch period or **epoch**. For such algorithms it is important to have accurate pitch markings: measurements of exactly where each pitch pulse or **epoch** occurs. An epoch can be defined by the instant of maximum glottal pressure, or alternatively by the instant of glottal closure. Note the distinction between **pitch marking** or **epoch detection** and **pitch tracking**. Pitch tracking gives the value of F0 (the average cycles per second of the glottis) at each particular point in time, averaged over a neighborhood. Pitch marking finds the exact point in time at each vibratory cycle at which the vocal folds reach some specific point (epoch).

Pitch marking

Pitch tracking

Epoch labeling can be done in two ways. The traditional way, and still the most accurate, is to use an **electroglottograph** or **EGG** (often also called a **laryngograph** or **Lx**). An EGG is a device that straps onto the (outside of the) speaker's neck near the larynx and sends a small current through the Adam's apple. A transducer detects whether the glottis is open or closed by measuring the impedance across the vocal folds. Some modern synthesis databases are still recorded with an EGG. The problem with using an EGG is that it must be attached to the speaker while he or she is recording the database. Although an EGG isn't particularly invasive, it is still annoying, and the EGG must be used during recording; it can't be used to pitch-mark speech that has already been collected. Modern epoch detectors are now approaching such a level of accuracy that EGGs are no longer used in most commercial TTS engines. Algorithms for epoch detection include Brookes and Loke (1999), and Veldhuis (2000).

Electroglotto-graph

EGG

Laryngograph

Lx

Given an epoch-labeled corpus, the intuition of TD-PSOLA is that we can modify the pitch and duration of a waveform by extracting a frame for each pitch period (windowed so that the frame doesn't have sharp edges) and then recombining these frames in various ways by simply overlapping and adding the windowed pitch period frames (we introduce the idea of windows in Section 9.3.2). The idea that we modify a signal by extracting frames, manipulating them in some way, and then recombining them by adding up the overlapped signals is called the **overlap-and-add** or **OLA** algorithm; TD-PSOLA is a special case of overlap-and-add in which the frames are pitch synchronous and the whole process takes place in the time domain.

Overlap-and-add

OLA

For example, to assign a specific duration to a diphone, we might want to lengthen the recorded master diphone. To lengthen a signal with TD-PSOLA, we simply insert extra copies of some of the pitch-synchronous frames, essentially duplicating a piece of the signal. Figure 8.16 shows the intuition.

TD-PSOLA can also be used to change the F0 value of a recorded diphone to give a higher or lower value. To increase the F0, we extract each pitch-synchronous frame from the original recorded diphone signal, place the frames closer together (overlapping them), with the amount of overlap determined by the desired period and hence frequency, and then add up the overlapping signals to produce the final signal. But note that by moving all the frames closer together, we make the signal shorter in time! Thus to change the pitch while holding the duration constant, we need to add duplicate frames.

Figure 8.17 shows the intuition; in this figure we have explicitly shown the extracted pitch-synchronous frames that are overlapped and added; note that the frames moved closer together (increasing the pitch) while extra frames have been added to hold the duration constant.

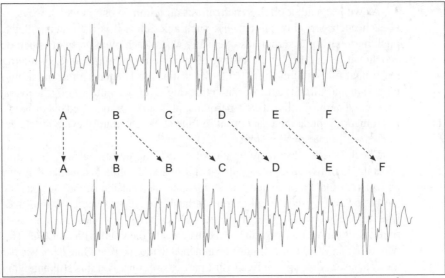

Figure 8.16   TD-PSOLA for duration modification. Individual pitch-synchronous frames can be duplicated to lengthen the signal (as shown here), or deleted to shorten the signal.

8.5   Unit Selection (Waveform) Synthesis

Diphone waveform synthesis suffers from two main problems. First, the stored diphone database must be modified by signal process methods like PSOLA to produce the desired prosody. Any kind of signal processing of the stored speech leaves artifacts in the speech that can make the speech sound unnatural. Second, diphone synthesis captures only the coarticulation due to a single neighboring phone. But there are many more global effects on phonetic realization, including more distant phones, syllable structure, the stress patterns of nearby phones, and even word-level effects.

Unit selection synthesis

For this reason, modern commercial synthesizers are based on a generalization of diphone synthesis called **unit selection synthesis**. Like diphone synthesis, unit selection synthesis is a kind of concatenative synthesis algorithm. The word **unit** means any stored piece of speech that is concatenated together to form an output. The intuition of unit selection synthesis is that we can store units of different sizes, which can be much larger that diphones. Unit selection thus differs from classic diphone synthesis in two ways:

1. In diphone synthesis, the database stores one copy of each diphone; in unit selection, the database is many hours long, with many copies of each diphone.

2. In diphone synthesis, the prosody of the units is modified by PSOLA or similar algorithms; in unit selection no (or minimal) signal processing is applied to the concatenated units.

The strengths of unit selection are due to the large unit database. In a sufficiently large database, entire words or phrases of the utterance we want to synthesize may already be present in the database, resulting in an extremely natural waveform for these

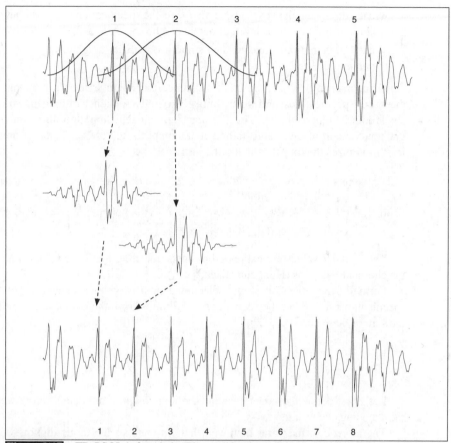

Figure 8.17 TD-PSOLA for pitch (F0) modification. To increase the pitch, we extract the individual pitch-synchronous frames, Hanning-window them, move them closer together and then add them up. To decrease the pitch, we move the frames further apart. Increasing the pitch will result in a shorter signal (since the frames are closer together), so we also need to duplicate frames if we want to change the pitch while holding the duration constant.

words or phrases. Thus we implicitly create larger units by selecting diphones that are consecutive in the database. In addition, in cases in which we can't find a large chunk and have to back off to individual diphones, many copies of each diphone make it more likely that we will find one that will fit in naturally.

The architecture of unit selection can be summarized as follows. We are given a large database of units; let's assume these are diphones (although it's also possible to do unit selection with other kinds of units such as half-phones, syllables, or half-syllables). We are also given a characterization of the target 'internal representation', that is, a phone string together with features such as stress values, word identity, F0 information, as described in Fig. 8.1 on page 250.

The goal of the synthesizer is to select from the database the best sequence of diphone units that corresponds to the target representation. What do we mean by the "best" sequence? Intuitively, the best sequence would be one in which

- each diphone unit we select exactly meets the specifications of the target diphone (in terms of F0, stress level, phonetic neighbors, etc.)
- each diphone unit concatenates smoothly with its neighboring units, with no perceptible break

Of course, in practice, we can't guarantee that there will be a unit that exactly meets our specifications, and we are unlikely to find a sequence of units in which every single join is imperceptible. Thus, in practice, unit selection algorithms implement a gradient version of these constraints, and attempt to find the sequence of unit that at least minimizes the **target cost** and the **join cost**:

Target cost

Join cost

> **Target cost** $T(u_t, s_t)$: how well the target specification s_t matches the potential unit u_t
>
> **Join cost** $J(u_t, u_{t+1})$: how well (perceptually) the potential unit u_t joins with its potential neighbor u_{t+1}

The T and J values are expressed as **costs**, meaning that high values indicate bad matches and bad joins (Hunt and Black, 1996).

Formally, then, the task of unit selection synthesis, given a sequence S of T target specifications, is to find the sequence $\hat{U}$ of T units from the database that minimizes the sum of these costs:

$$\hat{U} = \operatorname*{argmin}_{U} \sum_{t=1}^{T} T(s_t, u_t) + \sum_{t=1}^{T-1} J(u_t, u_{t+1}) \qquad (8.19)$$

Let's first define the target cost and the join cost in more detail before we turn to the decoding and training tasks.

The target cost measures how well the unit matches the target diphone specification. We can think of the specification for each diphone target as a feature vector; here are three sample vectors for three target diphone specifications, using dimensions (features) like *should the syllable be stressed*, and *where in the intonational phrase should the diphone come from*:

```
/ih-t/, +stress, phrase internal, high F0, content word
/n-t/, -stress, phrase final, high F0, function word
/dh-ax/, -stress, phrase initial, low F0, word 'the'
```

We'd like the distance between the target specification s and the unit to be some function of how different the unit is on each of these dimensions from the specification. Let's assume that for each dimension p, we can come up with some **subcost** $T_p(s_t[p], u_j[p])$. The subcost for a binary feature like *stress* might be 1 or 0. The subcost for a continuous feature like F0 might be the difference (or log difference) between the specification F0 and unit F0. Since some dimensions are more important to speech perceptions than others, we'll also want to weight each dimension. The simplest way to combine all these subcosts is just to assume that they are independent and additive. Using this model, the total target cost for a given target/unit pair is the weighted sum over all these subcosts for each feature/dimension:

$$T(s_t, u_j) = \sum_{p=1}^{P} w_p T_p(s_t[p], u_j[p]) \tag{8.20}$$

The target cost is a function of the desired diphone specification and a unit from the database. The **join cost**, by contrast, is a function of two units from the database. The goal of the join cost is to be low (0) when the join is completely natural, and high when the join would be perceptible or jarring. We meet this goal by measuring the acoustic similarity of the edges of the two units that we will be joining. If the two units have very similar energy, F0, and spectral features, they will probably join well. Thus as with the target cost, we compute a join cost by summing weighted subcosts:

$$J(u_t, u_{t+1}) = \sum_{p=1}^{P} w_p J_p(u_t[p], u_{t+1}[p]) \tag{8.21}$$

The three subcosts used in the classic Hunt and Black (1996) algorithm are the **cepstral distance** at the point of concatenation, and the absolute differences in both log power and F0. We introduce the cepstrum in Section 9.3.

In addition, if the two units u_t and u_{t+1} to be concatenated were consecutive diphones in the unit database (i.e., they followed each other in the original utterance), then we set the join cost to 0: $J(u_t, u_{t+1}) = 0$. This is an important feature of unit selection synthesis since it encourages large natural sequences of units to be selected from the database.

How do we find the best sequence of units that minimizes the sum of the target and join costs as expressed in Eq. 8.19? The standard method is to think of the unit selection problem as a hidden Markov model. The target units are the observed outputs, and the units in the database are the hidden states. Our job is to find the best hidden state sequence. We can use the Viterbi algorithm (Chapter 6) to solve this problem. Figure 8.18 shows a sketch of the search space as well as the best (Viterbi) path that determines the best unit sequence.

The weights for join and target costs are often set by hand because the number of weights is small (on the order of 20) and machine learning algorithms don't always achieve human performance. The system designer listens to entire sentences produced by the system and chooses values for weights that result in reasonable sounding utterances. Various automatic weight-setting algorithms do exist, however. Many of these assume we have some sort of distance function between the acoustics of two sentences, perhaps based on cepstral distance. The method of Hunt and Black (1996), for example, holds out a test set of sentences from the unit selection database. For each of these test sentences, we synthesize from the word sequence a sentence waveform (using units from the other sentences in the training database). Next we compare the acoustics of the synthesized sentence with the acoustics of the true human sentence. We now have a sequence of synthesized sentences, each one associated with a distance function to its human counterpart. We then use linear regression based on these distances to set the target cost weights so as to minimize the distance.

There are also more advanced methods of assigning both target and join costs. For example, above we computed target costs between two units by looking at the features

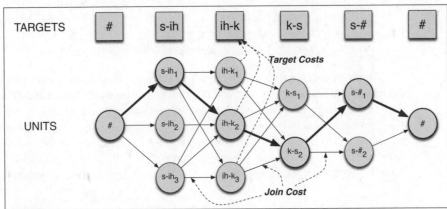

Figure 8.18   Decoding in unit selection, showing the sequence of target (specification) diphones for the word *six* and the set of possible database diphone units that we must search through. The best (Viterbi) path that minimizes the sum of the target and join costs is in bold.

of the two units, doing a weighted sum of feature costs, and choosing the lowest-cost unit. An alternative approach (which the new reader might need to come back to after learning the speech recognition techniques introduced in the next chapters) is to map the target unit into some acoustic space and then find a unit that is near the target in that acoustic space. The method of Donovan and Woodland (1995) and Donovan and Eide (1998), for example, clusters all the training units by using the decision tree algorithm of speech recognition described in Fig. 10.14 of Section 10.3. The decision tree is based on the same features described above, but here for each set of features, we follow a path down the decision tree to the leaf node that contains a cluster of units that have those features. This cluster of units can be parameterized by a Gaussian model, just as for speech recognition, so that we can map a set of features into a probability distribution over cepstral values and hence easily compute a distance between the target and a unit in the database. As for join costs, more sophisticated metrics make use of how perceivable a particular join might be (Wouters and Macon, 1998; Syrdal and Conkie, 2004; Bulyko and Ostendorf, 2001).

8.6   Evaluation

Speech synthesis systems are evaluated by human listeners. The development of a good automatic metric for synthesis evaluation, one that would eliminate the need for expensive and time-consuming human listening experiments, remains an open and exciting research topic.

Intelligibility   The minimal evaluation metric for speech synthesis systems is **intelligibility**: the ability of a human listener to correctly interpret the words and meaning of the synthesized utterance. A further metric is **quality**: an abstract measure of the naturalness,
Quality   fluency, or clarity of the speech.

Diagnostic Rhyme Test
DRT

The most local measures of intelligibility test the ability of a listener to discriminate between two phones. The **Diagnostic Rhyme Test** (**DRT**) (Voiers et al., 1975) tests the intelligibility of initial consonants. It is based on 96 pairs of confusable rhyming words differing only in a single phonetic feature, such as *dense/tense* or *bond/pond* (differing in voicing) or *mean/beat* or *neck/deck* (differing in nasality). For each pair, listeners hear one member of the pair and indicate which they think it is. The percentage of right answers is then used as an intelligibility metric. The **Modified Rhyme Test** (**MRT**) (House et al., 1965) is a similar test based on a different set of 300 words, consisting of 50 sets of 6 words. Each 6-word set differs in either initial or final consonants (e.g., *went, sent, bent, dent, tent, rent* or *bat, bad, back, bass, ban, bath*). Listeners are given a single word they must identify from a closed list of six words; the percentage of correct identifications is again used as an intelligibility metric.

Modified Rhyme Test
MRT

Since context effects are very important, both DRT and MRT words are embedded in **carrier phrases** like the following:

Carrier phrase

```
Now we will say <word> again.
```

To test units larger than single phones, we can use **semantically unpredictable sentences** (**SUS**) (Benoît et al., 1996). We construct such sentences by taking a simple POS template like DET ADJ NOUN VERB DET NOUN and inserting random English words in the slots, to produce sentences like

SUS

```
The unsure steaks closed the fish.
```

Measures of intelligibility like DRT/MRT and SUS factor out the role of context in measuring intelligibility. While this allows for a carefully controlled measure of a system's intelligibility, such acontextual or semantically unpredictable sentences aren't a good fit to how TTS is used in commercial applications. Thus, in commercial applications instead of DRT or SUS, we generally test intelligibility in situations that mimic the desired applications: reading addresses out loud, reading lines of news text, and so on.

To further evaluate the **quality** of the synthesized utterances, we can play a sentence for listeners and ask them to give a **mean opinion score** (**MOS**), a rating of how good the synthesized utterances are, usually on a scale from 1–5. We can then compare systems by comparing their MOS scores on the same sentences (using, e.g., t-tests to test for significant differences).

MOS

If we are comparing exactly two systems (perhaps to see if a particular change actually improved the system), we can use **AB tests**. In AB tests, we play the same sentence synthesized by two different systems (an A and a B system). The human listeners choose which of the two utterances they like better. We do this for 50 sentences and compare the number of sentences preferred for each system. To avoid listener bias, for each sentence we must present the two synthesized waveforms in random order.

AB tests

Bibliographical and Historical Notes

As we noted at the beginning of the chapter, speech synthesis is one of the earliest fields of speech and language processing. The 18th century saw a number of physical models of the articulation process, including the von Kempelen model mentioned above, as well as the 1773 vowel model of Kratzenstein in Copenhagen using organ pipes.

But the modern era of speech synthesis can clearly be said to have arrived by the early 1950s, when all three of the major paradigms of waveform synthesis—formant synthesis, articulatory synthesis, and concatenative synthesis— had been proposed.

Concatenative synthesis seems to have been first proposed by Harris (1953) at Bell Laboratories; he literally spliced together pieces of magnetic tape corresponding to phones. Harris's proposal was actually more like unit selection synthesis than diphone synthesis, in that he proposed storing multiple copies of each phone and proposed the use of a join cost (choosing the unit with the smoothest formant transitions with the neighboring unit). Harris's model was based on the phone, rather than the diphone, resulting in problems due to coarticulation. Peterson et al. (1958) added many of the basic ideas of unit selection synthesis, including the use of diphones, a database with multiple copies of each diphone with differing prosody, each labeled with prosodic features including F0, stress, and duration, and the use of join costs based on F0 and formant distance between neighboring units. They also proposed microconcatenation techniques such as windowing the waveforms. The Peterson et al. model was purely theoretical, however, and concatenative synthesis was not implemented until the 1960s and 1970s, when diphone synthesis was first implemented (Dixon and Maxey, 1968; Olive, 1977). Later diphone systems included larger units such as consonant clusters (Olive and Liberman, 1979). Modern unit selection, including the idea of large units of non-uniform length and the use of a target cost, was invented by Sagisaka (1988), Sagisaka et al. (1992). Hunt and Black (1996) formalized the model and put it in the form in which we have presented it in this chapter in the context of the ATR CHATR system (Black and Taylor, 1994). The idea of automatically generating synthesis units by clustering was first invented by Nakajima and Hamada (1988), but was developed mainly by (Donovan, 1996) who incorporated decision tree clustering algorithms from speech recognition. Many unit selection innovations took place as part of the AT&T NextGen synthesizer (Syrdal et al., 2000; Syrdal and Conkie, 2004).

We focused in this chapter on concatenative synthesis, but there are two other synthesis paradigms: **formant synthesis**, in which we try to build rules that generate artificial spectra, including especially formants; and **articulatory synthesis**, in which we try to directly model the physics of the vocal tract and articulatory process.

Formant synthesizers originally were inspired by attempts to mimic human speech by generating artificial spectrograms. The Haskins Laboratories Pattern Playback Machine generated a sound wave by painting spectrogram patterns on a moving transparent belt and using reflectance to filter the harmonics of a waveform (Cooper et al., 1951); other very early formant synthesizers include those of Lawrence (1953) and Fant (1951). Perhaps the most well-known of the formant synthesizers were the **Klatt formant synthesizer** and its successor systems, including the MITalk system (Allen et al., 1987) and the Klattalk software used in Digital Equipment Corporation's DECtalk (Klatt, 1982). See Klatt (1975) for details.

Articulatory synthesizers attempt to synthesize speech by modeling the physics of the vocal tract as an open tube. Representative models, both early and somewhat more recent include those of Stevens et al. (1953), Flanagan et al. (1975), and Fant (1986). See Klatt (1975) and Flanagan (1972) for more details.

Development of the text analysis components of TTS came somewhat later, as techniques were borrowed from other areas of natural language processing. The input to early synthesis systems was not text, but rather phonemes (typed in on punched cards). The first text-to-speech system to take text as input seems to have been the system of Umeda and Teranishi (Umeda et al., 1968; Teranishi and Umeda, 1968; Umeda, 1976). The system included a lexicalized parser that assigned prosodic boundaries, as well as accent and stress; the extensions in Coker et al. (1973) added more rules, for example, for deaccenting light verbs, and explored articulatory models as well. These early TTS systems used a pronunciation dictionary for word pronunciations. To expand to larger vocabularies, early formant-based TTS systems such as MITalk (Allen et al., 1987) used letter-to-sound rules instead of a dictionary since computer memory was far too expensive to store large dictionaries.

Modern grapheme-to-phoneme models derive from the influential early probabilistic grapheme-to-phoneme model of Lucassen and Mercer (1984), which was originally proposed in the context of speech recognition. The widespread use of such machine learning models was delayed, however, because early anecdotal evidence suggested that hand-written rules worked better than, for example, the neural networks of Sejnowski and Rosenberg (1987). The careful comparisons of Damper et al. (1999) showed that machine learning methods were generally superior. A number of such models make use of pronunciation by analogy (Byrd and Chodorow, 1985; Dedina and Nusbaum, 1991; Daelemans and van den Bosch, 1997; Marchand and Damper, 2000) or latent analogy (Bellegarda, 2005); HMMs (Taylor, 2005) have also been proposed.

Graphone The most recent work makes use of joint **graphone** models, in which the hidden variables are phoneme-grapheme pairs and the probabilistic model is based on joint rather than conditional likelihood (Deligne et al., 1995; Luk and Damper, 1996; Galescu and Allen, 2001; Bisani and Ney, 2002; Chen, 2003).

Fujisaki The literature on prosody is vast; another important computational model, for example, is the **Fujisaki** model (Fujisaki and Ohno, 1997). IViE (Grabe, 2001) is an extension of ToBI that focuses on labeling different varieties of English (Grabe et al., 2000). There is also much debate on the units of intonational structure, including **in-**

Intonation unit **tonational phrases** (Beckman and Pierrehumbert, 1986), **intonation units** (Du Bois

Tone unit et al., 1983) or **tone units** (Crystal, 1969), and their relation to clauses and other syntactic units (Chomsky and Halle, 1968; Langendoen, 1975; Streeter, 1978; Hirschberg and Pierrehumbert, 1986; Selkirk, 1986; Nespor and Vogel, 1986; Croft, 1995; Ladd, 1996; Ford and Thompson, 1996; Ford et al., 1996). Much recent work on speech synthesis has focused on generating emotional speech (Cahn, 1990; Bulut et al., 2002; Hamza et al., 2004; Eide et al., 2004; Lee et al., 2006; Schroder, 2006, among others).

HMM synthesis One of the most exciting new paradigms for speech synthesis is **HMM synthesis**, first proposed by Tokuda et al. (1995b) and elaborated in Tokuda et al. (1995a), Tokuda et al. (2000), and Tokuda et al. (2003). See also the textbook summary of HMM synthesis in Taylor (2008). Huang et al. (2001) and Gibbon et al. (2000) present more information on TTS evaluation. See also the annual speech synthesis competition

Blizzard Challenge called the **Blizzard Challenge** (Black and Tokuda, 2005; Bennett, 2005).

Two classic text-to-speech synthesis systems are described in Allen et al. (1987) (the MITalk system) and Sproat (1998b) (the Bell Labs system). Recent textbooks include Dutoit (1997), Huang et al. (2001), Taylor (2008), and Alan Black's online lec-

ture notes at `http://festvox.org/festtut/notes/festtut_toc.html`.
Influential collections of papers include van Santen et al. (1997), Sagisaka et al. (1997),
Narayanan and Alwan (2004). Conference publications appear in the main speech engineering conferences (INTERSPEECH, *IEEE ICASSP*) and the *Speech Synthesis Workshops*. Journals include *Speech Communication*, *Computer Speech and Language*, the *IEEE Transactions on Audio, Speech, and Language Processing*, and the *ACM Transactions on Speech and Language Processing*.

Exercises

8.1   Implement the text normalization routine that deals with MONEY, that is, mapping strings of dollar amounts like *$45*, *$320*, and *$4100* to words (either writing code directly or designing an FST). If there are multiple ways to pronounce a number you may pick your favorite way.

8.2   Implement the text normalization routine that deals with NTEL, that is, seven-digit phone numbers like *555-1212*, *555-1300*, and so on. Use a combination of the **paired** and **trailing unit** methods of pronunciation for the last four digits. (Again, either write code or design an FST).

8.3   Implement the text normalization routine that deals with type NDATE in Fig. 8.4.

8.4   Implement the text normalization routine that deals with type NTIME in Fig. 8.4.

8.5   (Suggested by Alan Black.) Download the free Festival speech synthesizer. Augment the lexicon to correctly pronounce the names of everyone in your class.

8.6   Download the Festival synthesizer. Using your own voice, record and train a diphone synthesizer.

8.7   Build a phrase boundary predictor. You can use any classifier you like, and you should implement some of the features described on page 263.

Chapter 9

Automatic Speech Recognition

When Frederic was a little lad he proved so brave and daring,
His father thought he'd 'prentice him to some career seafaring.
I was, alas! his nurs'rymaid, and so it fell to my lot
To take and bind the promising boy apprentice to a **pilot** —
A life not bad for a hardy lad, though surely not a high lot,
Though I'm a nurse, you might do worse than make your boy a pilot.
I was a stupid nurs'rymaid, on breakers always steering,
And I did not catch the word aright, through being hard of hearing;
Mistaking my instructions, which within my brain did gyrate,
I took and bound this promising boy apprentice to a **pirate.**
The Pirates of Penzance, Gilbert and Sullivan, 1877

Alas, this mistake by nurserymaid Ruth led to Frederic's long indenture as a pirate and, due to a slight complication involving 21st birthdays and leap years, nearly led to 63 extra years of apprenticeship. The mistake was quite natural, in a Gilbert-and-Sullivan sort of way; as Ruth later noted, "The two words were so much alike!" True, true; spoken language understanding is a difficult task, and it is remarkable that humans do

ASR as well at it as we do. The goal of **automatic speech recognition** (**ASR**) research is to address this problem computationally by building systems that map from an acoustic signal to a string of words. **Automatic speech understanding** (**ASU**) extends this goal to producing some sort of understanding of the sentence, rather than just the words.

The general problem of automatic transcription of speech by any speaker in any environment is still far from solved. But recent years have seen ASR technology mature to the point where it is viable in certain limited domains. One major application area is in human-computer interaction. While many tasks are better solved with visual or pointing interfaces, speech has the potential to be a better interface than the keyboard for tasks for which full natural language communication is useful or for which keyboards are not appropriate. This includes hands-busy or eyes-busy applications, such as where the user has objects to manipulate or equipment to control. Another important application area is telephony, where speech recognition is already used, for example, in spoken dialogue systems for entering digits, recognizing "yes" to accept collect calls, finding out airplane or train information, and call-routing ("Accounting, please", "Prof. Regier, please"). In some applications, a multimodal interface combining speech and pointing can be more efficient than a graphical user interface without speech (Cohen et al., 1998). Finally, ASR is applied to dictation, that is, to transcription of extended monologue by a single specific speaker. Dictation is common in fields such as law and is also important as part of augmentative communication (interaction between computers and humans with some disability resulting in the inability to type or the inability to speak). The blind Milton famously dictated *Paradise Lost* to his daughters, and Henry James dictated his later novels after a repetitive stress injury.

Before turning to architectural details, let's discuss some of the parameters of the speech recognition task. One dimension of variation in speech recognition tasks is

From Chapter 9 of *Speech and Language Processing*, Second Edition. Daniel Jurafsky, James H. Martin.

the vocabulary size. Speech recognition is easier if the number of distinct words we need to recognize is smaller. So tasks with a two-word vocabulary, like *yes* versus *no* detection, or an eleven-word vocabulary, like recognizing sequences of digits (*zero* to *nine* plus *oh*) in what is called the **digits task**, are relatively easy. On the other end, tasks with large vocabularies of 20,000 to 60,000 words, like transcribing human-human telephone conversations or transcribing broadcast news are much harder.

Digit recognition

A second dimension of variation is how fluent, natural, or conversational the speech is. **Isolated word** recognition, in which each word is surrounded by some sort of pause, is much easier than recognizing **continuous speech**, in which words run into each other and have to be segmented. Continuous speech tasks themselves vary greatly in difficulty. For example, human-to-machine speech turns out to be far easier to recognize than human-to-human speech. That is, recognizing speech of humans talking to machines, either reading out loud in **read speech** (which simulates the dictation task), or conversing with speech dialogue systems, is relatively easy. Recognizing the speech of two humans talking to each other in **conversational speech**, for example, for transcribing a business meeting, is much harder. It seems that when humans talk to machines, they simplify their speech quite a bit, talking more slowly and more clearly.

Isolated word
Continuous
speech

Read speech

Conversational
speech

A third dimension of variation is channel and noise. The **dictation** task (and much laboratory research in speech recognition) is done with high-quality, head-mounted microphones. Head-mounted microphones eliminate the distortion that occurs in a table microphone as the speaker's head moves around. Noise of any kind also makes recognition harder. Thus, recognizing a speaker dictating in a quiet office is much easier than recognizing a speaker in a noisy car on the highway with the window open.

A final dimension of variation is accent or speaker-class characteristics. Speech is easier to recognize if the speaker is speaking a standard dialect or, in general, one that matches the data the system was trained on. Recognition is thus harder on foreign-accented speech or speech of children (unless the system was specifically trained on exactly these kinds of speech).

Figure 9.1 shows the rough percentage of incorrect words (the **word error rate**, or WER, defined on page 328) from state-of-the-art systems on different ASR tasks.

Task	Vocabulary	Error Rate %
TI Digits	11 (zero–nine, oh)	.5
Wall Street Journal read speech	5,000	3
Wall Street Journal read speech	20,000	3
Broadcast News	64,000+	10
Conversational Telephone Speech (CTS)	64,000+	20

Figure 9.1   Rough word error rates (% of words misrecognized) reported around 2006 for ASR on various tasks; the error rates for Broadcast News and CTS are based on particular training and test scenarios and should be taken as ballpark numbers; error rates for differently defined tasks may range up to a factor of two.

Variation due to noise and accent increases the error rates quite a bit. The word error rate on strongly Japanese-accented or Spanish-accented English has been reported to be about 3 to 4 times higher than for native speakers on the same task (Tomokiyo, 2001).

And adding automobile noise with a 10 dB SNR (signal-to-noise ratio) can cause error rates to go up by 2 to 4 times.

In general, these error rates go down every year, because speech recognition performance has improved quite steadily. One estimate is that performance has improved roughly 10% a year over the last decade (Deng and Huang, 2004), due to a combination of algorithmic improvements and Moore's law.

While the algorithms we describe in this chapter are applicable across a wide variety of these speech tasks, we chose to focus this chapter on the fundamentals of one crucial area: **Large-Vocabulary Continuous Speech Recognition** (**LVCSR**). Large-vocabulary generally means that the systems have a vocabulary of roughly 20,000 to 60,000 words. We saw above that **continuous** means that the words are run together naturally. Furthermore, the algorithms we will discuss are generally **speaker-independent**; that is, they are able to recognize speech from people whose speech the system has never been exposed to before.

LVCSR

Speaker independent

The dominant paradigm for LVCSR is the HMM, and we focus on this approach in this chapter. Previous chapters have introduced most of the core algorithms used in HMM-based speech recognition. Chapter 7 introduced the key phonetic and phonological notions of **phone**, **syllable**, and intonation. Chapters 5 and 6 introduced the use of **Bayes' rule**, the **hidden Markov model** (**HMM**), the **Viterbi** algorithm, and the Baum-Welch (forward-backward) training algorithm. Chapter 4 introduced the *N*-**gram** language model and the **perplexity** metric. In this chapter, we begin with an overview of the architecture for HMM speech recognition, offer an overview of signal processing for feature extraction and the extraction of the important MFCC features, and then introduce Gaussian acoustic models. We then continue with how Viterbi decoding works in the ASR context and summarize the complete training procedure for ASR, called **embedded training**. Finally, we introduce word error rate, the standard evaluation metric. Chapter 10 continues with some advanced ASR topics.

9.1   Speech Recognition Architecture

The task of speech recognition is to take as input an acoustic waveform and produce as output a string of words. HMM-based speech recognition systems view this task using the metaphor of the noisy-channel. The intuition of the **noisy-channel** model (see Fig. 9.2) is to treat the acoustic waveform as a "noisy" version of the string of words, that is, a version that has been passed through a noisy communications channel. This channel introduces "noise", which makes it hard to recognize the "true" string of words. Our goal then is to build a model of the channel so that we can figure out how the channel modified this "true" sentence and hence recover the sentence.

Noisy-channel

The insight of the noisy-channel model is that if we know how the channel distorts the source, we could find the correct source sentence for a waveform by taking every possible sentence in the language, running each sentence through our noisy-channel model, and seeing if it matches the output. We then select the best matching source sentence as our desired source sentence.

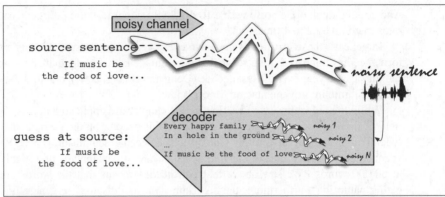

Figure 9.2   The noisy-channel model. We search through a huge space of potential "source" sentences and choose the one which has the highest probability of generating the "noisy" sentence. We need models of the prior probability of a source sentence (*N*-grams), the probability of words being realized as certain strings of phones (HMM lexicons), and the probability of phones being realized as acoustic or spectral features (Gaussian mixture models).

Implementing the noisy-channel model as we have expressed it in Fig. 9.2 requires solutions to two problems. First, to pick the sentence that best matches the noisy input, we will need a complete metric for a "best match". Because speech is so variable, an acoustic input sentence will never exactly match any model we have for this sentence. As in previous chapters, we use probability as our metric. This makes the speech recognition problem a special case of **Bayesian inference**, a method known since the work of Bayes (1763). Bayesian inference or Bayesian classification was applied successfully by the 1950s to language problems like optical character recognition (Bledsoe and Browning, 1959) and to authorship attribution tasks like the seminal work of Mosteller and Wallace (1964) on determining the authorship of the Federalist papers. Our goal is to combine various probabilistic models to get a complete estimate for the probability of a noisy acoustic observation-sequence given a candidate source sentence. We can then search through the space of all sentences, and choose the source sentence with the highest probability.

Bayesian

Second, since the set of all English sentences is huge, we need an efficient algorithm that will not search through all possible sentences but only consider ones that have a good chance of matching the input. This is the **decoding** or **search** problem, that we have already explored with the Viterbi decoding algorithm for HMMs in Chapters 5 and 6. Since the search space is so large in speech recognition, efficient search is an important part of the task, and we focus on a number of areas in search.

In the rest of this introduction we review the probabilistic or Bayesian model for speech recognition that we introduced for part-of-speech tagging in Chapter 5. We then introduce the various components of a modern HMM-based ASR system.

Recall that the goal of the probabilistic noisy-channel architecture for speech recognition can be summarized as follows:

What is the most likely sentence out of all sentences in the language $\mathscr{L}$ given some acoustic input O?

We can treat the acoustic input O as a sequence of individual "symbols" or "observations", for example by slicing up the input every 10 milliseconds, and representing each slice by floating-point values of the energy or frequencies of that slice. Each index then represents some time interval, and successive o_i indicate temporally consecutive slices of the input (note that capital letters stand for sequences of symbols and lower-case letters for individual symbols):

$$O = o_1, o_2, o_3, \ldots, o_t \tag{9.1}$$

Similarly, we treat a sentence as if it were composed of a string of words:

$$W = w_1, w_2, w_3, \ldots, w_n \tag{9.2}$$

Both of these are simplifying assumptions; for example, dividing sentences into words is sometimes too fine a division (we'd like to model facts about groups of words rather than individual words) and sometimes too gross a division (we need to deal with morphology). Usually in speech recognition a word is defined by orthography (after mapping every word to lower case): *oak* is treated as a different word than *oaks*, but the auxiliary *can* ("can you tell me...") is treated as the same word as the noun *can* ("i need a can of...").

The probabilistic implementation of our intuition above, then, can be expressed as

$$\hat{W} = \underset{W \in \mathscr{L}}{\operatorname{argmax}} P(W \, O) \tag{9.3}$$

Recall that the function $\operatorname{argmax}_x f(x)$ means "the x such that f(x) is largest". Eq. 9.3 is guaranteed to give us the optimal sentence W; we now need to make the equation operational. That is, for a given sentence W and acoustic sequence O we need to compute $P(W \, O)$. Recall that given any probability $P(x \, y)$, we can use Bayes' rule to break it down as follows:

$$P(x \, y) = \frac{P(y \, x) P(x)}{P(y)} \tag{9.4}$$

We saw in Chapter 5 that we can substitute Eq. 9.4 into Eq. 9.3 as follows:

$$\hat{W} = \underset{W \in \mathscr{L}}{\operatorname{argmax}} \frac{P(O \, W) P(W)}{P(O)} \tag{9.5}$$

The probabilities on the right-hand side of Eq. 9.5 are for the most part easier to compute than $P(W \, O)$. For example, $P(W)$, the prior probability of the word string itself, is what is estimated by the N-gram language models of Chapter 4. And we can see below that $P(O \, W)$ turns out to be easy to estimate as well. But $P(O)$, the probability of the acoustic observation sequence, is harder to estimate. Luckily, we can ignore $P(O)$ just as we saw in Chapter 5. Why? Since we are maximizing over all possible sentences, we will be computing $\frac{P(O \, W) P(W)}{P(O)}$ for each sentence in the language. But $P(O)$ doesn't change for each sentence! For each potential sentence we are still examining the same observations O, which must have the same probability $P(O)$. Thus,

$$\hat{W} = \underset{W \in \mathscr{L}}{\operatorname{argmax}} \frac{P(O \, W) P(W)}{P(O)} = \underset{W \in \mathscr{L}}{\operatorname{argmax}} P(O \, W) P(W) \tag{9.6}$$

To summarize, the most probable sentence W given some observation sequence O can be computed by taking the product of two probabilities for each sentence and choosing the sentence for which this product is greatest. The components of the speech recognizer that compute these two terms have names; $P(W)$, the **prior probability**, is computed by the **language model**. while $P(O\ W)$, the **observation likelihood**, is computed by the **acoustic model**.

Language model

Acoustic model

$$\hat{W} = \underset{W \in \mathscr{L}}{\operatorname{argmax}}\ \overbrace{P(O\ W)}^{\text{likelihood}}\ \overbrace{P(W)}^{\text{prior}} \qquad (9.7)$$

The language model (LM) prior $P(W)$ expresses the probability that a given string of words is a sentence of English. We saw in Chapter 4 how to compute such a language model prior $P(W)$ by using N-gram grammars, which assign a probability to a sentence by computing

$$P(w_1^n) \approx \prod_{k=1}^{n} P(w_k\ w_{k-N+1}^{k-1}) \qquad (9.8)$$

This chapter shows how the HMM we covered in Chapter 6 can be used to build an acoustic model (AM) that computes the likelihood $P(O\ W)$. Given the AM and LM probabilities, the probabilistic model can be operationalized in a search algorithm so as to compute the maximum probability word string for a given acoustic waveform. Figure 9.3 shows the components of an HMM speech recognizer as it processes a single utterance, indicating the computation of the prior and likelihood. The figure shows the recognition process in three stages. In the **feature extraction** or **signal processing** stage, the acoustic waveform is sampled into **frames** (usually of 10, 15, or 20 milliseconds) that are transformed into **spectral features**. Each time window is thus represented by a vector of around 39 features representing this spectral information as well as information about energy and spectral change. Section 9.3 gives an overview of the feature extraction process.

In the **acoustic modeling** or **phone recognition** stage, we compute the likelihood of the observed spectral feature vectors given linguistic units (words, phones, subparts of phones). For example, we use Gaussian mixture model (GMM) classifiers to compute for each HMM state q, corresponding to a phone or subphone, the likelihood of a given feature vector given this phone $p(o\ q)$. A (simplified) way of thinking of the output of this stage is as a sequence of probability vectors, one for each time frame, each vector at each time frame containing the likelihoods that each phone or subphone unit generated the acoustic feature vector observation at that time.

Finally, in the **decoding** phase, we take the acoustic model (AM), which consists of this sequence of acoustic likelihoods, plus an HMM dictionary of word pronunciations, combined with the language model (LM) (generally an N-gram grammar), and we output the most likely sequence of words. An HMM dictionary, as we show in Section 9.2, is a list of word pronunciations, each pronunciation represented by a string of phones. Each word can then be thought of as an HMM, where the phones (or sometimes subphones) are states in the HMM and the Gaussian likelihood estimators supply the HMM output likelihood function for each state. Most ASR systems use the Viterbi algorithm for decoding, speeding up the decoding with a wide variety of sophisticated augmentations such as pruning, fast-match, and tree-structured lexicons.

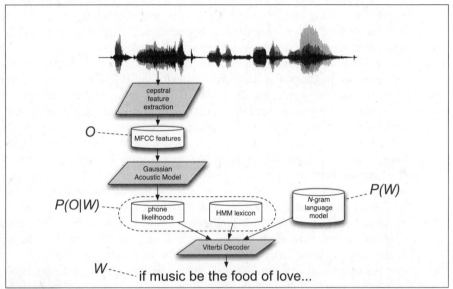

Figure 9.3 Schematic architecture for a simplified speech recognizer decoding a single sentence. A real recognizer is more complex since various kinds of pruning and fast matches are needed for efficiency. This architecture is only for decoding; we also need a separate architecture for training parameters.

9.2   The Hidden Markov Model Applied to Speech

Let's turn now to how the HMM model is applied to speech recognition. We saw in Chapter 6 that a hidden Markov model is characterized by the following components:

$Q = q_1 q_2 \ldots q_N$	a set of **states**
$A = a_{01} a_{02} \ldots a_{n1} \ldots a_{nn}$	a **transition probability matrix** A, each a_{ij} representing the probability of moving from state i to state j, s.t. $\sum_{j=1}^{n} a_{ij} = 1 \ \ \forall i$
$O = o_1 o_2 \ldots o_N$	a set of **observations**, each one drawn from a vocabulary $V = v_1, v_2, \ldots, v_V$.
$B = b_i(o_t)$	a set of **observation likelihoods**, also called **emission probabilities**, each expressing the probability of an observation o_t being generated from a state i
q_0, q_{end}	special **start and end states** that are not associated with observations

Furthermore, the chapter introduced the **Viterbi** algorithm for decoding HMMs, and the **Baum-Welch** or **Forward-Backward** algorithm for training HMMs.

All of these facets of the HMM paradigm play a crucial role in ASR. We begin here by discussing how the states, transitions, and observations map into the speech recognition task. We return to the ASR applications of Viterbi decoding in Section 9.6. The extensions to the Baum-Welch algorithms needed to deal with spoken language are covered in Sections 9.4 and 9.7. Recall the examples of HMMs we saw earlier in the book. In Chapter 5, the hidden states of the HMM were parts-of-speech, the observations were words, and the HMM decoding task mapped a sequence of words to a sequence of parts-of-speech. In Chapter 6, the hidden states of the HMM were weather, the observations were 'ice-cream consumptions', and the decoding task was to determine the weather sequence from a sequence of ice-cream consumptions. For speech, the hidden states are phones, parts of phones, or words, each observation is information about the spectrum and energy of the waveform at a point in time, and the decoding process maps this sequence of acoustic information to phones and words.

The observation sequence for speech recognition is a sequence of **acoustic feature vectors**. Each acoustic feature vector represents information such as the amount of energy in different frequency bands at a particular point in time. We return in Section 9.3 to the nature of these observations, but for now we simply note that each observation consists of a vector of 39 real-valued features indicating spectral information. Observations are generally drawn every 10 milliseconds, so 1 second of speech requires 100 spectral feature vectors, each vector of length 39.

The hidden states of hidden Markov models can be used to model speech in a number of different ways. For small tasks, like **digit recognition** (the recognition of the 11 digit words *zero* through *nine* plus *oh*) or for **yes-no** recognition (recognition of the two words **yes** and **no**), we could build an HMM whose states correspond to entire words. For most larger tasks, however, the hidden states of the HMM correspond to phone-like units, and words are sequences of these phone-like units.

Let's begin by describing an HMM model in which each state of an HMM corresponds to a single phone (if you've forgotten what a phone is, go back and look again at the definition in Chapter 7). In such a model, a word HMM thus consists of a concatenated sequence of HMM states. Figure 9.4 shows a schematic of the structure of a basic phone-state HMM for the word *six*.

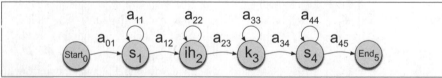

Figure 9.4   An HMM for the word *six*, consisting of four emitting states, two non-emitting states, and the transition probabilities A. The observation probabilities B are not shown.

Note that only certain connections between phones exist in Fig. 9.4. In the HMMs described in Chapter 6, there were arbitrary transitions between states; any state could transition to any other. This was also true of the HMMs for part-of-speech tagging in Chapter 5; although the probability of some tag transitions was low, any tag could, in principle, follow any other tag. Unlike other HMM applications, HMM models for speech recognition do not allow arbitrary transitions. Instead, they place strong constraints on transitions based on the sequential nature of speech. Except in unusual cases, HMMs for speech don't allow transitions from states to go to earlier states in the word; in other words, states can transition to themselves or to successive states. As we saw in Chapter 6, this kind of **left-to-right** HMM structure is called a **Bakis network**.

Bakis network

The most common model used for speech, illustrated in a simplified form in Fig. 9.4 is even more constrained, allowing a state to transition only to itself (self-loop) or to a single succeeding state. The use of self-loops allows a single phone to repeat so as to cover a variable amount of the acoustic input. Phone durations vary hugely, dependent on the phone identity, the speaker's rate of speech, the phonetic context, and the level of prosodic prominence of the word. Looking at the Switchboard corpus, the phone [aa] varies in length from 7 to 387 milliseconds (1 to 40 frames), and the phone [z] varies in duration from 7 milliseconds to more than 1.3 seconds (130 frames) in some utterances! Self-loops thus allow a single state to be repeated many times.

For very simple speech tasks (recognizing small numbers of words such as the digits), using an HMM state to represent a phone is sufficient. In general LVCSR tasks, however, a more fine-grained representation is necessary. This is because phones can last over 1 second, that is, over 100 frames, but the 100 frames are not acoustically identical. The spectral characteristics of a phone and the amount of energy vary dramatically across the phone. For example, recall from Chapter 7 that stop consonants have a closure portion, which has very little acoustic energy, followed by a release burst. Similarly, diphthongs are vowels whose F1 and F2 change significantly. Figure 9.5 shows these large changes in spectral characteristics over time for each of the two phones in the word "Ike", ARPAbet [ay k].

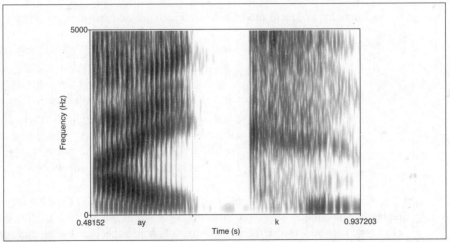

Figure 9.5   The two phones of the word "Ike", pronounced [ay k]. Note the continuous changes in the [ay] vowel on the left as F2 rises and F1 falls and the sharp differences between the silence and release parts of the [k] stop.

To capture this fact about the non-homogeneous nature of phones over time, in LVCSR we generally model a phone with more than one HMM state. The most common configuration is to use three HMM states: a beginning, middle, and end state. Each phone thus consists of three emitting HMM states instead of one (plus two non-emitting states at either end), as shown in Fig. 9.6. It is common to reserve the word **model** or **phone model** to refer to the entire five-state phone HMM and use the word **HMM state** (or just **state**) to refer to an individual subphone HMM state.

Phone model

HMM state

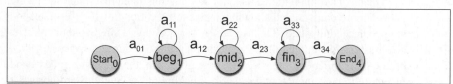

Figure 9.6   A standard five-state HMM model for a phone, consisting of three emitting states (corresponding to the transition-in, steady-state, and transition-out regions of the phone) and two non-emitting states.

To build an HMM for an entire word using these more complex phone models, we can simply replace each phone of the word model in Fig. 9.4 with a three-state phone HMM. We replace the non-emitting start and end states for each phone model with transitions directly to the emitting state of the preceding and following phone, leaving only two non-emitting states for the entire word. Figure 9.7 shows the expanded word.

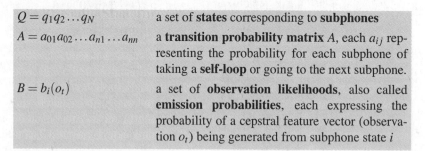

Figure 9.7   A composite word model for "six", [s ih k s], formed by concatenating four phone models, each with three emitting states.

In summary, an HMM model of speech recognition is parameterized by

$Q = q_1 q_2 \ldots q_N$	a set of **states** corresponding to **subphones**
$A = a_{01} a_{02} \ldots a_{n1} \ldots a_{nn}$	a **transition probability matrix** A, each a_{ij} representing the probability for each subphone of taking a **self-loop** or going to the next subphone.
$B = b_i(o_t)$	a set of **observation likelihoods**, also called **emission probabilities**, each expressing the probability of a cepstral feature vector (observation o_t) being generated from subphone state i

Another way of looking at the A probabilities and the states Q is that together they represent a **lexicon**: a set of pronunciations for words, each pronunciation consisting of a set of subphones, with the order of the subphones specified by the transition probabilities A.

We have now covered the basic structure of HMM states for representing phones and words in speech recognition. Later in this chapter we look at augmentations of the HMM model like triphone contexts and special silence phones. First, though, we need to turn to the next component of HMMs for speech recognition: the observation likelihoods. And to discuss observation likelihoods, we first need to introduce the actual acoustic observations: feature vectors. After discussing these in Section 9.3, we turn in Section 9.4 to the acoustic model and the computation of observation likelihoods. We then re-introduce Viterbi decoding and show how the acoustic model and language model are combined to choose the best sentence.

9.3   Feature Extraction: MFCC Vectors

Feature vector

MFCC
Cepstrum

Our goal in this section is to describe how we transform the input waveform into a sequence of acoustic **feature vectors**, each vector representing the information in a small time window of the signal. While there are many possible such feature representations, by far the most common in speech recognition is the **MFCC**, the **mel frequency cepstral coefficients**. These are based on the important idea of the **cepstrum**. We describe at a relatively high-level the process of extraction of MFCCs from a waveform; we strongly encourage students interested in more detail to follow up with a speech signal processing course.

Sampling
Sampling rate

We begin by repeating from Section 7.4.2 the process of digitizing and quantizing an analog speech waveform. Recall that the first step in processing speech is to convert the analog representations (first air pressure and then analog electric signals in a microphone) into a digital signal. This process of **analog-to-digital conversion** has two steps: **sampling** and **quantization**. A signal is sampled by measuring its amplitude at a particular time; the **sampling rate** is the number of samples taken per second. To accurately measure a wave, we must have at least two samples in each cycle: one measuring the positive part of the wave and one measuring the negative part. More than two samples per cycle increases the amplitude accuracy, but less than two samples will cause the frequency of the wave to be completely missed. Thus, the maximum frequency wave that can be measured is one whose frequency is half the sample rate (since every cycle needs two samples). This maximum frequency for a given sampling rate is called the **Nyquist frequency**. Most information in human speech is in frequencies below 10,000 Hz, so a 20,000 Hz sampling rate would be necessary for complete accuracy. But telephone speech is filtered by the switching network, and only frequencies less than 4,000 Hz are transmitted by telephones. Thus, an 8,000 Hz sampling rate is sufficient for **telephone-bandwidth** speech like the Switchboard corpus. A 16,000 Hz sampling rate (sometimes called **wideband**) is often used for microphone speech.

Nyquist frequency

*Telephone-
bandwidth*
Wideband

Even an 8,000 Hz sampling rate requires 8,000 amplitude measurements for each second of speech, so it is important to store amplitude measurements efficiently. They are usually stored as integers, either 8 bit (values from -128–127) or 16 bit (values from -32768–32767). This process of representing real-valued numbers as integers is called **quantization** because there is a minimum granularity (the quantum size) and all values that are closer together than this quantum size are represented identically.

Quantization

We refer to each sample in the digitized, quantized waveform as $x[n]$, where n is an index over time. Now that we have a digitized, quantized representation of the waveform, we are ready to extract MFCC features. The seven steps of this process are shown in Fig. 9.8 and individually described in each of the following sections.

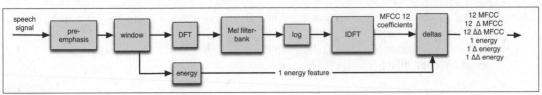

Figure 9.8   Extracting a sequence of 39-dimensional MFCC feature vectors from a digitized waveform.

9.3.1   Preemphasis

The first stage in MFCC feature extraction is to boost the amount of energy in the high frequencies. It turns out that if we look at the spectrum for voiced segments like vowels, there is more energy at the lower frequencies than at the higher frequencies. This drop

Spectral tilt   in energy across frequencies (which is called **spectral tilt**) is caused by the nature of the glottal pulse. Boosting the high frequency energy makes information from these higher formants more available to the acoustic model and improves phone detection accuracy.

This preemphasis is done with a filter.[1] Figure 9.9 shows an example of a spectral slice from the first author's pronunciation of the single vowel [aa] before and after preemphasis.

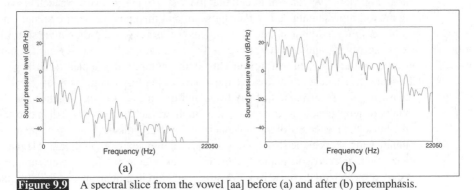

Figure 9.9   A spectral slice from the vowel [aa] before (a) and after (b) preemphasis.

9.3.2   Windowing

Recall that the goal of feature extraction is to provide spectral features that can help us build phone or subphone classifiers. We therefore don't want to extract our spectral features from an entire utterance or conversation, because the spectrum changes very

Non-stationary   quickly. Technically, we say that speech is a **non-stationary** signal, meaning that its statistical properties are not constant over time. Instead, we want to extract spectral features from a small **window** of speech that characterizes a particular subphone and

Stationary   for which we can make the (rough) assumption that the signal is **stationary** (that is, its statistical properties are constant within this region).

---

[1] For students who have had signal processing: this preemphasis filter is a first-order high-pass filter. In the time domain, with input $x[n]$ and $0.9 \leq \alpha \leq 1.0$, the filter equation is $y[n] = x[n] - \alpha x[n-1]$.

We extract this roughly stationary portion of speech by using a window which is non-zero inside some region and zero elsewhere, running this window across the speech signal and extracting the waveform inside this window.

We can characterize such a windowing process by three parameters: the **width** is the window (in milliseconds), the **offset** between successive windows, and the **shape** of the window. We call the speech extracted from each window a **frame**, we call the number of milliseconds in the frame the **frame size** and we call the number of milliseconds between the left edges of successive windows the **frame shift**.

Frame
Frame size
Frame shift

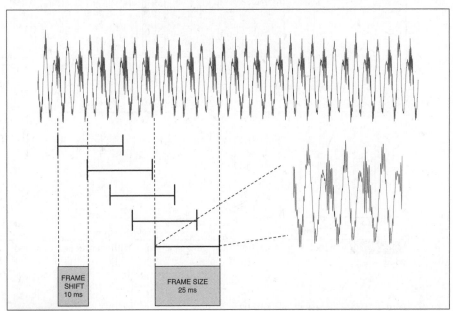

FRAME
SHIFT
10 ms

FRAME SIZE
25 ms

Figure 9.10   The windowing process, showing the frame shift and frame size, assuming a frame shift of 10 ms, a frame size of 25 ms, and a rectangular window.

To extract the signal we multiply the value of the signal at time n, $s[n]$ by the value of the window at time n, $w[n]$:

$$y[n] = w[n]s[n] \qquad (9.9)$$

Figure 9.10 suggests that these window shapes are rectangular since the extracted windowed signal looks just like the original signal. Indeed, the simplest window is the **rectangular** window. The rectangular window can cause problems, however, because it abruptly cuts off the signal at its boundaries. These discontinuities create problems when we do Fourier analysis. For this reason, a more common window used in MFCC extraction is the **Hamming** window, which shrinks the values of the signal toward zero at the window boundaries, avoiding discontinuities. Figure 9.11 shows both of these windows; the equations are as follows (assuming a window that is L frames long):

Rectangular

Hamming

$$rectangular \qquad w[n] = \begin{cases} 1 & 0 \le n \le L-1 \\ 0 & \text{otherwise} \end{cases} \qquad (9.10)$$

303

$$Hamming \quad w[n] \;=\; \begin{cases} 0.54 - 0.46\cos\left(\frac{2\pi n}{L}\right) & 0 \le n \le L-1 \\ 0 & \text{otherwise} \end{cases} \quad (9.11)$$

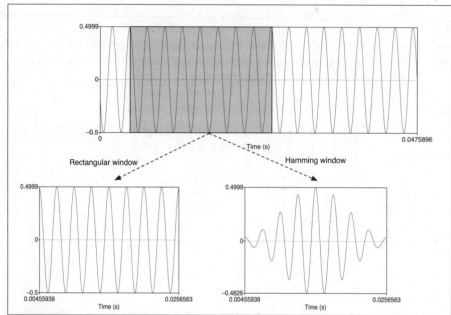

Figure 9.11   Windowing a portion of a pure sine wave with the rectangular and Hamming windows.

9.3.3   Discrete Fourier Transform

The next step is to extract spectral information for our windowed signal; we need to know how much energy the signal contains at different frequency bands. The tool for extracting spectral information for discrete frequency bands for a discrete-time (sampled) signal is the **discrete Fourier transform** or **DFT**.

Discrete Fourier transform
DFT

The input to the DFT is a windowed signal $x[n]...x[m]$, and the output, for each of N discrete frequency bands, is a complex number $X[k]$ representing the magnitude and phase of that frequency component in the original signal. If we plot the magnitude against the frequency, we can visualize the **spectrum** that we introduced in Chapter 7. For example, Fig. 9.12 shows a 25 ms Hamming-windowed portion of a signal and its spectrum as computed by a DFT (with some additional smoothing).

We do not introduce the mathematical details of the DFT here, except to note that Fourier analysis in general relies on **Euler's formula**, with j as the imaginary unit:

Euler's formula

$$e^{j\theta} = \cos\theta + j\sin\theta \qquad (9.12)$$

As a brief reminder for those students who have already studied signal processing, the DFT is defined as follows:

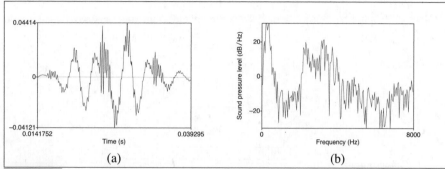

Figure 9.12   (a) A 25 ms Hamming-windowed portion of a signal from the vowel [iy] and   (b) its spectrum computed by a DFT.

$$X[k] = \sum_{n=0}^{N-1} x[n] e^{-j\frac{2\pi}{N}kn} \qquad (9.13)$$

Fast Fourier transform

FFT

A commonly used algorithm for computing the DFT is the **fast Fourier transform** or **FFT**. This implementation of the DFT is very efficient but only works for values of *N* that are powers of 2.

9.3.4   Mel Filter Bank and Log

The results of the FFT will be information about the amount of energy at each frequency band. Human hearing, however, is not equally sensitive at all frequency bands. It is less sensitive at higher frequencies, roughly above 1000 hertz. It turns out that modeling this property of human hearing during feature extraction improves speech recognition performance. The form of the model used in MFCCs is to warp the frequencies output by the DFT onto the **mel** scale mentioned in Chapter 7. A **mel** (Stevens *Mel* et al., 1937; Stevens and Volkmann, 1940) is a unit of pitch. By definition, pairs of sounds that are perceptually equidistant in pitch are separated by an equal number of mels. The mapping between frequency in hertz and the mel scale is linear below 1000 Hz and logarithmic above 1000 Hz. The mel frequency *m* can be computed from the raw acoustic frequency as follows:

$$mel(f) = 1127\ln(1 + \frac{f}{700}) \qquad (9.14)$$

During MFCC computation, we implement this intuition by creating a bank of filters that collect energy from each frequency band, with 10 filters spaced linearly below 1000 Hz and the remaining filters spread logarithmically above 1000 Hz. Figure 9.13 shows the bank of triangular filters that implement this idea.

Finally, we take the log of each of the mel spectrum values. In general, the human response to signal level is logarithmic; humans are less sensitive to slight differences in amplitude at high amplitudes than at low amplitudes. In addition, using a log makes the feature estimates less sensitive to variations in input such as power variations due to the speaker's mouth moving closer or further from the microphone.

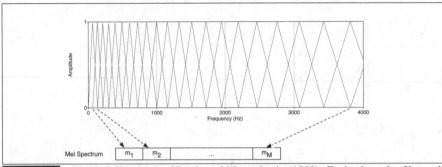

Figure 9.13 The mel filter bank of Davis and Mermelstein (1980). Each triangular filter collects energy from a given frequency range. Filters are spaced linearly below 1000 Hz and logarithmically above 1000 Hz.

9.3.5   The Cepstrum: Inverse Discrete Fourier Transform

While it would be possible to use the mel spectrum by itself as a feature representation for phone detection, the spectrum also has some problems, as we soon describe. For this reason, the next step in MFCC feature extraction is the computation of the *Cepstrum* **cepstrum**. The cepstrum has a number of useful processing advantages and also significantly improves phone recognition performance.

One way to think about the cepstrum is as a useful way of separating the **source** and **filter**. Recall from Section 7.4.6 that the speech waveform is created when a glottal source waveform of a particular fundamental frequency is passed through the vocal tract, which because of its shape has a particular filtering characteristic. But many characteristics of the glottal **source** (its fundamental frequency, the details of the glottal pulse, etc.) are not important for distinguishing different phones. Instead, the most useful information for phone detection is the **filter**, that is, the exact position of the vocal tract. If we knew the shape of the vocal tract, we would know which phone was being produced. This suggests that useful features for phone detection would find a way to deconvolve (separate) the source and filter and show us only the vocal tract filter. It turns out that the cepstrum is one way to do this.

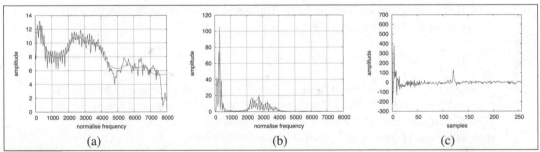

Figure 9.14 The magnitude spectrum (a), log magnitude spectrum (b), and cepstrum (c), from Taylor (2008), by permission. The two spectra have a smoothed spectral envelope laid on top to help visualize the spectrum.

For simplicity, let's ignore the preemphasis and mel warping that are part of the definition of MFCCs and look just at the basic definition of the cepstrum. The cepstrum can be thought of as the *spectrum of the log of the spectrum*. This may sound confusing. But let's begin with the easy part: the *log of the spectrum*. That is, the cepstrum begins with a standard magnitude spectrum, such as the one for a vowel shown in Fig. 9.14(a) from Taylor (2008). We then take the log, that is, replace each amplitude value in the magnitude spectrum with its log, as shown in Fig. 9.14(b).

The next step is to visualize the log spectrum *as if itself were a waveform*. In other words, consider the log spectrum in Fig. 9.14(b). Let's imagine removing the axis labels that tell us that this is a spectrum (frequency on the x-axis) and imagine that we are dealing with just a normal speech signal with time on the x-axis. What can we now say about the spectrum of this "pseudo-signal"? Notice that there is a high frequency repetitive component in this wave: small waves that repeat about 8 times in each 1000 along the x-axis, for a frequency of about 120 Hz. This high frequency component is caused by the fundamental frequency of the signal and represents the little peaks in the spectrum at each harmonic of the signal. In addition, there are some lower frequency components in this "pseudo-signal"; for example, the envelope or formant structure has about four large peaks in the window, for a much lower frequency.

Figure 9.14(c) shows the **cepstrum**: the spectrum that we have been describing of the log spectrum. This cepstrum (the word **cepstrum** is formed by reversing the first four letters of **spectrum**) is shown with **samples** along the x-axis. This is because by taking the spectrum of the log spectrum, we have left the frequency domain of the spectrum, and gone back to the time domain. It turns out that the correct unit of a cepstrum is the sample.

Examining this cepstrum, we see that there is indeed a large peak around 120, corresponding to the F0 and representing the glottal pulse. There are other various components at lower values on the x-axis. These represent the vocal tract filter (the position of the tongue and the other articulators). Thus, if we are interested in detecting phones, we can make use of just the lower cepstral values. If we are interested in detecting pitch, we can use the higher cepstral values.

For the purposes of MFCC extraction, we generally just take the first 12 cepstral values. These 12 coefficients will represent information solely about the vocal tract filter, cleanly separated from information about the glottal source.

It turns out that cepstral coefficients have the extremely useful property that the variance of the different coefficients tends to be uncorrelated. This is not true for the spectrum, where spectral coefficients at different frequency bands are correlated. The fact that cepstral features are uncorrelated means, as we show in the next section, that the Gaussian acoustic model (the Gaussian mixture model, or GMM) doesn't have to represent the covariance between all the MFCC features, which hugely reduces the number of parameters.

For those who have had signal processing, the cepstrum is more formally defined as the **inverse DFT of the log magnitude of the DFT of a signal**; hence, for a windowed frame of speech $x[n]$,

$$c[n] = \sum_{n=0}^{N-1} log \left(\left| \sum_{n=0}^{N-1} x[n] e^{-j\frac{2\pi}{N}kn} \right| \right) e^{j\frac{2\pi}{N}kn} \qquad (9.15)$$

9.3.6 Deltas and Energy

The extraction of the cepstrum with the inverse DFT from the previous section results in 12 cepstral coefficients for each frame. We next add a 13th feature: the energy from the frame. Energy correlates with phone identity and so is a useful cue for phone

Energy

detection (vowels and sibilants have more energy than stops, etc.). The **energy** in a frame is the sum over time of the power of the samples in the frame; thus, for a signal x in a window from time sample t_1 to time sample t_2, the energy is

$$Energy = \sum_{t=t_1}^{t_2} x^2[t] \tag{9.16}$$

Another important fact about the speech signal is that it is not constant from frame to frame. This change, such as the slope of a formant at its transitions, or the nature of the change from a stop closure to stop burst, can provide a useful cue for phone identity. For this reason, we also add features related to the change in cepstral features over time.

Delta feature

Double delta

We do this by adding for each of the 13 features (12 cepstral features plus energy) a **delta** or **velocity** feature and a **double delta** or **acceleration** feature. Each of the 13 delta features represents the change between frames in the corresponding cepstral/energy feature, and each of the 13 double delta features represents the change between frames in the corresponding delta features.

A simple way to compute deltas would be just to compute the difference between frames; thus the delta value $d(t)$ for a particular cepstral value $c(t)$ at time t can be estimated as

$$d(t) = \frac{c(t+1) - c(t-1)}{2} \tag{9.17}$$

Instead of this simple estimate, however, it is more common to make more sophisticated estimates of the slope, using a wider context of frames.

9.3.7 Summary: MFCC

After adding energy and then delta and double-delta features to the 12 cepstral features, we end up with 39 MFCC features:

12	cepstral coefficients
12	delta cepstral coefficients
12	double delta cepstral coefficients
1	energy coefficient
1	delta energy coefficient
1	double delta energy coefficient
39	MFCC features

Again, one of the most useful facts about MFCC features is that the cepstral coefficients tend to be uncorrelated, which turns out to make our acoustic model much simpler.

9.4 Acoustic Likelihood Computation

The last section showed how we can extract MFCC features representing spectral information from a wavefile and produce a 39-dimensional vector every 10 milliseconds. We are now ready to see how to compute the likelihood of these feature vectors given an HMM state. Recall from Chapter 6 that this output likelihood is computed by the B probability function of the HMM. Given an individual state q_i and an observation o_t, the observation likelihoods in B matrix gave us $p(o_t|q_i)$, which we called $b_t(i)$.

For part-of-speech tagging in Chapter 5, each observation o_t is a discrete symbol (a word), and we can compute the likelihood of an observation given a part-of-speech tag just by counting the number of times a given tag generates a given observation in the training set. But for speech recognition, MFCC vectors are real-valued numbers; we can't compute the likelihood of a given state (phone) generating an MFCC vector by counting the number of times each such vector occurs (since each one is likely to be unique).

In both decoding and training, we need an observation likelihood function that can compute $p(o_t|q_i)$ on real-valued observations. In decoding, we are given an observation o_t, and we need to produce the probability $p(o_t|q_i)$ for each possible HMM state so that we can choose the most likely sequence of states. Once we have this observation likelihood B function, we need to figure out how to modify the Baum-Welch algorithm of Chapter 6 to train it as part of training HMMs.

9.4.1 Vector Quantization

Vector quantization
VQ

One way to make MFCC vectors look like symbols we could count is to build a mapping function that maps each input vector into one of a small number of symbols. Then we could just compute probabilities on these symbols by counting, just as we did for words in part-of-speech tagging. This idea of mapping input vectors to discrete quantized symbols is called **vector quantization** or **VQ** (Gray, 1984). Although vector quantization is too simple to act as the acoustic model in modern LVCSR systems, it is a useful pedagogical step and plays an important role in various areas of ASR, so we use it to begin our discussion of acoustic modeling.

In vector quantization, we create the small symbol set by mapping each training feature vector into a small number of classes, and then we represent each class by a discrete symbol. More formally, a vector quantization system is characterized by a **codebook**, a **clustering algorithm**, and a **distance metric**.

Codebook
Prototype vector
Codeword

A **codebook** is a list of possible classes, a set of symbols constituting a vocabulary $V = v_1, v_2, ..., v_n$. For each symbol v_k in the codebook we list a **prototype vector**, also known as a **codeword**, which is a specific feature vector. For example, if we choose to use 256 codewords, we could represent each vector by a value from 0 to 255; (this is referred to as 8-bit VQ since we can represent each vector by a single 8-bit value). Each of these 256 values would be associated with a prototype feature vector.

Clustering

We create the codebook by using a **clustering** algorithm to cluster all the feature vectors in the training set into the 256 classes. Then we choose a representative feature vector from the cluster and make it the prototype vector or codeword for that cluster.

K-means clustering **K-means clustering** is often used, but we don't define clustering here; see Huang et al. (2001) or Duda et al. (2000) for detailed descriptions.

Once we've built the codebook, we compare each incoming feature vector to each of the 256 prototype vectors, select the prototype which is closest (by some **distance metric**), and replace the input vector by the index of this prototype vector. A schematic of this process is shown in Fig. 9.15.

The advantage of VQ is that since there are a finite number of classes, for each class v_k, we can compute the probability that it is generated by a given HMM state/subphone by simply counting the number of times it occurs in some training set when labeled by that state and normalizing.

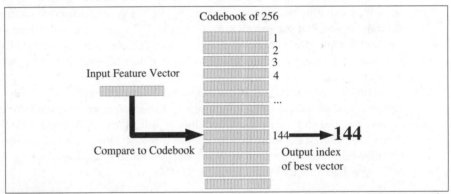

Figure 9.15 Schematic architecture of the (trained) vector quantization (VQ) process for choosing a symbol v_q for each input feature vector. The vector is compared to each codeword in the codebook, the closest entry (by some distance metric) is selected, and the index of the closest codeword is output.

Distance metric   Both the clustering process and the decoding process require a **distance metric** or **distortion** metric that specifies how similar two acoustic feature vectors are. The distance metric is used to build clusters, to find a prototype vector for each cluster, and to compare incoming vectors to the prototypes.

Euclidean distance   The simplest distance metric for acoustic feature vectors is **Euclidean distance**. Euclidean distance is the distance in N-dimensional space between the two points defined by the two vectors. We use the phrase "Euclidean distance" even though in practice we often mean the square of the Euclidean distance. Thus, given a vector x and a vector y of length D, the (square of the) Euclidean distance between them is defined as:

$$d_{\text{euclidean}}(x,y) = \sum_{i=1}^{D}(x_i - y_i)^2 \qquad (9.18)$$

The (squared) Euclidean distance described in Eq. 9.18) (and shown for two dimensions in Fig. 9.16) is also referred to as the sum-squared error and can also be expressed with the vector transpose operator as:

$$d_{\text{euclidean}}(x,y) = (x-y)^T(x-y) \qquad (9.19)$$

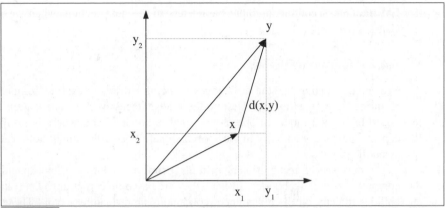

Figure 9.16   Euclidean distance in two dimensions; by the Pythagorean theorem, the distance between two points in a plane $x = (x1, y1)$ and $y = (x2, y2)$ $d(x,y) = \sqrt{(x_1 - x_2)^2 + (y_1 - y_2)^2}$.

The Euclidean distance metric assumes that each of the dimensions of a feature vector are equally important. But actually, each dimension has a different variance. If a dimension tends to have a lot of variance, then we'd like it to count less in the distance metric; a large difference in a dimension with low variance should count more than a large difference in a dimension with high variance. A slightly more complex distance metric, the **Mahalanobis distance**, takes into account the different variances of each of the dimensions.

Mahalanobis distance

If we assume that each dimension i of the acoustic feature vectors has a variance σ_i^2, then the Mahalanobis distance is

$$d_{\text{mahalanobis}}(x,y) = \sum_{i=1}^{D} \frac{(x_i - y_i)^2}{\sigma_i^2} \tag{9.20}$$

For those readers with more background in linear algebra here's the general form of Mahalanobis distance, which includes a full covariance matrix (covariance matrices are defined below):

$$d_{\text{mahalanobis}}(x,y) = (x-y)^T \Sigma^{-1} (x-y) \tag{9.21}$$

In summary, when decoding a speech signal, to compute an acoustic likelihood of a feature vector o_t given an HMM state q_j using VQ, we compute the Euclidean or Mahalanobis distance between the feature vector and each of the N codewords, choose the closest codeword, getting the codeword index v_k. We then look up the likelihood of the codeword index v_k given the HMM state j in the precomputed B likelihood matrix defined by the HMM:

$$\hat{b}_j(o_t) = b_j(v_k) \text{ s.t. } v_k \text{ is codeword of closest vector to } o_t \tag{9.22}$$

Since VQ is so rarely used, we don't use up space here giving the equations for modifying the EM algorithm to deal with VQ data; instead, we defer discussion of

EM training of continuous input parameters to the next section, when we introduce Gaussians.

9.4.2   Gaussian PDFs

Vector quantization has the advantages of being extremely easy to compute and of requiring very little storage. Despite these advantages, vector quantization turns out not to be a good model of speech. A small number of codewords is insufficient to capture the wide variability in the speech signal. Speech is simply not a categorical, symbolic process.

Probability density function

Modern speech recognition algorithms therefore do not use vector quantization to compute acoustic likelihoods. Instead, they are based on computing observation probabilities directly on the real-valued, continuous input feature vector. These acoustic models are based on the computation of a **probability density function** or **pdf** over a continuous space. By far the most common method for computing acoustic likelihoods is the **Gaussian mixture model (GMM)** pdfs, although neural networks, support vector machines (SVMs), and conditional random fields (CRFs), are also used.

Gaussian mixture model
GMM

Let's begin with the simplest use of Gaussian probability estimators, slowly building up to the more sophisticated models that are used.

Univariate Gaussians

Gaussian
Normal distribution
Mean

The **Gaussian** distribution, also known as the **normal distribution**, is the bell-curve function familiar from basic statistics. A Gaussian distribution is a function parameterized by a **mean**, or average value, and a **variance**, as shown in Fig. 9.17, which characterizes the average spread or dispersal from the mean. We will use μ to indicate the mean and σ^2 to indicate the variance, giving the following formula for a Gaussian function:

Variance

$$f(x\,\mu,\sigma) = \frac{1}{\sqrt{2\pi\sigma^2}} exp(-\frac{(x-\mu)^2}{2\sigma^2}) \tag{9.23}$$

Recall from basic statistics that the mean of a random variable X is the expected value of X. For a discrete variable X, this is the weighted sum over the values of X (for a continuous variable, it is the integral):

$$\mu = E(X) = \sum_{i=1}^{N} p(X_i)X_i \tag{9.24}$$

The variance of a random variable X is the weighted squared average deviation from the mean:

$$\sigma^2 = E(X_i - E(X))^2 = \sum_{i=1}^{N} p(X_i)(X_i - E(X))^2 \tag{9.25}$$

When a Gaussian function is used as a probability density function, the area under the curve is constrained to be equal to 1. We can then compute the probability that a

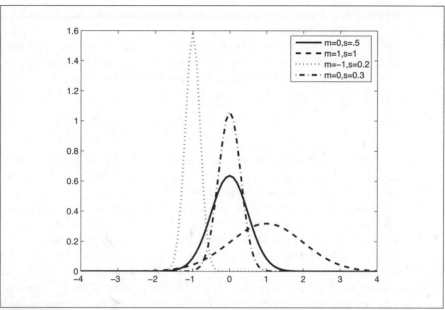

Figure 9.17   Gaussian functions with different means and variances.

random variable takes on any particular range of values by summing the area under the curve for that range of values. Figure 9.18 shows the probability expressed by the area under an interval of a Gaussian.

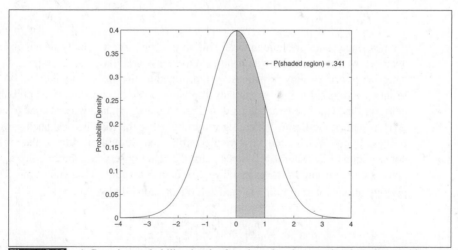

Figure 9.18   A Gaussian probability density function, showing a region from 0 to 1 with a total probability of .341. Thus for this sample Gaussian, the probability that a value on the X axis lies between 0 and 1 is .341.

We can use a univariate Gaussian pdf to estimate the probability that a particular HMM state j generates the value of a single dimension of a feature vector by assuming that the possible values of (this one dimension of the) observation feature vector o_t are normally distributed. In other words, we represent the observation likelihood function $b_j(o_t)$ for one dimension of the acoustic vector as a Gaussian. Taking, for the moment, our observation as a single real-valued number (a single cepstral feature) and assuming that each HMM state j has associated with it a mean value μ_j and variance σ_j^2, we compute the likelihood $b_j(o_t)$ using the equation for a Gaussian pdf:

$$b_j(o_t) = \frac{1}{\sqrt{2\pi\sigma_j^2}} exp\left(-\frac{(o_t - \mu_j)^2}{2\sigma_j^2}\right) \tag{9.26}$$

Equation 9.26 shows us how to compute $b_j(o_t)$, the likelihood of an individual acoustic observation given a single univariate Gaussian from state j with its mean and variance. We can now use this probability in HMM decoding.

But first we need to solve the training problem: how do we compute this mean and variance of the Gaussian for each HMM state q_i? Let's start by imagining the simpler situation of a completely labeled training set, in which each acoustic observation was labeled with the HMM state that produced it. In such a training set, we could compute the mean of each state by just taking the average of the values for each o_t that corresponded to state i, as shown in Eq. 9.27. The variance could just be computed from the sum-squared error between each observation and the mean, as shown in Eq. 9.28.

$$\hat{\mu}_i = \frac{1}{T}\sum_{t=1}^{T} o_t \text{ s.t. } q_t \text{ is state } i \tag{9.27}$$

$$\hat{\sigma}_j^2 = \frac{1}{T}\sum_{t=1}^{T} (o_t - \mu_i)^2 \text{ s.t. } q_t \text{ is state } i \tag{9.28}$$

But since states are hidden in an HMM, we don't know exactly which observation vector o_t was produced by which state. What we would like to do is assign each observation vector o_t to every possible state i, prorated by the probability that the HMM was in state i at time t. Luckily, we already know how to do this prorating; the probability of being in state i at time t was defined in Chapter 6 as $\xi_t(i)$, and we saw how to compute $\xi_t(i)$ as part of the Baum-Welch algorithm by using the forward and backward probabilities. Baum-Welch is an iterative algorithm, and we will need to do the probability computation of $\xi_t(i)$ iteratively since getting a better observation probability b will also help us be more sure of the probability ξ of being in a state at a certain time. Thus, we give equations for computing an updated mean and variance $\hat{\mu}$ and $\hat{\sigma^2}$:

$$\hat{\mu}_i = \frac{\sum_{t=1}^{T} \xi_t(i)o_t}{\sum_{t=1}^{T} \xi_t(i)} \tag{9.29}$$

$$\hat{\sigma}_i^2 = \frac{\sum_{t=1}^{T} \xi_t(i)(o_t - \mu_i)^2}{\sum_{t=1}^{T} \xi_t(i)} \tag{9.30}$$

Equations 9.29 and 9.30 are then used in the forward-backward (Baum-Welch) training of the HMM. As we show, the values of μ_i and σ_i are first set to some initial estimate, which is then re-estimated until the numbers converge.

Multivariate Gaussians

Equation 9.26 shows how to use a Gaussian to compute an acoustic likelihood for a single cepstral feature. Since an acoustic observation is a vector of 39 features, we'll need to use a multivariate Gaussian, which allows us to assign a probability to a 39-valued vector. Where a univariate Gaussian is defined by a mean μ and a variance σ^2, a multivariate Gaussian is defined by a mean vector $\vec{\mu}$ of dimensionality D and a covariance matrix Σ, defined below. As we discussed in the previous section, for a typical cepstral feature vector in LVCSR, D is 39.

$$f(\vec{x}\,\vec{\mu},\Sigma) = \frac{1}{(2\pi)^{\frac{D}{2}}\,\Sigma^{\frac{1}{2}}}\exp\left(-\frac{1}{2}(x-\mu)^{\mathrm{T}}\Sigma^{-1}(x-\mu)\right) \qquad (9.31)$$

The covariance matrix Σ captures the variance of each dimension as well as the covariance between any two dimensions.

Recall again from basic statistics that the covariance of two random variables X and Y is the expected value of the product of their average deviations from the mean:

$$\Sigma = E[(X-E(X))(Y-E(Y))] = \sum_{i=1}^{N}p(X_iY_i)(X_i-E(X))(Y_i-E(Y)) \qquad (9.32)$$

Thus, for a given HMM state with mean vector μ_j and covariance matrix Σ_j, and a given observation vector o_t, the multivariate Gaussian probability estimate is

$$b_j(o_t) = \frac{1}{(2\pi)^{\frac{D}{2}}\,\Sigma^{\frac{1}{2}}}\exp\left(-\frac{1}{2}(o_t-\mu_j)^{T}\Sigma_j^{-1}(o_t-\mu_j)\right) \qquad (9.33)$$

The covariance matrix Σ_j expresses the variance between each pair of feature dimensions. Suppose we made the simplifying assumption that features in different dimensions did not covary, that is, that there was no correlation between the variances of different dimensions of the feature vector. In this case, we could simply keep a distinct variance for each feature dimension. It turns out that keeping a separate variance for each dimension is equivalent to having a covariance matrix that is **diagonal**, that is, non-zero elements only appear along the main diagonal of the matrix. The main diagonal of such a diagonal covariance matrix contains the variances of each dimension, $\sigma_1^2, \sigma_2^2, \ldots \sigma_D^2$.

Diagonal

Let's look at some illustrations of multivariate Gaussians, focusing on the role of the full versus diagonal covariance matrix. We'll explore a simple multivariate Gaussian with only 2 dimensions, rather than the 39 that are typical in ASR. Figure 9.19 shows three different multivariate Gaussians in two dimensions. The leftmost figure shows a Gaussian with a diagonal covariance matrix, in which the variances of the two dimensions are equal. Figure 9.20 shows three contour plots corresponding to the Gaussians in Fig. 9.19; each is a slice through the Gaussian. The leftmost graph in Fig. 9.20 shows a slice through the diagonal equal-variance Gaussian. The slice is circular, since the variances are equal in both the X and Y directions.

The middle figure in Fig. 9.19 shows a Gaussian with a diagonal covariance matrix, but with unequal variances. It is clear from this figure, and especially from the contour slice shown in Fig. 9.20, that the variance is more than three times greater in one dimension than the other.

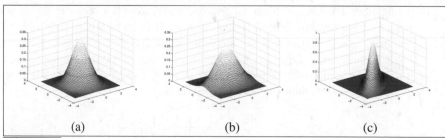

(a)   (b)   (c)

Figure 9.19   Three different multivariate Gaussians in two dimensions. The first two have diagonal covariance matrices, one with equal variance in the two dimensions $\begin{bmatrix} 1 & 0 \\ 0 & 1 \end{bmatrix}$ the second with different variances in the two dimensions, $\begin{bmatrix} .6 & 0 \\ 0 & 2 \end{bmatrix}$, and the third with non-zero elements in the off-diagonal of the covariance matrix: $\begin{bmatrix} 1 & .8 \\ .8 & 1 \end{bmatrix}$.

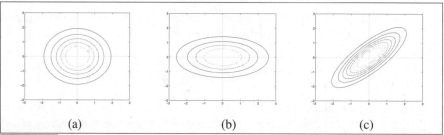

(a)   (b)   (c)

Figure 9.20   The same three multivariate Gaussians as in the previous figure. From left to right, a diagonal-covariance matrix with equal variance, diagonal with unequal variance, and non-diagonal covariance. With non-diagonal covariance, knowing the value on dimension X tells us something about the value on dimension Y.

The rightmost graph in Fig. 9.19 and Fig. 9.20 shows a Gaussian with a non-diagonal covariance matrix. Notice in the contour plot in Fig. 9.20 that the contour is not lined up with the two axes, as it is in the other two plots. Because of this, knowing the value in one dimension can help in predicting the value in the other dimension. Thus, having a non-diagonal covariance matrix allows us to model correlations between the values of the features in multiple dimensions.

A Gaussian with a full covariance matrix is thus a more powerful model of acoustic likelihood than one with a diagonal covariance matrix. And indeed, speech recognition performance is better using full-covariance Gaussians than diagonal-covariance Gaussians. But two problems with full-covariance Gaussians make them difficult to use in practice. First, they are slow to compute. A full-covariance matrix has D^2 parameters, whereas a diagonal-covariance matrix has only D. This makes a large difference in speed in real ASR systems. Second, a full-covariance matrix has many more parameters and hence requires much more data to train than does a diagonal-covariance matrix. Using a diagonal-covariance model means we can save our parameters for other things like the triphones (context-dependent phones) introduced in Section 10.3.

For this reason, most ASR systems use diagonal covariance in practice. We assume diagonal covariance for the remainder of this section.

Equation 9.33 can thus be simplified to the version in Eq. 9.34 in which instead of a covariance matrix, we simply keep a mean and variance for each dimension. Equation 9.34 thus describes how to estimate the likelihood $b_j(o_t)$ of a D-dimensional feature vector o_t given HMM state j, using a diagonal-covariance multivariate Gaussian.

$$b_j(o_t) = \prod_{d=1}^{D} \frac{1}{\sqrt{2\pi\sigma_{jd}^2}} exp\left(-\frac{1}{2}[\frac{(o_{td} - \mu_{jd})^2}{\sigma_{jd}^2}]\right) \tag{9.34}$$

Training a diagonal-covariance multivariate Gaussian is a simple generalization of training univariate Gaussians. We'll do the same Baum-Welch training, where we use the value of $\xi_t(i)$ to tell us the likelihood of being in state i at time t. Indeed, we'll use exactly the same equation as in Eq. 9.30, except that now we are dealing with vectors instead of scalars; the observation o_t is a vector of cepstral features, the mean vector $\vec{\mu}$ is a vector of cepstral means, and the variance vector $\vec{\sigma_i^2}$ is a vector of cepstral variances.

$$\hat{\mu}_i = \frac{\sum_{t=1}^{T} \xi_t(i)o_t}{\sum_{t=1}^{T} \xi_t(i)} \tag{9.35}$$

$$\hat{\sigma}_i^2 = \frac{\sum_{t=1}^{T} \xi_t(i)(o_t - \mu_i)(o_t - \mu_i)^T}{\sum_{t=1}^{T} \xi_t(i)} \tag{9.36}$$

Gaussian Mixture Models

The previous subsection showed that we can use a multivariate Gaussian model to assign a likelihood score to an acoustic feature vector observation. This models each dimension of the feature vector as a normal distribution. But a particular cepstral feature might have a very non-normal distribution; the assumption of a normal distribution may be too strong an assumption. For this reason, we often model the observation likelihood not with a single multivariate Gaussian, but with a weighted mixture of multivariate Gaussians. Such a model is called a **Gaussian mixture model** or **GMM**. Equation 9.37 shows the equation for the GMM function; the resulting function is the sum of M Gaussians. Figure 9.21 shows an intuition of how a mixture of Gaussians can model arbitrary functions.

Gaussian mixture model
GMM

$$f(x \mu, \Sigma) = \sum_{k=1}^{M} c_k \frac{1}{\sqrt{2\pi \Sigma_k}} exp[(x - \mu_k)^T \Sigma^{-1}(x - \mu_k)] \tag{9.37}$$

Equation 9.38 shows the definition of the output likelihood function $b_j(o_t)$.

$$b_j(o_t) = \sum_{m=1}^{M} c_{jm} \frac{1}{\sqrt{2\pi \Sigma_{jm}}} exp[(x - \mu_{jm})^T \Sigma_{jm}^{-1}(o_t - \mu_{jm})] \tag{9.38}$$

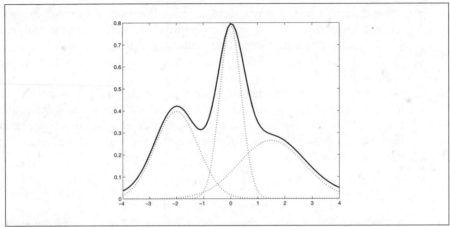

Figure 9.21   An arbitrary function approximated by a mixture of three Gaussians.

Let's turn to training the GMM likelihood function. This may seem hard to do; how can we train a GMM model if we don't know in advance which mixture is supposed to account for which part of each distribution? Recall that we could train a single multivariate Gaussian even if we didn't know which state accounted for each output, simply by using the Baum-Welch algorithm to tell us the likelihood of being in each state j at time t. It turns out the same trick will work for GMMs; we can use Baum-Welch to tell us the probability of a certain mixture accounting for the observation and iteratively update this probability.

We used the ξ function above to help us compute the state probability. By analogy with this function, let's define $\xi_{tm}(j)$ to mean the probability of being in state j at time t with the mth mixture component accounting for the output observation o_t. We can compute $\xi_{tm}(j)$ as follows:

$$\xi_{tm}(j) = \frac{\sum_{i=1} N \alpha_{t-1}(j) a_{ij} c_{jm} b_{jm}(o_t) \beta_t(j)}{\alpha_T(F)} \tag{9.39}$$

Now if we had the values of ξ from a previous iteration of Baum-Welch, we can use $\xi_{tm}(j)$ to recompute the mean, mixture weight, and covariance, using the following equations:

$$\hat{\mu}_{im} = \frac{\sum_{t=1}^{T} \xi_{tm}(i) o_t}{\sum_{t=1}^{T} \sum_{m=1}^{M} \xi_{tm}(i)} \tag{9.40}$$

$$\hat{c}_{im} = \frac{\sum_{t=1}^{T} \xi_{tm}(i)}{\sum_{t=1}^{T} \sum_{k=1}^{M} \xi_{tk}(i)} \tag{9.41}$$

$$\hat{\Sigma}_{im} = \frac{\sum_{t=1}^{T} \xi_t(i)(o_t - \mu_{im})(o_t - \mu_{im})^T}{\sum_{t=1}^{T} \sum_{k=1}^{M} \xi_{tm}(i)} \tag{9.42}$$

9.4.3   Probabilities, Log-Probabilities, and Distance Functions

Logprob

Up to now, all the equations we have given for acoustic modeling have used probabilities. It turns out, however, that a **log-probability** (or **logprob**) is much easier to work with than a probability. Thus, in practice throughout speech recognition (and related fields) we compute log-probabilities rather than probabilities.

One major reason that we can't use probabilities is numeric underflow. To compute a likelihood for a whole sentence, say, we are multiplying many small probability values, one for each 10 ms frame. Multiplying many probabilities results in smaller and smaller numbers, leading to underflow. The log of a small number like $.00000001 = 10^{-8}$, on the other hand, is a nice, easy-to-work-with number like -8. A second reason to use log probabilities is computational speed. Instead of multiplying probabilities, we add log-probabilities, and adding is faster than multiplying. Log-probabilities are particularly efficient when we are using Gaussian models since we can avoid exponentiating.

Thus, for example, for a single multivariate diagonal-covariance Gaussian model, instead of computing

$$b_j(o_t) = \prod_{d=1}^{D} \frac{1}{\sqrt{2\pi\sigma_{jd}^2}} exp\left(-\frac{1}{2}\frac{(o_{td}-\mu_{jd})^2}{\sigma_{jd}^2}\right) \tag{9.43}$$

we would compute

$$\log b_j(o_t) = -\frac{1}{2}\sum_{d=1}^{D}\left[log(2\pi) + \sigma_{jd}^2 + \frac{(o_{td}-\mu_{jd})^2}{\sigma_{jd}^2}\right] \tag{9.44}$$

With some rearrangement of terms, we can rewrite to pull out a constant C:

$$\log b_j(o_t) = C - \frac{1}{2}\sum_{d=1}^{D}\frac{(o_{td}-\mu_{jd})^2}{\sigma_{jd}^2} \tag{9.45}$$

where C can be precomputed:

$$C = -\frac{1}{2}\sum_{d=1}^{D}\left(\log(2\pi) + \sigma_{jd}^2\right) \tag{9.46}$$

In summary, computing acoustic models in the log domain means a much simpler computation, much of which can be precomputed for speed.

The perceptive reader may have noticed that Eq. 9.45 looks very much like the equation for Mahalanobis distance Eq. 9.20. Indeed, one way to think about a Gaussian logprob is as just a weighted distance metric.

A further point about Gaussian pdfs for those readers familiar with calculus. Although the equations for observation likelihood such as Eq. 9.26 are motivated by the use of Gaussian probability density functions, the values they return for the observation likelihood, $b_j(o_t)$, are not technically probabilities; they may in fact be greater than 1.

This is because we are computing the value of $b_j(o_t)$ at a single point, rather than integrating over a region. While the total area under the Gaussian pdf curve is constrained to 1, the actual value at any point could be greater than 1. (Imagine a very tall skinny Gaussian; the value could be greater than one at the center, although the area under the curve is still 1.0). If we were integrating over a region, we would be multiplying each point by its width dx, which would bring the value down below 1. The fact that the Gaussian estimate is not a true probability doesn't matter for choosing the most likely HMM state, since we are comparing different Gaussians, each of which is missing this dx factor.

In summary, the last few subsections introduced Gaussian models for acoustic training in speech recognition. Beginning with simple univariate Gaussian, we extended first to multivariate Gaussians to deal with the multidimensional acoustic feature vectors. We then introduced the diagonal covariance simplification of Gaussians and then introduced Gaussians mixtures (GMMs).

9.5   The Lexicon and Language Model

Since previous chapters contained extensive discussions of the N-gram language model (Chapter 4) and the pronunciation lexicon (Chapter 7), in this section we just briefly recall them to the reader.

Language models for LVCSR tend to be trigrams or even 4-grams; good toolkits are available to build and manipulate them (Stolcke, 2002; Young et al., 2005). Bigrams and unigram grammars are rarely used for large-vocabulary applications. Since trigrams require huge amounts of space, however, language models for applications like cell phones with tight memory constraints tend to use smaller contexts (or use compression techniques). As we will discuss in Chapter 24, some simple dialogue applications take advantage of their limited domain to use very simple finite-state or weighted finite-state grammars.

Lexicons are simply lists of words, with a pronunciation for each word expressed as a phone sequence. Publicly available lexicons like the CMU dictionary (CMU, 1993) can be used to extract the 60,000 word vocabularies commonly used for LVCSR. Most words have a single pronunciation, although some words such as homonyms and frequent function words may have more; the average number of pronunciations per word in most LVCSR systems seems to range from 1 to 2.5. Section 10.5.3 discusses the issue of pronunciation modeling.

9.6   Search and Decoding

We are now very close to having described all the parts of a complete speech recognizer. We have shown how to extract cepstral features for a frame and how to compute the acoustic likelihood $b_j(o_t)$ for that frame. We also know how to represent lexical knowledge, that each word HMM is composed of a sequence of phone models, and each phone model is composed of a set of subphone states. Finally, in Chapter 4 we showed how to use N-grams to build a model of word predictability.

Decoding

In this section we show how to combine all this knowledge to solve the problem of **decoding**: combining all these probability estimators to produce the most probable string of words. We can phrase the decoding question as "Given a string of acoustic observations, how should we choose the string of words that has the highest posterior probability?"

Recall from the beginning of the chapter the noisy-channel model for speech recognition. In this model, we use Bayes' rule, with the result that the best sequence of words is the one that maximizes the product of two factors, a language model prior and an acoustic likelihood:

$$\hat{W} = \underset{W \in \mathscr{L}}{\mathrm{argmax}} \; \overbrace{P(O\,W)}^{\text{likelihood}} \; \overbrace{P(W)}^{\text{prior}} \tag{9.47}$$

Now that we have defined both the acoustic model and language model we are ready to see how to find this maximum probability sequence of words. First, though, it turns out that we need to modify Eq. 9.47 because it relies on some incorrect independence assumptions. Recall that we trained a multivariate Gaussian mixture classifier to compute the likelihood of a particular acoustic observation (a frame) given a particular state (subphone). By computing separate classifiers for each acoustic frame and multiplying these probabilities to get the probability of the whole word, we are severely underestimating the probability of each subphone. This is because there is a lot of continuity across frames; if we were to take into account the acoustic context, we would have a greater expectation for a given frame and hence could assign it a higher probability. We must therefore reweight the two probabilities. We do this by adding

LMSF

in a **language model scaling factor** or **LMSF**, also called the **language weight**. This factor is an exponent on the language model probability $P(W)$. Because $P(W)$ is less than 1 and the LMSF is greater than 1 (between 5 and 15, in many systems), this has the effect of decreasing the value of the LM probability:

$$\hat{W} = \underset{W \in \mathscr{L}}{\mathrm{argmax}} \, P(O\,W)P(W)^{LMSF} \tag{9.48}$$

Reweighting the language model probability $P(W)$ in this way requires us to make one more change. This is because $P(W)$ has a side effect as a penalty for inserting words. It's simplest to see this in the case of a uniform language model, in which every word in a vocabulary of size V has an equal probability $\frac{1}{V}$. In this case, a sentence with N words will have a language model probability of $\frac{1}{V}$ for each of the N words, for a total penalty of $\frac{N}{V}$. The larger N is (the more words in the sentence), the more times this $\frac{1}{V}$ penalty multiplier is taken and the less probable the sentence will be. Thus, if (on average) the language model probability decreases (causing a larger penalty), the decoder will prefer fewer longer words. If the language model probability increases (larger penalty), the decoder will prefer more shorter words. Thus, our use of the LMSF to balance the acoustic model has the side effect of decreasing the word

Word insertion penalty insertion penalty. To offset this, we need to add back in a separate **word insertion penalty**:

$$\hat{W} = \underset{W \in \mathscr{L}}{\operatorname{argmax}} P(O \mid W) P(W)^{LMSF} WIP^N \tag{9.49}$$

Since in practice we use logprobs, the goal of our decoder is

$$\hat{W} = \underset{W \in \mathscr{L}}{\operatorname{argmax}} \log P(O \mid W) + LMSF \quad \log P(W) + N \quad \log WIP \tag{9.50}$$

Now that we have an equation to maximize, let's look at how to decode. It's the job of a decoder to simultaneously segment the utterance into words and identify each of these words. This task is made difficult by variation, both in terms of how words are pronounced in terms of phones and how phones are articulated in acoustic features. Just for an intuition of the difficulty of the problem, imagine a massively simplified version of the speech recognition task, in which the decoder is given a series of discrete phones. In such a case, we would know what each phone was with perfect accuracy, and yet decoding is still difficult. For example, try to decode the following sentence from the (hand-labeled) sequence of phones from the Switchboard corpus (don't peek ahead!):

[ay d ih s hh er d s ah m th ih ng ax b aw m uh v ih ng r ih s en l ih]

The answer is in the footnote.[2] The task is hard partly because of coarticulation and fast speech (e.g., [d] for the first phone of *just*). But it's also hard because speech, unlike English writing, has no spaces indicating word boundaries. The true decoding task, in which we have to identify the phones at the same time as we identify and segment the words is of course much harder.

For decoding, we start with the Viterbi algorithm that we introduced in Chapter 6, in the domain of **digit recognition**, a simple task with a vocabulary size of 11 (the numbers *one* through *nine* plus *zero* and *oh*).

Recall the basic components of an HMM model for speech recognition:

$Q = q_1 q_2 \ldots q_N$	a set of **states** corresponding to **subphones**.
$A = a_{01} a_{02} \ldots a_{n1} \ldots a_{nn}$	a **transition probability matrix** A, each a_{ij} representing the probability for each subphone of taking a **self-loop** or going to the next subphone. Together, Q and A implement a **pronunciation lexicon**, an HMM state graph structure for each word that the system is capable of recognizing.
$B = b_i(o_t)$	A set of **observation likelihoods**, also called **emission probabilities**, each expressing the probability of a cepstral feature vector (observation o_t) being generated from subphone state i.

The HMM structure for each word comes from a lexicon of word pronunciations. Generally, we use an off-the-shelf pronunciation dictionary such as the free CMUdict

---

2 I just heard something about moving recently.

dictionary described in Chapter 7. Recall from page 293 that the HMM structure for words in speech recognition is a simple concatenation of phone HMMs, each phone consisting of three subphone states, where every state has exactly two transitions: a self-loop and a loop to the next phones. Thus, we compute the HMM structure for each digit word in our digit recognizer simply by taking the phone string from the dictionary, expanding each phone into three subphones, and concatenating. In addition, we generally add an optional silence phone at the end of each word, allowing the possibility of pausing between words. We usually define the set of states Q from some version of the ARPAbet, augmented with silence phones and expanded to create three subphones for each phone.

The A and B matrices for the HMM are trained by the Baum-Welch algorithm in the **embedded training** procedure that we describe in Section 9.7. For now we'll assume that these probabilities have been trained.

Figure 9.22 shows the resulting HMM for digit recognition. Note that we've added non-emitting start and end states, with transitions from the end of each word to the end state, and a transition from the end state back to the start state to allow for sequences of digits. Note also the optional silence phones at the end of each word.

Digit recognizers often don't use word probabilities, since in many digit situations (phone numbers or credit card numbers) each digit may have an equal probability of appearing. But we've included transition probabilities into each word in Fig. 9.22, mainly to show where such probabilities would be for other kinds of recognition tasks. As it happens, there are cases in which digit probabilities do matter, such as in addresses (which are often likely to end in 0 or 00) or in cultures in which some numbers are lucky and hence more frequent, such as the lucky number "8" in Chinese.

Now that we have an HMM, we can use the same Viterbi algorithm (for decoding) and forward algorithm (as part of training and also stack decoding) that we introduced in Chapter 6. Let's first see how to use the forward algorithm to generate $P(O \lambda)$, the likelihood of an observation sequence O given an HMM. For illustration we'll use a pretend HMM consisting only of the single word "five" instead of all 11 digits. To compute this likelihood, we need to sum over all possible sequences of states; assuming *five* has the states [f], [ay], and [v], a 10-observation sequence includes many sequences such as the following:

```
f  ay ay ay ay v  v  v  v  v
f  f  ay ay ay ay v  v  v  v
f  f  f  f  ay ay ay ay v  v
f  f  ay ay ay ay ay ay v  v
f  f  ay ay ay ay ay v  v  v
...
```

The forward algorithm efficiently sums over this large number of sequences in $O(N^2 T)$ time.

Let's quickly review the forward algorithm. It is a dynamic programming algorithm, that is, an algorithm that uses a table to store intermediate values as it builds up the probability of the observation sequence. The forward algorithm computes the observation probability by summing over the probabilities of all possible paths that could generate the observation sequence.

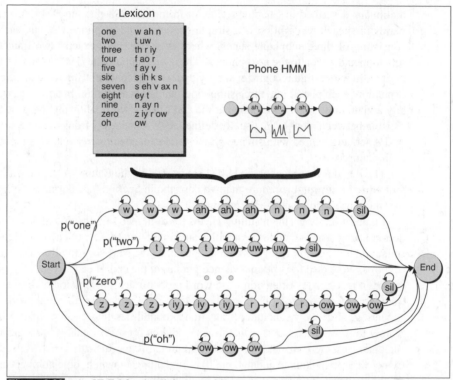

Figure 9.22   An HMM for the digit recognition task. A lexicon specifies the phone sequence, and each phone HMM is composed of three subphones, each with a Gaussian emission likelihood model. Combining these and adding an optional silence at the end of each word results in a single HMM for the whole task. Note the transition from the end state to the start state to allow digit sequences of arbitrary length.

Each cell of the forward algorithm trellis $\alpha_t(j)$ or *forward*$[t, j]$ represents the probability of being in state j after seeing the first t observations, given the automaton λ. We compute the value of each cell $\alpha_t(j)$ by summing over the probabilities of every path that could lead us to this cell. Formally, each cell expresses the following probability:

$$\alpha_t(j) = P(o_1, o_2 \ldots o_t, q_t = j \, \lambda) \tag{9.51}$$

Here $q_t = j$ means "the probability that the tth state in the sequence of states is state j". We compute this probability by summing over the extensions of all the paths that lead to the current cell. For a given state q_j at time t, the value $\alpha_t(j)$ is computed as

$$\alpha_t(j) = \sum_{i=1}^{N} \alpha_{t-1}(i) a_{ij} b_j(o_t) \tag{9.52}$$

The three factors that are multiplied in Eq˙ 9.52 in extending the previous paths to compute the forward probability at time t are

$\alpha_{t-1}(i)$ the **previous forward path probability** from the previous time step

a_{ij} the **transition probability** from previous state q_i to current state q_j

$b_j(o_t)$ the **state observation likelihood** of the observation symbol o_t given the current state j

The algorithm is described in Fig. 9.23.

---

function FORWARD(*observations* of len T, *state-graph* of len N) **returns** *forward-prob*

create a probability matrix *forward[N+2,T]*
for each state s **from** 1 **to** N **do**   ; initialization step
    $forward[s,1] \leftarrow a_{0,s} * b_s(o_1)$
for each time step t **from** 2 **to** T **do**   ; recursion step
    for each state s **from** 1 **to** N **do**
        $$forward[s,t] \leftarrow \sum_{s'=1}^{N} forward[s',t-1] * a_{s',s} * b_s(o_t)$$

$$forward[q_F,\mathrm{T}] \leftarrow \sum_{s=1}^{N} forward[s,T] * a_{s,q_F}$$; termination step
return $forward[q_F,T]$

Figure 9.23   The forward algorithm for computing likelihood of observation sequence given a word model. $a[s,s']$ is the transition probability from current state s to next state s', and $b[s',o_t]$ is the observation likelihood of s' given o_t. The observation likelihood $b[s',o_t]$ is computed by the **acoustic model**.

Let's see a trace of the forward algorithm running on a simplified HMM for the single word *five* given 10 observations; assuming a frame shift of 10 ms, this comes to 100 ms. The HMM structure is shown vertically along the left of Fig. 9.24, followed by the first three time steps of the forward trellis. The complete trellis is shown in Fig. 9.25, together with B values giving a vector of observation likelihoods for each frame. These likelihoods could be computed by any acoustic model (GMMs or other); in this example, we've hand-created simple values for pedagogical purposes.

Let's now turn to the question of decoding. Recall the Viterbi decoding algorithm from our description of HMMs in Chapter 6. The Viterbi algorithm returns the most likely state sequence (which is not the same as the most likely word sequence but is often a good enough approximation) in time $O(N^2T)$.

Each cell of the Viterbi trellis, $v_t(j)$, represents the probability that the HMM is in state j after seeing the first t observations and passing through the most likely state sequence $q_1...q_{t-1}$, given the automaton λ. We compute the value of each cell $v_t(j)$ by recursively taking the most probable path that could lead us to this cell. Formally, each cell expresses the following probability:

$$v_t(j) = P(q_0, q_1...q_{t-1}, o_1, o_2...o_t, q_t = j\ \lambda) \tag{9.53}$$

Like other dynamic programming algorithms, Viterbi fills each cell recursively. Given that we had already computed the probability of being in every state at time

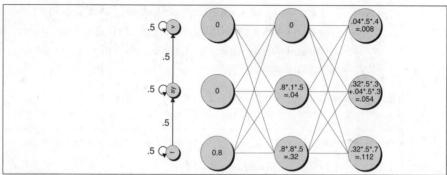

Figure 9.24   The first three time-steps of the forward trellis computation for the word *five*. The *A* transition probabilities are shown along the left edge; the *B* observation likelihoods are shown in Fig. 9.25.

V	0	0	0.008	0.0093	0.0114	0.00703	0.00345	0.00306	0.00206	0.00117
AY	0	0.04	0.054	0.0664	0.0355	0.016	0.00676	0.00208	0.000532	0.000109
F	0.8	0.32	0.112	0.0224	0.00448	0.000896	0.000179	4.48e-05	1.12e-05	2.8e-06
Time	1	2	3	4	5	6	7	8	9	10
	f 0.8	*f* 0.8	*f* 0.7	*f* 0.4	*f* 0.4	*f* 0.4	*f* 0.4	*f* 0.5	*f* 0.5	*f* 0.5
	ay 0.1	*ay* 0.1	*ay* 0.3	*ay* 0.8	*ay* 0.8	*ay* 0.8	*ay* 0.8	*ay* 0.6	*ay* 0.5	*ay* 0.4
B	*v* 0.6	*v* 0.6	*v* 0.4	*v* 0.3	*v* 0.3	*v* 0.3	*v* 0.3	*v* 0.6	*v* 0.8	*v* 0.9
	p 0.4	*p* 0.4	*p* 0.2	*p* 0.1	*p* 0.1	*p* 0.1	*p* 0.1	*p* 0.1	*p* 0.3	*p* 0.3
	iy 0.1	*iy* 0.1	*iy* 0.3	*iy* 0.6	*iy* 0.6	*iy* 0.6	*iy* 0.6	*iy* 0.5	*iy* 0.5	*iy* 0.4

Figure 9.25   The forward trellis for 10 frames of the word *five*, consisting of three emitting states (*f*, *ay*, *v*), plus non-emitting start and end states (not shown). The bottom half of the table gives part of the *B* observation likelihood vector for the observation *o* at each frame, $p(o\,q)$ for each phone *q*. *B* values are created by hand for pedagogical purposes. This table assumes the HMM structure for *five* shown in Fig. 9.24, each emitting state having a .5 loopback probability.

$t - 1$, we compute the Viterbi probability by taking the most probable of the extensions of the paths that lead to the current cell. For a given state q_j at time t, the value $v_t(j)$ is computed as

$$v_t(j) \; = \; \max_{i=1}^{N} v_{t-1}(i)\, a_{ij}\, b_j(o_t) \tag{9.54}$$

The three factors that are multiplied in Eq. 9.54 for extending the previous paths to compute the Viterbi probability at time t are

$v_{t-1}(i)$	the **previous Viterbi path probability** from the previous time step
a_{ij}	the **transition probability** from previous state q_i to current state q_j
$b_j(o_t)$	the **state observation likelihood** of the observation symbol o_t given the current state j

Figure 9.26 shows the Viterbi algorithm, repeated from Chapter 6.

Recall that the goal of the Viterbi algorithm is to find the best state sequence $q = (q_1 q_2 q_3 \ldots q_T)$ given the set of observations $o = (o_1 o_2 o_3 \ldots o_T)$. It needs to also find

---

function VITERBI(*observations* of len *T,state-graph* of len *N*) **returns** *best-path*

create a path probability matrix *viterbi[N+2,T]*
for each state *s* **from** 1 **to** *N* **do**   ;initialization step
    $viterbi[s,1] \leftarrow a_{0,s} * b_s(o_1)$
    $backpointer[s,1] \leftarrow 0$
for each time step *t* **from** 2 **to** *T* **do**   ;recursion step
  for each state *s* **from** 1 **to** *N* **do**
    $viterbi[s,t] \leftarrow \max\limits_{s'=1}^{N} viterbi[s',t-1] * a_{s',s} * b_s(o_t)$

    $backpointer[s,t] \leftarrow \operatorname*{argmax}\limits_{s'=1}^{N} viterbi[s',t-1] * a_{s',s}$

$viterbi[q_F,T] \leftarrow \max\limits_{s=1}^{N} viterbi[s,T] * a_{s,q_F}$; termination step

$backpointer[q_F,T] \leftarrow \operatorname*{argmax}\limits_{s=1}^{N} viterbi[s,T] * a_{s,q_F}$; termination step

return the backtrace path by following backpointers to states back in
        time from $backpointer[q_F,T]$

Figure 9.26   Viterbi algorithm for finding optimal sequence of hidden states. Given an observation sequence of words and an HMM (as defined by the *A* and *B* matrices), the algorithm returns the state path through the HMM that assigns maximum likelihood to the observation sequence. $a[s',s]$ is the transition probability from previous state s' to current state s, and $b_s(o_t)$ is the observation likelihood of s given o_t. Note that states 0 and F are non-emitting start and end states.

the probability of this state sequence (the joint probability of the state and observation sequences). Note that the Viterbi algorithm is identical to the forward algorithm except that it takes the MAX over the previous path probabilities where forward takes the SUM.

Figure 9.27 shows the computation of the first three time steps in the Viterbi trellis corresponding to the forward trellis in Fig. 9.24. We have again used the made-up probabilities for the cepstral observations; here we also follow common convention in not showing the zero cells in the upper-left corner. Note that only the middle cell in the third column differs from Viterbi to forward. Figure 9.25 shows the complete trellis.

Note the difference between the final values from the Viterbi and forward algorithms for this (made-up) example. The forward algorithm gives the probability of the observation sequence as .00128, which we get by summing the final column. The Viterbi algorithm gives the probability of the observation sequence given the best path, which we get from the Viterbi matrix as .000493. The Viterbi probability is much smaller than the forward probability, as we should expect since Viterbi comes from a single path, whereas the forward probability is the sum over all paths.

The real usefulness of the Viterbi decoder, of course, lies in its ability to decode a string of words. To do cross-word decoding, we need to augment the *A* matrix, which only has intraword state transitions, with the interword probability of transitioning from the end of one word to the beginning of another word. The digit HMM model in Fig. 9.22 on page 318 showed that we could just treat each word as independent,

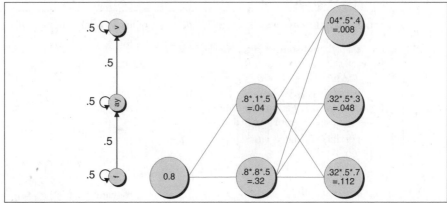

Figure 9.27   The first three time-steps of the Viterbi trellis computation for the word *five*. The *A* transition probabilities are shown along the left edge; the *B* observation likelihoods are shown in Fig. 9.28. Here we make the simplifying assumption that the probability of starting in state 1 (phone [f]) is 1.0.

V	0	0	0.008	0.0072	0.00672	0.00403	0.00188	0.00161	0.000667	0.000493
AY	0	0.04	0.048	0.0448	0.0269	0.0125	0.00538	0.00167	0.000428	8.78e-05
F	0.8	0.32	0.112	0.0224	0.00448	0.000896	0.000179	4.48e-05	1.12e-05	2.8e-06
Time	1	2	3	4	5	6	7	8	9	10
	f 0.8	*f* 0.8	*f* 0.7	*f* 0.4	*f* 0.4	*f* 0.4	*f* 0.4	*f* 0.5	*f* 0.5	*f* 0.5
	ay 0.1	*ay* 0.1	*ay* 0.3	*ay* 0.8	*ay* 0.8	*ay* 0.8	*ay* 0.8	*ay* 0.6	*ay* 0.5	*ay* 0.4
B	*v* 0.6	*v* 0.6	*v* 0.4	*v* 0.3	*v* 0.3	*v* 0.3	*v* 0.3	*v* 0.6	*v* 0.8	*v* 0.9
	p 0.4	*p* 0.4	*p* 0.2	*p* 0.1	*p* 0.1	*p* 0.1	*p* 0.1	*p* 0.1	*p* 0.3	*p* 0.3
	iy 0.1	*iy* 0.1	*iy* 0.3	*iy* 0.6	*iy* 0.6	*iy* 0.6	*iy* 0.6	*iy* 0.5	*iy* 0.5	*iy* 0.4

Figure 9.28   The Viterbi trellis for 10 frames of the word *five*, consisting of three emitting states (*f*, *ay*, *v*), plus non-emitting start and end states (not shown). The bottom half of the table gives part of the *B* observation likelihood vector for the observation *o* at each frame, $p(o\,q)$ for each phone *q*. *B* values are created by hand for pedagogical purposes. This table assumes the HMM structure for *five* shown in Fig. 9.27, each emitting state having a .5 loopback probability.

and use only the unigram probability. Higher-order *N*-grams are much more common. Figure 9.29, for example, shows an augmentation of the digit HMM with bigram probabilities.

A schematic of the HMM trellis for such a multi-word decoding task is shown in Fig. 9.30. The intraword transitions are exactly as shown in Fig. 9.27. But now we've added a transition between words. The transition probability on this arc comes from the language model $P(W)$ rather than from the *A* matrix inside each word.

Once the entire Viterbi trellis has been computed for the utterance, we can start from the most probable state at the final time step and follow the backtrace pointers backwards to get the most probable string of states, and hence the most probable string of words. Figure 9.31 shows the backtrace pointers being followed back from the best state, which happens to be at w_2, eventually through w_N and w_1, resulting in the final word string $w_1 w_N \quad w_2$.

Using the Viterbi algorithm is much more efficient than exponentially running the forward algorithm for each possible word string. Nonetheless, it is still slow, and much

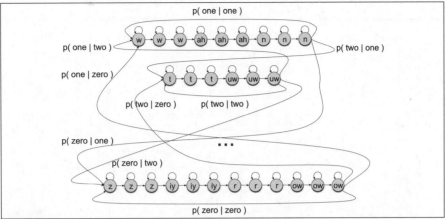

Figure 9.29 A bigram grammar network for the digit recognition task. The bigrams give the probability of transitioning from the end of one word to the beginning of the next.

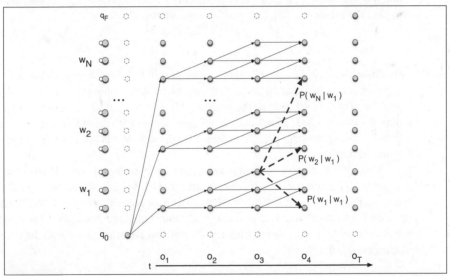

Figure 9.30 A schematic of the HMM Viterbi trellis for a bigram language model. The intraword transitions are the same as in Fig. 9.27. Between words, a potential transition is added (shown just from w_1 as a dark dashed line) from the end state of each word to the beginning state of every word, labeled with the bigram probability of the word pair.

modern research in speech recognition has focused on speeding up the decoding process. For example in practice in large-vocabulary recognition we do not consider all possible words when the algorithm is extending paths from one state column to the next. Instead, low-probability paths are **pruned** at each time step and not extended to the next state column.

Pruning

Beam search

This pruning is usually implemented by **beam search** (Lowerre, 1968). In beam search, at each time t, we first compute the probability of the best (most probable) state/path D. We then prune away any state that is worse than D by some fixed threshold

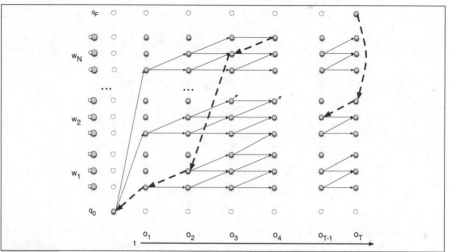

Figure 9.31   Viterbi backtrace in the HMM trellis. The backtrace starts in the final state, and results in a best phone string from which a word string is derived.

Beam width   (**beam width**) θ. We can talk about beam search in both the probability and negative log-probability domain. In the probability domain, any path/state whose probability is less than $\theta * D$ is pruned; in the negative log domain, any path whose cost is greater *Active list* than $\theta + D$ is pruned. Beam search is implemented with an **active list** of states that is kept for each time step. Only transitions from these words are extended when moving to the next time step.

Making this beam search approximation allows a significant speed-up at the cost of a degradation to the decoding performance. Huang et al. (2001) suggest that empirically a beam size of 5%–10% of the search space is sufficient; 90%–95% of the states are thus not considered. Because in practice most implementations of Viterbi use beam search, some of the literature uses the term **beam search** or **time-synchronous beam search** instead of Viterbi.

9.7   Embedded Training

We turn now to see how an HMM-based speech recognition system is trained. We've already seen some aspects of training. In Chapter 4 we showed how to train a language model. In Section 9.4, we saw how GMM acoustic models are trained by augmentation of the EM algorithm to deal with training the means, variances, and weights.

In this section, we complete the picture of HMM training by showing how this augmented EM training algorithm fits into the whole process of training acoustic models. For review, here are the three components of the **acoustic model**:

$Q = q_1 q_2 \ldots q_N$	the **subphones** represented as a set of **states**.
$A = a_{01} a_{02} \ldots a_{n1} \ldots a_{nn}$	a **subphone transition probability matrix** A, each a_{ij} representing the probability for each subphone of taking a **self-loop** or going to the next subphone. Together, Q and A implement a **pronunciation lexicon**, an HMM state graph structure for each word that the system is capable of recognizing.
$B = b_i(o_t)$	A set of **observation likelihoods**, also called **emission probabilities**, each expressing the probability of a cepstral feature vector (observation o_t) being generated from subphone state i.

We will assume that the pronunciation lexicon, and thus the basic HMM state graph structure for each word, is pre-specified as the simple linear HMM structures with loopbacks on each state that we saw in Fig. 9.7 and Fig. 9.22. In general, speech recognition systems do not attempt to learn the structure of the individual word HMMs. Thus, we need to train only the B matrix, and we need to train the probabilities of the non-zero (self-loop and next subphone) transitions in the A matrix. All the other probabilities in the A matrix are set to zero and never change.

The simplest possible training method is **hand-labeled isolated word** training, in which we train separately the B and A matrices for the HMMs for each word based on hand-aligned training data. We are given a training corpus of digits that has each instance of a spoken digit stored in a wavefile and has the start and end time of each word and phone marked by hand. Given such a database, we can compute the B Gaussians observation likelihoods and the A transition probabilities by merely counting in the training data! The A transition probabilities are specific to each word, but the B Gaussians are shared across words if the same phone occurred in multiple words.

Unfortunately, hand-segmented training data is rarely used in training systems for continuous speech. One reason is that it is very expensive to use humans to hand-label phonetic boundaries; it can take up to 400 times real time (i.e., 400 labeling hours to label each 1 hour of speech). Another reason is that humans don't do phonetic labeling well for units smaller than the phone; people are bad at consistently finding the boundaries of subphones. ASR systems aren't better than humans at finding boundaries, but their errors are at least consistent between the training and test sets.

For this reason, speech recognition systems train each phone HMM embedded in an entire sentence, and the segmentation and phone alignment are done automatically as part of the training procedure. This entire acoustic model training process is therefore called **embedded training**. Hand phone segmentation does still play some role, however, for example, for bootstrapping initial systems for discriminative (SVM; non-Gaussian) likelihood estimators or for tasks like phone recognition.

Embedded training

To train a simple digits system, we'll need a training corpus of spoken digit sequences. For simplicity, assume that the training corpus is separated into separate wavefiles, each containing a sequence of spoken digits. For each wavefile, we need the correct sequence of digit words. We thus associate with each wavefile a transcription (a string of words). We also need a pronunciation lexicon and a phoneset defining a set of (untrained) phone HMMs. From the transcription, lexicon, and phone HMMs, we can build a "whole sentence" HMM for each sentence, as shown in Fig. 9.32.

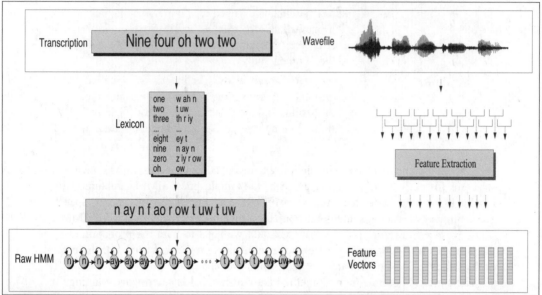

Figure 9.32 The input to the embedded training algorithm: a wavefile of spoken digits with a corresponding transcription. The transcription is converted into a raw HMM, ready to be aligned and trained against the cepstral features extracted from the wavefile.

We are now ready to train the transition matrix A and output likelihood estimator B for the HMMs. The beauty of the Baum-Welch-based paradigm for embedded training of HMMs is that this is all the training data we need. In particular, we don't need phonetically transcribed data. We don't even need to know where each word starts and ends. The Baum-Welch algorithm will sum over all possible segmentations of words and phones, using $\xi_j(t)$, the probability of being in state j at time t, and generating the observation sequence O.

Flat start We do, however, need an initial estimate for the transition and observation probabilities a_{ij} and $b_j(o_t)$. The simplest way to do this is with a **flat start**. In flat start, we first set to zero any HMM transitions that we want to be 'structurally zero', such as transitions from later phones back to earlier phones. The γ probability computation in Baum-Welch includes the previous value of a_{ij}, so those zero values will never change. Then we make all the rest of the (non-zero) HMM transitions equiprobable. Thus, the two transitions out of each state (the self-loop and the transition to the following subphone) each would have a probability of 0.5. For the Gaussians, a flat start initializes the mean and variance for each Gaussian identically, to the global mean and variance for the entire training data.

Now we have initial estimates for the A and B probabilities. For a standard Gaussian HMM system, we now run multiple iterations of the Baum-Welch algorithm on the entire training set. Each iteration modifies the HMM parameters, and we stop when the system converges. During each iteration, as discussed in Chapter 6, we compute the forward and backward probabilities for each sentence given the initial A and B probabilities and use the computed probabilities to re-estimate the A and B probabilities. We also apply the various modifications to EM discussed in the previous section to correctly update the Gaussian means and variances for multivariate Gaussians. We discuss in Section 10.3 in Chapter 10 how to modify the embedded training algorithm to handle mixture Gaussians.

In summary, the basic **embedded training procedure** is as follows:

Given: phoneset, pronunciation lexicon, and the transcribed wavefiles

1. Build a "whole sentence" HMM for each sentence, as shown in Fig. 9.32.

2. Initialize A probabilities to 0.5 (for loop-backs or for the correct next subphone) or to zero (for all other transitions).

3. Initialize B probabilities by setting the mean and variance for each Gaussian to the global mean and variance for the entire training set.

4. Run multiple iterations of the Baum-Welch algorithm.

The Baum-Welch algorithm is used repeatedly as a component of the embedded training process. Baum-Welch computes $\xi_t(i)$, the probability of being in state i at time t, by using forward-backward to sum over all possible paths that were in state i emitting symbol o_t at time t. This lets us accumulate counts for re-estimating the emission probability $b_j(o_t)$ from all the paths that pass through state j at time t. But Baum-Welch itself can be time consuming.

Viterbi training

There is an efficient approximation to Baum-Welch training that makes use of the Viterbi algorithm. In **Viterbi training**, instead of accumulating counts by a sum over all paths that pass through a state j at time t, we approximate this by choosing only the Viterbi (most probable) path. Thus, instead of running EM at every step of the embedded training, we repeatedly run Viterbi.

Forced alignment

Running the Viterbi algorithm over the training data in this way is called **forced Viterbi alignment** or just **forced alignment**. In Viterbi training (unlike in Viterbi decoding on the test set) we know which word string to assign to each observation sequence, so we can "force" the Viterbi algorithm to pass through certain words, by setting the a_{ij}s appropriately. A forced Viterbi is thus a simplification of the regular Viterbi decoding algorithm since it only has to figure out the correct state (subphone) sequence but doesn't have to discover the word sequence. The result is a **forced alignment**: the single best state path corresponding to the training observation sequence. We can now use this alignment of HMM states to observations to accumulate counts for re-estimating the HMM parameters. We saw earlier that forced alignment can also be used in other speech applications, like text-to-speech, whenever we have a word transcript and a wavefile in which we want to find boundaries.

The equations for retraining a (non-mixture) Gaussian from a Viterbi alignment are as follows:

$$\hat{\mu}_i = \frac{1}{T} \sum_{t=1}^{T} o_t \text{ s.t. } q_t \text{ is state } i \tag{9.55}$$

$$\hat{\sigma}_j^2 \;=\; \frac{1}{T} \sum_{t=1}^{T} (o_t - \mu_i)^2 \text{ s.t. } q_t \text{ is state } i \qquad (9.56)$$

We saw these equations already, as Eq. 9.27 and Eq. 9.28 on page 308, when we were "imagining the simpler situation of a completely labeled training set".

It turns out that this forced Viterbi algorithm is also used in the embedded training of hybrid models like HMM/MLP or HMM/SVM systems. We begin with an untrained MLP and, using its noisy outputs as the B values for the HMM, perform a forced Viterbi alignment of the training data. This alignment will be quite errorful since the MLP was random. Now this (quite errorful) Viterbi alignment give us a labeling of feature vectors with phone labels. We use this labeling to retrain the MLP. The counts of the transitions that are taken in the forced alignments can be used to estimate the HMM transition probabilities. We continue this hill-climbing process of neural-net training and Viterbi alignment until the HMM parameters begin to converge.

9.8   Evaluation: Word Error Rate

Word error   The standard evaluation metric for speech recognition systems is the **word error** rate. The word error rate is based on how much the word string returned by the recognizer (often called the **hypothesized** word string) differs from a correct or **reference** transcription. Given such a correct transcription, the first step in computing word error is to compute the **minimum edit distance** in words between the hypothesized and correct strings, as described in Chapter 3. The result of this computation will be the minimum number of word **substitutions**, word **insertions**, and word **deletions** necessary to map between the correct and hypothesized strings. The word error rate (WER) is then defined as follows (note that because the equation includes insertions, the error rate can be greater than 100%):

$$\text{Word Error Rate} \;=\; 100 \; \frac{\text{Insertions} + \text{Substitutions} + \text{Deletions}}{\text{Total Words in Correct Transcript}}$$

We sometimes also talk about the Sentence Error Rate (SER), which tells us how many sentences had at least one error:

$$\text{Sentence Error Rate} \;=\; 100 \; \frac{\text{\# of sentences with at least one word error}}{\text{total \# of sentences}}$$

Alignment   Here is a sample **alignment** between a reference and a hypothesis utterance from the CallHome corpus, showing the counts used to compute the error rate:

REF:	i	***	**	UM	the	PHONE	IS		i	LEFT	THE	portable	****	PHONE	UPSTAIRS	last	night
HYP:	i	GOT	IT	TO	the	*****	FULLEST	i	LOVE	TO		portable	FORM	OF		STORES	last	night
Eval:		I	I	S		D	S		S	S			I	S		S		

This utterance has six substitutions, three insertions, and one deletion:

$$\text{Word Error Rate} \;=\; 100 \frac{6+3+1}{13} = 76.9\%$$

The standard method for implementing minimum edit distance and computing word error rates is a free script called **sclite**, available from the National Institute of Standards and Technologies (NIST) (NIST, 2005). Sclite is given a series of reference (hand-transcribed, gold-standard) sentences and a matching set of hypothesis sentences. Besides performing alignments, and computing word error rate, sclite performs a number of other useful tasks. For example, for **error analysis** it gives useful information such as confusion matrices showing which words are often misrecognized for others, and summarizes statistics of words that are often inserted or deleted. `sclite` also gives error rates by speaker (if sentences are labeled for speaker ID), as well as useful statistics like the **sentence error rate**, the percentage of sentences with at least one word error.

Sentence error rate

Finally, `sclite` can be used to compute significance tests. Suppose we make some changes to our ASR system and find that our word error rate has decreased by 1%. To know if our changes really improved things, we need a statistical test to make sure that the 1% difference is not just due to chance. The standard statistical test for determining if two word error rates are different is the Matched-Pair Sentence Segment Word Error (MAPSSWE) test, which is also available in `sclite` (although the **McNemar test** is sometimes used as well).

McNemar test

The MAPSSWE test is a parametric test that looks at the difference between the number of word errors the two systems produce, averaged across a number of segments. The segments may be quite short or as long as an entire utterance; in general, we want to have the largest number of (short) segments in order to justify the normality assumption and to maximize power. The test requires that the errors in one segment be statistically independent of the errors in another segment. Since ASR systems tend to use trigram LMs, we can approximate this requirement by defining a segment as a region bounded on both sides by words that both recognizers get correct (or by turn/utterance boundaries). Here's an example from NIST (2007b) with four regions:

```
          I             II               III                IV
REF:   |it was|the best|of|times it|was the worst|of times|  |it was
SYS A: |ITS   |the best|of|times it|IS the worst |of times|OR|it was
SYS B: |it was|the best|  |times it|WON the TEST |of times|  |it was
```

In region I, system A has two errors (a deletion and an insertion) and system B has zero; in region III, system A has one error (a substitution) and system B has two. Let's define a sequence of variables Z representing the difference between the errors in the two systems as follows:

N_A^i the number of errors made on segment i by system A

N_B^i the number of errors made on segment i by system B

Z $N_A^i - N_B^i, i = 1, 2, \quad , n$ where n is the number of segments

In the example above, the sequence of Z values is $2, -1, -1, 1$. Intuitively, if the two systems are identical, we would expect the average difference, that is, the average of the Z values, to be zero. If we call the true average of the differences mu_z, we would thus like to know whether $mu_z = 0$. Following closely the original proposal and

335

notation of Gillick and Cox (1989), we can estimate the true average from our limited sample as $\hat{\mu}_z = \sum_{i=1}^{n} Z_i / n$.

The estimate of the variance of the Z_i's is

$$\sigma_z^2 = \frac{1}{n-1} \sum_{i=1}^{n} (Z_i - \mu_z)^2 \qquad (9.57)$$

Let

$$W = \frac{\hat{\mu}_z}{\sigma_z / \sqrt{n}} \qquad (9.58)$$

For a large enough n (> 50), W will approximately have a normal distribution with unit variance. The null hypothesis is $H_0 : \mu_z = 0$, and it can thus be rejected if $2 * P(Z \geq w) \leq 0.05$ (two-tailed) or $P(Z \geq w) \leq 0.05$ (one-tailed), where Z is standard normal and w is the realized value W; these probabilities can be looked up in the standard tables of the normal distribution.

Could we improve on word error rate as a metric? It would be nice, for example, to have something that didn't give equal weight to every word, perhaps valuing content words like *Tuesday* more than function words like *a* or *of*. While researchers generally agree that this would be a good idea, it has proved difficult to agree on a metric that works in every application of ASR. For dialogue systems, however, where the desired semantic output is more clear, a metric called *concept error rate* has proved extremely useful; it is discussed in Chapter 24 on page 837.

9.9   Summary

Together with Chapters 4 and 6, this chapter introduced the fundamental algorithms for addressing the problem of **Large-Vocabulary Continuous Speech Recognition**.

- The input to a speech recognizer is a series of acoustic waves. The **waveform**, **spectrogram**, and **spectrum** are among the visualization tools used to understand the information in the signal.

- In the first step in speech recognition, sound waves are **sampled**, **quantized**, and converted to some sort of **spectral representation**; a commonly used spectral representation is the **mel cepstrum** or **MFCC**, which provides a vector of features for each frame of the input.

- GMM acoustic models are used to estimate the **phonetic likelihoods** (also called **observation likelihoods**) of these **feature vectors** for each frame.

- **Decoding** or **search** or **inference** is the process of finding the optimal sequence of model states that matches a sequence of input observations. Incidentally, the fact that there are three terms for this process is a hint that speech recognition is inherently interdisciplinary and draws its metaphors from more than one field; **decoding** comes from information theory, and **search** and **inference** from artificial intelligence.

- We introduced the time-synchronous **Viterbi** decoding algorithm, which is usually implemented with pruning and then called **beam search**. The algorithm takes as input a sequence of cepstral feature vectors, a GMM acoustic model, and an N-gram language model and produces a string of words.

- The **embedded training** paradigm is the normal method for training speech recognizers. Given an initial lexicon with hand-built pronunciation structures, it can train the HMM transition probabilities and the HMM observation probabilities.

Bibliographical and Historical Notes

The first machine that recognized speech was probably a commercial toy named "Radio Rex" which was sold in the 1920s. Rex was a celluloid dog that moved (by means of a spring) when the spring was released by 500 Hz acoustic energy. Since 500 Hz is roughly the first formant of the vowel [eh] in "Rex", the dog seemed to come when he was called (David, Jr. and Selfridge, 1962).

By the late 1940s and early 1950s, a number of machine speech recognition systems had been built. An early Bell Labs system could recognize any of the 10 digits from a single speaker (Davis et al., 1952). This system had 10 speaker-dependent stored patterns, one for each digit, each of which roughly represented the first two vowel formants in the digit. They achieved 97%–99% accuracy by choosing the pattern that had the highest relative correlation coefficient with the input. Fry (1959) and Denes (1959) built a phoneme recognizer at University College, London, that recognized four vowels and nine consonants based on a similar pattern-recognition principle. Fry and Denes's system was the first to use phoneme transition probabilities to constrain the recognizer.

The late 1960s and early 1970s produced a number of important paradigm shifts. First were a number of feature-extraction algorithms, including the efficient fast Fourier transform (FFT) (Cooley and Tukey, 1965), the application of cepstral processing to speech (Oppenheim et al., 1968), and the development of LPC for speech coding (Atal *Warping* and Hanauer, 1971). Second were a number of ways of handling **warping**; stretching or shrinking the input signal to handle differences in speaking rate and segment length when matching against stored patterns. The natural algorithm for solving this problem was dynamic programming, and, as we saw in Chapter 6, the algorithm was reinvented multiple times to address this problem. The first application to speech processing was by Vintsyuk (1968), although his result was not picked up by other researchers, and was reinvented by Velichko and Zagoruyko (1970) and Sakoe and Chiba (1971) (and (1984)). Soon afterward, Itakura (1975) combined this dynamic programming idea with the LPC coefficients that had previously been used only for speech coding. The resulting system extracted LPC features from incoming words and used dynamic programming to match them against stored LPC templates. The non-probabilistic use of dynamic programming to match a template against incoming speech is called **dynamic** *Dynamic time* **time warping**. *warping*

The third innovation of this period was the rise of the HMM. Hidden Markov models seem to have been applied to speech independently at two laboratories around 1972. One application arose from the work of statisticians, in particular Baum and colleagues at the Institute for Defense Analyses in Princeton who applied HMMs to various prediction problems (Baum and Petrie, 1966; Baum and Eagon, 1967). James Baker learned of this work and applied the algorithm to speech processing (Baker, 1975) during his graduate work at CMU. Independently, Frederick Jelinek, Robert Mercer, and Lalit Bahl (drawing from their research in information-theoretical models influenced by the work of Shannon (1948)) applied HMMs to speech at the IBM Thomas J. Watson Research Center (Jelinek et al., 1975). IBM's and Baker's systems were very similar, particularly in their use of the Bayesian framework described in this chapter. One early difference was the decoding algorithm; Baker's DRAGON system used Viterbi (dynamic programming) decoding, while the IBM system applied Jelinek's stack decoding algorithm (Jelinek, 1969). Baker then joined the IBM group for a brief time before founding the speech-recognition company Dragon Systems. The HMM approach to speech recognition would turn out to completely dominate the field by the end of the century; indeed the IBM lab was the driving force in extending statistical models to natural language processing as well, including the development of class-based N-grams, HMM-based part-of-speech tagging, statistical machine translation, and the use of entropy/perplexity as an evaluation metric.

The use of the HMM slowly spread through the speech community. One cause was a number of research programs sponsored by ARPA, the Advanced Research Projects Agency of the U.S. Department of Defense. The first five-year program started in 1971, and was reviewed in Klatt (1977). The goal of this first program was to build speech understanding systems based on a few speakers, a constrained grammar and lexicon (1000 words), and less than 10% semantic error rate. Four systems were funded and compared with each other: the System Development Corporation (SDC) system, Bolt, Beranek and Newman (BBN)'s HWIM system, Carnegie-Mellon University's Hearsay-II system, and Carnegie-Mellon's Harpy system (Lowerre, 1968). The Harpy system used a simplified version of Baker's HMM-based DRAGON system and was the best of the tested systems and, according to Klatt the only one to meet the original goals of the ARPA project (with a semantic accuracy rate of 94% on a simple task).

Beginning in the mid-1980s, ARPA funded a number of new speech research programs. The first was the "Resource Management" (RM) task (Price et al., 1988), which like the earlier ARPA task involved transcription (recognition) of read speech (speakers reading sentences constructed from a 1000-word vocabulary) but which now included a component that involved speaker-independent recognition. Later tasks included recognition of sentences read from the *Wall Street Journal* (WSJ) beginning with limited systems of 5,000 words, and finally with systems of unlimited vocabulary (in practice most systems use approximately 60,000 words). Later speech recognition tasks moved away from read-speech to more natural domains; the Broadcast News domain (LDC, 1998; Graff, 1997) (transcription of actual news broadcasts, including quite difficult passages such as on-the-street interviews) and the Switchboard, CallHome, CallFriend, and Fisher domains (Godfrey et al., 1992; Cieri et al., 2004) (natural telephone conversations between friends or strangers). The Air Traffic Information System (ATIS) task (Hemphill et al., 1990) was an earlier speech understanding task whose goal was to simulate helping a user book a flight by answering questions about potential airlines, times, dates, and so forth.

Bakeoff   Each of the ARPA tasks involved an approximately annual **bakeoff** at which all ARPA-funded systems and many other "volunteer" systems from North America and Europe were evaluated against each other in terms of word error rate or semantic error rate. In the early evaluations, for-profit corporations did not generally compete, but eventually many (especially IBM and AT&T) competed regularly. The ARPA competitions resulted in wide-scale borrowing of techniques among labs since it was easy to see which ideas reduced errors the previous year, and the competitions were probably an important factor in the eventual spread of the HMM paradigm to virtually every major speech recognition lab. The ARPA program also resulted in a number of useful databases, originally designed for training and testing systems for each evaluation (TIMIT, RM, WSJ, ATIS, BN, CallHome, Switchboard, Fisher) but then made available for general research use.

Speech research includes a number of areas besides speech recognition; we already saw computational phonology in Chapter 7, speech synthesis in Chapter 8, and we will discuss spoken dialogue systems in Chapter 24. Another important area is **speaker** *Speaker* **recognition**, in which we identify a speaker. We generally distinguish the subtasks of *recognition* **speaker verification**, where we make a binary decision (is this speaker X or not?), such as for security when accessing personal information over the telephone, and **speaker identification**, where we make a one of N decision trying to match a speaker's voice against a database of many speakers (Reynolds and Rose, 1995; Shriberg et al., 2005; *Language* Doddington, 2001). These tasks are related to **language identification**, in which we *identification* are given a wavefile and must identify which language is being spoken; this is useful for automatically directing callers to human operators that speak appropriate languages.

A number of textbooks and reference books on speech recognition are good choices for readers who seek a more in-depth understanding of the material in this chapter: Huang et al. (2001) is the most comprehensive and up-to-date reference volume and is highly recommended. Jelinek (1997), Gold and Morgan (1999), and Rabiner and Juang (1993) are good comprehensive textbooks. The last two textbooks also discuss the history of the field and, together with the survey paper of Levinson (1995) have influenced our short history discussion in this chapter. O'Shaughnessy (2000) covers human as well as machine speech processing. Excellent textbooks on digital signal processing are Lyons (2004) and Rabiner and Schafer (1978). Our description of the forward-backward algorithm was modeled after Rabiner (1989), and we were also influenced by another useful tutorial paper, Knill and Young (1997). Research in the speech recognition field often appears in the proceedings of the annual INTER-SPEECH conference (which is called ICSLP and EUROSPEECH in alternate years) as well as the annual IEEE International Conference on Acoustics, Speech, and Signal Processing (ICASSP). Journals include *Speech Communication*, *Computer Speech and Language*, the *IEEE Transactions on Audio, Speech, and Language Processing*, and the *ACM Transactions on Speech and Language Processing*.

Exercises

9.1 Analyze each of the errors in the incorrectly recognized transcription of "um the phone is I left the..." on page 328. For each one, give your best guess as to whether you think it is caused by a problem in signal processing, pronunciation modeling, lexicon size, language model, or pruning in the decoding search.

9.2 In practice, as we mentioned earlier in Chapter 4, speech recognizers do all their probability computation by using the **log probability** (**logprob**) rather than actual probabilities. This helps avoid underflow for very small probabilities, but also makes the Viterbi algorithm very efficient since all probability multiplications can be implemented by adding logprobs. Rewrite the pseudocode for the Viterbi algorithm in Fig. 9.26 on page 321 to make use of logprobs instead of probabilities.

9.3 Now modify the Viterbi algorithm in Fig. 9.26 to implement the beam search described on page 323. Hint: You will probably need to add in code to check whether a given state is at the end of a word or not.

9.4 Finally, modify the Viterbi algorithm in Fig. 9.26 with more detailed pseudocode implementing the array of backtrace pointers.

9.5 Using the tutorials available as part of a publicly available recognizer like HTK or Sonic, build a digit recognizer.

9.6 Take the digit recognizer above and dump the phone likelihoods for a sentence. Show that your implementation of the Viterbi algorithm can successfully decode these likelihoods.

Credit

Fig. 9.14 (© Paul Taylor and Cambridge University Press)

Chapter 10

Speech Recognition: Advanced Topics

True, their voice-print machine was unfortunately a crude one. It could discriminate among only a few frequencies, and it indicated amplitude by indecipherable blots. But it had never been intended for such vitally important work.

Aleksandr I. Solzhenitsyn, *The First Circle*, p. 505

The *keju* civil service examination of Imperial China lasted almost 1300 years, from the year 606 until it was abolished in 1905. In its peak, millions of would-be officials from all over China competed for high-ranking government positions by participating in a uniform examination. For the final "metropolitan" part of this exam in the capital city, the candidates were locked in an examination compound for a grueling nine days and nights, answering questions about history, poetry, the Confucian classics, and policy.

Naturally, these millions of candidates didn't all show up in the capital. Instead, the exam had progressive levels; candidates who passed a one-day exam in their local prefecture could sit for the biannual provincial exam, and only upon passing that exam in the provincial capital was a candidate eligible for the metropolitan examination.

This algorithm for selecting capable officials is an instance of multistage search. The final 9-day process requires far too many resources (in both space and time) to examine every candidate. Instead, the algorithm uses a less intensive 1-day process to produce a preliminary list of candidates, and applies the final test only to this list.

The *keju* method can also be applied to speech recognition. We want to be able to use very expensive algorithms in recognition, such as 5-gram and parser-based language models or phone models that see four phones of context. But there are a huge number of potential transcriptions for each waveform, and it's too expensive (in time, space, or both) to apply such powerful algorithms to every candidate. Instead, we apply **multipass decoding**, in which efficient but dumb knowledge sources produce shortlists of potential candidates to be rescored by slow but smarter algorithms. We introduce such decoders, and knowledge sources like the **context-dependent acoustic model**, crucial for large-vocabulary recognition. We also briefly introduce the modeling of variation and the important topic of discriminative training.

10.1 Multipass Decoding: *N*-Best Lists and Lattices

The previous chapter applied the Viterbi algorithm for HMM decoding. There are two main limitations of the Viterbi decoder, however. First, the Viterbi decoder does not actually compute the sequence of words that is most probable given the input acoustics. Instead, it computes an approximation to this: the sequence of *states* (i.e., *phones* or *subphones*) that is most probable given the input. For example, consider any particular word sequence W. The true likelihood of the observation sequence O given W is computed by the forward algorithm by summing over all possible paths:

$$P(O\,W) = \sum_{S \in S_1^T} P(O, S\,W) \qquad (10.1)$$

The Viterbi algorithm approximates this sum by using the probability of the best state path through W:

$$P(O\,W) \approx \max_{S \in S_1^T} P(O, S\,W) \qquad (10.2)$$

Viterbi approximation

It turns out that this **Viterbi approximation** is not too bad, since the most probable sequence of phones usually turns out to correspond to the most probable sequence of words. But not always. Consider a speech recognition system whose lexicon has multiple pronunciations for each word. Suppose the correct word sequence includes a word with many pronunciations. Since the probabilities leaving the start arc of each word must sum to 1.0, each of these pronunciation paths through this multiple-pronunciation HMM word model will have a smaller probability than the path through a word with only a single pronunciation path. Thus, because the Viterbi decoder can only follow one of these pronunciation paths, it may ignore this many-pronunciation word in favor of an incorrect word with only one pronunciation path. In essence, the Viterbi approximation penalizes words with many pronunciations.

A second problem with the Viterbi decoder is that it is impossible or expensive for it to take advantage of many useful knowledge sources. The Viterbi algorithm as we have defined it cannot take complete advantage of any language model more complex than a bigram grammar. The reason is that a trigram grammar, for example, violates the **dynamic programming invariant**, as mentioned earlier. This invariant is the simplifying assumption that if the ultimate best path for the entire observation sequence happens to go through a state q_i, this best path must include the best path up to and including state q_i. Since a trigram grammar allows the probability of a word to be based on the two previous words, it is possible that the best trigram-probability path for the sentence may go through a word but not include the best path to that word. Such a situation could occur if a particular word w_x has a high trigram probability given w_y, w_z, but that conversely the best path to w_y didn't include w_z (i.e., $P(w_y\,w_q, w_z)$ was low for all q). For small domains like HMM part-of-speech tagging with 50 tags, we can solve this problem by considering all previous combinations of two or three states. But this approach is not possible in speech recognition, since the number of states is very large and the previous word may occur only many states previously. Advanced probabilistic LMs like PCFGs also violate the same dynamic programming assumptions.

There are two solutions to these problems with Viterbi decoding. The most common is to modify the Viterbi decoder to return multiple potential utterances instead of just the single best and then to use other high-level language models or pronunciation-modeling algorithms to re-rank these multiple outputs (Schwartz and Austin, 1991; Soong and Huang, 1990; Murveit et al., 1993). The second solution is to employ a

Stack decoder
A*

completely different decoding algorithm, such as the **stack decoder**, or **A*** decoder (Jelinek, 1969; Jelinek et al., 1975). We begin in this section with multiple-pass decoding and then return to stack decoding.

In **multiple-pass decoding** we break up the decoding process into two stages. In the first stage, we use fast, efficient knowledge sources or algorithms to perform a nonoptimal search. So, for example, we might use an unsophisticated but efficient language model like a bigram or use simplified acoustic models. In the second decoding pass we can apply more sophisticated but slower decoding algorithms on a reduced search space. The interface between these passes is an *N*-best list or **word lattice**.

N-best

The simplest algorithm for multipass decoding is to modify the Viterbi algorithm to return the *N*-best sentences (word sequences) for a given speech input. Suppose, for example, that a bigram grammar is used with such an *N*-best Viterbi algorithm to return the 1000 most highly probable sentences, each with its AM likelihood and LM prior score. This 1000-best list can now be passed to a more sophisticated language model, like a trigram grammar. This new LM replaces the bigram LM score of each hypothesized sentence with a new trigram LM probability. These priors can be combined with the acoustic likelihood of each sentence to generate a new posterior probability

Rescoring

for each sentence. Sentences are thus **rescored** and re-ranked according to this more sophisticated probability. Figure 10.1 shows an intuition for this algorithm.

Figure 10.1   The use of *N*-best decoding as part of a two-stage decoding model. Efficient but unsophisticated knowledge sources are used to return the *N*-best utterances. This significantly reduces the search space for second pass models, which can thus be sophisticated but slow.

A number of algorithms extend Viterbi to generate *N*-best hypotheses. While there is no polynomial-time admissible algorithm for finding the *N* most likely hypotheses (Young, 1984), there are a number of approximate (non-admissible) algorithms; we introduce one of them, the "Exact *N*-best" algorithm of Schwartz and Chow (1990). In Exact *N*-best, instead of each state maintaining a single path/backtrace, we maintain up to *N* different paths for each state. But we'd like to ensure that these paths correspond to different word paths; we don't want to waste our *N* paths on different state sequences that map to the same words. To do this, we keep for each path the **word history**, the entire sequence of words up to the current word/state. If two paths with the same word history come to a state at the same time, we merge the paths and sum the path probabilities. To keep the best *N* word sequences, the resulting algorithm requires $O(N)$ times the normal Viterbi time. This merging of paths also occurs in statistical machine translation, where it is called **hypothesis recombination**.

The result of any of these algorithms is an *N*-best list like the one shown in Fig. 10.2. In Fig. 10.2 the correct hypothesis happens to be the first one, but of course the reason

Rank	Path	AM logprob	LM logprob
1.	it's an area that's naturally sort of mysterious	-7193.53	-20.25
2.	that's an area that's naturally sort of mysterious	-7192.28	-21.11
3.	it's an area that's not really sort of mysterious	-7221.68	-18.91
4.	that scenario that's naturally sort of mysterious	-7189.19	-22.08
5.	there's an area that's naturally sort of mysterious	-7198.35	-21.34
6.	that's an area that's not really sort of mysterious	-7220.44	-19.77
7.	the scenario that's naturally sort of mysterious	-7205.42	-21.50
8.	so it's an area that's naturally sort of mysterious	-7195.92	-21.71
9.	that scenario that's not really sort of mysterious	-7217.34	-20.70
10.	there's an area that's not really sort of mysterious	-7226.51	-20.01

Figure 10.2   An example 10-Best list from the Broadcast News corpus, produced by the CU-HTK BN system (thanks to Phil Woodland). Logprobs use $\log_{10}$; the language model scale factor (LMSF) is 15.

to use N-best lists is that such isn't always the case. Each sentence in an N-best list is also annotated with an acoustic model probability and a language model probability. This allows a second-stage knowledge source to replace one of those two probabilities with an improved estimate.

One problem with an N-best list is that when N is large, listing all the sentences is extremely inefficient. Another problem is that N-best lists don't give quite as much information as we might want for a second-pass decoder. For example, we might want distinct acoustic model information for each word hypothesis so that we can reapply a new acoustic model for the word. Or we might want to have available different start and end times of each word so that we can apply a new duration model.

Word lattice For this reason, the output of a first-pass decoder is usually a more sophisticated representation called a **word lattice** (Murveit et al., 1993; Aubert and Ney, 1995). A word lattice is a directed graph that efficiently represents much more information about possible word sequences.[1] In some systems, nodes in the graph are words, and arcs are transitions between words. In others, arcs represent word hypotheses, and nodes are points in time. Let's use this latter model, so that each arc represents lots of information about the word hypothesis, including the start and end time, the acoustic model and language model probabilities, the sequence of phones (the pronunciation of the word), or even the phone durations. Figure 10.3 shows a sample lattice corresponding to the N-best list in Fig. 10.2. Note that the lattice contains many distinct links (records) for the same word, each with a slightly different starting or ending time. Such lattices are not produced from N-best lists; instead, a lattice is produced during first-pass decoding by including some of the word hypotheses that were active (in the beam) at each time-step. Since the acoustic and language models are context dependent, distinct links need to be created for each relevant context, resulting in a large number of links with the same word but different times and contexts. We could also produce N-best lists like Fig. 10.2 by first building a lattice like Fig. 10.3 and then tracing through the paths to produce N word strings.

---

[1] Actually, an ASR lattice is not the kind of lattice that may be familiar from mathematics, since it is not required to have the properties of a true lattice (i.e., be a partially ordered set with particular properties, such as a unique join for each pair of elements). Really, it's just a graph, but the convention is to call it a lattice.

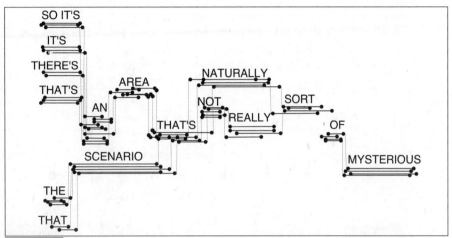

Figure 10.3   Word lattice corresponding to the *N*-best list in Fig. 10.2. The arcs beneath each word show the different start and end times for each word hypothesis in the lattice; for some of these we've shown schematically how each word hypothesis must start at the end of a previous hypothesis. Not shown in this figure are the acoustic and language model probabilities that decorate each arc.

The fact that each word hypothesis in a lattice is augmented separately with its acoustic model likelihood and language model probability allows us to rescore any path through the lattice, using either a more sophisticated language model or a more sophisticated acoustic model. As with *N*-best lists, the goal of this rescoring is to replace the **1-best utterance** with a different utterance that perhaps had a lower score on the first decoding pass. For this second-pass knowledge source to get a perfect word error rate, the actual correct sentence would have to be in the lattice or *N*-best list. If the correct sentence isn't there, the rescoring knowledge source can't find it. Thus, it is important when working with a lattice or *N*-best list to consider the baseline **lattice**
Lattice error rate   **error rate** (Woodland et al., 1995; Ortmanns et al., 1997): the lower-bound word error rate from the lattice. The lattice error rate is the word error rate we get if we chose the lattice path (the sentence) that has the lowest word error rate. Because it relies on
Oracle error rate   perfect knowledge of which path to pick, we call this an **oracle** error rate since we need some oracle to tell us which sentence/path to pick.
Lattice density   Another important lattice concept is the **lattice density**, which is the number of edges in a lattice divided by the number of words in the reference transcript. As we saw schematically in Fig. 10.3, real lattices are often extremely dense, with many copies of individual word hypotheses at slightly different start and end times. Because of this density, lattices are often pruned.

Besides being pruned, lattices are often simplified into a different, more schematic
Word graph   kind of lattice that is sometimes called a **word graph** or **finite-state machine**, although often it's still just referred to as a word lattice. In these word graphs, the timing information is removed and multiple overlapping copies of the same word are merged. The timing of the words is left implicit in the structure of the graph. In addition, the acoustic model likelihood information is removed, leaving only the language model probabilities. The resulting graph is a weighted FSA, which is a natural extension of an *N*-gram

347

language model; the word graph corresponding to Fig. 10.3 is shown in Fig. 10.4. This word graph can in fact be used as the language model for another decoding pass. Since such a word-graph language model vastly restricts the search space, it enables the use of a complicated acoustic model that is too slow to use in first-pass decoding.

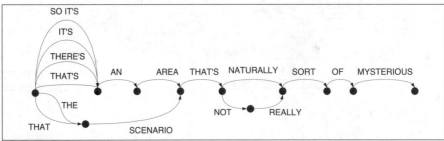

Figure 10.4   Word graph corresponding to the *N*-best list in Fig. 10.2. Each word hypothesis in the lattice also has language model probabilities (not shown in this figure).

A final type of lattice is used when we need to represent the posterior probability of individual words in a lattice. It turns out that in speech recognition, we almost never see the true posterior probability of anything, despite the fact that the goal of speech recognition is to compute the sentence with the maximum a posteriori probability. This is because in the fundamental equation of speech recognition, we ignore the denominator in our maximization:

$$\hat{W} = \operatorname*{argmax}_{W \in \mathscr{L}} \frac{P(O\,W)P(W)}{P(O)} = \operatorname*{argmax}_{W \in \mathscr{L}} P(O\,W)\,P(W) \qquad (10.3)$$

The product of the likelihood and the prior is **not** the posterior probability of the utterance (instead it's $P(O,W)$, the joint probability of the observation and the word sequence). The joint probability is fine for choosing the best hypothesis but the joint doesn't tell us how good this hypothesis is. Perhaps the best hypothesis is still really bad, and we need to ask the users to repeat themselves. If we had the posterior probabil-

Confidence   ity of a word, it could be used as a **confidence** metric since the posterior is an absolute rather than relative measure. Recognizers often pass a confidence metric to a higher-level process (like a dialogue manager; see Chapter 24) to indicate how confident the recognizer is that the word string it returns is a good one.

To compute the posterior probability of a word, we'll need to normalize over all the different word hypotheses available at a particular point in the utterances. At each point we'll need to know which words are competing or confusable. The lattices that

Confusion network   show these sequences of word confusions are called **confusion networks**, **meshes**,
Mesh   **sausages**, or **pinched lattices**. A confusion network consists of a sequence of word
Sausage   positions, as shown in Fig. 10.5. At each position is a set of mutually exclusive word
Pinched lattice   hypotheses. The network represents the set of sentences that can be created by a choice of one word from each position. Note that unlike in lattices or word graphs, when we build a confusion network we implicitly add paths that were not in the original lattice.

We build confusion networks by aligning the different hypothesis paths in the lattice with each other. We compute the posterior probability for each word by summing

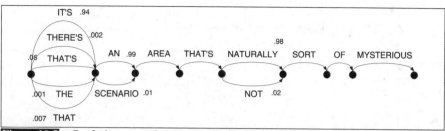

Figure 10.5   Confusion network corresponding to the word lattice in Fig. 10.3. Each word is associated with a posterior probability. Note that some of the words from the lattice have been pruned. (Probabilities computed by the SRI-LM toolkit).

over all paths passing through a word and then normalizing by the sum of the probabilities of all competing words. See Mangu et al. (2000), Evermann and Woodland (2000), Kumar and Byrne (2002), and Doumpiotis et al. (2003b) for details. Confusion networks are also used for minimizing error rate (by maximizing the improvement of the word posterior probability rather than the sentence likelihood), and for training discriminative classifiers that distinguish among words.

Standard publicly available language modeling toolkits like SRI-LM (Stolcke, 2002) (http://www.speech.sri.com/projects/srilm/) and the HTK language modeling toolkit (Young et al., 2005) (http://htk.eng.cam.ac.uk/) can be used to generate and manipulate lattices, *N*-best lists, and confusion networks.

Forward-backward   Other kinds of multiple-stage searches include the **forward-backward** search algorithm (not to be confused with the **forward-backward** algorithm for HMM parameter setting) (Austin et al., 1991), which performs a simple forward search followed by a detailed backward (i.e., time-reversed) search.

10.2   A* ("Stack") Decoding

Recall that the Viterbi algorithm approximated the forward computation, computing the likelihood of the single best (MAX) path through the HMM, while the forward algorithm computes the likelihood of the total (SUM) of all the paths through the HMM. The A* decoding algorithm allows us to use the complete forward probability, avoiding the Viterbi approximation. A* decoding also allows us to use any arbitrary language model. Thus, A* is a one-pass alternative to multipass decoding.

The A* decoding algorithm is a best-first search of the tree that implicitly defines the sequence of allowable words in a language. Consider the tree in Fig. 10.6, rooted in the START node on the left. Each leaf of this tree defines one sentence of the language; the one formed by concatenating all the words along the path from START to the leaf. We don't represent this tree explicitly, but the algorithm uses the tree implicitly as a way to structure the decoding search.

The algorithm performs a search from the root of the tree to the leaves, looking for the highest probability path and hence the highest-probability sentence. As we proceed from root toward the leaves, each branch leaving a given word node represents a word

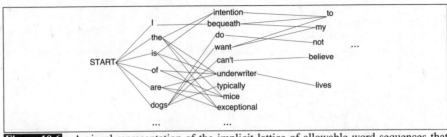

Figure 10.6   A visual representation of the implicit lattice of allowable word sequences that defines a language. The set of sentences of a language is far too large to represent explicitly, but the lattice gives a metaphor for exploring prefixes.

that may follow the current word. Each of these branches has a probability, which expresses the conditional probability of this next word given the part of the sentence we've seen so far. In addition, we can use the forward algorithm to assign each word a likelihood of producing some part of the observed acoustic data. The A* decoder must thus find a root-to-leaf path (word sequence) that has the highest probability, where a path probability is defined as the product of its language model probability (prior) and its acoustic match to the data (likelihood). It finds this path by keeping a **priority** **queue** of partial paths (i.e., prefixes of sentences, each annotated with a score). In a priority queue, each element has a score, and the *pop* operation returns the element with the highest score. The A* decoding algorithm iteratively chooses the best prefix-so-far, computes all the possible next words for that prefix, and adds these extended sentences to the queue. Figure 10.7 shows the complete algorithm.

Priority queue

---

function STACK-DECODING() **returns** *min-distance*

    Initialize the priority queue with a null sentence.
    Loop until queue is empty
        Pop the best (highest score) sentence *s* off the queue.
        If (*s* is marked end-of-sentence (EOS)) output *s* and terminate.
        Get list of candidate next words by doing fast matches.
        For each candidate next word *w*:
            Create a new candidate sentence $s + w$.
            Use forward algorithm to compute acoustic likelihood L of $s + w$.
            Compute language model probability P of extended sentence $s + w$.
            Compute "score" for $s + w$ (a function of L, P, and etc.).
            If (end-of-sentence) set EOS flag for $s + w$.
            Insert $s + w$ into the queue together with its score and EOS flag.

Figure 10.7   The A* decoding algorithm (modified from Paul (1991) and Jelinek (1997)). The evaluation function that is used to compute the score for a sentence is not completely defined here; possible evaluation functions are discussed below.

Let's consider a stylized example of an A* decoder working on a waveform for which the correct transcription is *If music be the food of love*. Figure 10.8 shows the search space after the decoder has examined paths of length one from the root. A

Fast match   **fast match** selects the likely next words. A fast match (discussed further below) is an algorithm for winnowing the number of possible following words, often by computing some approximation to the forward probability. At this point in our example, we've selected a subset of the possible next words based on the fast match and assigned each of them a score. The word *Alice* has the highest score. We haven't yet said exactly how the scoring works.

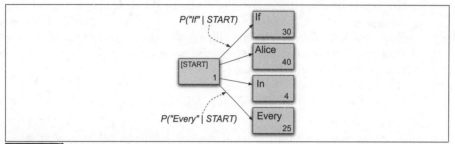

Figure 10.8   The beginning of the search for the sentence *If music be the food of love*. At this early stage *Alice* is the most likely hypothesis. (It has a higher score than the other hypotheses.)

Figure 10.9a shows the next stage in the search. We have expanded the *Alice* node. This means that the *Alice* node is no longer on the queue, but its children are. Note that now the node labeled *if* actually has a higher score than any of the children of *Alice*. Figure 10.9b shows the state of the search after we expanded the *if* node, removed it, and added *if music*, *if muscle*, and *if messy* on to the queue.

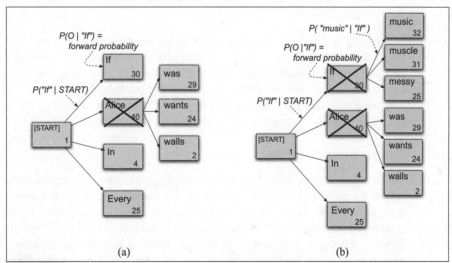

Figure 10.9   The next steps of the search for the sentence *If music be the food of love*. In (a) we've now expanded the *Alice* node and added three extensions that have a relatively high score; the highest-scoring node is *START if*, which is not along the *START Alice* path at all. In (b) we've expanded the *if* node. The hypothesis *START if music* then has the highest score.

We clearly want the scoring criterion for a hypothesis to be related to its probability. Indeed, it might seem that the score for a string of words w_1^i given an acoustic string y_1^j

should be the product of the prior and the likelihood:

$$P(y_1^j \; w_1^i)P(w_1^i)$$

Alas, we can't use this probability as the score because the probability will be smaller for a longer path than a shorter one. This is due to a basic fact about probabilities and substrings: any prefix of a string must have a higher probability than the string itself (e.g., P(START the ...) will be greater than P(START the book)). Thus, if we used probability as the score, the A* decoding algorithm would get stuck on the single-word hypotheses. Instead, we use the A* evaluation function (Nilsson, 1980; Pearl, 1984) $f^*(p)$ given a partial path p:

$$f^*(p) = g(p) + h^*(p)$$

$f^*(p)$ is the *estimated* score of the best complete path (complete sentence) that starts with the partial path p. In other words, it is an estimate of how well this path would do if we let it continue through the sentence. The A* algorithm builds this estimate from two components:

- $g(p)$ is the score from the beginning of utterance to the end of the partial path p. This g function can be nicely estimated by the probability of p given the acoustics so far (i.e., as $P(O \; W)P(W)$ for the word string W constituting p).

- $h^*(p)$ is an estimate of the best-scoring extension of the partial path to the end of the utterance.

Coming up with a good estimate of h^* is an unsolved and interesting problem. A simple approach is to chose an h^* estimate that correlates with the number of words remaining in the sentence (Paul, 1991). Slightly smarter is to estimate the expected likelihood per frame for the remaining frames and multiply this by the estimate of the remaining time. We can compute this expected likelihood by averaging the likelihood per frame in the training set. See Jelinek (1997) for further discussion.

Tree-Structured Lexicons

Tree-structured lexicon

We mentioned above that A* and other two-stage decoding algorithms require a **fast match** for quickly finding words in the lexicon that are likely candidates for matching some portion of the acoustic input. Many fast-match algorithms rely on a **tree-structured lexicon**, which stores word pronunciations in a structure that allows the forward probability computation to be shared for words that start with the same sequence of phones. The tree-structured lexicon was first suggested by Klovstad and Mondshein (1975) and can be used in both A* decoding (Gupta et al., 1988; Bahl et al., 1992) and Viterbi decoding (Ney et al., 1992; Nguyen and Schwartz, 1999). Figure 10.10 shows an example of a tree-structured lexicon like one used in the Sphinx-II recognizer (Ravishankar, 1996). Each tree root represents the first phone of all words beginning with that context-dependent phone (phone context may or may not be preserved across word boundaries), and each leaf is associated with a word.

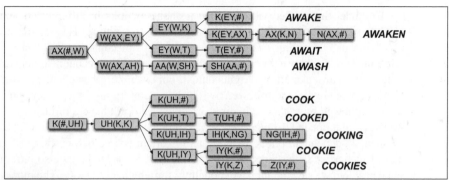

Figure 10.10   A tree-structured lexicon recognizer like the one used in the Sphinx-II recognizer (Ravishankar, 1996). Each node corresponds to a particular triphone, so EY(W,K) means the phone EY preceded by a W and followed by a K.

10.3   Context-Dependent Acoustic Models: Triphones

In our application in Section 9.4 of the HMM paradigm to ASR, we showed how an HMM could be created for each phone, with three emitting states corresponding to subphones at the beginning, middle, and end of the phone. We represented each subphone ("beginning of [eh]", "beginning of [t]", "middle of [ae]") with its own GMM.

The problem with using a fixed GMM for a subphone like "beginning of [eh]", however, is that phones vary enormously depending on the neighboring phones. This is because the movement of the articulators (tongue, lips, velum) during speech production is continuous and is subject to physical constraints like momentum. Thus, an articulator may start moving during one phone to get into place in time for the next phone. In Chapter 7 we defined the word **coarticulation** as the movement of articula-tors to anticipate the next sound or perseverate from the last sound. Figure 10.11 shows coarticulation due to neighboring phone contexts for the vowel [eh].

Coarticulation

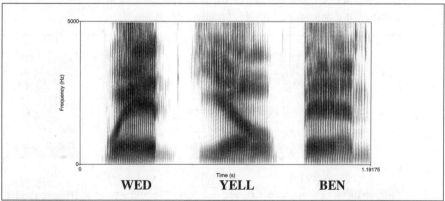

Figure 10.11   The vowel [eh] in three different triphone contexts, in the words *wed*, *yell*, and *Ben*. Notice the marked differences in the second formant (F2) at the beginning and end of the [eh] in all three cases.

353

CI phone
CD phone
Triphone

To model the marked variation that a phone exhibits in different contexts, most LVCSR systems replace the context-independent (**CI phone**) HMM with a context-dependent or **CD phone**. The most common kind of context-dependent model is a **triphone** HMM (Schwartz et al., 1985; Deng et al., 1990). A triphone model represents a phone in a particular left and right context. For example, the triphone *[y-eh+l]* means "[eh] preceded by [y] and followed by [l]". In general, [a-b+c] means "[b] preceded by [a] and followed by [c]". In situations in which we don't have a full triphone context, we use [a-b] to mean "[b] preceded by [a]" and [b+c] to mean "[b] followed by [c]".

Context-dependent phones capture an important source of variation and are a key part of modern ASR systems. But unbridled context-dependency also introduces the same problem we saw in language modeling: training data sparsity. The more complex the model we try to train, the less likely we are to have seen enough observations of each phone type to train on. For a phoneset with 50 phones, in principle we would need 50^3 or 125,000 triphones. In practice, not every sequence of three phones is possible (English doesn't seem to allow triphone sequences like [ae-eh+ow] or [m-j+t]). Young et al. (1994) found that 55,000 triphones are needed in the 20K *Wall Street Journal* task. But they found that only 18,500 of these triphones, that is, less than half, actually occurred in the SI84 section of the WSJ training data.

Tied states

Because of the problem of data sparsity, we must reduce the number of triphone parameters that we need to train. The most common way to do this is by clustering some of the contexts and **tying** subphones whose contexts fall into the same cluster (Young and Woodland, 1994). For example, the beginning of a phone with an [n] on its left may look much like the beginning of a phone with an [m] on its left. We can therefore tie together the first (beginning) subphone of, say, the [m-eh+d] and [n-eh+d] triphones. Tying two states together means that they share the same Gaussians. So we train only a single Gaussian model for the first subphone of the [m-eh+d] and [n-eh+d] triphones. Likewise, it turns out that the left context phones [r] and [w] produce a similar effect on the initial subphone of following phones.

Figure 10.12 shows, for example, the vowel [iy] preceded by the consonants [w], [r], [m], and [n]. Notice that the beginning of [iy] has a similar rise in F2 after [w] and [r]. And notice the similarity of the beginning of [m] and [n]; this speaker (the first author) has a nasal formant (N2) around 1000 Hz.

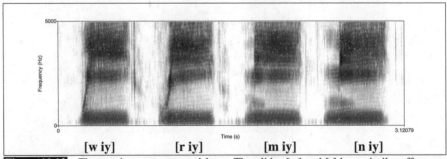

Figure 10.12 The words *we*, *re*, *me*, and *knee*. The glides [w] and [r] have similar effects on the beginning of the vowel [iy], as do the two nasals [n] and [m].

Figure 10.13 shows an example of the kind of triphone tying learned by the clustering algorithm. Each mixture Gaussian model is shared by the subphone states of various triphone HMMs.

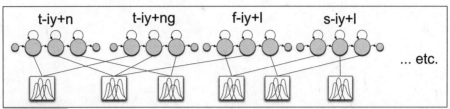

Figure 10.13   Four triphones showing the result of clustering. Notice that the initial subphone of [t-iy+n] and [t-iy+ng] is tied together, i.e., shares the same Gaussian mixture acoustic model. After Young et al. (1994).

How do we decide what contexts to cluster? The most common method is to use a decision tree. For each state (subphone) of each phone, a separate tree is built. Figure 10.14 shows a sample tree from the first (beginning) state of the phone /ih/, modified from Odell (1995). We begin at the root node of the tree with a single large cluster containing (the beginning state of) all triphones centered on /ih/. At each node in the tree, we split the current cluster into two smaller clusters by asking questions about the context. For example, the tree in Fig. 10.14 first splits the initial cluster into two clusters, one with nasal phone on the left, and one without. As we descend the tree from the root, each of these clusters is progressively split. The tree in Fig. 10.14 would split all beginning-state /ih/ triphones into five clusters, labeled A–E in the figure.

The questions used in the decision tree ask whether the phone to the left or right has a certain **phonetic feature**, of the type introduced in Chapter 7. Figure 10.15 shows a few decision tree questions; note that there are separate questions for vowels and consonants. Real trees would have many more questions.

How are decision trees like the one in Fig. 10.14 trained? The trees are grown top down from the root. At each iteration, the algorithm considers each possible question q and each node n in the tree. For each question, it considers how the new split would impact the acoustic likelihood of the training data. The algorithm computes the difference between the current acoustic likelihood of the training data and the new likelihood if the basis for the models being tied was splitting via question q. The algorithm picks the node n and question q that give the maximum likelihood. The procedure then iterates, stopping when each leaf node has a minimum threshold number of examples.

Cloning   We also need to modify the embedded training algorithm we saw in Section 9.7 to deal with context-dependent phones and also to handle mixture Gaussians. In both cases we use a more complex process that involves **cloning** and using extra iterations of EM, as described in Young et al. (1994).

To train context-dependent models, for example, we first use standard embedded training to train context-independent models using multiple passes of EM, resulting in separate single-Gaussian models for each subphone of each monophone /aa/, /ae/, etc. We then **clone** each monophone model, that is, make identical copies of the model with its three substates of Gaussians, one clone for each potential triphone. The *A* transition matrices are not cloned, but are tied together for all the triphone clones of a monophone. We then run an iteration of EM again and retrain the triphone Gaussians.

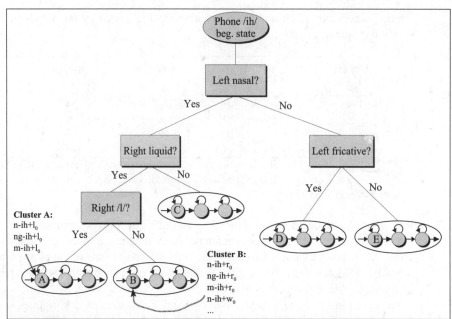

Figure 10.14 Decision tree for choosing which triphone states (subphones) to tie together. This tree will cluster state 0 (the beginning state) of the triphones /n-ih+l/, /ng-ih+l/, /m-ih+l/, into cluster class A, and other triphones into classes B–E. Adapted from Odell (1995).

Feature	Phones
Stop	b d g k p t
Nasal	m n ng
Fricative	ch dh f jh s sh th v z zh
Liquid	l r w y
Vowel	aa ae ah ao aw ax axr ay eh er ey ih ix iy ow oy uh uw
Front Vowel	ae eh ih ix iy
Central Vowel	aa ah ao axr er
Back Vowel	ax ow uh uw
High Vowel	ih ix iy uh uw
Rounded	ao ow oy uh uw w
Reduced	ax axr ix
Unvoiced	ch f hh k p s sh t th
Coronal	ch d dh jh l n r s sh t th z zh

Figure 10.15 Sample decision tree questions on phonetic features used by Odell (1995).

Now for each monophone we cluster all the context-dependent triphones by using the clustering algorithm described on page 347 to get a set of tied state clusters. One typical state is chosen as the exemplar for this cluster and the rest are tied to it.

We use this same cloning procedure to learn Gaussian mixtures. We first use embedded training with multiple iterations of EM to learn single-mixture Gaussian models for each tied triphone state, as described above. We then clone (split) each state into two identical Gaussians, perturb the values of each by some epsilon, and run EM again to retrain these values. We then split each of the two mixtures, resulting in four, perturb them, retrain. We continue until we have an appropriate number of mixtures for the number of observations in each state.

We thus create a full context-dependent GMM triphone model by applying these two cloning-and-retraining procedures in series, as shown schematically in Fig. 10.16.

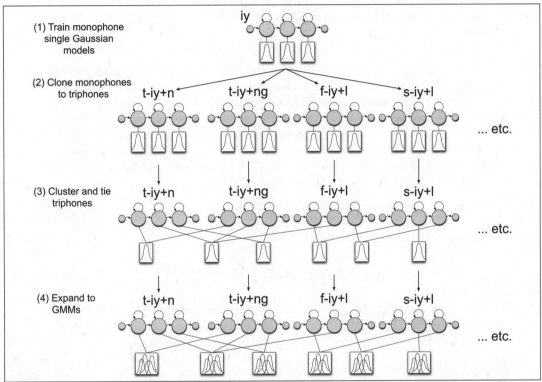

(1) Train monophone single Gaussian models

iy

(2) Clone monophones to triphones

t-iy+n   t-iy+ng   f-iy+l   s-iy+l

... etc.

(3) Cluster and tie triphones

t-iy+n   t-iy+ng   f-iy+l   s-iy+l

... etc.

(4) Expand to GMMs

t-iy+n   t-iy+ng   f-iy+l   s-iy+l

... etc.

Figure 10.16   The four stages in training a tied-mixture triphone acoustic model. After Young et al. (1994).

10.4   Discriminative Training

MLE
Discriminative
training

The Baum-Welch and embedded training models we have presented for training the HMM parameters (the A and B matrices) are based on maximizing the likelihood of the training data. An alternative to this **maximum likelihood estimation** (**MLE**) is to focus not on fitting the best model to the data but rather on **discriminating** the best model from all the other models. Such training procedures include Maximum Mutual Information Estimation (MMIE) (Woodland and Povey, 2002) and the use of neural net/SVM classifiers (Bourlard and Morgan, 1994), as well as other techniques like Minimum Classification Error training (Chou et al., 1993; McDermott and Hazen, 2004) or Minimum Bayes Risk estimation (Doumpiotis et al., 2003a). We summarize the first two of these in the next two subsections.

10.4.1   Maximum Mutual Information Estimation

Recall that in maximum likelihood estimation (MLE), we train our acoustic model parameters (A and B) so as to maximize the likelihood of the training data. Consider a particular observation sequence O, and a particular HMM model M_k corresponding to word sequence W_k, out of all the possible sentences $W' \in \mathscr{L}$. The MLE criterion thus maximizes

$$\mathscr{F}_{\text{MLE}}(\lambda) = P_\lambda(O \mid M_k) \tag{10.4}$$

Since our goal in speech recognition is to have the correct transcription for the largest number of sentences, we'd like, on average, the probability of the **correct** word string W_k to be high, certainly higher than the probability of all the **wrong** word strings $W_j s.t. j \neq k$. But the MLE criterion above does not guarantee this. Thus, we'd like to pick some other criterion which will let us chose the model λ that assigns the highest probability to the correct model, that is, maximizes $P_\lambda(M_k \mid O)$. Maximizing the probability of the word string rather than the probability of the observation sequence is called *CMLE*   **conditional maximum likelihood estimation** or **CMLE**:

$$\mathscr{F}_{\text{CMLE}}(\lambda) = P_\lambda(M_k \mid O) \tag{10.5}$$

Using Bayes' rule, we can express this as

$$\mathscr{F}_{\text{CMLE}}(\lambda) = P_\lambda(M_k \mid O) = \frac{P_\lambda(O \mid M_k)P(M_k)}{P_\lambda(O)} \tag{10.6}$$

Let's now expand $P_\lambda(O)$ by marginalizing (summing over all sequences that could have produced it). The total probability of the observation sequence is the weighted sum over all word strings of the observation likelihood given that word string:

$$P(O) = \sum_{W \in \mathscr{L}} P(O \mid W)P(W) \tag{10.7}$$

So a complete expansion of Eq. 10.6 is

$$\mathscr{F}_{\text{CMLE}}(\lambda) = P_\lambda(M_k \mid O) = \frac{P_\lambda(O \mid M_k)P(M_k)}{\sum_{M \in \mathscr{L}} P_\lambda(O \mid M)P(M)} \tag{10.8}$$

In a slightly confusing bit of standard nomenclature, CMLE is generally referred to instead as Maximum Mutual Information Estimation (MMIE). This is because it turns out that maximizing the posterior $P(W \mid O)$ and maximizing the mutual information $I(W, O)$ are equivalent if we assume that the language model probability of each sentence W is constant (fixed) during acoustic training, an assumption we usually make. Thus, from here on we will refer to this criterion as the MMIE criterion rather than the CMLE criterion, and so here is Eq. 10.8 restated:

$$\mathscr{F}_{\text{MMIE}}(\lambda) = P_\lambda(M_k \mid O) = \frac{P_\lambda(O \mid M_k)P(M_k)}{\sum_{M \in \mathscr{L}} P_\lambda(O \mid M)P(M)} \tag{10.9}$$

In a nutshell, then, the goal of MMIE estimation is to maximize Eq. 10.9 rather than Eq. 10.4. Now if our goal is to maximize $P_\lambda(M_k \mid O)$, we not only need to maximize the numerator of Eq. 10.9, but also to minimize the denominator. Notice that we can rewrite the denominator to make it clear that it includes a term equal to the model we are trying to maximize and a term for all other models:

$$P_\lambda(M_k \ O) = \frac{P_\lambda(O \ M_k)P(M_k)}{P_\lambda(O \ M_k)P(M_k) + \sum_{i \neq k} P_\lambda(O \ M_i)P(M_i)} \qquad (10.10)$$

Thus, to maximize $P_\lambda(M_k \ O)$, we will need to incrementally change λ so that it increases the probability of the correct model, while simultaneously decreasing the probability of each of the incorrect models. Thus, training with MMIE clearly fulfills the important goal of **discriminating** between the correct sequence and all other sequences.

The implementation of MMIE is quite complex, and we don't discuss it here except to mention that it relies on a variant of Baum-Welch training called Extended Baum-Welch that maximizes Eq. 10.9 instead of Eq. 10.4. Briefly, we can view this as a two step algorithm; we first use standard MLE Baum-Welch to compute the forward-backward counts for the training utterances. Then we compute another pass of forward-backward using all other possible utterances, and subtract these from the counts. Of course, it turns out that computing this full denominator is computationally extremely expensive, because it requires running a full recognition pass on all the training data. Recall that in normal EM, we don't need to run decoding on the training data, since we are only trying to maximize the likelihood of the *correct* word sequence; in MMIE, we need to compute the probabilities of *all* possible word sequences. Decoding is very time-consuming because of complex language models. Thus in practice MMIE algorithms estimate the denominator by summing over only the paths that occur in a word lattice, as an approximation to the full set of possible paths.

CMLE was first proposed by Nádas (1983) and MMIE by Bahl et al. (1986), but practical implementations that actually reduced word error rate came much later; see Woodland and Povey (2002) or Normandin (1996) for details.

10.4.2   Acoustic Models Based on Posterior Classifiers

Another kind of discriminative training involves replacing the Gaussian acoustic likelihood classifier with a frame-level classifier that is discriminative or gives a posterior estimate, such as multi-layer perceptrons (MLPs) or support vector machines (SVMs). When the GMM classifier of an HMM is replaced by an SVM or MLP, we call this a **HMM-SVM** or **HMM-MLP hybrid** approach (Bourlard and Morgan, 1994). The SVM or MLP approaches, like the Gaussian model, estimate the probability with respect to a cepstral feature vector at a single time t. The posterior approaches often use a larger window of acoustic information than the GMM models, including cepstral feature vectors from neighboring time periods. Thus the input to a typical acoustic MLP or SVM might be feature vectors for the current frame plus the four previous and four following frames, that is, a total of nine cepstral feature vectors instead of the single one that a GMM model uses. Because they have such a wide context, SVM or MLP models generally use phones rather than subphones or triphones, and compute a posterior for each phone.

The SVM or MLP classifiers are thus computing the posterior probability of a state j given the observation vectors, that is, $P(q_j\ o_t)$. (The computation is also conditioned on the context, but let's ignore that for the moment.) But the observation likelihood we need for the HMM, $b_j(o_t)$, is $P(o_t\ q_j)$. Bayes' rule can help us see how to compute one from the other. The classifier is computing

$$p(q_j\ o_t) = \frac{P(o_t\ q_j)p(q_j)}{p(o_t)} \qquad (10.11)$$

We can rearrange the terms as follows:

$$\frac{p(o_t\ q_j)}{p(o_t)} = \frac{P(q_j\ o_t)}{p(q_j)} \qquad (10.12)$$

The two terms on the right-hand side of Eq. 10.12 can be directly computed from the posterior classifier; the numerator is the output of the SVM or MLP, and the denominator is the total probability of a given state, summing over all observations (i.e., the sum over all t of $\xi_j(t)$). Thus although we cannot directly compute $P(o_t\ q_j)$, we

Scaled likelihood

can use Eq. 10.12 to compute $\frac{p(o_t\ q_j)}{p(o_t)}$, which is known as a **scaled likelihood** (the likelihood divided by the probability of the observation). In fact, the scaled likelihood is just as good as the regular likelihood since the probability of the observation $p(o_t)$ is a constant during recognition and it's presence in the equation doesn't hurt.

To train an SVM or MLP classifier we need to know the correct phone label q_j for each observation o_t. We can get this label with the **embedded training** algorithm that we saw for GMMs; we start with some initial version of our classifier and a word transcript for the training sentences. We run a forced alignment of the training data, producing a phone string, and now we retrain the classifier, and iterate.

10.5   Modeling Variation

As we noted at the beginning of this chapter, variation is one of the largest obstacles to successful speech recognition. We mentioned variation due to speaker differences from vocal characteristics or dialect, due to genre (such as spontaneous versus read speech), and due to the environment (such as noisy versus quiet environments). Handling this kind of variation is a major subject of modern research.

10.5.1   Environmental Variation and Noise

Environmental variation has received the most attention from the speech literature, and a number of techniques have been suggested for dealing with environmental noise.

Spectral subtraction
Additive noise

Spectral subtraction, for example, is used to combat **additive noise**. Additive noise is noise from external sound sources like engines or wind or fridges that is relatively constant and can be modeled as a noise signal that is just added in the time domain to the speech waveform to produce the observed signal. In spectral subtraction, we estimate the average noise during non-speech regions and then subtract this average value

Lombard effect

from the speech signal. Interestingly, speakers often compensate for high background-noise levels by increasing their amplitude, F0, and formant frequencies. This change in speech production due to noise is called the **Lombard effect**, named for Etienne Lombard who first described it in 1911 (Junqua, 1993).

Convolutional noise

Cepstral mean normalization

Other noise robustness techniques are used to deal with **convolutional noise**, noise introduced by channel characteristics like different microphones. For example, in **cepstral mean normalization** we compute the average of the cepstrum over time and subtract it from each frame; the average cepstrum models the fixed spectral characteristics of the microphone and the room acoustics (Atal, 1974).

Finally, non-verbal sounds, like coughs, loud breathing, and throat clearing, or environmental sounds, like beeps, telephone rings, and door slams can be modeled explicitly. For each sound, we create a special phone and add to the lexicon a word consisting only of that phone. We then add labels for these non-verbal words to the training data transcripts and train the phones normally with Baum-Welch training (Ward, 1989). The words also are added to the language model, often by allowing them to appear between any two words with some small constant probability.

10.5.2   Speaker Variation and Speaker Adaptation

Speech recognition systems are generally designed to be speaker independent since it's rarely practical to collect enough training data to build a single-user system. But when we do have enough data, speaker-dependent systems function better than speaker-independent systems. This makes sense; we can reduce the variability and increase the precision of our models if the test data looks more like the training data.

While it is rare to have enough data to train on an individual speaker, we do have enough data to train separate models for two important groups of speakers: men versus women. Since women and men have different vocal tracts and other acoustic and phonetic characteristics, we can split the training data by gender and train separate acoustic models for men and for women. Then, when a test sentence comes in, we use a gender detector to decide which of the two acoustic models to use. Gender detectors can be built out of binary GMM classifiers based on cepstral features. Such **gender-dependent acoustic modeling** is used in most LVCSR systems.

MLLR

It is important to **adapt** speaker-independent acoustic models to new speakers. For example the **maximum likelihood linear regression (MLLR)** technique (Leggetter and Woodland, 1995) adapts GMM acoustic models to a small amount of data from a new speaker. The idea is to use the small amount of data to train a linear transform to warp the means of the Gaussians. MLLR and other such techniques for **speaker adaptation** have been one of the largest sources of improvement in ASR performance in recent years.

Speaker adaptation

The MLLR algorithm begins with a trained acoustic model and a small adaptation dataset from a new speaker. The adaptation set can be as small as three sentences or ten seconds of speech. The idea is to learn a linear transform matrix (W) and a bias vector (ω) to transform the means of the acoustic model Gaussians. If the old mean of a Gaussian is μ, the equation for the new mean $\hat{\mu}$ is thus

$$\hat{\mu} = W\mu + \omega \tag{10.13}$$

In the simplest case, we can learn a single global transform and apply it to each Gaussian model. The resulting equation for the acoustic likelihood is thus only slightly modified:

$$b_j(o_t) = \frac{1}{\sqrt{2\pi\,\Sigma j}} \exp\left(-\frac{1}{2}(o_t - (W\mu_j + \omega))^T \Sigma_j^{-1} (o_t - (W\mu_j + \omega))\right) \quad (10.14)$$

The transform is learned by the use of linear regression to maximize the likelihood of the adaptation dataset. We first run forward-backward alignment on the adaptation set to compute the state occupation probabilities $\xi_j(t)$. We then compute W by solving a system of simultaneous equations involving $\xi_j(t)$. If enough data is available, it's also possible to learn a larger number of transforms.

MLLR is a type of **linear transform** approach to speaker adaptation, one of the three major classes of speaker adaptation methods; the other two are **MAP adaptation** and **Speaker Clustering** approaches. See Woodland (2001) for a comprehensive survey.

MLLR and other speaker-adaptation algorithms can also be used to address another large source of error in LVCSR, the problem of foreign or dialect-accented speakers. Word error rates go up when the test set speaker speaks a dialect or accent (such as Spanish-accented English or southern-accented Mandarin Chinese) that differs from the (usually standard) training set, Here, we can take an adaptation set of a few sentences from, say, 10 speakers and adapt to them as a group, creating an MLLR transform that addresses whatever characteristics are present in the dialect or accent (Huang et al., 2000; Tomokiyo and Waibel, 2001; Wang et al., 2003).

Another useful speaker adaptation technique is to control for the differing vocal tract lengths of speakers that is an important source of speech variation between speakers. Cues to the speaker's vocal tract length are present in the signal; for example, speakers with longer vocal tracts tend to have lower formants. Vocal tract length can *VTLN* therefore be detected and normalized in a process called **VTLN** (**Vocal Tract Length Normalization**); see the Notes at the end of the chapter for details and pointers.

10.5.3   Pronunciation Modeling: Variation Due to Genre

Why is conversational speech harder to recognize than read speech? Is it the difference in vocabulary or grammar? Or perhaps a fact about the recording situation?

Neither of these seems to be the cause. Weintraub et al. (1996) studied ASR performance on conversational versus read speech, controlling for these and other factors. Pairs of subjects in the lab conversed on the telephone. Weintraub et al. (1996) then hand-transcribed the conversations and had the participants come back and read their own transcripts over the same phone lines as if they were dictating. Both the natural and read conversations were recorded. Now Weintraub et al. (1996) had one natural corpus and one read speech corpus with identical transcripts, speakers, and microphones. They found that read speech was easier to recognize (WER = 29%) than conversational speech (WER = 53%). Since the speakers, words, and channel were controlled, this difference must be modelable somewhere in the acoustic model or lexicon.

Saraclar et al. (2000) tested the hypothesis that this difficulty with conversational speech was due to changed pronunciations, that is, to a mismatch between the phone strings in the lexicon and what people actually said. Recall from Chapter 7 the massive pronunciation variation in conversation speech (12 different Switchboard pronunciations for *because* and hundreds for *the*). Saraclar et al. (2000) showed in an oracle experiment that if a Switchboard recognizer is told which pronunciations to use for each word, the word error rate drops from 47% to 27%.

If knowing which pronunciation to use improves accuracy, could we improve recognition by simply adding more pronunciations for each word to the lexicon? Alas, it turns out that adding multiple pronunciations doesn't work well because of the extra confusability; if a common pronunciation of the word "of" is the single vowel [ax], it is now very confusable with the word "a" (Cohen, 1989). Multiple pronunciations also cause problems in Viterbi decoding. As we said on page 336, the Viterbi decoder finds the best **phone** string rather than the best **word** string. This means that Viterbi baises against words with many pronunciations, since the probability mass is split up among more pronunciations. Finally, using multiple pronunciations to model coarticulatory effects may be unnecessary because CD phones (triphones) already successfully model coarticulatory phenomena like flapping and vowel reduction (Jurafsky et al., 2001b).

Instead, most current LVCSR systems use a very small number of pronunciations per word. We generally start with a lexicon with many pronunciations, derived from dictionaries or from phonological rules of the type described in Chapter 7. A forced Viterbi phone alignment of the training set is then run using this lexicon. The result of the alignment is a phonetic transcription of the training corpus, showing the pronunciation that was used and the frequency of each pronunciation. We can then collapse similar pronunciations (e.g., if two pronunciations differ only in a single phone substitution we choose the more frequent pronunciation). We then choose the maximum likelihood pronunciation for each word. Only for very frequent words that have multiple high-frequency pronunciations do we add a second or third pronunciations. For such words, usually function words, we annotate the dictionary with a pronunciation probability that can be used in computing acoustic likelihood (Cohen, 1989; Hain et al., 2001; Hain, 2002).

Finding a better method to deal with pronunciation variation remains an unsolved research problem. One promising avenue is to focus on non-phonetic factors that affect pronunciation. For example, words that are highly predictable or at the beginning or end of intonation phrases or are followed by disfluencies are pronounced very differently (Fosler-Lussier and Morgan, 1999; Bell et al., 2003). Fosler-Lussier (1999) shows reductions in word errors by using these sorts of factors to predict which pronunciation to use. Another exciting line of research in pronunciation modeling uses a dynamic Bayesian network to model the complex overlap in articulators that produces phonetic reduction (Livescu and Glass, 2004b, 2004a).

Another important issue in pronunciation modeling is dealing with unseen words. In Web-based applications such as telephone-based interfaces to the Web, the recognizer lexicon must be automatically augmented with pronunciations for the millions of unseen words, particularly names, that occur on the Web. Grapheme-to-phoneme techniques like those described in Section 8.2.3 are used to solve this problem.

10.6   Metadata: Boundaries, Punctuation, and Disfluencies

The output of the speech recognition process as we have described it so far is just a string of raw words. Consider the following sample gold-standard transcript (i.e., assuming perfect word recognition) of part of a dialogue (Jones et al., 2003):

> yeah actually um i belong to a gym down here a gold's gym uh-huh and uh exercise i try to exercise five days a week um and i usually do that uh what type of exercising do you do in the gym

Compare the difficult transcript above with the following much clearer version:

> A: Yeah I belong to a gym down here. Gold's Gym. And I try to exercise five days a week. And I usually do that.
>
> B: What type of exercising do you do in the gym?

The raw transcript is not divided up among speakers, not punctuated or capitalized, and is littered with disfluencies making it harder to read (Jones et al., 2003, 2005). Adding punctuation to the transcript improves readability as well as the accuracy of information extraction algorithms on the transcribed text (Makhoul et al., 2005; Hillard et al., 2006). Post-processing ASR output involves tasks including the following:

Diarization **Diarization** is the task of assigning speaker labels (like **A:** and **B:** above) to speech regions in multispeaker tasks like meeting transcription.

Sentence segmentation **Sentence segmentation** is the task of finding sentence boundaries, which is easy from text (Chapters 3 and 8) because we have helpful punctuation like periods. Boundary detection in speech is harder because of the lack of punctuation and because the transcribed words will be errorful, but has the advantage that prosodic features like pauses and sentence-final intonation can be used as cues.

Truecasing **Truecasing** is the task of assigning the correct case for a word, so that sentence-initial words start with an upper-case letter, acronyms are all in capitals, and so on. This is often addressed as an HMM classification task like part-of-speech tagging, with hidden states like ALL-LOWER CASE, UPPER-CASE-INITIAL, *all-caps*, and so on.

Punctuation detection **Punctuation detection** is the task of assigning sentence-final punctuation (period, question mark, exclamation mark) as well as commas, quotation marks and so on.

Disfluency detection **Disfluency detection** is used to remove disfluencies from a transcript for readability, or at least marking them off with commas or font changes. Disfluency detection algorithms can also play an important role in avoiding the misrecognized words that often result from word fragments.

Metadata Marking punctuation, boundaries, and diarization in the text output is called **metadata** or **rich transcription**. Let's examine a few of these tasks in slightly more detail. **Sentence segmentation** can be modeled as a binary classification task, in which each junction between two words is labeled as a sentence boundary or as sentence-internal. Figure 10.17 shows the candidate boundary locations in a sample sentence. Such classifiers can use features discussed in Section 8.3.1, such as words and part-of-speech tags around each candidate boundary, length features such as the distance from the previously found boundary, and prosodic features like:

Duration: durations of the phone and rime (nucleus plus coda) preceding the candidate boundary, since sentence-final words tend to be lengthened. Each phone is usually normalized to the mean duration for that phone.

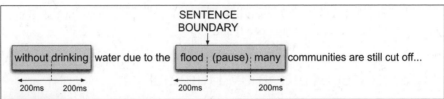

Figure 10.17   Candidate sentence boundaries computed at each inter-word boundary showing prosodic feature extraction regions from the Shriberg et al. (2000) algorithm.

Pause: duration of the interword pause at the candidate boundary.

Pitch reset

F0 features: the **change in pitch** across the boundary. Sentence boundaries often have **pitch reset** (an abrupt change in pitch), whereas non-boundaries are more likely to have continuous pitch across the boundary. Another useful F0 feature is the **pitch range** of the preboundary word; sentences often end with a **final fall** (Section 8.3.3) that is close to the speaker's F0 baseline.

For **punctuation detection**, similar features are used as for sentence boundary detection, but with multiple hidden classes (comma, sentence-final question mark, quotation mark, no punctuation) instead of just two. For both of these tasks, instead of a simple binary classifier, sequence information can be incorporated by modeling sentence segmentation as an HMM in which the hidden states correspond to sentence boundary decisions. The combination of prosodic and lexical features is discussed further for dialogue act detection in Section 24.5.2.

Disfluencies
Repair

Disfluencies or **repair** in conversation include phenomena like the following:

Disfluency Type	Example
fillers (or **filled pauses**):	But, *uh*, that was absurd
word fragments	A guy went to a *d-*, a landfill
repetitions:	it was just a *change of, change of* location
restarts	it's – I find it very strange

Interruption point

The ATIS sentence in Fig. 10.18 shows examples of a restart and the fillers *uh* and *I mean*, showing the **interruption point** that starts the **editing phase**.

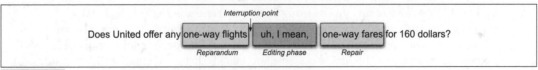

Figure 10.18   A disfluency example adapted from an ATIS sentence.

Detecting disfluencies is similar to detecting sentence boundaries; a classifier is trained to make a decision at each word boundary, using both text and prosodic features. Features include neighboring words and part-of-speech tags, the duration of pauses at the word boundary, the duration of the word and phones preceding the boundary, the difference in pitch values across the boundary, and so on. Fragment detection

Jitter
Spectral tilt

relies on features for detecting voice quality (Liu, 2004), including **jitter**, a measure of perturbation in the pitch period (Rosenberg, 1971), **spectral tilt**, the slope of the

Open quotient   spectrum (Section 9.3.1), and **open quotient**, the percentage of the glottal cycle in which the vocal folds are open (Fant, 1997).

10.7   Speech Recognition by Humans

Humans are of course much better at speech recognition than machines; current machines are roughly about five times worse than humans on clean speech, and the gap seems to increase with noisy speech.

ASR shares some features with human speech recognition, some of which were borrowed (PLP analysis (Hermansky, 1990), for example, was inspired by properties *Lexical access*   of the human auditory system). Three properties of human **lexical access** (the process of retrieving a word from the mental lexicon) are also shared by ASR models: **frequency**, **parallelism**, and **cue-based processing**. Human lexical access, like ASR with its N-gram language models, is sensitive to word **frequency**. Humans access high-frequency words faster, recognize them in noisier environments, and with less stimuli than low-frequency words (Howes, 1957; Grosjean, 1980; Tyler, 1984). Like ASR models, human lexical access is **parallel**: multiple words are active at the same time (Marslen-Wilson and Welsh, 1978; Salasoo and Pisoni, 1985, among others).

Finally, human speech perception integrates cues from many levels: acoustic cues, such as formant structure or voicing timing (Oden and Massaro, 1978; Miller, 1994), visual cues, such as lip movement (McGurk and Macdonald, 1976; Massaro and Cohen, 1983; Massaro, 1998), and lexical cues (Warren, 1970; Samuel, 1981; Con- *Phoneme*   nine and Clifton, 1987; Connine, 1990). For example, Warren (1970) demonstrated *restoration effect*   a **phoneme restoration effect**. They replaced one phone in a speech sample (e.g., the [s] in *legislature*) with a cough, and found that subjects listening to the modified sound *McGurk effect*   heard the entire word *legislature* including the [s]. In the **McGurk effect** McGurk and Macdonald (1976) showed that visual input can interfere with phone perception, causing subjects to perceive a completely different phone. They showed subjects a video of someone saying the syllable *ga* but the audio signal was dubbed with someone saying the syllable *ba*. Subjects reported hearing a third phone like *da* instead. We encourage the reader to try this from video demos on the Web; see, for example, `http://www.haskins.yale.edu/featured/heads/mcgurk.html`.

Word association   Other cues in human speech perception include semantic **word association** (words are accessed more quickly if a semantically related word has been heard recently) and *Repetition*   **repetition priming** (words are accessed more quickly if they themselves have just *priming*   been heard). The intuitions of both these results have been incorporated into the cache language model of Kuhn and De Mori (1990), which models repetition priming, the trigger language model of Rosenfeld (1996), and the LSA models of Coccaro and Jurafsky (1998) and Bellegarda (1999), which model word association (Chapter 4). In a fascinating reminder that good ideas are never discovered only once, Cole and Rudnicky (1983) point out that many of these insights about context effects on word and phone processing were actually discovered by William Bagley (1901). Bagley achieved his results, including an early version of the phoneme restoration effect, by recording speech on Edison phonograph cylinders, modifying it, and presenting it to subjects.

Bagley's results were forgotten and only rediscovered much later.

On-line processing

We have focused on the similarities between human and machine speech recognition; one difference is time course. While ASR models often emphasize optimization over the entire utterance, human processing seems to emphasize **on-line processing**: people incrementally segment an utterance into words and assign it an interpretation as they hear it. For example, Marslen-Wilson (1973) studied **close shadowers**: people who are able to shadow (repeat back) a passage as they hear it with lags as short as 250 ms. Marslen-Wilson found that when errors made by these shadowers were syntactically and semantically appropriate with the context, indicating that word segmentation, parsing, and interpretation took place within these 250 ms. Cole (1973) and Cole and Jakimik (1980) found similar effects in their work on the detection of mispronunciations. These results have led psychological models of human speech perception to focus on the time course of lexical access. For example, the neural-network TRACE model (McClelland and Elman, 1986) has three levels of computational units: features, phonemes, and words, each representing a hypothesis about its presence in the input and activated in parallel by the input. Activation flows excitatorily between units on different levels and inhibitorily between units on a single level so that the activation of a word slightly inhibits all other words. Human lexical access also exhibits **neighborhood effects** (the neighborhood of a word is the set of words that closely resemble it). Words with large frequency-weighted neighborhoods are accessed more slowly than words with fewer neighbors (Luce et al., 1990). ASR models don't focus on this word-level competition. Finally, humans make use of prosodic knowledge for word recognition Cutler and Norris (1988), Cutler and Carter (1987); using prosody in ASR is an important future research direction.

10.8 Summary

- We introduced two advanced decoding algorithms: The multipass (*N*-best or lattice) decoding algorithm and **stack** or **A*** decoding.
- Advanced acoustic models are based on context-dependent **triphones** rather than phones. Because the complete set of triphones would be too large, we use a smaller number of automatically clustered triphones instead.
- Acoustic models can be **adapted** to new speakers.
- Pronunciation variation is a source of errors in human-human speech recognition, but one that is not successfully handled by current technology.

Bibliographical and Historical Notes

A* search

See the previous chapter for most of the relevant speech recognition history. Note that although stack decoding is equivalent to the **A* search** developed in artificial intelligence, the stack decoding algorithm was developed independently in the information theory literature and the link with AI best-first search was noticed only later (Jelinek, 1976). Useful references on vocal tract length normalization include Cohen et al.

(1995), Wegmann et al. (1996), Eide and Gish (1996), Lee and Rose (1996), Welling et al. (2002), and Kim et al. (2004).

Many new directions in current speech recognition research involve alternatives to the HMM model, including new **graphical models** such as dynamic Bayes nets and factorial HMMs (Zweig, 1998; Bilmes, 2003; Livescu et al., 2003; Bilmes and Bartels, 2005; Frankel et al., 2007), as well as attempts to replace the **frame-based** HMM acoustic model (that makes a decision about each frame) with **segment-based recognizers** that attempt to detect variable-length segments (phones) (Digilakis, 1992; Ostendorf et al., 1996; Glass, 2003). New **landmark-based** recognizers and articulatory phonology-based recognizers focus on the use of distinctive features, defined acoustically or articulatorily, respectively (Niyogi et al., 1998; Livescu, 2005; Hasegawa-Johnson, 2005; Juneja and Espy-Wilson, 2003).

Frame-based

Segment-based

See Shriberg (2005) for an overview of metadata research. Shriberg (2002) and Nakatani and Hirschberg (1994) are computationally focused corpus studies of the acoustic and lexical properties of disfluencies. Early papers on sentence segmentation from speech include Wang and Hirschberg (1992) and Ostendorf and Ross (1997). See Shriberg et al. (2000) and Liu et al. (2006) for recent work on sentence segmentation, Kim and Woodland (2001) and Hillard et al. (2006) on punctuation detection, Nakatani and Hirschberg (1994), Honal and Schultz (2003, 2005), Lease et al. (2006), and a number of papers that jointly address multiple metadata extraction tasks (Heeman and Allen, 1999; Liu et al., 2005, 2006).

Exercises

10.1 Implement the Stack decoding algorithm of Fig. 10.7 on page 342. Pick a simple h^* function like an estimate of the number of words remaining in the sentence.

10.2 Modify the forward algorithm of Fig. 9.23 on page 319 to use the tree-structured lexicon of Fig. 10.10 on page 345.

10.3 Many ASR systems, including the Sonic and HTK systems, use a different algorithm for Viterbi called the **token-passing Viterbi** algorithm (Young et al., 1989). Read this paper and implement this algorithm.

Credits

Fig. 10.14 (© the authors; thanks to the Association of Computational Linguistics, the *Journal of Computational Linguistics* and its editor Robert Dale, and to Julian Odell)

Fig. 10.16 (© the authors; thanks to the Association of Computational Linguistics, the *Journal of Computational Linguistics* and its editor Robert Dale, and to Steve Young)

Chapter 11

Computational Phonology

bidakupadotigolabubidakutupiropadotigolabutupirobidaku...
Word segmentation stimulus (Saffran et al., 1996a)

Computational phonology

Phonology is the study of the systematic way that sounds are differently realized in different environments and how this system of sounds is related to the rest of the grammar. We've discussed various aspects of phonology in previous chapters, including phonemes, variation, and articulatory phonology in Chapter 7 and prosody and intonational phonology in Chapter 8. In this chapter we introduce **computational phonology**, the use of computational models in phonological theory.

Models in non-computational phonology are often framed in generative terms, expressing how an underlying phonological form is mapped to a surface phonological form. By contrast, in computational phonology, we are more interested in the inverse problem of **phonological parsing**; going from surface form to underlying structure. This includes the task of **syllabification**, determining the correct syllable structure for a surface word, or the task of determining the underlying string of phonemes or morphemes. Besides their theoretical interest, processes like syllabification turn out to be useful for speech processing. The chapter also discusses computational phonology methods like finite-state transducers and various versions of **optimality theory** and introduces a number of algorithms for the key problem of machine learning of phonological and morphological representations.

11.1 Finite-State Phonology

We applied finite-state transducers to spelling rules and morphology in Chapter 3. The application of automata to phonology is quite similar, and indeed came earlier (Kaplan and Kay, 1981). Figure 11.1 shows a motivating example; a transducer that models the simplified flapping rule in (11.1).

$$/t/ \rightarrow [dx] / \acute{V} \underline{\quad} V \tag{11.1}$$

The transducer in Fig. 11.1 accepts any string in which flaps occur in the correct places (after a stressed vowel, before an unstressed vowel) and rejects strings in which flapping doesn't occur or in which flapping occurs in the wrong environment.[1]

---

[1] For pedagogical purposes, this example ignores other important factors that influence flapping like social class, word frequency, rate of speech, and so on.

From Chapter 11 of *Speech and Language Processing*, Second Edition. Daniel Jurafsky, James H. Martin.

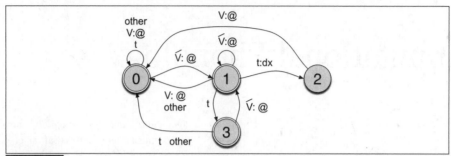

Figure 11.1   Transducer for English flapping: ARPAbet "dx" indicates a flap, and the "other" symbol means "any feasible pair not used elsewhere in the transducer". "@" means "any symbol not used elsewhere on any arc".

One way to think about transducers for phonological rules is the **two-level morphology** of Koskenniemi (1983) first mentioned in Chapter 3. The intuition of two-level morphology is to augment the notation for phonological rules to correspond more naturally to transducers. We motivate this idea by beginning with the notion of **rule ordering**. In a traditional phonological system, many phonological rules apply between a lexical form and a surface form. Sometimes these rules interact; the output from one rule affects the input to another rule. One way to implement rule interaction in a transducer system is to run transducers in a **cascade**. Consider, for example, the rules that are needed to deal with the phonological behavior of the English noun plural suffix -*s*. This suffix is pronounced [ix z] after any of [s/sh/z/zh/ch/jh] (so *peaches* is pronounced [p iy ch ix z]. This -s suffix is pronounced [z] after voiced sounds (so *pigs* is pronounced [p ih g z]), and pronounced [s] after unvoiced sounds (*cats* is pronounced [k ae t s]). We model this variation by writing phonological rules for the realization of the morpheme in different contexts.

From these three forms ([s], [z], [ix z]) we'll chose [z] as the "lexical" pronunciation of the suffix (because it turns out to simplify rule writing). Next we write two phonological rules. One, similar to the E-insertion spelling rule of page 64, inserts an [ix] after a morpheme-final sibilant and before the plural morpheme [z]. The other makes sure that the -*s* suffix is properly realized as [s] after unvoiced consonants.

$$\epsilon \rightarrow \text{ix} / \text{[+sibilant]} \ \hat{} \ \underline{\quad} \ \text{z} \ \# \qquad (11.2)$$

$$\text{z} \rightarrow \text{s} / \text{[-voice]} \ \hat{} \ \underline{\quad} \ \# \qquad (11.3)$$

These two rules must be **ordered**; rule (11.2) must apply before (11.3). This is because the environment of (11.2) includes z, and the rule (11.3) changes z. Consider running both rules on the lexical form *fox* concatenated with the plural -*s*:

Lexical form:	f aa k ˆ z
(11.2) applies:	f aa k s ˆ ix z
(11.3) doesn't apply:	f aa k sˆ ix z

If the devoicing rule (11.3) were ordered first, we would get the wrong result. This situation, in which one rule destroys the environment for another, is called **bleeding**:[2]

Bleeding

Lexical form: f aa k s ˆ z
(11.3) applies: f aa k s ˆ s
(11.2) doesn't apply: f aa k s ˆ s

As was suggested in Chapter 3, each of these rules can be represented by a transducer. Since the rules are ordered, the transducers would also need to be ordered. For example if they are placed in a cascade, the output of the first transducer would feed the input of the second transducer. Many rules can be cascaded together this way. As Chapter 3 discussed, running a cascade, particularly one with many levels, can be unwieldy, and so transducer cascades are usually replaced with a single, more complex, transducer by **composing** the individual transducers.

Two-level morphology is another way to solve the rule ordering problem. Koskenniemi (1983) observed that most phonological rules in a grammar are independent of one another; that feeding and bleeding relations between rules are not the norm. Koskenniemi therefore proposed that phonological rules be run in parallel rather than in series. The cases in which there is rule interaction (feeding or bleeding) we deal with by slightly modifying some rules. Koskenniemi's two-level rules can be thought of as a way of expressing **declarative constraints** on the well-formedness of the lexical-surface mapping. Two-level rules also differ from traditional phonological rules by explicitly coding when they are obligatory or optional, by using four differing **rule operators**; the ⇔ rule corresponds to traditional **obligatory** phonological rules, and the ⇒ rule implements **optional rules**:

Rule Type	Interpretation
a:b ⇐ c ___ d	*a* is **always** realized as *b* in the context *c* ___ *d*
a:b ⇒ c ___ d	*a* may be realized as *b* **only** in the context *c* ___ *d*
a:b ⇔ c ___ d	*a* must be realized as *b* in context *c* ___ *d* and nowhere else
a:b /⇐ c ___ d	*a* is **never** realized as *b* in the context *c* ___ *d*

The most important intuition of the two-level rules, and the mechanism that lets them avoid feeding and bleeding, is their ability to represent constraints on *two levels* using the colon (":") introduced in Chapter 3. The symbol *a:b* means a lexical *a* that maps to a surface *b*. Thus, *a:b* ⇔ *:c* ___ means *a* is realized as *b* after a **surface** c. By contrast, *a:b* ⇔ *c:* ___ means that *a* is realized as *b* after a **lexical** c. The symbol *c* with no colon is equivalent to *c:c*, that is, lexical *c* mapping to a surface *c*.

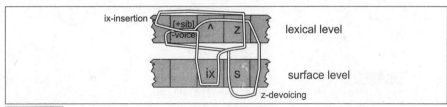

Figure 11.2   The constraints on ix-insertion and z-devoicing refer to *lexical* z, not *surface* z.

---

2 If we had represented the lexical form of *-s* as [s] rather than [z], we would have written the rule inversely to voice the *-s* after voiced sounds, but the rules would still need to be ordered (in reverse). Another rule relation is **feeding**, in which one rule creates the environment for another rule and so must be run beforehand.

Figure 11.2 shows an intuition for how the two-level approach avoids ordering for the ix-insertion and z-devoicing rules. The idea is that the z-devoicing rule maps a *lexical* z-insertion to a *surface* s and the ix rule refers to the *lexical* z. The two-level rules that model this constraint are shown in (11.4) and (11.5):

$$\epsilon : \text{ix} \iff [\text{+sibilant}]: \hat{\ } \underline{\quad} z: \# \qquad (11.4)$$

$$z : s \iff [\text{-voice}]: \hat{\ } \underline{\quad} \# \qquad (11.5)$$

As Chapter 3 discussed, rules can be automatically compiled into automata (see Kaplan and Kay (1994) and Antworth (1990) for details). The automata corresponding to the two rules are shown in Fig. 11.3 and Fig. 11.4. Figure 11.3 is based on Fig. 3.17 of Chapter 3; see page 64 for a reminder of how this automaton works. Note in Fig. 11.3 that the plural morpheme is represented by z:, indicating that the constraint is expressed about a lexical rather than surface z.

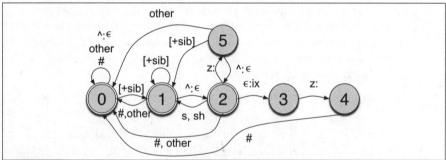

Figure 11.3   The transducer for the ix-insertion rule 11.2. The rule can be read *whenever a morpheme ends in a sibilant and the following morpheme is word-final z, insert [ix].*

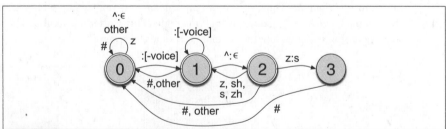

Figure 11.4   The transducer for the z-devoicing rule 11.3. This rule might be summarized *Devoice the morpheme z if it follows a morpheme-final voiceless consonant.*

Figure 11.5 shows the two automata running in parallel on the input [f aa k s ^ z]. Note that both the automata assume the default mapping ^:ε to remove the morpheme boundary and that both automata end in an accepting state.

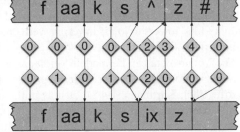

Figure 11.5   The transducer for ix-insertion (11.2) and z-devoicing (11.3) run in parallel.

11.2 Advanced Finite-State Phonology

Finite-state models of phonology have also been applied to more sophisticated phonological and morphological phenomena such as **harmony** and **templatic morphology**.

11.2.1 Harmony

Vowel harmony

Let's consider how a finite-state model deals with the complex interaction of three phonological rules in the Yawelmani dialect of Yokuts, a Native American language spoken in California.[3] First, Yokuts (like other languages such as Turkish and Hungarian) has **vowel harmony**, a process in which a vowel changes its form to look like a neighboring vowel. In Yokuts, a suffix vowel changes its form to agree in backness and roundness with the preceding stem vowel. That is, a front vowel like /i/ will appear as a back vowel [u] if the stem vowel is /u/. This **Harmony** rule applies if the suffix and stem vowels are of the same height (e.g., /u/ and /i/ both high, /o/ and /a/ both low):

	High Stem			**Low Stem**		
	Lexical	**Surface**	**Gloss**	**Lexical**	**Surface**	**Gloss**
Harmony	dub+hin	→ dubhun	"tangles"	bok'+al	→ bok'ol	"might eat"
No Harmony	xil+hin	→ xilhin	"leads by the hand"	xat'+al	→ xat'al	"might find"

The second relevant rule, **Lowering**, causes long high vowels to become low; /uː/ becomes [oː] and /iː/ becomes [eː], and the third rule, **Shortening**, shortens long vowels in closed syllables:

	Lowering		**Shortening**	
ʔuːt'+it	→ ʔoːt'ut	"steal, passive aorist"	sːap+hin	→ saphin
miːk'+it	→ meːk'+it	"swallow, passive aorist"	suduːk+hin	→ sudokhun

The three Yokuts rules must be ordered, just as the ix-insertion and z-devoicing rules had to be ordered. Harmony must be ordered before Lowering because the /uː/

---

[3] These rules were first proposed by Kisseberth (1969) drawing on Newman (1944). Our examples are from Cole and Kisseberth (1995); some details such as vowel underspecification have been removed for pedagogical simplification (Archangeli, 1984).

in the lexical form /ʔuːt'+it/ causes the /i/ to become [u] before it lowers in the surface form [ʔoːt'ut]. Lowering must be ordered before Shortening because the /uː/ in /suduːk+hin/ lowers to [o]; if lowering were ordered after shortening it would appear on the surface as [u].

The Yokuts data can be modeled either as a cascade of three rules in series or in the two-level formalism as three rules in parallel; Fig. 11.6 shows the two architectures (Lakoff, 1993; Karttunen, 1998). Just as in the two-level examples presented earlier, the rules work by referring sometimes to the lexical context, sometimes to the surface context; writing the rules is left as Exercise 11.4 for the reader.

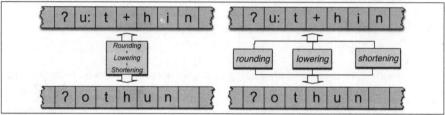

Figure 11.6   Combining the rounding, lowering, and shortening rules for Yawelmani Yokuts.

11.2.2   Templatic Morphology

Finite-state models have also been proposed for the templatic (non-concatenative) morphology (see page 52) common in Semitic languages like Arabic, Hebrew, and Syriac. Many of these models draw on the CV approach of McCarthy (1981), in which a word like /katab/ is represented by three separate morphemes; a **root morpheme** consisting of consonants (*ktb*), a **vocalic morpheme** consisting of vowels (*a*), and a CV pattern morpheme (sometimes called a **binyan** or a **CV skeleton**) (*CVCVC*). McCarthy repre-

tiers sented these morphemes on separate morphological **tiers** .

An influential model by Kay (1987), for example, uses separate tapes for each of McCarthy's tiers. A high-level intuition of Kay's model is shown in Fig. 11.7, which shows his special transducer that reads four tapes instead of two.

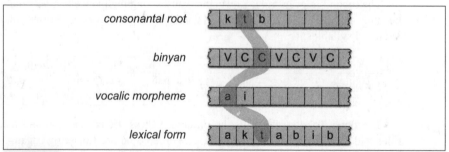

Figure 11.7   Kay's (1987) finite-state model of templatic ("non-concatenative") morphology.

A difficulty with a multitape model is in aligning the strings on the tapes; in Kay's model the binyan tape acted as an alignment guide. Kay's multitape intuition has led to a number of more fully worked out finite-state models of Semitic morphology; see the Historical Notes section at the end of the chapter for details and alternative models.

11.3   Computational Optimality Theory

Optimality Theory

OT

In a traditional phonological derivation, we are given an underlying lexical form and a surface form. The phonological system then consists of a sequence of rules that map the underlying form to the surface form. **Optimality Theory (OT)** (Prince and Smolensky, 1993) offers an alternative way of viewing phonological derivation, based on the metaphor of filtering rather than transforming. An OT model includes two functions (GEN and EVAL) and a set of ranked violable constraints (CON). Given an underlying form, the GEN function produces all imaginable surface forms, even those that couldn't possibly be a legal surface form for the input. The EVAL function then applies each constraint in CON to these surface forms in order of constraint rank. The surface form that best meets the constraints is chosen.

We briefly introduce OT, using some Yawlemani data, and then turn to the computational ramifications.[4] In addition to the interesting vowel harmony phenomena discussed above, Yawelmani has phonotactic constraints that rule out sequences of consonants; three consonants in a row (CCC) are not allowed to occur in a surface word. Sometimes, however, a word contains two consecutive morphemes such that the first one ends in two consonants and the second one starts with one consonant (or vice versa). What does the language do to solve this problem? It turns out that Yawelmani either deletes one of the consonants or inserts a vowel in between.

If a stem ends in a C and its suffix starts with CC, the first C of the suffix is deleted ("+" here means a morpheme boundary):

$$\textbf{C-deletion:}\ \ C \rightarrow \epsilon\ /\ C + \underline{\quad}\ C \qquad\qquad (11.6)$$

For example, simplifying somewhat, the CCVC "passive consequent adjunctive" morpheme hne:l drops the initial C if the previous morpheme ends in a consonant. Thus after diyel "guard", we would get the form diyel-ne:l-aw, "guard - passive consequent adjunctive - locative".

If a stem ends in CC and the suffix starts with C, the language instead inserts a vowel to break up the first two consonants:

$$\textbf{V-insertion:}\ \ \epsilon \rightarrow V\ /\ C \underline{\quad} C + C \qquad\qquad (11.7)$$

For example, an i is inserted into the root ?ilk- "sing" when it is followed by the C-initial suffix -hin, "past", producing ?ilik-hin, "sang", but not when followed by a V-initial suffix like -en, "future" in ?ilken "will sing".

Kisseberth (1970) proposed that these two rules have the same function: avoiding three consonants in a row. Let's restate this in terms of syllable structure. It happens

---

[4] The following explication of OT via the Yawelmani example draws heavily from Archangeli (1997) and a lecture by Jennifer Cole at the 1999 LSA Linguistic Institute.

Resyllabified

that Yawelmani syllables can only be of the form CVC or CV; complex onsets or complex codas that is, with multiple consonants, aren't allowed. Since CVCC syllables aren't allowed on the surface, CVCC roots must be **resyllabified** when they appear on the surface. From the point of view of syllabification, then, these insertions and deletions all happen so as to allow Yawelmani words to be properly syllabified. Here are examples of resyllabifications with no change, with an insertion, and with a deletion:

Underlying Morphemes	Surface Syllabification	Gloss
ʔilk-en	ʔil.ken	"will sing"
ʔilk-hin	ʔi.lik.hin	"sang"
diyel-hnil-aw	di.yel.neː.law	"guard – passive cons. adjunctive – locative"

The intuition of Optimality Theory is to try to directly represent these kinds of constraints on syllable structure directly, rather than using idiosyncratic insertion and deletion rules. One such constraint, *COMPLEX, says "No complex onsets or codas". Another class of constraints requires the surface form to be identical to (faithful to) the underlying form. Thus, FAITHV says "Don't delete or insert vowels", and FAITHC says "Don't delete or insert consonants". Given an underlying form, the GEN function produces all possible surface forms (i.e., every possible insertion and deletion of segments with every possible syllabification) and they are ranked by the EVAL function according to these (violable) constraints. The idea is that while, in general, insertion and deletion are dispreferred, in some languages and situations they are preferred over violating other constraints, such as those of syllable structure. Figure 11.8 shows the architecture.

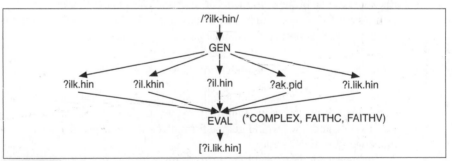

Figure 11.8   The architecture of a derivation in Optimality Theory.

The EVAL function works by applying each constraint in ranked order to each candidate, as shown in the table below.

	/ʔilk-hin/	*COMPLEX	FAITHC	FAITHV
	ʔilk.hin	*!		
	ʔil.khin	*!		
	ʔil.hin		*!	
☞	ʔi.lik.hin			*
	ʔak.pid		*!	

Starting with the highest-ranked constraints, if one candidate either violates no constraints or violates fewer constraints than all the other candidates, that candidate is declared optimal. If two candidates tie (have the same highest-ranked violation), then the next-highest ranked violation is considered. This evaluation is usually shown *Tableau* on a **tableau** (plural **tableaux**). The top left-hand cell shows the input, the constraints are listed in order of rank across the top row, and the possible outputs along the leftmost * column.[5] If a form violates a constraint, the relevant cell contains *****; a ***!** indicates the **!* fatal violation that causes a candidate to be eliminated. Cells for constraints that are irrelevant (since a higher-level constraint is already violated) are shaded.

One appeal of Optimality Theoretic derivations is that the constraints are presumed to be cross-linguistic generalizations. That is, all languages are presumed to have some version of faithfulness, some preference for simple syllables, and so on. Languages differ in how they rank the constraints; thus, English, presumably, ranks FAITHC higher than *COMPLEX. (How do we know this?) We return to this idea of **language universals** in Chapter 25.

11.3.1   Finite-State Transducer Models of Optimality Theory

Now that we've sketched the linguistic motivations for Optimality Theory, let's turn to two kinds of computational OT models: finite-state and stochastic. Frank and Satta (1998), following the foundational work of Ellison (1994), showed that an OT derivation can be computed by finite-state means (1) if GEN is a regular relation (e.g., assuming the input doesn't contain context-free trees of some sort) and (2) if the number of allowed violations of any constraint has some finite bound. The second constraint is relevant because of a property of OT that we haven't mentioned: if two candidates violate exactly the same number of constraints, the winning candidate is the one which has the smallest number of violations of the relevant constraint. Following this work and that of Hammond (1997), Karttunen (1998) proposed to implement OT as a finite-state transducer that is given an underlying form and produces a set of candidate forms. For example, for the syllabification example above, GEN would generate all strings that are variants of the input with consonant deletions or vowel insertions, and their syllabifications.

Each constraint is implemented as a filter transducer that lets pass only strings that meet the constraint. For legal strings, the transducer thus acts as the identity mapping. For example, *COMPLEX would be implemented with a transducer that mapped any input string to itself, unless the input string had two consonants in the onset or coda, in which case it would be mapped to null. The constraints can then be placed in a cascade, in which higher-ranked constraints are simply run first, as suggested in Fig. 11.9.

There is one crucial flaw with the cascade model in Fig. 11.9. Recall that the constraints-transducers filter out any candidate that violates a constraint. But in many derivations, including the proper derivation of ?i.lik.hin, even the optimal form still

---

[5]   Although there are an infinite number of candidates, it is traditional to show only the ones that are "close"; in the tableau below, we have shown the output ?ak.pid just to make it clear that even very different surface forms are to be included.

Figure 11.9   Version #1 ("merciless cascade") of Karttunen's cascade implementation of OT.

violates a constraint. The cascade in Fig. 11.8 would incorrectly filter it out, leaving no surface form at all! It is essential to enforce a constraint only if it does not reduce the candidate set to zero (Frank and Satta, 1998; Hammond, 1997).

Lenient composition

Karttunen (1998) formalizes this intuition with the **lenient composition** operator, a combination of regular composition and an operation called **priority union**. The basic idea is that if any candidates meet the constraint, these candidates will be passed through the filter as usual. If no output meets the constraint, lenient composition retains *all* of the candidates. Figure 11.10 shows the general idea; see Karttunen (1998) for the details.

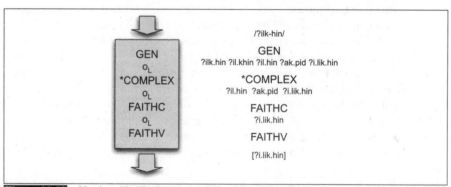

Figure 11.10   Version #2 ("lenient cascade") of Karttunen's cascade implementation of OT, showing a visualization of the candidate populations that would be passed through each FST constraint.

11.3.2   Stochastic Models of Optimality Theory

Classic OT was not designed to handle variation of the kind we saw in Section 7.3, since it assigns a single most harmonic output for each input. One way to deal with variation is to use the more dynamic concept of constraint ranking used in **Stochastic**

Stochastic OT

OT (Boersma and Hayes, 2001). In Stochastic OT, instead of the constraints being rank ordered, each constraint is associated with a value on a continuous scale. The continuous scale offers one thing a ranking cannot: the relative importance or weight of two constraints can be proportional to the distance between them. Figure 11.11

shows a sketch of such a continuous scale.

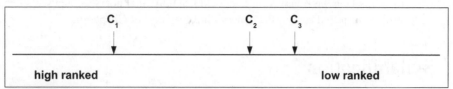

Figure 11.11   The Boersma and Hayes (2001) continuous scale in Stochastic OT.

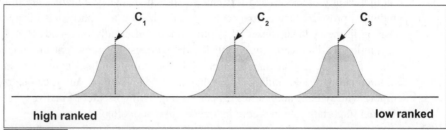

Figure 11.12   Three constraints in Stochastic OT that are strictly ranked; thus, non-stochastic OT is a special case of Stochastic OT.

How can the distance between constraints play a role in evaluation? Stochastic OT makes a further assumption about the values of constraints. Instead of each constraint having a fixed value as in Fig. 11.11 it has a Gaussian distribution of values centered on a fixed value as in Fig. 11.12. At evaluation time, a value for the constraint is drawn (a **selection point**) with a probability defined by the mean and variance of the Gaussian associated with each constraint.

If the distribution for two constraints is far enough apart, as shown in Fig. 11.12 there will be little or no probability of the lower-ranked constraint outranking the higher-ranked one. Thus, Stochastic OT includes non-stochastic OT as a special case.

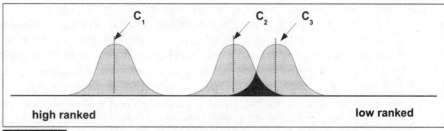

Figure 11.13   Three constraints in Stochastic OT in which C_3 will sometimes outrank C_2.

The interesting cases arise when two constraints in Stochastic OT overlap in their distribution, when there is some probability that a lower-ranked constraint will override a higher-ranked constraint. In Fig. 11.13, for example, constraint C_2 will generally outrank C_3 but occasionally outrank C_2. This allows Stochastic OT to model variation since for the same underlying form, differing selection points can cause different surface variants to be most highly ranked. In addition to the advantage of modeling variation, Stochastic OT differs from non-stochastic OT in having a stochastic learning theory, which we return to in Section 11.5.3. A final note; we can see stochastic OT itself as a special case of the general linear models of Chapter 6.

11.4   Syllabification

Syllabification

Syllabification, the task of segmenting a sequence of phones into syllables, is important in a variety of speech applications. In speech synthesis, syllables are important in predicting prosodic factors like accent; the realization of a phone also depends on its position in the syllable (onset [l] is pronounced differently than coda [l]). In speech recognition, syllabification is useful for recognizers that represent pronunciations in terms of syllables rather than phones. Syllabification can help find errors in pronunciation dictionaries by finding words that can't be syllabified, and it can help annotate corpora with syllable boundaries for corpus linguistics research. Finally, syllabification plays an important role in theoretical generative phonology.

One reason syllabification is a difficult computational task is that there is no completely agreed-upon definition of syllable boundaries. Different on-line syllabified dictionaries (such as the CMU and the CELEX lexicons) sometimes choose different syllabifications. Indeed, as Ladefoged (1993) points out, sometimes it isn't even clear how many syllables a word has; some words (*meal, teal, seal, hire, fire, hour*) can be viewed as having either one syllable or two.

Like much work in speech and language processing, syllabifiers can be based on hand-written rules or on machine learning from hand-labeled training sets. What kinds of knowledge can we use in designing either kind of syllabifier? One possible con-

Maximum Onset

straint is the **Maximum Onset** principle, which says that when a series of consonants occur word-medially before a vowel (VCCV), as many as possible (given the other constraints of the language) should be syllabified into the onset of the second syllable rather than the coda of the first syllable. Thus, the Maximum Onset principle favors the syllabification V.CCV over the syllabifications VC.CV or VCC.V.

Sonority

Another principle is to use the **sonority** of a sound, which is a measure of how perceptually salient, loud, or vowel-like it is. There are various attempts to define a

Sonority Hierarchy

sonority hierarchy; in general, all things being equal, vowels are more sonorous than glides (w, y), which are more sonorous than liquids (l, r), followed by nasals (n, m, ng), fricatives (z, s, sh, zh, v, f th, dh), and stops. The sonority constraint on syllable structure says that the nucleus of the syllable must be the most sonorous phone in a sequence (the **sonority peak**) and that sonority decreases monotonically out from the nucleus (toward the coda and toward the onset). Thus, in a syllable $C_1C_2VC_3C_4$, the nucleus V will be the most sonorous element, consonant C_2 will be more sonorous than C_1, and consonant C_3 will be more sonorant than consonant C_4.

Goldwater and Johnson (2005) implement a rule-based, language-independent classifier based only on maximum onset and sonority sequencing. Given a cluster of consonants between two syllable nuclei, sonority constrains the syllable boundary to be either just before or just after the consonant with the lowest sonority. Combining sonority with maximum onset, the Goldwater and Johnson classifier predicts a syllable boundary just before the consonant with the lowest sonority. This simple syllabifier correctly syllabifies 86%–87% of multisyllabic words in English and German.

While this error rate is not unreasonable, and further linguistic and some psychological evidence suggest these principles play a role in syllable structure, both Maximum Onset and sonority sequencing seem to have exceptions. For example, in the English syllable-initial clusters /sp st sk/ in words like *spell*, the less sonorous /p/ occurs between the more sonorous /s/ and the vowel, violating sonority sequencing (Blevins, 1995). Without some way to rule out onset clusters that are disallowed language-specifically, like /kn/ in English, the combination of sonority sequencing plus maximum onset incorrectly predicts the syllabification of words like *weakness* to be *wea.kness* rather than *weak.ness*. Furthermore, other constraints seem to be important, including the stress on a syllable (stressed syllables tend to have more complex codas), the presence or absence of morphological boundaries, and even the spelling of the word (Titone and Connine, 1997; Treiman et al., 2002).

Achieving higher performance thus requires the use of this sort of language-specific knowledge. The most commonly used rule-based syllabifier is based on the dissertation of Kahn (1976), available in an implementation by Fisher (1996). The Kahn algorithm makes use of language-specific information in the form of lists of allowable English initial clusters, allowable English final clusters, and "universally bad" clusters. The algorithm takes strings of phones, together with other information like word boundaries and stress if available, and assigns syllable boundaries between the phones. Syllables are built up incrementally according to three rules, as sketched in Fig. 11.14. Rule 1 forms nuclei at each syllabic segment, Rule 2a attaches onset consonants to the nucleus, and Rule 2b attaches coda consonants.[6] Rule 2a and 2b make use of lists of legal onset consonant sequences (including, e.g., [b], [b l], [b r], [b y], [ch], [d], [d r], [d w], [d y], [dh], [f], [f l], [f r], [f y], [g], [g l], [g r], [g w]) and legal coda clusters. English has a very large number of coda consonant clusters; some of the longer (4-consonant) clusters include

k s t s	l f th s	m f s t	n d th s	n k s t	r k t s	r p t s
k s th s	l k t s	m p f t	n t s t	n k t s	r l d z	r s t s
	l t s t	m p s t	n t th s	n k th s	r m p th	r t s t

The algorithm also takes a parameter indicating how fast or casual the speech is; the faster or more informal the speech, the more resyllabification happens, based on further rules we haven't shown.

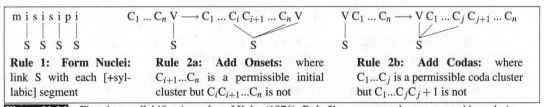

Rule 1: Form Nuclei: link S with each [+syllabic] segment

Rule 2a: Add Onsets: where $C_{i+1}...C_n$ is a permissible initial cluster but $C_iC_{i+1}...C_n$ is not

Rule 2b: Add Codas: where $C_1...C_j$ is a permissible coda cluster but $C_1...C_jC_{j+1}$ is not

Figure 11.14   First three syllabification rules of Kahn (1976). Rule 2b may not apply across word boundaries.

Instead of hand-written rules, we can apply a machine learning approach, using

---

6 Note that Rule 2a preceding Rule 2b can be seen as an implementation of Maximum Onset.

a hand-syllabified dictionary as a supervised training set. For example, the CELEX syllabified lexicon discussed in Section 7.5 is often used this way, selecting some words as a training set and reserving others as a dev-test and test set. Statistical classifiers can be used to predict syllabifications, including decision trees (van den Bosch, 1997), weighted finite-state transducers (Kiraz and Möbius, 1998), and probabilistic context-free grammars (Seneff et al., 1996; Müller, 2002, 2001; Goldwater and Johnson, 2005).

For example, the Kiraz and Möbius (1998) algorithm is a weighted finite-state transducer that inserts a syllable boundary in a sequence of phones (akin to the morpheme boundaries we saw in Chapter 3). A **weighted FST** (Pereira et al., 1994) is a simple augmentation of the finite transducer in which each arc is associated with a probability as well as a pair of symbols. The probability indicates how likely that path is to be taken; the probability on all the arcs leaving a node must sum to 1.

Weighted FST

The syllabification automaton of Kiraz and Möbius (1998) is composed of three separate weighted transducers, one for onsets, one for nuclei, and one for codas, concatenated into an FST that inserts a syllable marker after the end of the coda. Kiraz and Möbius (1998) compute path weights from frequencies in the training set; each path (e.g., the nucleus [iy]) of frequency f is assigned a weight of $1/f$. Another way to convert frequencies to costs is to use log probabilities. Figure 11.15 shows a sample automaton, simplified from Kiraz and Möbius (1998). We have shown the weights only for some of the nuclei. The arcs for each possible onset, nucleus, and coda are drawn from a language-dependent list like the one used in the Kahn algorithm above.

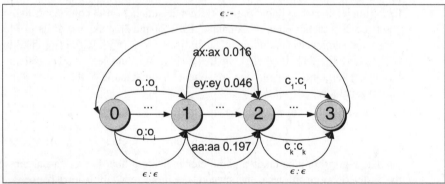

Figure 11.15   Simplified version of the Kiraz and Möbius (1998) syllabifier automaton showing onset (o), coda (c), and nucleus arcs. Costs on each arc shown only for some sample nucleus arcs. The syllable boundary marker '-' is inserted after every non-final syllable.

The automaton shown in Fig. 11.15 can be used to map from an input sequence like the phonetic representation of *weakness* [w iy k n eh s] into an output sequence that includes the syllabification marker like "-": [w iy k - n eh s]. If there are multiple possible legal syllabifications of a word, the Viterbi algorithm is used to choose the most likely path through the FST and hence the most probable segmentation. For example, the German word *Fenster*, "window", has three possible syllabifications: [fɛns-tɐ] <74>, [fɛn-stɐ] <75>, and [fɛnst-ɐ] <87> (with costs shown in angle brackets). Their syllabifier correctly chooses the lowest-cost syllabification, fɛns-tɐ, based on the frequencies of onsets and codas from the training set. Note that since morphological boundaries are also important for syllabification, the Kiraz and Möbius (1998) syllabification transducer can be placed after a morphological parsing transducer so that syllabification can be influenced by morphological structure.

More recent syllabifiers based on probabilistic context-free grammars (PCFGs) can model more complex hierarchical probabilistic dependencies between syllables (Seneff et al., 1996; Müller, 2002, 2001; Goldwater and Johnson, 2005). Together with other machine learning approaches like that of van den Bosch (1997), modern statistical syllabification approaches have a word accuracy of around 97%–98% correct, and probabilistic models of syllable structure have also been shown to predict human judgments of the acceptability of nonsense words (Coleman and Pierrehumbert, 1997).

There are a number of other directions in syllabification. One is the use of unsupervised machine learning algorithms (Ellison, 1992; Müller et al., 2000; Goldwater and Johnson, 2005). Another is the use of other cues for syllabification, such as allophonic details from a narrow phonetic transcription (Church, 1983).

11.5   Learning Phonology and Morphology

Machine learning of phonological structures is an active research area in computational phonology above and beyond the induction of syllable structure discussed in the previous section. Supervised learning work is based on a training set that is explicitly labeled for the phonological (or morphological) structure to be induced. Unsupervised work attempts to induce phonological or morphological structure without labeled training data. Let's look at three representative areas of learning: learning of phonological rules, learning of morphological rules, and learning of OT constraint rankings

11.5.1   Learning Phonological Rules

In this section we briefly summarize some early literature in learning phonological rules, generally couched either in terms of finite-state models of two-level phonology or as classic Chomsky-Halle rules.

Johnson (1984) gives one of the first computational algorithms for phonological rule induction. His algorithm works for rules of the form

$$a \rightarrow b/C \tag{11.8}$$

where C is the feature matrix of the segments around a. Johnson's algorithm sets up a system of constraint equations that C must satisfy, by considering both the positive contexts, that is, all the contexts C_i in which a b occurs on the surface, as well as all the negative contexts C_j in which an a occurs on the surface. Touretzky et al. (1990) extended Johnson's work by dealing, for example, with epenthesis and deletion rules.

The algorithm of Gildea and Jurafsky (1996) was designed to induce transducers representing two-level rules of the type we have discussed earlier. Gildea and Jurafsky's supervised algorithm was trained on pairs of underlying and surface forms. For example, they attempted to learn the rule of English flapping (focusing only on the phonetic context and ignoring social and other factors). The training set thus consisted of underlying/surface pairs, either with an underlying /t/ and surface flap [dx] or with an underlying /t/ and surface [t], as follows:

Flapping		Non-flapping	
butter /b ah t axr/ → [b ah dx axr]		*stop* /s t aa p/ → [s t aa p]	
meter /m iy t axr/ → [m iy dx axr]		*cat* /k ae t/ → [k ae t]	

The algorithm was based on OSTIA (Oncina et al., 1993), a general learning algorithm for **subsequential transducers** (page 59). Gildea and Jurafsky showed that by itself, the OSTIA algorithm was too general to learn phonological transducers, even given a large corpus of underlying-form/surface-form pairs. For example, given 25,000 underlying/surface pairs like the examples above, the algorithm ended up with the huge and incorrect automaton in Fig. 11.16(a). Gildea and Jurafsky then augmented OSTIA with learning biases specific to natural language phonology. For example they added a **Faithfulness** bias that underlying segments tend to be realized similarly on the surface (i.e., that all things being equal, an underlying /p/ was likely to emerge as a surface [p]), and knowledge about phonetic features. The biases enabled OSTIA to learn the automaton in Fig. 11.16(b), as well as correct automatons for other phonological rules.

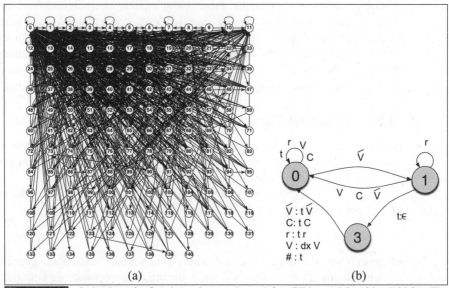

(a)   (b)

Figure 11.16   Induction of a flapping rule transducer (after Gildea and Jurafsky (1996)). The transducer in (a) is the initial attempt at learning. The transducer in (b) is the correct transducer induced after a faithfulness bias.

This work suggests that successful learning requires the integration of learning biases with empirical induction from data. In the next few sections we see these two factors applied in work on morphological learning and on ranking of OT constraints.

11.5.2   Learning Morphology

We discussed in Chapter 3 the use of finite-state transducers for morphological parsing. In general, these morphological parsers are built by hand and have relatively high accuracy, although there has also been some work on supervised machine learning of morphological parsers (van den Bosch, 1997). Recent work, however, has focused on unsupervised ways to automatically bootstrap morphological structure. The unsupervised (or weakly supervised) learning problem has practical applications since there are many languages for which a hand-built morphological parser, or a morphological segmented training corpus, does not yet exist. In addition, the learnability of linguistic structure is a much-discussed scientific topic in linguistics; unsupervised morphological learning may help us understand what makes language learning possible.

Approaches to unsupervised morphology induction have employed a wide variety of cues to a proper morphological parse. Early approaches were all essentially segmentation based; given a corpus of words, they attempted to segment each word into a stem and an affix by using various unsupervised heuristics. For example, the earliest work hypothesized morpheme boundaries at the point in a word where there is large uncertainty about the following letters (Harris, 1954, 1988; Hafer and Weiss, 1974). For *Trie* example, Fig. 11.17 shows a **trie**[7] that stores the words *car, care, cars, cares, cared,* etc. Note that certain nodes in the tree in Fig. 11.17 have a wide branching factor (after *car* and after *care*). If we think of the task of predicting the next letter giving the path in the trie so far, we can say that these points have a high conditional entropy; there are many possible continuations.[8] While this is a useful heuristic, it is not sufficient; in this example we would need a way to rule out the morpheme *car* as well as *care* being part of the word *careful*; this requires a complex set of thresholds.

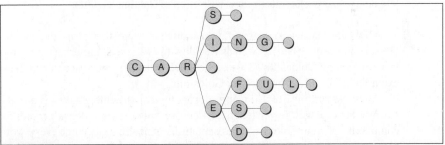

Figure 11.17   Example of a letter trie. A Harris style algorithm would insert morpheme boundaries after *car* and *care*. After Schone and Jurafsky (2000).

Minimum description length
MDL

Another class of segmentation-based approaches to morphology induction focuses on globally optimizing a single criterion for the whole grammar, the criterion of **minimum description length**, or **MDL**. The MDL principle is widely used in language learning, and we see it again in grammar induction in Chapter 14. The idea is that we

---

[7] A **trie** is a tree structure used for storing strings, in which a string is represented as a path from the root to a leaf. Each non-terminal node in the tree thus stores a prefix of a string; every common prefix is represented by a node. The word **trie** comes from *retrieval* and is pronounced either [t r iy] or [t r ay].

[8] Interestingly, this idea of placing boundaries at regions of low predictability has been shown to be used by infants for word segmentation (Saffran et al., 1996b).

are trying to learn the optimal probabilistic model of some data. Given any proposed model, we can assign a likelihood to the entire data set. We can also use the proposed model to assign a compressed length to this data (with probabilistic models we can use the intuition that the compressed length of the data is related to the entropy, which we can estimate from the log-probability). We can also assign a length to the proposed model itself. The MDL principle says to choose the model for which the sum of the data length and the model length is the smallest. The principle is often viewed from a Bayesian perspective. If we are attempting to learn the best model $\hat{M}$ out of all models M for some data D which has the maximum a posteriori probability $P(M D)$, we can use Bayes Rule to express the best model $\hat{M}$ as

$$\hat{M} = argmax_M P(M D) = argmax_M \frac{P(D M)P(M)}{P(D)} = argmax_M P(D M)P(M)$$

Thus, the best model is the one that maximizes two terms: the likelihood of the data $P(D M)$ and the prior of the model $P(M)$. The MDL principle can be viewed as saying that the prior term on the model should be related to the length of the model.

cooked cooks cooking	cook	ed
played plays playing	play	s
boiled boils boiling	boil	ing

(a) Word list with no structure   (b) Word list with morphological structure
Total letter count: 54   Total letter count: 18 letters

Figure 11.18   Naive version of MDL, showing the reduction in the description length of a lexicon with morphological structure; adapted from Goldsmith (2001).

MDL approaches to segmentation induction were first proposed by de Marcken (1996) and Brent (1999), as well as Kazakov (1997); we summarize from a more recent instantiation by Goldsmith (2001). The MDL intuition can be seen from the schematic example in Fig. 11.18 inspired by Goldsmith.

As we see in Fig. 11.18, using morphological structure makes it possible to represent a lexicon with fewer letters. Of course, this example doesn't represent the true complexity of morphological representations, since in reality not every word is combinable with every affix. An improvement is to use a **signature**, a list of suffixes that can appear with a particular stem, like the following from Goldsmith (2001):

Signature

Signature	Example
NULL.ed.ing.s	remain remained remaining remains
NULL.s	cow cows
e.ed.es.ing	notice noticed notices noticing

The Goldsmith (2001) version of MDL considers all possible segmentations of every word into a stem and a suffix. It then chooses for the whole corpus the set of segmentations that jointly minimize the compressed length of the corpus and the length of the model. The length of the model is the sum of the lengths of the affixes, the stems, and the signatures. The algorithm estimates the compressed length of the corpus by assigning a probability to the corpus and then computing the cross-entropy of the corpus given the model.

While stem and affix statistics are quite successful in morphological learning, other features have been proposed to deal with cases where MDL oversegments (e.g., segmenting the word *ally* to *all+y*), or undersegments (e.g., missing the link between *dirt* and *dirty*). For example, Schone and Jurafsky (2000, 2001) propose that semantics plays a role, noting that *ally* and *all* are not semantically related, while *dirt* and *dirty* are. The Schone and Jurafsky (2000) algorithm uses a trie to come up with "pairs of potential morphological variants" (PPMVs), words that differ only in potential affixes. For each pair, they compute the semantic similarity between the words, using the Latent Semantic Analysis (LSA) algorithm (Chapter 20). LSA is an unsupervised model of word similarity that is induced directly from the distributions of word in context. Schone and Jurafsky (2000) showed that using the semantic similarity alone was as good a predictor of morphological structure as MDL. The table below shows the LSA-based similarity between PPMVs; in this example, the similarity is high only for words that are morphologically related.

PPMV	Score	PPMV	Score	PPMV	Score	PPMV	Score
ally/allies	6.5	dirty/dirt	2.4	car/cares	-0.14	car/cared	-.096
car/cars	5.6	rating/rate	0.97	car/caring	-0.71	ally/all	-1.3

Schone and Jurafsky (2001) extended the algorithm to learn prefixes and circumfixes and incorporated other useful features, including syntactic and other effects of neighboring word context (Jacquemin, 1997) and the Levenshtein distance between the PPMVs (Gaussier, 1999).

The algorithms we've mentioned focus on learning regular morphology. Yarowsky and Wicentowski (2000) address the more complex problem of learning *irregular* morphology. Their idea is to probabilistically align an inflected form (such as English *took* or Spanish *juegan*) with each potential stem (such as English *take* or Spanish *jugar*). The result of their alignment-based algorithm is an inflection-root mapping, with both an optional stem change and a suffix, as shown in the following table.

English				Spanish			
Root	Inflection	Stem Change	Suffix	Root	Inflection	Stem Change	Suffix
take	took	ake→ook	+ϵ	jugar	juega	gar→eg	+a
take	taking	e→ϵ	+ing	jugar	jugamos	ar→ϵ	+amos
skip	skipped	ϵ→p	+ed	tener	tienen	ener→ien	+en

The Yarowsky and Wicentowski (2000) algorithm assumes knowledge of the regular inflectional affixes of the language and a list of open class stems, both of which might be induced by one of the above algorithms. Given an inflected form, the Yarowsky and Wicentowski (2000) algorithm uses various knowledge sources to weight the potential stem, including the relative frequency of the inflected form and potential stem, the similarity in lexical context, and the Levenshtein distance between them.

11.5.3   Learning in Optimality Theory

Let's conclude with a brief sketch of work on learning in Optimality Theory. Most work on OT learning has assumed that the constraints are already given and the task is just to learn the ranking. Two algorithms for learning rankings have been worked out in some detail; the **constraint demotion** algorithm of Tesar and Smolensky (2000) and the **gradual learning algorithm** of Boersma and Hayes (2001).

Constraint demotion

The **constraint demotion** algorithm makes two assumptions: that we know all the possible OT constraints of the language and that each surface form is annotated with its complete parse and underlying form. The intuition of the algorithm is that each of these surface observations gives us implicit evidence about the constraint ranking.

Given the underlying form, we can use the GEN algorithm to implicitly form the set of competitors. We can now construct a set of pairs consisting of the correct observed grammatical form and each competitor. The learner must find a constraint ranking that prefers the observed learning *winner* over each (non-observed) competitor *loser*. Because the set of constraints is given, we can use the standard OT parsing architecture to determine for each winner or loser exactly which constraints they violate.

For example, consider the learning algorithm that has observed Candidate 1, but whose current constraint ranking prefers Candidate 2, as follows (this example and the following tables are modified from Boersma and Hayes (2001)):

/underlying form/	C_1	C_2	C_3	C_4	C_5	C_6	C_7	C_8
Candidate 1 (learning observation)	*!	**	*		*			*
☞ Candidate 2 (learner's output)		*	*	*		*		*

Given a set of such *winner/loser* pairs, the constraint demotion algorithm needs to demote each constraint that is violated by the winner Candidate 2 until the observed form (Candidate 1) is preferred. The algorithm first cancels any marks due to violations that are identical between the two candidates:

/underlying form/	C_1	C_2	C_3	C_4	C_5	C_6	C_7	C_8
Candidate 1 (learning observation)	*!	~~**~~	~~*~~		*			~~*~~
☞ Candidate 2 (learner's output)		~~*~~	~~*~~	*		*		~~*~~

These constraints are pushed down in the hierarchy until they are dominated by the constraints violated by the loser. The algorithm divides constraints into **strata** and tries to find a lower strata to move the constraints into. Here's a simplification of this intuition as C_1 and C_2 get moved below C_8:

/underlying form/	C_3	C_4	C_5	C_6	C_7	C_8	C_1	C_2
☞ Candidate 1 (learning observation)				*			*	*
Candidate 2 (learner's output)		*!		*				

Gradual learning algorithm

The **gradual learning algorithm** (GLA) of (Boersma and Hayes, 2001) is a generalization of constraint demotion that learns constraint rankings in Stochastic OT. Since OT is a special case of Stochastic OT, the algorithm also learns OT rankings. It generalizes constraint demotion by being able to learn from cases of free variation. Recall from Section 11.3 that in Stochastic OT each constraint is associated with a **ranking value** on a continuous scale. The ranking value is defined as the mean of the Gaussian distribution for the constraint. The goal of the GLA is to assign a ranking value for each constraint. The algorithm is a simple extension to the constraint demotion algorithm and follows exactly the same steps until the final step. Instead of demoting constraints to a lower strata, the ranking value of each constraint violated by the learning observation (Candidate 1) is decreased slightly, and the ranking value of each constraint violated by the learner's output (Candidate 2) is increased slightly:

/underlying form/	C_1	C_2	C_3	C_4	C_5	C_6	C_7	C_8
Candidate 1 (learning observation)	$*! \rightarrow$	$* \rightarrow$			$* \rightarrow$			
☞ Candidate 2 (learner's output)				$\leftarrow *$		$\leftarrow *$		

11.6   Summary

This chapter has introduced many of the important concepts of phonetics and computational phonology.

- **Transducers** can be used to model phonological rules just as they were used in Chapter 3 to model spelling rules. **Two-level morphology** models phonological rules as finite-state **well-formedness constraints** on the mapping between lexical and surface form.

- **Optimality theory** is a theory of phonological well-formedness; there are computational implementations and relationships to transducers.

- Computational models exist for **syllabification**, inserting syllable boundaries in phone strings.

- There are numerous algorithms for learning phonological and morphological rules, both supervised and unsupervised.

Bibliographical and Historical Notes

The idea that phonological rules could be modeled as regular relations dates to Johnson (1972), who showed that any phonological system that didn't allow rules to apply to their own output (i.e., a system without recursive rules) could be modeled with regular relations. Virtually all phonological rules that had been formulated at the time had this property (except some rules with integral-valued features, like early stress and tone rules). Johnson's insight unfortunately did not attract the attention of the community, and was independently discovered by Ronald Kaplan and Martin Kay; see Chapter 3 for the rest of the history of two-level morphology. Earlier computational finite-state models that deal with templatic morphology in languages like Arabic include Kataja and Koskenniemi (1988), Kornai (1991), Bird and Ellison (1994), and Beesley (1996). Extensions of the Kay (1987) model include Kiraz (1997, 2000, 2001). Recent models based on extensions to the finite-state calculus include Beesley and Karttunen (2000). Karttunen (1993) gives a tutorial introduction to two-level morphology that includes more of the advanced details than we were able to present here; the definitive text on finite-state morphology is Beesley and Karttunen (2003). Other FSA models of phonology include Bird and Ellison (1994).

Optimality theory was developed by Prince and Smolensky and circulated as a technical report (Prince and Smolensky, 1993) until its publication more than a decade later (Prince and Smolensky, 2004). The extensive finite-state literature in OT includes Eisner (1997, 2000b, 2002a), Gerdemann and van Noord (2000), and Riggle (2005).

Recent work on phonological learning has focused on some new areas. One is learning **phonotactic constraints** on the allowable word-internal sequences in the language, including probabilistic (Coleman and Pierrehumbert, 1997; Frisch et al., 2000; Bailey and Hahn, 2001; Hayes and Wilson, 2008; Albright, 2007) as well as non-probabilistic phonotactic constraints (Hayes, 2004; Prince and Tesar, 2004; Tesar and Prince, 2007). A related task is the learning of **underlying forms** and phonological alternations given the observed surface forms and the set of constraints. Many of the unsupervised algorithms for learning underlying forms are based on a constraint satisfaction approach, in which sets of possible underlying forms are proposed by examining alternating surface forms, and then iteratively ruling out possible underlying forms (Tesar and Prince, 2007; Alderete et al., 2005; Tesar, 2006a, 2006b). The recent unsupervised Maximum Likelihood Learning of Lexicons and Grammars (MLG) model of Jarosz (2006, 2008) learns underlying forms and constraint rankings given surface forms in a probabilistic version of OT using the Expectation Maximization (EM) algorithm described in Chapter 6.

Indeed, in addition to this probabilistic model of Jarosz (2008), as well as the Stochastic OT described earlier in the chapter, much recent work in computational phonology has focused on models with weighted constraints, including **Harmonic Grammar** and **maximum entropy models**. For example, **Harmonic Grammar** is an extension to Optimality Theory (or more properly is the theory that Optimality Theory originally grew out of) in which optimality for a form is defined as maximal **harmony**. Harmony is defined by the sum of weighted constraints (Smolensky and Legendre, 2006). In using sums of weight rather than OT-style rankings, Harmony Theory resembles the log-linear models of Chapter 6. Recent computational work include the application to OT of maximum entropy models (Goldwater and Johnson, 2003) and the Harmonic Grammar-related models of Pater et al. (2007) and Pater (2008).

Harmonic Grammar

Harmony

Word segmentation is one of the earliest problems in computational linguistics, and models date back to Harris (1954). Among the many modern models are Bayesian ones like Brent (1999) and Goldwater et al. (2006). The word segmentation problem is important also in computational developmental psycholinguistics; for representative recent work, see Christiansen et al. (1998), Kuhl et al. (2003), Thiessen and Saffran (2004), and Thiessen et al. (2005). Recent work on morphology induction includes Baroni et al. (2002), Clark (2002), and Albright and Hayes (2003).

Readers with further interest in phonology should consult phonology textbooks like Odden (2005) and Kager (2000).

Exercises

11.1 Build an automaton for rule (11.3).

11.2 Some Canadian dialects of English exhibit **Canadian raising**: /aɪ/ is raised to [ʌɪ] and /aʊ/ to [ʌʊ] in stressed position before a voiceless consonant (Bromberger and Halle, 1989). A simplified rule dealing only with /aɪ/ can be stated as:

$$/aɪ/ \rightarrow [ʌɪ] / \underline{\quad} \begin{bmatrix} C \\ -voice \end{bmatrix} \qquad (11.9)$$

In some Canadian dialects this rule interacts with the flapping rule, causing different pronunciations for the words *rider* ([raɪɾɚ]) and *writer* ([rʌɪɾɚ]). Write a two-level rule and an automaton for the raising and flapping rules that correctly models this distinction, making simplifying assumptions as needed.

11.3 Write the lexical entry for the pronunciation of the English past tense (preterite) suffix *-d*, and the two-level rules that express the difference in its pronunciation depending on the previous context. Don't worry about the spelling rules. Make sure you correctly handle the pronunciation of the past tenses of the words *add*, *pat*, *bake*, and *bag*.

11.4 Write two-level rules for the Yawelmani Yokuts Harmony, Shortening, and Lowering phenomena from page 365. Make sure your rules can run in parallel.

Credit

Fig. 11.18 (© the authors; thanks to the Association of Computational Linguistics, the *Journal of Computational Linguistics* and its editor Robert Dale, and to John Goldsmith)

Chapter 12

Formal Grammars of English

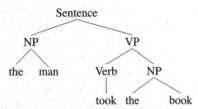

The first context-free grammar parse tree (Chomsky, 1956)

If on a winter's night a traveler by Italo Calvino
Nuclear and Radiochemistry by Gerhart Friedlander et al.
The Fire Next Time by James Baldwin
A Tad Overweight, but Violet Eyes to Die For by G. B. Trudeau
Sometimes a Great Notion by Ken Kesey
Dancer from the Dance by Andrew Holleran

Six books in English whose titles are not constituents, from Pullum (1991, p. 195)

The study of grammar has an ancient pedigree; Panini's grammar of Sanskrit was written over two thousand years ago and is still referenced today in teaching Sanskrit. By contrast, Geoff Pullum noted in a recent talk that "almost everything most educated Americans believe about English grammar is wrong". In this chapter, we make a preliminary stab at addressing some of these gaps in our knowledge of grammar and syntax, as well as introducing some of the formal mechanisms that are available for capturing this knowledge.

Syntax   The word **syntax** comes from the Greek *sýntaxis*, meaning "setting out together or arrangement", and refers to the way words are arranged together. We have seen various syntactic notions in previous chapters. The regular languages introduced in Chapter 2 offered a simple way to represent the ordering of strings of words, and Chapter 4 showed how to compute probabilities for these word sequences. Chapter 5 showed that part-of-speech categories could act as a kind of equivalence class for words. This chapter and the following ones introduce sophisticated notions of syntax and grammar that go well beyond these simpler notions. In this chapter, we introduce three main new ideas: **constituency**, **grammatical relations**, and **subcategorization and dependency**.

The fundamental idea of constituency is that groups of words may behave as a single unit or phrase, called a constituent. For example, we will see that a group of words called a **noun phrase** often acts as a unit; noun phrases include single words like *she* or *Michael* and phrases like *the house*, *Russian Hill*, and *a well-weathered* *three-story structure*. This chapter introduces the use of **context-free grammars**, a formalism that will allow us to model these constituency facts.

Grammatical relations are a formalization of ideas from traditional grammar such as SUBJECTS and OBJECTS and other related notions. In the following sentence, the noun phrase *She* is the SUBJECT and *a mammoth breakfast* is the OBJECT:

(12.1) She ate a mammoth breakfast.

Subcategorization and **dependency relations** refer to certain kinds of relations between words and phrases. For example, the verb *want* can be followed by an infinitive, as in *I want to fly to Detroit*, or a noun phrase, as in *I want a flight to Detroit*. But the verb *find* cannot be followed by an infinitive (**I found to fly to Dallas*). These are called facts about the *subcategorization* of the verb.

As we show, none of the syntactic mechanisms that we've discussed up until now can easily capture such phenomena. They can be modeled much more naturally by grammars that are based on context-free grammars. Context-free grammars are thus the backbone of many formal models of the syntax of natural language (and, for that matter, of computer languages). As such they are integral to many computational applications, including grammar checking, semantic interpretation, dialogue understanding, and machine translation. They are powerful enough to express sophisticated relations among the words in a sentence, yet computationally tractable enough that efficient algorithms exist for parsing sentences with them (as we show in Chapter 13). Later in Chapter 14 we show that adding probability to context-free grammars gives us a model of disambiguation and also helps model certain aspects of human parsing.

In addition to an introduction to the grammar formalism, this chapter also provides a brief overview of the grammar of English. We have chosen a domain that has relatively simple sentences, the Air Traffic Information System (ATIS) domain (Hemphill et al., 1990). ATIS systems are an early example of spoken language systems for helping book airline reservations. Users try to book flights by conversing with the system, specifying constraints like *I'd like to fly from Atlanta to Denver*. The U.S. government funded a number of different research sites to collect data and build ATIS systems in the early 1990s. The sentences we model in this chapter are drawn from the corpus of user queries to the system.

12.1   Constituency

Noun phrase   How do words group together in English? Consider the **noun phrase**, a sequence of words surrounding at least one noun. Here are some examples of noun phrases (thanks to Damon Runyon):

Harry the Horse	a high-class spot such as Mindy's
the Broadway coppers	the reason he comes into the Hot Box
they	three parties from Brooklyn

How do we know that these words group together (or "form constituents")? One piece of evidence is that they can all appear in similar syntactic environments, for example, before a verb.

> three parties from Brooklyn *arrive*...
> a high-class spot such as Mindy's *attracts*...
> the Broadway coppers *love*...
> they *sit*

But while the whole noun phrase can occur before a verb, this is not true of each of the individual words that make up a noun phrase. The following are not grammatical sentences of English (recall that we use an asterisk (*) to mark fragments that are not grammatical English sentences):

> *from *arrive*...   *as *attracts*...
> *the *is*...   *spot *sat*...

Thus, to correctly describe facts about the ordering of these words in English, we must be able to say things like "*Noun Phrases can occur before verbs*".

Preposed
Postposed
Other kinds of evidence for constituency come from what are called **preposed** or **postposed** constructions. For example, the prepositional phrase *on September seventeenth* can be placed in a number of different locations in the following examples, including preposed at the beginning and postposed at the end:

> *On September seventeenth*, I'd like to fly from Atlanta to Denver
> I'd like to fly *on September seventeenth* from Atlanta to Denver
> I'd like to fly from Atlanta to Denver *on September seventeenth*

But again, while the entire phrase can be placed differently, the individual words making up the phrase cannot be

> *On September, I'd like to fly seventeenth from Atlanta to Denver
> *On I'd like to fly September seventeenth from Atlanta to Denver
> *I'd like to fly on September from Atlanta to Denver seventeenth

Section 12.6 gives other motivations for context-free grammars based on their ability to model recursive structures. See Radford (1988) for further examples of groups of words behaving as a single constituent.

12.2   Context-Free Grammars

CFG
The most commonly used mathematical system for modeling constituent structure in English and other natural languages is the **Context-Free Grammar**, or **CFG**. Context-free grammars are also called **Phrase-Structure Grammars**, and the formalism is equivalent to what is also called **Backus-Naur Form**, or **BNF**. The idea of basing a grammar on constituent structure dates back to the psychologist Wilhelm Wundt (1900) but was not formalized until Chomsky (1956) and, independently, Backus (1959).

Rules
A context-free grammar consists of a set of **rules** or **productions**, each of which expresses the ways that symbols of the language can be grouped and ordered together, *Lexicon* and a **lexicon** of words and symbols. For example, the following productions express *NP* that an **NP** (or **noun phrase**) can be composed of either a *ProperNoun* or a determiner

(*Det*) followed by a *Nominal*; a *Nominal* can be one or more *Noun*s.

$$NP \;\rightarrow\; Det\ Nominal$$
$$NP \;\rightarrow\; ProperNoun$$
$$Nominal \;\rightarrow\; Noun \quad Nominal\ Noun$$

Context-free rules can be hierarchically embedded, so we can combine the previous rules with others, like the following, that express facts about the lexicon:

$$Det \;\rightarrow\; a$$
$$Det \;\rightarrow\; the$$
$$Noun \;\rightarrow\; flight$$

Terminal

Non-terminal

The symbols that are used in a CFG are divided into two classes. The symbols that correspond to words in the language ("the", "nightclub") are called **terminal** symbols; the lexicon is the set of rules that introduce these terminal symbols. The symbols that express clusters or generalizations of these are called **non-terminals**. In each context-free rule, the item to the right of the arrow ($\rightarrow$) is an ordered list of one or more terminals and non-terminals; to the left of the arrow is a single non-terminal symbol expressing some cluster or generalization. Notice that in the lexicon, the non-terminal associated with each word is its lexical category, or part-of-speech, which we defined in Chapter 5.

A CFG can be thought of in two ways: as a device for generating sentences and as a device for assigning a structure to a given sentence. We saw this same dualism in our discussion of finite-state transducers in Chapter 3. Viewing a CFG as a generator, we can read the $\rightarrow$ arrow as "rewrite the symbol on the left with the string of symbols on the right".

So starting from the symbol:	*NP*
we can use rule 12.2 to rewrite *NP* as:	*Det Nominal*
and then rule 12.2:	*Det Noun*
and finally with 12.2 and 12.2 as:	*a flight*

Derivation

Parse tree

We say the string *a flight* can be derived from the non-terminal *NP*. Thus, a CFG can be used to generate a set of strings. This sequence of rule expansions is called a **derivation** of the string of words. It is common to represent a derivation by a **parse tree** (commonly shown inverted with the root at the top). Figure 12.1 shows the tree representation of this derivation.

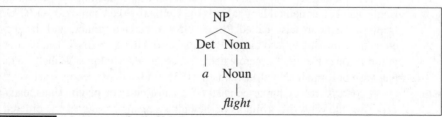

Figure 12.1   A parse tree for "a flight".

In the parse tree shown in Fig. 12.1, we can say that the node *NP* **dominates** all the nodes in the tree (*Det, Nom, Noun, a, flight*). We can say further that it immediately dominates the nodes *Det* and *Nom*.

The formal language defined by a CFG is the set of strings that are derivable from the designated **start symbol**. Each grammar must have one designated start symbol, which is often called *S*. Since context-free grammars are often used to define sentences, *S* is usually interpreted as the "sentence" node, and the set of strings that are derivable from *S* is the set of sentences in some simplified version of English.

Let's add to our list of rules a few higher-level rules that expand *S*, and a couple of others. One rule will express the fact that a sentence can consist of a noun phrase followed by a **verb phrase**:

$$S \rightarrow NP\ VP \quad \text{I prefer a morning flight}$$

A verb phrase in English consists of a verb followed by assorted other things; for example, one kind of verb phrase consists of a verb followed by a noun phrase:

$$VP \rightarrow Verb\ NP \quad \text{prefer a morning flight}$$

Or the verb may be followed by a noun phrase and a prepositional phrase:

$$VP \rightarrow Verb\ NP\ PP \quad \text{leave Boston in the morning}$$

Or the verb phrase may have a verb followed by a prepositional phrase alone:

$$VP \rightarrow Verb\ PP \quad \text{leaving on Thursday}$$

A prepositional phrase generally has a preposition followed by a noun phrase. For example, a common type of prepositional phrase in the ATIS corpus is used to indicate location or direction:

$$PP \rightarrow Preposition\ NP \quad \text{from Los Angeles}$$

The *NP* inside a *PP* need not be a location; *PP*s are often used with times and dates, and with other nouns as well; they can be arbitrarily complex. Here are ten examples from the ATIS corpus:

to Seattle	on these flights
in Minneapolis	about the ground transportation in Chicago
on Wednesday	of the round trip flight on United Airlines
in the evening	of the AP fifty seven flight
on the ninth of July	with a stopover in Nashville

Figure 12.2 gives a sample lexicon, and Fig. 12.3 summarizes the grammar rules we've seen so far, which we'll call $\mathcal{L}_0$. Note that we can use the or-symbol to indicate that a non-terminal has alternate possible expansions.

We can use this grammar to generate sentences of this "ATIS-language". We start with *S*, expand it to *NP VP*, then choose a random expansion of *NP* (let's say, to *I*), and a random expansion of *VP* (let's say, to *Verb NP*), and so on until we generate the string *I prefer a morning flight*. Figure 12.4 shows a parse tree that represents a complete derivation of *I prefer a morning flight*.

Noun →	*flights breeze trip morning*
Verb →	*is prefer like need want fly*
Adjective →	*cheapest non-stop first latest*
	other direct
Pronoun →	*me I you it*
Proper-Noun →	*Alaska Baltimore Los Angeles*
	Chicago United American
Determiner →	*the a an this these that*
Preposition →	*from to on near*
Conjunction →	*and or but*

Figure 12.2   The lexicon for $\mathcal{L}_0$.

Grammar Rules	**Examples**
S → *NP VP*	I + want a morning flight
NP → *Pronoun*	I
Proper-Noun	Los Angeles
Det Nominal	a + flight
Nominal → *Nominal Noun*	morning + flight
Noun	flights
VP → *Verb*	do
Verb NP	want + a flight
Verb NP PP	leave + Boston + in the morning
Verb PP	leaving + on Thursday
PP → *Preposition NP*	from + Los Angeles

Figure 12.3   The grammar for $\mathcal{L}_0$, with example phrases for each rule.

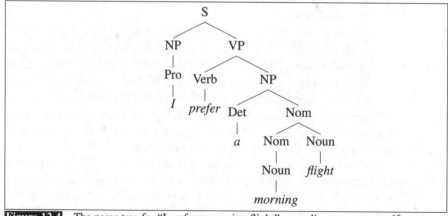

Figure 12.4   The parse tree for "I prefer a morning flight" according to grammar $\mathcal{L}_0$.

Bracketed notation

It is sometimes convenient to represent a parse tree in a more compact format called **bracketed notation**, essentially the same as LISP tree representations; here is the bracketed representation of the parse tree of Fig. 12.4:

(12.2) [$_S$ [$_{NP}$ [$_{Pro}$ I]] [$_{VP}$ [$_V$ prefer] [$_{NP}$ [$_{Det}$ a] [$_{Nom}$ [$_N$ morning] [$_{Nom}$ [$_N$ flight]]]]]]

Grammatical
Ungrammatical

A CFG like that of $\mathscr{L}_0$ defines a formal language. We saw in Chapter 2 that a formal language is a set of strings. Sentences (strings of words) that can be derived by a grammar are in the formal language defined by that grammar, and are called **grammatical** sentences. Sentences that cannot be derived by a given formal grammar are not in the language defined by that grammar and are referred to as **ungrammatical**. This hard line between "in" and "out" characterizes all formal languages but is only a very simplified model of how natural languages really work. This is because determining whether a given sentence is part of a given natural language (say, English) often depends on the context. In linguistics, the use of formal languages to model natural languages is called **generative grammar** since the language is defined by the set of possible sentences "generated" by the grammar.

Generative grammar

12.2.1   Formal Definition of Context-Free Grammar

We conclude this section by way of summary with a quick, formal description of a context-free grammar and the language it generates. A context-free grammar G is defined by four parameters: N, Σ, R, S (technically this is a "4-tuple").

N	a set of **non-terminal symbols** (or **variables**)
Σ	a set of **terminal symbols** (disjoint from N)
R	a set of **rules** or productions, each of the form $A \rightarrow \beta$,
	where A is a non-terminal,
	β is a string of symbols from the infinite set of strings $(\Sigma \cup N)*$
S	a designated **start symbol**

For the remainder of the book we adhere to the following conventions when discussing the formal properties of context-free grammars (as opposed to explaining particular facts about English or other languages).

Capital letters like A, B, and S	Non-terminals
S	The start symbol
Lower-case Greek letters like α, β, and γ	Strings drawn from $(\Sigma \cup N)*$
Lower-case Roman letters like u, v, and w	Strings of terminals

A language is defined through the concept of derivation. One string derives another one if it can be rewritten as the second one by some series of rule applications. More formally, following Hopcroft and Ullman (1979),

Directly derives

if $A \rightarrow \beta$ is a production of P and α and γ are any strings in the set $(\Sigma \cup N)*$, then we say that $\alpha A \gamma$ **directly derives** $\alpha \beta \gamma$, or $\alpha A \gamma \Rightarrow \alpha \beta \gamma$.

Derivation is then a generalization of direct derivation:

Let $\alpha_1, \alpha_2, \ldots, \alpha_m$ be strings in $(\Sigma \cup N)*, m \geq 1$, such that

$$\alpha_1 \Rightarrow \alpha_2, \alpha_2 \Rightarrow \alpha_3, \ldots, \alpha_{m-1} \Rightarrow \alpha_m$$

Derives   We say that α_1 **derives** α_m, or $\alpha_1 \overset{*}{\Rightarrow} \alpha_m$.

We can then formally define the language $\mathscr{L}_G$ generated by a grammar G as the set of strings composed of terminal symbols that can be derived from the designated start symbol S.

$$\mathscr{L}_G = \quad w \mid w \text{ is in } \Sigma* \text{ and } S \overset{*}{\Rightarrow} w$$

Syntactic parsing   The problem of mapping from a string of words to its parse tree is called **syntactic parsing**; we define algorithms for parsing in Chapter 13.

12.3   Some Grammar Rules for English

In this section, we introduce a few more aspects of the phrase structure of English; for consistency we will continue to focus on sentences from the ATIS domain. Because of space limitations, our discussion is necessarily limited to highlights. Readers are strongly advised to consult a good reference grammar of English, such as Huddleston and Pullum (2002).

12.3.1   Sentence-Level Constructions

In the small grammar $\mathscr{L}_0$, we provided only one sentence-level construction for declarative sentences like *I prefer a morning flight*. Among the large number of constructions for English sentences, four are particularly common and important: declarative structure, imperative structure, yes-no question structure, and wh-question structure.

Declarative   Sentences with **declarative** structure have a subject noun phrase followed by a verb phrase, like "I prefer a morning flight". Sentences with this structure have a great number of different uses that we follow up on in Chapter 24. Here are a number of examples from the ATIS domain:

> The flight should be eleven a.m. tomorrow
> The return flight should leave at around seven p.m.
> I'd like to fly the coach discount class
> I want a flight from Ontario to Chicago
> I plan to leave on July first around six thirty in the evening

Imperative   Sentences with **imperative** structure often begin with a verb phrase and have no subject. They are called imperative because they are almost always used for commands and suggestions; in the ATIS domain they are commands to the system.

> Show the lowest fare
> Show me the cheapest fare that has lunch
> Give me Sunday's flights arriving in Las Vegas from New York City

List all flights between five and seven p.m.
Show me all flights that depart before ten a.m. and have first class fares
Please list the flights from Charlotte to Long Beach arriving after lunch time
Show me the last flight to leave

We can model this sentence structure with another rule for the expansion of *S*:

$$S \rightarrow VP$$

Yes-no question   Sentences with **yes-no question** structure are often (though not always) used to ask questions (hence the name); they begin with an auxiliary verb, followed by a subject *NP*, followed by a *VP*. Here are some examples. Note that the third example is not really a question but a command or suggestion; Chapter 24 discusses the uses of these question forms to perform different **pragmatic** functions such as asking, requesting, or suggesting.

Do any of these flights have stops?
Does American's flight eighteen twenty five serve dinner?
Can you give me the same information for United?

Here's the rule:

$$S \rightarrow Aux\ NP\ VP$$

Wh-phrase   The most complex of the sentence-level structures we examine are the various **wh-structures**. These are so named because one of their constituents is a **wh-phrase**, that
Wh-word   is, one that includes a **wh-word** (*who, whose, when, where, what, which, how, why*). These may be broadly grouped into two classes of sentence-level structures. The **wh-subject-question** structure is identical to the declarative structure, except that the first noun phrase contains some wh-word.

What airlines fly from Burbank to Denver?
Which flights depart Burbank after noon and arrive in Denver by six p.m?
Whose flights serve breakfast?
Which of these flights have the longest layover in Nashville?

Here is a rule. Exercise 12.10 discusses rules for the constituents that make up the *Wh-NP*.

$$S \rightarrow Wh\text{-}NP\ VP$$

Wh-non-subject question   In the **wh-non-subject-question** structure, the wh-phrase is not the subject of the sentence, and so the sentence includes another subject. In these types of sentences the auxiliary appears before the subject *NP*, just as in the yes-no question structures. Here is an example followed by a sample rule:

What flights do you have from Burbank to Tacoma Washington?

$$S \rightarrow Wh\text{-}NP\ Aux\ NP\ VP$$

Long-distance dependencies   Constructions like the **wh-non-subject-question** contain what are called **long-distance dependencies** because the *Wh-NP what flights* is far away from the predicate that it is semantically related to, the main verb *have* in the *VP*. In some models of parsing and understanding compatible with the grammar rule above, long-distance dependencies like the relation between *flights* and *have* are thought of as a semantic relation. In such models, the job of figuring out that *flights* is the argument of *have* is done during semantic interpretation. In other models of parsing, the relationship between *flights* and *have* is considered to be a syntactic relation, and the grammar is modified to insert a small marker called a **trace** or **empty category** after the verb. We return to such empty-category models when we introduce the Penn Treebank on page 404.

There are other sentence-level structures we won't try to model here, like **topicalization** or other fronting constructions. In topicalization (also treated as a long-distance dependency in the Penn Treebank), a phrase is placed at the beginning of the sentence for discourse purposes.

> On Tuesday, I'd like to fly from Detroit to Saint Petersburg

12.3.2   Clauses and Sentences

Before we move on, we should clarify the status of the *S* rules in the grammars we just described. *S* rules are intended to account for entire sentences that stand alone as fundamental units of discourse. However, as we'll see, *S* can also occur on the right-hand side of grammar rules and hence can be embedded within larger sentences. Clearly then, there's more to being an *S* than just standing alone as a unit of discourse.

Clause

What differentiates sentence constructions (i.e., the *S* rules) from the rest of the grammar is the notion that they are in some sense *complete*. In this way they correspond to the notion of a **clause**, which traditional grammars often describe as forming a complete thought. One way of making this notion of "complete thought" more precise is to say an *S* is a node of the parse tree below which the main verb of the *S* has all of its **arguments**. We define verbal arguments later, but for now let's just see an illustration from the tree for *I prefer a morning flight* in Fig. 12.4 on page 390. The verb *prefer* has two arguments: the subject *I* and the object *a morning flight*. One of the arguments appears below the *VP* node, but the other one, the subject *NP*, appears only below the *S* node.

12.3.3   The Noun Phrase

Our $\mathcal{L}_0$ grammar introduced three of the most frequent types of noun phrases that occur in English: pronouns, proper nouns and the *NP → Det Nominal* construction. While pronouns and proper nouns can be complex in their own ways, the central focus of this section is on the last type since that is where the bulk of the syntactic complexity resides. We can view these noun phrases as consisting of a head, the central noun in the noun phrase, along with various modifiers that can occur before or after the head noun. Let's take a close look at the various parts.

The Determiner

Noun phrases can begin with simple lexical determiners, as in the following examples:

a stop	the flights	this flight
those flights	any flights	some flights

The role of the determiner in English noun phrases can also be filled by more complex expressions, as follows:

United's flight
United's pilot's union
Denver's mayor's mother's canceled flight

In these examples, the role of the determiner is filled by a possessive expression consisting of a noun phrase followed by an *'s* as a possessive marker, as in the following rule.

$$Det \rightarrow NP \text{ 's}$$

The fact that this rule is recursive (since an *NP* can start with a *Det*) helps us model the last two examples above, in which a sequence of possessive expressions serves as a determiner.

Under some circumstances determiners are optional in English. For example, determiners may be omitted if the noun they modify is plural:

(12.3) Show me *flights* from San Francisco to Denver on weekdays

As we saw in Chapter 5, **mass nouns** also don't require determination. Recall that mass nouns often (not always) involve something that is treated like a substance (including e.g., *water* and *snow*), don't take the indefinite article "*a*", and don't tend to pluralize. Many abstract nouns are mass nouns (*music, homework*). Mass nouns in the ATIS domain include *breakfast, lunch,* and *dinner*:

(12.4) Does this flight serve dinner?

Exercise 12.4 asks the reader to represent this fact in the CFG formalism.

The Nominal

The nominal construction follows the determiner and contains any pre- and post-head noun modifiers. As indicated in grammar $\mathscr{L}_0$, in its simplest form a nominal can consist of a single noun.

$$Nominal \rightarrow Noun$$

As we'll see, this rule also provides the basis for the bottom of various recursive rules used to capture more complex nominal constructions.

Before the Head Noun

Cardinal numbers
Ordinal numbers
Quantifiers

A number of different kinds of word classes can appear before the head noun (the "postdeterminers") in a nominal. These include **cardinal numbers**, **ordinal numbers**, and **quantifiers**. Examples of cardinal numbers:

two friends   one stop

Ordinal numbers include *first, second, third,* and so on, but also words like *next, last, past, other,* and *another*:

the first one	the next day	the second leg
the last flight	the other American flight	

Some quantifiers (*many*, *(a) few*, *several*) occur only with plural count nouns:

many fares

The quantifiers *much* and *a little* occur only with non-count nouns.
Adjectives occur after quantifiers but before nouns.

a *first-class* fare	a *non-stop* flight
the *longest* layover	the *earliest* lunch flight

Adjective phrase   Adjectives can also be grouped into a phrase called an **adjective phrase** or AP. APs can have an adverb before the adjective (see Chapter 5 for definitions of adjectives and adverbs):

the *least expensive* fare

We can combine all the options for prenominal modifiers with one rule as follows:

$$NP \rightarrow (Det) \ (Card) \ (Ord) \ (Quant) \ (AP) \ Nominal$$

This simplified noun phrase rule has a flatter structure and hence is simpler than would be assumed by most modern generative theories of grammar; as we discuss in Section 12.4, flat structures are often used for simplicity in computational applications (and indeed, there is no universally agreed-upon internal constituency for the noun phrase).

Note the use of parentheses "( )" to mark **optional constituents**. A rule with one set of parentheses is really a shorthand for two rules, one with the optional constituent, and one without.

After the Head Noun

A head noun can be followed by **postmodifiers**. Three kinds of nominal postmodifiers are common in English:

prepositional phrases	all flights *from Cleveland*
non-finite clauses	any flights *arriving after eleven a.m.*
relative clauses	a flight *that serves breakfast*

Prepositional phrase postmodifiers are particularly common in the ATIS corpus since they are used to mark the origin and destination of flights. Here are some examples, with brackets inserted to show the boundaries of each PP; note that two or more PPs can be strung together:

any stopovers *[for Delta seven fifty one]*
all flights *[from Cleveland] [to Newark]*
arrival *[in San Jose] [before seven p.m.]*
a reservation *[on flight six oh six] [from Tampa] [to Montreal]*

Here's a new nominal rule to account for postnominal *PP*s:

$$Nominal \rightarrow Nominal \ PP$$

The three most common kinds of **non-finite** postmodifiers are the gerundive (*-ing*), *-ed*, and infinitive forms.

Gerundive postmodifiers are so called because they consist of a verb phrase that begins with the gerundive (*-ing*) form of the verb. In the following examples, the verb phrases happen to all have only prepositional phrases after the verb, but in general this verb phrase can have anything in it (i.e., anything semantically and syntactically compatible with the gerund verb).

> any of those *[leaving on Thursday]*
> any flights *[arriving after eleven a.m.]*
> flights *[arriving within thirty minutes of each other]*

We can define the *Nominals* with gerundive modifiers as follows, making use of a new non-terminal *GerundVP*:

$$Nominal \;\rightarrow\; Nominal\; GerundVP$$

We can make rules for *GerundVP* constituents by duplicating all of our VP productions, substituting *GerundV* for *V*.

$$GerundVP \;\rightarrow\; GerundV\; NP$$
$$GerundV\; PP \quad GerundV \quad GerundV\; NP\; PP$$

GerundV can then be defined as

$$GerundV \;\rightarrow\; being \quad arriving \quad leaving \quad \ldots$$

The phrases in italics below are examples of the two other common kinds of non-finite clauses, infinitives and *-ed* forms:

> the last flight *to arrive in Boston*
> I need to have dinner *served*
> Which is the aircraft *used by this flight*?

A postnominal relative clause (more correctly a **restrictive relative clause**), is a clause that often begins with a **relative pronoun** (*that* and *who* are the most common). The relative pronoun functions as the subject of the embedded verb (is a **subject relative**) in the following examples:

> a flight *that serves breakfast*
> flights *that leave in the morning*
> the United flight *that arrives in San Jose around ten p.m.*
> the one *that leaves at ten thirty five*

We might add rules like the following to deal with these:

$$Nominal \;\rightarrow\; Nominal\; RelClause$$
$$RelClause \;\rightarrow\; (who \quad that)\; VP$$

The relative pronoun may also function as the object of the embedded verb, as in the following example; we leave for the reader the exercise of writing grammar rules for more complex relative clauses of this kind.

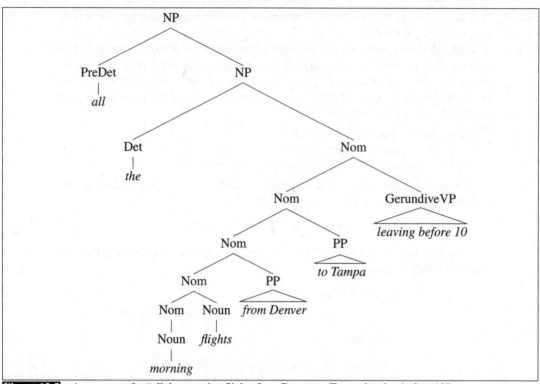

Figure 12.5   A parse tree for "all the morning flights from Denver to Tampa leaving before 10".

the earliest American Airlines flight that I can get

Various postnominal modifiers can be combined, as the following examples show:

a flight *[from Phoenix to Detroit] [leaving Monday evening]*
I need a flight *[to Seattle] [leaving from Baltimore] [making a stop in Minneapolis]*
evening flights *[from Nashville to Houston] [that serve dinner]*
a friend *[living in Denver] [that would like to visit me here in Washington DC]*

Before the Noun Phrase

Predeterminers   Word classes that modify and appear before *NP*s are called **predeterminers**. Many of these have to do with number or amount; a common predeterminer is *all*:

all the flights   all flights   all non-stop flights

The example noun phrase given in Fig. 12.5 illustrates some of the complexity that arises when these rules are combined.

12.3.4   Agreement

In Chapter 3 we discussed English inflectional morphology. Recall that most verbs in English can appear in two forms in the present tense: the form used for third-person, singular subjects (*the flight does*), and the form used for all other kinds of subjects (*all the flights do, I do*). The third-person-singular (*3sg*) form usually has a final *-s* where the non-3sg form does not. Here are some examples, again using the verb *do*, with various subjects:

> Do [NP all of these flights] offer first class service?
> Do [NP I] get dinner on this flight?
> Do [NP you] have a flight from Boston to Forth Worth?
> Does [NP this flight] stop in Dallas?

Here are more examples with the verb *leave*:

> What flights *leave* in the morning?
> What flight *leaves* from Pittsburgh?

This agreement phenomenon occurs whenever a verb has some noun acting as its subject. Note that sentences in which the subject does not agree with the verb are ungrammatical:

> *[What flight] *leave* in the morning?
> *Does [NP you] have a flight from Boston to Forth Worth?
> *Do [NP this flight] stop in Dallas?

How can we modify our grammar to handle these agreement phenomena? One way is to expand our grammar with multiple sets of rules, one rule set for *3sg* subjects and one for non-*3sg* subjects. For example, the rule that handled these yes-no questions used to look like this:

$$S \rightarrow Aux\ NP\ VP$$

We could replace this with two rules of the following form:

$$S \rightarrow 3sgAux\ 3sgNP\ VP$$
$$S \rightarrow Non3sgAux\ Non3sgNP\ VP$$

We could then add rules for the lexicon like these:

$$3sgAux \rightarrow does\ has\ can\ \ldots$$
$$Non3sgAux \rightarrow do\ have\ can\ \ldots$$

But we would also need to add rules for *3sgNP* and *Non3sgNP*, again by making two copies of each rule for *NP*. While pronouns can be first, second, or third person, full lexical noun phrases can only be third person, so for them we just need to distinguish between singular and plural (dealing with the first and second person pronouns is left as an exercise):

$$3SgNP \rightarrow Det\ SgNominal$$
$$Non3SgNP \rightarrow Det\ PlNominal$$
$$SgNominal \rightarrow SgNoun$$
$$PlNominal \rightarrow PlNoun$$
$$SgNoun \rightarrow flight\ fare\ dollar\ reservation\ \ldots$$
$$PlNoun \rightarrow flights\ fares\ dollars\ reservations\ \ldots$$

The problem with this method of dealing with number agreement is that it doubles the size of the grammar. Every rule that refers to a noun or a verb needs to have a "singular" version and a "plural" version. Unfortunately, subject-verb agreement is only the tip of the iceberg. We'll also have to introduce copies of rules to capture the fact that head nouns and their determiners have to agree in number as well:

this flight	*this flights
those flights	*those flight

Case
Nominative
Accusative

Rule proliferation will also have to happen for the noun's **case**; for example, English pronouns have **nominative** (*I, she, he, they*) and **accusative** (*me, her, him, them*) versions. We will need new versions of every *NP* and *N* rule for each of these.

Gender agreement

These problems are compounded in languages like German or French, which not only have number-agreement as in English but also have **gender agreement**. We mentioned briefly in Chapter 3 that the gender of a noun must agree with the gender of its modifying adjective and determiner. This adds another multiplier to the rule sets of the language.

Chapter 15 introduces a way to deal with these agreement problems without exploding the size of the grammar, by effectively **parameterizing** each non-terminal of the grammar with **feature structures** and **unification**. But for many practical computational grammars, we simply rely on CFGs and make do with the large numbers of rules.

12.3.5   The Verb Phrase and Subcategorization

The verb phrase consists of the verb and a number of other constituents. In the simple rules we have built so far, these other constituents include *NP*s and *PP*s and combinations of the two:

$$VP \rightarrow Verb \quad \text{disappear}$$
$$VP \rightarrow Verb\,NP \quad \text{prefer a morning flight}$$
$$VP \rightarrow Verb\,NP\,PP \quad \text{leave Boston in the morning}$$
$$VP \rightarrow Verb\,PP \quad \text{leaving on Thursday}$$

Verb phrases can be significantly more complicated than this. Many other kinds of constituents, such as an entire embedded sentence, can follow the verb. These are called **sentential complements**:

Sentential
complements

You [$_{VP}$ [$_V$ said [$_S$ there were two flights that were the cheapest]]]
You [$_{VP}$ [$_V$ said [$_S$ you had a two hundred sixty six dollar fare]]
[$_{VP}$ [$_V$ Tell] [$_{NP}$ me] [$_S$ how to get from the airport in Philadelphia to downtown]]
I [$_{VP}$ [$_V$ think [$_S$ I would like to take the nine thirty flight]]

Here's a rule for these:

$$VP \rightarrow Verb\,S$$

Another potential constituent of the *VP* is another VP. This is often the case for verbs like *want, would like, try, intend, need*:

I want [$_{VP}$ to fly from Milwaukee to Orlando]

Hi, I want [$_{VP}$ to arrange three flights]

Hello, I'm trying [$_{VP}$ to find a flight that goes from Pittsburgh to Denver after two p.m.]

Recall from Chapter 5 that verbs can also be followed by *particles*, words that resemble a preposition but that combine with the verb to form a *phrasal verb* like *take off*. These particles are generally considered to be an integral part of the verb in a way that other post-verbal elements are not; phrasal verbs are treated as individual verbs composed of two words.

While a verb phrase can have many possible kinds of constituents, not every verb is compatible with every verb phrase. For example, the verb *want* can be used either with an *NP* complement (*I want a flight ...*) or with an infinitive *VP* complement (*I want to fly to ...*). By contrast, a verb like *find* cannot take this sort of *VP* complement (* *I found to fly to Dallas*).

Transitive

Intransitive

This idea that verbs are compatible with different kinds of complements is a very old one; traditional grammar distinguishes between **transitive** verbs like *find*, which take a direct object *NP* (*I found a flight*), and **intransitive** verbs like *disappear*, which do not (**I disappeared a flight*).

Subcategorize

Where traditional grammars **subcategorize** verbs into these two categories (transitive and intransitive), modern grammars distinguish as many as 100 subcategories. (In fact, tagsets for many such subcategorization frames exist; see Macleod et al. (1998) for the COMLEX tagset, Sanfilippo (1993) for the ACQUILEX tagset, and further discussion in Chapter 15.) We say that a verb like *find* **subcategorizes for** an *NP*, and a verb like *want* subcategorizes for either an *NP* or a non-finite *VP*. We also call these constituents the **complements** of the verb (hence our use of the term **sentential complement** above). So we say that *want* can take a *VP* complement. These possible sets of complements are called the **subcategorization frame** for the verb. Another way of talking about the relation between the verb and these other constituents is to think of the verb as a logical predicate and the constituents as logical arguments of the predicate. So we can think of such predicate-argument relations as FIND(I, A FLIGHT) or WANT(I, TO FLY). We talk more about this view of verbs and arguments in Chapter 17 when we talk about predicate calculus representations of verb semantics.

Subcategorizes for

Complements

Subcategorization frame

Frame	Verb	Example
$\emptyset$	eat, sleep	I ate
NP	prefer, find, leave	Find [$_{NP}$ the flight from Pittsburgh to Boston]
NP NP	show, give	Show [$_{NP}$ me] [$_{NP}$ airlines with flights from Pittsburgh]
PP_{from} PP_{to}	fly, travel	I would like to fly [$_{PP}$ from Boston] [$_{PP}$ to Philadelphia]
NP PP_{with}	help, load	Can you help [$_{NP}$ me] [$_{PP}$ with a flight]
VPto	prefer, want, need	I would prefer [$_{VPto}$ to go by United airlines]
VPbrst	can, would, might	I can [$_{VPbrst}$ go from Boston]
S	mean	Does this mean [$_S$ AA has a hub in Boston]

Figure 12.6   Subcategorization frames for a set of example verbs.

Subcategorization frames for a set of example verbs are given in Fig. 12.6. Note that a verb can subcategorize for a particular type of verb phrase, such as a verb phrase whose verb is an infinitive (*VPto*) or a verb phrase whose verb is a bare stem (un-inflected: *VPbrst*). Note also that a single verb can take different subcategorization frames. The verb *find*, for example, can take an *NP NP* frame (*find me a flight*) as well as an *NP* frame.

How can we represent the relation between verbs and their complements in a context-free grammar? One thing we could do is to do what we did with agreement features: make separate subtypes of the class Verb (*Verb-with-NP-complement*, *Verb-with-Inf-VP-complement*, *Verb-with-S-complement*, and so on):

$$Verb\text{-}with\text{-}NP\text{-}complement \rightarrow find \quad leave \quad repeat \quad \dots$$
$$Verb\text{-}with\text{-}S\text{-}complement \rightarrow think \quad believe \quad say \quad \dots$$
$$Verb\text{-}with\text{-}Inf\text{-}VP\text{-}complement \rightarrow want \quad try \quad need \quad \dots$$

Each *VP* rule could then be modified to require the appropriate verb subtype:

$$VP \rightarrow Verb\text{-}with\text{-}no\text{-}complement \quad \text{disappear}$$
$$VP \rightarrow Verb\text{-}with\text{-}NP\text{-}comp \; NP \quad \text{prefer a morning flight}$$
$$VP \rightarrow Verb\text{-}with\text{-}S\text{-}comp \; S \quad \text{said there were two flights}$$

The problem with this approach, as with the same solution to the agreement feature problem, is a vast explosion in the number of rules. The standard solution to both of these problems is the **feature structure**, which is introduced in Chapter 15, where we also discuss the fact that nouns, adjectives, and prepositions can subcategorize for complements just as verbs can.

12.3.6   Auxiliaries

Auxiliaries

Modal verb

Perfect

Progressive

Passive

The subclass of verbs called **auxiliaries** or **helping verbs** have particular syntactic constraints that can be viewed as a kind of subcategorization. Auxiliaries include the **modal** verbs *can, could, may, might, must, will, would, shall*, and *should*, the **perfect** auxiliary *have*, the **progressive** auxiliary *be*, and the **passive** auxiliary *be*. Each of these verbs places a constraint on the form of the following verb, and each of these must also combine in a particular order.

Modal verbs subcategorize for a *VP* whose head verb is a bare stem; for example, *can go in the morning, will try to find a flight*. The perfect verb *have* subcategorizes for a *VP* whose head verb is the past participle form: *have booked 3 flights*. The progressive verb *be* subcategorizes for a *VP* whose head verb is the gerundive participle: *am going from Atlanta*. The passive verb *be* subcategorizes for a *VP* whose head verb is the past participle: *was delayed by inclement weather*.

A sentence can have multiple auxiliary verbs, but they must occur in a particular order: *modal* < *perfect* < *progressive* < *passive*. Here are some examples of multiple auxiliaries:

modal perfect	*could have been* a contender
modal passive	*will be* married
perfect progressive	*have been* feasting
modal perfect passive	*might have been* prevented

Auxiliaries are often treated just like verbs such as *want, seem,* or *intend,* which subcategorize for particular kinds of *VP* complements. Thus, *can* would be listed in the lexicon as a *verb-with-bare-stem-VP-complement.* One way of capturing the ordering constraints among auxiliaries, commonly used in the **systemic grammar** of Halliday (1985), is to introduce a special constituent called the **verb group**, whose subconstituents include all the auxiliaries as well as the main verb. Some of the ordering constraints can also be captured in a different way. Since modals, for example, do not have a progressive or participle form, they simply will never be allowed to follow progressive or passive *be* or perfect *have*. Exercise 12.8 asks the reader to write grammar rules for auxiliaries.

The passive construction has a number of properties that make it different from other auxiliaries. One important difference is a semantic one; while the subject of non-passive (**active**) sentence is often the semantic agent of the event described by the verb (*I prevented a catastrophe*), the subject of the passive is often the undergoer or patient of the event (*a catastrophe was prevented*). This is discussed further in Chapter 19.

12.3.7   Coordination

The major phrase types discussed here can be conjoined with **conjunctions** like *and, or,* and *but* to form larger constructions of the same type. For example, a **coordinate** noun phrase can consist of two other noun phrases separated by a conjunction:

Please repeat [$_{NP}$ [$_{NP}$ the flights] *and* [$_{NP}$ the costs]]
I need to know [$_{NP}$ [$_{NP}$ the aircraft] *and* [$_{NP}$ the flight number]]

Here's a rule that allows these structures:

$$NP \rightarrow NP \ and \ NP$$

Note that the ability to form coordinate phrases through conjunctions is often used as a test for constituency. Consider the following examples, which differ from the ones given above in that they lack the second determiner.

Please repeat the [$_{Nom}$ [$_{Nom}$ flights] *and* [$_{Nom}$ costs]]
I need to know the [$_{Nom}$ [$_{Nom}$ aircraft] *and* [$_{Nom}$ flight number]]

The fact that these phrases can be conjoined is evidence for the presence of the underlying *Nominal* constituent we have been making use of. Here's a new rule for this:

$$Nominal \rightarrow Nominal \ and \ Nominal$$

The following examples illustrate conjunctions involving *VP*s and *S*s.

What flights do you have [$_{VP}$ [$_{VP}$ leaving Denver] *and* [$_{VP}$ arriving in San Francisco]]
[$_S$ [$_S$ I'm interested in a flight from Dallas to Washington] *and* [$_S$ I'm also interested in going to Baltimore]]

The rules for *VP* and *S* conjunctions mirror the *NP* one given above.

$$VP \rightarrow VP \ and \ VP$$
$$S \rightarrow S \ and \ S$$

Metarules

Since all the major phrase types can be conjoined in this fashion, it is also possible to represent this conjunction fact more generally; a number of grammar formalisms such as Gazdar et al. (1985) do this using **metarules** such as the following:

$$X \rightarrow X \, and \, X$$

This metarule simply states that any non-terminal can be conjoined with the same non-terminal to yield a constituent of the same type. Of course, the variable X must be designated as a variable that stands for any non-terminal rather than a non-terminal itself.

12.4   Treebanks

Treebank

Context-free grammar rules of the type that we have explored so far in this chapter can in principle be used to assign a parse tree to any sentence. This means that it is possible to build a corpus in which every sentence is syntactically annotated with a parse tree. Such a syntactically annotated corpus is called a **treebank**. Treebanks play an important role in parsing, as we discuss in Chapter 13, and in various empirical investigations of syntactic phenomena.

Penn Treebank

A wide variety of treebanks have been created, generally by the use of parsers (of the sort described in the next two chapters) to automatically parse each sentence, followed by the use of humans (linguists) to hand-correct the parses. The **Penn Treebank** project (whose POS tagset we introduced in Chapter 5) has produced treebanks from the Brown, Switchboard, ATIS, and *Wall Street Journal* corpora of English, as well as treebanks in Arabic and Chinese. Other treebanks include the Prague Dependency Treebank for Czech, the Negra treebank for German, and the Susanne treebank for English.

12.4.1   Example: The Penn Treebank Project

Figure 12.7 shows sentences from the Brown and ATIS portions of the Penn Treebank.[1] Note the formatting differences for the part-of-speech tags; such small differences are common and must be dealt with in processing treebanks. The Penn Treebank part-of-speech tagset was defined in Chapter 5. The use of LISP-style parenthesized notation for trees is extremely common and resembles the bracketed notation we saw above in (12.2). For those who are not familiar with it we show a standard node-and-line tree representation in Fig. 12.8.

Traces
Syntactic movement

Figure 12.9 shows a tree from the *Wall Street Journal*. This tree shows another feature of the Penn Treebanks: the use of **traces** (–NONE– nodes) to mark long-distance dependencies or **syntactic movement**. For example, quotations often follow a quotative verb like *say*. But in this example, the quotation "We would have to wait until

---

[1] The Penn Treebank project released treebanks in multiple languages and in various stages; for example, there were Treebank I (Marcus et al., 1993), Treebank II (Marcus et al., 1994), and Treebank III releases of English treebanks. We use Treebank III for our examples.

```
((S
   (NP-SBJ (DT That)
      (JJ cold) (, ,)                    ((S
      (JJ empty) (NN sky) )                 (NP-SBJ The/DT flight/NN )
   (VP (VBD was)                             (VP should/MD
      (ADJP-PRD (JJ full)                       (VP arrive/VB
         (PP (IN of)                               (PP-TMP at/IN
            (NP (NN fire)                             (NP eleven/CD a.m/RB ))
               (CC and)                            (NP-TMP tomorrow/NN )))))
               (NN light) ))))
   (. .) ))
              (a)                                          (b)
```

Figure 12.7   Parsed sentences from the LDC Treebank3 version of the Brown (a) and ATIS (b) corpora.

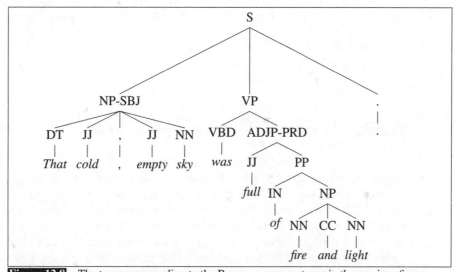

Figure 12.8   The tree corresponding to the Brown corpus sentence in the previous figure.

we have collected on those assets" precedes the words *he said*. An empty *S* containing only the node −NONE− marks the position after *said* where the quotation sentence often occurs. This empty node is marked (in Treebanks II and III) with the index 2, as is the quotation *S* at the beginning of the sentence. Such co-indexing may make it easier for some parsers to recover the fact that this fronted or topicalized quotation is the complement of the verb *said*. A similar −NONE− node marks the fact that there is no syntactic subject right before the verb *to wait*; instead, the subject is the earlier *NP We*. Again, they are both co-indexed with the index 1.

The Penn Treebank II and Treebank III releases added further information to make it easier to recover the relationships between predicates and arguments. Certain phrases were marked with tags indicating the grammatical function of the phrase (as surface

```
( (S ('' '')
   (S-TPC-2
     (NP-SBJ-1 (PRP We) )
     (VP (MD would)
       (VP (VB have)
         (S
           (NP-SBJ (-NONE- *-1) )
           (VP (TO to)
             (VP (VB wait)
               (SBAR-TMP (IN until)
                 (S
                   (NP-SBJ (PRP we) )
                   (VP (VBP have)
                     (VP (VBN collected)
                       (PP-CLR (IN on)
                         (NP (DT those)(NNS assets))))))))))))))))))
   (, ,) ('' '')
   (NP-SBJ (PRP he) )
   (VP (VBD said)
     (S (-NONE- *T*-2) ))
   (. .) ))
```

Figure 12.9   A sentence from the *Wall Street Journal* portion of the LDC Penn Treebank. Note the use of the empty -NONE- nodes.

subject, logical topic, cleft, non-VP predicates) its presence in particular text categories (headlines, titles), and its semantic function (temporal phrases, locations) (Marcus et al., 1994; Bies et al., 1995). Figure 12.9 shows examples of the -SBJ (surface subject) and -TMP (temporal phrase) tags. Figure 12.8 shows in addition the -PRD tag, which is used for predicates that are not VPs (the one in Fig. 12.8 is an ADJP). Figure 12.20 on page 420 shows the tag -UNF in NP-UNF meaning "unfinished or incomplete phrase".

12.4.2   Treebanks as Grammars

The sentences in a treebank implicitly constitute a grammar of the language. For example, from the three parsed sentences in Fig. 12.7 and Fig. 12.9, we can extract each of the CFG rules in them. For simplicity, let's strip off the rule suffixes (-SBJ and so on). The resulting grammar is shown in Fig. 12.10.

The grammar used to parse the Penn Treebank is relatively flat, resulting in very many and very long rules. For example, among the approximately 4,500 different rules for expanding VPs are separate rules for PP sequences of any length and every possible arrangement of verb arguments:

```
VP  →  VBD PP
VP  →  VBD PP PP
```

Grammar	Lexicon
$S \rightarrow NP\ VP$.	$PRP \rightarrow we \quad he$
$S \rightarrow NP\ VP$	$DT \rightarrow the \quad that \quad those$
$S \rightarrow$ " S " , $NP\ VP$.	$JJ \rightarrow cold \quad empty \quad full$
$S \rightarrow$ -NONE-	$NN \rightarrow sky \quad fire \quad light \quad flight \quad tomorrow$
$NP \rightarrow DT\ NN$	$NNS \rightarrow assets$
$NP \rightarrow DT\ NNS$	$CC \rightarrow and$
$NP \rightarrow NN\ CC\ NN$	$IN \rightarrow of \quad at \quad until \quad on$
$NP \rightarrow CD\ RB$	$CD \rightarrow eleven$
$NP \rightarrow DT\ JJ , JJ\ NN$	$RB \rightarrow a.m.$
$NP \rightarrow PRP$	$VB \rightarrow arrive \quad have \quad wait$
$NP \rightarrow$ -NONE-	$VBD \rightarrow was \quad said$
$VP \rightarrow MD\ VP$	$VBP \rightarrow have$
$VP \rightarrow VBD\ ADJP$	$VBN \rightarrow collected$
$VP \rightarrow VBD\ S$	$MD \rightarrow should \quad would$
$VP \rightarrow VBN\ PP$	$TO \rightarrow to$
$VP \rightarrow VB\ S$	
$VP \rightarrow VB\ SBAR$	
$VP \rightarrow VBP\ VP$	
$VP \rightarrow VBN\ PP$	
$VP \rightarrow TO\ VP$	
$SBAR \rightarrow IN\ S$	
$ADJP \rightarrow JJ\ PP$	
$PP \rightarrow IN\ NP$	

Figure 12.10   A sample of the CFG grammar rules and lexical entries that would be extracted from the three treebank sentences in Fig. 12.7 and Fig. 12.9.

```
VP  →  VBD PP PP PP
VP  →  VBD PP PP PP PP
VP  →  VB ADVP PP
VP  →  VB PP ADVP
VP  →  ADVP VB PP
```

as well as even longer rules, such as

```
VP  →  VBP PP PP PP PP PP ADVP PP
```

which comes from the *VP* marked in italics:

(12.5) This mostly happens because we *go from football in the fall to lifting in the winter to football again in the spring*.

Some of the many thousands of *NP* rules include

```
NP  →  DT JJ NN
NP  →  DT JJ NNS
NP  →  DT JJ NN NN
NP  →  DT JJ JJ NN
NP  →  DT JJ CD NNS
NP  →  RB DT JJ NN NN
NP  →  RB DT JJ JJ NNS
NP  →  DT JJ JJ NNP NNS
NP  →  DT NNP NNP NNP NNP JJ NN
```

417

```
NP  →  DT JJ NNP CC JJ JJ NN NNS
NP  →  RB DT JJS NN NN SBAR
NP  →  DT VBG JJ NNP NNP CC NNP
NP  →  DT JJ NNS , NNS CC NN NNS NN
NP  →  DT JJ JJ VBG NN NNP NNP FW NNP
NP  →  NP JJ , JJ '' SBAR '' NNS
```

The last two of those rules, for example, come from the following two NPs:

(12.6) [$_{DT}$ The] [$_{JJ}$ state-owned] [$_{JJ}$ industrial] [$_{VBG}$ holding] [$_{NN}$ company] [$_{NNP}$ Instituto] [$_{NNP}$ Nacional] [$_{FW}$ de] [$_{NNP}$ Industria]

(12.7) [$_{NP}$ Shearson's] [$_{JJ}$ easy-to-film,] [$_{JJ}$ black-and-white] "[$_{SBAR}$ Where We Stand]" [$_{NNS}$ commercials]

Viewed as a large grammar in this way, the Penn Treebank III *Wall Street Journal* corpus, which contains about 1 million words, also has about 1 million non-lexical rule tokens, consisting of about 17,500 distinct rule types.

Various facts about the treebank grammars, such as their large numbers of flat rules, pose problems for probabilistic parsing algorithms. For this reason, it is common to make various modifications to a grammar extracted from a treebank. We discuss these further in Chapter 14.

12.4.3   Treebank Searching

It is often important to search through a treebank to find examples of particular grammatical phenomena, either for linguistic research or for answering analytic questions about a computational application. But neither the regular expressions used for text search nor the Boolean expressions over words used for Web search are a sufficient search tool. What is needed is a language that can specify constraints about nodes and links in a parse tree so as to search for specific patterns.

Various such tree-searching languages exist in different tools. **Tgrep** (Pito, 1993) and **TGrep2** (Rohde, 2005) are publicly available tools for searching treebanks that use a similar language for expressing tree constraints. We'll describe the more recent language used by **TGrep2**, drawing from the on-line manual (Rohde, 2005).

A pattern in **tgrep** or **TGrep2** consists of a specification of a node, possibly followed by links to other nodes. A node specification can then be used to return the subtree rooted at that node. For example, the pattern

```
NP
```

returns all subtrees in a corpus whose root is NP. Nodes can be specified by a name, a regular expression inside slashes, or a disjunction of these. For example, we can specify a singular or plural noun (NN or NNS) in Penn Treebank notation as either of the following:

```
/NNS?/        NN|NNS
```

A node that is either the word *bush* or else ends in the string *tree* can be expressed as

```
/tree$/|bush
```

The power of **tgrep/TGrep2** patterns lies in the ability to specify information about links. The operator < means **immediately dominates**; the following pattern thus matches an *NP* immediately dominating a PP:

```
NP < PP
```

The relation < < specifies dominance; this pattern matches an *NP* dominating a PP:

```
NP << PP
```

This previous pattern would thus match either of the following trees:

```
(12.8) (NP (NP (NN reinvestment))
           (PP (IN of)
               (NP (NNS dividends))))
```

```
(12.9) (NP (NP
               (DT the) (JJ austere) (NN company) (NN dormitory))
           (VP (VBN run)
               (PP (IN by)
                   (NP (DT a) (JJ prying) (NN caretaker)))))
```

The relation . marks linear precedence. The following pattern matches an *NP* that immediately dominates a JJ and is immediately followed by a PP, for example, matching the *NP* dominating *the austere company dormitory* in (12.9) above:[2]

```
NP < JJ . VP
```

Each of the relations in a **tgrep/TGrep2** expression is interpreted as referring to the first or root node. Thus, for example, the following expression means an *NP* that both precedes a *PP* and dominates an S:

```
NP . PP < S
```

If we wanted instead to specify that the *PP* dominated the S, we could use parentheses as follows:

```
NP . (PP < S)
```

Figure 12.11 gives the major link operations for **TGrep2**.

12.4.4   Heads and Head Finding

We suggested informally earlier that syntactic constituents could be associated with a lexical **head**; *N* is the head of an *NP*, *V* is the head of a *VP*. This idea of a head for each constituent dates back to Bloomfield (1914). It is central to linguistic formalisms such as Head-Driven Phrase Structure Grammar (Pollard and Sag, 1994), and has become extremely popular in computational linguistics with the rise of lexicalized grammars (Chapter 14).

In one simple model of lexical heads, each context-free rule is associated with a head (Charniak, 1997; Collins, 1999). The head is the word in the phrase that is grammatically the most important. Heads are passed up the parse tree; thus, each

---

[2] The definition of linear precedence differs slightly between **tgrep** and **TGrep2**. See Rohde (2005) for more details.

Link	Explanation
A < B	A is the parent of (immediately dominates) B.
A > B	A is the child of B.
A <N B	B is the Nth child of A (the first child is <1).
A >N B	A is the Nth child of B (the first child is >1).
A <, B	Synonymous with A <1 B.
A >, B	Synonymous with A >1 B.
A <-N B	B is the Nth-to-last child of A (the last child is <-1).
A >-N B	A is the Nth-to-last child of B (the last child is >-1).
A <- B	B is the last child of A (synonymous with A <-1 B).
A >- B	A is the last child of B (synonymous with A >-1 B).
A <' B	B is the last child of A (also synonymous with A <-1 B).
A >' B	A is the last child of B (also synonymous with A >-1 B).
A <: B	B is the only child of A.
A >: B	A is the only child of B.
A << B	A dominates B (A is an ancestor of B).
A >> B	A is dominated by B (A is a descendant of B).
A <<, B	B is the leftmost descendant of A.
A >>, B	A is the leftmost descendant of B.
A <<' B	B is the rightmost descendant of A.
A >>' B	A is the rightmost descendant of B.
A <<: B	There is a single path of descent from A and B is on it.
A >>: B	There is a single path of descent from B and A is on it.
A . B	A immediately precedes B.
A , B	A immediately follows B.
A .. B	A precedes B.
A ,, B	A follows B.
A $ B	A is a sister of B (and A ≠ B).
A $. B	A is a sister of and immediately precedes B.
A $, B	A is a sister of and immediately follows B.
A $.. B	A is a sister of and precedes B.
A $,, B	A is a sister of and follows B.

Figure 12.11   Links in **TGrep2**, summarized from Rohde (2005).

non-terminal in a parse tree is annotated with a single word, which is its lexical head. Figure 12.12 shows an example of such a tree from Collins (1999), in which each non-terminal is annotated with its head. "Workers dumped sacks into a bin" is a shortened form of a WSJ sentence.

For the generation of such a tree, each CFG rule must be augmented to identify one right-side constituent to be the head daughter. The headword for a node is then set to the headword of its head daughter. Choosing these head daughters is simple for textbook examples (*NN* is the head of *NP*) but is complicated and indeed controversial for most phrases. (Should the complementizer *to* or the verb be the head of an infinite verb-phrase?) Modern linguistic theories of syntax generally include a component that defines heads (see, e.g., Pollard and Sag, 1994).

An alternative approach to finding a head is used in most practical computational systems. Instead of specifying head rules in the grammar itself, heads are identified dynamically in the context of trees for specific sentences. In other words, once a sentence

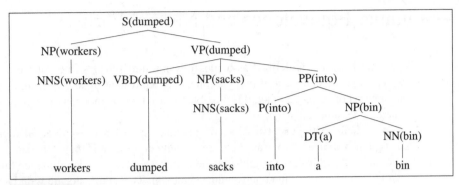

Figure 12.12 A lexicalized tree from Collins (1999).

is parsed, the resulting tree is walked to decorate each node with the appropriate head. Most current systems rely on a simple set of hand-written rules, such as a practical one for Penn Treebank grammars given in Collins (1999) but developed originally by Magerman (1995). For example, the rule for finding the head of an *NP* is as follows (Collins, 1999, p. 238):

- If the last word is tagged POS, return last-word.
- Else search from right to left for the first child which is an NN, NNP, NNPS, NX, POS, or JJR.
- Else search from left to right for the first child which is an NP.
- Else search from right to left for the first child which is a $, ADJP, or PRN.
- Else search from right to left for the first child which is a CD.
- Else search from right to left for the first child which is a JJ, JJS, RB or QP.
- Else return the last word

Selected other rules from this set are shown in Fig. 12.13. For example, for *VP* rules of the form $VP \rightarrow Y_1 \quad Y_n$, the algorithm would start from the left of $Y_1 \quad Y_n$ looking for the first Y_i of type TO; if no TOs are found, it would search for the first Y_i of type VBD; if no VBDs are found, it would search for a VBN, and so on. See Collins (1999) for more details.

Parent	Direction	Priority List
ADJP	Left	NNS QP NN $ ADVP JJ VBN VBG ADJP JJR NP JJS DT FW RBR RBS SBAR RB
ADVP	Right	RB RBR RBS FW ADVP TO CD JJR JJ IN NP JJS NN
PRN	Left	
PRT	Right	RP
QP	Left	$ IN NNS NN JJ RB DT CD NCD QP JJR JJS
S	Left	TO IN VP S SBAR ADJP UCP NP
SBAR	Left	WHNP WHPP WHADVP WHADJP IN DT S SQ SINV SBAR FRAG
VP	Left	TO VBD VBN MD VBZ VB VBG VBP VP ADJP NN NNS NP

Figure 12.13 Selected head rules from Collins (1999). The set of head rules is often called a **head percolation table**.

12.5   Grammar Equivalence and Normal Form

A formal language is defined as a (possibly infinite) set of strings of words. This suggests that we could ask if two grammars are equivalent by asking if they generate the same set of strings. In fact, it is possible to have two distinct context-free grammars generate the same language.

We usually distinguish two kinds of grammar equivalence: **weak equivalence** and **strong equivalence**. Two grammars are strongly equivalent if they generate the same set of strings *and* if they assign the same phrase structure to each sentence (allowing merely for renaming of the non-terminal symbols). Two grammars are weakly equivalent if they generate the same set of strings but do not assign the same phrase structure to each sentence.

Normal form

Chomsky normal form

Binary branching

It is sometimes useful to have a **normal form** for grammars, in which each of the productions takes a particular form. For example, a context-free grammar is in **Chomsky normal form** (CNF) (Chomsky, 1963) if it is ϵ-free and if in addition each production is either of the form $A \rightarrow B\ C$ or $A \rightarrow a$. That is, the right-hand side of each rule either has two non-terminal symbols or one terminal symbol. Chomsky normal form grammars are **binary branching**, that is they have binary trees (down to the prelexical nodes). We make use of this binary branching property in the CKY parsing algorithm in Chapter 13.

Any grammar can be converted into a weakly equivalent Chomsky normal form grammar. For example, a rule of the form

$$A \rightarrow B\ C\ D$$

can be converted into the following two CNF rules (Exercise 12.11 asks the reader to formulate the complete algorithm):

$$A \rightarrow B\ X$$
$$X \rightarrow C\ D$$

Sometimes using binary branching can actually produce smaller grammars. For example, the sentences that might be characterized as

```
VP -> VBD NP PP*
```

are represented in the Penn Treebank by this series of rules:

```
VP → VBD NP PP
VP → VBD NP PP PP
VP → VBD NP PP PP PP
VP → VBD NP PP PP PP PP
...
```

but could also be generated by the following two-rule grammar:

```
VP → VBD NP PP
VP → VP PP
```

Chomsky-
adjunction
The generation of a symbol A with a potentially infinite sequence of symbols B with a rule of the form A → A B is known as **Chomsky-adjunction**.

12.6   Finite-State and Context-Free Grammars

We argued in Section 12.1 that adequate models of grammar need to be able to represent complex interrelated facts about constituency, subcategorization, and dependency relations, and we implied that at the least the power of context-free grammars is needed to accomplish this. But why is it that we can't just use finite-state methods to capture these syntactic facts? The answer to this question is critical since, as shown in Chapter 13, a considerable price is paid in terms of processing speed when we switch from regular languages to context-free ones.

There are two answers to this question. The first is mathematical; we show in Chapter 16 that given certain assumptions, that certain syntactic structures present in English and other natural languages make them not regular languages. The second answer is more subjective and has to do with notions of expressiveness; even when finite-state methods are capable of dealing with the syntactic facts in question, they often don't express them in ways that make generalizations obvious, lead to understandable formalisms, or produce structures of immediate use in subsequent semantic processing.

The mathematical objection is discussed more fully in Chapter 16, but we'll briefly review it here. We mentioned in passing in Chapter 2 that a completely equivalent alternative to finite-state machines and regular expressions, called regular grammars, can describe regular languages. The rules in a regular grammar are a restricted form of the rules in a context-free grammar because they are in right-linear or left-linear form. In a right-linear grammar, for example, the rules are all of the form $A \rightarrow w*$ or $A \rightarrow w * B$, that is, the non-terminals expand either to a string of terminals or to a string of terminals followed by a non-terminal. These rules look a lot like the rules we've been using throughout this chapter, so what can't they do? What they can't do is express recursive **center-embedding** rules like the following, where a non-terminal is rewritten as itself, surrounded by (non-empty) strings:

$$A \stackrel{*}{\Rightarrow} \alpha A \beta \tag{12.10}$$

In other words, a language can be generated by a finite-state machine if and only if the grammar that generates L does not have any **center-embedded** recursions of this form (Chomsky, 1959a; Bar-Hillel et al., 1961; Nederhof, 2000). Intuitively, this is because grammar rules in which the non-terminal symbols are always on either the right or left edge of a rule can be processed iteratively rather than recursively. Such center-embedding rules are needed to deal with artificial problems, such as the language $a^n b^n$, or for practical problems, such as checking for correctly matching delimiters in programming and markup languages. It turns out that there are no slam-dunk examples of this for English, but examples like the following give a flavor of the problem.

(12.11) The luggage arrived.

(12.12) The luggage that the passengers checked arrived.

(12.13) The luggage that the passengers that the storm delayed checked arrived.

At least in theory, this kind of embedding could go on, although it gets increasingly difficult to process such examples and they are luckily fairly rare outside textbooks like this one. Chapter 16 discusses this and related issues as to whether or not even context-free grammars are up to the task.

So, is there no role for finite-state methods in syntactic analysis? A quick review of the rules used for noun phrases in this chapter, as well as those used in the Penn *Noun group* treebank grammar, reveals that a considerable portion of them can be handled by finite-state methods. Consider the following rule for a **noun group**, the prenominal and nominal portions of a noun phrase:

$$Nominal \rightarrow (Det)\ (Card)\ (Ord)\ (Quant)\ (AP)\ Nominal$$

Assuming we convert the prenominal elements of this rule into terminals, this rule is effectively right-linear and can be captured by a finite-state machine. Indeed, it is possible to automatically build a regular grammar that is an approximation of a given context-free grammar; see the references at the end of the chapter. Thus, for many practical purposes for which matching syntactic and semantic rules aren't necessary, finite-state rules are quite sufficient.

12.7   Dependency Grammars

We have focused in this chapter on context-free grammars because many available treebanks and parsers produce these kinds of syntactic representations. But in a class of *Dependency* grammar formalisms called **dependency grammars**, which are becoming quite im-*grammar* portant in speech and language processing, constituents and phrase-structure rules do not play any fundamental role. Instead, the syntactic structure of a sentence is described purely in terms of words and binary semantic or syntactic relations between these words. Dependency grammars often draw heavily on the work of Tesnière (1959), *Dependency* and the name **dependency** might have been used first by early computational linguist David Hays. But this lexical dependency notion of grammar is, in fact, older than the relatively recent phrase-structure or constituency grammars, and has its roots in the ancient Greek and Indian linguistic traditions. Indeed, the notion in traditional grammar of "parsing a sentence into subject and predicate" is based on lexical relations rather than constituent relations.

Figure 12.14 shows a typed dependency parse of the sentence *They hid the letter on the shelf*, using the dependency grammar formalism of de Marneffe et al. (2006). Note that there are no non-terminal or phrasal nodes; each link in the parse tree holds *Typed dependency* between two lexical nodes. This is a **typed dependency parse** because the links are labeled (typed), from a fixed inventory of 48 grammatical relations, a subset of which is shown in Fig. 12.15. Other dependency-based computational grammars, such as *Link Grammar* **Link Grammar** (Sleator and Temperley, 1993), use different but roughly overlapping links. In untyped dependency parses the links are unlabeled.

As shown in Chapter 14, one advantage of dependency formalisms is the strong predictive parsing power that words have for their dependents. Knowing the identity

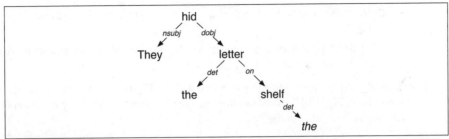

Figure 12.14 A typed dependency parse from the Stanford Parser (de Marneffe et al., 2006).

Argument Dependencies	Description
nsubj	nominal subject
csubj	clausal subject
dobj	direct object
iobj	indirect object
pobj	object of preposition
Modifier Dependencies	**Description**
tmod	temporal modifier
appos	appositional modifier
det	determiner
prep	prepositional modifier

Figure 12.15 Some of the grammatical relations from de Marneffe et al. (2006).

Free word order

of the verb can help in deciding which noun is the subject or the object. Dependency grammar researchers argue that another advantage of dependency grammars is their ability to handle languages with relatively **free word order**. For example, word order in Czech is much more flexible than in English; an *object* might occur before or after a *location adverbial* or a **comp**. A phrase-structure grammar would need a separate rule for each possible place in the parse tree where such an adverbial phrase could occur. A dependency grammar would just have one link type representing this particular adverbial relation. Thus, a dependency grammar abstracts from word-order variation, representing only the information that is necessary for the parse.

Computational implementations of dependency grammars include (for English) Link Grammar (Sleator and Temperley, 1993), Constraint Grammar (Karlsson et al., 1995), MINIPAR (Lin, 2003), and the Stanford Parser (de Marneffe et al., 2006). Dependency resources in other languages include the 500,000 word Prague Dependency Treebank for Czech Hajič (1998), which has been used to train probabilistic dependency parsers (Collins et al., 1999).

12.7.1   The Relationship Between Dependencies and Heads

The reader may have noticed the similarity between dependency graphs like Fig. 12.14 and head structures like Fig. 12.12. In fact, an unlabeled dependency graph can be automatically derived from a context-free parse through the use of head rules; here's an algorithm from Xia and Palmer (2001):

1. Mark the head child of each node in a phrase structure, using the head percolation table.

2. In the dependency structure, make the head of each non-head-child depend on the head of the head-child.

This algorithm applied to the parse tree in Fig. 12.16 would produce the dependency structure in Fig. 12.17. Hand-written patterns can then be used to type the dependencies (de Marneffe et al., 2006).

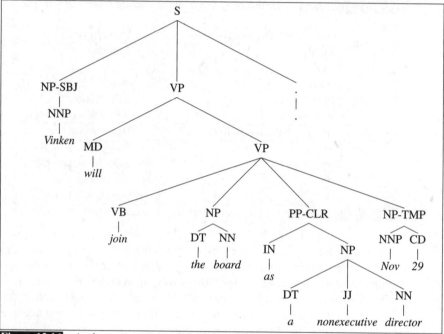

Figure 12.16   A phrase-structure tree from the *Wall Street Journal* component of the Penn Treebank 3.

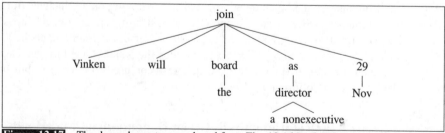

Figure 12.17   The dependency tree produced from Fig. 12.16 by the algorithm given above.

We return to the discussion of heads and dependencies when we discuss lexicalized parsing in Chapter 14 and again when we introduce head features and subcategorization in Chapter 15.

12.7.2   Categorial Grammar

Categorial grammar

Combinatory categorial grammar

Categorial grammar is an early lexicalized grammar model (Adjukiewicz, 1935; Bar-Hillel, 1953). In this section, we give a simplified overview of one important extension to categorial grammar, **combinatory categorial grammar**, or CCG (Steedman, 1996, 1989, 2000). A categorial grammar has two components. The **categorial lexicon** associates each word with a syntactic and semantic category. The **combinatory rules** allow functions and arguments to be combined. There are two types of categories: functors and arguments. Arguments, like nouns, have simple categories like N. Verbs or determiners act as functors. For example, a determiner can be thought of as a function that applies to an N on its right to produce an NP. Such complex categories are built with the X/Y and X\Y operators. X/Y means a function from Y to X, that is, something that combines with a Y on its right to produce an X. Determiners thus receive the category NP/N: something that combines with an N on its right to produce an NP. Transitive verbs might have the category VP/NP: something that combines with an *NP* on the right to produce a VP. Ditransitive verbs like *give* might have the category (VP/NP)/NP: something that combines with an *NP* on its right to yield a transitive verb. The simplest **combination rules** just combine an X/Y with a Y on its right to produce an X or an X\Y with a Y on its left to produce an X.

Consider the simple sentence *Harry eats apples* from Steedman (1989). Instead of using a primitive *VP* category, let's assume that a finite verb phrase like *eat apples* has the category (S\NP): something that combines with an NP on the left to produce a sentence. *Harry* and *apples* are both NPs. *Eats* is a finite transitive verb which combines with an *NP* on the right to produce a finite VP: (S\NP)/NP. The derivation of *S* proceeds as follows:

(12.14)

$$
\frac{\dfrac{\text{Harry}}{\text{NP}} \quad \dfrac{\dfrac{\text{eats}}{\text{(S\backslash NP)/NP}} \quad \dfrac{\text{apples}}{\text{NP}}}{\text{S\backslash NP}}}{\text{S}}
$$

Modern categorial grammars include more complex combinatory rules that are needed for coordination and other complex phenomena, and also include composition of semantic categories as well as syntactic ones. See the end of the chapter for a pointer to useful references.

12.8   Spoken Language Syntax

The grammar of written English and the grammar of conversational spoken English share many features but also differ in a number of respects. This section gives a quick sketch of a number of the characteristics of the syntax of spoken English.

Utterance

We usually use the term **utterance** rather than **sentence** for the units of spoken language. Figure 12.18 shows some sample spoken ATIS utterances that exhibit many aspects of spoken language grammar.

This is a standard style of transcription used in transcribing speech corpora for speech recognition. The comma "," marks a short pause, and each period "." marks a

the . [exhale] . . . [inhale] . . uh does American airlines . offer any . one way flights . uh one way fares, for one hundred and sixty one dollars

[mm] i'd like to leave i guess between um . [smack] . five o'clock no, five o'clock and uh, seven o'clock . P M

all right, [throat_clear] . . i'd like to know the . give me the flight . times . in the morning . for September twentieth . nineteen ninety one

uh one way

. w- wha- what is the lowest, cost, fare

[click] . i need to fly, betwee- . leaving . Philadelphia . to, Atlanta [exhale]

on United airlines . . give me, the . . time . . from New York . [smack] . to Boise-, to . I'm sorry . on United airlines . [uh] give me the flight, numbers, the flight times from . [uh] Boston . to Dallas

Figure 12.18   Sample spoken utterances from users interacting with an ATIS system.

long pause. **Fragments** (incomplete words like *wha-* for incomplete *what*) are marked with a dash, and the square brackets "[smack]" mark non-verbal events (**lipsmacks**, **breaths**, etc.).

These utterances differ from written English sentences in a number of ways. One is in the lexical statistics; for example, spoken English is much higher in pronouns than written English; the subject of a spoken sentence is almost invariably a pronoun. Spoken sentences often consist of short fragments or phrases (*one way* or *around four p.m.*, which are less common in written English). Spoken sentences have phonological, prosodic, and acoustic characteristics that of course written utterances don't have; we discussed these in Chapter 8. Finally, spoken sentences have various kinds of disfluencies (hesitations, repairs, restarts, etc.), discussed below.

12.8.1   Disfluencies and Repair

Perhaps the most salient syntactic feature that distinguishes spoken and written language is the class of phenomena known individually as disfluencies and collectively as the phenomenon of repair.

Restarts   Disfluencies include the use of the words *uh* and *um*, word repetitions, **restarts**, and word fragments. The ATIS sentence in Fig. 12.19 shows examples of a restart and the use of *uh*. The restart here occurs when the speaker starts by asking for *one-way flights* and then stops and corrects herself, restarts and asks about *one-way fares*.

Reparandum   The segment *one-way flights* is referred to as the **reparandum**, and the replacing
Repair   sequence *one-way fares* is referred to as the **repair**. The **interruption point**, where the
Interruption point   speaker breaks off the original word sequence, here occurs right after the word *flights*.
Edit terms   In the editing phase we see what are often called **edit terms**, such as *you know, I mean, uh*, and *um*.

Filled pauses   The words *uh* and *um* (sometimes called **filled pauses** or **fillers**) are generally treated like regular words in speech recognition lexicons and grammars.

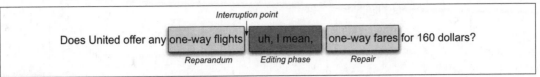

Figure 12.19   A disfluency example (from Fig. 10.18) adapted from an ATIS sentence.

Fragments   Incomplete words like *wha-* and *betwee-* in Fig. 12.18 are known as **fragments**. Fragments are extremely problematic for speech recognition systems since they are often incorrectly attached to previous or following words, resulting in word missegmentation.

Disfluencies are very common. One count in the Switchboard Treebank corpus found that 37% of the sentences with more than two words were disfluent in some way. Indeed, the word *uh* is one of the most frequent words in Switchboard.

For applications like speech understanding, where our goal is to build a meaning for the input sentence, it may be useful to detect these restarts in order to edit out what the speaker probably considered the "corrected" words. For example, in the sentence above, if we could detect that there was a restart, we could just delete the reparandum and parse the remaining parts of the sentence:

> Does United offer any ~~one-way flights uh I mean~~ one-way fares for 160 dollars?

How do disfluencies interact with the constituent structure of the sentence? Hindle (1983) showed that the repair often has the same structure as the constituent just before the interruption point. Thus, in the example above, the repair is an NP, as is the reparandum. This means that if it is possible to automatically find the interruption point, it is also often possible to automatically detect the boundaries of the reparandum.

There are other interactions between disfluencies and syntactic structure. For example, when there is a disfluency immediately after a subject NP, the repair always repeats the subject but not the preceding discourse marker. If the repair happens after an auxiliary or main verb, the verb and subject are (almost) always recycled together (Fox and Jasperson, 1995). We discuss the automatic detection of disfluencies in Section 10.6.

12.8.2   Treebanks for Spoken Language

Treebanks for spoken corpora like Switchboard use an augmented notation to deal with spoken language phenomena like disfluencies. Figure 12.20 shows the parse tree for Switchboard sentence (12.15). This sentence shows how the Treebank marks disfluencies; square brackets delineate the entire repair area, including the reparandum, editing phase, and the repair. The plus symbol marks the end of the reparandum.

(12.15) But I don't have [any, + F uh,   any] real idea

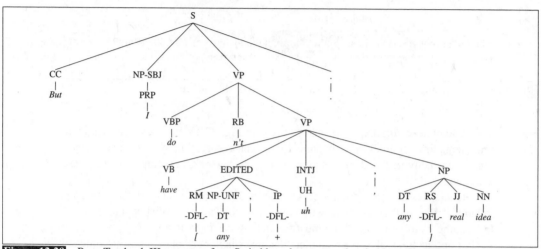

Figure 12.20   Penn Treebank III parse tree for a Switchboard sentence, showing how the disfluency information is represented in the parse tree. Note the .EDITED node, with the .RM and .RS nodes marking the beginning and end of the repair portion, and note the use of the filled pause *uh*.

12.9   Grammars and Human Processing

Do people use context-free grammars in their mental processing of language? It has proved very difficult to find clear-cut evidence that they do. For example, some early experiments asked subjects to judge which words in a sentence were more closely connected (Levelt, 1970), finding that their intuitive groupings corresponded to syntactic constituents. Other experimenters examined the role of constituents in auditory comprehension by having subjects listen to sentences while also listening to short "clicks" at different times. Fodor and Bever (1965) found that subjects often mis-heard the clicks as if they occurred at constituent boundaries. Fodor and Bever argued that the constituent was thus a "perceptual unit" that resisted interruption. Unfortunately, there were severe methodological problems with the click paradigm (see, e.g., Clark and Clark (1977) for a discussion).

A broader problem with all these early studies is that they do not control for the fact that constituents are often semantic units as well as syntactic units. Thus, as is discussed further in Chapter 18, *a single odd block* is a constituent (an *NP*) but also a semantic unit (an object of type BLOCK that has certain properties). Thus, experiments that show that people notice the boundaries of constituents could simply be measuring a semantic rather than syntactic fact.

Thus, it is necessary to find evidence for a constituent that is *not* a semantic unit. Furthermore, because of the many non-constituent-based theories of grammar based on lexical dependencies, it is important to find evidence that cannot be interpreted as a *lexical* fact; that is, evidence for constituency that is not based on particular words.

One series of experiments arguing for constituency has come from Kathryn Bock and her colleagues. Bock and Loebell (1990), for example, avoided all these earlier pitfalls by studying whether a subject who uses a particular syntactic constituent (e.g., a verb phrase of a particular type, like *V NP PP*), is more likely to use the constituent in following sentences. In other words, they asked whether use of a constituent *primes* its use in subsequent sentences. As we saw in previous chapters, priming is a common way to test for the existence of a mental structure. Bock and Loebell relied on the English **ditransitive alternation**. A ditransitive verb is one like *give* that can take two arguments:

(12.16) The wealthy widow gave [$_{NP}$ the church] [$_{NP}$ her Mercedes].

The verb *give* allows another possible subcategorization frame, called a **prepositional dative**, in which the indirect object is expressed as a prepositional phrase:

(12.17) The wealthy widow gave [$_{NP}$ her Mercedes] [$_{PP}$ to the church].

Alternations   As we discussed on page 402, many verbs other than *give* have such **alternations** (*send*, *sell*, etc.; see Levin (1993) for a summary of many different alternation patterns). Bock and Loebell relied on these alternations by giving subjects a picture and asking them to describe it in one sentence. The picture was designed to elicit verbs like *give* or *sell* by showing an event such as a boy handing an apple to a teacher. Since these verbs alternate, subjects might, for example, say *The boy gave the apple to the teacher* or *The boy gave the teacher an apple*.

Before describing the picture, subjects were asked to read an unrelated "priming" sentence out loud; the priming sentences had either *V NP NP* or *V NP PP* structure. Crucially, while these priming sentences had the same *constituent structure* as the dative alternation sentences, they did not have the same *semantics*. For example, the priming sentences might be prepositional *locatives*, rather than *datives*:

(12.18) IBM moved [$_{NP}$ a bigger computer] [$_{PP}$ to the Sears store].

Bock and Loebell found that subjects who had just read a *V NP PP* sentence were more likely to use a *V NP PP* structure in describing the picture. This suggested that the use of a particular constituent *primed* the later use of that constituent, and hence that the constituent must be mentally represented in order to prime and be primed.

In more recent work, Bock and her colleagues have continued to find evidence for this kind of constituency structure.

12.10   Summary

This chapter has introduced a number of fundamental concepts in syntax through the use of **context-free grammars**.

- In many languages, groups of consecutive words act as a group or a **constituent**, which can be modeled by **context-free grammars** (which are also known as **phrase-structure grammars**).

- A context-free grammar consists of a set of **rules** or **productions**, expressed over a set of **non-terminal** symbols and a set of **terminal** symbols. Formally, a particular **context-free language** is the set of strings that can be **derived** from a particular **context-free grammar**.

- A **generative grammar** is a traditional name in linguistics for a formal language that is used to model the grammar of a natural language.

- There are many sentence-level grammatical constructions in English; **declarative**, **imperative**, **yes-no question**, and **wh-question** are four common types; these can be modeled with context-free rules.

- An English **noun phrase** can have **determiners**, **numbers**, **quantifiers**, and **adjective phrases** preceding the **head noun**, which can be followed by a number of **postmodifiers**; **gerundive** VPs, **infinitives** VPs, and **past participial** VPs are common possibilities.

- **Subjects** in English **agree** with the main verb in person and number.

- Verbs can be **subcategorized** by the types of **complements** they expect. Simple subcategories are **transitive** and **intransitive**; most grammars include many more categories than these.

- The correlate of **sentences** in spoken language are generally called **utterances**. Utterances may be **disfluent**, containing **filled pauses** like *um* and *uh*, **restarts**, and **repairs**.

- **Treebanks** of parsed sentences exist for many genres of English and for many languages. Treebanks can be searched with tree-search tools.

- Any context-free grammar can be converted to **Chomsky normal form**, in which the right-hand side of each rule has either two non-terminals or a single terminal.

- Context-free grammars are more powerful than finite-state automata, but it is nonetheless possible to **approximate** a context-free grammar with a FSA.

- There is some evidence that constituency plays a role in the human processing of language.

Bibliographical and Historical Notes

[The origin of the idea of phrasal constituency, cited in Percival (1976)]:
den sprachlichen Ausdruck für die willkürliche
Gliederung einer Gesammtvorstellung in ihre
in logische Beziehung zueinander gesetzten Bestandteile'
[the linguistic expression for the arbitrary division of a total idea
into its constituent parts placed in logical relations to one another]
W. Wundt

According to Percival (1976), the idea of breaking up a sentence into a hierarchy of constituents appeared in the *Völkerpsychologie* of the groundbreaking psychologist Wilhelm Wundt (Wundt, 1900). Wundt's idea of constituency was taken up into linguistics by Leonard Bloomfield in his early book *An Introduction to the Study of Language* (Bloomfield, 1914). By the time of his later book, *Language* (Bloomfield, 1933), what was then called "immediate-constituent analysis" was a well-established method of syntactic study in the United States. By contrast, traditional European grammar, dat-ing from the Classical period, defined relations between *words* rather than constituents, and European syntacticians retained this emphasis on such **dependency** grammars.

American Structuralism saw a number of specific definitions of the immediate constituent, couched in terms of their search for a "discovery procedure": a methodological algorithm for describing the syntax of a language. In general, these attempt to capture the intuition that "The primary criterion of the immediate constituent is the degree in which combinations behave as simple units" (Bazell, 1966, p. 284). The most well known of the specific definitions is Harris' idea of distributional similarity to individual units, with the *substitutability* test. Essentially, the method proceeded by breaking up a construction into constituents by attempting to substitute simple structures for possible constituents—if a substitution of a simple form, say, *man*, was substitutable in a construction for a more complex set (like *intense young man*), then the form *intense young man* was probably a constituent. Harris's test was the beginning of the intuition that a constituent is a kind of equivalence class.

The first formalization of this idea of hierarchical constituency was the **phrase-structure grammar** defined in Chomsky (1956) and further expanded upon (and argued against) in Chomsky (1957) and Chomsky (1975). From this time on, most generative linguistic theories were based at least in part on context-free grammars or generalizations of them (such as Head-Driven Phrase Structure Grammar (Pollard and Sag, 1994), Lexical-Functional Grammar (Bresnan, 1982), Government and Binding (Chomsky, 1981), and Construction Grammar (Kay and Fillmore, 1999), inter alia); many of these theories used schematic context-free templates known as **X-bar schemata**, which also relied on the notion of syntactic head.

X-bar schemata

Shortly after Chomsky's initial work, the context-free grammar was reinvented by Backus (1959) and independently by Naur et al. (1960) in their descriptions of the ALGOL programming language; Backus (1996) noted that he was influenced by the productions of Emil Post and that Naur's work was independent of his (Backus') own. (Recall the discussion on page 13 of multiple invention in science.) After this early work, a great number of computational models of natural language processing were based on context-free grammars because of the early development of efficient algorithms to parse these grammars (see Chapter 13).

As we have already noted, grammars based on context-free rules are not ubiquitous. Various classes of extensions to CFGs are designed specifically to handle long-distance dependencies. We noted earlier that some grammars treat long-distance-dependent items as being related semantically but not syntactically; the surface syntax does not represent the long-distance link (Kay and Fillmore, 1999; Culicover and Jackendoff, 2005). But there are alternatives. One extended formalism is **Tree Adjoining Grammar** (TAG) (Joshi, 1985). The primary TAG data structure is the tree, rather than the rule. Trees come in two kinds: **initial trees** and **auxiliary trees**. Initial trees might, for example, represent simple sentential structures, and auxiliary trees add recursion into a tree. Trees are combined by two operations called **substitution** and **adjunction**. The adjunction operation handles long-distance dependencies. See Joshi (1985) for more details. An extension of Tree Adjoining Grammar, called Lexicalized Tree Adjoining Grammars is discussed in Chapter 14. Tree Adjoining Grammar is a member of the family of **mildly context-sensitive languages**, introduced in Chapter 16.

We mentioned on page 404 another way of handling long-distance dependencies, based on the use of empty categories and co-indexing. The Penn Treebank uses this model, which draws (in various Treebank corpora) from the Extended Standard Theory and Minimalism (Radford, 1997).

Representative examples of grammars that are based on word relations rather than constituency include the dependency grammar of Mel'čuk (1979), the Word Grammar of Hudson (1984), and the Constraint Grammar of Karlsson et al. (1995).

There are a variety of algorithms for building a regular grammar that approximates a CFG (Pereira and Wright, 1997; Johnson, 1998a; Langendoen and Langsam, 1987; Nederhof, 2000; Mohri and Nederhof, 2001).

Readers interested in the grammar of English should get one of the three large reference grammars of English: Huddleston and Pullum (2002), Biber et al. (1999), and Quirk et al. (1985). Another useful reference is McCawley (1998).

Generative

There are many good introductory textbooks on syntax from different perspectives. Sag et al. (2003) is an introduction to syntax from a **generative** perspective, focusing on the use of phrase-structure rules, unification, and the type hierarchy in Head-Driven Phrase Structure Grammar. Van Valin, Jr. and La Polla (1997) is an introduction from

Functional

a **functional** perspective, focusing on cross-linguistic data and on the functional motivation for syntactic structures.

See Bach (1988) for an introduction to basic categorial grammar. Various extensions to categorial grammars are presented in Lambek (1958), Dowty (1979), and Ades and Steedman (1982) inter alia; the other papers in Oehrle et al. (1988) give a survey of extensions. Combinatory categorial grammar is presented in Steedman (1989, 2000); see Steedman and Baldridge (2007) for a tutorial introduction. See Chapter 18 for a discussion of semantic composition.

Exercises

12.1 Draw tree structures for the following ATIS phrases:

1. Dallas
2. from Denver
3. after five p.m.
4. arriving in Washington
5. early flights
6. all redeye flights
7. on Thursday
8. a one-way fare
9. any delays in Denver

12.2 Draw tree structures for the following ATIS sentences:

1. Does American airlines have a flight between five a.m. and six a.m.?
2. I would like to fly on American airlines.
3. Please repeat that.
4. Does American 487 have a first-class section?

5. I need to fly between Philadelphia and Atlanta.

6. What is the fare from Atlanta to Denver?

7. Is there an American airlines flight from Philadelphia to Dallas?

12.3 Augment the grammar rules on page 399 to handle pronouns. Deal properly with person and case.

12.4 Modify the noun phrase grammar of Sections 12.3.3–12.3.4 to correctly model mass nouns and their agreement properties

12.5 How many types of *NP*s would the rule on page 396 expand to if we didn't allow parentheses in our grammar formalism?

12.6 Assume a grammar that has many *VP* rules for different subcategorizations, as expressed in Section 12.3.5, and differently subcategorized verb rules like *Verb-with-NP-complement*. How would the rule for postnominal relative clauses (12.5) need to be modified if we wanted to deal properly with examples like *the earliest flight that you have*? Recall that in such examples the pronoun *that* is the object of the verb *get*. Your rules should allow this noun phrase but should correctly rule out the ungrammatical *S *I get*.

12.7 Does your solution to the previous problem correctly model the NP *the earliest flight that I can get*? How about *the earliest flight that I think my mother wants me to book for her*? Hint: this phenomenon is called **long-distance dependency**.

12.8 Write rules expressing the verbal subcategory of English auxiliaries; for example, you might have a rule *verb-with-bare-stem-VP-complement* → *can*.

Possessive
Genitive
12.9 *NP*s like *Fortune's office* or *my uncle's marks* are called **possessive** or **genitive** noun phrases. We can be model possessive noun phrases by treating the sub-NP like *Fortune's* or *my uncle's* as a determiner of the following head noun. Write grammar rules for English possessives. You may treat *'s* as if it were a separate word (i.e., as if there were always a space before *'s*).

12.10 Page 393 discussed the need for a *Wh-NP* constituent. The simplest *Wh-NP* is one of the *Wh-pronouns* (*who, whom, whose, which*). The Wh-words *what* and *which* can be determiners: *which four will you have?*, *what credit do you have with the Duke?* Write rules for the different types of *Wh-NP*s.

12.11 Write an algorithm for converting an arbitrary context-free grammar into Chomsky normal form.

Chapter 13

Syntactic Parsing

There are and can exist but two ways of investigating and discovering truth. The one hurries on rapidly from the senses and particulars to the most general axioms, and from them. . . derives and discovers the intermediate axioms. The other constructs its axioms from the senses and particulars, by ascending continually and gradually, till it finally arrives at the most general axioms.

Francis Bacon, *Novum Organum* Book I.19 (1620)

We defined parsing in Chapter 3 as a combination of recognizing an input string and assigning a structure to it. Syntactic parsing, then, is the task of recognizing a sentence and assigning a syntactic structure to it. This chapter focuses on the kind of structures assigned by context-free grammars of the kind described in Chapter 12. However, since they are based on a purely declarative formalism, context-free grammars don't specify *how* the parse tree for a given sentence should be computed. We therefore need to specify algorithms that employ these grammars to produce trees. This chapter presents three of the most widely used parsing algorithms for automatically assigning a complete context-free (phrase-structure) tree to an input sentence.

These kinds of parse trees are directly useful in applications such as **grammar checking** in word-processing systems: a sentence that cannot be parsed may have grammatical errors (or at least be hard to read). More typically, however, parse trees serve as an important intermediate stage of representation for **semantic analysis** (as we show in Chapter 18) and thus play an important role in applications like **question answering** and **information extraction**. For example, to answer the question

What books were written by British women authors before 1800?

we'll need to know that the subject of the sentence was *what books* and that the by-adjunct was *British women authors* to help us figure out that the user wants a list of books (and not a list of authors).

Before presenting any parsing algorithms, we begin by describing some of the factors that motivate the standard algorithms. First, we revisit the **search metaphor** for parsing and recognition, which we introduced for finite-state automata in Chapter 2, and talk about the **top-down** and **bottom-up** search strategies. We then discuss how the ambiguity problem rears its head again in syntactic processing and how it ultimately makes simplistic approaches based on backtracking infeasible.

The sections that follow then present the Cocke-Kasami-Younger (CKY) algorithm (Kasami, 1965; Younger, 1967), the Earley algorithm (Earley, 1970), and the chart parsing approach (Kay, 1982; Kaplan, 1973). These approaches all combine insights from bottom-up and top-down parsing with dynamic programming to efficiently handle complex inputs. Recall that we've already seen several applications of dynamic

From Chapter 13 of *Speech and Language Processing*, Second Edition. Daniel Jurafsky, James H. Martin.

Grammar	**Lexicon**
$S \rightarrow NP\ VP$	$Det \rightarrow that \quad this \quad a$
$S \rightarrow Aux\ NP\ VP$	$Noun \rightarrow book \quad flight \quad meal \quad money$
$S \rightarrow VP$	$Verb \rightarrow book \quad include \quad prefer$
$NP \rightarrow Pronoun$	$Pronoun \rightarrow I \quad she \quad me$
$NP \rightarrow Proper\text{-}Noun$	$Proper\text{-}Noun \rightarrow Houston \quad NWA$
$NP \rightarrow Det\ Nominal$	$Aux \rightarrow does$
$Nominal \rightarrow Noun$	$Preposition \rightarrow from \quad to \quad on \quad near \quad through$
$Nominal \rightarrow Nominal\ Noun$	
$Nominal \rightarrow Nominal\ PP$	
$VP \rightarrow Verb$	
$VP \rightarrow Verb\ NP$	
$VP \rightarrow Verb\ NP\ PP$	
$VP \rightarrow Verb\ PP$	
$VP \rightarrow VP\ PP$	
$PP \rightarrow Preposition\ NP$	

Figure 13.1   The $\mathcal{L}_1$ miniature English grammar and lexicon.

programming algorithms in earlier chapters — Minimum-Edit-Distance, Viterbi, Forward. Finally, we discuss **partial parsing methods**, for use in situations in which a superficial syntactic analysis of an input may be sufficient.

13.1   Parsing as Search

Chapters 2 and 3 showed that finding the right path through a finite-state automaton or finding the right transduction for an input can be viewed as a search problem. For finite-state automata, the search is through the space of all possible paths through a machine. In syntactic parsing, the parser can be viewed as searching through the space of possible parse trees to find the correct parse tree for a given sentence. Just as the search space of possible paths was defined by the structure of an automaton, so the search space of possible parse trees is defined by a grammar. Consider the following ATIS sentence:

(13.1) Book that flight.

Figure 13.1 introduces the $\mathcal{L}_1$ grammar, which consists of the $\mathcal{L}_0$ grammar from the last chapter with a few additional rules. Given this grammar, the correct parse tree for this example would be the one shown in Fig. 13.2.

How can we use $\mathcal{L}_1$ to assign the parse tree in Fig. 13.2 to this example? The goal of a parsing search is to find all the trees whose root is the start symbol S and that cover exactly the words in the input. Regardless of the search algorithm we choose, two kinds of constraints should help guide the search. One set of constraints comes from the data, that is, the input sentence itself. Whatever else is true of the final parse tree, we know that there must be three leaves and that they must be the words *book*, *that*, and *flight*. The second kind of constraint comes from the grammar. We know that

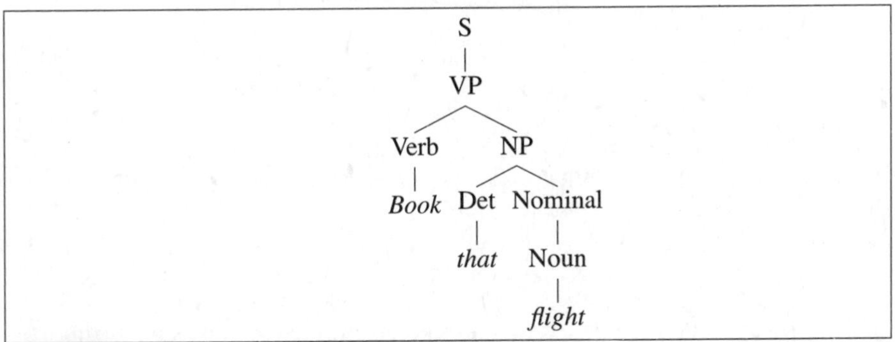

Figure 13.2   The parse tree for the sentence *Book that flight* according to grammar $\mathscr{L}_1$.

whatever else is true of the final parse tree, it must have one root, which must be the start symbol *S*.

These two constraints, invoked by Bacon at the start of this chapter, give rise to the two search strategies underlying most parsers: **top-down** or **goal-directed search**, and **bottom-up** or **data-directed search**. These constraints are more than just search strategies. They reflect two important insights in the western philosophical tradition: the **rationalist** tradition, which emphasizes the use of prior knowledge, and the **empiricist** tradition, which emphasizes the data in front of us.

Rationalist
Empiricist

13.1.1   Top-Down Parsing

Top-down

A **top-down** parser searches for a parse tree by trying to build from the root node *S* down to the leaves. Let's consider the search space that a top-down parser explores, assuming for the moment that it builds all possible trees in parallel. The algorithm starts by assuming that the input can be derived by the designated start symbol *S*. The next step is to find the tops of all trees that can start with *S*, by looking for all the grammar rules with *S* on the left-hand side. In the grammar in Fig. 13.1, three rules expand *S*, so the second **ply**, or level, of the search space in Fig. 13.3 has three partial trees.

Ply

We next expand the constituents in these three new trees, just as we originally expanded *S*. The first tree tells us to expect an *NP* followed by a *VP*, the second expects an *Aux* followed by an *NP* and a *VP*, and the third a *VP* by itself. To fit the search space on the page, we have shown in the third ply of Fig. 13.3 only a subset of the trees that result from the expansion of the leftmost leaves of each tree. At each ply of the search space we use the right-hand sides of the rules to provide new sets of expectations for the parser, which are then used to recursively generate the rest of the trees. Trees are grown downward until they eventually reach the part-of-speech categories at the bottom of the tree. At this point, trees whose leaves fail to match all the words in the input can be rejected, leaving behind those trees that represent successful parses. In Fig. 13.3, only the fifth parse tree in the third ply (the one that has expanded the rule *VP → Verb NP*) will eventually match the input sentence *Book that flight*.

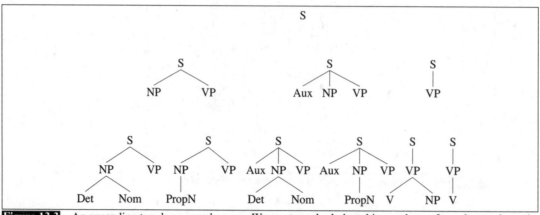

Figure 13.3   An expanding top-down search space. We create each ply by taking each tree from the previous ply, replacing the leftmost non-terminal with each of its possible expansions and collecting each of these trees into a new ply.

13.1.2   Bottom-Up Parsing

Bottom-up   **Bottom-up** parsing is the earliest known parsing algorithm (it was first suggested by Yngve (1955)) and is used in the shift-reduce parsers common for computer languages (Aho and Ullman, 1972). In bottom-up parsing the parser starts with the words of the input, and tries to build trees from the words up, again by applying rules from the grammar one at a time. The parse is successful if the parser succeeds in building a tree rooted in the start symbol *S* that covers all of the input. Figure 13.4 shows the bottom-up search space, beginning with the sentence *Book that flight*. The parser begins by looking up each input word in the lexicon and building three partial trees with the part-of-speech for each word. But the word *book* is ambiguous; it can be a noun or a verb. Thus, the parser must consider two possible sets of trees. The first two plies in Fig. 13.4 show this initial bifurcation of the search space.

Each of the trees in the second ply is then expanded. In the parse on the left (the one in which *book* is incorrectly considered a noun), the *Nominal → Noun* rule is applied to both of the nouns (*book* and *flight*). This same rule is also applied to the sole noun (*flight*) on the right, producing the trees on the third ply.

In general, the parser extends one ply to the next by looking for places in the parse-in-progress where the right-hand side of some rule might fit. This contrasts with the earlier top-down parser, which expanded trees by applying rules when their left-hand side matched an unexpanded non-terminal.

Thus, in the fourth ply, in the first and third parse, the sequence *Det Nominal* is recognized as the right-hand side of the *NP → Det Nominal* rule.

In the fifth ply, the interpretation of *book* as a noun has been pruned from the search space. This is because this parse cannot be continued: there is no rule in the grammar with the right-hand side *Nominal NP*. The final ply of the search space (not shown in Fig. 13.4) contains the correct parse (see Fig. 13.2).

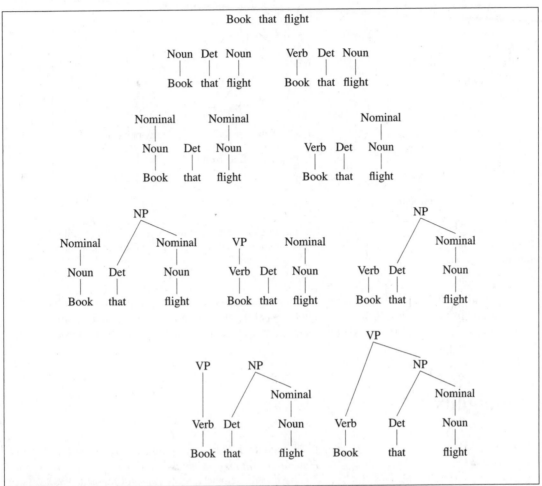

Figure 13.4   An expanding bottom-up search space for the sentence *Book that flight*. This figure does not show the final phase of the search with the correct parse tree (see Fig. 13.2). Make sure you understand how that final parse tree follows from the search space in this figure.

13.1.3   Comparing Top-Down and Bottom-Up Parsing

Each of these two architectures has its own advantages and disadvantages. The top-down strategy never wastes time exploring trees that cannot result in an *S*, since it begins by generating just those trees. This means it also never explores subtrees that cannot find a place in some *S*-rooted tree. In the bottom-up strategy, by contrast, trees that have no hope of leading to an *S* or fitting in with any of their neighbors are generated with wild abandon.

The top-down approach has its own inefficiencies. While it does not waste time with trees that do not lead to an *S*, it does spend considerable effort on *S* trees that are not consistent with the input. Note that the first four of the six trees in the third ply in Fig. 13.3 all have left branches that cannot match the word *book*. None of these trees

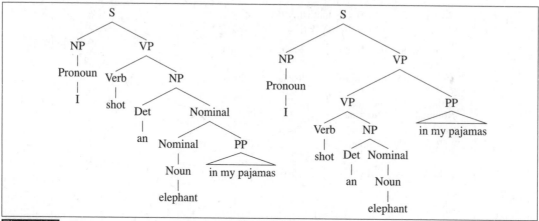

Figure 13.5   Two parse trees for an ambiguous sentence. The parse on the left corresponds to the humorous reading in which the elephant is in the pajamas, the parse on the right corresponds to the reading in which Captain Spaulding did the shooting in his pajamas.

could possibly be used in parsing this sentence. This weakness in top-down parsers arises from the fact that they generate trees before ever examining the input. Bottom-up parsers, on the other hand, never suggest trees that are not at least locally grounded in the input.

13.2   Ambiguity

> *One morning I shot an elephant in my pajamas.*
> *How he got into my pajamas I don't know.*
>
> Groucho Marx, *Animal Crackers*, 1930

Structural ambiguity

Ambiguity is perhaps the most serious problem faced by parsers. Chapter 5 introduced the notions of **part-of-speech ambiguity** and **part-of-speech disambiguation**. In this section we introduce a new kind of ambiguity, called **structural ambiguity**, which arises in the syntactic structures used in parsing. Structural ambiguity occurs when the grammar assigns more than one possible parse to a sentence. Groucho Marx's well-known line as Captain Spaulding is ambiguous because the phrase *in my pajamas* can be part of the *NP* headed by *elephant* or of the verb phrase headed by *shot*. Figure 13.5 illustrates these two analyses of Marx's line.

Attachment ambiguity

Structural ambiguity, appropriately enough, comes in many forms. Two common kinds of ambiguity are **attachment ambiguity** and **coordination ambiguity**.

A sentence has an **attachment ambiguity** if a particular constituent can be attached to the parse tree at more than one place. The Groucho Marx sentence above is an example of *PP*-attachment ambiguity. Various kinds of adverbial phrases are also subject to this kind of ambiguity. For instance, in the following example the gerundive-*VP* *flying to Paris* can be part of a gerundive sentence whose subject is *the Eiffel Tower* or it can be an adjunct modifying the *VP* headed by *saw*:

(13.2) We saw the Eiffel Tower flying to Paris.

Coordination
ambiguity

In **coordination ambiguity** different sets of phrases can be conjoined by a conjunction like *and*. For example, the phrase *old men and women* can be bracketed as *[old [men and women]]*, referring to *old men* and *old women*, or as *[old men] and [women]*, in which case it is only the men who are old.

These ambiguities combine in complex ways in real sentences. A program that summarized the news, for example, would need to be able to parse sentences like the following from the Brown corpus:

(13.3) President Kennedy today pushed aside other White House business to devote all his time and attention to working on the Berlin crisis address he will deliver tomorrow night to the American people over nationwide television and radio.

This sentence has a number of ambiguities, although since they are semantically unreasonable, it requires a careful reading to see them. The last noun phrase could be parsed *[nationwide [television and radio]]* or *[[nationwide television] and radio]*. The direct object of *pushed aside* should be *other White House business* but could also be the bizarre phrase *[other White House business to devote all his time and attention to working]* (i.e., a structure like *Kennedy affirmed [his intention to propose a new budget to address the deficit]*). Then the phrase *on the Berlin crisis address he will deliver tomorrow night to the American people* could be an adjunct modifying the verb *pushed*. A *PP* like *over nationwide television and radio* could be attached to any of the higher *VPs* or *NPs* (e.g., it could modify *people* or *night*).

Syntactic
disambiguation

The fact that there are many unreasonable parses for naturally occurring sentences is an extremely irksome problem that affects all parsers. Ultimately, most natural-language processing systems need to be able to choose the correct parse from the multitude of possible parses through a process known as **syntactic disambiguation**. Unfortunately, effective disambiguation algorithms generally require statistical, semantic, and pragmatic knowledge not readily available during syntactic processing (techniques for making use of such knowledge are introduced in Chapter 14 and Chapter 18).

Lacking such knowledge, we are left with the choice of simply returning all the possible parse trees for a given input. Unfortunately, generating all the possible parses from robust, highly ambiguous, wide-coverage grammars such as the Penn Treebank grammar described in Chapter 12 is problematic. The reason for this lies in the potentially exponential number of parses that are possible for certain inputs. Consider the following ATIS example:

(13.4) Show me the meal on Flight UA 386 from San Francisco to Denver.

The recursive *VP → VP PP* and *Nominal → Nominal PP* rules conspire with the three prepositional phrases at the end of this sentence to yield a total of 14 parse trees for this sentence. For example, *from San Francisco* could be part of the *VP* headed by *show* (which would have the bizarre interpretation that the showing was happening from San Francisco). Figure 13.6 illustrates a reasonable parse for this sentence. Church and Patil (1982) showed that the number of parses for sentences of this type grows exponentially at the same rate as the number of parenthesizations of arithmetic expressions.

Local ambiguity

Even if a sentence isn't ambiguous (i.e., it doesn't have more than one parse in the end), it can be inefficient to parse because of **local ambiguity**. Local ambiguity occurs

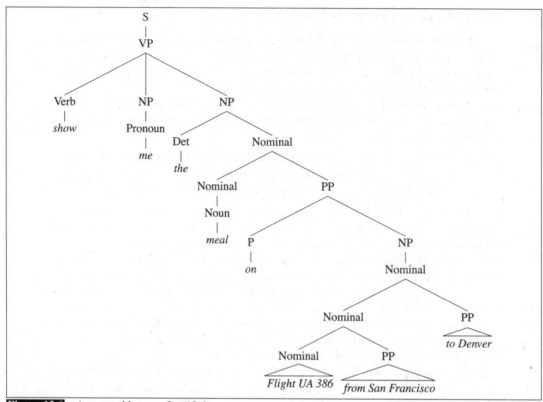

Figure 13.6   A reasonable parse for (13.4).

when some part of a sentence is ambiguous, that is, has more than one parse, even if the whole sentence is not ambiguous. For example, the sentence *Book that flight* is unambiguous, but when the parser sees the first word *Book*, it cannot know if the word is a verb or a noun until later. Thus, it must consider both possible parses.

13.3   Search in the Face of Ambiguity

To fully understand the problem that local and global ambiguity pose for syntactic parsing, let's return to our earlier description of top-down and bottom-up parsing. There we made the simplifying assumption that we could explore all possible parse trees in parallel. Thus, each ply of the search in Fig. 13.3 and Fig. 13.4 showed parallel expansions of the parse trees on the previous plies. Although it is certainly possible to implement this method directly, it typically requires an unrealistic amount of memory to store the space of trees as they are constructed. This is especially true since realistic grammars have much more ambiguity than the miniature grammar we've been using.

A common alternative approach to exploring complex search spaces is to use an agenda-based backtracking strategy such as those used to implement the various finite-state machines in Chapters 2 and 3. A backtracking approach expands the search space incrementally by systematically exploring one state at a time. The state chosen for expansion can be based on simple systematic strategies, such as depth-first or breadth-first methods, or on more complex methods that make use of probabilistic and semantic considerations. When the given strategy arrives at a tree that is inconsistent with the input, the search continues by returning to an unexplored option already on the agenda. The net effect of this strategy is a parser that single-mindedly pursues trees until they either succeed or fail before returning to work on trees generated earlier in the process.

Unfortunately, the pervasive ambiguity in typical grammars leads to intolerable inefficiencies in any backtracking approach. Backtracking parsers will often build valid trees for portions of the input and then discard them during backtracking, only to find that they have to be rebuilt again. Consider the top-down backtracking process involved in finding a parse for the *NP* in (13.5):

(13.5) a flight from Indianapolis to Houston on NWA

The preferred complete parse is shown as the bottom tree in Fig. 13.7. While this phrase has numerous parses, we focus here on the amount of repeated work expended on the path to retrieving this single preferred parse.

A typical top-down, depth-first, left-to-right backtracking strategy leads to small parse trees that fail because they do not cover all of the input. These successive failures trigger backtracking events that lead to parses that incrementally cover more and more of the input. The sequence of trees attempted on the way to the correct parse by this top-down approach is shown in Fig. 13.7.

This figure clearly illustrates the kind of reduplication of work that arises in backtracking approaches. Except for its topmost component, every part of the final tree is derived more than once. The work done on this simple example would, of course, be magnified by any ambiguity introduced at the verb phrase or sentential level. Note that although this example is specific to top-down parsing, similar examples of wasted effort exist for bottom-up parsing as well.

13.4   Dynamic Programming Parsing Methods

The previous section presented some of the ambiguity problems that afflict standard bottom-up or top-down parsers. Luckily, a single class of algorithms can solve these problems. **Dynamic programming** once again provides a framework for solving this problem, just as it helped us with the Minimum Edit Distance, Viterbi, and Forward algorithms. Recall that dynamic programming approaches systematically fill in tables of solutions to sub-problems. When complete, the tables contain the solution to all the sub-problems needed to solve the problem as a whole.

In the case of parsing, such tables store subtrees for each constituent in the input as it is discovered. The efficiency gain arises because these subtrees are discovered once, stored, and then used in all parses calling for that constituent. This solves the re-parsing problem (subtrees are looked up, not re-parsed) and partially solves the ambiguity problem (the dynamic programming table implicitly stores all possible parses

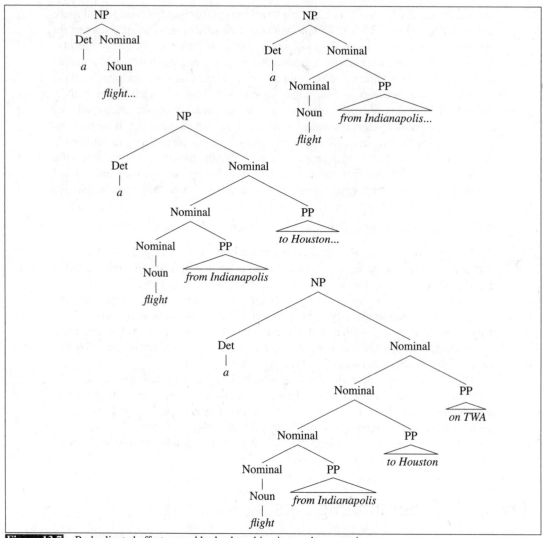

Figure 13.7   Reduplicated effort caused by backtracking in top-down parsing.

by storing all the constituents with links that enable the parses to be reconstructed). As we mentioned earlier, the three most widely used methods are the Cocke-Kasami-Younger (CKY) algorithm, the Earley algorithm, and chart parsing.

13.4.1 CKY Parsing

Let's begin our investigation of the CKY algorithm by examining one of its major requirements: the grammars used with it must be in Chomsky normal form (CNF). Recall from Chapter 12 that grammars in CNF are restricted to rules of the form $A \rightarrow B\ C$ or $A \rightarrow w$. That is, the right-hand side of each rule must expand either to two non-terminals or to a single terminal. Recall also that restricting a grammar to CNF does not lead to any loss in expressiveness, since any context-free grammar can be converted into a corresponding CNF grammar that accepts exactly the same set of strings as the original grammar. This single restriction gives rise to an extremely simple and elegant table-based parsing method.

Conversion to Chomsky Normal Form

Let's start with the process of converting a generic CFG into one represented in CNF. Assuming we're dealing with an ϵ-free grammar, there are three situations we need to address in any generic grammar: rules that mix terminals with non-terminals on the right-hand side, rules that have a single non-terminal on the right, and rules in which the length of the right-hand side is greater than 2.

The remedy for rules that mix terminals and non-terminals is to simply introduce a new dummy non-terminal that covers only the original terminal. For example, a rule for an infinitive verb phrase such as *INF-VP* $\rightarrow$ *to VP* would be replaced by the two rules *INF-VP* $\rightarrow$ *TO VP* and *TO* $\rightarrow$ *to*.

Unit productions   Rules with a single non-terminal on the right are called **unit productions**. We can eliminate unit productions by rewriting the right-hand side of the original rules with the right-hand side of all the non-unit production rules that they ultimately lead to. More formally, if $A \overset{*}{\Rightarrow} B$ by a chain of one or more unit productions and $B \rightarrow \gamma$ is a non-unit production in our grammar, then we add $A \rightarrow \gamma$ for each such rule in the grammar and discard all the intervening unit productions. As we demonstrate with our toy grammar, this can lead to a substantial *flattening* of the grammar and a consequent promotion of terminals to fairly high levels in the resulting trees.

Rules with right-hand sides longer than 2 are normalized through the introduction of new non-terminals that spread the longer sequences over several new rules. Formally, if we have a rule like

$$A \rightarrow B\,C\,\gamma$$

we replace the leftmost pair of non-terminals with a new non-terminal and introduce a new production result in the following new rules:

$$X1 \rightarrow B\,C$$
$$A \rightarrow X1\,\gamma$$

In the case of longer right-hand sides, we simply iterate this process until the offending rule has been replaced by rules of length 2. The choice of replacing the leftmost pair of non-terminals is purely arbitrary; any systematic scheme that results in binary rules would suffice.

In our current grammar, the rule $S \rightarrow Aux\,NP\,VP$ would be replaced by the two rules $S \rightarrow X1\,VP$ and $X1 \rightarrow Aux\,NP$.

The entire conversion process can be summarized as follows:

1. Copy all conforming rules to the new grammar unchanged.
2. Convert terminals within rules to dummy non-terminals.
3. Convert unit-productions.
4. Make all rules binary and add them to new grammar.

$\mathcal{L}_1$ **Grammar**	$\mathcal{L}_1$ **in CNF**
$S \rightarrow NP\ VP$	$S \rightarrow NP\ VP$
$S \rightarrow Aux\ NP\ VP$	$S \rightarrow X1\ VP$
	$X1 \rightarrow Aux\ NP$
$S \rightarrow VP$	$S \rightarrow book\quad include\quad prefer$
	$S \rightarrow Verb\ NP$
	$S \rightarrow X2\ PP$
	$S \rightarrow Verb\ PP$
	$S \rightarrow VP\ PP$
$NP \rightarrow Pronoun$	$NP \rightarrow I\quad she\quad me$
$NP \rightarrow Proper\text{-}Noun$	$NP \rightarrow TWA\quad Houston$
$NP \rightarrow Det\ Nominal$	$NP \rightarrow Det\ Nominal$
$Nominal \rightarrow Noun$	$Nominal \rightarrow book\quad flight\quad meal\quad money$
$Nominal \rightarrow Nominal\ Noun$	$Nominal \rightarrow Nominal\ Noun$
$Nominal \rightarrow Nominal\ PP$	$Nominal \rightarrow Nominal\ PP$
$VP \rightarrow Verb$	$VP \rightarrow book\quad include\quad prefer$
$VP \rightarrow Verb\ NP$	$VP \rightarrow Verb\ NP$
$VP \rightarrow Verb\ NP\ PP$	$VP \rightarrow X2\ PP$
	$X2 \rightarrow Verb\ NP$
$VP \rightarrow Verb\ PP$	$VP \rightarrow Verb\ PP$
$VP \rightarrow VP\ PP$	$VP \rightarrow VP\ PP$
$PP \rightarrow Preposition\ NP$	$PP \rightarrow Preposition\ NP$

Figure 13.8 $\mathcal{L}_1$ Grammar and its conversion to CNF. Note that although they aren't shown here, all the original lexical entries from $\mathcal{L}_1$ carry over unchanged as well.

Figure 13.8 shows the results of applying this entire conversion procedure to the $\mathcal{L}_1$ grammar introduced earlier on page 428. Note that this figure doesn't show the original lexical rules; since these original lexical rules are already in CNF, they all carry over unchanged to the new grammar. Figure 13.8 does, however, show the various places where the process of eliminating unit productions has, in effect, created new lexical rules. For example, all the original verbs have been promoted to both *VP*s and to *S*s in the converted grammar.

CKY Recognition

With our grammar now in CNF, each non-terminal node above the part-of-speech level in a parse tree will have exactly two daughters. A simple two-dimensional matrix can be used to encode the structure of an entire tree. More specifically, for a sentence of length n, we are working with the upper-triangular portion of an $(n+1) \quad (n+1)$ matrix. Each cell $[i, j]$ in this matrix contains a set of non-terminals that represent all the constituents that span positions i through j of the input. Since our indexing scheme begins with 0, it's natural to think of the indexes as pointing at the gaps between the input words (as in $_0$ *Book* $_1$ *that* $_2$ *flight* $_3$). It follows then that the cell that represents the entire input resides in position $[0, n]$ in the matrix.

Since our grammar is in CNF, the non-terminal entries in the table have exactly two daughters in the parse. Therefore, for each constituent represented by an entry $[i, j]$ in the table, there must be a position in the input, k, where it can be split into two parts such that $i < k < j$. Given such a position k, the first constituent $[i,k]$ must lie to the left of entry $[i,j]$ somewhere along row i, and the second entry $[k,j]$ must lie beneath it, along column j.

To make this more concrete, consider the following example with its completed parse matrix, shown in Fig. 13.9.

(13.6) Book the flight through Houston.

The superdiagonal row in the matrix contains the parts of speech for each input word in the input. The subsequent diagonals above that superdiagonal contain constituents that cover all the spans of increasing length in the input.

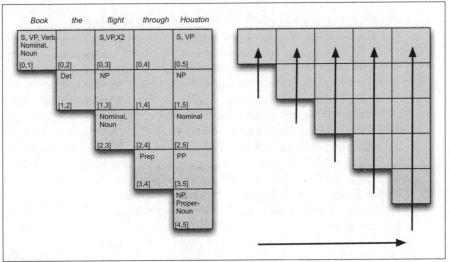

Figure 13.9   Completed parse table for *Book the flight through Houston*.

Given all this, CKY recognition is simply a matter of filling the parse table in the right way. To do this, we'll proceed in a bottom-up fashion so that at the point where we are filling any cell $[i,j]$, the cells containing the parts that could contribute to this entry (i.e., the cells to the left and the cells below) have already been filled. There are several ways to do this; as the right side of Fig. 13.9 illustrates, the algorithm given in Fig. 13.10 fills the upper-triangular matrix a column at a time working from left to right. Each column is then filled from bottom to top. This scheme guarantees that at each point in time we have all the information we need (to the left, since all the columns to the left have already been filled, and below since we're filling bottom to top). It also mirrors on-line parsing since filling the columns from left to right corresponds to processing each word one at a time.

The outermost loop of the algorithm given in Fig. 13.10 iterates over the columns, and the second loop iterates over the rows, from the bottom up. The purpose of the innermost loop is to range over all the places where a substring spanning i to j in the input might be split in two. As k ranges over the places where the string can be split, the pairs of cells we consider move, in lockstep, to the right along row i and down along

```
function CKY-PARSE(words, grammar) returns table

for j ← from 1 to LENGTH(words) do
    table[j − 1, j] ← A   A → words[j] ∈ grammar
    for i ← from j − 2 downto 0 do
        for k ← i + 1 to j − 1 do
            table[i,j] ← table[i,j] ∪
                            A   A → BC ∈ grammar,
                            B ∈ table[i, k],
                            C ∈ table[k, j]
```

Figure 13.10   The CKY algorithm.

column *j*. Figure 13.11 illustrates the general case of filling cell $[i, j]$. At each such split, the algorithm considers whether the contents of the two cells can be combined in a way that is sanctioned by a rule in the grammar. If such a rule exists, the non-terminal on its left-hand side is entered into the table.

Figure 13.12 shows how the five cells of column 5 of the table are filled after the word *Houston* is read. The arrows point out the two spans that are being used to add an entry to the table. Note that the action in cell $[0,5]$ indicates the presence of three alternative parses for this input, one where the *PP* modifies the *flight*, one where it modifies the booking, and one that captures the second argument in the original *VP → Verb NP PP* rule, now captured indirectly with the *VP → X2 PP* rule.

In fact, since our current algorithm manipulates *sets* of non-terminals as cell entries, it won't include multiple copies of the same non-terminal in the table; the second *S* and *VP* discovered while processing $[0,5]$ would have no effect. We revisit this behavior in the next section.

CKY Parsing

The algorithm given in Fig. 13.10 is a recognizer, not a parser; for it to succeed, it simply has to find an *S* in cell $[0,N]$. To turn it into a parser capable of returning all possible parses for a given input, we can make two simple changes to the algorithm: the first change is to augment the entries in the table so that each non-terminal is paired with pointers to the table entries from which it was derived (more or less as shown in Fig. 13.12), the second change is to permit multiple versions of the same non-terminal to be entered into the table (again as shown in Fig. 13.12). With these changes, the completed table contains all the possible parses for a given input. Returning an arbitrary single parse consists of choosing an *S* from cell $[0,n]$ and then recursively retrieving its component constituents from the table.

Of course, returning all the parses for a given input may incur considerable cost. As we saw earlier, an exponential number of parses may be associated with a given input. In such cases, returning all the parses will have an unavoidable exponential cost. Looking forward to Chapter 14, we can also think about retrieving the best parse for a given input by further augmenting the table to contain the probabilities of each entry. Retrieving the most probable parse consists of running a suitably modified version of the Viterbi algorithm from Chapter 5 over the completed parse table.

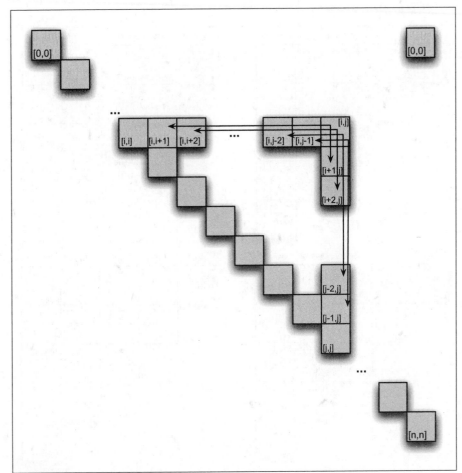

Figure 13.11   All the ways to fill the $[i, j]$th cell in the CKY table.

CKY in Practice

Finally, we should note that while the restriction to CNF does not pose a problem theoretically, it does pose some non-trivial problems in practice. Obviously, as things stand now, our parser isn't returning trees that are consistent with the grammar given to us by our friendly syntacticians. In addition to making our grammar developers unhappy, the conversion to CNF will complicate any syntax-driven approach to semantic analysis.

One approach to getting around these problems is to keep enough information around to transform our trees back to the original grammar as a post-processing step of the parse. This is trivial in the case of the transformation used for rules with length greater than 2. Simply deleting the new dummy non-terminals and promoting their daughters restores the original tree.

In the case of unit productions, it turns out to be more convenient to alter the basic CKY algorithm to handle them directly than it is to store the information needed to recover the correct trees. Exercise 13.3 asks you to make this change. Many of the

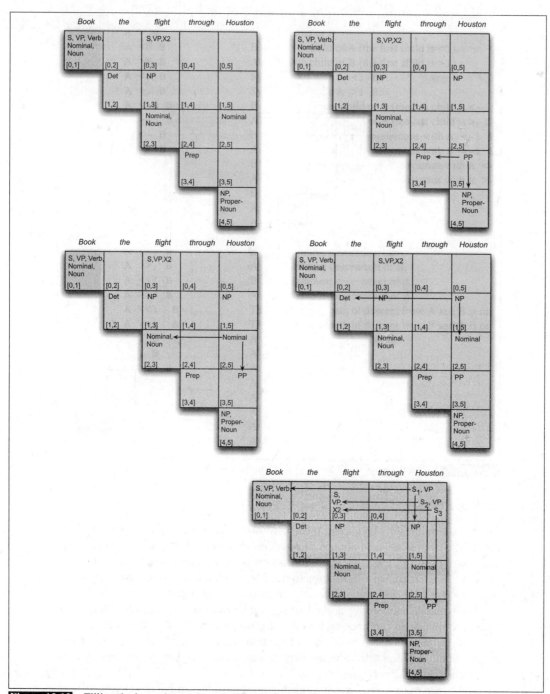

Figure 13.12   Filling the last column after reading the word *Houston*.

probabilistic parsers presented in Chapter 14 use the CKY algorithm altered in just this manner. Another solution is to adopt a more complex dynamic programming solution that simply accepts arbitrary CFGs. The next section presents such an approach.

13.4.2   The Earley Algorithm → *top down*

In contrast with the bottom-up search implemented by the CKY algorithm, the Earley algorithm (Earley, 1970) uses dynamic programming to implement a **top-down search** of the kind discussed earlier in Section 13.1.1. The core of the Earley algorithm is a

Chart   single left-to-right pass that fills an array—we'll call it a **chart**—that has $N + 1$ entries. For each word position in the sentence, the chart contains a list of states representing the partial parse trees that have been generated so far. As with the CKY algorithm, the indexes represent the locations between the words in an input (as in $_0Book_1that_2flight_3$). By the end of the sentence, the chart compactly encodes all the possible parses of the input. Each possible subtree is represented only once and can thus be shared by all the parses that need it.

The individual states contained within each chart entry contain three kinds of information: a subtree corresponding to a single grammar rule, information about the progress made in completing this subtree, and the position of the subtree with respect to the input. We'll use a • within the right-hand side of a state's grammar rule to indi-

Dotted rule   cate the progress made in recognizing it. The resulting structure is called a **dotted rule**. A state's position with respect to the input is represented by two numbers indicating where the state begins and where its dot lies.

Consider the following example states, which would be among those created by the Earley algorithm in the course of parsing (13.7):

(13.7) Book that flight.

$$S \;\rightarrow\; \bullet \, VP, \; [0,0]$$
$$NP \;\rightarrow\; Det \bullet Nominal, \; [1,2]$$
$$VP \;\rightarrow\; V \, NP \bullet, \; [0,3]$$

The first state, with its dot to the left of its constituent, represents a top-down prediction for this particular kind of S. The first 0 indicates that the constituent predicted by this state should begin at the start of the input; the second 0 reflects the fact that the dot lies at the beginning as well. The second state, created at a later stage in the processing of this sentence, indicates that an NP begins at position 1, that a Det has been successfully parsed, and that a $Nominal$ is expected next. The third state, with its dot to the right of its two constituents, represents the successful discovery of a tree corresponding to a VP that spans the entire input.

The basic operation of an Earley parser is to march through the $N + 1$ sets of states in the chart in a left-to-right fashion, processing the states within each set in order. At each step, one of the three operators described below is applied to each state, depending on its status. In each case, this results in the addition of new states to the end of either the current or the next set of states in the chart. The algorithm always moves forward through the chart, making additions as it goes; states are never removed and the algorithm never backtracks to a previous chart entry once it has moved on. The presence of a state $S \rightarrow \alpha\bullet$, $[0, N]$ in the list of states in the last chart entry indicates a successful parse. Figure 13.13 gives the complete algorithm.

---

function EARLEY-PARSE(*words, grammar*) **returns** *chart*

  ENQUEUE(($\gamma \rightarrow \bullet S$, $[0,0]$), *chart[0]*)
  for $i \leftarrow$ **from** 0 **to** LENGTH(*words*) **do**
   for each *state* **in** *chart[i]* **do**
    if INCOMPLETE?(*state*) **and**
         NEXT-CAT(*state*) is not a part of speech **then**
     PREDICTOR(*state*)
    elseif INCOMPLETE?(*state*) **and**
         NEXT-CAT(*state*) is a part of speech **then**
     SCANNER(*state*)
    else
     COMPLETER(*state*)
   end
  end
  return(*chart*)

procedure PREDICTOR(($A \rightarrow \alpha \bullet B\beta$, $[i, j]$))
  for each ($B \rightarrow \gamma$) **in** GRAMMAR-RULES-FOR(B, *grammar*) **do**
    ENQUEUE(($B \rightarrow \bullet \gamma$, $[j, j]$), *chart[j]*)
  end

procedure SCANNER(($A \rightarrow \alpha \bullet B\beta$, $[i, j]$))
  if B $\subset$ PARTS-OF-SPEECH(*word[j]*) **then**
    ENQUEUE(($B \rightarrow word[j]$, $[j, j+1]$), *chart[j+1]*)

procedure COMPLETER(($B \rightarrow \gamma \bullet$, $[j,k]$))
  for each ($A \rightarrow \alpha \bullet B\beta$, $[i, j]$) **in** *chart[j]* **do**
    ENQUEUE(($A \rightarrow \alpha B \bullet \beta$, $[i,k]$), *chart[k]*)
  end

procedure ENQUEUE(*state, chart-entry*)
  if *state* is not already in *chart-entry* **then**
    PUSH(*state, chart-entry*)
  end

Figure 13.13   The Earley algorithm.

The following three sections describe in detail the three operators used to process states in the chart. Each takes a single state as input and derives new states from it. These new states are then added to the chart as long as they are not already present. PREDICTOR and COMPLETER add states to the chart entry being processed, and SCAN-NER adds a state to the next chart entry.

PREDICTOR

As might be guessed from its name, the job of PREDICTOR is to create new states representing top-down expectations generated during the parsing process. PREDICTOR is applied to any state that has a non-terminal immediately to the right of its dot when the non-terminal is not a part-of-speech category. This application results in the creation of one new state for each alternative expansion of that non-terminal provided by the grammar. These new states are placed into the same chart entry as the generating state. They begin and end at the point in the input where the generating state ends.

For example, applying PREDICTOR to the state $S \rightarrow \bullet VP$, $[0,0]$ results in the addition of the following five states to the first chart entry.

$$VP \rightarrow \bullet Verb, [0,0]$$
$$VP \rightarrow \bullet Verb\,NP, [0,0]$$
$$VP \rightarrow \bullet Verb\,NP\,PP, [0,0]$$
$$VP \rightarrow \bullet Verb\,PP, [0,0]$$
$$VP \rightarrow \bullet VP\,PP, [0,0]$$

SCANNER

When a state has a part-of-speech category to the right of the dot, SCANNER is called to examine the input and incorporate into the chart a state corresponding to the prediction of a word with a particular part-of-speech. SCANNER accomplishes this by creating a new state from the input state with the dot advanced over the predicted input category. Note that unlike CKY, Earley uses top-down input to help deal with part-of-speech ambiguities; only those parts-of-speech of a word that are predicted by some existing state will find their way into the chart.

Returning to our example, when the state $VP \rightarrow \bullet Verb\,NP$, $[0,0]$ is processed, SCANNER consults the current word in the input since the category following the dot is a part-of-speech. It then notes that *book* can be a verb, matching the expectation in the current state. This results in the creation of the new state $Verb \rightarrow book\bullet$, $[0,1]$. This new state is then added to the chart entry that *follows* the one currently being processed. The noun sense of *book* never enters the chart since it is not predicted by any rule at this position in the input.

We should note that our version of SCANNER and PREDICTOR differs slightly from the corresponding operations in the original formulation of the algorithm (Earley, 1970). There terminals were treated uniformly as ordinary parts of the grammar by both PREDICTOR and SCANNER. In this approach, a state like $VP \rightarrow \bullet Verb\,NP$, $[0,0]$ would trigger predicted states corresponding to any rule that had *Verb* as its left-hand side. In our current example, the state $Verb \rightarrow \bullet book$ would be predicted. The original SCANNER would subsequently encounter this predicted state and match the current input token against the predicted token, resulting in a new state with the dot advanced, $Verb \rightarrow book\bullet$.

Unfortunately, this approach is not practical for applications with large lexicons, since states representing *every* word in a given word class would be entered into the chart as soon as that class was predicted. In our current example, states representing every known verb would be added in addition to the one for *book*. For this reason, our version of the PREDICTOR does not create states representing predictions for individual lexical items. SCANNER makes up for this by explicitly inserting states representing completed lexical items despite the fact that no states in the chart predict them.

COMPLETER

COMPLETER is applied to a state when its dot has reached the right end of the rule. The presence of such a state represents the fact that the parser has successfully discovered a particular grammatical category over some span of the input. The purpose of COMPLETER is to find, and advance, all previously created states that were looking for this grammatical category at this position in the input. COMPLETER then creates states **copying** the older state, advancing the dot over the expected category, and installing the new state in the current chart entry.

In the current example, when the state $NP \rightarrow Det\ Nominal\bullet$, $[1,3]$ is processed, COMPLETER looks for incomplete states ending at position 1 and expecting an NP. It finds the states $VP \rightarrow Verb\bullet NP$, $[0,1]$ and $VP \rightarrow Verb\bullet NP\ PP$, $[0,1]$. This results in the addition of the new complete state, $VP \rightarrow Verb\ NP\bullet$, $[0,3]$, and the new incomplete state, $VP \rightarrow Verb\ NP\bullet PP$, $[0,3]$ to the chart.

A Complete Example

Figure 13.14 shows the sequence of states created during the complete processing of (13.7); each row indicates the state number for reference, the dotted rule, the start and end points, and finally the function that added this state to the chart. The algorithm begins by seeding the chart with a top-down expectation for an S, that is, by adding a dummy state $\gamma \rightarrow \bullet S, [0,0]$ to Chart[0]. When this state is processed, it is passed to PREDICTOR, leading to the creation of the three states representing predictions for each possible type of S and transitively passed to states for all of the left corners of those trees. When the state $VP \rightarrow \bullet\ Verb, [0,0]$ is reached, SCANNER is called and the first word is read. A state representing the verb sense of *Book* is added to the entry for Chart[1]. Note that when the subsequent sentence initial VP states are processed, SCANNER will be called again. However, new states are not added since they would be identical to the *Verb* state already in the chart.

When all the states of Chart[0] have been processed, the algorithm moves on to Chart[1], where it finds the state representing the verb sense of *book*. This is a complete state with its dot to the right of its constituent and is therefore passed to COMPLETER. COMPLETER then finds the four previously existing VP states expecting a *Verb* at this point in the input. These states are copied with their dots advanced and added to Chart[1]. The completed state corresponding to an intransitive VP then leads to the creation of an S representing an imperative sentence. Alternatively, the dot in the transitive verb phrase leads to the creation of the three states predicting different forms of NPs. The state $NP \rightarrow \bullet\ Det\ Nominal$, $[1,1]$ causes SCANNER to read the word *that* and add a corresponding state to Chart[2].

Moving on to Chart[2], the algorithm finds the state representing the determiner sense of *that*. This complete state leads to the advancement of the dot in the NP state

Chart[0]	S0	$\gamma \rightarrow \bullet S$	[0,0]	Dummy start state
	S1	$S \rightarrow \bullet NP\ VP$	[0,0]	Predictor
	S2	$S \rightarrow \bullet Aux\ NP\ VP$	[0,0]	Predictor
	S3	$S \rightarrow \bullet VP$	[0,0]	Predictor
	S4	$NP \rightarrow \bullet Pronoun$	[0,0]	Predictor
	S5	$NP \rightarrow \bullet Proper\text{-}Noun$	[0,0]	Predictor
	S6	$NP \rightarrow \bullet Det\ Nominal$	[0,0]	Predictor
	S7	$VP \rightarrow \bullet Verb$	[0,0]	Predictor
	S8	$VP \rightarrow \bullet Verb\ NP$	[0,0]	Predictor
	S9	$VP \rightarrow \bullet Verb\ NP\ PP$	[0,0]	Predictor
	S10	$VP \rightarrow \bullet Verb\ PP$	[0,0]	Predictor
	S11	$VP \rightarrow \bullet VP\ PP$	[0,0]	Predictor
Chart[1]	S12	$Verb \rightarrow book \bullet$	[0,1]	Scanner
	S13	$VP \rightarrow Verb \bullet$	[0,1]	Completer
	S14	$VP \rightarrow Verb \bullet NP$	[0,1]	Completer
	S15	$VP \rightarrow Verb \bullet NP\ PP$	[0,1]	Completer
	S16	$VP \rightarrow Verb \bullet PP$	[0,1]	Completer
	S17	$S \rightarrow VP \bullet$	[0,1]	Completer
	S18	$VP \rightarrow VP \bullet PP$	[0,1]	Completer
	S19	$NP \rightarrow \bullet Pronoun$	[1,1]	Predictor
	S20	$NP \rightarrow \bullet Proper\text{-}Noun$	[1,1]	Predictor
	S21	$NP \rightarrow \bullet Det\ Nominal$	[1,1]	Predictor
	S22	$PP \rightarrow \bullet Prep\ NP$	[1,1]	Predictor
Chart[2]	S23	$Det \rightarrow that \bullet$	[1,2]	Scanner
	S24	$NP \rightarrow Det \bullet Nominal$	[1,2]	Completer
	S25	$Nominal \rightarrow \bullet Noun$	[2,2]	Predictor
	S26	$Nominal \rightarrow \bullet Nominal\ Noun$	[2,2]	Predictor
	S27	$Nominal \rightarrow \bullet Nominal\ PP$	[2,2]	Predictor
Chart[3]	S28	$Noun \rightarrow flight \bullet$	[2,3]	Scanner
	S29	$Nominal \rightarrow Noun \bullet$	[2,3]	Completer
	S30	$NP \rightarrow Det\ Nominal \bullet$	[1,3]	Completer
	S31	$Nominal \rightarrow Nominal \bullet Noun$	[2,3]	Completer
	S32	$Nominal \rightarrow Nominal \bullet PP$	[2,3]	Completer
	S33	$VP \rightarrow Verb\ NP \bullet$	[0,3]	Completer
	S34	$VP \rightarrow Verb\ NP \bullet PP$	[0,3]	Completer
	S35	$PP \rightarrow \bullet Prep\ NP$	[3,3]	Predictor
	S36	$S \rightarrow VP \bullet$	[0,3]	Completer
	S37	$VP \rightarrow VP \bullet PP$	[0,3]	Completer

Figure 13.14   Chart entries created during an Earley parse of *Book that flight*. Each entry shows the state, its start and end points, and the function that placed it in the chart.

predicted in Chart[1] and also to the predictions for the various kinds of *Nominal*. The first of these causes SCANNER to be called for the last time to process the word *flight*.

Finally, moving on to Chart[3]: the presence of the state representing *flight* leads in succession to the completion of an *NP*, a transitive *VP*, and an *S*. The presence of the state $S \rightarrow VP\bullet$, $[0,3]$ in the last chart entry signals the discovery of a successful parse.

It is useful to contrast this example with the CKY example given earlier. Although Earley managed to avoid adding an entry for the noun sense of *book*, its overall behavior

Chart[1]	S12	$Verb \rightarrow book \bullet$	[0,1]	Scanner
Chart[2]	S23	$Det \rightarrow that \bullet$	[1,2]	Scanner
Chart[3]	S28	$Noun \rightarrow flight \bullet$	[2,3]	Scanner
	S29	$Nominal \rightarrow Noun \bullet$	[2,3]	(S28)
	S30	$NP \rightarrow Det\ Nominal \bullet$	[1,3]	(S23, S29)
	S33	$VP \rightarrow Verb\ NP \bullet$	[0,3]	(S12, S30)
	S36	$S \rightarrow VP \bullet$	[0,3]	(S33)

Figure 13.15   States that participate in the final parse of *Book that flight*, including structural parse information.

is clearly much more promiscuous than that of CKY. This promiscuity arises from the purely top-down nature of the predictions that Earley makes. Exercise 13.6 asks you to improve the algorithm by eliminating some of these unnecessary predictions.

Retrieving Parse Trees from a Chart

As with the CKY algorithm, this version of the Earley algorithm is a recognizer, not a parser. Valid sentences will simply leave the state $S \rightarrow \alpha \bullet$, $[0,N]$ in the chart. To retrieve parses from the chart, we need to add an additional field to each state with information about the completed states that generated its constituents.

The information needed to fill these fields can be gathered by a simple change to the COMPLETER function. Recall that COMPLETER creates new states by advancing existing incomplete states when the constituent following the dot has been found. We just change COMPLETER to add a pointer to the older state onto a list of constituent-states for the new state. Retrieving a parse tree from the chart is then merely a matter of following pointers, starting with the state (or states) representing a complete S in the final chart entry. Figure 13.15 shows the chart entries produced by an appropriately updated COMPLETER that participated in the final parse for this example.

13.4.3   Chart Parsing

In both the CKY and Earley algorithms, the order in which events occur (adding entries to the table, reading words, making predictions, etc.) is statically determined by the procedures that make up these algorithms. Unfortunately, dynamically determining the order in which events occur based on the current information is often necessary for a *Chart parsing* variety of reasons. Fortunately, **chart parsing**, an approach advanced by Martin Kay and his colleagues (Kaplan, 1973; Kay, 1982), permits a more flexible determination of the order in which chart entries are processed. This is accomplished through the use of an explicit *agenda*. In this scheme, as states (called **edges** in this approach) are created, they are added to an agenda that is kept ordered according to a policy that is specified *separately* from the main parsing algorithm. This can be viewed as another instance of a state-space search that we've seen several times before. The FSA and FST recognition and parsing algorithms in Chapters 2 and 3 employed agendas with simple static policies, and the A* decoding algorithm described in Chapter 9 is driven by an agenda that is ordered probabilistically.

Figure 13.16 presents a generic version of a parser based on such a scheme. The main part of the algorithm consists of a single loop that removes an edge from the front of an agenda, processes it, and then moves on to the next entry in the agenda. When the agenda is empty, the parser stops and returns the chart. The policy used to order the elements in the agenda thus determines the order in which further edges are created and predictions are made.

---

function CHART-PARSE(*words, grammar, agenda-strategy*) **returns** *chart*

  INITIALIZE(*chart, agenda, words*)
  while *agenda*
    current-edge ← POP(*agenda*)
    PROCESS-EDGE(*current-edge*)
  return(*chart*)

  procedure PROCESS-EDGE(*edge*)
    ADD-TO-CHART(*edge*)
    if INCOMPLETE?(*edge*)
      FORWARD-FUNDAMENTAL-RULE(*edge*)
    else
      BACKWARD-FUNDAMENTAL-RULE(*edge*)
    MAKE-PREDICTIONS(*edge*)

  procedure FORWARD-FUNDAMENTAL(($A \rightarrow \alpha \bullet B\ \beta, [i,j]$))
    for each($B \rightarrow \gamma \bullet, [j,k]$) **in** *chart*
      ADD-TO-AGENDA($A \rightarrow \alpha B \bullet \beta, [i,k]$)

  procedure BACKWARD-FUNDAMENTAL(($B \rightarrow \gamma \bullet, [j,k]$))
    for each($A \rightarrow \alpha \bullet B\ \beta, [i,j]$) **in** *chart*
      ADD-TO-AGENDA($A \rightarrow \alpha B \bullet \beta, [i,k]$)

  procedure ADD-TO-CHART(*edge*)
    if *edge* is not already in *chart* **then**
      Add *edge* to *chart*

  procedure ADD-TO-AGENDA(*edge*)
    if *edge* is not already in *agenda* **then**
      APPLY(*agenda-strategy, edge, agenda*)

Figure 13.16   A chart parsing algorithm.

Fundamental rule

The key principle in processing edges in this approach is what Kay termed the **fundamental rule** of chart parsing. The fundamental rule states that when the chart contains two contiguous edges where one of the edges provides the constituent that the other one needs, a new edge should be created that spans the original edges and incorporates the provided material. More formally, the fundamental rule states the following: if the chart contains two edges $A \rightarrow \alpha \bullet B\ \beta, [i,j]$ and $B \rightarrow \gamma \bullet, [j,k]$, then we should add the new edge $A \rightarrow \alpha B \bullet \beta [i,k]$ to the chart. It should be clear that the fundamental rule is a generalization of the basic table-filling operations found in both the CKY and Earley algorithms.

The fundamental rule is triggered in Fig. 13.16 when an edge is removed from the agenda and passed to the PROCESS-EDGE procedure. Note that the fundamental rule itself does not specify which of the two edges involved has triggered the processing. PROCESS-EDGE handles both cases by checking to see whether or not the edge in question is complete. If it is complete, then the algorithm looks earlier in the chart to see if any existing edge can be advanced; if it is incomplete, then the algorithm looks later in the chart to see if it can be advanced by any pre-existing edge later in the chart.

The next piece of the algorithm to specify is the method for making predictions based on the edge being processed. There are two key components to making predictions in chart parsing: the events that trigger predictions and the nature of the prediction. These components vary depending on whether we are pursuing a top-down or bottom-up strategy. As in Earley, top-down predictions are triggered by expectations that arise from incomplete edges that have been entered into the chart; bottom-up predictions are triggered by the discovery of completed constituents. Figure 13.17 illustrates how these two strategies can be integrated into the chart parsing algorithm.

---

procedure MAKE-PREDICTIONS(*edge*)
  if *Top-Down* **and** INCOMPLETE?(*edge*)
    TD-PREDICT(*edge*)
  elseif *Bottom-Up* **and** COMPLETE?(*edge*)
    BU-PREDICT(*edge*)

procedure TD-PREDICT(($A \rightarrow \alpha \bullet B \beta, [i, j]$))
  for each($B \rightarrow \gamma$) in *grammar* **do**
    ADD-TO-AGENDA($B \rightarrow \bullet \gamma, [j, j]$)

procedure BU-PREDICT(($B \rightarrow \gamma \bullet, [i, j]$))
  for each($A \rightarrow B \beta$) in *grammar*
    ADD-TO-AGENDA($A \rightarrow B \bullet \beta, [i, j]$)

Figure 13.17 More of the chart parsing algorithm.

Obviously, we've left out many of the bookkeeping details that would have to be specified to turn this approach into a real parser. Among the details that have to be worked out are how the INITIALIZE procedure gets things started, how and when words are read, how the chart is organized, and how to specify an agenda strategy. Indeed, in *Algorithm schema* describing this approach, Kay (1982) refers to it as an **algorithm schema** rather than an algorithm, since it more accurately specifies an entire family of parsers rather than any particular parser. Exercise 13.7 asks you to explore some of the available choices by implementing various chart parsers.

13.5 Partial Parsing

Many language processing tasks do not require complex, complete parse trees for all inputs. For these tasks, a **partial parse**, or **shallow parse**, of input sentences may be *Partial parse* *Shallow parse* sufficient. For example, information extraction systems generally do not extract *all* the possible information from a text: they simply identify and classify the segments in a text that are likely to contain valuable information. Similarly, information retrieval systems may index texts according to a subset of the constituents found in them.

There are many different approaches to partial parsing. Some make use of cascades of FSTs, of the kind discussed in Chapter 3, to produce tree-like representations. These approaches typically produce flatter trees than the ones we've been discussing in this chapter and the previous one. This flatness arises from the fact that FST cascade approaches generally defer decisions that may require semantic or contextual factors, such as prepositional phrase attachments, coordination ambiguities, and nominal compound analyses. Nevertheless, the intent is to produce parse trees that link all the major constituents in an input.

Chunking   An alternative style of partial parsing is known as **chunking**. Chunking is the process of identifying and classifying the flat, non-overlapping segments of a sentence that constitute the basic non-recursive phrases corresponding to the major parts-of-speech found in most wide-coverage grammars. This set typically includes noun phrases, verb phrases, adjective phrases, and prepositional phrases; in other words, the phrases that correspond to the content-bearing parts-of-speech. Of course, not all applications require the identification of all of these categories; indeed, the most common chunking task is to simply find all the base noun phrases in a text.

Since chunked texts lack a hierarchical structure, a simple bracketing notation is sufficient to denote the location and the type of the chunks in a given example. The following example illustrates a typical bracketed notation.

(13.8) [$_{NP}$ The morning flight] [$_{PP}$ from] [$_{NP}$ Denver] [$_{VP}$ has arrived.]

This bracketing notation makes clear the two fundamental tasks that are involved in chunking: finding the non-overlapping extents of the chunks and assigning the correct label to the discovered chunks.

Note that in this example all the words are contained in some chunk. This will not be the case in all chunking applications. Many words in any input will often fall outside of any chunk, for example, in systems searching for base *NP*s in their inputs, as in the following:

(13.9)   [$_{NP}$ The morning flight] from [$_{NP}$ Denver] has arrived.

The details of what constitutes a syntactic base phrase for any given system varies according to the syntactic theories underlying the system and whether the phrases are being derived from a treebank. Nevertheless, some standard guidelines are followed in most systems. First and foremost, base phrases of a given type do not recursively contain any constituents of the same type. Eliminating this kind of recursion leaves us with the problem of determining the boundaries of the non-recursive phrases. In most approaches, base phrases include the headword of the phrase, along with any pre-head material within the constituent, while crucially excluding any post-head material. Eliminating post-head modifiers from the major categories automatically removes the need to resolve attachment ambiguities. Note that this exclusion does lead to certain oddities, such as *PP*s and *VP*s often consisting solely of their heads. Thus, our earlier example *a flight from Indianapolis to Houston on NWA* is reduced to the following:

(13.10) [$_{NP}$ a flight] [$_{PP}$ from] [$_{NP}$ Indianapolis][$_{PP}$ to][$_{NP}$ Houston][$_{PP}$ on][$_{NP}$ NWA]

13.5.1   Finite-State Rule-Based Chunking

Syntactic base phrases of the kind we're considering can be characterized by finite-state automata (or finite-state rules, or regular expressions) of the kind discussed in Chapters 2 and 3. In finite-state rule-based chunking, rules are hand-crafted to capture the phrases of interest for any particular application. In most rule-based systems, chunking proceeds from left to right, finding the longest matching chunk from the beginning of the sentence and continuing with the first word after the end of the previously recognized chunk. The process continues until the end of the sentence. This is a greedy process and is not guaranteed to find the best global analysis for any given input.

The primary limitation placed on these chunk rules is that they cannot contain any recursion; the right-hand side of the rule cannot reference directly or indirectly the category that the rule is designed to capture. In other words, rules of the form $NP \rightarrow Det\ Nominal$ are fine, but rules such as $Nominal \rightarrow Nominal\ PP$ are not. Consider the following example chunk rules adapted from Abney (1996).

$$NP \rightarrow (DT)\ NN^*\ NN$$
$$NP \rightarrow NNP$$
$$VP \rightarrow VB$$
$$VP \rightarrow Aux\ VB$$

The process of turning these rules into a single finite-state transducer is the same process we introduced in Chapter 3 to capture spelling and phonological rules for English. Finite-state transducers are created corresponding to each rule and are then unioned together to form a single machine that can be determinized and minimized.

As we saw in Chapter 3, a major benefit of the finite-state approach is the ability to use the output of earlier transducers as inputs to subsequent transducers to form **cascades**. In **partial parsing**, this technique can be used to more closely approximate the output of true context-free parsers. In this approach, an initial set of transducers is used, in the way just described, to find a subset of syntactic base phrases. These base phrases are then passed as input to further transducers that detect larger and larger constituents such as prepositional phrases, verb phrases, clauses, and sentences. Consider the following rules, again adapted from Abney (1996).

$$FST_2 \quad PP \rightarrow IN\ NP$$
$$FST_3 \quad S \rightarrow PP^*\ NP\ PP^*\ VP\ PP^*$$

Combining these two machines with the earlier ruleset results in a three-machine cascade. The application of this cascade to (13.8) is shown in Fig. 13.18.

13.5.2   Machine Learning-Based Approaches to Chunking

As with part-of-speech tagging, an alternative to rule-based processing is to use supervised machine learning techniques to *train* a chunker by using annotated data as a training set. As described earlier in Chapter 6, we can view the task as one of **sequential classification**, where a classifier is trained to label each element of the input

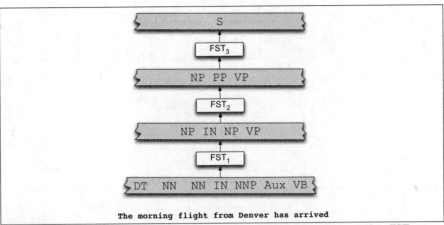

Figure 13.18   Chunk-based partial parsing through a set of finite-state cascades. FST₁ transduces from part-of-speech tags to base noun phrases and verb phrases. FST₂ finds prepositional phrases. Finally, FST₃ detects sentences.

in sequence. Any of the standard approaches to training classifiers apply to this problem. In the work that pioneered this approach, Ramshaw and Marcus (1995) used the transformation-based learning method described in Chapter 5.

The critical first step in such an approach is to be able to view the chunking process in a way that is amenable to sequential classification. A particularly fruitful approach is to treat chunking as a tagging task similar to part-of-speech tagging (Ramshaw and Marcus, 1995). In this approach, a small tagset simultaneously encodes both the segmentation and the labeling of the chunks in the input. The standard way to do this has come to be called **IOB tagging** and is accomplished by introducing tags to represent the beginning (B) and internal (I) parts of each chunk, as well as those elements of the input that are outside (O) any chunk. Under this scheme, the size of the tagset is $(2n+1)$, where n is the number of categories to be classified. The following example shows the bracketing notation of (13.8) on page 451 reframed as a tagging task:

IOB tagging

(13.11)   *The   morning flight from Denver has   arrived*
        B_NP I_NP   I_NP B_PP B_NP   B_VP I_VP

The same sentence with only the base-NPs tagged illustrates the role of the O tags.

(13.12)   *The   morning flight from Denver has arrived.*
        B_NP I_NP   I_NP O   B_NP O O

Notice that there is no explicit encoding of the end of a chunk in this scheme; the end of any chunk is implicit in any transition from an I or B to a B or O tag. This encoding reflects the notion that when sequentially labeling words, it is generally easier (at least in English) to detect the beginning of a new chunk than it is to know when a chunk has ended. Not surprisingly, a variety of other tagging schemes represent chunks in subtly different ways, including some that explicitly mark the end of constituents. Tjong Kim Sang and Veenstra (1999) describe three variations on this basic tagging scheme and investigate their performance on a variety of chunking tasks.

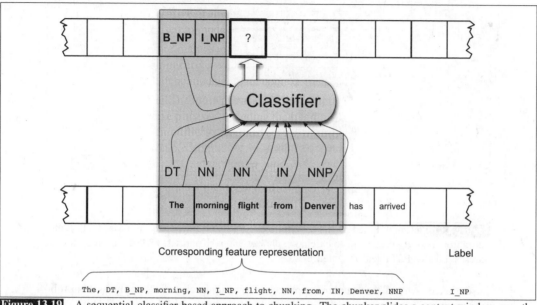

Corresponding feature representation   Label

The, DT, B_NP, morning, NN, I_NP, flight, NN, from, IN, Denver, NNP   I_NP

Figure 13.19   A sequential-classifier-based approach to chunking. The chunker slides a context window over the sentence, classifying words as it proceeds. At this point, the classifier is attempting to label *flight*. Features derived from the context typically include the words, part-of-speech tags as well as the previously assigned chunk tags.

Given such a tagging scheme, building a chunker consists of training a classifier to label each word of an input sentence with one of the IOB tags from the tagset. Of course, training requires training data consisting of the phrases of interest delimited and marked with the appropriate category. The direct approach is to annotate a representative corpus. Unfortunately, annotation efforts can be both expensive and time consuming. It turns out that the best place to find such data for chunking is in an existing treebank such as the Penn Treebank described in Chapter 12.

Such treebanks provide a complete parse for each corpus sentence, allowing base syntactic phrases to be extracted from the parse constituents. To find the phrases we're interested in, we just need to know the appropriate non-terminal names in the corpus. Finding chunk boundaries requires finding the head and then including the material to the left of the head, ignoring the text to the right. This is somewhat error-prone since it relies on the accuracy of the head-finding rules described in Chapter 12.

Having extracted a training corpus from a treebank, we must now cast the training data into a form that's useful for training classifiers. In this case, each input can be represented as a set of features extracted from a context window that surrounds the word to be classified. Using a window that extends two words before and two words after the word being classified seems to provide reasonable performance. Features extracted from this window include the words themselves, their parts-of-speech, and the chunk tags of the preceding inputs in the window.

Figure 13.19 illustrates this scheme with the example given earlier. During training, the classifier would be provided with a training vector consisting of the values of 13 features; the two words to the left of the decision point, their parts-of-speech and chunk tags, the word to be tagged along with its part-of-speech, the two words that follow along with their parts-of speech, and finally the correct chunk tag, in this case, I_NP. During classification, the classifier is given the same vector without the answer and assigns the most appropriate tag from its tagset.

13.5.3   Chunking-System Evaluations

As with the evaluation of part-of-speech taggers, the evaluation of chunkers proceeds by comparing chunker output with gold-standard answers provided by human annotators. However, unlike part-of-speech tagging, word-by-word accuracy measures are not appropriate. Instead, chunkers are evaluated according to the notions of precision, recall, and the *F*-measure borrowed from the field of information retrieval.

Precision   **Precision** measures the percentage of system-provided chunks that were correct. Correct here means that both the boundaries of the chunk and the chunk's label are correct. Precision is therefore defined as

$$\text{Precision:} = \frac{\text{Number of correct chunks given by system}}{\text{Total number of chunks given by system}}$$

Recall   **Recall** measures the percentage of chunks actually present in the input that were correctly identified by the system. Recall is defined as

$$\text{Recall:} = \frac{\text{Number of correct chunks given by system}}{\text{Total number of actual chunks in the text}}$$

F-measure   The **F-measure** (van Rijsbergen, 1975) provides a way to combine these two measures into a single metric. The F-measure is defined as

$$F_\beta = \frac{(\beta^2 + 1)PR}{\beta^2 P + R}$$

The β parameter differentially weights the importance of recall and precision, based perhaps on the needs of an application. Values of $\beta > 1$ favor recall, while values of $\beta < 1$ favor precision. When $\beta = 1$, precision and recall are equally balanced; this is sometimes called $F_{\beta=1}$ or just F_1:

$$F_1 = \frac{2PR}{P + R} \tag{13.13}$$

F-measure comes from a weighted harmonic mean of precision and recall. The harmonic mean of a set of numbers is the reciprocal of the arithmetic mean of reciprocals:

$$\text{HarmonicMean}(a_1, a_2, a_3, a_4, ..., a_n) = \frac{n}{\frac{1}{a_1} \frac{1}{a_2} \frac{1}{a_3} ... \frac{1}{a_n}} \tag{13.14}$$

and hence F-measure is

$$F = \frac{1}{\frac{1}{\alpha P} \quad \frac{1}{(1-\alpha)R}} \quad \text{or} \left(\text{with } \beta^2 = \frac{1-\alpha}{\alpha}\right) \quad F = \frac{(\beta^2 + 1)PR}{\beta^2 P + R} \tag{13.15}$$

The best current systems achieve an F-measure of around .96 on the task of base-NP chunking. Learning-based systems designed to find a more complete set of base phrases, such as the ones given in Fig. 13.20, achieve *F*-measures in the .92 to .94 range. The choice of learning approach seems to have little impact; a wide range of machine learning approaches achieve similar results (Cardie et al., 2000). FST-based systems (Section 13.5.1) achieve *F*-measures ranging from .85 to .92 on this task.

Statistical significance on chunking results can be computed using matched-pair tests such as McNemar's test, or variants such as the Matched-Pair Sentence Segment Word Error (MAPSSWE) test described on page 329.

Factors limiting the performance of current systems include part-of-speech tagging accuracy, inconsistencies in the training data introduced by the process of extracting chunks from parse trees, and difficulty resolving ambiguities involving conjunctions. Consider the following examples that involve pre-nominal modifiers and conjunctions.

(13.16)   [*NP* Late arrivals and departures] are commonplace during winter.

(13.17)   [*NP* Late arrivals] and [*NP* cancellations] are commonplace during winter.

In the first example, *late* is shared by both *arrivals* and *departures*, yielding a single long base-NP. In the second example, *late* is not shared and modifies *arrivals* alone, thus yielding two base-NPs. Distinguishing these two situations, and others like them, requires access to semantic and context information unavailable to current chunkers.

Label	Category	Proportion (%)	Example
NP	Noun Phrase	51	*The most frequently cancelled flight*
VP	Verb Phrase	20	*may not arrive*
PP	Prepositional Phrase	20	*to Houston*
ADVP	Adverbial Phrase	4	*earlier*
SBAR	Subordinate Clause	2	*that*
ADJP	Adjective Phrase	2	*late*

Figure 13.20   Most frequent base phrases used in the 2000 CONLL shared task. These chunks correspond to the major categories contained in the Penn Treebank.

13.6   Summary

The two major ideas introduced in this chapter are those of **parsing** and **partial parsing**. Here's a summary of the main points we covered about these ideas:

- Parsing can be viewed as a **search** problem.
- Two common architectural metaphors for this search are **top-down** (starting with the root *S* and growing trees down to the input words) and **bottom-up** (starting with the words and growing trees up toward the root *S*).
- **Ambiguity** combined with the **repeated parsing of subtrees** poses problems for simple backtracking algorithms.
- A sentence is **structurally ambiguous** if the grammar assigns it more than one possible parse. Common kinds of structural ambiguity include **PP-attachment**, **coordination ambiguity**, and **noun-phrase bracketing ambiguity**.

- **Dynamic programming** parsing algorithms use a table of partial parses to efficiently parse ambiguous sentences. The **CKY**, **Earley**, and **chart parsing** algorithms all use dynamic programming to solve the repeated parsing of subtrees problem.

- The CKY algorithm restricts the form of the grammar to Chomsky normal form (CNF); the Earley and chart parsers accept unrestricted context-free grammars.

- Many practical problems, including **information extraction** problems, can be solved without full parsing.

- **Partial parsing** and **chunking** are methods for identifying shallow syntactic constituents in a text.

- High-accuracy partial parsing can be achieved either through rule-based or machine learning-based methods.

Bibliographical and Historical Notes

Writing about the history of compilers, Knuth notes:

> In this field there has been an unusual amount of parallel discovery of the
> same technique by people working independently.

Well, perhaps not unusual, if multiple discovery is the norm (see page 13). But there has certainly been enough parallel publication that this history errs on the side of succinctness in giving only a characteristic early mention of each algorithm; the interested reader should see Aho and Ullman (1972).

Bottom-up parsing seems to have been first described by Yngve (1955), who gave a breadth-first, bottom-up parsing algorithm as part of an illustration of a machine translation procedure. Top-down approaches to parsing and translation were described (presumably independently) by at least Glennie (1960), Irons (1961), and Kuno and Oettinger (1963). Dynamic programming parsing, once again, has a history of independent discovery. According to Martin Kay (personal communication), a dynamic programming parser containing the roots of the CKY algorithm was first implemented by John Cocke in 1960. Later work extended and formalized the algorithm, as well as proving its time complexity (Kay, 1967; Younger, 1967; Kasami, 1965). The related *WFST* **well-formed substring table** (**WFST**) seems to have been independently proposed by Kuno (1965) as a data structure that stores the results of all previous computations in the course of the parse. Based on a generalization of Cocke's work, a similar data structure had been independently described by Kay (1967, 1973). The top-down application of dynamic programming to parsing was described in Earley's Ph.D. dissertation (Earley, 1968, 1970). Sheil (1976) showed the equivalence of the WFST and the Earley algorithm. Norvig (1991) shows that the efficiency offered by dynamic programming can be captured in any language with a *memoization* function (such as in LISP) simply by wrapping the *memoization* operation around a simple top-down parser.

While parsing via cascades of finite-state automata had been common in the early history of parsing (Harris, 1962), the focus shifted to full CFG parsing quite soon afterward. Church (1980) argued for a return to finite-state grammars as a processing model for natural language understanding; other early finite-state parsing models include Ejerhed (1988). Abney (1991) argued for the important practical role of shallow parsing. Much recent work on shallow parsing applies machine learning to the task of learning the patterns; see, for example, Ramshaw and Marcus (1995), Argamon et al. (1998), Munoz et al. (1999).

The classic reference for parsing algorithms is Aho and Ullman (1972); although the focus of that book is on computer languages, most of the algorithms have been applied to natural language. A good programming languages textbook such as Aho et al. (1986) is also useful.

Exercises

13.1 Implement the algorithm to convert arbitrary context-free grammars to CNF. Apply your program to the $\mathscr{L}_1$ grammar.

13.2 Implement the CKY algorithm and test it with your converted $\mathscr{L}_1$ grammar.

13.3 Rewrite the CKY algorithm given in Fig. 13.10 on page 440 so that it can accept grammars that contain unit productions.

13.4 Augment the Earley algorithm of Fig. 13.13 to enable parse trees to be retrieved from the chart by modifying the pseudocode for COMPLETER as described on page 448.

13.5 Implement the Earley algorithm as augmented in the previous exercise. Check it on a test sentence by using the $\mathscr{L}_1$ grammar.

13.6 Alter the Earley algorithm so that it makes better use of bottom-up information to reduce the number of useless predictions.

13.7 Attempt to recast the CKY and Earley algorithms in the chart-parsing paradigm.

13.8 Discuss the relative advantages and disadvantages of partial versus full parsing.

13.9 Implement a more extensive finite-state grammar for noun groups by using the examples given in Section 13.5 and test it on some *NP*s. Use an on-line dictionary with parts-of-speech if available; if not, build a more restricted system by hand.

13.10 Discuss how to augment a parser to deal with input that may be incorrect, for example, containing spelling errors or mistakes arising from automatic speech recognition.

Chapter 14

Statistical Parsing

Two roads diverged in a wood, and I –
I took the one less traveled by...
Robert Frost, *The Road Not Taken*

The characters in Damon Runyon's short stories are willing to bet "on any proposition whatever", as Runyon says about Sky Masterson in *The Idyll of Miss Sarah Brown*, from the probability of getting aces back-to-back to the odds against a man being able to throw a peanut from second base to home plate. There is a moral here for language processing: with enough knowledge we can figure the probability of just about anything. The last two chapters have introduced sophisticated models of syntactic structure and its parsing. In this chapter we show that it is possible to build probabilistic models of syntactic knowledge and use some of this probabilistic knowledge in efficient probabilistic parsers.

One crucial use of probabilistic parsing is to solve the problem of **disambiguation**. Recall from Chapter 13 that sentences on average tend to be syntactically ambiguous because of problems like **coordination ambiguity** and **attachment ambiguity**. The CKY and Earley parsing algorithms could represent these ambiguities in an efficient way but were not equipped to resolve them. A probabilistic parser offers a solution to the problem: compute the probability of each interpretation and choose the most probable interpretation. Thus, due to the prevalence of ambiguity, most modern parsers used for natural language understanding tasks (thematic role labeling, summarization, question-answering, machine translation) are of necessity probabilistic.

Another important use of probabilistic grammars and parsers is in **language modeling** for speech recognition. We saw that *N*-gram grammars are used in speech recognizers to predict upcoming words, helping constrain the acoustic model search for words. Probabilistic versions of more sophisticated grammars can provide additional predictive power to a speech recognizer. Of course, humans have to deal with the same problems of ambiguity as do speech recognizers, and it is interesting that psychological experiments suggest that people use something like these probabilistic grammars in human language processing tasks (e.g., human reading or speech understanding).

The most commonly used probabilistic grammar is the **probabilistic context-free grammar** (PCFG), a probabilistic augmentation of context-free grammars in which each rule is associated with a probability. We introduce PCFGs in the next section, showing how they can be trained on a hand-labeled Treebank grammar and how they can be parsed. We present the most basic parsing algorithm for PCFGs, which is the probabilistic version of the **CKY algorithm** that we saw in Chapter 13.

We then show a number of ways that we can improve on this basic probability model (PCFGs trained on Treebank grammars). One method of improving a trained

From Chapter 14 of *Speech and Language Processing*, Second Edition. Daniel Jurafsky, James H. Martin.

Treebank grammar is to change the names of the non-terminals. By making the non-terminals sometimes more specific and sometimes more general, we can come up with a grammar with a better probability model that leads to improved parsing scores. Another augmentation of the PCFG works by adding more sophisticated conditioning factors, extending PCFGs to handle probabilistic **subcategorization** information and probabilistic **lexical dependencies**.

Finally, we describe the standard PARSEVAL metrics for evaluating parsers and discuss some psychological results on human parsing.

14.1   Probabilistic Context-Free Grammars

PCFG
SCFG

The simplest augmentation of the context-free grammar is the **Probabilistic Context-Free Grammar** (**PCFG**), also known as the **Stochastic Context-Free Grammar** (**SCFG**), first proposed by Booth (1969). Recall that a context-free grammar G is defined by four parameters (N, Σ, R, S); a probabilistic context-free grammar is also defined by four parameters, with a slight augmentation to each of the rules in R:

> N a set of **non-terminal symbols** (or **variables**)
>
> Σ a set of **terminal symbols** (disjoint from N)
>
> R a set of **rules** or productions, each of the form $A \rightarrow \beta \; [p]$,
>
>   where A is a non-terminal,
>
> β is a string of symbols from the infinite set of strings $(\Sigma \cup N)*$,
>
>   and p is a number between 0 and 1 expressing $P(\beta \, A)$
>
> S a designated **start symbol**

That is, a PCFG differs from a standard CFG by augmenting each rule in R with a conditional probability:

$$A \rightarrow \beta \; [p] \tag{14.1}$$

Here p expresses the probability that the given non-terminal A will be expanded to the sequence β. That is, p is the conditional probability of a given expansion β given the left-hand-side (LHS) non-terminal A. We can represent this probability as

$$P(A \rightarrow \beta)$$

or as

$$P(A \rightarrow \beta \, A)$$

or as

$$P(RHS \, LHS)$$

Thus, if we consider all the possible expansions of a non-terminal, the sum of their probabilities must be 1:

$$\sum_{\beta} P(A \rightarrow \beta) = 1$$

Grammar		Lexicon	
$S \rightarrow NP\ VP$	[.80]	$Det \rightarrow that$ [.10] a [.30] the [.60]	
$S \rightarrow Aux\ NP\ VP$	[.15]	$Noun \rightarrow book$ [.10] $flight$ [.30]	
$S \rightarrow VP$	[.05]	$meal$ [.15] $money$ [.05]	
$NP \rightarrow Pronoun$	[.35]	$flights$ [.40] $dinner$ [.10]	
$NP \rightarrow Proper\text{-}Noun$	[.30]	$Verb \rightarrow book$ [.30] $include$ [.30]	
$NP \rightarrow Det\ Nominal$	[.20]	$prefer;$ [.40]	
$NP \rightarrow Nominal$	[.15]	$Pronoun \rightarrow I$ [.40] she [.05]	
$Nominal \rightarrow Noun$	[.75]	me [.15] you [.40]	
$Nominal \rightarrow Nominal\ Noun$	[.20]	$Proper\text{-}Noun \rightarrow Houston$ [.60]	
$Nominal \rightarrow Nominal\ PP$	[.05]	NWA [.40]	
$VP \rightarrow Verb$	[.35]	$Aux \rightarrow does$ [.60] can [40]	
$VP \rightarrow Verb\ NP$	[.20]	$Preposition \rightarrow from$ [.30] to [.30]	
$VP \rightarrow Verb\ NP\ PP$	[.10]	on [.20] $near$ [.15]	
$VP \rightarrow Verb\ PP$	[.15]	$through$ [.05]	
$VP \rightarrow Verb\ NP\ NP$	[.05]		
$VP \rightarrow VP\ PP$	[.15]		
$PP \rightarrow Preposition\ NP$	[1.0]		

Figure 14.1   A PCFG that is a probabilistic augmentation of the $\mathscr{L}_1$ miniature English CFG grammar and lexicon of Fig. 13.1. These probabilities were made up for pedagogical purposes and are not based on a corpus (since any real corpus would have many more rules, so the true probabilities of each rule would be much smaller).

Figure 14.1 shows a PCFG: a probabilistic augmentation of the $\mathscr{L}_1$ miniature English CFG grammar and lexicon. Note that the probabilities of all of the expansions of each non-terminal sum to 1. Also note that these probabilities were made up for pedagogical purposes. A real grammar has a great many more rules for each non-terminal; hence, the probabilities of any particular rule would tend to be much smaller.

Consistent   A PCFG is said to be **consistent** if the sum of the probabilities of all sentences in the language equals 1. Certain kinds of recursive rules cause a grammar to be inconsistent by causing infinitely looping derivations for some sentences. For example, a rule $S \rightarrow S$ with probability 1 would lead to lost probability mass due to derivations that never terminate. See Booth and Thompson (1973) for more details on consistent and inconsistent grammars.

How are PCFGs used? A PCFG can be used to estimate a number of useful probabilities concerning a sentence and its parse tree(s), including the probability of a particular parse tree (useful in disambiguation) and the probability of a sentence or a piece of a sentence (useful in language modeling). Let's see how this works.

14.1.1   PCFGs for Disambiguation

A PCFG assigns a probability to each parse tree T (i.e., each **derivation**) of a sentence S. This attribute is useful in **disambiguation**. For example, consider the two parses of the sentence "Book the dinner flight" shown in Fig. 14.2. The sensible parse on the left means "Book a flight that serves dinner". The nonsensical parse on the right, however, would have to mean something like "Book a flight on behalf of 'the dinner'" just as a structurally similar sentence like "Can you book John a flight?" means something like "Can you book a flight on behalf of John?"

The probability of a particular parse T is defined as the product of the probabilities of all the n rules used to expand each of the n non-terminal nodes in the parse tree T, where each rule i can be expressed as $LHS_i \rightarrow RHS_i$:

$$P(T,S) = \prod_{i=1}^{n} P(RHS_i\, LHS_i) \tag{14.2}$$

The resulting probability $P(T,S)$ is both the joint probability of the parse and the sentence and also the probability of the parse $P(T)$. How can this be true? First, by the definition of joint probability:

$$P(T,S) = P(T)P(S\ T) \tag{14.3}$$

But since a parse tree includes all the words of the sentence, $P(S\ T)$ is 1. Thus,

$$P(T,S) = P(T)P(S\ T) = P(T) \tag{14.4}$$

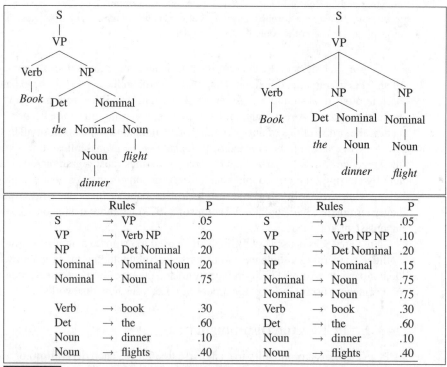

	Rules		P		Rules		P
S	$\rightarrow$	VP	.05	S	$\rightarrow$	VP	.05
VP	$\rightarrow$	Verb NP	.20	VP	$\rightarrow$	Verb NP NP	.10
NP	$\rightarrow$	Det Nominal	.20	NP	$\rightarrow$	Det Nominal	.20
Nominal	$\rightarrow$	Nominal Noun	.20	NP	$\rightarrow$	Nominal	.15
Nominal	$\rightarrow$	Noun	.75	Nominal	$\rightarrow$	Noun	.75
				Nominal	$\rightarrow$	Noun	.75
Verb	$\rightarrow$	book	.30	Verb	$\rightarrow$	book	.30
Det	$\rightarrow$	the	.60	Det	$\rightarrow$	the	.60
Noun	$\rightarrow$	dinner	.10	Noun	$\rightarrow$	dinner	.10
Noun	$\rightarrow$	flights	.40	Noun	$\rightarrow$	flights	.40

Figure 14.2   Two parse trees for an ambiguous sentence. The transitive parse on the left corresponds to the sensible meaning "Book a flight that serves dinner", while the ditransitive parse on the right corresponds to the nonsensical meaning "Book a flight on behalf of 'the dinner' ".

We can compute the probability of each of the trees in Fig. 14.2 by multiplying the probabilities of each of the rules used in the derivation. For example, the probability of the left tree in Fig. 14.2a (call it T_{left}) and the right tree (Fig. 14.2b or T_{right}) can be computed as follows:

$$P(T_{left}) = .05 * .20 * .20 * .20 * .75 * .30 * .60 * .10 * .40 = \mathbf{2.2} \quad \mathbf{10}^{-6}$$
$$P(T_{right}) = .05 * .10 * .20 * .15 * .75 * .75 * .30 * .60 * .10 * .40 = \mathbf{6.1} \quad \mathbf{10}^{-7}$$

We can see that the left (transitive) tree in Fig. 14.2 has a much higher probability than the ditransitive tree on the right. Thus, this parse would correctly be chosen by a disambiguation algorithm that selects the parse with the highest PCFG probability.

Let's formalize this intuition that picking the parse with the highest probability is the correct way to do disambiguation. Consider all the possible parse trees for a given *Yield* sentence S. The string of words S is called the **yield** of any parse tree over S. Thus, out of all parse trees with a yield of S, the disambiguation algorithm picks the parse tree that is most probable given S:

$$\hat{T}(S) = \underset{T s.t. S=\text{yield}(T)}{\text{argmax}} P(T \mid S) \tag{14.5}$$

By definition, the probability $P(T \mid S)$ can be rewritten as $P(T,S)/P(S)$, thus leading to

$$\hat{T}(S) = \underset{T s.t. S=\text{yield}(T)}{\text{argmax}} \frac{P(T,S)}{P(S)} \tag{14.6}$$

Since we are maximizing over all parse trees for the same sentence, $P(S)$ will be a constant for each tree, so we can eliminate it:

$$\hat{T}(S) = \underset{T s.t. S=\text{yield}(T)}{\text{argmax}} P(T,S) \tag{14.7}$$

Furthermore, since we showed above that $P(T,S) = P(T)$, the final equation for choosing the most likely parse neatly simplifies to choosing the parse with the highest probability:

$$\hat{T}(S) = \underset{T s.t. S=\text{yield}(T)}{\text{argmax}} P(T) \tag{14.8}$$

14.1.2   PCFGs for Language Modeling

A second attribute of a PCFG is that it assigns a probability to the string of words constituting a sentence. This is important in **language modeling**, whether for use in speech recognition, machine translation, spelling correction, augmentative communication, or other applications. The probability of an unambiguous sentence is $P(T,S) = P(T)$ or just the probability of the single parse tree for that sentence. The probability of an ambiguous sentence is the sum of the probabilities of all the parse trees for the sentence:

$$P(S) = \sum_{T s.t. S = \text{yield}(T)} P(T, S) \qquad (14.9)$$

$$= \sum_{T s.t. S = \text{yield}(T)} P(T) \qquad (14.10)$$

An additional feature of PCFGs that is useful for language modeling is their ability to assign a probability to substrings of a sentence. For example, suppose we want to know the probability of the next word w_i in a sentence given all the words we've seen so far $w_1, ..., w_{i-1}$. The general formula for this is

$$P(w_i\, w_1, w_2, ..., w_{i-1}) = \frac{P(w_1, w_2, ..., w_{i-1}, w_i, ...)}{P(w_1, w_2, ..., w_{i-1}, ...)} \qquad (14.11)$$

We saw in Chapter 4 a simple approximation of this probability using N-grams, conditioning on only the last word or two instead of the entire context; thus, the **bigram approximation** would give us

$$P(w_i\, w_1, w_2, ..., w_{i-1}) \approx \frac{P(w_{i-1}, w_i)}{P(w_{i-1})} \qquad (14.12)$$

But the fact that the N-gram model can only make use of a couple words of context means it is ignoring potentially useful prediction cues. Consider predicting the word *after* in the following sentence from Chelba and Jelinek (2000):

(14.13) the contract ended with a loss of 7 cents after trading as low as 9 cents

A trigram grammar must predict *after* from the words *7 cents*, while it seems clear that the verb *ended* and the subject *contract* would be useful predictors that a PCFG-based parser could help us make use of. Indeed, it turns out that PCFGs allow us to condition on the entire previous context $w_1, w_2, ..., w_{i-1}$ shown in Eq. 14.11. We discuss the details of ways to use PCFGs and augmentations of PCFGs as language models in Section 14.9.

In summary, this section and the previous one have shown that PCFGs can be applied both to disambiguation in syntactic parsing and to word prediction in language modeling. Both of these applications require that we be able to compute the probability of parse tree T for a given sentence S. The next few sections introduce some algorithms for computing this probability.

14.2   Probabilistic CKY Parsing of PCFGs

The parsing problem for PCFGs is to produce the most-likely parse $\hat{T}$ for a given sentence S, that is,

$$\hat{T}(S) = \underset{T s.t. S = \text{yield}(T)}{\text{argmax}} P(T) \qquad (14.14)$$

Probabilistic CKY

The algorithms for computing the most likely parse are simple extensions of the standard algorithms for parsing; there are probabilistic versions of both the CKY and Earley algorithms of Chapter 13. Most modern probabilistic parsers are based on the **probabilistic CKY** algorithm, first described by Ney (1991).

As with the CKY algorithm, we assume for the probabilistic CKY algorithm that the PCFG is in Chomsky normal form. Recall from page 412 that grammars in CNF are restricted to rules of the form $A \rightarrow B\,C$, or $A \rightarrow w$. That is, the right-hand side of each rule must expand to either two non-terminals or to a single terminal.

For the CKY algorithm, we represented each sentence as having indices between the words. Thus, an example sentence like

(14.15) Book the flight through Houston.

would assume the following indices between each word:

(14.16) ⓪ Book ① the ② flight ③ through ④ Houston ⑤

Using these indices, each constituent in the CKY parse tree is encoded in a two-dimensional matrix. Specifically, for a sentence of length n and a grammar that contains V non-terminals, we use the upper-triangular portion of an $(n+1)$ $(n+1)$ matrix. For CKY, each cell $table[i, j]$ contained a list of constituents that could span the sequence of words from i to j. For probabilistic CKY, it's slightly simpler to think of the constituents in each cell as constituting a third dimension of maximum length V. This third dimension corresponds to each non-terminal that can be placed in this cell, and the value of the cell is then a probability for that non-terminal/constituent rather than a list of constituents. In summary, each cell $[i, j, A]$ in this $(n+1)$ $(n+1)$ V matrix is the probability of a constituent A that spans positions i through j of the input.

Figure 14.3 gives pseudocode for this probabilistic CKY algorithm, extending the basic CKY algorithm from Fig. 13.10.

---

function PROBABILISTIC-CKY(*words,grammar*) **returns** most probable parse
                                                                  and its probability

for $j \leftarrow$ **from** 1 **to** LENGTH(*words*) **do**
   for all A $A \rightarrow words[j] \in grammar$
    $table[j-1, j, A] \leftarrow P(A \rightarrow words[j])$
   for $i \leftarrow$ **from** $j-2$ **downto** 0 **do**
     for $k \leftarrow i+1$ **to** $j-1$ **do**
      for all A $A \rightarrow BC \in grammar,$
          and $table[i, k, B] > 0$ **and** $table[k, j, C] > 0$
        if $(table[i,j,A] < P(A \rightarrow BC)$ $table[i,k,B]$ $table[k,j,C])$ **then**
         $table[i,j,A] \leftarrow P(A \rightarrow BC)$ $table[i,k,B]$ $table[k,j,C]$
         $back[i,j,A] \leftarrow$ k,B,C
  return BUILD_TREE(*back*[1, LENGTH(*words*), *S*]), *table*[1, LENGTH(*words*), *S*]

Figure 14.3 The probabilistic CKY algorithm for finding the maximum probability parse of a string of *num_words* words given a PCFG grammar with *num_rules* rules in Chomsky normal form. *back* is an array of backpointers used to recover the best parse. The *build_tree* function is left as an exercise to the reader.

Like the CKY algorithm, the probabilistic CKY algorithm as shown in Fig. 14.3 requires a grammar in Chomsky normal form. Converting a probabilistic grammar to CNF requires that we also modify the probabilities so that the probability of each parse remains the same under the new CNF grammar. Exercise 14.2 asks you to modify the algorithm for conversion to CNF in Chapter 13 so that it correctly handles rule probabilities.

In practice, we more often use a generalized CKY algorithm that handles unit productions directly rather than converting them to CNF. Recall that Exercise 13.3 asked you to make this change in CKY; Exercise 14.3 asks you to extend this change to probabilistic CKY.

Let's see an example of the probabilistic CKY chart, using the following mini-grammar, which is already in CNF:

S	$\rightarrow NP\ VP$	.80	Det	$\rightarrow the$	.40
NP	$\rightarrow Det\ N$	.30	Det	$\rightarrow a$	.40
VP	$\rightarrow V\ NP$	.20	N	$\rightarrow meal$	.01
V	$\rightarrow includes$	.05	N	$\rightarrow flight$	.02

Given this grammar, Fig. 14.4 shows the first steps in the probabilistic CKY parse of this sentence:

(14.17) The flight includes a meal

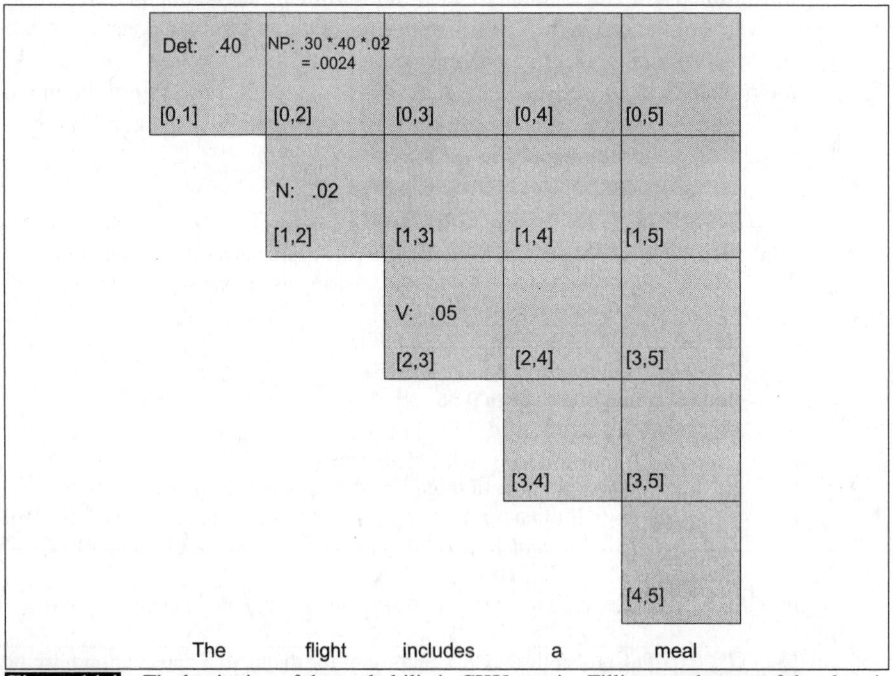

Figure 14.4   The beginning of the probabilistic CKY matrix. Filling out the rest of the chart is left as Exercise 14.4 for the reader.

14.3   Ways to Learn PCFG Rule Probabilities

Where do PCFG rule probabilities come from? There are two ways to learn probabilities for the rules of a grammar. The simplest way is to use a treebank, a corpus of already parsed sentences. Recall that we introduced in Chapter 12 the idea of treebanks and the commonly used **Penn Treebank** (Marcus et al., 1993), a collection of parse trees in English, Chinese, and other languages that is distributed by the Linguistic Data Consortium. Given a treebank, we can compute the probability of each expansion of a non-terminal by counting the number of times that expansion occurs and then normalizing.

$$P(\alpha \rightarrow \beta \mid \alpha) = \frac{\text{Count}(\alpha \rightarrow \beta)}{\sum_{\gamma} \text{Count}(\alpha \rightarrow \gamma)} = \frac{\text{Count}(\alpha \rightarrow \beta)}{\text{Count}(\alpha)} \qquad (14.18)$$

If we don't have a treebank but we do have a (non-probabilistic) parser, we can generate the counts we need for computing PCFG rule probabilities by first parsing a corpus of sentences with the parser. If sentences were unambiguous, it would be as simple as this: parse the corpus, increment a counter for every rule in the parse, and then normalize to get probabilities.

But wait! Since most sentences are ambiguous, that is, have multiple parses, we don't know which parse to count the rules in. Instead, we need to keep a separate count for each parse of a sentence and weight each of these partial counts by the probability of the parse it appears in. But to get these parse probabilities to weight the rules, we need to already have a probabilistic parser.

The intuition for solving this chicken-and-egg problem is to incrementally improve our estimates by beginning with a parser with equal rule probabilities, then parse the sentence, compute a probability for each parse, use these probabilities to weight the counts, re-estimate the rule probabilities, and so on, until our probabilities converge. The standard algorithm for computing this solution is called the **inside-outside** algorithm; it was proposed by Baker (1979) as a generalization of the forward-backward algorithm of Chapter 6. Like forward-backward, inside-outside is a special case of the Expectation Maximization (EM) algorithm, and hence has two steps: the **expectation step**, and the **maximization step**. See Lari and Young (1990) or Manning and Schütze (1999) for a complete description of the algorithm.

Inside-outside

Expectation step
Maximization step

This use of the inside-outside algorithm to estimate the rule probabilities for a grammar is actually a kind of limited use of inside-outside. The inside-outside algorithm can actually be used not only to set the rule probabilities but even to induce the grammar rules themselves. It turns out, however, that grammar induction is so difficult that inside-outside by itself is not a very successful grammar inducer; see the Historical Notes at the end of the chapter for pointers to other grammar induction algorithms.

477

14.4   Problems with PCFGs

While probabilistic context-free grammars are a natural extension to context-free grammars, they have two main problems as probability estimators:

Poor independence assumptions: CFG rules impose an independence assumption on probabilities, resulting in poor modeling of structural dependencies across the parse tree.

Lack of lexical conditioning: CFG rules don't model syntactic facts about specific words, leading to problems with subcategorization ambiguities, preposition attachment, and coordinate structure ambiguities.

Because of these problems, most current probabilistic parsing models use some augmented version of PCFGs, or modify the Treebank-based grammar in some way. In the next few sections after discussing the problems in more detail we introduce some of these augmentations.

14.4.1   Independence Assumptions Miss Structural Dependencies Between Rules

Let's look at these problems in more detail. Recall that in a CFG the expansion of a non-terminal is independent of the context, that is, of the other nearby non-terminals in the parse tree. Similarly, in a PCFG, the probability of a particular rule like $NP \rightarrow Det\ N$ is also independent of the rest of the tree. By definition, the probability of a group of independent events is the product of their probabilities. These two facts explain why in a PCFG we compute the probability of a tree by just multiplying the probabilities of each non-terminal expansion.

Unfortunately, this CFG independence assumption results in poor probability estimates. This is because in English the choice of how a node expands can after all depend on the location of the node in the parse tree. For example, in English it turns out that *NP*s that are syntactic **subjects** are far more likely to be pronouns, and *NP*s that are syntactic **objects** are far more likely to be non-pronominal (e.g., a proper noun or a determiner noun sequence), as shown by these statistics for *NP*s in the Switchboard corpus (Francis et al., 1999):[1]

	Pronoun	Non-Pronoun
Subject	91%	9%
Object	34%	66%

Unfortunately, there is no way to represent this contextual difference in the probabilities in a PCFG. Consider two expansions of the non-terminal *NP* as a pronoun or as a determiner+noun. How shall we set the probabilities of these two rules? If we set

---

[1]   Distribution of subjects from 31,021 declarative sentences; distribution of objects from 7,489 sentences. This tendency is caused by the use of subject position to realize the **topic** or old information in a sentence (Givón, 1990). Pronouns are a way to talk about old information, while non-pronominal ("lexical") noun-phrases are often used to introduce new referents. We talk more about new and old information in Chapter 21.

their probabilities to their overall probability in the Switchboard corpus, the two rules
have about equal probability.

$$NP \rightarrow DT\ NN \quad .28$$
$$NP \rightarrow PRP \quad\quad .25$$

Because PCFGs don't allow a rule probability to be conditioned on surrounding
context, this equal probability is all we get; there is no way to capture the fact that in
subject position, the probability for $NP \rightarrow PRP$ should go up to .91, while in object
position, the probability for $NP \rightarrow DT\ NN$ should go up to .66.

These dependencies could be captured if the probability of expanding an NP as a
pronoun (e.g., $NP \rightarrow PRP$) versus a lexical NP (e.g., $NP \rightarrow DT\ NN$) were *conditioned*
on whether the NP was a subject or an object. Section 14.5 introduces the technique of
parent annotation for adding this kind of conditioning.

14.4.2   Lack of Sensitivity to Lexical Dependencies

A second class of problems with PCFGs is their lack of sensitivity to the words in the
parse tree. Words do play a role in PCFGs since the parse probability includes the
probability of a word given a part-of-speech (i.e., from rules like $V \rightarrow sleep$, $NN \rightarrow$
book, etc.).

But it turns out that lexical information is useful in other places in the grammar,
such as in resolving prepositional phrase (*PP*) attachment ambiguities. Since prepositional phrases in English can modify a noun phrase or a verb phrase, when a parser
finds a prepositional phrase, it must decide where to attach it into the tree. Consider
the following example:

(14.19) Workers dumped sacks into a bin.

Figure 14.5 shows two possible parse trees for this sentence; the one on the left
is the correct parse; Fig. 14.6 shows another perspective on the preposition attachment
problem, demonstrating that resolving the ambiguity in Fig. 14.5 is equivalent to deciding whether to attach the prepositional phrase into the rest of the tree at the *NP* or *VP*
VP attachment   nodes; we say that the correct parse requires **VP attachment**, and the incorrect parse
NP attachment   implies **NP attachment**.

Why doesn't a PCFG already deal with *PP* attachment ambiguities? Note that the
two parse trees in Fig. 14.5 have almost exactly the same rules; they differ only in that
the left-hand parse has this rule:

$$VP \rightarrow VBD\ NP\ PP$$

while the right-hand parse has these:

$$VP \rightarrow VBD\ NP$$
$$NP \rightarrow NP\ PP$$

Depending on how these probabilities are set, a PCFG will **always** either prefer *NP*
attachment or *VP* attachment. As it happens, *NP* attachment is slightly more common
in English, so if we trained these rule probabilities on a corpus, we might always prefer
NP attachment, causing us to misparse this sentence.

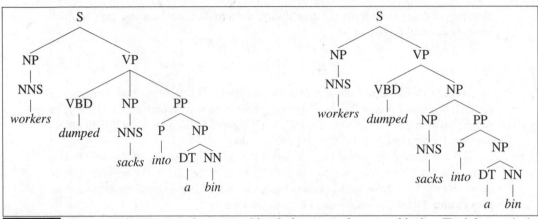

Figure 14.5   Two possible parse trees for a **prepositional phrase attachment ambiguity**. The left parse is the sensible one, in which "into a bin" describes the resulting location of the sacks. In the right incorrect parse, the sacks to be dumped are the ones which are already "into a bin", whatever that might mean.

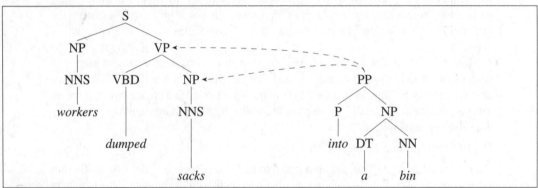

Figure 14.6   Another view of the preposition attachment problem. Should the *PP* on the right attach to the *VP* or *NP* nodes of the partial parse tree on the left?

But suppose we set the probabilities to prefer the *VP* attachment for this sentence. Now we would misparse the following sentence, which requires *NP* attachment:

(14.20) fishermen caught tons of herring

What information in the input sentence lets us know that (14.20) requires *NP* attachment while (14.19) requires *VP* attachment?

It should be clear that these preferences come from the identities of the verbs, nouns, and prepositions. It seems that the affinity between the verb *dumped* and the preposition *into* is greater than the affinity between the noun *sacks* and the preposition *into*, thus leading to *VP* attachment. On the other hand, in (14.20) the affinity between *tons* and *of* is greater than that between *caught* and *of*, leading to *NP* attachment.

Thus, to get the correct parse for these kinds of examples, we need a model that

Lexical dependency

somehow augments the PCFG probabilities to deal with these **lexical dependency** statistics for different verbs and prepositions.

Coordination ambiguities are another case in which lexical dependencies are the key to choosing the proper parse. Figure 14.7 shows an example from Collins (1999) with two parses for the phrase *dogs in houses and cats*. Because *dogs* is semantically a better conjunct for *cats* than *houses* (and because most dogs can't fit inside cats), the parse *[dogs in [$_{NP}$ houses and cats]]* is intuitively unnatural and should be dispreferred. The two parses in Fig. 14.7, however, have exactly the same PCFG rules, and thus a PCFG will assign them the same probability.

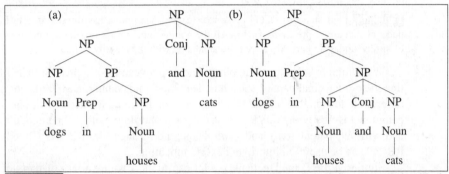

Figure 14.7   An instance of coordination ambiguity. Although the left structure is intuitively the correct one, a PCFG will assign them identical probabilities since both structures use exactly the same rules. After Collins (1999).

In summary, we have shown in this section and the previous one that probabilistic context-free grammars are incapable of modeling important **structural** and **lexical** dependencies. In the next two sections we sketch current methods for augmenting PCFGs to deal with both these issues.

14.5   Improving PCFGs by Splitting Non-Terminals

Let's start with the first of the two problems with PCFGs mentioned above: their inability to model structural dependencies, like the fact that NPs in subject position tend to be pronouns, whereas *NP*s in object position tend to have full lexical (non-pronominal) form. How could we augment a PCFG to correctly model this fact? One idea would *Split* be to **split** the *NP* non-terminal into two versions: one for subjects, one for objects. Having two nodes (e.g., $NP_{subject}$ and NP_{object}) would allow us to correctly model their different distributional properties, since we would have different probabilities for the rule $NP_{subject} \rightarrow PRP$ and the rule $NP_{object} \rightarrow PRP$.

Parent annotation   One way to implement this intuition of splits is to do **parent annotation** (Johnson, 1998b), in which we annotate each node with its parent in the parse tree. Thus, an *NP* node that is the subject of the sentence and hence has parent *S* would be annotated *NP^S*, while a direct object *NP* whose parent is *VP* would be annotated *NP^VP*. Figure 14.8 shows an example of a tree produced by a grammar that parent-annotates the phrasal non-terminals (like *NP* and *VP*).

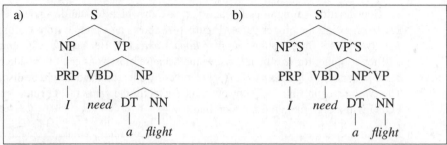

Figure 14.8   A standard PCFG parse tree (a) and one which has **parent annotation** on the nodes which aren't pre-terminal (b). All the non-terminal nodes (except the pre-terminal part-of-speech nodes) in parse (b) have been annotated with the identity of their parent.

In addition to splitting these phrasal nodes, we can also improve a PCFG by splitting the pre-terminal part-of-speech nodes (Klein and Manning, 2003b). For example, different kinds of adverbs (RB) tend to occur in different syntactic positions: the most common adverbs with ADVP parents are *also* and *now*, with *VP* parents *n't* and *not*, and with *NP* parents *only* and *just*. Thus, adding tags like RB^ADVP, RB^VP, and RB^NP can be useful in improving PCFG modeling.

Similarly, the Penn Treebank tag IN can mark a wide variety of parts-of-speech, including subordinating conjunctions (*while*, *as*, *if*), complementizers (*that*, *for*), and prepositions (*of*, *in*, *from*). Some of these differences can be captured by parent annotation (subordinating conjunctions occur under S, prepositions under PP), while others require specifically splitting the pre-terminal nodes. Figure 14.9 shows an example from Klein and Manning (2003b) in which even a parent-annotated grammar incorrectly parses *works* as a noun in *to see if advertising works*. Splitting pre-terminals to allow *if* to prefer a sentential complement results in the correct verbal parse.

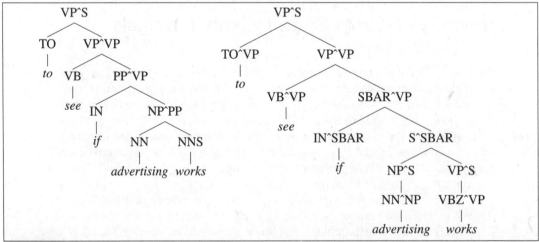

Figure 14.9   An incorrect parse even with a parent-annotated parse (left). The correct parse (right), was produced by a grammar in which the pre-terminal nodes have been split, allowing the probabilistic grammar to capture the fact that *if* prefers sentential complements. Adapted from Klein and Manning (2003b).

To deal with cases in which parent annotation is insufficient, we can also hand-write rules that specify a particular node split based on other features of the tree. For example, to distinguish between complementizer IN and subordinating conjunction IN, both of which can have the same parent, we could write rules conditioned on other aspects of the tree such as the lexical identity (the lexeme *that* is likely to be a complementizer, *as* a subordinating conjunction).

Split and merge

Node-splitting is not without problems; it increases the size of the grammar and hence reduces the amount of training data available for each grammar rule, leading to overfitting. Thus, it is important to split to just the correct level of granularity for a particular training set. While early models employed hand-written rules to try to find an optimal number of non-terminals (Klein and Manning, 2003b), modern models automatically search for the optimal splits. The **split and merge** algorithm of Petrov et al. (2006), for example, starts with a simple X-bar grammar, alternately splits the non-terminals, and merges non-terminals, finding the set of annotated nodes that maximizes the likelihood of the training set treebank. As of the time of this writing, the performance of the Petrov et al. (2006) algorithm was the best of any known parsing algorithm on the Penn Treebank.

14.6 Probabilistic Lexicalized CFGs

The previous section showed that a simple probabilistic CKY algorithm for parsing raw PCFGs can achieve extremely high parsing accuracy if the grammar rule symbols are redesigned by automatic splits and merges.

In this section, we discuss an alternative family of models in which instead of modifying the grammar rules, we modify the probabilistic model of the parser to allow for **lexicalized** rules. The resulting family of lexicalized parsers includes the well-known **Collins parser** (Collins, 1999) and **Charniak parser** (Charniak, 1997), both of which are publicly available and widely used throughout natural language processing.

Collins parser

Charniak parser

Lexicalized grammar

We saw in Section 12.4.4 that syntactic constituents could be associated with a lexical **head**, and we defined a **lexicalized grammar** in which each non-terminal in the tree is annotated with its lexical head, where a rule like $VP \rightarrow VBD\ NP\ PP$ would be extended as

$$VP(dumped) \rightarrow VBD(dumped)\ NP(sacks)\ PP(into) \quad (14.21)$$

Head tag

In the standard type of lexicalized grammar, we actually make a further extension, which is to associate the **head tag**, the part-of-speech tags of the headwords, with the non-terminal symbols as well. Each rule is thus lexicalized by both the headword and the head tag of each constituent resulting in a format for lexicalized rules like

$$VP(dumped,VBD) \rightarrow VBD(dumped,VBD)\ NP(sacks,NNS)\ PP(into,IN) \quad (14.22)$$

We show a lexicalized parse tree with head tags in Fig. 14.10, extended from Fig. 12.12.

To generate such a lexicalized tree, each PCFG rule must be augmented to identify one right-hand constituent to be the head daughter. The headword for a node is then set

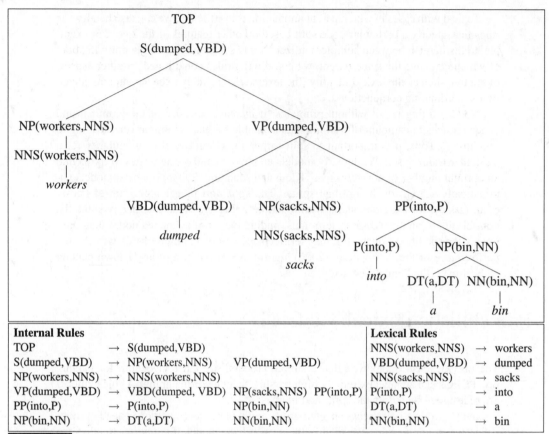

Internal Rules		
TOP	→ S(dumped,VBD)	
S(dumped,VBD)	→ NP(workers,NNS)	VP(dumped,VBD)
NP(workers,NNS)	→ NNS(workers,NNS)	
VP(dumped,VBD)	→ VBD(dumped, VBD)	NP(sacks,NNS) PP(into,P)
PP(into,P)	→ P(into,P)	NP(bin,NN)
NP(bin,NN)	→ DT(a,DT)	NN(bin,NN)

Lexical Rules	
NNS(workers,NNS)	→ workers
VBD(dumped,VBD)	→ dumped
NNS(sacks,NNS)	→ sacks
P(into,P)	→ into
DT(a,DT)	→ a
NN(bin,NN)	→ bin

Figure 14.10   A lexicalized tree, including head tags, for a WSJ sentence, adapted from Collins (1999). Below we show the PCFG rules that would be needed for this parse tree, internal rules on the left, and lexical rules on the right.

to the headword of its head daughter, and the head tag to the part-of-speech tag of the headword. Recall that we gave in Fig. 12.13 a set of hand-written rules for identifying the heads of particular constituents.

A natural way to think of a lexicalized grammar is as a parent annotation, that is, as a simple context-free grammar with many copies of each rule, one copy for each possible headword/head tag for each constituent. Thinking of a probabilistic lexicalized CFG in this way would lead to the set of simple PCFG rules shown below the tree in Fig. 14.10.

Lexical rules
Internal rule

Note that Fig. 14.10 shows two kinds of rules: **lexical rules**, which express the expansion of a pre-terminal to a word, and **internal rules**, which express the other rule expansions. We need to distinguish these kinds of rules in a lexicalized grammar because they are associated with very different kinds of probabilities. The lexical rules are deterministic, that is, they have probability 1.0 since a lexicalized pre-terminal like $NN(bin,NN)$ can only expand to the word *bin*. But for the internal rules, we need to estimate probabilities.

Suppose we were to treat a probabilistic lexicalized CFG like a really big CFG that just happened to have lots of very complex non-terminals and estimate the probabilities for each rule from maximum likelihood estimates. Thus, according to Eq. 14.18, the MLE estimate for the probability for the rule $P(VP(dumped,VBD) \rightarrow VBD(dumped, VBD) NP(sacks,NNS) PP(into,P))$ would be

$$\frac{Count(VP(dumped,VBD) \rightarrow VBD(dumped, VBD) NP(sacks,NNS) PP(into,P))}{Count(VP(dumped,VBD))} \quad (14.23)$$

But there's no way we can get good estimates of counts like those in (14.23) because they are so specific: we're unlikely to see many (or even any) instances of a sentence with a verb phrase headed by *dumped* that has one *NP* argument headed by *sacks* and a *PP* argument headed by *into*. In other words, counts of fully lexicalized PCFG rules like this will be far too sparse, and most rule probabilities will come out 0.

The idea of lexicalized parsing is to make some further independence assumptions to break down each rule so that we would estimate the probability

$$P(VP(dumped,VBD) \rightarrow VBD(dumped, VBD) NP(sacks,NNS) PP(into,P)) \quad (14.24)$$

as the product of smaller independent probability estimates for which we could acquire reasonable counts. The next section summarizes one such method, the Collins parsing method.

14.6.1   The Collins Parser

Modern statistical parsers differ in exactly which independence assumptions they make. In this section we describe a simplified version of Collins's (1999) Model 1, but a number of other parsers are worth knowing about; see the summary at the end of the chapter.

The first intuition of the Collins parser is to think of the right-hand side of every (internal) CFG rule as consisting of a head non-terminal, together with the non-terminals to the left of the head and the non-terminals to the right of the head. In the abstract, we think about these rules as follows:

$$LHS \rightarrow L_n L_{n-1} \ldots L_1 H R_1 \ldots R_{n-1} R_n \quad (14.25)$$

Since this is a lexicalized grammar, each of the symbols like L_1 or R_3 or H or LHS is actually a complex symbol representing the category and its head and head tag, like *VP(dumped,VP)* or *NP(sacks,NNS)*.

Now, instead of computing a single MLE probability for this rule, we are going to break down this rule via a neat generative story, a slight simplification of what is called Collins Model 1. This new generative story is that given the left-hand side, we first generate the head of the rule and then generate the dependents of the head, one by one, from the inside out. Each of these generation steps will have its own probability.

We also add a special STOP non-terminal at the left and right edges of the rule; this non-terminal allows the model to know when to stop generating dependents on a given side. We generate dependents on the left side of the head until we've generated STOP on the left side of the head, at which point we move to the right side of the head and start generating dependents there until we generate STOP. So it's as if we are generating a rule augmented as follows:

$$P(VP(dumped,VBD) \rightarrow \quad (14.26)$$
$$\text{STOP } VBD(dumped, VBD) \, NP(sacks,NNS) \, PP(into,P) \text{ STOP})$$

Let's see the generative story for this augmented rule. We make use of three kinds of probabilities: P_H for generating heads, P_L for generating dependents on the left, and P_R for generating dependents on the right.

1) Generate the head VBD(dumped,VBD) with probability
P(H LHS) = P(VBD(dumped,VBD) VP(dumped,VBD))

    VP(dumped,VBD)
    |
    VBD(dumped,VBD)

2) Generate the left dependent (which is STOP, since there isn't one) with probability
P(STOP VP(dumped,VBD) VBD(dumped,VBD))

    VP(dumped,VBD)
    STOP VBD(dumped,VBD)

3) Generate right dependent NP(sacks,NNS) with probability
P_r(NP(sacks,NNS VP(dumped,VBD), VBD(dumped,VBD))

    VP(dumped,VBD)
    STOP VBD(dumped,VBD) NP(sacks,NNS)

4) Generate the right dependent PP(into,P) with probability
P_r(PP(into,P) VP(dumped,VBD), VBD(dumped,VBD))

    VP(dumped,VBD)
    STOP VBD(dumped,VBD) NP(sacks,NNS) PP(into,P)

5) Generate the right dependent STOP with probability
P_r(STOP VP(dumped,VBD), VBD(dumped,VBD))

    VP(dumped,VBD)
    STOP VBD(dumped,VBD) NP(sacks,NNS) PP(into,P) STOP

In summary, the probability of this rule

$$P(VP(dumped,VBD) \rightarrow \quad (14.27)$$
$$VBD(dumped, VBD) \, NP(sacks,NNS) \, PP(into,P))$$

is estimated as

$$P_H(VBD \, VP, dumped) \quad P_L(STOP \, VP,VBD,dumped) \quad (14.28)$$
$$P_R(NP(sacks,NNS) \, VP,VBD,dumped)$$
$$P_R(PP(into,P) \, VP,VBD,dumped)$$
$$P_R(STOP \, VP,VBD,dumped)$$

Each of these probabilities can be estimated from much smaller amounts of data than the full probability in (14.27). For example, the maximum likelihood estimate for the component probability $P_R(NP(sacks,NNS) \, VP,VBD,dumped)$ is

$$\frac{\text{Count}(\ VP(dumped,VBD)\ \text{with}\ NNS(sacks)\text{as a daughter somewhere on the right}\ )}{\text{Count}(\ VP(dumped,VBD)\ )} \quad (14.29)$$

These counts are much less subject to sparsity problems than are complex counts like those in (14.27).

More generally, if we use h to mean a headword together with its tag, l to mean a word+tag on the left, and r to mean a word+tag on the right, then the probability of an entire rule can be expressed as follows:

1. Generate the head of the phrase $H(hw,ht)$ with probability:

$$P_H(H(hw,ht)\ P,hw,ht)$$

2. Generate modifiers to the left of the head with total probability

$$\prod_{i=1}^{n+1} P_L(L_i(lw_i,lt_i)\ P,H,hw,ht)$$

such that $L_{n+1}(lw_{n+1},lt_{n+1})$ =STOP, and we stop generating once we've generated a STOP token.

3. Generate modifiers to the right of the head with total probability:

$$\prod_{i=1}^{n+1} P_P(R_i(rw_i,rt_i)\ P,H,hw,ht)$$

such that $R_{n+1}(rw_{n+1},rt_{n+1}) = STOP$, and we stop generating once we've generated a STOP token.

14.6.2   Advanced: Further Details of the Collins Parser

The actual Collins parser models are more complex (in a couple of ways) than the simple model presented in the previous section. Collins Model 1 includes a **distance** feature. Thus, instead of computing P_L and P_R as follows,

Distance

$$P_L(L_i(lw_i,lt_i)\ P,H,hw,ht) \quad (14.30)$$
$$P_R(R_i(rw_i,rt_i)\ P,H,hw,ht) \quad (14.31)$$

Collins Model 1 conditions also on a distance feature:

$$P_L(L_i(lw_i,lt_i)\ P,H,hw,ht,distance_L(i-1)) \quad (14.32)$$
$$P_R(R_i(rw_i,rt_i)\ P,H,hw,ht,distance_R(i-1)) \quad (14.33)$$

The distance measure is a function of the sequence of words *below* the previous modifiers (i.e., the words that are the yield of each modifier non-terminal we have

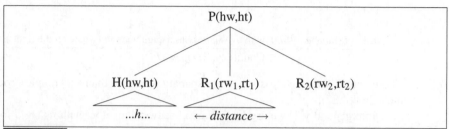

Figure 14.11 R_2 is generated with probability $P(R_2(rh_2, rt_2)\ P, H, hw, ht, distance_R(1))$. The distance is the yield of the previous dependent non-terminal R_1. Had there been another intervening dependent, its yield would have been included as well. Adapted from Collins (2003).

already generated on the left). Figure 14.11, adapted from Collins (2003), shows the computation of the probability $P(R_2(rh_2, rt_2)\ P, H, hw, ht, distance_R(1))$.

The simplest version of this distance measure is just a tuple of two binary features based on the surface string below these previous dependencies: (1) Is the string of length zero? (i.e., were no previous words generated?) (2) Does the string contain a verb?

Collins Model 2 adds more sophisticated features, conditioning on subcategorization frames for each verb and distinguishing arguments from adjuncts.

Finally, smoothing is as important for statistical parsers as it was for N-gram models. This is particularly true for lexicalized parsers, since the lexicalized rules will otherwise condition on many lexical items that may never occur in training (even using the Collins or other methods of independence assumptions).

Consider the probability $P_R(R_i(rw_i, rt_i)\ P, hw, ht)$. What do we do if a particular right-hand constituent never occurs with this head? The Collins model addresses this problem by interpolating three backed-off models: fully lexicalized (conditioning on the headword), backing off to just the head tag, and altogether unlexicalized.

Backoff Level	$P_R(R_i(rw_i, rt_i\ ...)$	Example
1	$P_R(R_i(rw_i, rt_i)\ P, hw, ht)$	$P_R(NP(sacks, NNS)\ VP, VBD, dumped)$
2	$P_R(R_i(rw_i, rt_i)\ P, ht)$	$P_R(NP(sacks, NNS)\ VP, VBD)$
3	$P_R(R_i(rw_i, rt_i)\ P)$	$P_R(NP(sacks, NNS)\ VP)$

Similar backoff models are built also for P_L and P_H. Although we've used the word "backoff", in fact these are not backoff models but interpolated models. The three models above are linearly interpolated, where e_1, e_2, and e_3 are the maximum likelihood estimates of the three backoff models above:

$$P_R(...) = \lambda_1 e_1 + (1 - \lambda_1)(\lambda_2 e_2 + (1 - \lambda_2)e_3) \tag{14.34}$$

The values of $\lambda_1\ and\ \lambda_2$ are set to implement Witten-Bell discounting (Witten and Bell, 1991) following Bikel et al. (1997).

The Collins model deals with unknown words by replacing any unknown word in the test set, and any word occurring less than six times in the training set, with a special UNKNOWN word token. Unknown words in the test set are assigned a part-of-speech tag in a preprocessing step by the Ratnaparkhi (1996) tagger; all other words are tagged as part of the parsing process.

The parsing algorithm for the Collins model is an extension of probabilistic CKY; see Collins (2003). Extending the CKY algorithm to handle basic lexicalized probabilities is left as Exercises 14.5 and 14.6 for the reader.

14.7   Evaluating Parsers

The standard techniques for evaluating parsers and grammars are called the PARSE-VAL measures; they were proposed by Black et al. (1991) and were based on the same ideas from signal-detection theory that we saw in earlier chapters. The intuition of the PARSEVAL metric is to measure how much the **constituents** in the hypothesis parse tree look like the constituents in a hand-labeled, gold-reference parse. PARSEVAL thus assumes we have a human-labeled "gold standard" parse tree for each sentence in the test set; we generally draw these gold-standard parses from a treebank like the Penn Treebank.

Given these gold-standard reference parses for a test set, a given constituent in a hypothesis parse C_h of a sentence s is labeled "correct" if there is a constituent in the reference parse C_r with the same starting point, ending point, and non-terminal symbol.

We can then measure the precision and recall just as we did for chunking in the previous chapter.

$$\textbf{labeled recall:} = \frac{\text{\# of correct constituents in hypothesis parse of } s}{\text{\# of correct constituents in reference parse of } s}$$

$$\textbf{labeled precision:} = \frac{\text{\# of correct constituents in hypothesis parse of } s}{\text{\# of total constituents in hypothesis parse of } s}$$

F-measure   As with other uses of precision and recall, instead of reporting them separately, we often report a single number, the **F-measure** (van Rijsbergen, 1975): The F-measure is defined as

$$F_\beta = \frac{(\beta^2 + 1)PR}{\beta^2 P + R}$$

The β parameter differentially weights the importance of recall and precision, based perhaps on the needs of an application. Values of $\beta > 1$ favor recall and values of $\beta < 1$ favor precision. When $\beta = 1$, precision and recall are equally balanced; this is sometimes called $F_{\beta=1}$ or just F_1:

$$F_1 = \frac{2PR}{P+R} \tag{14.35}$$

The F-measure derives from a weighted harmonic mean of precision and recall. Remember that the harmonic mean of a set of numbers is the reciprocal of the arithmetic mean of the reciprocals:

$$\text{HarmonicMean}(a_1, a_2, a_3, a_4, ..., a_n) = \frac{n}{\frac{1}{a_1} \frac{1}{a_2} \frac{1}{a_3} ... \frac{1}{a_n}} \tag{14.36}$$

and hence the *F*-measure is

$$F = \frac{1}{\frac{1}{\alpha P} \quad \frac{1}{(1-\alpha)R}} \quad \text{or} \left(\text{with } \beta^2 = \frac{1-\alpha}{\alpha} \right) \quad F = \frac{(\beta^2+1)PR}{\beta^2 P + R} \qquad (14.37)$$

We additionally use a new metric, crossing brackets, for each sentence *s*:

cross-brackets: the number of constituents for which the reference parse has a bracketing such as ((A B) C) but the hypothesis parse has a bracketing such as (A (B C)).

As of the time of this writing, the performance of modern parsers that are trained and tested on the *Wall Street Journal* treebank was somewhat higher than 90% recall, 90% precision, and about 1% cross-bracketed constituents per sentence.

For comparing parsers that use different grammars, the PARSEVAL metric includes a canonicalization algorithm for removing information likely to be grammar-specific (auxiliaries, pre-infinitival "to", etc.) and for computing a simplified score. The interested reader should see Black et al. (1991). The canonical publicly available imple-

evalb   mentation of the PARSEVAL metrics is called **evalb** (Sekine and Collins, 1997).

You might wonder why we don't evaluate parsers by measuring how many *sentences* are parsed correctly instead of measuring *constituent* accuracy. The reason we use constituents is that measuring constituents gives us a more fine-grained metric. This is especially true for long sentences, where most parsers don't get a perfect parse. If we just measured sentence accuracy, we wouldn't be able to distinguish between a parse that got most of the constituents wrong and one that just got one constituent wrong.

Nonetheless, constituents are not always an optimal unit for parser evaluation. For example, using the PARSEVAL metrics requires that our parser produce trees in the exact same format as the gold standard. That means that if we want to evaluate a parser which produces different styles of parses (dependency parses, or LFG feature-structures, etc.) against, say, the Penn Treebank (or against another parser that produces Treebank format), we need to map the output parses into Treebank format. A related problem is that constituency may not be the level we care the most about. We might be more interested in how well the parser does at recovering grammatical dependencies (subject, object, etc.), which could give us a better metric for how useful the parses would be to semantic understanding. For these purposes, we can use alternative evaluation metrics based on measuring the precision and recall of labeled dependencies, where the labels indicate the grammatical relations (Lin, 1995; Carroll et al., 1998; Collins et al., 1999). Kaplan et al. (2004), for example, compared the Collins (1999) parser with the Xerox XLE parser (Riezler et al., 2002), which produces much richer semantic representations by converting both parse trees to a dependency representation.

14.8   Advanced: Discriminative Reranking

The models we have seen of parsing so far, the PCFG parser and the Collins lexicalized parser, are generative parsers. By this we mean that the probabilistic model implemented in these parsers gives us the probability of generating a particular sentence by assigning a probability to each choice the parser could make in this generation procedure.

Generative models have some significant advantages; they are easy to train with maximum likelihood, and they give us an explicit model of how different sources of evidence are combined. But generative parsing models also make it hard to incorporate arbitrary kinds of information into the probability model. This is because the probability is based on the generative derivation of a sentence; it is difficult to add features that are not local to a particular PCFG rule.

Consider, for example, how to represent global facts about tree structure. Parse trees in English tend to be right-branching; we'd therefore like our model to assign a higher probability to a tree that is more right-branching, all else being equal. It is also the case that heavy constituents (those with a large number of words) tend to appear later in the sentence. Or we might want to condition our parse probabilities on global facts like the identity of the speaker (perhaps some speakers are more likely to use complex relative clauses or to use the passive). Or we might want to condition on complex discourse factors across sentences. None of these kinds of global factors are trivial to incorporate into the generative models we have been considering. A simplistic model that, for example, makes each non-terminal dependent on how right-branching the tree is in the parse so far, or makes each *NP* non-terminal sensitive to the number of relative clauses the speaker or writer used in previous sentences, would result in counts that are far too sparse.

We discussed this problem in Chapter 6, where the need for these kinds of global features motivated the use of log-linear (MEMM) models for POS tagging instead of HMMs. For parsing, there are two broad classes of discriminative models: dynamic programming approaches and two-stage models of parsing that use discriminative reranking. We discuss discriminative reranking in the rest of this section; see the end of the chapter for pointers to discriminative dynamic programming approaches.

In the first stage of a discriminative reranking system, we can run a normal statistical parser of the type we've described so far. But instead of just producing the single best parse, we modify the parser to produce a ranked list of parses together with their probabilities. We call this ranked list of N parses the **N-best list** (the N-best list was first introduced in Chapter 9 in a discussion of multiple-pass decoding models for speech recognition). There are various ways to modify statistical parsers to produce an N-best list of parses; see the end of the chapter for pointers to the literature. For each sentence in the training set and the test set, we run this N-best parser and produce a set of N parse/probability pairs.

N-best list

The second stage of a discriminative reranking model is a classifier that takes each of these sentences with their N parse/probability pairs as input, extracts some large set of features, and chooses the single best parse from the N-best list. We can rerank with any type of classifier, such as the log-linear classifiers introduced in Chapter 6.

A wide variety of features can be used for reranking. One important feature to include is the parse probability assigned by the first-stage statistical parser. Other features might include each of the CFG rules in the tree, the number of parallel conjuncts, the heaviness of each constituent, measures of how right-branching the parse tree is, the number of times various tree fragments occur, bigrams of adjacent non-terminals in the tree, and so on.

The two-stage architecture has a weakness: the accuracy rate of the complete architecture can never be better than the accuracy rate of the best parse in the first-stage *N*-best list. This is because reranking methods merely choose one of the *N*-best parses; even if we picked the very best parse in the list, we can't get 100% accuracy if the correct parse isn't in the list! Therefore, it is important to consider the ceiling **ora-**

Oracle accuracy   **cle accuracy** (often measured in *F*-measure) of the *N*-best list. The oracle accuracy of a particular *N*-best list is the accuracy we get if we chose the parse that had the highest accuracy. We call this an **oracle** accuracy because it relies on perfect knowledge (as if from an oracle) of which parse to pick.[2] Of course it only makes sense to implement discriminative reranking if the *N*-best *F*-measure is higher than the 1-best *F*-measure. Luckily, this is often the case; for example the Charniak (2000) parser has an *F*-measure of 0.897 on section 23 of the Penn Treebank, but the Charniak and Johnson (2005) algorithm for producing the 50-best parses has a much higher oracle *F*-measure of 0.968.

14.9   Advanced: Parser-Based Language Modeling

We said earlier that statistical parsers can take advantage of longer-distance information than *N*-grams, which suggests that they might do a better job at language modeling/word prediction. It turns out that if we have a very large amount of training data, a 4-gram or 5-gram grammar is nonetheless still the best way to do language modeling. But in situations in which there is not enough data for such huge models, parser-based language models that have higher accuracy than *N*-gram models are beginning to be developed.

Two common applications for language modeling are speech recognition and machine translation. The simplest way to use a statistical parser for language modeling for either of these applications is through a two-stage algorithm of the type discussed in the previous section and in Section 10.1. In the first stage, we run a normal speech recognition decoder, or machine translation decoder, using a normal *N*-gram grammar. But instead of just producing the single best transcription or translation sentence, we modify the decoder to produce a ranked *N*-best list of transcriptions/translations sentences, each one together with its probability (or, alternatively, a lattice).

Then in the second stage, we run our statistical parser and assign a parse probability to each sentence in the *N*-best list or lattice. We then rerank the sentences based on this parse probability and choose the single best sentence. This algorithm can work better than using a simple trigram grammar. For example, on the task of recognizing

---

[2]   We introduced this same oracle idea in Chapter 9 when we talked about the **lattice error rate**.

spoken sentences from the *Wall Street Journal* with this two-stage architecture, the probabilities assigned by the Charniak (2001) parser improved the word error rate by about 2% absolute, over a simple trigram grammar computed on 40 million words (Hall and Johnson, 2003). We can either use the parse probabilities assigned by the parser as-is or we can linearly combine it with the original *N*-gram probability.

An alternative to the two-pass architecture, at least for speech recognition, is to modify the parser to run strictly left to right, so that it can incrementally give the probability of the next word in the sentence. This would allow the parser to be fit directly into the first-pass decoding pass and would obviate the second pass altogether. While a number of such left-to-right, parser-based language modeling algorithms exist (Stolcke, 1995; Jurafsky et al., 1995; Roark, 2001; Xu et al., 2002), it is fair to say that it is still early days for the field of parser-based statistical language models.

14.10   Human Parsing

Human sentence processing

Are the kinds of probabilistic parsing models we have been discussing also used by humans when they are parsing? The answer to this question lies in a field called **human sentence processing**. Recent studies suggest that there are at least two ways in which humans apply probabilistic parsing algorithms, although there is still disagreement on the details.

Reading time

One family of studies has shown that when humans read, the predictability of a word seems to influence the **reading time**; more predictable words are read more quickly. One way of defining predictability is from simple bigram measures. For example, Scott and Shillcock (2003) used an eye-tracker to monitor the gaze of participants reading sentences. They constructed the sentences so that some would have a verb-noun pair with a high bigram probability (such as (14.38a)) and others a verb-noun pair with a low bigram probability (such as (14.38b)).

(14.38)   a) **HIGH PROB:** One way to **avoid confusion** is to make the changes during vacation

           b) **LOW PROB:** One way to **avoid discovery** is to make the changes during vacation

They found that the higher the bigram predictability of a word, the shorter the time that participants looked at the word (the **initial-fixation duration**).

While this result provides evidence only for *N*-gram probabilities, more recent experiments have suggested that the probability of an upcoming word given the syntactic parse of the preceding sentence prefix also predicts word reading time (Hale, 2001; Levy, 2008).

Interestingly, this effect of probability on reading time has also been shown for morphological structure; the time to recognize a word is influenced by entropy of the word and the entropy of the word's morphological paradigm (Moscoso del Prado Martín et al., 2004b).

The second family of studies has examined how humans disambiguate sentences that have multiple possible parses, suggesting that humans prefer whichever parse is

Garden-path

more probable. These studies often rely on a specific class of temporarily ambiguous sentences called **garden-path** sentences. These sentences, first described by Bever (1970), are sentences that are cleverly constructed to have three properties that combine to make them very difficult for people to parse:

1. They are **temporarily ambiguous**: The sentence is unambiguous, but its initial portion is ambiguous.
2. One of the two or more parses in the initial portion is somehow preferable to the human parsing mechanism.
3. But the dispreferred parse is the correct one for the sentence.

The result of these three properties is that people are "led down the garden path" toward the incorrect parse and then are confused when they realize it's the wrong one. Sometimes this confusion is quite conscious, as in Bever's example (14.39); in fact, this sentence is so hard to parse that readers often need to be shown the correct structure. In the correct structure, *raced* is part of a reduced relative clause modifying *The horse*, and means "The horse [which was raced past the barn] fell"; this structure is also present in the sentence "Students taught by the Berlitz method do worse when they get to France".

(14.39) The horse raced past the barn fell.

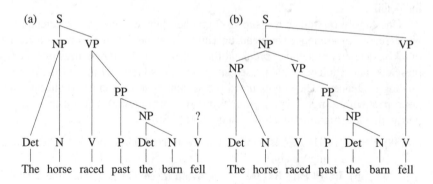

In Marti Hearst's example (14.40), readers often misparse the verb *houses* as a noun (analyzing *the complex houses* as a noun phrase, rather than a noun phrase and a verb). Other times, the confusion caused by a garden-path sentence is so subtle that it can only be measured by a slight increase in reading time. Thus, in (14.41) readers often misparse *the solution* as the direct object of *forgot* rather than as the subject of an embedded sentence. This misparse is subtle, and is only noticeable because experimental participants take longer to read the word *was* than in control sentences. This "mini garden path" effect at the word *was* suggests that subjects had chosen the direct object parse and had to reanalyze or rearrange their parse now that they realize they are in a sentential complement.

(14.40) The complex houses married and single students and their families.

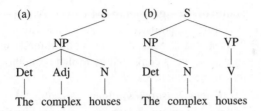

(14.41) The student forgot the solution was in the back of the book.

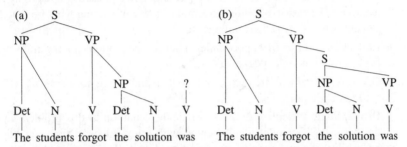

While many factors seem to play a role in these preferences for a particular (incorrect) parse, at least one factor seems to be syntactic probabilities, especially lexicalized (subcategorization) probabilities. For example, the probability of the verb *forgot* taking a direct object ($VP \rightarrow V\,NP$) is higher than the probability of it taking a sentential complement ($VP \rightarrow V\,S$); this difference causes readers to expect a direct object after *forget* and be surprised (longer reading times) when they encounter a sentential complement. By contrast, a verb which prefers a sentential complement (like *hope*) didn't cause extra reading time at *was*.

The garden path in (14.40) may arise from the fact that $P(houses\ Noun)$ is higher than $P(houses\ Verb)$ and $P(complex\ Adjective)$ is higher than $P(complex\ Noun)$, and the garden path in (14.39) at least partially caused by the low probability of the reduced relative clause construction.

Besides grammatical knowledge, human parsing is affected by many other factors which we describe later, including resource constraints (such as memory limitations, discussed in Chapter 16), thematic structure (such as whether a verb expects semantic *agents* or *patients*, discussed in Chapter 19) and discourse constraints (Chapter 21).

14.11   Summary

This chapter has sketched the basics of **probabilistic** parsing, concentrating on **probabilistic context-free grammars** and **probabilistic lexicalized context-free grammars**.

- Probabilistic grammars assign a probability to a sentence or string of words while attempting to capture more sophisticated syntactic information than the *N*-gram grammars of Chapter 4.

- A **probabilistic context-free grammar** (**PCFG**) is a context-free grammar in which every rule is annotated with the probability of that rule being chosen. Each PCFG rule is treated as if it were **conditionally independent**; thus, the probability of a sentence is computed by **multiplying** the probabilities of each rule in the parse of the sentence.
- The probabilistic CKY (**Cocke-Kasami-Younger**) algorithm is a probabilistic version of the CKY parsing algorithm. There are also probabilistic versions of other parsers like the Earley algorithm.
- PCFG probabilities can be learned by counting in a **parsed corpus** or by parsing a corpus. The **inside-outside** algorithm is a way of dealing with the fact that the sentences being parsed are ambiguous.
- Raw PCFGs suffer from poor independence assumptions among rules and lack of sensitivity to lexical dependencies.
- One way to deal with this problem is to split and merge non-terminals (automatically or by hand).
- **Probabilistic lexicalized CFG**s are another solution to this problem in which the basic PCFG model is augmented with a **lexical head** for each rule. The probability of a rule can then be conditioned on the lexical head or nearby heads.
- Parsers for lexicalized PCFGs (like the Charniak and Collins parsers) are based on extensions to probabilistic CKY parsing.
- Parsers are evaluated with three metrics: **labeled recall**, **labeled precision**, and **cross-brackets**.
- Evidence from **garden-path sentences** and other on-line sentence-processing experiments suggest that the human parser uses some kinds of probabilistic information about grammar.

Bibliographical and Historical Notes

Many of the formal properties of probabilistic context-free grammars were first worked out by Booth (1969) and Salomaa (1969). Baker (1979) proposed the inside-outside algorithm for unsupervised training of PCFG probabilities, and used a CKY-style parsing algorithm to compute inside probabilities. Jelinek and Lafferty (1991) extended the CKY algorithm to compute probabilities for prefixes. Stolcke (1995) drew on both of these algorithms in adapting the Earley algorithm to use with PCFGs.

A number of researchers starting in the early 1990s worked on adding lexical dependencies to PCFGs and on making PCFG rule probabilities more sensitive to surrounding syntactic structure. For example, Schabes et al. (1988) and Schabes (1990) presented early work on the use of heads. Many papers on the use of lexical dependencies were first presented at the DARPA Speech and Natural Language Workshop in June 1990. A paper by Hindle and Rooth (1990) applied lexical dependencies to the problem of attaching prepositional phrases; in the question session to a later paper, Ken Church suggested applying this method to full parsing (Marcus, 1990). Early work on such probabilistic CFG parsing augmented with probabilistic dependency information includes Magerman and Marcus (1991), Black et al. (1992), Bod (1993), and Jelinek et al. (1994), in addition to Collins (1996), Charniak (1997), and Collins (1999) discussed above. Other recent PCFG parsing models include Klein and Manning (2003a) and Petrov et al. (2006).

This early lexical probabilistic work led initially to work focused on solving specific parsing problems like preposition-phrase attachment by using methods including transformation-based learning (TBL) (Brill and Resnik, 1994), maximum entropy (Ratnaparkhi et al., 1994), memory-based Learning (Zavrel and Daelemans, 1997), log-linear models (Franz, 1997), decision trees that used semantic distance between heads (computed from WordNet) (Stetina and Nagao, 1997), and boosting (Abney et al., 1999b).

Another direction extended the lexical probabilistic parsing work to build probabilistic formulations of grammars other than PCFGs, such as probabilistic TAG grammar (Resnik, 1992; Schabes, 1992), based on the TAG grammars discussed in Chapter 12, probabilistic LR parsing (Briscoe and Carroll, 1993), and probabilistic link grammar (Lafferty et al., 1992). An approach to probabilistic parsing called **supertagging** extends the part-of-speech tagging metaphor to parsing by using very complex tags that are, in fact, fragments of lexicalized parse trees (Bangalore and Joshi, 1999; Joshi and Srinivas, 1994), based on the lexicalized TAG grammars of Schabes et al. (1988). For example, the noun *purchase* would have a different tag as the first noun in a noun compound (where it might be on the left of a small tree dominated by Nominal) than as the second noun (where it might be on the right). Supertagging has also been applied to CCG parsing and HPSG parsing (Clark and Curran, 2004a; Matsuzaki et al., 2007; Blunsom and Baldwin, 2006). Non-supertagging statistical parsers for CCG include Hockenmaier and Steedman (2002).

Supertagging

Goodman (1997), Abney (1997), and Johnson et al. (1999) gave early discussions of probabilistic treatments of feature-based grammars. Other recent work on building statistical models of feature-based grammar formalisms like HPSG and LFG includes Riezler et al. (2002), Kaplan et al. (2004), and Toutanova et al. (2005).

We mentioned earlier that discriminative approaches to parsing fall into the two broad categories of dynamic programming methods and discriminative reranking methods. Recall that discriminative reranking approaches require N-best parses. Parsers based on A* search can easily be modified to generate N-best lists just by continuing the search past the first-best parse (Roark, 2001). Dynamic programming algorithms like the ones described in this chapter can be modified by the elimination of the dynamic programming with heavy pruning (Collins, 2000; Collins and Koo, 2005; Bikel, 2004), or through new algorithms (Jiménez and Marzal, 2000; Charniak and Johnson, 2005; Huang and Chiang, 2005), some adapted from speech recognition algorithms such as those of Schwartz and Chow (1990) (see Section 10.1).

In dynamic programming methods, instead of outputting and then reranking an N-best list, the parses are represented compactly in a chart, and log-linear and other methods are applied for decoding directly from the chart. Such modern methods include Johnson (2001), Clark and Curran (2004b), and Taskar et al. (2004). Other reranking developments include changing the optimization criterion (Titov and Henderson, 2006).

Another important recent area of research is dependency parsing; algorithms include Eisner's bilexical algorithm (Eisner, 1996b, 1996a, 2000a), maximum spanning tree approaches (using on-line learning) (McDonald et al., 2005a, 2005b), and approaches based on building classifiers for parser actions (Kudo and Matsumoto, 2002; Yamada and Matsumoto, 2003; Nivre et al., 2006; Titov and Henderson, 2007). A dis-

Non-projective dependencies

tinction is usually made between projective and **non-projective dependencies**. Non-projective dependencies are those in which the dependency lines can cross; this is not common in English but is very common in many languages with more free word order. Non-projective dependency algorithms include McDonald et al. (2005b) and Nivre (2007). The Klein-Manning parser combines dependency and constituency information (Klein and Manning, 2003c).

Collins' (1999) dissertation includes a very readable survey of the field and an introduction to his parser. Manning and Schütze (1999) extensively cover probabilistic parsing.

The field of grammar induction is closely related to statistical parsing, and a parser is often used as part of a grammar induction algorithm. One of the earliest statistical works in grammar induction was Horning (1969), who showed that PCFGs could be induced without negative evidence. Early modern probabilistic grammar work showed that simply using EM was insufficient (Lari and Young, 1990; Carroll and Charniak, 1992). Recent probabilistic work, such as Yuret (1998), Clark (2001), Klein and Manning (2002), and Klein and Manning (2004), are summarized in Klein (2005) and Adriaans and van Zaanen (2004). Work since that summary includes Smith and Eisner (2005), Haghighi and Klein (2006), and Smith and Eisner (2007).

Exercises

14.1 Implement the CKY algorithm.

14.2 Modify the algorithm for conversion to CNF from Chapter 13 to correctly handle rule probabilities. Make sure that the resulting CNF assigns the same total probability to each parse tree.

14.3 Recall that Exercise 13.3 asked you to update the CKY algorithm to handle unit productions directly rather than converting them to CNF. Extend this change to probabilistic CKY.

14.4 Fill out the rest of the probabilistic CKY chart in Fig. 14.4.

14.5 Sketch how the CKY algorithm would have to be augmented to handle lexicalized probabilities.

14.6 Implement your lexicalized extension of the CKY algorithm.

14.7 Implement the PARSEVAL metrics described in Section 14.7. Next, either use a treebank or create your own hand-checked parsed testset. Now use your CFG (or other) parser and grammar, parse the test set and compute labeled recall, labeled precision, and cross-brackets.

Credits

Chapter 15

Features and Unification

> FRIAR FRANCIS: *If either of you know any inward impediment why you should not be conjoined, charge you, on your souls, to utter it.*
>
> William Shakespeare, *Much Ado About Nothing*

From a reductionist perspective, the history of the natural sciences over the last few hundred years can be seen as an attempt to explain the behavior of larger structures by the combined action of smaller primitives. In biology, the properties of inheritance have been explained by the action of genes, and then again the properties of genes have been explained by the action of DNA. In physics, matter was reduced to atoms, and then again to subatomic particles. The appeal of reductionism has not escaped computational linguistics. In this chapter we introduce the idea that grammatical categories like *VPto*, *Sthat*, *Non3sgAux*, or *3sgNP*, as well as the grammatical rules like $S \rightarrow NP\ VP$ that make use of them, should be thought of as *objects* that can have complex sets of *properties* associated with them. The information in these properties is represented by **constraints**, and so these kinds of models are often called **constraint-based formalisms**.

Constraint-based formalisms

Why do we need a more fine-grained way of representing and placing constraints on grammatical categories? One problem arose in Chapter 12, where we saw that naive models of grammatical phenomena such as agreement and subcategorization can lead to overgeneration problems. For example, to avoid ungrammatical noun phrases such as *this flights* and verb phrases like *disappeared a flight*, we were forced to create a huge proliferation of primitive grammatical categories such as *Non3sgVPto*, *NPmass*, *3sgNP*, and *Non3sgAux*. These new categories led, in turn, to an explosion in the number of grammar rules and a corresponding loss of generality in the grammar. A constraint-based representation scheme will allow us to represent fine-grained information about number and person agreement, and subcategorization, as well as semantic categories like mass/count.

Constraint-based formalisms have other advantages that we do not cover in this chapter, such as the ability to model more complex phenomena than does context-free grammar, and the ability to efficiently and conveniently compute semantics for syntactic representations.

Consider briefly how this approach might work in the case of grammatical number. As we saw in Chapter 12, noun phrases like *this flight* and *those flights* can be distinguished according to whether they are singular or plural. This distinction can be captured if we associate a property called NUMBER that can have the value singular or plural with appropriate members of the *NP* category. Given this ability, we can say that *this flight* is a member of the *NP* category and, in addition, has the value singular for its NUMBER property. This same property can be used in the same way to distinguish singular and plural members of the *VP* category, such as *serves lunch* and *serve lunch*.

Of course, simply associating these properties with various words and phrases does not solve any of our overgeneration problems. To make these properties useful, we need the ability to perform simple operations, such as equality tests, on them. By pairing such tests with our grammar rules, we can add various constraints to help ensure that only grammatical strings are generated by the grammar. For example, we might want to ask whether a given noun phrase and verb phrase have the same values for their respective number properties. Such a test is illustrated by the following kind of rule:

$$S \rightarrow NP\ VP$$

only if the number of the NP is equal to the number of the VP.

The remainder of this chapter provides the details of one computational implementation of a constraint-based formalism, based on feature structures and unification. The next section describes feature structures, the representation used to capture the kinds of grammatical properties we have in mind. Section 15.2 then introduces the unification operator that implements basic operations over feature structures and Section 15.3 covers the integration of these structures into a grammatical formalism. Section 15.4 then introduces the unification algorithm and its required data structures. Next, Section 15.5 describes how feature structures and the unification operator can be integrated into a parser. Finally, Section 15.6 discusses the most significant extension to this constraint-based formalism, the use of types and inheritance, as well as other extensions.

15.1   Feature Structures

Feature structures

Attribute-value matrix

One of the simplest ways to encode the kind of properties that we have in mind is through the use of **feature structures**. These are simply sets of feature-value pairs, where features are unanalyzable atomic symbols drawn from some finite set, and values are either atomic symbols or feature structures themselves. Such feature structures are illustrated with the following kind of diagram, called an **attribute-value matrix** or AVM:

$$\begin{bmatrix} \text{FEATURE}_1 & value_1 \\ \text{FEATURE}_2 & value_2 \\ \vdots & \\ \text{FEATURE}_n & value_n \end{bmatrix}$$

To make this concrete, consider the number property discussed above. To capture this property, we use the symbol NUMBER to designate this grammatical attribute, and the symbols *sg* and *pl* (introduced in Chapter 3) to designate the possible values it can take on in English. A simple feature structure consisting of this single feature would then be illustrated as follows:

$$\begin{bmatrix} \text{NUMBER} & sg \end{bmatrix}$$

Adding an additional feature-value pair to capture the grammatical notion of person leads to the following feature structure:

$$\begin{bmatrix} \text{NUMBER} & sg \\ \text{PERSON} & 3rd \end{bmatrix}$$

Next we can encode the grammatical category of the constituent that this structure corresponds to through the use of the CAT feature. For example, we can indicate that these features are associated with a noun phrase by using the following structure:

$$\begin{bmatrix} \text{CAT} & NP \\ \text{NUMBER} & sg \\ \text{PERSON} & 3rd \end{bmatrix}$$

This structure can be used to represent the *3sgNP* category introduced in Chapter 12 to capture a restricted subcategory of noun phrases.

As mentioned earlier, features are not limited to atomic symbols as their values; they can also have other feature structures as their values. This is particularly useful when we wish to bundle a set of feature-value pairs for similar treatment. As an example of this, consider that the NUMBER and PERSON features are often lumped together since grammatical subjects must agree with their predicates in both their number and person properties. This lumping together can be captured by an AGREEMENT feature that takes a feature structure consisting of the NUMBER and PERSON feature-value pairs as its value. Introducing this feature into our third-person singular noun phrase yields the following kind of structure:

$$\begin{bmatrix} \text{CAT} & NP \\ \text{AGREEMENT} & \begin{bmatrix} \text{NUMBER} & sg \\ \text{PERSON} & 3rd \end{bmatrix} \end{bmatrix}$$

Given this kind of arrangement, we can test for the equality of the values for both the NUMBER and PERSON features of two constituents by testing for the equality of their AGREEMENT features.

Feature path

This ability to use feature structures as values leads fairly directly to the notion of a **feature path**. A feature path is nothing more than a sequence of features through a feature structure leading to a particular value. For example, in the last feature structure, we can say that the ⟨AGREEMENT NUMBER⟩ path leads to the value *sg*, while the ⟨AGREEMENT PERSON⟩ path leads to the value *3rd*. This notion of a path leads naturally to an alternative way of illustrating feature structures, shown in Figure 15.1, which, as we discuss in Section 15.4, is suggestive of how they will be implemented. In these diagrams, feature structures are depicted as directed graphs where features appear as labeled edges and values as nodes.

Reentrant structures

While this notion of paths will prove useful in a number of settings, we introduce it here to help explain an additional important kind of feature structure: one that contains features that actually share some feature structure as a value. Such feature structures are referred to as **reentrant structures**. What we have in mind here is not the simple idea that two features might have equal values, but rather that they share precisely the same feature structure (or node in the graph). These two cases can be distinguished

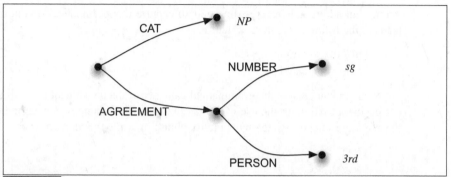

Figure 15.1   A feature structure with shared values. The location (value) found by following the ⟨HEAD SUBJECT AGREEMENT⟩ path is the same as that found via the ⟨HEAD AGREEMENT⟩ path.

clearly if we think in terms of paths through a graph. In the case of simple equality, two paths lead to distinct nodes in the graph that anchor identical, but distinct, structures. In the case of a reentrant structure, two feature paths actually lead to the same node in the structure.

Figure 15.2 illustrates a simple example of reentrancy. In this structure, the ⟨HEAD SUBJECT AGREEMENT⟩ path and the ⟨HEAD AGREEMENT⟩ path lead to the same location. We denote shared structures like this in our AVM diagrams by adding numerical indexes that signal the values to be shared. The AVM version of the feature structure from Fig. 15.2 would be denoted as follows, using the notation of the PATR-II system (Shieber, 1986), based on Kay (1979):

$$\begin{bmatrix} \text{CAT} & S \\ & \begin{bmatrix} \text{AGREEMENT} & \boxed{1}\begin{bmatrix} \text{NUMBER} & sg \\ \text{PERSON} & 3rd \end{bmatrix} \\ \text{SUBJECT} & \begin{bmatrix} \text{AGREEMENT} & \boxed{1} \end{bmatrix} \end{bmatrix} \end{bmatrix}$$

These simple structures give us the ability to express linguistic generalizations in surprisingly compact and elegant ways.

15.2   Unification of Feature Structures

As noted earlier, feature structures would be of little use without our being able to perform reasonably efficient and powerful operations on them. As we show, the two principal operations we need to perform are merging the information content of two structures and rejecting the merger of structures that are incompatible. Fortunately, *Unification*   a single computational technique, called **unification**, suffices for both of these purposes. The bulk of this section illustrates through a series of examples how unification instantiates these notions of merger and compatibility. Discussion of the unification algorithm and its implementation is deferred to Section 15.4.

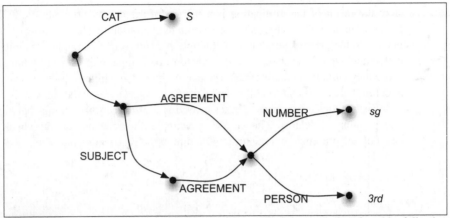

Figure 15.2   A feature structure with shared values. The location (value) found by following the ⟨HEAD SUBJECT AGREEMENT⟩ path is the same as that found via the ⟨HEAD AGREEMENT⟩ path.

We begin with the following simple application of the unification operator.

$$\begin{bmatrix} \text{NUMBER} & sg \end{bmatrix} \sqcup \begin{bmatrix} \text{NUMBER} & sg \end{bmatrix} = \begin{bmatrix} \text{NUMBER} & sg \end{bmatrix}$$

As the equation illustrates, unification is a binary operation (represented here as ⊔) that accepts two feature structures as arguments and returns a feature structure when it succeeds. In this example, unification is being used to perform a simple equality check. The unification succeeds because the corresponding NUMBER features in each structure agree as to their values. In this case, since the original structures are identical, the output is the same as the input. The following similar kind of check fails since the NUMBER features in the two structures have incompatible values.

$$\begin{bmatrix} \text{NUMBER} & sg \end{bmatrix} \sqcup \begin{bmatrix} \text{NUMBER} & pl \end{bmatrix} \quad \textit{Fails!}$$

This next unification illustrates an important aspect of the notion of compatibility in unification.

$$\begin{bmatrix} \text{NUMBER} & sg \end{bmatrix} \sqcup \begin{bmatrix} \text{NUMBER} & [] \end{bmatrix} = \begin{bmatrix} \text{NUMBER} & sg \end{bmatrix}$$

In this situation, these features structures are taken to be compatible and are hence capable of being merged, despite the fact that the given values for the respective NUMBER features are different. The [] value in the second structure indicates that the value has been left unspecified. A feature with such a [] value can be successfully matched to any value in a corresponding feature in another structure. Therefore, in this case, the value *sg* from the first structure can match the [] value from the second and as is indicated by the output shown, the result of this type of unification is a structure with the value provided by the more specific, non-null, value.

The next example illustrates another of the merger aspects of unification.

$$\begin{bmatrix} \text{NUMBER} & sg \end{bmatrix} \sqcup \begin{bmatrix} \text{PERSON} & 3rd \end{bmatrix} = \begin{bmatrix} \text{NUMBER} & sg \\ \text{PERSON} & 3rd \end{bmatrix}$$

Here the result of the unification is a merger of the original two structures into one larger structure. This larger structure contains the union of all the information stored in each of the original structures. Although this is a simple example, it is important to understand why these structures are judged to be compatible: they are compatible because they contain no features that are explicitly incompatible—that they each contain a feature-value pair that the other lacks does not cause the unification to fail.

We now consider a series of cases involving the unification of somewhat more complex reentrant structures. The following example illustrates an equality check complicated by the presence of a reentrant structure in the first argument.

$$
\begin{bmatrix} \text{AGREEMENT} & \boxed{1} \begin{bmatrix} \text{NUMBER} & sg \\ \text{PERSON} & 3rd \end{bmatrix} \\ \text{SUBJECT} & \begin{bmatrix} \text{AGREEMENT} & \boxed{1} \end{bmatrix} \end{bmatrix}
$$

$$
\sqcup \begin{bmatrix} \text{SUBJECT} & \begin{bmatrix} \text{AGREEMENT} & \begin{bmatrix} \text{PERSON} & 3rd \\ \text{NUMBER} & sg \end{bmatrix} \end{bmatrix} \end{bmatrix}
$$

$$
= \begin{bmatrix} \text{AGREEMENT} & \boxed{1} \begin{bmatrix} \text{NUMBER} & sg \\ \text{PERSON} & 3rd \end{bmatrix} \\ \text{SUBJECT} & \begin{bmatrix} \text{AGREEMENT} & \boxed{1} \end{bmatrix} \end{bmatrix}
$$

The important elements in this example are the SUBJECT features in the two input structures. The unification of these features succeeds because the values found in the first argument by following the $\boxed{1}$ numerical index match those that are directly present in the second argument. Note that, by itself, the value of the AGREEMENT feature in the first argument would have no bearing on the success of unification since the second argument lacks an AGREEMENT feature at the top level. It becomes relevant only because the value of the AGREEMENT feature is shared with the SUBJECT feature.

The following example illustrates the copying capabilities of unification.

$$
(15.1) \begin{bmatrix} \text{AGREEMENT} & \boxed{1} \\ \text{SUBJECT} & \begin{bmatrix} \text{AGREEMENT} & \boxed{1} \end{bmatrix} \end{bmatrix}
$$

$$
\sqcup \begin{bmatrix} \text{SUBJECT} & \begin{bmatrix} \text{AGREEMENT} & \begin{bmatrix} \text{PERSON} & 3rd \\ \text{NUMBER} & sg \end{bmatrix} \end{bmatrix} \end{bmatrix}
$$

$$
= \begin{bmatrix} \text{AGREEMENT} & \boxed{1} \\ \text{SUBJECT} & \begin{bmatrix} \text{AGREEMENT} & \boxed{1} \begin{bmatrix} \text{PERSON} & 3rd \\ \text{NUMBER} & sg \end{bmatrix} \end{bmatrix} \end{bmatrix}
$$

Here the value found via the second argument's ⟨SUBJECT AGREEMENT⟩ path is copied over to the corresponding place in the first argument. In addition, the AGREEMENT feature of the first argument receives a value as a side effect of the index linking it to the value at the end of the ⟨SUBJECT AGREEMENT⟩ path.

The next example demonstrates the important difference between features that actually share values versus those that merely have identical-looking values.

(15.2)
$$\begin{bmatrix} \text{AGREEMENT} & \begin{bmatrix} \text{NUMBER} & sg \end{bmatrix} \\ \text{SUBJECT} & \begin{bmatrix} \text{AGREEMENT} & \begin{bmatrix} \text{NUMBER} & sg \end{bmatrix} \end{bmatrix} \end{bmatrix}$$

$$\sqcup \begin{bmatrix} \text{SUBJECT} & \begin{bmatrix} \text{AGREEMENT} & \begin{bmatrix} \text{PERSON} & 3 \\ \text{NUMBER} & sg \end{bmatrix} \end{bmatrix} \end{bmatrix}$$

$$= \begin{bmatrix} \text{AGREEMENT} & \begin{bmatrix} \text{NUMBER} & sg \end{bmatrix} \\ \text{SUBJECT} & \begin{bmatrix} \text{AGREEMENT} & \begin{bmatrix} \text{NUMBER} & sg \\ \text{PERSON} & 3 \end{bmatrix} \end{bmatrix} \end{bmatrix}$$

The values at the end of the ⟨SUBJECT AGREEMENT⟩ path and the ⟨AGREEMENT⟩ path are the same, but not shared, in the first argument. The unification of the SUBJECT features of the two arguments adds the PERSON information from the second argument to the result. However, since no index links the AGREEMENT feature to the ⟨SUBJECT AGREEMENT⟩ path, this information is not added to the value of the AGREEMENT feature.

Finally, consider the following example of a failure to unify.

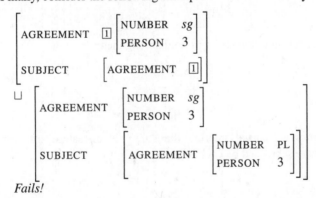

Fails!

Proceeding through the features in order, we first find that the AGREEMENT features in these examples successfully match. However, when we move on to the SUBJECT features, we find that the values found at the respective ⟨SUBJECT AGREEMENT NUMBER⟩ paths differ, causing a unification failure.

Feature structures are a way of representing partial information about some linguistic object or placing informational constraints on what the object can be. Unification can be seen as a way of merging the information in each feature structure or of describing objects that satisfy both sets of constraints. Intuitively, unifying two feature structures produces a new feature structure that is more specific (has more information) than, or is identical to, either of the input feature structures. We say that a less specific (more abstract) feature structure **subsumes** an equally or more specific one.

Subsumes

Subsumption is represented by the operator $\sqsubseteq$. A feature structure F subsumes a feature structure G ($F \sqsubseteq G$) if and only if

1. For every feature x in F, $F(x) \sqsubseteq G(x)$ (where $F(x)$ means "the value of the feature x of feature structure F").
2. For all paths p and q in F such that $F(p) = F(q)$, it is also the case that $G(p) = G(q)$.

For example, consider these feature structures:

(15.3) $\begin{bmatrix} \text{NUMBER} & sg \end{bmatrix}$

(15.4) $\begin{bmatrix} \text{PERSON} & 3 \end{bmatrix}$

(15.5) $\begin{bmatrix} \text{NUMBER} & sg \\ \text{PERSON} & 3 \end{bmatrix}$

(15.6) $\begin{bmatrix} \text{CAT} & \text{VP} \\ \text{AGREEMENT} & \boxed{1} \\ \text{SUBJECT} & \begin{bmatrix} \text{AGREEMENT} & \boxed{1} \end{bmatrix} \end{bmatrix}$

(15.7) $\begin{bmatrix} \text{CAT} & \text{VP} \\ \text{AGREEMENT} & \boxed{1} \\ \text{SUBJECT} & \begin{bmatrix} \text{AGREEMENT} & \boxed{1} \begin{bmatrix} \text{PERSON} & 3 \\ \text{NUMBER} & sg \end{bmatrix} \end{bmatrix} \end{bmatrix}$

The following subsumption relations hold among them:

$$15.3 \sqsubseteq 15.5$$
$$15.4 \sqsubseteq 15.5$$
$$15.6 \sqsubseteq 15.7$$

Subsumption is a partial ordering; there are pairs of feature structures that neither subsume nor are subsumed by each other:

$$15.3 \not\sqsubseteq 15.4$$
$$15.4 \not\sqsubseteq 15.3$$

Semilattice

Monotonic

Since every feature structure is subsumed by the empty structure [], the relation among feature structures can be defined as a **semilattice**. Unification can be defined in terms of the subsumption semilattice. Given two feature structures F and G, $F \sqcup G$ is defined as the most general feature structure H such that $F \sqsubseteq H$ and $G \sqsubseteq H$. Since the information ordering defined by subsumption is a semilattice, the unification operation is **monotonic** (Pereira and Shieber, 1984; Rounds and Kasper, 1986; Moshier, 1988). This means that if some description is true of a feature structure, unifying it with another feature structure results in a feature structure that still satisfies the original description. The unification operation is therefore associative; given a finite set of feature structures to unify, we can check them in any order and get the same result.

To summarize, unification is a way of implementing the integration of knowledge from different constraints. Given two compatible feature structures as input, unification produces the most general feature structure that nonetheless contains all the information in the inputs. Given two incompatible feature structures, it fails.

15.3   Feature Structures in the Grammar

Our primary purpose in introducing feature structures and unification has been to provide a way to elegantly express syntactic constraints that would be difficult to express with the mechanisms of context-free grammars alone. Our next step, therefore, is to specify a way to integrate feature structures and unification operations into the specification of a grammar. We can accomplish this by *augmenting* the rules of ordinary context-free grammars with attachments that specify feature structures for the constituents of the rules, along with appropriate unification operations that express constraints on those constituents. From a grammatical point of view, these attachments are used to accomplish the following goals:

- to associate complex feature structures with both lexical items and instances of grammatical categories
- to guide the composition of feature structures for larger grammatical constituents, based on the feature structures of their component parts
- to enforce compatibility constraints between specified parts of grammatical constructions

We use the following notation to denote the grammar augmentations that will allow us to accomplish all of these goals, based on the PATR-II system described in Shieber (1986):

$$\beta_0 \rightarrow \beta_1 \quad \beta_n$$
$$set\ of\ constraints$$

The specified constraints have one of the following forms:

$$\langle \beta_i\ feature\ path \rangle \quad = \quad Atomic\ value$$
$$\langle \beta_i\ feature\ path \rangle \quad = \quad \langle \beta_j\ feature\ path \rangle$$

The notation $\langle \beta_i\ feature\ path \rangle$ denotes a feature path through the feature structure associated with the β_i component of the context-free part of the rule. The first style of constraint specifies that the value found at the end of the given path must unify with the specified atomic value. The second form specifies that the values found at the end of the two given paths must be unifiable.

To illustrate the use of these constraints, let us return to the informal solution to the number agreement problem proposed at the beginning of this chapter.

$$S \rightarrow NP\ VP$$

only if the number of the NP is equal to the number of the VP.

Using the new notation, this rule can now be expressed as follows.

$$S \rightarrow NP \; VP$$
$$\langle NP \; \text{NUMBER} \rangle = \langle VP \; \text{NUMBER} \rangle$$

Note that in cases of two or more constituents of the same syntactic category in a rule, we subscript the constituents to keep them straight, as in $VP \rightarrow V \, NP_1 \, NP_2$.

Taking a step back from the notation, it is important to note that in this approach the simple generative nature of context-free rules has been fundamentally changed by this augmentation. Ordinary context-free rules are based on the simple notion of concatenation; an *NP* followed by a *VP* is an *S*; or generatively, to produce an *S*, all we need to do is concatenate an *NP* to a *VP*. In the new scheme, this concatenation must be accompanied by a successful unification operation. This leads naturally to questions about the computational complexity of the unification operation and its effect on the generative power of this new grammar. These issues are discussed in Chapter 16.

To review, there are two fundamental components to this approach.

- The elements of context-free grammar rules will have feature-based constraints associated with them. This reflects a shift from atomic grammatical categories to more complex categories with properties.

- The constraints associated with individual rules can make reference to the feature structures associated with the parts of the rule to which they are attached.

The following sections present applications of unification constraints to four interesting linguistic phenomena: agreement, grammatical heads, subcategorization, and long-distance dependencies.

15.3.1   Agreement

As discussed in Chapter 12, agreement phenomena show up in a number of different places in English. This section illustrates how unification can be used to capture the two main types of English agreement phenomena: subject-verb agreement and determiner-nominal agreement. We will use the following ATIS sentences as examples throughout this discussion to illustrate these phenomena.

(15.8) This flight serves breakfast.

(15.9) Does this flight serve breakfast?

(15.10) Do these flights serve breakfast?

Notice that the constraint used to enforce SUBJECT-VERB agreement given above is deficient in that it ignores the PERSON feature. The following constraint, which makes use of the AGREEMENT feature, takes care of this problem.

$$S \rightarrow NP \; VP$$
$$\langle NP \; \text{AGREEMENT} \rangle = \langle VP \; \text{AGREEMENT} \rangle$$

Examples 15.9 and 15.10 illustrate a minor variation on SUBJECT-VERB agreement. In these yes-no questions, the subject *NP* must agree with the auxiliary verb, rather than the main verb of the sentence, which appears in a non-finite form. This agreement constraint can be handled by the following rule.

$$S \rightarrow Aux\ NP\ VP$$
$$\langle Aux\ \text{AGREEMENT} \rangle = \langle NP\ \text{AGREEMENT} \rangle$$

Agreement between determiners and nominals in noun phrases is handled in a similar fashion. The basic task is to permit the expressions given above but block the unwanted *this flights and *those flight expressions where the determiners and nominals clash in their NUMBER feature. Again, the logical place to enforce this constraint is in the grammar rule that brings the parts together.

$$NP \rightarrow Det\ Nominal$$
$$\langle Det\ \text{AGREEMENT} \rangle = \langle Nominal\ \text{AGREEMENT} \rangle$$
$$\langle NP\ \text{AGREEMENT} \rangle = \langle Nominal\ \text{AGREEMENT} \rangle$$

This rule states that the AGREEMENT feature of the *Det* must unify with the AGREEMENT feature of the *Nominal* and, moreover, that the AGREEMENT feature of the *NP* must also unify with the *Nominal*.

Having expressed the constraints needed to enforce subject-verb and determiner-nominal agreement, we must now fill in the rest of the machinery needed to make these constraints work. Specifically, we must consider how the various constituents that take part in these constraints (the *Aux*, *VP*, *NP*, *Det*, and *Nominal*) acquire values for their various agreement features.

We can begin by noting that our constraints involve both lexical and non-lexical constituents. The simpler lexical constituents, *Aux* and *Det*, receive values for their respective agreement features directly from the lexicon, as in the following rules:

$$Aux \rightarrow do$$
$$\langle Aux\ \text{AGREEMENT NUMBER} \rangle = pl$$
$$\langle Aux\ \text{AGREEMENT PERSON} \rangle = 3rd$$
$$Aux \rightarrow does$$
$$\langle Aux\ \text{AGREEMENT NUMBER} \rangle = sg$$
$$\langle Aux\ \text{AGREEMENT PERSON} \rangle = 3rd$$
$$Det \rightarrow this$$
$$\langle Det\ \text{AGREEMENT NUMBER} \rangle = sg$$
$$Det \rightarrow these$$
$$\langle Det\ \text{AGREEMENT NUMBER} \rangle = pl$$

Returning to our first *S* rule, let us first consider the AGREEMENT feature for the *VP* constituent. The constituent structure for this *VP* is specified by the following rule:

$$VP \rightarrow Verb\ NP$$

It seems clear that the agreement constraint for this constituent must be based on its constituent verb. This verb, as with the previous lexical entries, can acquire its agreement feature values directly from lexicon as in the following rules:

$$Verb \rightarrow serve$$
$$\langle Verb\ \text{AGREEMENT NUMBER}\rangle = pl$$
$$Verb \rightarrow serves$$
$$\langle Verb\ \text{AGREEMENT NUMBER}\rangle = sg$$
$$\langle Verb\ \text{AGREEMENT PERSON}\rangle = 3rd$$

All that remains is to stipulate that the agreement feature of the parent *VP* is constrained to be the same as its verb constituent.

$$VP \rightarrow Verb\ NP$$
$$\langle VP\ \text{AGREEMENT}\rangle = \langle Verb\ \text{AGREEMENT}\rangle$$

In other words, non-lexical grammatical constituents can acquire values for at least some of their features from their component constituents.

The same technique works for the remaining *NP* and *Nominal* categories. The values for the agreement features for these categories are derived from the nouns *flight* and *flights*.

$$Noun \rightarrow flight$$
$$\langle Noun\ \text{AGREEMENT NUMBER}\rangle = sg$$
$$Noun \rightarrow flights$$
$$\langle Noun\ \text{AGREEMENT NUMBER}\rangle = pl$$

Nominal features can be constrained to have the same values as their constituent nouns.

$$Nominal \rightarrow Noun$$
$$\langle Nominal\ \text{AGREEMENT}\rangle = \langle Noun\ \text{AGREEMENT}\rangle$$

Note that this section has only scratched the surface of the English agreement system and that the agreement system of other languages can be considerably more complex than English.

15.3.2   Head Features

To account for the way that compositional grammatical constituents such as noun phrases, nominals, and verb phrases come to have agreement features, the preceding section introduced the notion of copying feature structures from phrase-structure children to their parents. This turns out to be a specific instance of a much more general phenomenon in constraint-based grammars. Specifically, the features for most grammatical categories are copied from *one* of the children to the parent. The child that provides the features is called the head of the phrase, and the features copied are referred to as **head features**.

Head features

This notion of heads, first introduced in Section 12.4.4, plays an important role in constraint-based grammars. Consider the following three rules from the last section.

$$VP \rightarrow Verb\ NP$$
$$\langle VP\ \text{AGREEMENT} \rangle = \langle Verb\ \text{AGREEMENT} \rangle$$
$$NP \rightarrow Det\ Nominal$$
$$\langle Det\ \text{AGREEMENT} \rangle = \langle Nominal\ \text{AGREEMENT} \rangle$$
$$\langle NP\ \text{AGREEMENT} \rangle = \langle Nominal\ \text{AGREEMENT} \rangle$$
$$Nominal \rightarrow Noun$$
$$\langle Nominal\ \text{AGREEMENT} \rangle = \langle Noun\ \text{AGREEMENT} \rangle$$

In each of these rules, the constituent providing the agreement feature structure to its parent is the head of the phrase. More specifically, the verb is the head of the verb phrase, the nominal is the head of the noun phrase, and the noun is the head of the nominal. As a result, we can say that the agreement feature structure is a head feature. We can rewrite our rules to reflect these generalizations by placing the agreement feature structure under a HEAD feature and then copying that feature upward as in the following constraints.

$$VP \rightarrow Verb\ NP \tag{15.11}$$
$$\langle VP\ \text{HEAD} \rangle = \langle Verb\ \text{HEAD} \rangle$$

$$NP \rightarrow Det\ Nominal \tag{15.12}$$
$$\langle NP\ \text{HEAD} \rangle = \langle Nominal\ \text{HEAD} \rangle$$
$$\langle Det\ \text{HEAD AGREEMENT} \rangle = \langle Nominal\ \text{HEAD AGREEMENT} \rangle$$

$$Nominal \rightarrow Noun \tag{15.13}$$
$$\langle Nominal\ \text{HEAD} \rangle = \langle Noun\ \text{HEAD} \rangle$$

Similarly, the lexical entries that introduce these features must now reflect this HEAD notion, as in the following:

$$Noun \rightarrow flights$$
$$\langle Noun\ \text{HEAD AGREEMENT NUMBER} \rangle = pl$$
$$Verb \rightarrow serves$$
$$\langle Verb\ \text{HEAD AGREEMENT NUMBER} \rangle = sg$$
$$\langle Verb\ \text{HEAD AGREEMENT PERSON} \rangle = 3rd$$

15.3.3   Subcategorization

Recall that subcategorization is the notion that verbs can be picky about the patterns of arguments they will allow themselves to appear with. In Chapter 12, to prevent the generation of ungrammatical sentences with verbs and verb phrases that do not match, we were forced to split the category of verb into multiple subcategories. These more specific verb categories were then used in the definition of the specific verb phrases that they were allowed to occur with, as in the following:

$$Verb\text{-}with\text{-}S\text{-}comp \;\rightarrow\; think$$
$$VP \;\rightarrow\; Verb\text{-}with\text{-}S\text{-}comp \; S$$

Clearly, this approach introduces exactly the same undesirable proliferation of categories that we saw with the similar approach to solving the number problem. The proper way to avoid this proliferation is to introduce feature structures to distinguish among the various members of the verb category. We can accomplish this goal by associating with each of the verbs in the lexicon an atomic feature, called SUBCAT, with an appropriate value. For example, the transitive version of *serves* could be assigned the following feature structure in the lexicon:

$$Verb \;\rightarrow\; serves$$
$$\langle Verb \text{ HEAD AGREEMENT NUMBER}\rangle = sg$$
$$\langle Verb \text{ HEAD SUBCAT}\rangle = trans$$

The SUBCAT feature signals to the rest of the grammar that this verb should only appear in verb phrases with a single noun phrase argument. We enforce this constraint by adding corresponding constraints to all the verb phrase rules in the grammar, as in the following:

$$VP \;\rightarrow\; Verb$$
$$\langle VP \text{ HEAD}\rangle = \langle Verb \text{ HEAD}\rangle$$
$$\langle VP \text{ HEAD SUBCAT}\rangle = intrans$$
$$VP \;\rightarrow\; Verb \; NP$$
$$\langle VP \text{ HEAD}\rangle = \langle Verb \text{ HEAD}\rangle$$
$$\langle VP \text{ HEAD SUBCAT}\rangle = trans$$
$$VP \;\rightarrow\; Verb \; NP \; NP$$
$$\langle VP \text{ HEAD}\rangle = \langle Verb \text{ HEAD}\rangle$$
$$\langle VP \text{ HEAD SUBCAT}\rangle = ditrans$$

The first unification constraint in these rules states that the verb phrase receives its HEAD features from its verb constituent, and the second constraint specifies what the value of that SUBCAT feature must be. Any attempt to use a verb with an inappropriate verb phrase will fail since the value of the SUBCAT feature of the *VP* will fail to unify with the atomic symbol given in the second constraint. Note that this approach requires unique symbols for each of the 50–100 verb phrase frames in English.

This is a somewhat clumsy approach since these unanalyzable SUBCAT symbols do not directly encode either the number or type of the arguments that the verb expects to take. To see this, note that we cannot simply examine a verb's entry in the lexicon and know what its subcategorization frame is. Rather, we must use the value of the SUBCAT feature indirectly as a pointer to those verb phrase rules in the grammar that can accept the verb in question.

A more elegant solution, which makes better use of the expressive power of feature structures, allows the verb entries to directly specify the order and type of their arguments. The following entry for *serves* is an example of one such approach, in which the verb's subcategory feature expresses a list of its objects and complements.

$$Verb \rightarrow serves$$
$$\langle Verb \text{ HEAD AGREEMENT NUMBER} \rangle = sg$$
$$\langle Verb \text{ HEAD SUBCAT FIRST CAT} \rangle = NP$$
$$\langle Verb \text{ HEAD SUBCAT SECOND} \rangle = end$$

This entry uses the FIRST feature to state that the first post-verbal argument must be an *NP*; the value of the SECOND feature indicates that this verb expects only one argument. A verb like *leave Boston in the morning*, with two arguments, would have the following kind of entry.

$$Verb \rightarrow leaves$$
$$\langle Verb \text{ HEAD AGREEMENT NUMBER} \rangle = sg$$
$$\langle Verb \text{ HEAD SUBCAT FIRST CAT} \rangle = NP$$
$$\langle Verb \text{ HEAD SUBCAT SECOND CAT} \rangle = PP$$
$$\langle Verb \text{ HEAD SUBCAT THIRD} \rangle = end$$

This scheme is, of course, a rather baroque way of encoding a list; it is also possible to use the idea of types defined in Section 15.6 to define a list type more cleanly.

The individual verb phrase rules must now check for the presence of exactly the elements specified by their verb, as in the following transitive rule:

$$VP \rightarrow Verb\,NP \qquad\qquad (15.14)$$
$$\langle VP \text{ HEAD} \rangle = \langle Verb \text{ HEAD} \rangle$$
$$\langle VP \text{ HEAD SUBCAT FIRST CAT} \rangle = \langle NP \text{ CAT} \rangle$$
$$\langle VP \text{ HEAD SUBCAT SECOND} \rangle = end$$

The second constraint in this rule's constraints states that the category of the first element of the verb's SUBCAT list must match the category of the constituent immediately following the verb. The third constraint goes on to state that this verb phrase rule expects only a single argument.

Subcategorization frames   Our previous examples have shown rather simple subcategorization structures for verbs. In fact, verbs can subcategorize for quite complex **subcategorization frames**, (e.g., *NP PP*, *NP NP*, or *NP S*) and these frames can be composed of many different phrasal types. To come up with a list of possible subcategorization frames for English verbs, we first need a list of possible phrase types that can make up these frames. Figure 15.3 shows one short list of possible phrase types for making up subcategorization frames for verbs; this list is modified from one used to create verb subcategorization frames in the FrameNet project (Johnson, 1999; Baker et al., 1998) and includes phrase types for special subjects of verbs like *there* and *it*, as well as for objects and complements.

Noun Phrase Types		
There	nonreferential there	**There** *is still much to learn*
It	nonreferential it	**It** *was evident that my ideas*
NP	noun phrase	*As he was relating* **his story**
Preposition Phrase Types		
PP	preposition phrase	*couch their message* **in terms**
PPing	gerundive PP	*censured him* **for not having intervened**
PPpart	particle	*turn it* **off**
Verb Phrase Types		
VPbrst	bare stem VP	*she could* **discuss it**
VPto	to-marked infin. VP	*Why do you want* **to know**?
VPwh	wh-VP	*it is worth considering* **how to write**
VPing	gerundive VP	*I would consider* **using it**
Complement Clause types		
Sfin	finite clause	*maintain* **that the situation was unsatisfactory**
Swh	wh-clause	*it tells us* **where we are**
Sif	whether/if clause	*ask* **whether Aristophanes is depicting a**
Sing	gerundive clause	*see* **some attention being given**
Sto	to-marked clause	*know* **themselves to be relatively unhealthy**
Sforto	for-to clause	*She was waiting* **for him to make some reply**
Sbrst	bare stem clause	*commanded* **that his sermons be published**
Other Types		
AjP	adjective phrase	*thought it* **possible**
Quo	quotes	*asked* **"What was it like?"**

Figure 15.3   A small set of potential phrase types which can be combined to create a set of potential subcategorization frames for verbs. Modified from the FrameNet tagset (Johnson, 1999; Baker et al., 1998). The sample sentence fragments are from the British National Corpus.

For the phrase types in Fig. 15.3 to be used in a unification grammar, each phrase type could be described by features. For example, the form **VPto**, which is subcategorized for by *want*, might be expressed as

$$Verb \rightarrow want$$
$$\langle Verb \ \text{HEAD SUBCAT FIRST CAT} \rangle = VP$$
$$\langle Verb \ \text{HEAD SUBCAT FIRST FORM} \rangle = infinitive$$

Each of the 50 to 100 possible verb subcategorization frames in English would be described as a list drawn from these phrase types. For instance, here is an example of the two-complement *want*. We can use this example to demonstrate two different notational possibilities. First, lists can be represented with an angle brackets notation $\langle$ and $\rangle$. Second, instead of using a rewrite rule annotated with path equations, we can represent the lexical entry as a single feature structure:

Subcat	Example
Quo	asked [$_{Quo}$ "What was it like?"]
NP	asking [$_{NP}$ a question]
Swh	asked [$_{Swh}$ what trades you're interested in]
Sto	ask [$_{Sto}$ him to tell you]
PP	that means asking [$_{PP}$ at home]
Vto	asked [$_{Vto}$ to see a girl called Evelyn]
NP Sif	asked [$_{NP}$ him] [$_{Sif}$ whether he could make]
NP NP	asked [$_{NP}$ myself] [$_{NP}$ a question]
NP Swh	asked [$_{NP}$ him] [$_{Swh}$ why he took time off]

Figure 15.4   A set of sample subcategorization patterns for the verb *ask* with examples from the BNC.

$$\begin{bmatrix} \text{ORTH} & want \\ \text{CAT} & Verb \\ \text{HEAD} & \begin{bmatrix} \text{SUBCAT} & \left\langle \begin{bmatrix} \text{CAT } NP \end{bmatrix}, \begin{bmatrix} \text{CAT } VP \\ \text{HEAD} \begin{bmatrix} \text{VFORM } infinitival \end{bmatrix} \end{bmatrix} \right\rangle \end{bmatrix} \end{bmatrix}$$

Combining even a limited set of phrase types results in a very large set of possible subcategorization frames. Furthermore, each verb allows many different subcategorization frames. Figure 15.4 provides a set of subcategorization patterns for the verb *ask*, with examples from the BNC.

A number of comprehensive subcategorization-frame tagsets exist, such as the COMLEX set (Macleod et al., 1998), which includes subcategorization frames for verbs, adjectives, and nouns, and the ACQUILEX tagset of verb subcategorization frames (Sanfilippo, 1993). Many subcategorization-frame tagsets add other information about the complements, such as specifying the identity of the implicit subject in a lower verb phrase that has no overt subject; this is called **control** information. For example, *Temmy promised Ruth to go* implies (at least in some dialects) that Temmy will do the going, while *Temmy persuaded Ruth to go* implies that Ruth will do the going. Some of the multiple possible subcategorization frames for a verb can be partially predicted by the semantics of the verb; for example, many verbs of transfer (like *give*, *send*, *carry*) predictably take the two subcategorization frames *NP NP* and *NP PP*:

Control

NP NP   sent FAA Administrator James Busey a letter
NP PP   sent a letter to the chairman of the Armed Services Committee

Alternations

These relationships among subcategorization frames across classes of verbs are called argument-structure **alternations** and are discussed in Chapter 19 when we discuss the semantics of verbal argument structure. Chapter 14 introduces probabilities for modeling the fact that verbs generally have preferences even among the different subcategorization frames they allow.

Subcategorization in Other Parts of Speech

Valence

Although the notion of subcategorization, or **valence** as it is often called, was originally conceived for verbs, more recent work has focused on the fact that many other kinds of words exhibit forms of valence-like behavior. Consider the following contrasting uses of the prepositions *while* and *during*.

(15.15) Keep your seatbelt fastened while *we are taking off*.

(15.16) *Keep your seatbelt fastened while *takeoff*.

(15.17) Keep your seatbelt fastened during *takeoff*.

(15.18) *Keep your seatbelt fastened during *we are taking off*.

Despite the apparent similarities between these words, they make quite different demands on their arguments. Representing these differences is left as Exercise 15.5 for the reader.

Many adjectives and nouns also have subcategorization frames. Here are some examples that use the adjectives *apparent*, *aware*, and *unimportant* and the nouns *assumption* and *question*:

It was **apparent** [$_{Sfin}$ that the kitchen was the only room...]
It was **apparent** [$_{PP}$ from the way she rested her hand over his]
aware [$_{Sfin}$ he may have caused offense]
it is **unimportant** [$_{Swheth}$ whether only a little bit is accepted]
the **assumption** [$_{Sfin}$ that wasteful methods have been employed]
the **question** [$_{Swheth}$ whether the authorities might have decided]

See Nomlex (Macleod et al., 1998), FrameNet, Johnson (1999), and NomBank (Meyers et al., 2004) for descriptions of subcategorization frames for nouns and adjectives.

Verbs express subcategorization constraints on their subjects as well as their complements. For example, we need to represent the lexical fact that the verb *seem* can take an **Sfin** as its subject (*That she was affected seems obvious*), whereas the verb *paint* cannot. The SUBJECT feature can be used to express these constraints.

15.3.4   Long-Distance Dependencies

The model of subcategorization we have developed so far has two components. Each headword has a SUBCAT feature that contains a list of the complements it expects. Then, phrasal rules like the *VP* rule in (15.14) match up each expected complement in the SUBCAT list with an actual constituent. This mechanism works fine when the complements of a verb are in fact to be found in the verb phrase.

Long-distance dependencies

Sometimes, however, a constituent subcategorized for by the verb is not locally instantiated but stands in a **long-distance** relationship with its predicate. Here are some examples of such **long-distance dependency**:

What cities does Continental service?
What flights do you have from Boston to Baltimore?
What time does that flight leave Atlanta?

In the first example, the constituent *what cities* is subcategorized for by the verb *service*, but because the sentence is an example of a **wh-non-subject-question**, the object is located at the front of the sentence. Recall from Chapter 12 that a (simple) phrase structure rule for a **wh-non-subject-question** is something like the following:

$$S \rightarrow \textit{Wh-NP Aux NP VP}$$

Now that we have features, we can augment this phrase structure rule to require the *Aux* and the *NP* to agree (since the *NP* is the subject). But we also need some way to augment the rule to tell it that the *Wh-NP* should fill some subcategorization slot in the *VP*. The representation of such long-distance dependencies is a quite difficult problem because the verb whose subcategorization requirement is being filled can be quite distant from the filler. In the following (made-up) sentence, for example, the *wh*-phrase *which flight* must fill the subcategorization requirements of the verb *book*, despite the fact that there are two other verbs (*want* and *have*) in between:

Which flight do you want me to have the travel agent book?

Many solutions to representing long-distance dependencies in unification grammars involve keeping a list, often called a **gap list**, implemented as a feature GAP that is passed up from phrase to phrase in the parse tree. The **filler** (e.g., *which flight* above) is put on the gap list and must eventually be unified with the subcategorization frame of some verb. See Sag and Wasow (1999) for an explanation of such a strategy, together with a discussion of the many other complications that must be modeled in long-distance dependencies.

Gap list
Filler

15.4   Implementation of Unification

The unification operator takes two feature structures as input and returns a single merged feature structure if successful or a failure signal if the two inputs are not compatible. The input feature structures are represented as directed acyclic graphs (DAGs), where features are depicted as labels on directed edges, and feature values are either atomic symbols or DAGs. As we show, the implementation of the operator is a relatively straightforward recursive, graph-matching algorithm, suitably tailored to accommodate the various requirements of unification. Roughly speaking, the algorithm loops through the features in one input and attempts to find a corresponding feature in the other. If all of the respective feature values match, then the unification is successful. If there is a mismatch, then the unification fails. The recursion is motivated by the need to correctly match those features that have feature structures as their values.

A notable aspect of this algorithm is that rather than constructing a new feature structure with the unified information from the two arguments, it destructively alters the arguments so that in the end they point to exactly the same information. Thus, the result of a successful call to the unification operator consists of suitably altered versions of the arguments. As is discussed in the next section, the destructive nature of this algorithm necessitates certain minor extensions to the simple graph version of feature structures as DAGs that we have been assuming.

15.4.1   Unification Data Structures

To facilitate the destructive merger aspect of the algorithm, we add a small complication to the DAGs used to represent the input feature structures: feature structures are represented by DAGs with additional edges, or fields. Specifically, each feature structure consists of two fields: a content field and a pointer field. The content field may be null or contain an ordinary feature structure. Similarly, the pointer field may be null or contain a pointer to another feature structure. If the pointer field of the DAG is null, then the content field of the DAG contains the actual feature structure to be processed. If, on the other hand, the pointer field is non-null, then the destination of the pointer represents the actual feature structure to be processed. The merger aspects of unification are achieved by the alteration of the pointer field of DAGs during processing.

To see how this works, let's consider the extended DAG representation for the following familiar feature structure:

(15.19) $\begin{bmatrix} \text{NUMBER} & sg \\ \text{PERSON} & 3rd \end{bmatrix}$

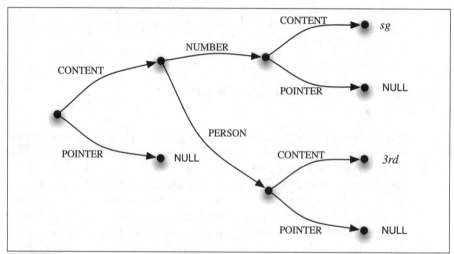

Figure 15.5   An extended DAG notation for (15.19).

Figure 15.5 shows this extended representation in its graphical form. Note that the extended representation contains content and pointer links both for the top-level layer of features and for each of the embedded feature structures all the way down to the atomic values.

Before presenting the details of the unification algorithm, let's illustrate the use of this extended DAG representation with the following simple example.

(15.20) $\begin{bmatrix} \text{NUMBER} & sg \end{bmatrix} \sqcup \begin{bmatrix} \text{PERSON} & 3rd \end{bmatrix} = \begin{bmatrix} \text{NUMBER} & sg \\ \text{PERSON} & 3rd \end{bmatrix}$

This unification results in the creation of a new structure containing the union of the information from the two original arguments. With the extended notation, we can see how the unification is accomplished by some additions to the original arguments and a change to some of the pointers from one structure to the other so that in the end they contain the same content. In this example, we accomplish this by first adding a PERSON feature to the first argument and then assigning it a value by filling its POINTER field with a pointer to the appropriate location in the second argument, as shown in Fig. 15.6.

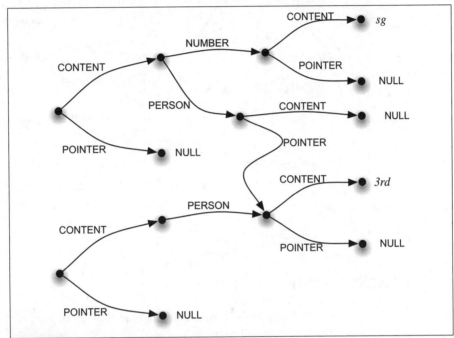

Figure 15.6   The arguments after assigning the first argument's new PERSON feature to the appropriate value in the second argument.

The process is, however, not yet complete. While it is clear from Fig. 15.6 that the first argument now contains all the correct information, the second one does not; it lacks a NUMBER feature. We could, of course, add a NUMBER feature to this argument with a pointer to the appropriate place in the first one. This change would result in the two arguments having all the correct information from this unification.

Unfortunately, this solution is inadequate since it does not meet our requirement that the two arguments be truly unified. Since the two arguments are not completely unified at the top level, future unifications involving one of the arguments would not show up in the other. The solution to this problem is to simply set the POINTER field of the second argument to point at the first one. When this is done, any future change to either argument will be immediately reflected in both. The result of this final change is shown in Figure 15.7.

15.4.2   The Unification Algorithm

The unification algorithm that we have been leading up to is shown in Figure 15.8. This algorithm accepts two feature structures represented using the extended DAG representation and returns as its value a modified version of one of the arguments, or a failure signal in the event that the feature structures are incompatible.

521

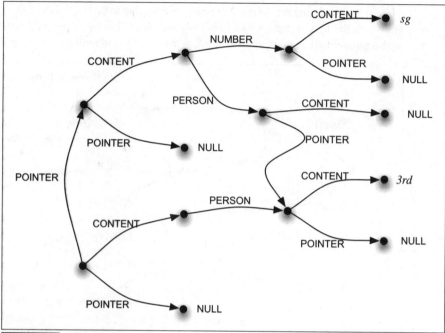

Figure 15.7   The final result of unifying F1 and F2.

The first step in this algorithm is to acquire the true contents of both of the arguments. Recall that if the pointer field of an extended feature structure is non-null, then we can find the real content of that structure by following the pointer found in pointer field. The variables *f1* and *f2* are the result of this pointer following process, often referred to as **dereferencing**.

Dereferencing

As with all recursive algorithms, the next step is to test for the various base cases of the recursion before proceeding to a recursive call involving some part of the original arguments. In this case, there are three possible base cases:

- The arguments are identical.
- One or both of the arguments have a null value.
- The arguments are non-null and non-identical.

If the structures are identical, then the pointer of the first is set to the second and the second is returned. It is important to understand why this pointer change is done in this case. After all, since the arguments are identical, returning either one would appear to suffice. This might be true for a single unification, but recall that we want the two arguments to the unification operator to be truly unified. The pointer change is necessary since we want the arguments to be truly identical so that any subsequent unification that adds information to one will add it to both.

In the case in which either of the arguments is null, the pointer field for the null argument is changed to point to the other argument, which is then returned. The result is that both structures now point at the same value.

```
function UNIFY(f1-orig, f2-orig) returns f-structure or failure

  f1 ← Dereferenced contents of f1-orig
  f2 ← Dereferenced contents of f2-orig

  if f1 and f2 are identical then
    f1.pointer ← f2
    return f2
  else if f1 is null then
    f1.pointer ← f2
    return f2
  else if f2 is null then
    f2.pointer ← f1
    return f1
  else if both f1 and f2 are complex feature structures then
    f2.pointer ← f1
    for each f2-feature in f2 do
      f1-feature ← Find or create a corresponding feature in f1
      if UNIFY(f1-feature.value, f2-feature.value) returns failure then
        return failure
    return f1
  else return failure
```

Figure 15.8   The unification algorithm.

If neither of the preceding tests is true, then there are two possibilities: they are non-identical atomic values or they are non-identical complex structures. The former case signals an incompatibility in the arguments that leads the algorithm to return a failure signal. In the latter case, a recursive call is needed to ensure that the component parts of these complex structures are compatible. In this implementation, the key to the recursion is a loop over all the features of the *second* argument, $f2$. This loop attempts to unify the value of each feature in $f2$ with the corresponding feature in $f1$. In this loop, if a feature is encountered in $f2$ that is missing from $f1$, then a feature is added to $f1$ and given the value NULL. Processing then continues as if the feature had been there to begin with. If *every* one of these unifications succeeds, then the pointer field of $f2$ is set to $f1$, completing the unification of the structures, and $f1$ is returned as the value of the unification.

An Example

To illustrate this algorithm, let's walk through the following example.

$$(15.21) \quad \begin{bmatrix} \text{AGREEMENT} & \boxed{1}\begin{bmatrix} \text{NUMBER} & sg \end{bmatrix} \\ \text{SUBJECT} & \begin{bmatrix} \text{AGREEMENT} & \boxed{1} \end{bmatrix} \end{bmatrix}$$
$$\sqcup \quad \begin{bmatrix} \text{SUBJECT} & \begin{bmatrix} \text{AGREEMENT} & \begin{bmatrix} \text{PERSON} & 3rd \end{bmatrix} \end{bmatrix} \end{bmatrix}$$

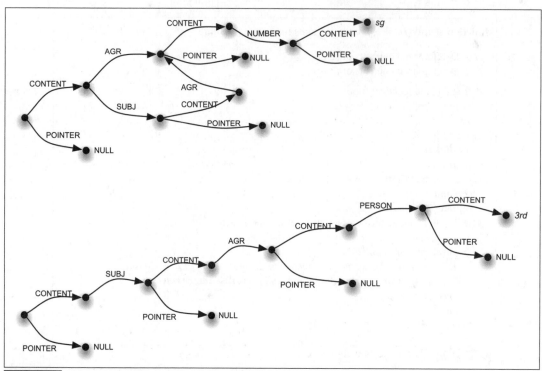

Figure 15.9   The initial arguments *f1* and *f2* to (15.21).

Figure 15.9 shows the extended representations for the arguments to this unification. These original arguments are not identical, null, or atomic, so the main loop is entered. Looping over the features of *f2*, the algorithm is led to a recursive attempt to unify the values of the corresponding SUBJECT features of *f1* and *f2*.

$$\left[\text{AGREEMENT}\quad \boxed{1}\right] \sqcup \left[\text{AGREEMENT}\quad \left[\text{PERSON}\quad 3rd\right]\right]$$

These arguments are also non-identical, non-null, and non-atomic, so the loop is entered again, leading to a recursive check of the values of the AGREEMENT features.

$$\left[\text{NUMBER}\quad sg\right] \sqcup \left[\text{PERSON}\quad 3rd\right]$$

In looping over the features of the second argument, the fact that the first argument lacks a PERSON feature is discovered. A PERSON feature initialized with a NULL value is, therefore, added to the first argument. This, in effect, changes the previous unification to the following:

$$\begin{bmatrix}\text{NUMBER} & sg \\ \text{PERSON} & null\end{bmatrix} \sqcup \left[\text{PERSON}\quad 3rd\right]$$

After creating this new PERSON feature, the next recursive call leads to the unification of the NULL value of the new feature in the first argument with the *3rd* value of the second argument. Since there are no further features to check in the *f2* argument at any level of recursion, each of the recursive calls to UNIFY returns. The result is shown in Figure 15.10.

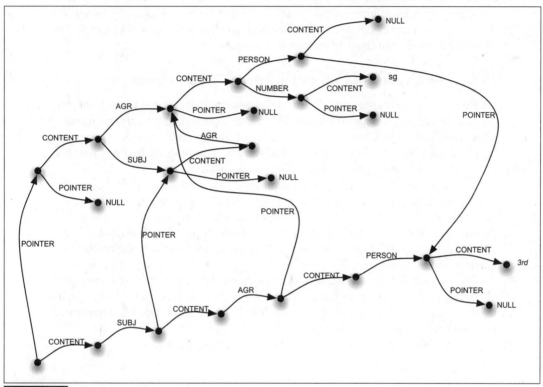

Figure 15.10   The final structures of *f1* and *f2* at the end.

15.5   Parsing with Unification Constraints

We now have all the pieces necessary to integrate feature structures and unification into a parser. Fortunately, the order-independent nature of unification allows us to largely ignore the actual search strategy used in the parser. Once we have associated unification constraints with the context-free rules of the grammar, and feature structures with the states of the search, we can use any of the standard search algorithms described in Chapter 13.

Of course, this leaves a fairly large range of possible implementation strategies. We could, for example, simply parse as we did before, using the context-free components of the rules, and then build the feature structures for the resulting trees after the fact, filtering out those parses that contain unification failures. Although such an approach would result in only well-formed structures in the end, it fails to use the power of unification to reduce the size of the parser's search space during parsing.

The next section describes an approach that makes better use of the power of unification by integrating unification constraints directly into the Earley parsing process, allowing ill-formed structures to be eliminated as soon as they are proposed. As we show, this approach requires only minimal changes to the basic Earley algorithm. We then move on to briefly consider an approach to unification-based parsing that moves even further away from standard context-free methods.

15.5.1   Integration of Unification into an Earley Parser

We have two goals in integrating feature structures and unification into the Earley algorithm: to use feature structures to provide a richer representation for the constituents of the parse and to block entry into the chart of ill-formed constituents that violate unification constraints. We show that these goals can be accomplished by fairly minimal changes to the original Earley scheme given on page 444.

The first change involves the various representations used in the original code. Recall that the Earley algorithm operates by using a set of unadorned context-free grammar rules to fill in a data structure, called a chart, with a set of states. At the end of the parse, the states that make up this chart represent all possible parses of the input. Therefore, we begin our changes by altering the representations of both the context-free grammar rules and the states in the chart.

The rules are altered in such a way that in addition to their current components, they also include a feature structure derived from their unification constraints. More specifically, we use the constraints listed with a rule to build a feature structure, represented as a DAG, for use with that rule during parsing.

Consider the following context-free rule with unification constraints:

$$S \rightarrow NP\ VP$$
$$\langle NP \text{ HEAD AGREEMENT} \rangle = \langle VP \text{ HEAD AGREEMENT} \rangle$$
$$\langle S \text{ HEAD} \rangle = \langle VP \text{ HEAD} \rangle$$

Converting these constraints into a feature structure results in the following structure:

$$
\begin{bmatrix}
S & \begin{bmatrix} \text{HEAD} & \boxed{1} \end{bmatrix} \\
NP & \begin{bmatrix} \text{HEAD} & \begin{bmatrix} \text{AGREEMENT} & \boxed{2} \end{bmatrix} \end{bmatrix} \\
VP & \begin{bmatrix} \text{HEAD} & \boxed{1} \begin{bmatrix} \text{AGREEMENT} & \boxed{2} \end{bmatrix} \end{bmatrix}
\end{bmatrix}
$$

In this derivation, we combined the various constraints into a single structure by first creating top-level features for each of the parts of the context-free rule, S, NP, and VP in this case. We then add further components to this structure by following the path equations in the constraints. Note that this is a purely notational conversion; the DAGs and the constraint equations contain the same information. However, tying the constraints together in a single feature structure puts it in a form that can be passed directly to our unification algorithm.

The second change involves the states used to represent partial parses in the Earley chart. The original states contain fields for the context-free rule being used, the position of the dot representing how much of the rule has been completed, the positions of the beginning and end of the state, and a list of other states that represent the completed subparts of the state. To this set of fields, we simply add an additional field to contain the DAG representing the feature structure corresponding to the state. Note that when a rule is first used by PREDICTOR to create a state, the DAG associated with the state will simply consist of the DAG retrieved from the rule. For example, when PREDICTOR uses the above S rule to enter a state into the chart, the DAG given above will be its initial DAG. We denote states like this as follows, where Dag denotes the feature structure given above.

$$S \rightarrow \bullet NP\ VP,\ [0,0],\ [],Dag$$

Given these representational additions, we can move on to altering the algorithm itself. The most important change concerns the actions that take place when a new state is created by the extension of an existing state, which takes place in the COMPLETER routine. Recall that COMPLETER is called when a completed constituent has been added to the chart. Its task is to attempt to find, and extend, existing states in the chart that are looking for constituents that are compatible with the newly completed constituent. COMPLETER is, therefore, a function that creates new states by *combining* the information from two other states, and as such is a likely place to apply the unification operation.

To be more specific, COMPLETER adds a new state into the chart by finding an existing state whose $\bullet$ can be advanced by the newly completed state. A $\bullet$ can be advanced when the category of the constituent immediately following it matches the category of the newly completed constituent. To accommodate the use of feature structures, we can alter this scheme by unifying the feature structure associated with the newly completed state with the appropriate part of the feature structure being advanced. If this unification succeeds, then the DAG of the new state receives the unified structure and is entered into the chart. If it fails, then no new state is entered into the chart. The appropriate alterations to COMPLETER are shown in Figure 15.11.

Consider this process in the context of parsing the phrase *That flight*, where the *That* has already been seen, as is captured by the following state.

$$NP \rightarrow Det\bullet Nominal[0,1],[S_{Det}],Dag_1$$

$$Dag_1 \begin{bmatrix} NP & \begin{bmatrix} HEAD & \boxed{1} \end{bmatrix} \\ DET & \begin{bmatrix} HEAD & \begin{bmatrix} AGREEMENT & \boxed{2} \begin{bmatrix} NUMBER & SG \end{bmatrix} \end{bmatrix} \end{bmatrix} \\ NOMINAL & \begin{bmatrix} HEAD & \boxed{1} \begin{bmatrix} AGREEMENT & \boxed{2} \end{bmatrix} \end{bmatrix} \end{bmatrix}$$

Now consider the later situation in which the parser has processed *flight* and has subsequently produced the following state:

$$Nominal \rightarrow Noun\bullet, [1,2], [S_{Noun}], Dag_2$$

$$Dag_2 \begin{bmatrix} \text{NOMINAL} & \begin{bmatrix} \text{HEAD} & \boxed{1} \end{bmatrix} \\ \text{NOUN} & \begin{bmatrix} \text{HEAD} & \boxed{1} \begin{bmatrix} \text{AGREEMENT} & \begin{bmatrix} \text{NUMBER} & \text{SG} \end{bmatrix} \end{bmatrix} \end{bmatrix} \end{bmatrix}$$

To advance the *NP* rule, the parser unifies the feature structure found under the NOMINAL feature of Dag_2, with the feature structure found under the NOMINAL feature of the *NP*'s Dag_1. As in the original algorithm, a new state is created to represent the fact that an existing state has been advanced. This new state's DAG is given the DAG that resulted from this unification.

The final change to the original algorithm concerns the check for states already contained in the chart. In the original algorithm, the ENQUEUE function refused to enter into the chart any state that was *identical* to one already present in the chart. "Identical" meant the same rule, with the same start and finish positions, and the same position of the •. It was this check that allowed the algorithm to, among other things, avoid the infinite recursion problems associated with left-recursive rules.

The problem, of course, is that our states are now more complex since they have complex feature structures associated with them. States that appeared identical under the original criteria might in fact now be different since their associated DAGs may differ. One solution to this problem is to extend the identity check to include the DAGs associated with the states, but it turns out that we can improve on this solution.

The motivation for the improvement lies in the motivation for the identity check. Its purpose is to prevent the wasteful addition of a state into the chart whose effect on the parse would be accomplished by an already existing state. Put another way, we want to prevent the entry into the chart of any state that would duplicate the work that will eventually be done by other states. Of course, this will clearly be the case with identical states, but it turns out it is also the case for states in the chart that are *more general* than new states being considered.

Consider the situation in which the chart contains the following state, where the *Dag* places no constraints on the *Det*.

$$NP \rightarrow \bullet Det\, NP, [i,i], [], Dag$$

Such a state simply says that it is expecting a *Det* at position i and that any *Det* will do.

Now consider the situation in which the parser wants to insert into the chart a new state that is identical to this one, with the exception that its DAG restricts the *Det* to be singular. In this case, although the states in question are not identical, the addition of the new state to the chart would accomplish nothing and should therefore be prevented.

To see this, let's consider all the cases. If the new state is added, then a subsequent singular *Det* will match both rules and advance both. As a result of the unification of features, both will have DAGs indicating that their *Det*s are singular, with the net result being duplicate states in the chart. If a plural *Det* is encountered, the new state will

```
function EARLY-PARSE(words, grammar) returns chart

    ADDTOCHART((γ → • S, [0,0], dag_γ), chart[0])
    for i ← from 0 to LENGTH(words) do
      for each state in chart[i] do
        if INCOMPLETE?(state) and
                NEXT-CAT(state) is not a part of speech then
            PREDICTOR(state)
        elseif INCOMPLETE?(state) and
                NEXT-CAT(state) is a part of speech then
            SCANNER(state)
        else
            COMPLETER(state)
      end
    end
    return(chart)

    procedure PREDICTOR((A → α • B β, [i,j], dag_A))
        for each (B → γ) in GRAMMAR-RULES-FOR(B, grammar) do
            ADDTOCHART((B → • γ, [j,j], dag_B), chart[j])
        end

    procedure SCANNER((A → α • B β, [i,j], dag_A))
        if B ∈ PARTS-OF-SPEECH(word[j]) then
            ADDTOCHART((B → word[j]•, [j,j+1], dag_B), chart[j+1])

    procedure COMPLETER((B → γ •, [j,k], dag_B))
        for each (A → α • B β, [i,j], dag_A) in chart[j] do
            if new-dag ← UNIFY-STATES(dag_B, dag_A, B) ≠ Fails!
                ADDTOCHART((A → α B • β, [i,k], new-dag), chart[k])
        end

    procedure UNIFY-STATES(dag1, dag2, cat)
        dag1-cp ← COPYDAG(dag1)
        dag2-cp ← COPYDAG(dag2)
        UNIFY(FOLLOW-PATH(cat, dag1-cp), FOLLOW-PATH(cat, dag2-cp))

    procedure ADDTOCHART(state, chart-entry)
        if state is not subsumed by a state in chart-entry then
            PUSH-ON-END(state, chart-entry)
        end
```

Figure 15.11 Modifications to the Earley algorithm to include unification.

reject it and not advance, while the old rule will advance, entering a single new state into the chart. On the other hand, if the new state is not placed in the chart, a subsequent plural or singular *Det* will match the more general state and advance it, leading to the addition of one new state into the chart. Note that this leaves us in exactly the same situation as if the new state had been entered into the chart, with the exception that the duplication is avoided. In sum, nothing worthwhile is accomplished by entering into the chart a state that is more specific than a state already in the chart.

Fortunately, the notion of subsumption introduced earlier gives us a formal way to talk about the generalization and specialization relations among feature structures. The proper way to alter ENQUEUE is to check whether a newly created state is *subsumed* by any existing states in the chart. If it is, then it will not be allowed into the chart. More specifically, if a new state is identical in terms of its rule, start and finish positions, subparts, and • position, to an existing state, then that state will not be entered into the chart if its DAG is subsumed by the DAG of an existing state (i.e., if $Dag_{old} \sqsubseteq Dag_{new}$). The necessary change to the original ENQUEUE procedure is shown in Figure 15.11.

The Need for Copying

The calls to COPYDAG within the UNIFY-STATE procedure require some elaboration. Recall that one of the strengths of the Earley algorithm (and of the dynamic programming approach in general) is that once states have been entered into the chart, they may be used again and again as part of different derivations, including ones that in the end do not lead to successful parses. This ability is the motivation for the fact that states already in the chart are not updated to reflect the progress of their • but instead are copied and then updated, leaving the original states intact so that they can be used again in further derivations.

The call to COPYDAG in UNIFY-STATE is required in order to preserve this behavior because of the destructive nature of our unification algorithm. If we simply unified the DAGs associated with the existing states, those states would be altered by the unification and hence would not be available in the same form for subsequent uses by the COMPLETER function. Note that this has negative consequences regardless of whether the unification succeeds or fails, since in either case the original states are altered.

Let's consider what would happen if the call to COPYDAG were absent in the following example where an early unification attempt fails.

(15.22) Show me morning flights.

Let's assume that our parser has the following entry for the ditransitive version of the verb *show*, as well as the following transitive and ditransitive verb phrase rules.

$Verb \rightarrow show$

$\langle Verb$ HEAD SUBCAT FIRST CAT$\rangle = NP$

$\langle Verb$ HEAD SUBCAT SECOND CAT$\rangle = NP$

$\langle Verb$ HEAD SUBCAT THIRD$\rangle = END$

$VP \rightarrow Verb\ NP$

$\langle VP$ HEAD$\rangle = \langle Verb$ HEAD$\rangle$

$\langle VP$ HEAD SUBCAT FIRST CAT$\rangle = \langle NP$ CAT$\rangle$

$\langle VP$ HEAD SUBCAT SECOND$\rangle = END$

$VP \rightarrow Verb\ NP\ NP$

$\langle VP$ HEAD$\rangle = \langle Verb$ HEAD$\rangle$

$\langle VP$ HEAD SUBCAT FIRST CAT$\rangle = \langle NP_1$ CAT$\rangle$

$\langle VP$ HEAD SUBCAT SECOND CAT$\rangle = \langle NP_2$ CAT$\rangle$

$\langle VP$ HEAD SUBCAT THIRD$\rangle = END$

When the word *me* is read, the state representing the transitive verb phrase will be completed since its dot has moved to the end. COMPLETER will, therefore, call UNIFY-STATES before attempting to enter this complete state into the chart. The call will fail since the SUBCAT structures of these two rules cannot be unified. This is, of course, exactly what we want since this version of *show* is ditransitive. Unfortunately, because of the destructive nature of our unification algorithm, we have already altered the DAG attached to the state representing *show*, as well as the one attached to the *VP*, thereby ruining them for use with the correct verb phrase rule later on. Thus, to make sure that states can be used again and again with multiple derivations, we copy the DAGs associated with states before attempting any unifications involving them.

All of this copying can be quite expensive. As a result, a number of alternative techniques have been developed that attempt to minimize this cost (Pereira, 1985; Karttunen and Kay, 1985; Tomabechi, 1991; Kogure, 1990). Kiefer et al. (1999) and Penn and Munteanu (2003) describe a set of related techniques to speed up a large unification-based parsing system.

15.5.2   Unification-Based Parsing

A more radical approach to using unification in parsing can be motivated by a look at an alternative way of denoting our augmented grammar rules. Consider the following *S* rule that we have been using throughout this chapter:

$$S \rightarrow NP\ VP$$
$$\langle NP \text{ HEAD AGREEMENT} \rangle = \langle VP \text{ HEAD AGREEMENT} \rangle$$
$$\langle S \text{ HEAD} \rangle = \langle VP \text{ HEAD} \rangle$$

An interesting way to alter the context-free part of this rule is to change the way its grammatical categories are specified. In particular, we can place the categorical information about the parts of the rule inside the feature structure, rather than inside the context-free part of the rule. A typical instantiation of this approach would give us the following rule (Shieber, 1986):

$$X_0 \rightarrow X_1\ X_2$$
$$\langle X_0 \text{ CAT} \rangle = S$$
$$\langle X_1 \text{ CAT} \rangle = NP$$
$$\langle X_2 \text{ CAT} \rangle = VP$$
$$\langle X_1 \text{ HEAD AGREEMENT} \rangle = \langle X_2 \text{ HEAD AGREEMENT} \rangle$$
$$\langle X_0 \text{ HEAD} \rangle = \langle X_2 \text{ HEAD} \rangle$$

Focusing solely on the context-free component of the rule, we can say that this rule now states that the X_0 constituent consists of two components and that the X_1 constituent is immediately to the left of the X_2 constituent. The information about the actual categories of these components is placed inside the rule's feature structure, in this case, indicating that X_0 is an *S*, X_1 is an *NP*, and X_2 is a *VP*. Altering the Earley algorithm to deal with this notational change is trivial. Instead of seeking the categories of constituents in the context-free components of the rule, the algorithm simply needs to look at the CAT feature in the DAG associated with a rule.

Of course, since it is the case that these two rules contain precisely the same information, it isn't clear that there is any benefit to this change. To see the potential benefit of this change, consider the following rules.

$$X_0 \rightarrow X_1 \, X_2$$
$$\langle X_0 \text{ CAT} \rangle = \langle X_1 \text{ CAT} \rangle$$
$$\langle X_2 \text{ CAT} \rangle = PP$$
$$X_0 \rightarrow X_1 \textit{ and } X_2$$
$$\langle X_1 \text{ CAT} \rangle = \langle X_2 \text{ CAT} \rangle$$
$$\langle X_0 \text{ CAT} \rangle = \langle X_1 \text{ CAT} \rangle$$

The first rule is an attempt to generalize over various rules that we have already seen, such as $NP \rightarrow NP\,PP$ and $VP \rightarrow VP\,PP$. It simply states that any category can be followed by a prepositional phrase and that the resulting constituent has the same category as the original. Similarly, the second rule is an attempt to generalize over rules such as $S \rightarrow S \textit{ and } S$, $NP \rightarrow NP \textit{ and } NP$, and so on.[1] It states that any constituent can be conjoined with a constituent of the same category to yield a new category of the same kind. What these rules have in common is their use of phrase-structure rules that contain constituents with constrained, but unspecified, categories, something that can not be accomplished with our old rule format.

Of course, since these rules rely on the use of the CAT feature, their effect could be approximated in the old format by a simple enumeration of all the various instantiations of the rule. A more compelling case for the new approach is motivated by the existence of grammatical rules, or constructions, that contain constituents that are not easily characterized by any existing syntactic category.

Consider the following examples of the English HOW-MANY construction from the WSJ (Jurafsky, 1992).

(15.23) **How early** does it open?

(15.24) **How deep** is her Greenness?

(15.25) **How papery** are your profits?

(15.26) **How quickly** we forget.

(15.27) **How many of you** can name three famous sporting Blanchards?

As is illustrated in these examples, the HOW-MANY construction has two components: the lexical item *how* and a lexical item or phrase that is rather hard to characterize syntactically. It is this second element that is of interest to us here. As these examples show, it can be an adjective, adverb, or some kind of quantified phrase (although not all members of these categories yield grammatical results). Clearly, a better way to describe this second element is as a *scalar* concept, a constraint that can be captured by feature structures, as in the following rule:

$$X_0 \rightarrow X_1 \, X_2$$

---

[1]   These rules should not be mistaken for correct, or complete, accounts of the phenomena in question.

$$\langle X_1 \text{ ORTH} \rangle = \langle \textit{how} \rangle$$
$$\langle X_2 \text{ SEM} \rangle = \langle \text{SCALAR} \rangle$$

A complete account of rules like this involves semantics and must therefore have to wait for Chapter 17. The key point here is that by using feature structures, a grammatical rule can place constraints on its constituents in a manner that does not make any use of the notion of a syntactic category.

Of course, dealing with this kind of rule requires some changes to our parsing scheme. All of the parsing approaches we have considered thus far are driven by the syntactic category of the various constituents in the input. More specifically, they are based on simple atomic matches between the categories that have been predicted and categories that have been found. Consider, for example, the operation of the COMPLETER function shown in Figure 15.11 on page 517. This function searches the chart for states that can be advanced by a newly completed state. COMPLETER accomplishes this by matching the category of the newly completed state to the category of the constituent following the • in the existing state. Clearly, this approach will run into trouble when there are no such categories to consult.

The remedy for this problem with COMPLETER is to search the chart for states whose DAGs *unify* with the DAG of the newly completed state. This eliminates any requirement that states or rules have a category. The PREDICTOR can be changed in a similar fashion by having it add states to the chart states whose X_0 DAG component can unify with the constituent following the • of the predicting state. Exercise 15.6 asks you to make the necessary changes to the pseudocode in Figure 15.11 to effect this style of parsing. Exercise 15.7 asks you to consider some of the implications of these alterations, particularly with respect to prediction.

15.6 Types and Inheritance

> *I am surprised that ancient and modern writers have not attributed greater*
> *importance to the laws of inheritance...*
> Alexis de Tocqueville, *Democracy in America*, 1840

The basic feature structures we have presented so far have two problems that have led to extensions to the formalism. The first problem is that there is no way to place a constraint on what can be the value of a feature. For example, we have implicitly assumed that the NUMBER attribute can take only *sg* and *pl* as values. But in our current system, there is nothing, for example, to stop NUMBER from having the value *3rd* or *feminine* as values:

$$\left[\text{NUMBER} \quad \textit{feminine} \right]$$

This problem has caused many unification-based grammatical theories to add various mechanisms to try to constrain the possible values of a feature. Formalisms like Functional Unification Grammar (FUG) (Kay, 1979, 1984, 1985) and Lexical Functional Grammar (LFG) (Bresnan, 1982), for example, focused on ways to keep intransitive verbs like *sneeze* from unifying with a direct object (*Marin sneezed Toby*). This

None was addressed in FUG by addition of a special atom **none**, which is not allowed to unify with anything, and in LFG by addition of **coherence** conditions that specified when a feature should not be filled. The Generalized Phrase Structure Grammar (GPSG) (Gazdar et al., 1985, 1988) added a class of **feature co-occurrence restrictions**, to prevent, for example, nouns from having some verbal properties.

The second problem with simple feature structures is that there is no way to capture generalizations across them. For example, the many types of English verb phrases described in the Subcategorization section on page 501 share many features, as do the many kinds of subcategorization frames for verbs. Syntacticians were looking for ways to express these generalities.

Types A general solution to both of these problems is the use of **types**. Type systems for unification grammars have the following characteristics:

1. Each feature structure is labeled by a type.

Appropriateness 2. Conversely, each type has **appropriateness conditions** expressing which features are appropriate for it and what types of values they can take.

Type hierarchy 3. The types are organized into a **type hierarchy**, in which more specific types inherit properties of more abstract ones.

4. The unification operation is modified to unify the types of feature structures in addition to unifying the attributes and values.

Typed feature structures In such **typed feature structure** systems, types are a new class of objects, just like attributes and values were for standard feature structures. Types come in two *Simple types* kinds: **simple types** (also called **atomic types**) and **complex types**. A simple type *Complex types* is an atomic symbol like **sg** or **pl** (we will use **boldface** for all types), and replaces the simple atomic values used in standard feature structures. All types are organized into a multiple-inheritance **type hierarchy** (a kind of **partial order** called a **lattice**). Figure 15.12 shows the type hierarchy for the new type **agreement**, which will be the type of the kind of atomic object that can be the value of an AGREE feature.

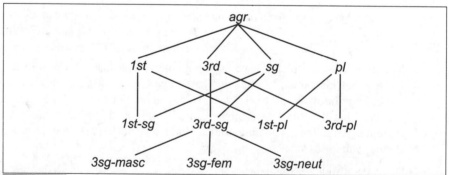

Figure 15.12   Carpenter's (1992) simple type hierarchy for the subtypes of type **agr** which can be the value of the AGREE attribute.

Subtype In the hierarchy in Fig. 15.12, **3rd** is a **subtype** of **agr**, and **3-sg** is a **subtype** of both **3rd** and **sg**. Types can be unified in the type hierarchy; the unification of any two types is the most general type that is more specific than the two input types. Thus:

3rd ⊔ **sg** = **3sg**
1st ⊔ **pl** = **1pl**
1st ⊔ **agr** = **1st**
3rd ⊔ **1st** = *undefined*

Fail type
The unification of two types that do not have a defined unifier is undefined, although it is also possible to explicitly represent this **fail type** with the symbol ⊥ (Aït-Kaci, 1984).

The second kind of types are complex types, which specify

- a set of features that are appropriate for that type
- restrictions on the values of those features (expressed in terms of types)
- equality constraints between the values

Consider a simplified representation of the complex type **verb**, which just represents agreement and verbal morphology information. A definition of **verb** would define the two appropriate features, AGREE and VFORM, and would also define the type of the values of the two features. Let's suppose that the AGREE feature takes values of type **agr** defined in Fig. 15.12 above and the VFORM feature takes values of type **vform**, where **vform** subsumes the seven subtypes **finite**, **infinitive**, **gerund**, **base**, **present-participle**, **past-participle**, and **passive-participle**. Thus, **verb** would be defined as follows (where the convention is to indicate the type either at the top of the AVM or just to the lower left of the left bracket):

$$
\begin{bmatrix}
\textbf{verb} & \\
\text{AGREE} & \textbf{agr} \\
\text{VFORM} & \textbf{vform}
\end{bmatrix}
$$

By contrast, the type **noun** might be defined with the AGREE feature, but without the VFORM feature:

$$
\begin{bmatrix}
\textbf{noun} & \\
\text{AGREE} & \textbf{agr}
\end{bmatrix}
$$

The unification operation is augmented for typed feature structures just by requiring that the types of the two structures unify in addition to the values of the component features unifying.

$$
\begin{bmatrix}
\textbf{verb} & \\
\text{AGREE} & \textbf{1st} \\
\text{VFORM} & \textbf{gerund}
\end{bmatrix}
\sqcup
\begin{bmatrix}
\textbf{verb} & \\
\text{AGREE} & \textbf{sg} \\
\text{VFORM} & \textbf{gerund}
\end{bmatrix}
=
\begin{bmatrix}
\textbf{verb} & \\
\text{AGREE} & \textbf{1-sg} \\
\text{VFORM} & \textbf{gerund}
\end{bmatrix}
$$

Complex types are also part of the type hierarchy. Subtypes of complex types inherit all the features of their parents, together with the constraints on their values. Sanfilippo (1993), for example, uses a type hierarchy to encode the hierarchical structure of the lexicon. Figure 15.13 shows a small part of this hierarchy, the part that models the various subcategories of verbs that take sentential complements; these are divided into the transitive ones (which take direct objects: (*ask yourself whether you have become better informed*) and the intransitive ones (*Monsieur asked whether I wanted to ride*). The type **trans-comp-cat** would introduce the required direct object, constraining it to be of type **noun-phrase**, and types like **sbase-comp-cat** would introduce the baseform (bare stem) complement and constrain its vform to be the baseform.

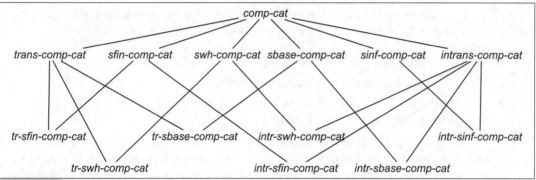

Figure 15.13   Part of the Sanfilippo (1993) type hierarchy for the verb type **verb-cat**, showing the subtypes of the **comp-cat** type. These are all subcategories of verbs that take sentential complements.

15.6.1   Advanced: Extensions to Typing

Defaults

Typed feature structures can be extended by allowing for inheritance with **default unification**. Default systems have mainly been used in lexical type hierarchies of the sort described in the previous section, to encode generalizations and subregular exceptions to them. In early versions of default unification the operation was order dependent, based on the **priority union** operation (Kaplan, 1987). More recent architectures are order independent (Lascarides and Copestake, 1997; Young and Rounds, 1993), related to Reiter's default logic (Reiter, 1980).

Priority union

Many unification-based theories of grammar, including HPSG (Pollard and Sag, 1987, 1994) and LFG (Bresnan, 1982), use an additional mechanism besides inheritance for capturing lexical generalizations: the **lexical rule**. Lexical rules (Jackendoff, 1975) express lexical generalizations by allowing a reduced, hence more redundancy free, lexicon to be automatically expanded by the rules. See Pollard and Sag (1994) for examples, Carpenter (1991) on complexity issues, and Meurers and Minnen (1997) on efficient implementation. Conversely, see Krieger and Nerbonne (1993) on using the type hierarchy to replace lexical rules.

Lexical rule

Types can also be used to represent constituency. Rules like (15.11) on page 501 use a normal phrase structure rule template and add the features through path equations, but the whole phrase-structure rule can also be represented as a type. To do this, we need a way to represent constituents as features. One way, following Sag and Wasow (1999), is to take a type **phrase**, which has a feature called DTRS ("daughters"), whose value is a list of **phrases**. For example, the phrase *I love New York* could have the following representation (showing only the DTRS feature):

$$
\begin{bmatrix}
\textbf{phrase} \\
\text{DTRS } \langle
\begin{bmatrix}
\text{CAT } PRO \\
\text{ORTH } I
\end{bmatrix},
\begin{bmatrix}
\text{CAT } VP \\
\text{DTRS } \langle
\begin{bmatrix}
\text{CAT } Verb \\
\text{ORTH } love
\end{bmatrix},
\begin{bmatrix}
\text{CAT } NP \\
\text{ORTH } New\ York
\end{bmatrix} \rangle
\end{bmatrix} \rangle
\end{bmatrix}
$$

15.6.2   Other Extensions to Unification

Path inequalities

Negation

Set-valued features

Disjunction

There are many other extensions to unification besides typing, including **path inequalities** (Moshier, 1988; Carpenter, 1992; Carpenter and Penn, 1994), **negation** (Johnson, 1988, 1990), **set-valued features** (Pollard and Moshier, 1990), and **disjunction** (Kay, 1979; Kasper and Rounds, 1986). In some unification systems, these operations are incorporated into feature structures. Kasper and Rounds (1986) and others, by contrast, implement them in a separate metalanguage that *describes* feature structures. This idea derives from the work of Pereira and Shieber (1984) and even earlier work by Kaplan and Bresnan (1982), all of whom distinguished between a metalanguage for describing feature structures and the actual feature structures themselves. The descriptions may thus use negation and disjunction to describe a set of feature structures (i.e., a certain feature must not contain a certain value or may contain any of a set of values), but an actual instance of a feature structure that meets the description would not have negated or disjoint values.

The unification grammars as described so far have no mechanism for disambiguation. Much recent work in unification grammars has focused on this disambiguation problem, particularly through the use of probabilistic augmentations. See the Historical Notes section for important references.

15.7   Summary

This chapter introduced feature structures and the unification operation that combines them.

- A feature structure is a set of features-value pairs, where features are unanalyzable atomic symbols drawn from some finite set and values are either atomic symbols or feature structures. They are represented either as **attribute-value matrices** (**AVMs**) or as directed acyclic graphs (**DAGs**), where features are directed labeled edges and feature values are nodes in the graph.

- **Unification** is the operation for both combining information (merging the information content of two feature structures) and comparing information (rejecting the merger of incompatible features).

- A phrase-structure rule can be augmented with feature structures and with feature constraints expressing relations among the feature structures of the constituents of the rule. **Subcategorization** constraints can be represented as feature structures on head verbs (or other predicates). The elements that are subcategorized for by a verb may appear in the verb phrase or may be realized apart from the verb, as a **long-distance dependency**.

- Feature structures can be **typed**. The resulting **typed feature structures** place constraints on which type of values a given feature can take; they can also be organized into a **type hierarchy** to capture generalizations across types.

Bibliographical and Historical Notes

The use of features in linguistic theory comes originally from phonology. Anderson (1985) credits Jakobson (1939) with being the first to use features (called **distinctive features**) as an ontological type in a theory, drawing on previous uses of features by Trubetskoi (1939) and others. The semantic use of features followed soon after; see Chapter 19 for the history of componential analysis in semantics. Features in syntax were well established by the 1950s and were popularized by Chomsky (1965).

The unification operation in linguistics was developed independently by Kay (1979) (feature structure unification) and Colmerauer (1970, 1975) (term unification) (see page 13). Both were working in machine translation and looking for a reversible formalism for combining linguistic information. Colmerauer's original Q-system was a bottom-up parser, based on a series of rewrite rules that contained logical variables, designed for a English-to-French machine translation system. The rewrite rules were reversible to allow them to work for both parsing and generation. Colmerauer, Fernand Didier, Robert Pasero, Philippe Roussel, and Jean Trudel designed the Prolog language, based on extending Q-systems to full unification using the resolution principle of Robinson (1965), and implemented a French analyzer based on it (Colmerauer and Roussel, 1996). The modern use of Prolog and term unification for natural *Definite Clause* language with **Definite Clause Grammars** was based on Colmerauer's (1975) meta-*Grammars* morphosis grammars, and was developed and named by Pereira and Warren (1980). Meanwhile, Martin Kay and Ron Kaplan had been working with Augmented Transi-*ATN* tion Network (**ATN**) grammars. An ATN is a Recursive Transition Network (RTN) in which the nodes are augmented with feature registers. In an ATN analysis of a passive, the first NP would be assigned to the subject register, then when the passive verb was encountered, the value would be moved into the object register. To make this process reversible, they restricted assignments to registers so that certain registers could only be filled once, that is, couldn't be overwritten once written. They thus moved toward the concepts of logical variables without realizing it. Kay's original unification algorithm was designed for feature structures rather than terms (Kay, 1979). The integration of unification into an Earley-style approach given in Section 15.5 is based on Shieber (1985b).

See Shieber (1986) for a clear introduction to unification, and Knight (1989) for a multidisciplinary survey of unification.

Inheritance and appropriateness conditions were first proposed for linguistic knowledge by Bobrow and Webber (1980) in the context of an extension of the KL-ONE knowledge representation system (Brachman and Schmolze, 1985). Simple inheritance without appropriateness conditions was taken up by number of researchers; early users include Jacobs (1985, 1987). Aït-Kaci (1984) borrowed the notion of inheritance in unification from the logic programming community. Typing of feature structures, including both inheritance and appropriateness conditions, was independently proposed by Calder (1987), Pollard and Sag (1987), and Elhadad (1990). Typed feature structures were formalized by King (1989) and Carpenter (1992). There is an extensive literature on the use of type hierarchies in linguistics, particularly for capturing lexical generalizations; besides the papers previously discussed, the interested reader should consult Evans and Gazdar (1996) for a description of the DATR language, designed for defining inheritance networks for linguistic knowledge representation, Fraser and Hudson (1992) for the use of inheritance in a dependency grammar, and Daelemans et al. (1992) for a general overview. Formalisms and systems for the implementation of constraint-based grammars through typed feature structures include the PAGE system using the TDL language (Krieger and Schäfer, 1994), ALE (Carpenter and Penn, 1994), ConTroll (Götz et al., 1997), and LKB (Copestake, 2002).

Efficiency issues in unification parsing are discussed by Kiefer et al. (1999), Malouf et al. (2000), and Munteanu and Penn (2004).

Grammatical theories based on unification include Lexical Functional Grammar (LFG) (Bresnan, 1982), Head-Driven Phrase Structure Grammar (HPSG) (Pollard and Sag, 1987, 1994), Construction Grammar (Kay and Fillmore, 1999), and Unification Categorial Grammar (Uszkoreit, 1986).

Much recent computational work on unification grammars has focused on probabilistic augmentations for disambiguation. Key relevant papers include Abney (1997), Goodman (1997), Johnson et al. (1999), Riezler et al. (2000), Geman and Johnson (2002), Riezler et al. (2002, 2003), Kaplan et al. (2004), Miyao and Tsujii (2005), Toutanova et al. (2005), Ninomiya et al. (2006), and Blunsom and Baldwin (2006).

Exercises

15.1 Draw the DAGs corresponding to the AVMs given in Examples 15.1–15.2.

15.2 Consider the following examples from the Berkeley Restaurant Project (BERP), focusing on their use of pronouns.

> I want to spend lots of money.
> Tell me about Chez Panisse.
> I'd like to take her to dinner.
> She doesn't like Italian.

Assuming that these pronouns all belong to the category *Pro*, write lexical and grammatical entries with unification constraints that block the following examples.

> *Me want to spend lots of money.
> *Tell I about Chez Panisse.

*I would like to take she to dinner.
*Her doesn't like Italian.

15.3 Draw a picture of the subsumption semilattice corresponding to the feature structures in Examples 15.3 to 15.7. Be sure to include the most general feature structure [].

15.4 Consider the following examples.

The sheep are baaaaing.
The sheep is baaaaing.

Create appropriate lexical entries for the words *the*, *sheep*, and *baaaaing*. Show that your entries permit the correct assignment of a value to the NUMBER feature for the subjects of these examples, as well as their various parts.

15.5 Create feature structures expressing the different SUBCAT frames for *while* and *during* shown on page 506.

15.6 Alter the pseudocode shown in Figure 15.11 so that it performs the more radical kind of unification-based parsing described on page 519.

15.7 Consider the following problematic grammar suggested by Shieber (1985b).

$$S \rightarrow T$$
$$\langle T \text{ F} \rangle = a$$
$$T_1 \rightarrow T_2 \, A$$
$$\langle T_1 \text{ F} \rangle = \langle T_2 \text{ F F} \rangle$$
$$S \rightarrow A$$
$$A \rightarrow a$$

Show the first S state entered into the chart by using your modified PREDICTOR from the previous exercise, then describe any problematic behavior displayed by PREDICTOR on subsequent iterations. Discuss the cause of the problem and how it might be remedied.

15.8 Using the list approach to representing a verb's subcategorization frame, show how a grammar could handle any number of verb subcategorization frames with only the following two *VP* rules. More specifically, show the constraints that would have to be added to these rules to make this work.

$$VP \rightarrow Verb$$
$$VP \rightarrow VP \, X$$

The solution to this problem involves thinking about a recursive walk down a verb's subcategorization frame. This is a hard problem; you might consult Shieber (1986) if you get stuck.

15.9 Page 524 showed how to use typed feature structures to represent constituency. Use that notation to represent rules 15.11, 15.12, and 15.13 shown on page 501.

Chapter 16

Language and Complexity

> *This is the dog, that worried the cat, that killed the rat, that ate the malt, that lay in the house that Jack built.*
>
> Mother Goose, *The House that Jack Built*

> *This is the malt that the rat that the cat that the dog worried killed ate.*
> Victor H. Yngve (1960)

Much of the humor in musical comedy and comic operetta comes from entwining the main characters in fabulously complicated plot twists. Casilda, the daughter of the Duke of Plaza-Toro in Gilbert and Sullivan's *The Gondoliers*, is in love with her father's attendant Luiz. Unfortunately, Casilda discovers she has already been married (by proxy) as a babe of six months to "the infant son and heir of His Majesty the immeasurably wealthy King of Barataria". It is revealed that this infant son was spirited away by the Grand Inquisitor and raised as a gondolier by a "highly respectable gondolier" in Venice. The gondolier had a baby of the same age and could never remember which child was which, and so Casilda was in the unenviable position, as she puts it, of "being married to one of two gondoliers, but it is impossible to say which". By way of consolation, the Grand Inquisitor informs her that "such complications frequently occur".

Luckily, such complications don't frequently occur in natural language. Or do they? In fact, there are sentences that are so complex that they are hard to understand, such as Yngve's sentence above or the sentence:

> *"The Republicans who the senator who she voted for chastised were trying to cut all benefits for veterans".*

Studying such sentences, and more generally understanding what level of complexity tends to occur in natural language, is an important area of language processing. Complexity plays an important role, for example, in deciding when we need to use a particular formal mechanism. Formal mechanisms like finite automata, Markov models, transducers, phonological rewrite rules, and context-free grammars can be described in terms of their **power**, or equivalently in terms of the **complexity** of the phenomena they can describe. This chapter introduces the Chomsky hierarchy, a theoretical tool that allows us to compare the expressive power or complexity of these different formal mechanisms. With this tool in hand, we summarize arguments about the correct formal power of the syntax of natural languages, in particular, English but also including a famous Swiss dialect of German that has the interesting syntactic property called **cross-serial dependencies**. This property has been used to argue that context-free grammars are insufficiently powerful to model the morphology and syntax of natural language.

In addition to using complexity as a metric for understanding the relation between natural language and formal models, the field of complexity is also concerned with what makes individual constructions or sentences hard to understand. For example, we saw above that certain **nested** or **center-embedded** sentences are difficult for people to process. Understanding what makes some sentences difficult for people to process is an important part of understanding human parsing.

16.1   The Chomsky Hierarchy

How are automata, context-free grammars, and phonological rewrite rules related? What they have in common is that each describes a **formal language**, which we have seen is a set of strings over a finite alphabet. But the kinds of grammars we can write with each of these formalism are of different **generative power**. One grammar is of greater generative power or **complexity** than another if it can define a language that the other cannot define. We show, for example, that a context-free grammar can be used to describe formal languages that cannot be described with a finite-state automaton.

Generative power

It is possible to construct a hierarchy of grammars, where the set of languages describable by grammars of greater power subsumes the set of languages describable by grammars of lesser power. There are many possible such hierarchies; the one that is most commonly used in computational linguistics is the **Chomsky hierarchy** (Chomsky, 1959a), which includes four kinds of grammars. Figure 16.1 shows the four grammars in the Chomsky hierarchy as well as a useful fifth type, the *mildly context-sensitive* languages.

Chomsky hierarchy

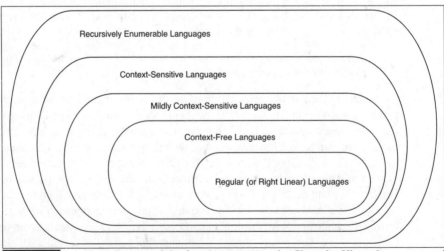

Figure 16.1   A Venn diagram of the four languages on the Chomsky Hierarchy, augmented with a fifth class, the mildly context-sensitive languages.

This decrease in the generative power of languages from the most powerful to the weakest can in general be accomplished by placing constraints on the way the grammar rules are allowed to be written. Figure 16.2 shows the five types of grammars in the extended Chomsky hierarchy, defined by the constraints on the form that rules must take. In these examples, A is a single non-terminal, and α, β, and γ are arbitrary strings of terminal and non-terminal symbols. They may be empty unless this is specifically disallowed below. x is an arbitrary string of terminal symbols.

Type	Common Name	Rule Skeleton	Linguistic Example
0	Turing Equivalent	$\alpha \rightarrow \beta$, s.t. $\alpha \neq \epsilon$	HPSG, LFG, Minimalism
1	Context Sensitive	$\alpha A \beta \rightarrow \alpha \gamma \beta$, s.t. $\gamma \neq \epsilon$	
–	Mildly Context Sensitive		TAG, CCG
2	Context Free	$A \rightarrow \gamma$	Phrase-Structure Grammars
3	Regular	$A \rightarrow xB$ or $A \rightarrow x$	Finite-State Automata

Figure 16.2   The Chomsky Hierarchy, augumented by the mildly context-sensitive grammars.

Turing-equivalent, **Type 0**, or **unrestricted** grammars have no restrictions on the form of their rules, except that the left-hand side cannot be the empty string ϵ. Any (non-null) string can be written as any other string (or as ϵ). Type 0 grammars characterize the **recursively enumerable** languages, that is, those whose strings can be listed (enumerated) by a Turing Machine.

Recursively enumerable

Context-sensitive grammars have rules that rewrite a non-terminal symbol A in the context $\alpha A \beta$ as any non-empty string of symbols. They can be written either in the form $\alpha A \beta \rightarrow \alpha \gamma \beta$ or in the form $A \rightarrow \gamma / \alpha \_\_ \beta$. We have seen this latter version in the Chomsky-Halle representation of phonological rules (Chomsky and Halle, 1968), like this flapping rule:

Context-sensitive

$$/t/ \rightarrow [dx] / \acute{V} \_\_ V$$

While the form of these rules seems context-sensitive, Chapter 7 showed that phonological rule systems that do not have recursion are actually equivalent in power to the regular grammars.

Another way of conceptualizing a rule in a context-sensitive grammar is as rewriting a string of symbols δ as another string of symbols ϕ in a "nondecreasing" way such that ϕ has at least as many symbols as δ.

We studied **context-free** grammars in Chapter 12. Context-free rules allow any single non-terminal to be rewritten as any string of terminals and non-terminals. A non-terminal may also be rewritten as ϵ, although we didn't make use of this option in Chapter 12.

Context-free

Regular grammars are equivalent to regular expressions. That is, a given regular language can be characterized either by a regular expression of the type we discussed in Chapter 2 or by a regular grammar. Regular grammars can either be **right-linear** or **left-linear**. A rule in a right-linear grammar has a single non-terminal on the left, and at most one non-terminal on the right-hand side. If there is a non-terminal on the right-hand side, it must be the last symbol in the string. The right-hand side of left-linear grammars is reversed (the right-hand side must start with (at most) a single non-terminal). All regular languages have both a left-linear and a right-linear grammar. For the rest of our discussion, we consider only the right-linear grammars.

Right-linear

Left-linear

For example, consider the following regular (right-linear) grammar:

$$S \rightarrow aA$$
$$S \rightarrow bB$$
$$A \rightarrow aS$$
$$B \rightarrow bbS$$
$$S \rightarrow \epsilon$$

It is regular, since the left-hand side of each rule is a single non-terminal and each right-hand side has at most one (rightmost) non-terminal. Here is a sample derivation in the language:

$$S \Rightarrow aA \Rightarrow aaS \Rightarrow aabB \Rightarrow aabbbS \Rightarrow aabbbaA$$
$$\Rightarrow aabbbaaS \Rightarrow aabbbaa$$

We can see that each time S expands, it produces either *aaS* or *bbbS*; thus, readers should convince themselves that this language corresponds to the regular expression $(aa \cup bbb)*$.

We do not present the proof that a language is regular if and only if it is generated by a regular grammar; it was first proved by Chomsky and Miller (1958) and can be found in textbooks like Hopcroft and Ullman (1979) and Lewis and Papadimitriou (1988). The intuition is that since the non-terminals are always at the right or left edge of a rule, they can be processed iteratively rather than recursively.

Mildly context-sensitive

The fifth class of languages and grammars that is useful to consider is the **mildly context-sensitive grammars** and the **mildly context-sensitive languages**. Mildly context-sensitive languages are a proper subset of the context-sensitive languages and a proper superset of the context-free languages. The rules for mildly context-sensitive languages can be described in a number of ways; indeed, it turns out that various grammar formalisms, including Tree-Adjoining Grammars (Joshi, 1985), Head Grammars (Pollard, 1984), Combinatory Categorial Grammars (CCG), (Steedman, 1996, 2000), and also a specific version of Minimalist Grammars (Stabler, 1997) are all weakly equivalent (Joshi et al., 1991).

16.2   Ways to Tell if a Language Isn't Regular

How do we know which type of rules to use for a given problem? Could we use regular expressions to write a grammar for English? Or do we need to use context-free rules or even context-sensitive rules? It turns out that for formal languages there are methods for deciding this. That is, we can say for a given formal language whether it is representable by a regular expression or whether it instead requires a context-free grammar, and so on.

So if we want to know if some part of natural language (the phonology of English, let's say, or perhaps the morphology of Turkish) is representable by a certain class of grammars, we need to find a formal language that models the relevant phenomena and to figure out which class of grammars is appropriate for this formal language.

Why should we care whether (say) the syntax of English is representable by a regular language? The main reason is that we'd like to know which type of rule to use in writing computational grammars for English. If English is regular, we would write regular expressions and use efficient automata to process the rules. If English is context-free, we would write context-free rules and use the CKY algorithm to parse sentences, and so on.

Another reason to care is that it tells us something about the formal properties of different aspects of natural language; it would be nice to know where a language "keeps" its complexity; whether the phonological system of a language is simpler than the syntactic system, or whether a certain kind of morphological system is inherently simpler than another kind. It would be a strong and exciting claim, for example, if we could show that the phonology of English was capturable by a finite-state machine rather than the context-sensitive rules that are traditionally used; it would mean that English phonology has quite simple formal properties. Indeed, this fact was shown by Johnson (1972) and helped lead to the modern work in finite-state methods described in Chapters 3 and 11.

16.2.1   The Pumping Lemma

The most common way to prove that a language is regular is to actually build a regular expression for the language. In doing this, we can rely on the fact that the regular languages are closed under union, concatenation, Kleene star, complementation, and intersection. We saw examples of union, concatenation, and Kleene star in Chapter 2. So if we can independently build a regular expression for two distinct parts of a language, we can use the union operator to build a regular expression for the whole language, proving that the language is regular.

Pumping lemma   Sometimes we want to prove that a given language is *not* regular. An extremely useful tool for doing this is the **pumping lemma**. There are two intuitions behind this lemma. (Our description of the pumping lemma draws from Lewis and Papadimitriou (1988) and Hopcroft and Ullman (1979).) First, if a language can be modeled by a finite automaton with a finite number of states, we must be able to decide with a bounded amount of memory whether any string was in the language or not. This amount of memory can be different for different automata, but for a given automaton it can't grow larger for different strings (since a given automaton has a fixed number of states). Thus, the memory needs must not be proportional to the length of the input. This means, for example, that languages like $a^n b^n$ are not likely to be regular, since we would need some way to remember what n was in order to make sure that there were an equal number of a's and b's. The second intuition relies on the fact that if a regular language has any long strings (longer than the number of states in the automaton), there must be some sort of loop in the automaton for the language. We can use this fact by showing that if a language *doesn't* have such a loop, then it can't be regular.

Let's consider a language L and the corresponding deterministic FSA M, which has N states. Consider an input string also of length N. The machine starts out in state q_0; after seeing one symbol it will be in state q_1; after N symbols, it will be in state q_n. In other words, a string of length N will go through $N+1$ states (from q_0 to q_N). But there are only N states in the machine. This means that at least two of the states along the accepting path (call them q_i and q_j) must be the same. In other words, somewhere on an accepting path from the initial to final state, there must be a loop. Figure 16.3 illustrates this point. Let x be the string of symbols that the machine reads on going from the initial state q_0 to the beginning of the loop q_i. y is the string of symbols that the machine reads in going through the loop. z is the string of symbols from the end of the loop (q_j) to the final accepting state (q_N).

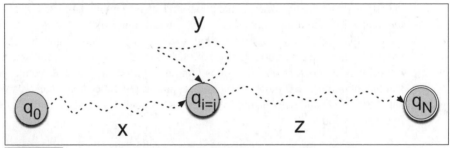

Figure 16.3   A machine with N states accepting a string xyz of N symbols.

The machine accepts the concatenation of these three strings of symbols, that is, xyz. But if the machine accepts xyz, it must accept xz! This is because the machine could just skip the loop in processing xz. Furthermore, the machine could also go around the loop any number of times; thus, it must also accept $xyyz$, $xyyyz$, $xyyyyz$, and so on. In fact, it must accept any string of the form xy^nz for $n \geq 0$.

The version of the pumping lemma we give is a simplified one for infinite regular languages; stronger versions can be stated that also apply to finite languages, but this one gives the flavor of this class of lemmas:

> **Pumping lemma**. Let L be an infinite regular language. Then, there are strings x, y, and z, such that $y \neq \epsilon$ and $xy^nz \in L$ for $n \geq 0$.

The pumping lemma states that if a language is regular, then there is some string y that can be "pumped" appropriately. But this doesn't mean that if we can pump some string y, the language must be regular. Non-regular languages may also have strings that can be pumped. Thus, the lemma is not used for showing that a language *is* regular. Rather, it is used for showing that a language *isn't* regular, by showing that in some language there is no possible string that can be pumped in the appropriate way.

Let's use the pumping lemma to show that the language a^nb^n (i.e., the language consisting of strings of a's followed by an equal number of b's) is not regular. We must show that any possible string s that we pick cannot be divided into three parts x, y, and z such that y can be pumped. Given a random string s from a^nb^n, we can distinguish three ways of breaking s up and show that no matter which way we pick, we cannot find some y that can be pumped:

1. y is composed only of a's. (This implies that x is all a's too, and z contains all the b's, perhaps preceded by some a's.) But if y is all a's, that means xy^nz has more a's than xyz. But this means it has more a's than b's, and so cannot be a member of the language a^nb^n!

2. y is composed only of b's. The problem here is similar to case 1; If y is all b's, that means xy^nz has more b's than xyz, and hence has more b's than a's.

3. y is composed of both a's and b's (this implies that x is only a's, while z is only b's). This means that xy^nz must have some b's before a's, and again cannot be a member of the language a^nb^n!

Thus, no string in a^nb^n can be divided into x, y, z in such a way that y can be pumped, and hence a^nb^n is not a regular language.

But while a^nb^n is not a regular language, it is a context-free language. In fact, the context-free grammar that models a^nb^n only takes two rules! Here they are:

$$S \rightarrow a\,S\,b$$
$$S \rightarrow \epsilon$$

Figure 16.4 illustrates a sample parse tree using this grammar to derive the sentence *aabb*.

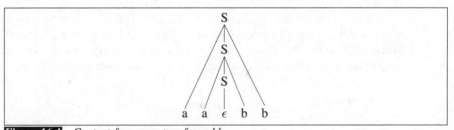

Figure 16.4   Context-free parse tree for *aabb*.

There is also a pumping lemma for context-free languages, one that can be used whether or not a language is context-free; for more complete discussions see Hopcroft and Ullman (1979) and Partee et al. (1990).

16.2.2   Proofs that Various Natural Languages Are Not Regular

> *"How's business?" I asked.*
> *"Lousy and terrible." Fritz grinned richly. "Or I pull off a new deal in the next month or I go as a gigolo,"*
> *"Either . . . or . . . ," I corrected, from force of professional habit.*
> *"I'm speaking a lousy English just now," drawled Fritz, with great self-satisfaction. "Sally says maybe she'll give me a few lessons."*
>
> Christopher Isherwood, "Sally Bowles", from
> *Goodbye to Berlin.* 1935

Consider a formal version of the English language modeled as a set of strings of words. Is this language a regular language? It is generally agreed that natural languages like English, viewed in this way, are not regular, although most attempted proofs of this are widely known to be incorrect.

One kind of argument that is often made informally is that English number agreement cannot be captured by a regular grammar because of the potentially unbounded distance between the subject and the verb in sentences like these:

(16.1) Which *problem* did your professor say she thought *was* unsolvable?

(16.2) Which *problems* did your professor say she thought *were* unsolvable?

In fact, a simple regular grammar *can* model number agreement, as Pullum and Gazdar (1982) show. Here's their regular (right-linear) grammar that models these sentences:

$$S \ \rightarrow \ \text{Which problem did your professor say T}$$
$$S \ \rightarrow \ \text{Which problems did your professor say U}$$
$$T \ \rightarrow \ \text{she thought T} \quad \text{you thought T} \quad \text{was unsolvable}$$
$$U \ \rightarrow \ \text{she thought U} \quad \text{you thought U} \quad \text{were unsolvable}$$

So, a regular grammar could model English agreement. This grammar isn't elegant, and would have a huge explosion in the number of grammar rules, but that's not relevant to the question of the regularity or non-regularity of English.

Another common flaw with previously attempted proofs, pointed out by Mohri and Sproat (1998), is that a language L containing a subset L' at position P' in the Chomsky hierarchy does not imply that the language L is also at position P'. For example, a regular language can contain as a proper subset a context-free language; L_1 is context-free,

$$L_1 = \ a^n b^n : n \in N \tag{16.3}$$

and yet L_1 is contained in the regular language L:

$$L = \ a^p b^q : p, q \in N \tag{16.4}$$

Thus, the fact that a language L contains a sublanguage that is very complex says nothing about the overall complexity of language L.

There are correct proofs, based on the pumping lemma, that English (or rather "the set of strings of English words considered as a formal language") is not a regular language. A proof by Partee et al. (1990), for example, is based on a famous class of *Center-embedded* sentences with **center-embedded** structures (Yngve, 1960); here is a variant of these sentences:

The cat likes tuna fish.
The cat the dog chased likes tuna fish.
The cat the dog the rat bit chased likes tuna fish.
The cat the dog the rat the elephant admired bit chased likes tuna fish.

These sentences get harder to understand as they get more complex. For now, let's assume that the grammar of English allows an indefinite number of embeddings. Then, to show that English is not regular, we need to show that languages with sentences like these are isomorphic to some non-regular language. Since every fronted *NP* must have its associated verb, these sentences are of the form

(the + noun)^n (transitive verb)$^{n-1}$ likes tuna fish.

The idea of the proof will be to show that sentences of these structures can be produced by intersecting English with a regular expression. We can then use the pumping lemma to prove that the resulting language isn't regular.

In order to build a simple regular expression that we can intersect with English to produce these sentences, we define regular expressions for the noun groups (*A*) and the verbs (*B*):

$A =$ the cat, the dog, the rat, the elephant, the kangaroo, ...
$B =$ chased, bit, admired, ate, befriended, ...

Now, if we take the regular expression /A* B* likes tuna fish/ and intersect it with English (considered as a set of strings), the resulting language is

$$L = x^n y^{n-1} \text{ likes tuna fish}, \ x \in A, y \in B$$

This language L can be shown to be non-regular via the pumping lemma (see Exercise 16.2). Since the intersection of English with a regular language is not a regular language, English cannot be a regular language either (since the regular languages are closed under intersection).

A well-known flaw, or at least an overly strong assumption with this proof is the assumption that these structures can be nested indefinitely. Sentences of English are clearly bounded by some finite length; perhaps we can safely say that all sentences of English are less than a billion words long. If the set of sentences is finite, then all natural languages are clearly finite-state. This is a flaw with all such proofs about the formal complexity of natural language. We will ignore this objection for now, since conveniently imagining that English has an infinite number of sentences can prove enlightening in understanding the properties of finite English.

A more worrisome potential flaw with this proof is that it depends on the assumption that these double relativizations of objects are strictly grammatical (even if hard to process). The research of Karlsson (2007) suggests that while some kinds of center-embeddings are grammatical, these double relativizations of objects are in fact ungrammatical. In any case, sentences like this get hard much faster than a billion words and are difficult to understand after a couple nestings. We return to this issue in Section 16.4.

16.3   Is Natural Language Context Free?

The previous section argued that English (considered as a set of strings) doesn't seem like a regular language. The natural next question to ask is whether English is a context-free language. This question was first asked by Chomsky (1956) and has an interesting history; a number of well-known attempts to prove English and other languages non-context-free have been published, and all except two have been disproved after publication. One of these two correct (or at least not yet disproved) arguments derives from the syntax of a dialect of Swiss German; the other from the morphology of Bambara, a Northwestern Mande language spoken in Mali and neighboring countries (Culy, 1985). The interested reader should see Pullum (1991, pp. 131–146) for an extremely witty history of both the incorrect and correct proofs; this section merely summarizes one of the correct proofs, the one based on Swiss German.

Both of the correct arguments, and most of the incorrect ones, make use of the fact that the following languages and ones that have similar properties are not context-free:

$$xx \quad x \in \{a, b\}^* \tag{16.5}$$

This language consists of sentences containing two identical strings concatenated. The following related language is also not context free:

$$a^n b^m c^n d^m \tag{16.6}$$

The non-context-free nature of such languages can be shown with the pumping lemma for context-free languages.

The attempts to prove that the natural languages are not a subset of the context-free languages do this by showing that natural languages have a property of these xx languages called **cross-serial dependencies**. In a cross-serial dependency, words or larger structures are related in left-to-right order as shown in Fig. 16.5. A language that has arbitrarily long cross-serial dependencies can be mapped to the xx languages.

Cross-serial dependencies

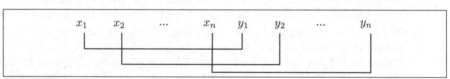

Figure 16.5   A schematic of a cross-serial dependency.

The successful proof, independently proposed by Huybregts (1984) and Shieber (1985a) (as we might expect from the prevalence of multiple discovery in science; see page 13) shows that a dialect of Swiss German spoken in Zürich has cross-serial constraints that make certain parts of that language equivalent to the non-context-free language $a^n b^m c^n d^m$. The intuition is that Swiss German allows a sentence to have a string of dative nouns followed by a string of accusative nouns, followed by a string of dative-taking verbs, followed by a string of accusative-taking verbs.

We will follow the version of the proof presented in Shieber (1985a). First, he notes that Swiss German allows verbs and their arguments to be ordered cross-serially. Assume that all the example clauses we present below are preceded by the string *"Jan säit das"* ("Jan says that"):

(16.7) ...*mer em Hans es huus   hälfed aastriiche.*
　　　 ...we Hans/DAT the house/ACC helped paint.

　　　 "...we helped Hans paint the house."

Notice the cross-serial nature of the semantic dependency: both nouns precede both verbs, and *em Hans* (Hans) is the argument of *hälfed* (helped), and *es huus* (the house) is the argument of *aastriiche* (paint). Furthermore, there is a cross-serial case dependency between the nouns and verbs; *hälfed* (helped) requires the dative, and *em Hans* is dative, while *aastriiche* (paint) takes the accusative, and *es huus* (the house) is accusative.

Shieber points out that this case marking can occur even across triply embedded cross-serial clauses like the following:

(16.8) ...*mer d'chind*   *em Hans   es huus   haend   wele   laa*
        ...we the children/ACC Hans/DAT the house/ACC have   wanted to let
        hälfe aastriiche.
        help paint.

        "...we have wanted to let the children help Hans paint the house."

Shieber notes that among such sentences, those with all dative *NP*s preceding all accusative *NP*s and all dative-subcategorizing *V*s preceding all accusative-subcategorizing *V*s are acceptable.

(16.9) Jan säit das mer (d'chind)* (em Hans)* es huus haend wele laa* hälfe*
        aastriche.

Let's call the regular expression above R. Since it's a regular expression (you see it only has concatenation and Kleene stars), it must define a regular language, and so we can intersect R with Swiss German; if the result is context-free, so is Swiss German.

But it turns out that Swiss German requires that the number of verbs requiring dative objects (*hälfe*) must equal the number of dative NPs (*em Hans*) and similarly for accusatives. Furthermore, an arbitrary number of verbs can occur in a subordinate clause of this type (subject to performance constraints). This means that the result of intersecting this regular language with Swiss German is the following language:

(16.10) L = Jan säit das mer (d'chind)^n(em Hans)^m es huus haend wele (laa)^n (hälfe)^m
         aastriiche.

But this language is of the form $wa^nb^mxc^nd^my$, which is not context-free!
So we can conclude that Swiss German is not context free.

16.4   Complexity and Human Processing

We noted in passing earlier that many of the sentences that were used to argue for the non-finite-state nature of English (like the center-embedded sentences) are quite difficult to understand. If you are a speaker of Swiss German (or if you have a friend who is), you will notice that the long cross-serial sentences in Swiss German are also rather difficult to follow. Indeed, as Pullum and Gazdar (1982) point out,

> precisely those construction-types that figure in the various proofs that English is not context-free appear to cause massive difficulty in the human processing system...

This brings us to a second use of the term **complexity**. In the previous section we talked about the complexity of a language. Here we turn to a question that is as much psychological as computational: the complexity of an individual sentence. Why are certain sentences hard to comprehend? Can this tell us anything about computational processes?

Many things can make a sentence hard to understand. For example, we saw in Chapter 14 that a word is read more slowly if it is unpredictable; that is, if it has a low N-gram probability or a low parse probability. We also saw in Chapter 14 how ambiguity arising from **garden-path sentences** can cause difficulty; if there are multiple possible parses, a human reader (or listener) sometimes chooses the incorrect parse, leading to a double-take when switching back to the other parse. Other factors that affect sentence difficulty include implausible meanings and bad handwriting.

Another kind of difficulty seems to be related to human memory limitations, and it is this particular kind of complexity (often called "linguistic complexity" or "syntactic complexity") that bears an interesting relation to the formal-language complexity from the previous section.

Consider these sentences from Gibson (1998) that cause difficulties when people try to read them (we will use the # to mean that a sentence causes extreme processing difficulty). In each case, the (ii) example is significantly more complex than the (i) example:

(16.11) (i) The cat likes tuna fish.

       (ii) #The cat the dog the rat the goat licked bit chased likes tuna fish.

(16.12) (i) The child damaged the pictures which were taken by the photographer who the professor met at the party.

       (ii) #The pictures which the photographer who the professor met at the party took were damaged by the child.

(16.13) (i) The fact that the employee who the manager hired stole office supplies worried the executive.

       (ii) #The executive who the fact that the employee stole office supplies worried hired the manager.

The earliest work on sentences of this type noticed that they all exhibit *nesting* or *center embedding* (Chomsky, 1957; Yngve, 1960; Chomsky and Miller, 1963; Miller and Chomsky, 1963). That is, they all contain examples in which a syntactic category A is nested within another category B, and surrounded by other words (X and Y):

$$[_B \; X \; [_A] \; Y]$$

In each of the examples above, part (i) has zero or one embedding, while part (ii) has two or more embeddings. For example, (16.11ii) has three reduced relative clauses embedded inside each other:

(16.14) # $[_S$ The cat $[_{S'}$ the dog $[_{S'}$ the rat $[_{S'}$ the goat licked] bit] chased] likes tuna fish].

In (16.12ii), the relative clause *who the professor met at the party* is nested in between *the photographer* and *took*. The relative clause *which the photographer . . . took* is then nested between *The pictures* and *were damaged by the child.*

(16.15) #The pictures [which the photographer [who the professor met at the party] took] were damaged by the child.

The difficulty with these nested structures is not caused by ungrammaticality, since the structures that are used in the complex sentences in (16.11ii)–(16.13ii) are the same ones used in the easier sentences (16.11i)–(16.13i). The difference between the easy and complex sentences seems to relate to the number of embeddings. But there is no natural way to write a grammar that allows N embeddings but not $N + 1$ embeddings. Rather, the complexity of these sentences seems to be a processing phenomenon; some fact about the human parsing mechanism is unable to deal with these kinds of multiple nestings in English and in other languages (Cowper, 1976; Babyonyshev and Gibson, 1999).

The difficulty of these sentences seems to have something to do with *memory limitations*. Early formal grammarians suggested that this might have something to do with how the parser processed embeddings. For example, Yngve (1960) suggested that the human parser is based on a limited-size stack and that the more incomplete phrase-structure rules the parser needs to store on the stack, the more complex the sentence. *Self-embedded* Miller and Chomsky (1963) hypothesized that **self-embedded** structures are particularly difficult. A self-embedded structure contains a syntactic category A nested within another example of A and surrounded by other words (x and y below); such structures might be difficult because a stack-based parser might confuse two copies of the rule on the stack.

The intuitions of these early models are important, although we no longer believe that the complexity problems have to do with an actual stack. For example, we now know that between sentences having the same number of embeddings there are complexity differences such as the well-known difference between subject-extracted relative clauses (16.16ii) and object-extracted relative clauses (16.16i):

(16.16)   (i) [$_S$ The reporter [$_{S'}$ who [$_S$ the senator attacked]] admitted the error].
           (ii) [$_S$ The reporter [$_{S'}$ who [$_S$ attacked the senator]] admitted the error].

The object-extracted relative clauses are more difficult to process, as measured, for example, by the amount of time it takes to read them, and other factors (MacWhinney, 1977, 1982; MacWhinney and Csaba Pléh, 1988; Ford, 1983; Wanner and Maratsos, 1978; King and Just, 1991; Gibson, 1998). Indeed, Karlsson (2007) has shown in a study of seven languages that the grammaticality of center embeddings depends a lot on the particular syntactic structure (e.g., relative clauses versus double relativization of objects) being embedded. Another problem for the old-fashioned stack-based models is the fact that discourse factors can make some doubly nested relative clauses easier to process, such as the following double nested example:

(16.17) The pictures [that the photographer [who I met at the party] took] turned out very well.

What seems to make this structure less complex is that one of the embedded NPs is the word *I*; pronouns like *I* and *you* seem to be easier to process, perhaps because they do not introduce a new entity to the discourse.

One human parsing model that accounts for this data is the Dependency Locality Theory (Gibson, 1998, 2003). The intuition of the DLT is that object relatives are difficult because they have two nouns that appear before any verb. The reader must hold on to these two nouns without knowing how they will fit into the sentences.

More specifically, the DLT proposes that the processing cost of integrating a new word w is proportional to the distance between w and the syntactic item with which w is being integrated. Distance is measured not just in words but also in how many new phrases or discourse referents have to be held in memory at the same time. Thus, the memory load for a word is higher if there have been many intervening *new discourse referents* since the word has been predicted. Thus, the DLT predicts that a sequence of NPs can be made easier to process if one of them is a pronoun that is already active in the discourse, explaining (16.17).

In summary, the complexity of these center-embedded and other examples does seem to be related to memory, although not in as direct a link to parsing stack size as was first thought 40 years ago. Recent research has focused on the relationship between complexity and probabilistic parsing, suggesting that complexity can be caused by unexpected (low probability, high entropy) structures (Hale, 2006; Levy, 2008; Moscoso del Prado Martín et al., 2004b; Juola, 1998). Understanding the relationship between complexity due to memory factors and due to information-theoretic and statistical parsing factors is an exciting research area that is just beginning to be investigated.

16.5   Summary

This chapter introduced two different ideas of **complexity**: the complexity of a formal language and the complexity of a human sentence.

- Grammars can be characterized by their **generative power**. One grammar is of greater generative power or **complexity** than another if it can define a language that the other cannot define. The **Chomsky hierarchy** is a hierarchy of grammars based on their generative power. It includes **Turing equivalent**, **context-sensitive**, **context-free**, and **regular** grammars.

- The **pumping lemma** can be used to prove that a given language is **not regular**. English is not a regular language, although the kinds of sentences that make English non-regular are exactly those that are hard for people to parse. Despite many decades of attempts to prove the contrary, English does, however, seem to be a context-free language. The syntax of Swiss-German and the morphology of Bambara, by contrast, are not context-free and seem to require mildly context-sensitive grammars.

- Certain **center-embedded** sentences are hard for people to parse. Many theories agree that this difficulty is somehow caused by **memory limitations** of the human parser.

Bibliographical and Historical Notes

Chomsky (1956) first asked whether finite-state automata or context-free grammars were sufficient to capture the syntax of English. His suggestion in that paper that English syntax contained "examples that are not easily explained in terms of phrase structure" was a motivation for his development of syntactic transformations.

Chomsky's proof was based on the language $xx^R : x \in {a,b}^*$. x^R means "the reverse of x", so each sentence of this language consists of a string of a's and b's followed by the reverse or "mirror image" of the string. This language is not regular; Partee et al. (1990) shows this by intersecting it with the regular language aa^*bbaa^*. The resulting language is $a^n b^2 a^n$; it is left as an exercise for the reader (Exercise 16.3) to show by the pumping lemma that this is not regular.

Chomsky's proof showed that English had mirror-like properties, relying on multiple embeddings of the following English syntactic structures, where $S_1, S_2, \ldots, S_n$ are declarative sentences in English,

- If S_1, then S_2
- Either S_3, or S_4
- The man who said S_5 is arriving today

See Chomsky (1956) for details.

Pullum (1991, pp. 131–146) is the definitive historical study of research on the non-context-free-ness of natural language. The early history of attempts to prove natural languages non-context-free is summarized in Pullum and Gazdar (1982). The pumping lemma was originally presented by Bar-Hillel et al. (1961), who also offer a number of important proofs about the closure and decidability properties of finite-state and context-free languages. Further details, including the pumping lemma for context-free languages (also in Bar-Hillel et al. (1961)) can be found in a textbook on automata theory such as Hopcroft and Ullman (1979).

Yngve's idea that the difficulty of center-embedded sentences could be explained if the human parser was finite-state was taken up by Church (1980) in his master's thesis. He showed that a finite-state parser that implements this idea could also explain a number of other grammatical and psycholinguistic phenomena. While the cognitive modeling field has turned toward more sophisticated models of complexity, Church's work can be seen as the beginning of the return to finite-state models in speech and language processing that characterized the 1980s and 1990s.

NP-complete We didn't have space to go into a number of other ways of looking at complexity. One is whether language processing is NP-complete. **NP-complete** is the name of a class of problems that are suspected to be particularly difficult to process. Barton, Jr. et al. (1987) prove a number of complexity results about the NP-completeness of natural language recognition and parsing. Among other things, they showed that

1. Maintaining lexical and agreement feature ambiguities over a potentially infinite-length sentence causes the problem of recognizing sentences in some unification-based formalisms like Lexical Functional Grammar to be NP-complete.

2. Two-level morphological parsing (or even just mapping between lexical and surface form) is also NP-complete.

Finally, recent work has looked at the expressive power of different kinds of probabilistic grammars, showing, for example, that weighted context-free grammars (in which each rule has a weight) and probabilistic context-free grammars (in which the weights of the rules for a non-terminal must sum to 1) are equally expressive (Smith and Johnson, 2007; Abney et al., 1999a; Chi, 1999).

Exercises

16.1 Is the language $a^n b^2 a^n$ context free?

16.2 Use the pumping lemma to show this language is not regular:

$$L = x^n y^{n-1} \, likes \, tuna \, fish, x \in A, y \in B$$

16.3 Partee et al. (1990) showed that the language $xx^R, x \in a, b*$ is not regular, by intersecting it with the regular language $aa^* bbaa^*$. The resulting language is $a^n b^2 a^n$. Use the pumping lemma to show that this language is not regular, completing the proof that $xx^R, x \in a, b*$ is not regular.

16.4 Build a context-free grammar for the language

$$L = \quad xx^R \; x \in a, b*$$

Chapter 17

The Representation of Meaning

> ISHMAEL: *Surely all this is not without meaning.*
> Herman Melville, *Moby Dick*

Meaning representations

Meaning representation languages

The approach to semantics that is introduced here, and elaborated on in the next four chapters, is based on the notion that the meaning of linguistic expressions can be captured in formal structures, which we call **meaning representations**. Correspondingly, the frameworks that specify the syntax and semantics of these representations are called **meaning representation languages**. These meaning representations play a role analogous to that of the phonological, morphological, and syntactic representations introduced in earlier chapters.

The need for meaning representations arises when neither the raw linguistic inputs nor any of the structures derivable from them by any of the transducers we have studied thus far facilitate the kind of semantic processing that is required. More specifically, what we need are representations that bridge the gap from linguistic inputs to the non-linguistic knowledge of the world needed to perform tasks involving the meaning of linguistic inputs. To illustrate this notion, consider the following everyday language tasks that require some form of semantic processing of natural language:

- Answering essay questions on an exam
- Deciding what to order at a restaurant by reading a menu
- Learning to use a new piece of software by reading the manual
- Realizing that you've been insulted
- Following recipes

Simply having access to the phonological, morphological, and syntactic representations that we have already discussed will not get us very far toward accomplishing any of these tasks. Rather, they require access to representations that link the linguistic elements involved in the task to the non-linguistic *knowledge of the world* needed to successfully accomplish them. For example, some of the world knowledge needed to perform the above tasks would include the following:

- Answering and grading essay questions requires background knowledge about the topic of the question, the desired knowledge level of the students, and how such questions are *normally* answered.
- Reading a menu and deciding what to order, giving advice about where to go to dinner, following a recipe, and generating new recipes all require knowledge about food, how it is prepared, what people like to eat, and what restaurants are like.

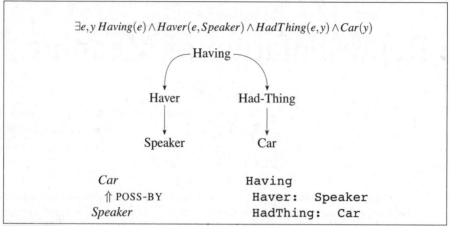

$$\exists e,y \, Having(e) \land Haver(e, Speaker) \land HadThing(e,y) \land Car(y)$$

Figure 17.1   A list of symbols, two directed graphs, and a record structure: a sampler of meaning representations for *I have a car*.

- Learning to use a piece of software by reading a manual, or giving advice about how to use the software, requires knowledge about current computers, the specific software in question, similar software applications, and knowledge about users in general.

In the representational approach presented here and elaborated on in the next four chapters, we assume that linguistic expressions have meaning representations that are made up of the *same kind of stuff* that is used to represent this kind of everyday common-sense knowledge of the world. The process whereby such representations are created and assigned to linguistic inputs is called **semantic analysis**.

Semantic analysis

To make these notions a bit more concrete, consider Fig. 17.1, which shows sample meaning representations for the sentence *I have a car*, using four representative meaning representation languages. The first row illustrates a sentence in **First-Order Logic**, which is covered in detail in Section 17.3; the graph in the center is an example of **Semantic Network**, which is discussed further in Section 17.5; the third row contains a **Conceptual Dependency** diagram, discussed in more detail in Chapter 19, and finally a **Frame-Based** representation, discussed in Section 17.5 and again in Chapter 22.

While there are non-trivial differences among these approaches, at an abstract level they all share as a common foundation the notion that a meaning representation consists of structures composed from a set of symbols, or representational vocabulary. When appropriately arranged, these symbol structures are taken to *correspond* to objects, properties of objects, and relations among objects in some state of affairs being represented. In this case, all four representations make use of symbols corresponding to the speaker, a car, and relations denoting the possession of one by the other.

It is important to note that these representations can be viewed from at least two distinct perspectives in all four of these approaches: as representations of the meaning of the particular linguistic input *I have a car* and as representations of the state of affairs in some world. It is this dual perspective that allows these representations to be used to link linguistic inputs to the world and to our knowledge of it.

The structure of this part of the book parallels that of the previous parts. We alternate discussions of the nature of meaning representations with discussions of the computational processes that can produce them. More specifically, this chapter introduces the basics of what is needed in a meaning representation, and Chapter 18 introduces a number of techniques for assigning meanings to linguistic inputs. Chapter 19 explores a range of complex representational issues related to the meanings of words. Chapter 20 then explores some robust computational methods designed to exploit these lexical representations.

Since the focus of this chapter is on some of the basic requirements for meaning representations, we defer a number of extremely important issues to later chapters. In particular, the focus of this chapter is on representing what is sometimes called the *Literal meaning* **literal meaning** of sentences. By this, we have in mind representations that are closely tied to the conventional meanings of the words that are used to create them and that do not reflect much of the context in which they occur. The shortcomings of such representations with respect to phenomena such as idioms and metaphor are discussed in Chapter 19; the task of producing representations for larger stretches of discourse is discussed in Chapter 21.

There are five major parts to this chapter. Section 17.1 explores some of the key computational requirements for what we need in a meaning representation language. Section 17.2 discusses how we can provide some guarantees that these representations will actually do what we need them to do—provide a correspondence to the state of affairs being represented. Section 17.3 then introduces First-Order Logic, which has historically been the primary technique for investigating issues in natural language semantics. Section 17.4 then describes how FOL can be used to capture the semantics of events and states in English.

17.1   Computational Desiderata for Representations

We begin by considering the issue of why meaning representations are needed and what they should do for us. To focus this discussion, we consider in more detail the task of giving advice about restaurants to tourists. In this discussion, we assume that we have a computer system that accepts spoken language queries from tourists and constructs appropriate responses by using a knowledge base of relevant domain knowledge. A series of examples will serve to introduce some of the basic requirements that a meaning representation must fulfill and some of the complications that inevitably arise in the process of designing such meaning representations. In each of these examples, we will examine the role that the representation of the meaning of the request must play in the process of satisfying it.

17.1.1   Verifiability

Let us begin by considering the following simple question:

(17.1) Does Maharani serve vegetarian food?

This example illustrates the most basic requirement for a meaning representation: it must be possible to use the representation to determine the relationship between the meaning of a sentence and the world as we know it. In other words, we need to be able to determine the truth of our representations. Section 17.2 explores this topic in some detail. For now, let's assume that we can give computational systems the ability to compare, or *match*, the representation of the meaning of a expressions with the representations in a **knowledge base**, its store of information about its world.

Knowledge base

In this example, let us assume that the meaning of this question contains, as a component, the meaning underlying the proposition *Maharani serves vegetarian food*. For now, we will simply gloss this representation as

$$Serves(Maharani, VegetarianFood) \qquad (17.2)$$

It is this representation of the input that will be matched against the knowledge base of facts about a set of restaurants. If the system finds a representation matching the input proposition in its knowledge base, it can return an affirmative answer. Otherwise, it must either say *No* if its knowledge of local restaurants is complete or say that it does not know if there is reason to believe that its knowledge is incomplete.

Verifiability

This notion, known as **verifiability**, concerns a system's ability to compare the state of affairs described by a representation to the state of affairs in some world as modeled in a knowledge base.

17.1.2   Unambiguous Representations

The domain of semantics, like all the other domains we have studied, is subject to ambiguity. Specifically, individual linguistic expressions can legitimately have different meaning representations assigned to them based on the circumstances in which they occur. Consider the following example from the BERP corpus:

(17.3) I wanna eat someplace that's close to ICSI.

Given the allowable argument structures for the verb *eat*, this sentence can either mean that the speaker wants to eat *at* some nearby location, or under a Godzilla-as-speaker interpretation, the speaker may want to devour some nearby location. The answer generated by the system for this request will depend on which interpretation is chosen as the correct one.

Since ambiguities such as this abound in all genres of all languages, some means of determining that certain interpretations are preferable (or alternatively, not as preferable) to others is needed. The various linguistic phenomena that give rise to such ambiguities and the techniques that can be employed to deal with them are discussed in detail in the next four chapters.

Our concern in this chapter, however, is with the status of our meaning representations with respect to ambiguity, and not with the means by which we might arrive at correct interpretations. Since we reason about, and act upon, the semantic content of linguistic inputs, the final representation of an input's meaning should be free from any ambiguity.[1]

---

[1] This does not preclude the use of intermediate semantic representations that maintain some level of ambiguity on the way to a single unambiguous form. Examples of such representations are discussed in Chapter 18.

Vagueness A concept closely related to ambiguity is **vagueness**. Like ambiguity, vagueness can make it difficult to determine what to do with a particular input on the basis of its meaning representation. Vagueness, however, does not give rise to multiple representations. Consider the following request as an example:

(17.4) I want to eat Italian food.

While the use of the phrase *Italian food* may provide enough information for a restaurant advisor to provide reasonable recommendations, it is nevertheless quite *vague* as to what the user really wants to eat. Therefore, a vague representation of the meaning of this phrase may be appropriate for some purposes, while a more specific representation may be needed for other purposes. It will, therefore, be advantageous for a meaning representation language to support representations that maintain a certain level of vagueness. Note that it is not always easy to distinguish ambiguity from vagueness. Zwicky and Sadock (1975) provide a useful set of tests that can be used as diagnostics.

17.1.3   Canonical Form

The notion that single sentences can be assigned multiple meanings leads to the related phenomenon of distinct inputs that should be assigned the same meaning representation. Consider the following alternative ways of expressing (17.1):

(17.5) Does Maharani have vegetarian dishes?

(17.6) Do they have vegetarian food at Maharani?

(17.7) Are vegetarian dishes served at Maharani?

(17.8) Does Maharani serve vegetarian fare?

Given that these alternatives use different words and have widely varying syntactic analyses, it would not be unreasonable to expect them to have substantially different meaning representations. Such a situation would, however, have undesirable consequences for how we determine the truth of our representations. If the system's knowledge base contains only a single representation of the fact in question, then the representations underlying all but one of our alternatives will fail to produce a match. We could, of course, store all possible alternative representations of the same fact in the knowledge base, but doing so would lead to an enormous number of problems related to keeping such a knowledge base consistent.

The way out of this dilemma is motivated by the fact that since the answers given for each of these alternatives should be the same in all situations, we might say that they all mean the same thing, at least for the purposes of giving restaurant recommendations. In other words, at least in this domain, we can legitimately consider assigning the same meaning representation to the propositions underlying each of these requests. Taking such an approach would guarantee that our simple scheme for answering yes-no questions will still work.

Canonical form The notion that inputs that mean the same thing should have the same meaning representation is known as the doctrine of **canonical form**. This approach greatly simplifies various reasoning tasks since systems need only deal with a single meaning representation for a potentially wide range of expressions.

Canonical form does, of course, complicate the task of semantic analysis. To see this, note that the alternatives given above use completely different words and syntax to refer to vegetarian fare and to what restaurants do with it. More specifically, to assign the same representation to all of these requests, our system would have to conclude that *vegetarian fare*, *vegetarian dishes*, and *vegetarian food* refer to the same thing in this context, that the use here of *having* and *serving* are similarly equivalent, and that the different syntactic parses underlying these requests are all compatible with the same meaning representation.

Being able to assign the same representation to such diverse inputs is a tall order. Fortunately, some systematic meaning relationships among word senses and among grammatical constructions can be exploited to make this task tractable. Consider the issue of the meanings of the words *food*, *dish*, and *fare* in these examples. A little introspection or a glance at a dictionary reveals that these words have a fair number of distinct uses. However, it also reveals that at least one sense is shared among them all. If a system has the ability to choose that shared sense, then an identical meaning representation can be assigned to the phrases containing these words.

Word senses

Word sense disambiguation

In general, we say that these words all have various **word senses** and that some of the senses are synonymous with one another. The process of choosing the right sense in context is called **word sense disambiguation**, or word sense tagging, by analogy to part-of-speech tagging. The topics of synonymy, sense tagging, and a host of other topics related to word meanings is covered in Chapters 19 and 20. Suffice it to say here that the fact that inputs may use different words does not preclude the assignment of identical meanings to them.

Just as there are systematic relationships among the meanings of different words, there are similar relationships related to the role that syntactic analyses play in assigning meanings to sentences. Specifically, alternative syntactic analyses often have meanings that are, if not identical, at least systematically related to one another. Consider the following pair of examples:

(17.9) Maharani serves vegetarian dishes.

(17.10) Vegetarian dishes are served by Maharani.

Despite the different placement of the arguments to *serve* in these examples, we can still assign *Maharani* and *vegetarian dishes* to the same roles in both of these examples because of our knowledge of the relationship between active and passive sentence constructions. In particular, we can use knowledge of where grammatical subjects and direct objects appear in these constructions to assign *Maharani* to the role of the server, and *vegetarian dishes* to the role of thing being served in both of these examples, despite the fact that they appear in different surface locations. The precise role of the grammar in the construction of meaning representations is covered in Chapter 18.

17.1.4   Inference and Variables

Continuing with the topic of the computational purposes that meaning representations should serve, we should consider more complex requests such as the following:

(17.11) Can vegetarians eat at Maharani?

Here, it would be a mistake to invoke canonical form to force our system to assign the same representation to this request as for the previous examples. That this request results in the same answer as the others arises, not because they mean the same thing, but because there is a common-sense connection between what vegetarians eat and what vegetarian restaurants serve. This is a fact about the world and not a fact about any particular kind of linguistic regularity. This implies that no approach based on canonical form and simple matching will give us an appropriate answer to this request. What is needed is a systematic way to connect the meaning representation of this request with the facts about the world as they are represented in a knowledge base.

Inference   We use the term **inference** to refer generically to a system's ability to draw valid conclusions based on the meaning representation of inputs and its store of background knowledge. It must be possible for the system to draw conclusions about the truth of propositions that are not explicitly represented in the knowledge base but that are nevertheless logically derivable from the propositions that are present.

Now consider the following somewhat more complex request:

(17.12) I'd like to find a restaurant where I can get vegetarian food.

Unlike our previous examples, this request does not make reference to any particular restaurant. The user is expressing a desire for information about an unknown and unnamed entity that is a restaurant that serves vegetarian food. Since this request does not mention any particular restaurant, the kind of simple matching-based approach we have been advocating is not going to work. Rather, answering this request requires a more complex kind of matching that involves the use of variables. We can gloss a representation containing such variables as follows:

$$Serves(x, VegetarianFood) \qquad (17.13)$$

Matching such a proposition succeeds only if the variable x can be replaced by some known object in the knowledge base in such a way that the entire proposition will then match. The concept that is substituted for the variable can then be used to fulfill the user's request. Of course, this simple example only hints at the issues involved in the use of such variables. Suffice it to say that linguistic inputs contain many instances of all kinds of indefinite references, and it is, therefore, critical for any meaning representation language to be able to handle this kind of expression.

17.1.5   Expressiveness

Finally, to be useful, a meaning representation scheme must be expressive enough to handle an extremely wide range of subject matter. The ideal situation, of course, would be to have a single meaning representation language that could adequately represent the meaning of any sensible natural language utterance. Although this is probably too much to expect from any single representational system, First-Order Logic, as described in Section 17.3, is expressive enough to handle quite a lot of what needs to be represented.

17.2   Model-Theoretic Semantics

The last two sections focused on various desiderata for meaning representations and on some of the ways in which natural languages convey meaning. We haven't said much formally about what it is about meaning representation languages that allows them to do all the things we want them to. In particular, we might like to have some kind of guarantee that these representations can do the work that we require of them: bridge the gap from merely formal representations to representations that tell us something about some state of affairs in the world.

To see how we might provide such a guarantee, let's start with the basic notions shared by most meaning representation schemes. What they all have in common is the ability to represent objects, properties of objects, and relations among objects. This *Model* point of view can be formalized by the notion of a **model**. The basic idea is that a model is a formal construct that stands for the particular state of affairs in the world that we're trying to represent. Expressions in a meaning representation language can then be mapped in a systematic way to the elements of the model. If the model accurately captures the facts we're interested in concerning some state of affairs in the world, then a systematic mapping between the meaning representation and model provides the necessary bridge between the meaning representation and world being considered. As we show, models provide a surprisingly simple and powerful way to ground the expressions in meaning representation languages.

Non-logical vocabulary

Logical vocabulary

Before we start, here is some terminology. The vocabulary of a meaning representation consists of two parts: the non-logical vocabulary and the logical vocabulary. The **non-logical vocabulary** consists of the open-ended set of names for the objects, properties, and relations that make up the world we're trying to represent. These appear in various schemes as predicates, nodes, labels on links, or labels in slots in frames, The **logical vocabulary** consists of the closed set of symbols, operators, quantifiers, links, etc., that provide the formal means for composing expressions in a given meaning representation language.

Denotation

Domain

We'll start by requiring that each element of the non-logical vocabulary of a meaning representation have a **denotation** in the model. By denotation, we simply mean that every element of the non-logical vocabulary corresponds to a fixed, well-defined part of the model. Let's start with objects, the most basic notion in most representational schemes. The **domain** of a model is simply the set of objects that are part of the application, or state of affairs, being represented. Each distinct concept, category, or individual in an application denotes a unique element in the domain. A domain is therefore formally a set. Note that it isn't mandatory that every element of the domain have a corresponding concept in our meaning representation; it's perfectly acceptable to have domain elements that aren't mentioned or conceived of in the meaning representation. Nor do we require that elements of the domain have a single denoting concept in the meaning representation; a given element in the domain might have several distinct representations denoting it, such as *Mary*, *WifeOf(Abe)*, or *MotherOf(Robert)*.

We can capture properties of objects in a model by denoting those domain elements that have the property in question; that is, properties denote sets. Similarly, relations among objects denote sets of ordered lists, or tuples, of domain elements that take

Extensional

part in the corresponding relations. This approach to properties and relations is thus an **extensional** one: the denotation of properties like *red* is the set of things we think are red, the denotation of a relation like *Married* is simply the set of pairs of domain elements that are married. To summarize:

- Objects denote *elements* of the domain
- Properties denote *sets of elements* of the domain
- Relations denote *sets of tuples of elements* of the domain

There is one additional element that we need to make this scheme work. We need a mapping that systematically gets us from our meaning representation to the corresponding denotations. More formally, we need a function that maps from the non-logical vocabulary of our meaning representation to the proper denotations in the model. We'll call such a mapping an **interpretation**.

Interpretation

To make these notions more concrete, let's return to the realm of restaurants we introduced in Chapter 4. Assume that our application concerns a particular set of restaurant patrons and restaurants, various facts about the likes and dislikes of the patrons, and facts about the restaurants such as their cuisine, typical cost, and noise level.

To begin populating our domain, $\mathscr{D}$, let's assume that in the current state of affairs we're dealing with four patrons designated by the non-logical symbols *Matthew*, *Franco*, *Katie*, and *Caroline*. These four symbols will denote four unique domain elements. We'll use the constants a, b, c and, d to stand for these domain elements. Note that we're deliberately using meaningless, non-mnemonic names for our domain elements to emphasize the fact that whatever it is that we know about these entities has to come from the formal properties of the model and not from the names of the symbols. Continuing, let's assume that our application includes three restaurants, designated as *Frasca*, *Med*, and *Rio* in our meaning representation, that denote the domain elements e, f, and g. Finally, let's assume that we're dealing with the three cuisines *Italian*, *Mexican*, and *Eclectic*, denoting i, j, and k in our model.

Having populated the domain, let's move on to the properties and relations we believe to be true in this particular state of affairs. Let's assume that in our application we need to represent some properties of restaurants such as the fact that some are noisy or expensive. Properties like *Noisy* denote the subset of restaurants from our domain that are known to be noisy. Two-place relational notions, such as which restaurants individual patrons *Like*, denote ordered pairs, or tuples, of the objects from the domain. Similarly, since we decided to represent cuisines as objects in our model, we can also capture which restaurants *Serve* which cuisines as a set of tuples. One particular state of affairs using this scheme is given in Fig. 17.2.

Given this simple scheme, we can ground the meaning of pretty much any of the representations shown earlier in Fig. 17.1 by simply consulting the appropriate denotations in the corresponding model. We can evaluate a representation claiming, for example, that *Matthew likes the Rio*, or that the *The Med serves Italian* by mapping the objects in the meaning representations to their corresponding domain elements and mapping any links, predicates, or slots in the meaning representation to the appropriate relations in the model. More concretely, we can verify a representation asserting that *Matthew likes Frasca* by first using our interpretation function to map the symbol *Matthew* to its denotation a, *Frasca* to e, and the *Likes* relation to the appropriate set of

Domain	$\mathscr{D} = a, b, c, d, e, f, g, h, i, j$
Matthew, Franco, Katie and Caroline	a, b, c, d
Frasca, Med, Rio	e, f, g
Italian, Mexican, Eclectic	h, i, j
Properties	
Noisy	$Noisy = e, f, g$
Frasca, Med, and Rio are noisy	
Relations	
Likes	$Likes = \langle a, f \rangle, \langle c, f \rangle, \langle c, g \rangle, \langle b, e \rangle, \langle d, f \rangle, \langle d, g \rangle$
Matthew likes the Med	
Katie likes the Med and Rio	
Franco likes Frasca	
Caroline likes the Med and Rio	
Serves	$Serves = \langle e, j \rangle, \langle f, i \rangle, \langle e, h \rangle$
Med serves eclectic	
Rio serves Mexican	
Frasca serves Italian	

Figure 17.2   A model of the restaurant world.

tuples. We then simply check that set of tuples for the presence of the tuple $\langle a, e \rangle$. If, as it is in this case, the tuple is present in the model, then we can conclude that *Matthew likes Frasca* is true; if it isn't then we can't.

This is all pretty straightforward—we're simply using sets and operations on sets to ground the expressions in our meaning representations. Of course, the more interesting part comes when we consider more complex examples such as the following:

(17.14) Katie likes the Rio and Matthew likes the Med.

(17.15) Katie and Caroline like the same restaurants.

(17.16) Franco likes noisy, expensive restaurants.

(17.17) Not everybody likes Frasca.

Clearly, our simple scheme for grounding the meaning of representations is not adequate for examples such as these. Plausible meaning representations for these examples will not map directly to individual entities, properties, or relations. Instead, they involve complications such as conjunctions, equality, quantified variables, and negations. To assess whether these statements are consistent with our model, we'll have to tear them apart, assess the parts, and then determine the meaning of the whole from the meaning of the parts according to the details of how the whole is assembled.

Consider the first example given above. A typical meaning representation for examples like this will include two distinct propositions expressing the individual patron's preferences, conjoined with some kind of implicit or explicit conjunction operator. Obviously, our model doesn't have a relation that encodes the pairwise preferences for all of the patrons and restaurants in our model, nor does it need to. We know from our model that *Matthew likes the Med* and separately that *Katie likes the Rio* (that is, we know that the tuples $\langle a, f \rangle$ and $\langle c, g \rangle$ are members of the set denoted by the *Likes* relation). All we really need to know is how to deal with the semantics of the conjunction operator. If we assume the simplest possible semantics for the English word *and*, the whole statement is true if it is the case that each of the components is true in our model. In this case, both components are true since the appropriate tuples are present and therefore the sentence as a whole is true.

Truth-conditional semantics

What we've done with this example is provide what is called **truth-conditional semantics** for the assumed conjunction operator in some meaning representation. That is, we've provided a method for determining the truth of a complex expression from the meanings of the parts (by consulting a model) and the meaning of an operator by essentially consulting a truth table. The various representations that populate Fig. 17.1 are truth-conditional to the extent that they give a formal specification as to how we can assess the meaning of complex sentences from the meaning of their parts. In particular, we need to know the semantics of the entire logical vocabulary of the meaning representation scheme being used.

Note that although the details of how this happens depends on details of the particular meaning representation being used, it should be clear that assessing the truth conditions of examples like these involves nothing beyond the simple set operations we've been discussing. We return to these issues in the next section, where we discuss them in the context of the semantics of First-Order Logic.

17.3   First-Order Logic

First-Order Logic (FOL) is a flexible, well-understood, and computationally tractable approach to the representation of knowledge that satisfies many of the desiderata given in Section 17.1 for a meaning representation language. Specifically, it provides a sound computational basis for the verifiability, inference, and expressiveness requirements, as well as a sound model-theoretic semantics.

In addition, an attractive feature of FOL is that it makes very few specific commitments as to how things ought to be represented. As we show, the specific commitments it does make are ones that are fairly easy to live with and that are shared by many of the schemes mentioned earlier; the represented world consists of objects, properties of objects, and relations among objects.

The remainder of this section introduces the basic syntax and semantics of FOL and then describes the application of FOL to the representation of events. Section 17.6 then discusses the connections between FOL and some of the other representational approaches.

17.3.1   Basic Elements of First-Order Logic

We will explore FOL in a bottom-up fashion by first examining its various atomic elements and then showing how they can be composed to create larger meaning representations. Figure 17.3, which provides a complete context-free grammar for the particular syntax of FOL that we will use, is our roadmap for this section.

$$
\begin{aligned}
\textit{Formula} &\rightarrow \textit{AtomicFormula} \\
& \textit{Formula Connective Formula} \\
& \textit{Quantifier Variable,\ldots Formula} \\
& \textit{Formula} \\
& (\textit{Formula}) \\
\textit{AtomicFormula} &\rightarrow \textit{Predicate}(\textit{Term},\ldots) \\
\textit{Term} &\rightarrow \textit{Function}(\textit{Term},\ldots) \\
& \textit{Constant} \\
& \textit{Variable} \\
\textit{Connective} &\rightarrow \land \quad \lor \quad \Rightarrow \\
\textit{Quantifier} &\rightarrow \forall \quad \exists \\
\textit{Constant} &\rightarrow A \quad \textit{VegetarianFood} \quad \textit{Maharani} \\
\textit{Variable} &\rightarrow x \quad y \\
\textit{Predicate} &\rightarrow \textit{Serves} \quad \textit{Near} \\
\textit{Function} &\rightarrow \textit{LocationOf} \quad \textit{CuisineOf}
\end{aligned}
$$

Figure 17.3   A context-free grammar specification of the syntax of First-Order Logic representations. Adapted from Russell and Norvig (2002)

Term   Let's begin by examining the notion of a **term**, the FOL device for representing objects. As can be seen from Fig. 17.3, FOL provides three ways to represent these basic building blocks: constants, functions, and variables. Each of these devices can be thought of as a way of naming, or pointing to, an object in the world under consideration.

Constants   **Constants** in FOL refer to specific objects in the world being described. Such constants are conventionally depicted as either single capitalized letters such as A and B or single capitalized words that are often reminiscent of proper nouns such as *Maharani* and *Harry*. Like programming language constants, FOL constants refer to exactly one object. Objects can, however, have multiple constants that refer to them.

Functions   **Functions** in FOL correspond to concepts that are often expressed in English as genitives such as *Frasca's location*. A FOL translation of such an expression might look like the following.

$$LocationOf(Frasca) \qquad\qquad (17.18)$$

FOL functions are syntactically the same as single argument predicates. It is important to remember, however, that while they have the appearance of predicates, they are in fact *terms* in that they refer to unique objects. Functions provide a convenient way to refer to specific objects without having to associate a named constant with them. This is particularly convenient in cases in which many named objects, like restaurants, have a unique concept such as a location associated with them.

Variable   The notion of a **variable** is our final FOL mechanism for referring to objects. Variables, which are normally depicted as single lower-case letters, let us make assertions and draw inferences about objects without having to make reference to any particular named object. This ability to make statements about anonymous objects comes in two flavors: making statements about a particular unknown object and making statements about all the objects in some arbitrary world of objects. We return to the topic of variables after we have presented quantifiers, the elements of FOL that make variables useful.

Now that we have the means to refer to objects, we can move on to the FOL mechanisms that are used to state relations that hold among objects. Predicates are symbols that refer to, or name, the relations that hold among some fixed number of objects in a given domain. Returning to the example introduced informally in Section 17.1, a reasonable FOL representation for *Maharani serves vegetarian food* might look like the following formula:

$$Serves(Maharani, VegetarianFood) \qquad (17.19)$$

This FOL sentence asserts that *Serves*, a two-place predicate, holds between the objects denoted by the constants *Maharani* and *VegetarianFood*.

A somewhat different use of predicates is illustrated by the following fairly typical representation for a sentence like *Maharani is a restaurant*:

$$Restaurant(Maharani) \qquad (17.20)$$

This is an example of a one-place predicate that is used, not to relate multiple objects, but rather to assert a property of a single object. In this case, it encodes the category membership of *Maharani*.

With the ability to refer to objects, to assert facts about objects, and to relate objects to one another, we can create rudimentary composite representations. These representations correspond to the atomic formula level in Fig. 17.3. This ability to compose complex representations is, however, not limited to the use of single predicates. Larger composite representations can also be put together through the use of **logical connectives**. As can be seen from Fig. 17.3, logical connectives let us create larger representations by conjoining logical formulas using one of three operators. Consider, for example, the following BERP sentence and one possible representation for it:

Logical connectives

(17.21) I only have five dollars and I don't have a lot of time.

$$Have(Speaker, FiveDollars) \land Have(Speaker, LotOfTime) \qquad (17.22)$$

The semantic representation for this example is built up in a straightforward way from semantics of the individual clauses through the use of the $\land$ and operators. Note that the recursive nature of the grammar in Fig. 17.3 allows an infinite number of logical formulas to be created through the use of these connectives. Thus, as with syntax, we can use a finite device to create an infinite number of representations.

17.3.2   Variables and Quantifiers

We now have all the machinery necessary to return to our earlier discussion of variables. As noted above, variables are used in two ways in FOL: to refer to particular anonymous objects and to refer generically to all objects in a collection. These two uses are made possible through the use of operators known as **quantifiers**. The two operators that are basic to FOL are the existential quantifier, which is denoted ∃ and is pronounced as "there exists", and the universal quantifier, which is denoted ∀ and is pronounced as "for all".

Quantifiers

The need for an existentially quantified variable is often signaled by the presence of an indefinite noun phrase in English. Consider the following example:

(17.23) a restaurant that serves Mexican food near ICSI.

Here, reference is being made to an anonymous object of a specified category with particular properties. The following would be a reasonable representation of the meaning of such a phrase:

$$\exists x Restaurant(x) \ \wedge \ Serves(x, MexicanFood) \tag{17.24}$$
$$\wedge \ Near((LocationOf(x), LocationOf(ICSI)))$$

The existential quantifier at the head of this sentence instructs us on how to interpret the variable x in the context of this sentence. Informally, it says that for this sentence to be true there must be at least one object such that if we were to substitute it for the variable x, the resulting sentence would be true. For example, if *AyCaramba* is a Mexican restaurant near ICSI, then substituting *AyCaramba* for x results in the following logical formula:

$$Restaurant(AyCaramba) \wedge Serves(AyCaramba, MexicanFood) \tag{17.25}$$
$$\wedge Near((LocationOf(AyCaramba), LocationOf(ICSI)))$$

Based on the semantics of the $\wedge$ operator, this sentence will be true if all of its three component atomic formulas are true. These in turn will be true if they are either present in the system's knowledge base or can be inferred from other facts in the knowledge base.

The use of the universal quantifier also has an interpretation based on substitution of known objects for variables. The substitution semantics for the universal quantifier takes the expression *for all* quite literally; the $\forall$ operator states that for the logical formula in question to be true, the substitution of *any* object in the knowledge base for the universally quantified variable should result in a true formula. This is in marked contrast to the $\exists$ operator, which only insists on a single valid substitution for the sentence to be true.

Consider the following example:

(17.26) All vegetarian restaurants serve vegetarian food.

A reasonable representation for this sentence would be something like the following:

$$\forall x VegetarianRestaurant(x) \ \Rightarrow \ Serves(x, VegetarianFood) \tag{17.27}$$

For this sentence to be true, it must be the case that every substitution of a known object for x must result in a sentence that is true. We can divide the set of all possible substitutions into the set of objects consisting of vegetarian restaurants and the set consisting of everything else. Let us first consider the case in which the substituted object actually is a vegetarian restaurant; one such substitution would result in the following sentence:

$$VegetarianRestaurant(Maharani) \ \Rightarrow \ Serves(Maharani, VegetarianFood) \tag{17.28}$$

If we assume that we know that the consequent clause

$$Serves(Maharani, VegetarianFood) \tag{17.29}$$

is true, then this sentence as a whole must be true. Both the antecedent and the consequent have the value *True* and, therefore, according to the first two rows of Fig. 17.4 on page 561 the sentence itself can have the value *True*. This result will be the same for all possible substitutions of *Terms* representing vegetarian restaurants for *x*.

Remember, however, that for this sentence to be true, it must be true for all possible substitutions. What happens when we consider a substitution from the set of objects that are not vegetarian restaurants? Consider the substitution of a non-vegetarian restaurant such as *Ay Caramba's* for the variable *x*:

$$VegetarianRestaurant(AyCaramba) \Rightarrow Serves(AyCaramba, VegetarianFood)$$

Since the antecedent of the implication is *False*, we can determine from Fig. 17.4 that the sentence is always *True*, again satisfying the $\forall$ constraint.

Note that it may still be the case that *Ay Caramba* serves vegetarian food without actually being a vegetarian restaurant. Note also, that despite our choice of examples, there are no implied categorical restrictions on the objects that can be substituted for *x* by this kind of reasoning. In other words, there is no restriction of *x* to restaurants or concepts related to them. Consider the following substitution:

$$VegetarianRestaurant(Carburetor) \Rightarrow Serves(Carburetor, VegetarianFood)$$

Here the antecedent is still false, and hence, the rule remains true under this kind of irrelevant substitution.

To review, variables in logical formulas must be either existentially ($\exists$) or universally ($\forall$) quantified. To satisfy an existentially quantified variable, at least one substitution must result in a true sentence. Sentences with universally quantified variables must be true under all possible substitutions.

17.3.3   Lambda Notation

Lambda notation

The final element we need to complete our discussion of FOL is called the **lambda notation** (Church, 1940). This notation provides a way to abstract from fully specified FOL formula in a way that will be particularly useful for semantic analysis. The lambda notation extends the syntax of FOL to include expressions of the following form:

$$\lambda x.P(x) \tag{17.30}$$

Such expressions consist of the Greek symbol λ, followed by one or more variables, followed by a FOL formula that makes use of those variables.

The usefulness of these λ-expressions is based on the ability to apply them to logical terms to yield new FOL expressions where the formal parameter variables are bound to the specified terms. This process is known as λ-**reduction** and consists of a simple

λ-reduction

textual replacement of the λ variables with the specified FOL terms, accompanied by the subsequent removal of the λ. The following expressions illustrate the application of a λ-expression to the constant *A*, followed by the result of performing a λ-reduction on this expression:

$$\lambda x.P(x)(A) \tag{17.31}$$
$$P(A)$$

An important and useful variation of this technique is the use of one λ-expression as the body of another as in the following expression:

$$\lambda x.\lambda y.Near(x,y) \tag{17.32}$$

This fairly abstract expression can be glossed as the state of something being near something else. The following expressions illustrate a single λ-application and subsequent reduction with this kind of embedded λ-expression:

$$\lambda x.\lambda y.Near(x,y)(Bacaro) \tag{17.33}$$
$$\lambda y.Near(Bacaro,y)$$

The important point here is that the resulting expression is still a λ-expression; the first reduction bound the variable x and removed the outer λ, thus revealing the inner expression. As might be expected, this resulting λ-expression can, in turn, be applied to another term to arrive at a fully specified logical formula, as in the following:

$$\lambda y.Near(Bacaro,y)(Centro) \tag{17.34}$$
$$Near(Bacaro,Centro)$$

Currying   This general technique, called **currying**[2] (Schönkfinkel, 1924) is a way of converting a predicate with multiple arguments into a sequence of single-argument predicates.

As we show in Chapter 18, the λ-notation provides a way to incrementally gather arguments to a predicate when they do not all appear together as daughters of the predicate in a parse tree.

17.3.4   The Semantics of First-Order Logic

The various objects, properties, and relations represented in a FOL knowledge base acquire their meanings by virtue of their correspondence to objects, properties, and relations out in the external world being modeled. We can accomplish this by employing the model-theoretic approach introduced in Section 17.2. Recall that this approach employs simple set-theoretic notions to provide a truth-conditional mapping from the expressions in a meaning representation to the state of affairs being modeled. We can apply this approach to FOL by going through all the elements in Fig. 17.3 on page 556 and specifying how each should be accounted for.

We can start by asserting that the objects in our world, FOL terms, denote elements in a domain, and asserting that atomic formulas are captured either as sets of domain elements for properties, or as sets of tuples of elements for relations. As an example, consider the following:

(17.35) Centro is near Bacaro.

Capturing the meaning of this example in FOL involves identifying the *Terms* and *Predicates* that correspond to the various grammatical elements in the sentence and

---

[2] *Currying* is the standard term, although Heim and Kratzer (1998) present an interesting argument for the term *Schönkfinkelization* over currying, since Curry *later* built on Schönfinkel's work.

creating logical formulas that capture the relations implied by the words and syntax of the sentence. For this example, such an effort might yield something like the following:

$$Near(Centro, Bacaro) \tag{17.36}$$

The meaning of this logical formula is based on whether the domain elements denoted by the terms *Centro* and *Bacaro* are contained among the tuples denoted by the relation denoted by the predicate *Near* in the current model.

The interpretations of formulas involving logical connectives is based on the meaning of the components in the formulas combined with the meanings of the connectives they contain. Figure 17.4 gives interpretations for each of the logical operators shown in Fig. 17.3.

P	Q	$\neg P$	$P \wedge Q$	$P \vee Q$	$P \Rightarrow Q$
False	False	True	False	False	True
False	True	True	False	True	True
True	False	False	False	True	False
True	True	False	True	True	True

Figure 17.4   Truth table giving the semantics of the various logical connectives.

The semantics of the $\wedge$ (and) and $\neg$ (not) operators are fairly straightforward, and are correlated with at least some of the senses of the corresponding English terms. However, it is worth pointing out that the $\vee$ (or) operator is not disjunctive in the same way that the corresponding English word is, and that the $\Rightarrow$ (implies) operator is only loosely based on any common-sense notions of implication or causation.

The final bit we need to address involves variables and quantifiers. Recall that there are no variables in our set-based models, only elements of the domain and relations that hold among them. We can provide a model-based account for formulas with variables by employing the notion of a substitution introduced earlier on page 557. Formulas involving $\exists$ are true if a substitution of terms for variables results in a formula that is true in the model. Formulas involving $\forall$ must be true under all possible substitutions.

17.3.5   Inference

One of the most important desiderata given in Section 17.1 for a meaning representation language is that it should support inference, or deduction. That is, the ability to add valid new propositions to a knowledge base or to determine the truth of propositions not explicitly contained within a knowledge base. This section briefly discusses **modus ponens**, the most widely implemented inference method provided by FOL. Applications of modus ponens to inference in discourse is discussed in Chapter 21.

Modus ponens   **Modus ponens** is a familiar form of inference that corresponds to what is informally known as *if-then* reasoning. We can abstractly define modus ponens as follows, where α and β should be taken as FOL formulas:

$$\frac{\alpha \qquad\qquad}{\beta} \tag{17.37}$$
$$\frac{\alpha \Rightarrow \beta}{\beta}$$

A schema like this indicates that the formula below the line can be inferred from the formulas above the line by some form of inference. Modus ponens simply states that if the left-hand side of an implication rule is true, then the right-hand side of the rule can be inferred. In the following discussions, we will refer to the left-hand side of an implication as the antecedent and the right-hand side as the consequent.

For a typical use of modus ponens, consider the following example, which uses a rule from the last section:

$$\frac{VegetarianRestaurant(Leaf) \qquad \forall x VegetarianRestaurant(x) \Rightarrow Serves(x, VegetarianFood)}{Serves(Leaf, VegetarianFood)} \qquad (17.38)$$

Here, the formula $VegetarianRestaurant(Leaf)$ matches the antecedent of the rule, thus allowing us to use modus ponens to conclude $Serves(Leaf, VegetarianFood)$.

Modus ponens can be put to practical use in one of two ways: forward chaining and *Forward chaining* backward chaining. In **forward chaining** systems, modus ponens is used in precisely the manner just described. As individual facts are added to the knowledge base, modus ponens is used to fire all applicable implication rules. In this kind of arrangement, as soon as a new fact is added to the knowledge base, all applicable implication rules are found and applied, each resulting in the addition of new facts to the knowledge base. These new propositions in turn can be used to fire implication rules applicable to them. The process continues until no further facts can be deduced.

The forward chaining approach has the advantage that facts will be present in the knowledge base when needed, because, in a sense all inference is performed in advance. This can substantially reduce the time needed to answer subsequent queries since they should all amount to simple lookups. The disadvantage of this approach is that facts that will never be needed may be inferred and stored.

Production systems **Production systems**, which are used extensively in cognitive modeling research, are forward chaining inference systems augmented with additional control knowledge that governs which rules are to be fired.

Backward chaining In **backward chaining**, modus ponens is run in reverse to prove specific propositions called queries. The first step is to see if the query formula is true by determining if it is present in the knowledge base. If it is not, then the next step is to search for applicable implication rules present in the knowledge base. An applicable rule is one whereby the consequent of the rule matches the query formula. If there are any such rules, then the query can be proved if the antecedent of any one them can be shown to be true. Not surprisingly, this can be performed recursively by backward chaining on the antecedent as a new query. The Prolog programming language is a backward chaining system that implements this strategy.

To see how this works, let's assume that we have been asked to verify the truth of the proposition $Serves(Leaf, VegetarianFood)$, assuming the facts given above the line in (17.38). Since this proposition is not present in the knowledge base, a search for an applicable rule is initiated resulting in the rule given above. After substituting the constant *Leaf* for the variable x, our next task is to prove the antecedent of the rule, $VegetarianRestaurant(Leaf)$, which, of course, is one of the facts we are given.

Note that it is critical to distinguish between reasoning by backward chaining from queries to known facts and reasoning backwards from known consequents to unknown antecedents. To be specific, by reasoning backwards we mean that if the consequent of a rule is known to be true, we assume that the antecedent will be as well. For example, let's assume that we know that *Serves*(*Leaf*, *VegetarianFood*) is true. Since this fact matches the consequent of our rule, we might reason backwards to the conclusion that *VegetarianRestaurant*(*Leaf*).

Abduction

While backward chaining is a sound method of reasoning, reasoning backwards is an invalid, though frequently useful, form of *plausible reasoning*. Plausible reasoning from consequents to antecedents is known as **abduction**, and as we show in Chapter 21, is often useful in accounting for many of the inferences people make while analyzing extended discourses.

Complete

Resolution

While forward and backward reasoning are sound, neither is **complete**. This means that there are valid inferences that cannot be found by systems using these methods alone. Fortunately, there is an alternative inference technique called **resolution** that is sound and complete. Unfortunately, inference systems based on resolution are far more computationally expensive than forward or backward chaining systems. In practice, therefore, most systems use some form of chaining and place a burden on knowledge-base developers to encode the knowledge in a fashion that permits the necessary inferences to be drawn.

17.4   Event and State Representations

Much of the semantics that we need to capture in language consists of representations of states and events. Roughly speaking, states are conditions, or properties, that remain unchanged over some period of time, and events denote changes in some state of affairs. The representation of both can involve a host of participants, props, times and locations.

The representations for events and states that we have employed thus far have consisted of single predicates with as many arguments as are needed to incorporate all the roles associated with a given example. For example, the representation for an expression such as *Leaf serves vegetarian fare* consists of a single predicate with arguments for the entity doing the serving and the thing served.

$$Serves(Leaf, VegetarianFare) \tag{17.39}$$

Such an approach simply assumes that the predicate denoting the meaning of a verb has the same number of arguments as are present in the verb's syntactic subcategorization frame. Unfortunately, four problems with this approach make it awkward to apply in practice:

- Determining the correct number of roles for any given event
- Representing facts about the roles associated with an event
- Ensuring that all the correct inferences can be derived directly from the representation of an event
- Ensuring that no incorrect inferences can be derived from the representation of an event

We will explore these and other related issues by considering a series of representations for events. This discussion will focus on the following examples of the verb *eat*:

(17.40) I ate.

(17.41) I ate a turkey sandwich.

(17.42) I ate a turkey sandwich at my desk.

(17.43) I ate at my desk.

(17.44) I ate lunch.

(17.45) I ate a turkey sandwich for lunch.

(17.46) I ate a turkey sandwich for lunch at my desk.

Arity

Clearly, the variable number of arguments for a predicate-bearing verb like *eat* poses a tricky problem. While we would like to think that all of these examples denote the same kind of event, predicates in FOL have fixed **arity** — they take a fixed number of arguments.

One possible solution is suggested by the way that examples like these are handled syntactically. For example, the solution given in Chapter 15 was to create one subcategorization frame for each of the configurations of arguments that a verb allows. The semantic analog to this approach is to create as many different *eating* predicates as are needed to handle all of the ways that *eat* behaves. Such an approach would yield the following kinds of representations for (17.40) through (17.46).

$$Eating_1(Speaker)$$
$$Eating_2(Speaker, TurkeySandwich)$$
$$Eating_3(Speaker, TurkeySandwich, Desk)$$
$$Eating_4(Speaker, Desk)$$
$$Eating_5(Speaker, Lunch)$$
$$Eating_6(Speaker, TurkeySandwich, Lunch)$$
$$Eating_7(Speaker, TurkeySandwich, Lunch, Desk)$$

This approach simply sidesteps the issue of how many arguments the *Eating* predicate should have by creating distinct predicates for each of the subcategorization frames. Unfortunately, this approach comes at a rather high cost. Other than the suggestive names of the predicates, nothing ties these events to one another even though there are obvious logical relations among them. Specifically, if (17.46) is true, then all of the other examples are true as well. Similarly, if (17.45) is true, then (17.40), (17.41), and (17.44) must also be true. Such logical connections cannot be made on the basis of these predicates alone. Moreover, we would expect a common-sense knowledge base to contain logical connections between concepts like *Eating* and related concepts like *Hunger* and *Food*.

Meaning postulates

One way to solve these problems involves the use of what are called **meaning postulates**. Consider the following example postulate:

$$\forall w, x, y, z \, Eating_7(w, x, y, z) \Rightarrow Eating_6(w, x, y) \tag{17.47}$$

This postulate explicitly ties together the semantics of two of our predicates. Other postulates could be created to handle the rest of the logical relations among the various *Eatings* and the connections from them to other related concepts.

Although such an approach might be made to work in small domains, it clearly has scalability problems. A somewhat more sensible approach is to say that (17.40) through (17.46) all reference the same predicate with some of the arguments missing from some of the surface forms. Under this approach, as many arguments are included in the definition of the predicate as ever appear with it in an input. Adopting the structure of a predicate like $Eating_7$ as an example would give us a predicate with four arguments denoting the eater, thing eaten, meal being eaten, and the location of the eating. The following formulas would then capture the semantics of our examples:

$$\exists w, x, y \, Eating(Speaker, w, x, y)$$
$$\exists w, x \, Eating(Speaker, TurkeySandwich, w, x)$$
$$\exists w \, Eating(Speaker, TurkeySandwich, w, Desk)$$
$$\exists w, x \, Eating(Speaker, w, x, Desk)$$
$$\exists w, x \, Eating(Speaker, w, Lunch, x)$$
$$\exists w \, Eating(Speaker, TurkeySandwich, Lunch, w)$$
$$Eating(Speaker, TurkeySandwich, Lunch, Desk)$$

This approach directly yields the obvious logical connections among these formulas without the use of meaning postulates. Specifically, all of the sentences with ground terms as arguments logically imply the truth of the formulas with existentially bound variables as arguments.

Unfortunately, this approach has at least two glaring deficiencies: it makes too many commitments and it does not let us individuate events. As an example of how it makes too many commitments, consider how we accommodated the *for lunch* complement in (17.44) through (17.46); a third argument, the meal being eaten, was added to the *Eating* predicate. The presence of this argument implicitly makes it the case that all eating events are associated with a meal (i.e., breakfast, lunch, or dinner). More specifically, the existentially quantified variable for the meal argument in the above examples states that some formal meal is associated with each of these eatings. This is flawed since one can certainly eat something without its being associated with a meal.

To see how this approach fails to properly individuate events, consider the following formulas.

$$\exists w, x \, Eating(Speaker, w, x, Desk)$$
$$\exists w, x \, Eating(Speaker, w, Lunch, x)$$
$$\exists w, x \, Eating(Speaker, w, Lunch, Desk)$$

If we knew that the first two formulas were referring to the same event, they could be combined to create the third representation. Unfortunately, with the current representation we have no way of telling if this is possible. The independent facts that *I ate at my desk* and *I ate lunch* do not permit us to conclude that *I ate lunch at my desk*. What is lacking in this approach is some way of referring to the particular events in question.

Event variable

We can solve these problems if we employ reification to elevate events to entities that can be quantified over. To accomplish this elevation, we can add an **event variable** as the first argument to the representation of any event. Consider the representation of (17.46) under this kind of approach.

$$\exists e \, Eating(e, Speaker, TurkeySandwich, Lunch, Desk) \tag{17.48}$$

The variable *e* now gives us a handle on the event in question. If we need to make additional assertions about this event, we can do so through this variable. For example, if we subsequently determine that this *Eating* event happened on a Tuesday, we can assert that as follows:

$$\exists e\, Eating(e, Speaker, TurkeySandwich, Lunch, Desk) \wedge Time(e, Tuesday) \quad (17.49)$$

Davidsonian

Events represented in this fashion are referred to as **Davidsonian** event representations after the philosopher Donald Davidson who introduced the technique (Davidson, 1967).

This approach still leaves us with the problem of deciding a fixed set of semantic roles for each predicate and then capturing other ancillary facts with additional predications. For example, in (17.49) we captured the location of the event as the fourth argument to the *Eating* predicate, and we captured the time with the *Time* relation. We can eliminate this dichotomy by capturing all the event arguments with additional relations.

$$\exists e\, Eating(e) \; \wedge \; Eater(e, Speaker) \wedge Eaten(e, TurkeySandwich) \quad (17.50)$$
$$\wedge \; Meal(e, Lunch) \wedge Location(e, Desk) \wedge Time(e, Tuesday)$$

Neo-Davidsonian

This style of representation distills the representation of events to a single argument that stands for the event itself. Everything else is captured by additional predications. Representations of this sort are typically referred to as **neo-Davidsonian** event representations (Parsons, 1990). To summarize, in the neo-Davidsonian approach to event representations:

- There is no need to specify a fixed number of arguments for a given surface predicate; rather, as many roles and fillers can be glued on as appear in the input.

- No more roles are postulated than are mentioned in the input.

- The logical connections among closely related examples are satisfied without the need for meaning postulates.

17.4.1   Representing Time

In our discussion of events, we did not seriously address the issue of capturing the time when the represented events are supposed to have occurred. The representation

Temporal logic

of such information in a useful form is the domain of **temporal logic**. This discussion introduces the most basic concerns of temporal logic and briefly discusses the means by which human languages convey temporal information, which, among other things,

Tense logic

includes **tense logic**, the ways that verb tenses convey temporal information. A more detailed discussion of robust approaches to the representation and analysis of temporal expressions is presented in Chapter 22.

The most straightforward theory of time holds that it flows inexorably forward and that events are associated with either points or intervals in time, as on a timeline. Given these notions, we can order distinct events by situating them on the timeline. More specifically, we can say that one event *precedes* another if the flow of time leads from the first event to the second. Accompanying these notions in most theories is the idea of the current moment in time. Combining this notion with the idea of a temporal ordering relationship yields the familiar notions of past, present, and future.

Not surprisingly, a large number of schemes can represent this kind of temporal information. The one presented here is a fairly simple one that stays within the FOL framework of reified events that we have been pursuing. Consider the following examples:

(17.51) I arrived in New York.

(17.52) I am arriving in New York.

(17.53) I will arrive in New York.

These sentences all refer to the same kind of event and differ solely in the tense of the verb. In our current scheme for representing events, all three would share the following kind of representation, which lacks any temporal information:

$$\exists e Arriving(e) \wedge Arriver(e, Speaker) \wedge Destination(e, NewYork) \qquad (17.54)$$

The temporal information provided by the tense of the verbs can be exploited by predicating additional information about the event variable e. Specifically, we can add temporal variables representing the interval corresponding to the event, the end point of the event, and temporal predicates relating this end point to the current time as indicated by the tense of the verb. Such an approach yields the following representations for our *arriving* examples:

$$\exists e, i, n, t \, Arriving(e) \quad \wedge \quad Arriver(e, Speaker) \wedge Destination(e, NewYork)$$
$$\wedge \quad IntervalOf(e, i) \wedge EndPoint(i, e) \wedge Precedes(e, Now)$$

$$\exists e, i, n, t \, Arriving(e) \quad \wedge \quad Arriver(e, Speaker) \wedge Destination(e, NewYork)$$
$$\wedge \quad IntervalOf(e, i) \wedge MemberOf(i, Now)$$

$$\exists e, i, n, t \, Arriving(e) \quad \wedge \quad Arriver(e, Speaker) \wedge Destination(e, NewYork)$$
$$\wedge \quad IntervalOf(e, i) \wedge EndPoint(e, n) \wedge Precedes(Now, e)$$

This representation introduces a variable to stand for the interval of time associated with the event and a variable that stands for the end of that interval. The two-place predicate *Precedes* represents the notion that the first time-point argument precedes the second in time; the constant *Now* refers to the current time. For past events, the end point of the interval must precede the current time. Similarly, for future events the current time must precede the end of the event. For events happening in the present, the current time is contained within the event interval.

Unfortunately, the relation between simple verb tenses and points in time is by no means straightforward. Consider the following examples:

(17.55) Ok, we fly from San Francisco to Boston at 10.

(17.56) Flight 1390 will be at the gate an hour now.

In the first example, the present tense of the verb *fly* is used to refer to a future event, while in the second the future tense is used to refer to a past event.

More complications occur when we consider some of the other verb tenses. Consider the following examples:

(17.57) Flight 1902 arrived late.

(17.58) Flight 1902 had arrived late.

Although both refer to events in the past, representing them in the same way seems wrong. The second example seems to have another unnamed event lurking in the background (e.g., Flight 1902 had already arrived late *when* something else happened). To account for this phenomena, Reichenbach (1947) introduced the notion of a **reference** *Reference point*   **point**. In our simple temporal scheme, the current moment in time is equated with the time of the utterance and is used as a reference point for when the event occurred (before, at, or after). In Reichenbach's approach, the notion of the reference point is separated from the utterance time and the event time. The following examples illustrate the basics of this approach:

(17.59) When Mary's flight departed, I ate lunch.

(17.60) When Mary's flight departed, I had eaten lunch.

In both of these examples, the eating event has happened in the past, that is, prior to the utterance. However, the verb tense in the first example indicates that the eating event began when the flight departed, while the second example indicates that the eating was accomplished prior to the flight's departure. Therefore, in Reichenbach's terms the *departure* event specifies the reference point. These facts can be accommodated by additional constraints relating the *eating* and *departure* events. In the first example, the reference point precedes the *eating* event, and in the second example, the eating precedes the reference point. Figure 17.5 illustrates Reichenbach's approach with the primary English tenses. Exercise 17.6 asks you to represent these examples in FOL.

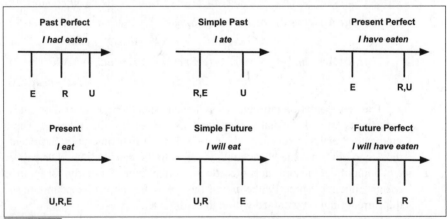

Figure 17.5   Reichenbach's approach applied to various English tenses. In these diagrams, time flows from left to right, an **E** denotes the time of the event, an **R** denotes the reference time, and an **U** denotes the time of the utterance.

This discussion has focused narrowly on the broad notions of past, present, and future and how they are signaled by various English verb tenses. Of course, languages also have many other more direct and more specific ways to convey temporal information, including the use of a wide variety of temporal expressions, as in the following ATIS examples:

(17.61) I'd like to go at 6:45, in the morning.

(17.62) Somewhere around noon, please.

As we show in Chapter 22, grammars for such temporal expressions are of considerable practical importance to information extraction and question-answering applications.

Finally, we should note that a systematic conceptual organization is reflected in examples like these. In particular, temporal expressions in English are frequently expressed in spatial terms, as is illustrated by the various uses of *at, in, somewhere*, and *near* in these examples (Lakoff and Johnson, 1980; Jackendoff, 1983). Metaphorical organizations such as these, in which one domain is systematically expressed in terms of another, will be discussed in more detail in Chapter 19.

17.4.2 Aspect

Aspect

In the last section, we discussed ways to represent the time of an event with respect to the time of an utterance describing it. In this section, we address the notion of **aspect**, which concerns a cluster of related topics, including whether an event has ended or is ongoing, whether it is conceptualized as happening at a point in time or over some interval, and whether any particular state in the world comes about because of it. Based on these and related notions, event expressions have traditionally been divided into four general classes illustrated in the following examples:

Stative: I know my departure gate.

Activity: John is flying.

Accomplishment: Sally booked her flight.

Achievement: She found her gate.

Although the earliest versions of this classification were discussed by Aristotle, the one presented here is due to Vendler (1967). In the following discussion, we'll present a brief characterization of each of the four classes, along with some diagnostic techniques suggested in Dowty (1979) for identifying examples of each kind.

Stative expressions

Stative expressions represent the notion of an event participant having a particular property, or being in a state, at a given point in time. As such, these expressions can be thought of as capturing an aspect of a world at a single point in time. Consider the following ATIS examples.

(17.63) I like Flight 840 arriving at 10:06.

(17.64) I need the cheapest fare.

(17.65) I want to go first class.

In examples like these, the event participant denoted by the subject can be seen as experiencing something at a specific point in time. Whether or not the experiencer was in the same state earlier or will be in the future is left unspecified.

There are a number of diagnostic tests for identifying statives. As an example, stative verbs are distinctly odd when used in the progressive form.

(17.66) *I am needing the cheapest fare on this day.

(17.67) *I am wanting to go first class.

We should note that in these and subsequent examples, we use an * to indicate a broadened notion of ill-formedness that may include both semantic and syntactic factors.

Statives are also odd when used as imperatives.

(17.68) *Need the cheapest fare!

Finally, statives are not easily modified by adverbs like *deliberately* and *carefully*.

(17.69) *I deliberately like Flight 840 arriving at 10:06.

(17.70) *I carefully like Flight 840 arriving at 10:06.

Activity expressions

Activity expressions describe events undertaken by a participant and have no particular end point. Unlike statives, activities are seen as occurring over some span of time and are therefore not associated with single points in time. Consider the following examples:

(17.71) She drove a Mazda.

(17.72) I live in Brooklyn.

These examples both specify that the subject is engaged in, or has engaged in, the activity specified by the verb for some period of time.

Unlike statives, activity expressions are fine in both the progressive and imperative forms.

(17.73) She is living in Brooklyn.

(17.74) Drive a Mazda!

However, like statives, activity expressions are odd when temporally modified with temporal expressions using *in*.

(17.75) *I live in Brooklyn in a month.

(17.76) *She drove a Mazda in an hour.

They can, however, successfully be used with *for* temporal adverbials, as in the following examples:

(17.77) I live in Brooklyn for a month.

(17.78) She drove a Mazda for an hour.

Accomplishment expressions

Unlike activities, **accomplishment expressions** describe events that have a natural end point and result in a particular state. Consider the following examples:

(17.79) He booked me a reservation.

(17.80) United flew me to New York.

In these examples, an event is seen as occurring over some period of time that ends when the intended state is accomplished.

A number of diagnostics can be used to distinguish accomplishment events from activities. Consider the following examples, which make use of the word *stop* as a test.

(17.81) I stopped living in Brooklyn.

(17.82) She stopped booking my flight.

In the first example, which is an activity, one can safely conclude the statement *I lived in Brooklyn* even though this activity came to an end. However, from the second example, one cannot conclude the statement *She booked her flight*, since the activity was stopped before the intended state was accomplished. Therefore, although stopping an activity entails that the activity took place, stopping an accomplishment event indicates that the event did not succeed.

Activities and accomplishments can also be distinguished by how they can be modified by various temporal adverbials. Consider the following examples:

(17.83) *I lived in Brooklyn in a year.

(17.84) She booked a flight in a minute.

In general, accomplishments can be modified by *in* temporal expressions, while simple activities can not.

Achievement expressions

The final aspectual class, **achievement expressions**, is similar to accomplishments in that these expressions result in a state. Consider the following examples:

(17.85) She found her gate.

(17.86) I reached New York.

Unlike accomplishments, achievement events are thought of as happening in an instant and are not equated with any particular activity leading up to the state. To be more specific, the events in these examples may have been preceded by extended *searching* or *traveling* events, but the events corresponding directly to *found* and *reach* are conceived of as points, not intervals.

The point-like nature of these events has implications for how they can be temporally modified. In particular, consider the following examples:

(17.87) I lived in New York for a year.

(17.88) *I reached New York for a few minutes.

Unlike activity and accomplishment expressions, achievements cannot be modified by *for* adverbials.

Achievements can also be distinguished from accomplishments by employing the word *stop*, as we did earlier. Consider the following examples:

(17.89) I stopped booking my flight.

(17.90) *I stopped reaching New York.

As we saw earlier, using *stop* with an accomplishment expression results in a failure to reach the intended state. Note, however, that the resulting expression is perfectly well-formed. On the other hand, using *stop* with an achievement example is unacceptable.

Telic eventualities

We should note that since both accomplishments and achievements are events that result in a state, they are sometimes characterized as subtypes of a single aspectual class. Members of this combined class are known as **telic eventualities**.

Before moving on, we should make two points about this classification scheme. The first point is that event expressions can easily be shifted from one class to another. Consider the following examples:

(17.91) I flew.

(17.92) I flew to New York.

The first example is a simple activity; it has no natural end point and cannot be temporally modified by *in* temporal expressions. On the other hand, the second example is clearly an accomplishment event since it has an end point, results in a particular state, and can be temporally modified in all the ways that accomplishments can. Clearly, the classification of an event is not solely governed by the verb, but by the semantics of the entire expression in context.

The second point is that while classifications such as this one are often useful, they do not *explain* why it is that events expressed in natural languages fall into these particular classes. We revisit this issue in Chapter 19 where we sketch a representational approach from Dowty (1979) that accounts for these classes.

17.5   Description Logics

Semantic networks
Frames
Slot-filler

Over the years, a fair number of representational schemes have been invented to capture the meaning of linguistic utterances for use in natural language processing systems. Other than FOL, the most widely used schemes have been **semantic networks** and **frames**, which are also sometimes called **slot-filler** representations.

In semantic networks, objects are represented as nodes in a graph, with relations between objects being represented by named links. In frame-based systems, objects are represented as feature structures similar to those discussed in Chapter 15, which can, of course, also be naturally represented as graphs. In this approach, features are called slots and the values, or fillers, of these slots can either be atomic values or other embedded frames.

It is now widely accepted that meanings represented in these approaches can, in principle, be translated into equivalent statements in FOL with relative ease. The difficulty is that in many of these approaches the semantics of a statement are defined procedurally. That is, the meaning arises from whatever the system that interprets it does with it.

Description logics can be viewed as an effort to better understand and specify the semantics of these earlier structured network representations and to provide a conceptual framework that is especially well suited to certain kinds of domain modeling. Formally, the term Description Logics refers to a family of logical approaches that correspond to varying subsets of FOL. The various restrictions placed on the expressiveness of Description Logics serve to guarantee the tractability of various critical kinds of inference. Our focus here, however, will be on the modeling aspects of DLs rather than on computational complexity issues.

Terminology
TBox
ABox
Ontology

When using Description Logics to model an application domain, we emphasize the representation of knowledge about categories, individuals that belong to those categories, and the relationships that can hold among these individuals. The set of categories, or concepts, that make up a particular application domain is called its **terminology**. The portion of a knowledge base that contains the terminology is traditionally called the **TBox**; this is in contrast to the **ABox** that contains facts about individuals. The terminology is typically arranged into a hierarchical organization called an **ontology** that captures the subset/superset relations among the categories.

To illustrate this approach, let's return to our earlier culinary domain, which included notions like restaurants, cuisines, and patrons, among others. We represented concepts like these in FOL by using unary predicates such as *Restaurant*(x); the DL equivalent simply omits the variable, so the category corresponding to the notion of a restaurant is simply written as Restaurant.[3] To capture the notion that a particular domain element, such as *Frasca*, is a restaurant, we simply assert Restaurant(Frasca) in much the same way we would in FOL. The semantics of these categories are specified in precisely the same way that was introduced earlier in Section 17.2: a category like Restaurant simply denotes the set of domain elements that are restaurants.

Having specified the categories of interest in a state of affairs, the next step is to arrange these categories into a hierarchical structure. There are two ways to capture the hierarchical relationships present in a terminology: we can directly assert relations between categories that are related hierarchically, or we can provide complete definitions for our concepts and then rely on these definitions to infer hierarchical relationships. The choice between these methods hinges on the use to which the resulting categories will be put and the feasibility of formulating precise definitions for many naturally occurring categories. We'll discuss the first option here and return to the notion of definitions later in this section.

Subsumption   To directly specify a hierarchical structure, we can assert **subsumption** relations between the appropriate concepts in a terminology. The subsumption relation is conventionally written as $C \sqsubseteq D$ and is read as C is subsumed by D; that is, all members of the category C are also members of the category D. Not surprisingly, the formal semantics of this relation are provided by a simple set relation; any domain element that is in the set denoted by C is also in the set denoted by D.

Continuing with our restaurant theme, adding the following statements to the TBox asserts that all restaurants are commercial establishments and, moreover, that there are various subtypes of restaurants.

$$\text{Restaurant} \sqsubseteq \text{CommercialEstablishment} \tag{17.93}$$
$$\text{ItalianRestaurant} \sqsubseteq \text{Restaurant} \tag{17.94}$$
$$\text{ChineseRestaurant} \sqsubseteq \text{Restaurant} \tag{17.95}$$
$$\text{MexicanRestaurant} \sqsubseteq \text{Restaurant} \tag{17.96}$$

Ontologies such as this are conventionally illustrated with diagrams such as the one shown in Fig. 17.6, where subsumption relations are denoted by links between the nodes representing the categories.

Note, however, that it was precisely the vague nature of network diagrams like this that motivated the development of Description Logics. For example, from this diagram we can't tell whether the given set of categories is exhaustive or disjoint. That is, we can't tell if these are all the kinds of restaurants that we'll be dealing with in our domain or whether there might be others. We also can't tell if an individual restaurant must fall into only *one* of these categories, or if it is possible, for example, for a restaurant to be *both* Italian and Chinese. The DL statements given above are more transparent in

---

[3] DL statements are conventionally typeset with a sans serif font. We'll follow that convention here, reverting to our standard mathematical notation when giving FOL equivalents of DL statements.

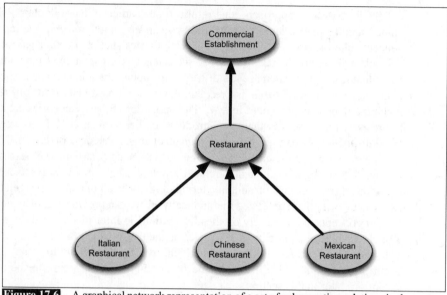

Figure 17.6   A graphical network representation of a set of subsumption relations in the restaurant domain.

their meaning; they simply assert a set of subsumption relations between categories and make no claims about coverage or mutual exclusion.

If an application requires coverage and disjointness information, then such information must be made explicitly. The simplest ways to capture this kind of information is through the use of negation and disjunction operators. For example, the following assertion would tell us that Chinese restaurants can't also be Italian restaurants.

$$\text{ChineseRestaurant} \sqsubseteq \textbf{not ItalianRestaurant} \tag{17.97}$$

Specifying that a set of subconcepts covers a category can be achieved with disjunction, as in the following:

$$\text{Restaurant} \sqsubseteq \tag{17.98}$$
$$(\textbf{or ItalianRestaurant ChineseRestaurant MexicanRestaurant})$$

Of course, having a hierarchy such as the one given in Fig. 17.6 tells us next to nothing about the concepts in it. We certainly don't know anything about what makes a restaurant a restaurant, much less Italian, Chinese, or expensive. What is needed are additional assertions about what it means to be a member of any of these categories. In Description Logics such statements come in the form of relations between the concepts being described and other concepts in the domain. In keeping with its origins in structured network representations, relations in Description Logics are typically binary and are often referred to as roles, or role-relations.

To see how such relations work, let's consider some of the facts about restaurants discussed earlier in the chapter. We'll use the hasCuisine relation to capture information as to what kinds of food restaurants serve and the hasPriceRange relation to capture how pricey particular restaurants tend to be. We can use these relations to say something more concrete about our various classes of restaurants. Let's start with our ItalianRestaurant concept. As a first approximation, we might say something uncontroversial like Italian restaurants serve Italian cuisine. To capture these notions, let's first add some new concepts to our terminology to represent various kinds of cuisine.

$$
\begin{array}{llll}
\text{MexicanCuisine} & \sqsubseteq & \text{Cuisine} \qquad & \text{ExpensiveRestaurant} \sqsubseteq \text{Restaurant} \\
\text{ItalianCuisine} & \sqsubseteq & \text{Cuisine} & \text{ModerateRestaurant} \sqsubseteq \text{Restaurant} \\
\text{ChineseCuisine} & \sqsubseteq & \text{Cuisine} & \text{CheapRestaurant} \sqsubseteq \text{Restaurant} \\
\text{VegetarianCuisine} & \sqsubseteq & \text{Cuisine}
\end{array}
$$

Next, let's revise our earlier version of ItalianRestaurant to capture cuisine information.

$$
\text{ItalianRestaurant} \ \sqsubseteq \ \text{Restaurant} \sqcap \exists \text{hasCuisine.ItalianCuisine} \qquad (17.99)
$$

The correct way to read this expression is that individuals in the category Italian-Restaurant are subsumed both by the category Restaurant and by an unnamed class defined by the existential clause — the set of entities that serve Italian cuisine. An equivalent statement in FOL would be

$$
\forall x ItalianRestaurant(x) \ \rightarrow \ Restaurant(x) \qquad (17.100)
$$
$$
\land (\exists y Serves(x,y) \land ItalianCuisine(y))
$$

This FOL translation should make it clear what the DL assertions given above do and do not entail. In particular, they don't say that domain entities classified as Italian restaurants can't engage in other relations like being expensive or even serving Chinese cuisine. And critically, they don't say much about domain entities that we know do serve Italian cuisine. In fact, inspection of the FOL translation makes it clear that we cannot *infer* that any new entities belong to this category based on their characteristics. The best we can do is infer new facts about restaurants that we're explicitly told are members of this category.

Of course, inferring the category membership of individuals given certain characteristics is a common and critical reasoning task that we need to support. This brings us back to the alternative approach to creating hierarchical structures in a terminology: actually providing a definition of the categories we're creating in the form of necessary and sufficient conditions for category membership. In this case, we might explicitly provide a definition for ItalianRestaurant as being those restaurants that serve Italian cuisine, and ModerateRestaurant as being those whose price range is moderate.

$$
\text{ItalianRestaurant} \ \equiv \ \text{Restaurant} \sqcap \exists \text{hasCuisine.ItalianCuisine} \qquad (17.101)
$$
$$
\text{ModerateRestaurant} \ \equiv \ \text{Restaurant} \sqcap \text{hasPriceRange.ModeratePrices} \qquad (17.102)
$$

While our earlier statements provided necessary conditions for membership in these categories, these statements provide both necessary and sufficient conditions.

Finally, let's now consider the superficially similar case of vegetarian restaurants. Clearly, vegetarian restaurants are those that serve vegetarian cuisine. But they don't merely serve vegetarian fare, that's all they serve. We can accommodate this kind of constraint by adding an additional restriction in the form of a universal quantifier to our earlier description of VegetarianRestaurants, as follows:

$$VegetarianRestaurant \equiv Restaurant \qquad (17.103)$$
$$\sqcap \exists hasCuisine.VegetarianCuisine$$
$$\sqcap \forall hasCuisine.VegetarianCuisine$$

Inference

Paralleling the focus of Description Logics on categories, relations, and individuals is a processing focus on a restricted subset of logical inference. Rather than employing the full range of reasoning permitted by FOL, DL reasoning systems emphasize the closely coupled problems of subsumption and instance checking.

Subsumption

Subsumption, as a form of inference, is the task of determining, based on the facts asserted in a terminology, whether a superset/subset relationship exists between two concepts. Correspondingly, **instance checking** asks if an individual can be a member of a particular category given the facts we know about both the individual and the terminology. The inference mechanisms underlying subsumption and instance checking go beyond simply checking for explicitly stated subsumption relations in a terminology. They must explicitly reason using the relational information asserted about the terminology to infer appropriate subsumption and membership relations.

Instance checking

Returning to our restaurant domain, let's add a new kind of restaurant using the following statement:

$$IlFornaio \sqsubseteq ModerateRestaurant \sqcap \exists hasCuisine.ItalianCuisine \qquad (17.104)$$

Given this assertion, we might ask whether the IlFornaio chain of restaurants might be classified as an Italian restaurant or a vegetarian restaurant. More precisely, we can pose the following questions to our reasoning system:

$$IlFornaio \sqsubseteq ItalianRestaurant \qquad (17.105)$$
$$IlFornaio \sqsubseteq VegetarianRestaurant \qquad (17.106)$$

The answer to the first question is positive since IlFornaio meets the criteria we specified for the category ItalianRestaurant: it's a Restaurant since we explicitly classified it as a ModerateRestaurant, which is a subtype of Restaurant, and it meets the has.Cuisine class restriction since we've asserted that directly.

The answer to the second question is negative. Recall, that our criteria for vegetarian restaurants contains two requirements: it has to serve vegetarian fare, and that's all it can serve. Our current definition for IlFornaio fails on both counts since we have not asserted any relations that state that IlFornaio serves vegetarian fare, and the relation we have asserted, hasCuisine.ItalianCuisine, contradicts the second criteria.

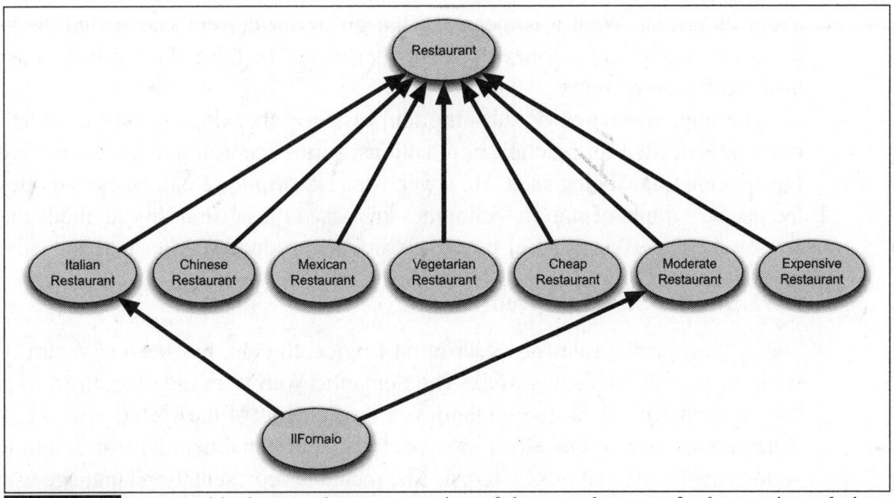

Figure 17.7   A graphical network representation of the complete set of subsumption relations in the restaurant domain given the current set of assertions in the TBox.

Implied hierarchy   A related reasoning task, based on the basic subsumption inference, is to derive the **implied hierarchy** for a terminology given facts about the categories in the terminology. This task roughly corresponds to a repeated application of the subsumption operator to pairs of concepts in the terminology. Given our current collection of statements, the expanded hierarchy shown in Fig. 17.7 can be inferred. You should convince yourself that this diagram contains all and only the subsumption links that should be present given our current knowledge.

Instance checking is the task of determining whether a particular individual can be classified as a member of a particular category. This process takes what is known about a given individual, in the form of relations and explicit categorical statements, and then compares that information with what is known about the current terminology. It then returns a list of *the most specific* categories to which the individual can belong.

As an example of a categorization problem, consider an establishment that we're told is a restaurant and serves Italian cuisine.

$$\text{Restaurant(Gondolier)} \qquad (17.107)$$

$$\text{hasCuisine(Gondolier, ItalianCuisine)} \qquad (17.108)$$

Here, we're being told that the entity denoted by the term Gondolier is a restaurant and serves Italian food. Given this new information and the contents of our current TBox, we might reasonably like to ask if this is an Italian restaurant, if it is a vegetarian restaurant, or if it has moderate prices.

Assuming the definitional statements given earlier, we can indeed categorize the Gondolier as an Italian restaurant. That is, the information we've been given about it meets the necessary and sufficient conditions required for membership in this category. And as with the IlFornaio category, this individual fails to match the stated criteria for the VegetarianRestaurant. Finally, the Gondolier might also turn out to be a moderately priced restaurant, but we can't tell at this point since we don't know anything about its prices. What this means is that given our current knowledge the answer to the query ModerateRestaurant(Gondolier) would be false since it lacks the required hasPriceRange relation.

The implementation of subsumption, instance checking, as well as other kinds of inferences needed for practical applications, varies according to the expressivity of the Description Logic being used. However, for a Description Logic of even modest power, the primary implementation techniques are based on satisfiability methods that in turn rely on the underlying model-based semantics introduced earlier in this chapter.

OWL and the Semantic Web

The highest-profile role for Description Logics, to date, has been as a part of the development of the Semantic Web. The Semantic Web is an ongoing effort to provide a way to formally specify the semantics of the contents of the Web (Fensel et al., 2003). A key component of this effort involves the creation and deployment of ontologies for various application areas of interest. The meaning representation language used to represent this knowledge is the **Web Ontology Language** (OWL) (McGuiness and van Harmelen, 2004). OWL embodies a Description Logic that corresponds roughly to the one we've been describing here.

Web Ontology Language

17.6   Embodied and Situated Approaches to Meaning

The notion that the translation of linguistic expressions into formal representations made up of discrete symbols adequately captures the notion of meaning is subject to considerable debate. The following discussion gives a brief overview of an alternative approaches that seek to ground the meaning of linguistic expressions in various ways.

Meaning as action

An approach that holds considerable appeal when we consider the semantics of imperative sentences is the notion of **meaning as action**. Under this view, utterances are viewed as actions, and the meanings of these utterances reside in procedures that are activated in the hearer as a result of hearing the utterance. This approach was followed in the creation of the historically important SHRDLU system and is summed up well by its creator Terry Winograd (1972b).

> One of the basic viewpoints underlying the model is that all language use can be thought of as a way of activating procedures within the hearer. We can think of an utterance as a program—one that indirectly causes a set of operations to be carried out within the hearer's cognitive system.

Unfortunately, while the approach employed in SHRDLU was procedural, it nevertheless consisted of arbitrary symbols that were not grounded in any meaningful way.

X-schema

A more sophisticated procedural model of semantics is the **executing schema** or **x-schema** model of Bailey et al. (1997), Narayanan (1997), and Chang et al. (1998). The intuition of this model is that various parts of the semantics of events, including the *aspectual* factors discussed on page 569, are based on schematized descriptions of sensory-motor processes like inception, iteration, enabling, completion, force, and effort. The model represents the aspectual semantics of events via a kind of probabilistic

Petri net   automaton called a **Petri net** (Murata, 1989). The nets used in the model have states like *ready, process, finish, suspend,* and *result.*

The meaning representation of an example like *Jack is walking to the store* activates the *process* state of the walking event. An accomplishment event like *Jack walked to the store* activates the *result* state. An iterative activity like *Jack walked to the store every week* is simulated in the model by an iterative activation of the *process* and *result* nodes. The key insight of this approach is that these processes have direct analogs in the human motor control system.

This use of sensory motor primitives as a foundation for semantic description is also based on the work of Regier (1996) on the role of visual primitives in a computational model of learning the semantics of spatial prepositions. Siskind (2001) presents an approach with similar goals based on the force dynamics work of Talmy (1988).

Of course, much of what we talk about is abstract and thus cannot be directly grounded in visual, haptic, or motor control processes. However, as we show in Chapter 19, many, if not most, abstract concepts can be expressed using metaphors that do make a connection to concepts that are grounded in perceptual or motor primitives. Consider the following example from Narayanan (1999).

(17.109) In 1991, in response to World Bank pressure, India boldly set out on a path of liberalization.

Drawing on the metaphor work of Lakoff and Johnson (1980), Narayanan presents a system that can analyze metaphorical expressions such as this and demonstrates that it can draw appropriate inferences based on a mapping from the conceptual domain to lower-level perceptual and motor primitives.

The focus of much of this work has been on grounded representations for events, states, and actions. However, the representations of objects and their properties in these systems is fairly similar to the approach taken in logic-based approaches, namely unanalyzed constants that stand for the objects under discussion. Roy (2005b) presents a framework that extends the notion of a grounded schema to provide a uniform treatment of events, states, objects, and properties. In brief, in this approach the representations of objects and their properties arise directly from the set of grounded schemas that an agent possesses. For example, instead of relying on a logical constant like *BALL* to represent what we know about balls, its meaning consists of the constraints expressed by the grounded set of schemas that involve balls.

An impressive aspect of Roy's grounded schema approach is that it is based on the design and implementation of a series of language-processing robots that can both perceive and act in the world (Roy et al., 2004; Roy, 2005a; Roy and Mukherjee, 2005). In these robots, grounded schemas represent the robot's model of its world, guide its actions, and drive its language comprehension process.

17.7   Summary

This chapter has introduced the representational approach to meaning. The following are some of the highlights of this chapter:

- A major approach to meaning in computational linguistics involves the creation of **formal meaning representations** that capture the meaning-related content of linguistic inputs. These representations are intended to bridge the gap from language to common-sense knowledge of the world.

- The frameworks that specify the syntax and semantics of these representations are called **meaning representation languages**. A wide variety of such languages are used in natural language processing and artificial intelligence.

- Such representations need to be able to support the practical computational requirements of semantic processing. Among these are the need to determine **the truth of propositions**, to support **unambiguous representations**, to represent **variables**, to support **inference**, and to be sufficiently **expressive**.

- Human languages have a wide variety of features that are used to convey meaning. Among the most important of these is the ability to convey a **predicate-argument structure**.

- **First-Order Logic** is a well-understood, computationally tractable meaning representation language that offers much of what is needed in a meaning representation language.

- Important elements of semantic representation including **states** and **events** can be captured in FOL.

- **Semantic networks** and **frames** can be captured within the FOL framework.

- Modern **Description Logics** consist of useful and computationally tractable subsets of full First-Order Logic. The most prominent use of a description logic is the **Web Ontology Language** (OWL), used in the specification of the Semantic Web.

Bibliographical and Historical Notes

The earliest computational use of declarative meaning representations in natural language processing was in the context of question-answering systems (Green et al., 1961; Raphael, 1968; Lindsey, 1963). These systems employed ad hoc representations for the facts needed to answer questions. Questions were then translated into a form that could be matched against facts in the knowledge base. Simmons (1965) provides an overview of these early efforts.

Woods (1967) investigated the use of FOL-like representations in question answering as a replacement for the ad hoc representations in use at the time. Woods (1973) further developed and extended these ideas in the landmark Lunar system. Interestingly, the representations used in Lunar had both truth-conditional and procedural semantics. Winograd (1972b) employed a similar representation based on the Micro-Planner language in his SHRDLU system.

During this same period, researchers interested in the cognitive modeling of language and memory had been working with various forms of associative network representations. Masterman (1957) was the first to make computational use of a semantic network-like knowledge representation, although semantic networks are generally credited to Quillian (1968). A considerable amount of work in the semantic network framework was carried out during this era (Norman and Rumelhart, 1975; Schank, 1972; Wilks, 1975c, 1975b; Kintsch, 1974). It was during this period that a number of researchers began to incorporate Fillmore's notion of case roles (Fillmore, 1968) into their representations. Simmons (1973) was the earliest adopter of case roles as part of representations for natural language processing.

Detailed analyses by Woods (1975) and Brachman (1979) aimed at figuring out what semantic networks actually mean led to the development of a number of more sophisticated network-like languages including KRL (Bobrow and Winograd, 1977) and KL-ONE (Brachman and Schmolze, 1985). As these frameworks became more sophisticated and well defined, it became clear that they were restricted variants of FOL coupled with specialized indexing inference procedures. A useful collection of papers covering much of this work can be found in Brachman and Levesque (1985). Russell and Norvig (2002) describe a modern perspective on these representational efforts.

Linguistic efforts to assign semantic structures to natural language sentences in the generative era began with the work of Katz and Fodor (1963). The limitations of their simple feature-based representations and the natural fit of logic to many of the linguistic problems of the day quickly led to the adoption of a variety of predicate-argument structures as preferred semantic representations (Lakoff, 1972; McCawley, 1968). The subsequent introduction by Montague (1973) of the truth-conditional model-theoretic framework into linguistic theory led to a much tighter integration between theories of formal syntax and a wide range of formal semantic frameworks. Good introductions to Montague semantics and its role in linguistic theory can be found in Dowty et al. (1981) and Partee (1976).

The representation of events as reified objects is due to Davidson (1967). The approach presented here, which explicitly reifies event participants, is due to Parsons (1990). Most current computational approaches to temporal reasoning are based on Allen's notion of temporal intervals (Allen, 1984); see Chapter 22. ter Meulen (1995) provides a modern treatment of tense and aspect. Davis (1990) describes the use of FOL to represent knowledge across a wide range of common-sense domains including quantities, space, time, and beliefs.

A recent comprehensive treatment of logic and language can be found in van Benthem and ter Meulen (1997). A classic semantics text is Lyons (1977). McCawley (1993) is an indispensable textbook covering a wide range of topics concerning logic and language. Chierchia and McConnell-Ginet (1991) also broadly covers semantic issues from a linguistic perspective. Heim and Kratzer (1998) is a more recent text written from the perspective of current generative theory.

Exercises

17.1 Peruse your daily newspaper for three examples of ambiguous sentences or headlines. Describe the various sources of the ambiguities.

17.2 Consider a domain in which the word *coffee* can refer to the following concepts in a knowledge-based system: a caffeinated or decaffeinated beverage, ground coffee used to make either kind of beverage, and the beans themselves. Give arguments as to which of the following uses of coffee are ambiguous and which are vague.

1. I've had my coffee for today.
2. Buy some coffee on your way home.
3. Please grind some more coffee.

17.3 The following rule, which we gave as a translation for Example 17.26, is not a reasonable definition of what it means to be a vegetarian restaurant.

$$\forall x VegetarianRestaurant(x) \Rightarrow Serves(x, VegetarianFood)$$

Give a FOL rule that better defines vegetarian restaurants in terms of what they serve.

17.4 Give FOL translations for the following sentences:

1. Vegetarians do not eat meat.
2. Not all vegetarians eat eggs.

17.5 Give a set of facts and inferences necessary to prove the following assertions:

1. McDonald's is not a vegetarian restaurant.
2. Some vegetarians can eat at McDonald's.

Don't just place these facts in your knowledge base. Show that they can be inferred from some more general facts about vegetarians and McDonald's.

17.6 For the following sentences, give FOL translations that capture the temporal relationships between the events.

1. When Mary's flight departed, I ate lunch.
2. When Mary's flight departed, I had eaten lunch.

17.7 On page 560, we gave the representation *Near*(*Centro, Bacaro*) as a translation for the sentence *Centro is near Bacaro*. In a truth-conditional semantics, this formula is either true or false given some model. Critique this truth-conditional approach with respect to the meaning of words like *near*.

Chapter 18

Computational Semantics

"Then you should say what you mean," the March Hare went on.
"I do," Alice hastily replied; "at least–at least I mean what I say–that's the same thing, you know."
"Not the same thing a bit!" said the Hatter. "You might just as well say that 'I see what I eat' is the same thing as 'I eat what I see'!"

Lewis Carroll, *Alice in Wonderland*

Semantic analysis

This chapter presents a principled computational approach to the problem of **semantic analysis**, the process whereby meaning representations of the kind discussed in the last chapter are composed for linguistic expressions. The automated creation of accurate and expressive meaning representations necessarily involves a wide range of knowledge sources and inference techniques. Among the sources of knowledge that are typically involved are the meanings of words, the conventional meanings associated with grammatical constructions, knowledge about the structure of the discourse, common-sense knowledge about the topic at hand, and knowledge about the state of affairs in which the discourse is occurring.

Syntax-driven semantic analysis

The focus of this chapter is a kind of **syntax-driven semantic analysis** that is fairly modest in its scope. In this approach, meaning representations are assigned to sentences solely on the basis of knowledge gleaned from the lexicon and the grammar. When we refer to an expression's meaning or meaning representation, we have in mind a representation that is both context independent and free of inference. Representations of this type correspond to the traditional notion of literal meaning discussed in the previous chapter.

There are two motivations for proceeding along these lines: first, to provide useful input to those domains, including question answering, in which such primitive representations suffice to produce useful results, and second to use these impoverished representations as inputs to subsequent processes that produce richer, more complete, meaning representations. Chapters 21 and 24 will discuss how these meaning representations can be used in processing extended discourses and dialogs.

18.1 Syntax-Driven Semantic Analysis

Principle of compositionality

The approach detailed in this section is based on the **principle of compositionality**. The key idea behind this approach is that the meaning of a sentence can be constructed from the meanings of its parts. When interpreted superficially, this principle is somewhat less than useful. We know that sentences are composed of words and that words

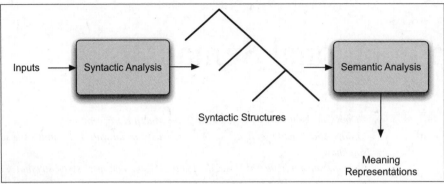

Figure 18.1   A simple pipeline approach to semantic analysis.

are the primary carriers of meaning in language. It would seem then that all this principle tells us is that we should compose the meaning representation for sentences from the meanings of the words that make them up.

Fortunately, the Mad Hatter has provided us with a hint as to how to make this principle useful. The meaning of a sentence is not based solely on the words that make it up, but also on the ordering and grouping of words and on the relations among the words in the sentence. This is just another way of saying that the meaning of a sentence is partially based on its syntactic structure. Therefore, in syntax-driven semantic analysis, the composition of meaning representations is guided by the syntactic *components* and *relations* provided by the kind of grammars discussed in Chapter 12.

Let's begin by assuming that the syntactic analysis of an input sentence serves as the input to a semantic analyzer. Figure 18.1 illustrates an obvious pipeline-oriented approach that follows directly from this assumption. An input is first passed through a parser to derive its syntactic analysis. This analysis is then passed as input to a **se-**

Semantic analyzer   **mantic analyzer** to produce a meaning representation. Note that although this diagram shows a parse tree as input, other syntactic representations such as flat chunks, feature structures, or dependency structures can also be used. For the remainder of this chapter we assume tree-like inputs.

Before moving on, we should touch on the role of ambiguity in this story. As we've seen, ambiguous representations can arise from numerous sources, including competing syntactic analyses, ambiguous lexical items, competing anaphoric references, and as we show later in this chapter, ambiguous quantifier scopes. In the syntax-driven approach presented here, we assume that syntactic, lexical, and anaphoric ambiguities are not a problem. That is, we'll assume that some larger system is capable of iterating through the possible ambiguous interpretations and passing them individually to the kind of semantic analyzer described here.

Let's consider how such an analysis might proceed with the following example:

(18.1) Franco likes Frasca.

Figure 18.2 shows a simplified parse tree (lacking any feature attachments), along with a plausible meaning representation for this example. As suggested by the dashed arrows, a semantic analyzer given this tree as input might fruitfully proceed by first re-

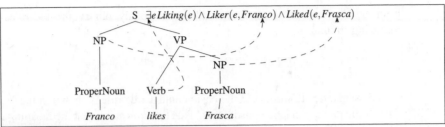

Figure 18.2   Parse tree for the sentence *Franco likes Frasca*.

trieving a skeletal meaning representation from the subtree corresponding to the verb *likes*. The analyzer would then retrieve or compose meaning representations corresponding to the two noun phrases in the sentence. Then, using the representation acquired from the verb as a kind of template, the analyzer would use the noun phrase meaning representations to bind the appropriate variables in the verb representation, thus producing the meaning representation for the sentence as a whole.

Unfortunately, there are a number of serious difficulties with this simplified story. As described, the function used to interpret the tree in Fig. 18.2 must know, among other things, that the verb carries the template upon which the final representation is based, where its corresponding arguments are, and which argument fills which role in the verb's meaning representation. In other words, the function requires a good deal of specific knowledge about *this particular example and its parse tree* to create the required meaning representation. Given that there are an infinite number of such trees for any reasonable grammar, any approach based on one semantic function for every possible tree is in serious trouble.

Fortunately, we have faced this problem before. We do not define languages by enumerating the strings or trees that are permitted, but rather by specifying finite devices that are capable of generating the desired set of outputs. It would seem, therefore, that the right place for semantic knowledge in a syntax-directed approach is with the finite set of devices that generate trees in the first place: the grammar rules and the lexical entries. This is known as the **rule-to-rule hypothesis** (Bach, 1976).

Rule-to-rule hypothesis

Designing an analyzer based on this approach brings us back to the notion of parts and what it means for them to have meanings. The following section is an attempt to answer two questions:

- What does it mean for a syntactic constituent to have a meaning?
- What characteristics must these meanings have so that they can be composed into larger meanings?

18.2   Semantic Augmentations to Syntactic Rules

Semantic attachments

In keeping with the approach used in Chapter 15, we will begin by augmenting our context-free grammar rules with **semantic attachments**. These attachments are instructions that specify how to compute the meaning representation of a construction

597

from the meanings of its constituent parts. Abstractly, our augmented rules have the following structure:

$$A \rightarrow \alpha_1 \ldots \alpha_n \qquad f(\alpha_j.sem, \ldots, \alpha_k.sem) \qquad (18.2)$$

The semantic attachment to the basic context-free rule is shown in the ... to the right of the rule's syntactic constituents. This notation states that the meaning representation assigned to the construction A, which we denote as $A.sem$, can be computed by running the function f on some subset of the semantic attachments of As constituents.

There are myriad ways to instantiate this style of rule-to-rule approach. Our semantic attachments could, for example, take the form of arbitrary programming language fragments. We could then construct a meaning representation for a given derivation by passing the appropriate fragments to an interpreter in a bottom-up fashion and then storing the resulting representations as the value for the associated non-terminals.[1] Such an approach would allow us to create any meaning representation we might like. Unfortunately, the unrestricted power of this approach would also allow us to create representations that have no correspondence at all with the kind of formal logical expressions described in the last chapter. Moreover, this approach would afford us very little guidance as to how to go about designing the semantic attachments to our grammar rules.

For these reasons, more principled approaches are typically used to instantiate the rule-to-rule approach. We introduce two such constrained approaches in this chapter. The first makes direct use of FOL and the λ-calculus notation introduced in Chapter 17. This approach essentially uses a logical notation to guide the creation of logical forms in a principled fashion. The second approach, described later in Section 18.4 is based on the feature-structure and unification formalisms introduced in Chapter 15.

To get started, let's take a look at a basic example along with a simplified target semantic representation.

(18.3) Maharani closed.

$$Closed(Maharani) \qquad (18.4)$$

Let's work our way bottom-up through the rules involved in this example's derivation. Starting with the proper noun, the simplest possible approach is to assign a unique FOL constant to it, as in the following.

$$ProperNoun \rightarrow Maharani \qquad Maharani \qquad (18.5)$$

The non-branching NP rule that dominates this one doesn't add anything semantically, so we just copy the semantics of the $ProperNoun$ up unchanged to the NP.

$$NP \rightarrow ProperNoun \qquad ProperNoun.sem \qquad (18.6)$$

Moving on to the VP, the semantic attachment for the verb needs to provide the name of the predicate, specify its arity, and provide the means to incorporate an argument

---

[1] Those familiar with compiler tools such as YACC and Bison will recognize this approach.

once it's discovered. We can make use of a λ-expression to accomplish these tasks.

$$VP \rightarrow Verb \qquad Verb.sem \qquad\qquad (18.7)$$

$$Verb \rightarrow closed \qquad \lambda x.Closed(x) \qquad\qquad (18.8)$$

This attachment stipulates that the verb *closed* has a unary predicate *Closed* as its representation. The λ-notation lets us leave unspecified, as the x variable, the entity that is closing. As with our earlier *NP* rule, the intransitive *VP* rule that dominates the verb simply copies upward the semantics of the verb below it.

Proceeding upward, it remains for the semantic attachment for the S rule to bring things together by inserting the semantic representation of the subject *NP* as the first argument to the predicate.

$$S \rightarrow NP\ VP \qquad VP.sem(NP.sem) \qquad\qquad (18.9)$$

Since the value of *VP.sem* is a λ-expression and the value of *NP.sem* is a simply a FOL constant, we can create our desired final meaning representation by using λ-reduction to apply the *VP.sem* to the *NP.sem*.

$$\lambda x.Closed(x)(Maharani) \qquad\qquad (18.10)$$

$$Closed(Maharani) \qquad\qquad (18.11)$$

This example illustrates a general pattern which repeats itself throughout this chapter. The semantic attachments to our grammar rules consist primarily of λ-reductions, whereby one element of an attachment serves as a functor and the rest serve as arguments to it. As we show, the real work resides in the lexicon where the bulk of the meaning representations are introduced.

Although this example illustrates the basic approach, the full story is a bit more complex. Let's begin by replacing our earlier target representation with one that is more in keeping with the neo-Davidsonian representations introduced in the last chapter, and by considering an example with a more complex noun phrase as its subject.

(18.12) Every restaurant closed.

The target representation for this example should be the following.

$$\forall x\ Restaurant(x) \Rightarrow \exists e\ Closed(e) \wedge ClosedThing(e,x) \qquad\qquad (18.13)$$

Clearly, the semantic contribution of the subject noun phrase in this example is much more extensive than in our previous one. In our earlier example, the FOL constant representing the subject was simply plugged into the correct place in the *Closed* predicate by a single λ-reduction. Here, the final result involves a complex intertwining of the content provided by the *NP* and the content provided by the *VP*. We'll have to do some work if we want to rely on λ-reduction to produce what we want here.

The first step is to determine exactly what we'd like the meaning representation of *Every restaurant* to be. Let's start by assuming that *Every* invokes the $\forall$ quantifier and that *restaurant* specifies the category of concept that we're quantifying over, which we call the **restriction** of the noun phrase. Putting these together, we might expect the meaning representation to be something like $\forall x\, Restaurant(x)$. Although this is a valid FOL formula, its not a terribly useful one, since it says that everything is a restaurant. What's missing from it is the notion that noun phrases like *every restaurant* are normally embedded in expressions that stipulate something about the universally quantified variable. That is, we're probably trying to *say something* about all restaurants.

This notion is traditionally referred to as the *NP*'s **nuclear scope**. In this case, the nuclear scope of this noun phrase is *closed*.

We can capture these notions in our target representation by adding a dummy predicate, Q, representing the scope and attaching that predicate to the restriction predicate with an $\Rightarrow$ logical connective, leaving us with the following expression:

$$\forall x\, Restaurant(x) \Rightarrow Q(x)$$

Ultimately, what we need to do to make this expression meaningful is to replace Q with the logical expression corresponding to the nuclear scope. Fortunately, the λ-calculus can come to our rescue again. All we need do is permit λ-variables to range over FOL predicates as well as terms. The following expression captures exactly what we need.

$$\lambda Q.\forall x\, Restaurant(x) \Rightarrow Q(x)$$

The following series of grammar rules with their semantic attachments serve to produce this desired meaning representation for this kind of *NP*.

$$NP \rightarrow Det\ Nominal \qquad Det.Sem(Nominal.Sem) \qquad (18.14)$$

$$Det \rightarrow every \qquad \lambda P.\lambda Q.\forall x\, P(x) \Rightarrow Q(x) \qquad (18.15)$$

$$Nominal \rightarrow Noun \qquad Noun.sem \qquad (18.16)$$

$$Noun \rightarrow restaurant \qquad \lambda x.Restaurant(x) \qquad (18.17)$$

The critical step in this sequence involves the λ-reduction in the *NP* rule. This rule applies the λ-expression attached to the *Det* to the semantic attachment of the *Nominal*, which is itself a λ-expression. The following are the intermediate steps in this process.

$$\lambda P.\lambda Q.\forall x\, P(x) \Rightarrow Q(x)(\lambda x.Restaurant(x))$$

$$\lambda Q.\forall x\, \lambda x.Restaurant(x)(x) \Rightarrow Q(x)$$

$$\lambda Q.\forall x\, Restaurant(x) \Rightarrow Q(x)$$

The first expression is the expansion of the *Det.Sem(Nominal.Sem)* semantic attachment to the *NP* rule. The second formula is the result of this λ-reduction. Note that this second formula has a λ-application embedded in it. Reducing this expression in place gives us the final form.

$$\forall x \, Restaurant(x) \Rightarrow \exists e \, Closed(e) \wedge ClosedThing(e,x)$$

$$\lambda Q.\forall x \, Restaurant(x) \Rightarrow Q(x) \qquad \lambda x.\exists e \, Closed(e) \wedge ClosedThing(e,x)$$

$$closed$$

$$\lambda P.\lambda Q.\forall x P(x) \Rightarrow Q(x) \qquad \lambda x.Restaurant(x)$$

Every   *restaurant*

Figure 18.3   Intermediate steps in the semantic interpretation of *Every restaurant closed*.

Having revised our semantic attachment for the subject noun phrase portion of our example, let's move to the *S* and *VP* and *Verb* rules to see how they need to change to accommodate these revisions. Let's start with the *S* rule and work our way down. Since the meaning of the subject *NP* is now a λ-expression, it makes sense to consider it as a functor to be called with the meaning of the *VP* as its argument. The following attachment accomplishes this.

$$S \rightarrow NP \, VP \qquad NP.sem(VP.sem) \qquad (18.18)$$

Note that we've flipped the role of functor and argument from our original proposal for this *S* rule.

The last attachment to revisit is the one for the verb *close*. We need to update it to provide a proper event-oriented representation and to make sure that it interfaces well with the new *S* and *NP* rules. The following attachment accomplishes both goals.

$$Verb \rightarrow close \qquad \lambda x.\exists e Closed(e) \wedge ClosedThing(e,x) \qquad (18.19)$$

This attachment is passed unchanged to the *VP* constituent through the intransitive *VP* rule. It is then combined with the meaning representation of *Every restaurant* as dictated by the semantic attachment for the *S* given earlier. The following expressions illustrate the intermediate steps in this process.

$$\lambda Q.\forall x Restaurant(x) \Rightarrow Q(x)(\lambda y.\exists e Closed(e) \wedge ClosedThing(e,y))$$

$$\forall x Restaurant(x) \Rightarrow \lambda y.\exists e Closed(e) \wedge ClosedThing(e,y)(x)$$

$$\forall x Restaurant(x) \Rightarrow \exists e Closed(e) \wedge ClosedThing(e,x)$$

These steps achieve our goal of getting the *VP*'s meaning representation spliced in as the nuclear scope in the *NP*'s representation. Figure 18.3 shows these steps in the context of the parse tree underlying (18.12).

As is always the case with any kind of grammar engineering effort, we now need to make sure that our earlier simpler examples still work. One area that we need to revisit is our representation of proper nouns. Let's consider them in the context of our earlier example.

(18.20) Maharani closed.

The *S* rule now expects the subject *NP*'s semantic attachment to be a functor applied to the semantics of the *VP*, so our earlier representation of proper nouns as FOL constants won't do. Fortunately, we can once again exploit the flexibility of the λ-calculus to accomplish what we need:

$$\lambda x.x(Maharani)$$

This trick turns a simple FOL constant into a λ-expression, which when reduced serves to inject the constant into a larger expression. You should work through our original example with all of the new semantic rules to make sure that you can come up with the following intended representation:

$$\exists e\ Closed(e) \land ClosedThing(Maharani)$$

As one final exercise, let's see how this approach extends to an expression involving a transitive verb phrase, as in the following:

(18.21) Matthew opened a restaurant.

If we've done things correctly we ought to be able to specify the semantic attachments for transitive verb phrases, for the verb *open* and for the determiner *a*, while leaving the rest of our rules alone.

Let's start by modeling the semantics for the determiner *a* on our earlier attachment for *every*.

$$Det \rightarrow a \qquad \lambda P.\lambda Q.\exists x\, P(x) \land Q(x) \qquad\qquad (18.22)$$

This rule differs from the attachment for *every* in two ways. First, we're using the existential quantifier $\exists$ to capture the semantics of *a*. And second, we've replaced the implies $\Rightarrow$ operator with a logical $\land$. The overall framework remains the same, with the λ-variables P and Q standing for the restriction and the nuclear scopes, to be filled in later. With this addition, our existing *NP* rule will create the appropriate representation for *a restaurant*:

$$\lambda Q.\exists x\, Restaurant(x) \land Q(x)$$

Next, let's move on to the *Verb* and *VP* rules. Two arguments need to be incorporated into the underlying meaning representation. One argument is available at the level of the transitive *VP* rule, and the second at the *S* rule. Let's assume the following form for the *VP* semantic attachment.

$$VP \rightarrow Verb\ NP \qquad Verb.Sem(NP.Sem) \qquad\qquad (18.23)$$

This attachment assumes that the verb's semantic attachment will be applied as a functor to the semantics of its noun phrase argument. And let's assume for now that the representations we developed earlier for quantified noun phrases and proper nouns will remain unchanged. With these assumptions in mind, the following attachment for the verb *opened* will do what we want.

Grammar Rule	Semantic Attachment
$S \rightarrow NP\ VP$	$NP.sem(VP.sem)$
$NP \rightarrow Det\ Nominal$	$Det.sem(Nominal.sem)$
$NP \rightarrow ProperNoun$	$ProperNoun.sem$
$Nominal \rightarrow Noun$	$Noun.sem$
$VP \rightarrow Verb$	$Verb.sem$
$VP \rightarrow Verb\ NP$	$Verb.sem(NP.sem)$
$Det \rightarrow every$	$\lambda P.\lambda Q.\forall x P(x) \Rightarrow Q(x)$
$Det \rightarrow a$	$\lambda P.\lambda Q.\exists x P(x) \wedge Q(x)$
$Noun \rightarrow restaurant$	$\lambda r.Restaurant(r)$
$ProperNoun \rightarrow Matthew$	$\lambda m.m(Matthew)$
$ProperNoun \rightarrow Franco$	$\lambda f.f(Franco)$
$ProperNoun \rightarrow Frasca$	$\lambda f.f(Frasca)$
$Verb \rightarrow closed$	$\lambda x.\exists eClosed(e) \wedge ClosedThing(e,x)$
$Verb \rightarrow opened$	$\lambda w.\lambda z.w(\lambda x.\exists eOpened(e) \wedge Opener(e,z)$
	$\wedge Opened(e,x))$

Figure 18.4   Semantic attachments for a fragment of our English grammar and lexicon.

$$Verb \rightarrow opened \qquad (18.24)$$
$$\lambda w.\lambda z.w(\lambda x.\exists e\ Opened(e) \wedge Opener(e,z) \wedge OpenedThing(e,x))$$

With this attachment in place, the transitive *VP* rule will incorporate the variable standing for *a restaurant* as the second argument to *opened*, incorporate the entire expression representing the *opening* event as the nuclear scope of *a restaurant*, and finally produce a λ-expression suitable for use with our *S* rule. As with the previous example, you should walk through this example step by step to make sure that you arrive at our intended meaning representation.

$$\exists xRestaurant(x) \wedge \exists eOpened(e) \wedge Opener(e,Matthew) \wedge OpenedThing(e,x)$$

The list of semantic attachments we've developed for this small grammar fragment is shown in Fig. 18.4.

In walking through these examples, we have introduced three techniques that instantiate the rule-to-rule approach to semantic analysis introduced at the beginning of this section:

1. Associating complex, function-like λ-expressions with lexical items
2. Copying semantic values from children to parents in non-branching rules
3. Applying the semantics of one of the children of a rule to the semantics of the other children of the rule through λ-reduction.

These techniques serve to illustrate a general division of labor that guides the design of semantic attachments in this compositional framework. In general, the lexical rules introduce quantifiers, predicates, and terms into our meaning representations. The semantic attachments for grammar rules put these elements together in the right ways but generally do not introduce new elements into the representations being created.

18.3 Quantifier Scope Ambiguity and Underspecification

The grammar fragment developed in the last section should handle examples like the following that contain multiple quantified noun phrases.

(18.25) Every restaurant has a menu.

Systematically applying the rules given in Fig. 18.4 to this example produces the following perfectly reasonable meaning representation:

$$\forall x\, Restaurant(x) \Rightarrow \exists y\, (Menu(y) \wedge \exists e\, (Having(e) \wedge Haver(e,x) \wedge Had(e,y)))$$

This formula more or less corresponds to the common-sense notion that all restaurants have menus.

Unfortunately, this isn't the only possible interpretation for this example. The following is also possible:

$$\exists y\, Menu(y) \wedge \forall x\, (Restaurant(x) \Rightarrow \exists e\, (Having(e) \wedge Haver(e,x) \wedge Had(e,y)))$$

This formula asserts that there is one menu out there in the world and all restaurants share it. From a common-sense point of view, this seems pretty unlikely, but remember that our semantic analyzer only has access to the semantic attachments in the grammar and the lexicon in producing meaning representations. Of course, world knowledge and contextual information can be used to select between these two readings, but only if we are able to produce both.

This example illustrates that expressions containing quantified terms can give rise to ambiguous representations even in the absence of syntactic, lexical, or anaphoric ambiguities. This is known as the problem of **quantifier scoping**. The difference between the two interpretations given above arises from which of the two quantified variables has the outer scope (i.e., which is outside the other in the expression).

Quantifier scoping

The approach outlined in the last section cannot handle this phenomena. The interpretation that is produced is based on the order in which the λ-expressions are reduced as dictated by the grammar and its semantic attachments. To fix this, we need the following capabilities.

- The ability to efficiently create *underspecified representations* that embody all possible readings without explicitly enumerating them
- A means to generate, or extract, all of the possible readings from this representation
- The ability to choose among the possible readings

The following sections outline approaches to the first two problems. The solution to the last, most important, problem requires the use of context and world knowledge and, unfortunately, the problem remains largely unsolved.

18.3.1 Store and Retrieve Approaches

One way to address the quantifier scope problem is to rethink our notion of what the semantic expressions attached to syntactic constituents should consist of. To see this,

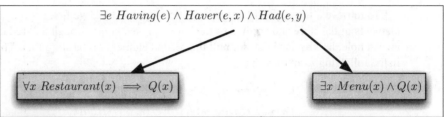

$$\exists e \; Having(e) \wedge Haver(e,x) \wedge Had(e,y)$$

$$\forall x \; Restaurant(x) \implies Q(x) \qquad \exists x \; Menu(x) \wedge Q(x)$$

Figure 18.5   An abstract depiction of how component meaning representations contribute to the meaning of (18.25).

let's examine the various parts that play a common role in both of the representations given earlier for (18.25). Ignoring the λ-expressions, the representations provided by *has*, *every restaurant*, and *a menu* are as follows.

$$\exists e \; Having(e) \wedge Haver(e,x) \wedge Had(e,y)$$

$$\forall x Restaurant(x) \Rightarrow Q(x)$$

$$\exists x Menu(x) \wedge Q(x)$$

An underspecified representation of this sentence's meaning should specify what we know about how these representations combine and no more. In particular, it would capture that the *restaurant* fills the *Haver* role and that the *menu* fills the *Had* role. However, it should remain agnostic about the placement of the quantifiers in the final representation. Figure 18.5 illustrates these facts graphically.

Cooper storage   To provide this kind of functionality, we introduce the notion of **Cooper storage** (Cooper, 1983) and once again leverage the power of λ-expressions. Recall that in our original approach to semantic analysis, we assigned a single FOL formula to each node in a parse tree. In the new approach, we replace this single semantic attachment with a store. The store includes a core meaning representation for a node along with an indexed list of quantified expressions gathered from the nodes below this node in the tree. These quantified expressions are in the form of λ-expressions that can be combined with the core meaning representation to incorporate the quantified expressions in the right way.

The following store would be associated with the node at the top of the parse tree for (18.25).

$$\exists e \; Having(e) \wedge Haver(e,s_1) \wedge Had(e,s_2)$$
$$(\lambda Q.\forall x \; Restaurant(x) \Rightarrow Q(x),1),$$
$$(\lambda Q.\exists x \; Menu(x) \wedge Q(x),2)$$

This store contains exactly what we said we needed—the *Haver* and *Had* roles have been correctly assigned just as in our earlier approach but we also have access to the original quantified expressions through the indexes on the variables s_1 and s_2. These indexes pick out the corresponding quantified expressions in the store. Note that contents of this store correspond directly to the representations given in Fig. 18.5.

605

To retrieve a fully-specified representation from a store, we first choose one of the elements of the store and apply it to the core representation through a λ-reduction. As an example, let's assume that we pull the second element of the store first. This results in the following λ-application

$$\lambda Q.\exists x \, (Menu(x) \wedge Q(x))$$
$$(\lambda s_2.\exists e \, Having(e) \wedge Haver(e, s_1) \wedge Had(e, s_2))$$

and its subsequent reduction.

$$\exists x \, (Menu(x) \wedge \exists e \, Having(e) \wedge Haver(e, s_1) \wedge Had(e, x))$$

Note that we use the index variable s_2 as the λ-variable for core representation's λ-expression. This ensures that the quantified expression retrieved from the store will be assigned to the correct role in the core representation.

The store now contains this new core representation and one remaining quantified λ-expression. Pulling that expression out of the store and applying it to the core results in the following λ-application

$$\lambda Q.\forall x \, (Restaurant(x) \Rightarrow Q(x))$$
$$(\lambda .s_1 \exists y \, (Menu(y) \wedge \exists e \, Having(e) \wedge Haver(e, s_1) \wedge Had(e, x))$$

and subsequent reduction.

$$\forall x \, Restaurant(x) \Rightarrow \exists y \, Menu(y) \wedge \exists e \, Having(e) \wedge Haver(e, x) \wedge Had(e, y))$$

This process yields exactly the same expression that we got with our original approach. To get the alternative interpretation, in which *a menu* has the outer scope, we simply pull the elements out of the store in the opposite order.

In working through this example, we assumed that we already had the contents of the store for this sentence. But how did this store get populated? For the core representations in the store, we simply apply our semantic attachments in exactly the same fashion as we normally would. That is, we either copy them up unchanged from child to parent in the tree, or we apply the core representation of one child to the representation of the others as dictated by our semantic attachments in the grammar. We store the result as the core representation in the parent's store. Any quantified indexed expressions in the store are simply copied up to the store of the parent.

To see how this works, let's consider the *VP* node in the derivation of (18.25). Figure 18.6 illustrates the stores for all of the nodes in this example. The core representation for this *VP* results from the application of the transitive *VP* rule given earlier in Fig. 18.4. In this case, we apply the representation of the *Verb* to the representation of the argument *NP*. The indexed quantified expression in the *NP*'s store is copied up to the *VP*'s store.

Things get more interesting in the computation of the store for *a menu*. The relevant rule in Fig. 18.4 instructs us to apply the meaning representation of the *Det* to the representation of the *Nominal*, thus providing us with the representation shown as the second element of the *NP*'s store in Fig. 18.6. Now, if we were to store this expression

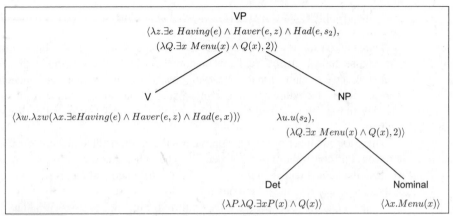

Figure 18.6   Semantic stores for the *VP* subtree for (18.25).

as the core representation for this *NP* we would be right back to our original formulation. It would subsequently be consumed by the *VP* node and a hard commitment to the placement of this quantified term would be made.

To avoid this, we use the same representational trick we used earlier to turn FOL constants into λ-expressions. When a quantified *NP* is introduced, we create a new index variable, in this case s_2, and wrap a λ-application around that variable. This index on the variable points at the corresponding quantified expression in the store. This new λ-expression serves as the core representation for the new *NP*. And, as is shown in Fig. 18.6, it is this variable that is subsequently bound as the appropriate semantic argument in the event representation.

18.3.2   Constraint-Based Approaches

Unfortunately, this storage-based approach suffers from two problems. First, it only addresses the problem of scope ambiguities introduced by quantified noun phrases. However, a wide array of syntactic constructions and lexical items also introduce similar ambiguities. Consider the following example and its associated interpretations.

(18.26) Every restaurant did not close.

$$(\forall x\, Restaurant(x) \;\Rightarrow\; \exists e\, Closing(e) \wedge Closed(e,x))$$

$$\forall x\, Restaurant(x) \;\Rightarrow\; (\exists e\, Closing(e) \wedge Closed(e,x))$$

Nothing in the store-and-retrieve method allows us to handle this problem. Of course, we could incorporate additional mechanisms into the method to handle negation but the resulting approach becomes more and more ad hoc as additional problems are encountered.

Even if we could extend the store-and-retrieve approach to handle additional sources of ambiguity, there is a second more critical shortcoming. Although it allows us to enumerate all the possible scopings for a given expression, it doesn't allow us to impose additional constraints on those possibilities. This is an ability that is crucial if we wish to be able to apply specific lexical, syntactic, and pragmatic knowledge to narrow down the range of possibilities for any given expression.

The solution to these problems lies in a change of perspective. Instead of taking what is essentially a procedural focus on how to retrieve fully-specified representations from stores, we ought to focus instead on how to effectively represent underspecified representations, including any constraints that any final representation must satisfy. In this view, any fully-specified FOL expression that is consistent with the constraints is valid.

Hole semantics

There are a number of current approaches that address the underspecification problem from this constraint-based perspective. The **hole semantics** (Bos, 1996) approach we describe here is representative of the field. The Historical Notes section at the end of the chapter surveys the other constraint-based approaches.

Hole

Labels

To get a feel for this approach, let's return to Fig. 18.5 on page 593. The Q predicates in the quantified expressions are place-holders that will eventually be replaced by arbitrary FOL expressions through a series of coordinated λ-reductions. In the hole semantics approach, we replace these λ-variables with **holes**. Instead of using λ-reductions to fill these holes, we first add **labels** to all of the candidate FOL subexpressions. In a fully-specified formula, all holes will be filled with labeled subexpressions.

Dominance constraints

Of course, we can't fill holes with just any labeled expression, so we'll add **dominance constraints** between holes and labels that restrict which labels can fill which holes. More formally, an expression of the form $l \leq h$ asserts that the expression containing hole h dominates the expression with label l. This simply means that the expression containing h must ultimately have l as a subexpression, and not the other way around.

Let's walk through this in the context of (18.25). As we showed in Fig. 18.5 on page 593, there are three quantified expressions that play a role in this example: the *restaurant*, the *menu*, and the *having*. Let's label them l_1, l_2, and l_3, respectively. We'll use the hole h_0 as a place-holder for the final representation. Replacing the λ-variables, we'll use h_1 to stand for the nuclear scope of *restaurant*, and h_1 to stand for the nuclear scope of *menu*.

Since h_0 stands for the entire expression it trivially dominates all of the expressions in the underspecified representation. Moreover, we know that in both of the two possible interpretations, the holes h_1 and h_2 outscope the event labeled by l_3. However, since we want to remain agnostic about how l_1 and l_2 relate to each other no dominance relations are specified concerning them. This leaves us with the following underspecified representation for (18.25)

$$l_1 : \forall x\, Restaurant(x) \Rightarrow h_1$$
$$l_2 : \exists x\, Menu(y) \wedge h_2$$
$$l_3 : \exists e\, Having(e) \wedge Haver(e,x) \wedge Had(e,y)$$
$$l_1 \leq h_0, l_2 \leq h_0, l_3 \leq h_1, l_3 \leq h_2$$

Figure 18.7 captures these facts graphically.

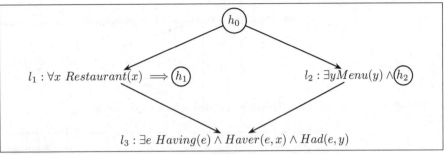

Figure 18.7   Hole semantic representation for *Every restaurant has a menu.*

Plugging

Now that we have an underspecified representation, how can we retrieve a fully-specified FOL representation? Clearly, what we need is a **plugging** that fills all the holes with labeled expressions in a way that respects all of the stated constraints. More formally, a plugging is a one-to-one mapping from holes to labels that satisfies all the given constraints. When we have plugged all the holes consistently, we have a fully-specified representation.

Let's start by filling h_0. The two candidate plugs for this hole are l_1 and l_2. Since h_0 dominates both l_1 and l_2 and neither one dominates the other, the choice is arbitrary. Let's assume that we plug h_0 with l_1, denoted as $P(h_0) = l_1$. Once we've made this choice, the remaining assignments are fully determined by the constraints; that is, $P(h_1) = l_2$ and $P(h_2) = l_3$. This plugging corresponds to the following interpretation where $\forall x\ Restaurant(x)$ has the outer-scope.

$$\forall x Restaurant(x) \Rightarrow \exists y(Menu(y) \wedge \exists e Having(e) \wedge Haver(e,x) \wedge Had(e,y))$$

Figure 18.8 illustrates the steps in this process graphically. Not surprisingly, the alternative interpretation in which *menu* has the outer scope is obtained by starting with the assignment $P(h_0) = l_2$.

To implement this approach, we have to define a language to associate labels and holes with FOL expressions and to express dominance constraints between holes and labels. Blackburn and Bos (2005) describe a meta-language based on FOL and λ-expressions for doing just that. These FOL statements play the role of our semantic attachments to grammar rules.

This constraint-based approach to underspecification addresses many of the problems with the store-and-retrieve approach that we raised at the beginning of this section. First, the approach is not specific to any particular grammatical construction or source of scope ambiguity. This follows since we can label, or designate as holes, essentially arbitrary pieces of FOL formula. Second, and perhaps more importantly, dominance constraints give us the power to express constraints that can rule out unwanted interpretations. The source of these constraints can come from specific lexical and syntactic knowledge and can be expressed directly in the semantic attachments to lexical entries and grammar rules.

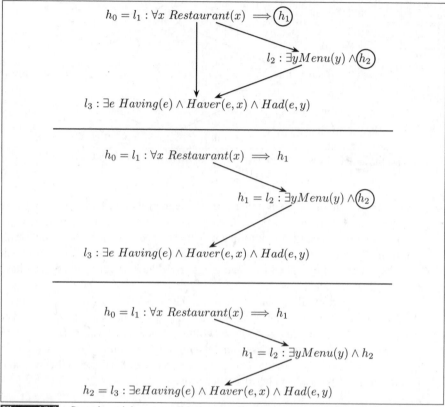

Figure 18.8   Steps in arriving at a valid plugging for *Every restaurant has a menu.*

18.4   Unification-Based Approaches to Semantic Analysis

As mentioned in Section 18.2, feature structures and the unification operator provide an effective way to implement syntax-driven semantic analysis. Recall that in Chapter 15 we paired complex feature structures with individual context-free grammar rules to encode syntactic constraints such as number agreement and subcategorization, constraints that were awkward or in some cases impossible to convey directly with context-free grammars. For example, the following rule was used to capture agreement constraints on English noun phrases:

$$NP \rightarrow Det\ Nominal$$
$$\langle Det\ \text{AGREEMENT} \rangle = \langle Nominal\ \text{AGREEMENT} \rangle$$
$$\langle NP\ \text{AGREEMENT} \rangle = \langle Nominal\ \text{AGREEMENT} \rangle$$

Rules such as this serve two functions at the same time: they ensure that the grammar rejects expressions that violate this constraint, and more importantly for our current topic, they create complex structures that can be associated with parts of grammatical derivations. The following structure, for example, results from the application of the above rule to a singular noun phrase.

$$\begin{bmatrix} \text{AGREEMENT} & \begin{bmatrix} \text{NUMBER} & sg \end{bmatrix} \end{bmatrix}$$

We'll use this latter capability to compose meaning representations and associate them with constituents in parse.

In this unification-based approach, our FOL representations and λ-based semantic attachments are replaced by complex feature structures and unification equations. To see how this works, let's walk through a series of examples similar to those discussed earlier in Section 18.2. Let's start with a simple intransitive sentence with a proper noun as its subject.

(18.27) Rhumba closed

With an event-oriented approach, the meaning representation for this sentence should be something like the following.

$$\exists e\, Closing(e) \wedge Closed(e, Rhumba)$$

Our first task is to show that we can encode representations like this within a feature-structure framework. The most straightforward way to approach this task is to simply follow the BNF-style definition of FOL statements given in Chapter 17. The relevant elements of this definition stipulate that FOL formulas come in three varieties: atomic formulas consisting of predicates with the appropriate number of term arguments; formulas conjoined with other formulas by the ∧, ∨ and ⇒ operators; and quantified formulas that consist of a quantifier, variables, and a formula. Using this definition as a guide, we can capture this FOL expression with the following feature structure.

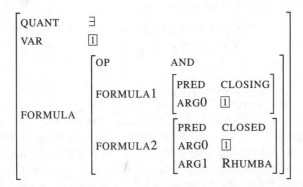

Figure 18.9 shows this expression in the DAG-style notation introduced in Chapter 15. The figure reveals how variables are handled. Instead of introducing explicit FOL variables, we use the path-based, feature-sharing capability of feature structures to accomplish the same goal. In this example, the event variable *e* is captured by the three paths leading to the same shared node.

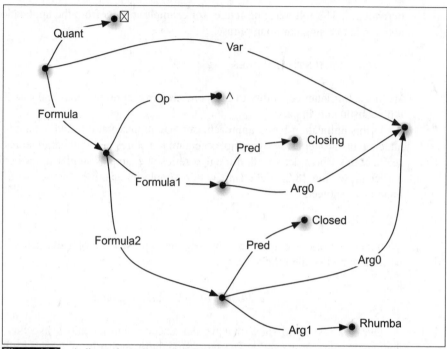

Figure 18.9   A directed graph notation for semantic feature structures.

Our next step is to associate unification equations with the grammar rules involved in this example's derivation. Let's start at the top with the *S* rule.

$$S \rightarrow NP\ VP$$
$$\langle S\ \text{SEM} \rangle = \langle NP\ \text{SEM} \rangle$$
$$\langle VP\ \text{ARG0} \rangle = \langle NP\ \text{INDEXVAR} \rangle$$
$$\langle NP\ \text{SCOPE} \rangle = \langle VP\ \text{SEM} \rangle$$

The first equation equates the meaning representation of the *NP* (encoded under the SEM feature) with our top-level *S*. The second equation assigns the subject *NP* to the appropriate role inside the *VP*'s meaning representation. More concretely, the second equation fills the appropriate role in the *VP*'s semantic representation by unifying the ARG0 feature with a path that leads to a representation of the semantics of the *NP*. Finally, the third equation unifies the SCOPE feature in the *NP*'s meaning representation with a pointer to the VP's meaning representation. As we show, this is a somewhat convoluted way to bring the representation of an event up to where it belongs in the representation. The motivation for this apparatus should become clear in the ensuing discussion when we consider quantified noun phrases.

Carrying on, let's consider the attachments for the *NP* and *ProperNoun* parts of this derivation.

$$NP \rightarrow ProperNoun$$
$$\langle NP \text{ SEM} \rangle = \langle ProperNoun \text{ SEM} \rangle$$
$$\langle NP \text{ SCOPE} \rangle = \langle \text{ProperNoun SCOPE} \rangle$$
$$\langle NP \text{ INDEXVAR} \rangle = \langle ProperNoun \text{ INDEXVAR} \rangle$$

$$ProperNoun \rightarrow Rhumba$$
$$\langle ProperNoun \text{ SEM PRED} \rangle = \text{RHUMBA}$$
$$\langle ProperNoun \text{ INDEXVAR} \rangle = \langle ProperNoun \text{ SEM PRED} \rangle$$

As we saw earlier, there isn't much to the semantics of proper nouns in this approach. Here we're just introducing a constant and providing an index variable to point at that constant.

Next, let's move on to the semantic attachments for the *VP* and *Verb* rules.

$$VP \rightarrow Verb$$
$$\langle VP \text{ SEM} \rangle = \langle \text{Verb SEM} \rangle$$
$$\langle VP \text{ ARG0} \rangle = \langle \text{Verb ARG0} \rangle$$

$$Verb \rightarrow closed$$
$$\langle Verb \text{ SEM QUANT} \rangle = \exists$$
$$\langle Verb \text{ SEM FORMULA OP} \rangle = \wedge$$
$$\langle Verb \text{ SEM FORMULA FORMULA1 PRED} \rangle = \text{CLOSING}$$
$$\langle Verb \text{ SEM FORMULA FORMULA1 ARG0} \rangle = \langle Verb \text{ SEM VAR} \rangle$$
$$\langle Verb \text{ SEM FORMULA FORMULA2 PRED} \rangle = \text{CLOSED}$$
$$\langle Verb \text{ SEM FORMULA FORMULA2 ARG0} \rangle = \langle Verb \text{ SEM VAR} \rangle$$
$$\langle Verb \text{ SEM FORMULA FORMULA2 ARG1} \rangle = \langle Verb \text{ ARG0} \rangle$$

The attachments for the *VP* rule parallel our earlier treatment of non-branching grammatical rules. These unification equations are simply making the appropriate semantic fragments of the *Verb* available at the *VP* level. In contrast, the unification equations for the *Verb* introduce the bulk of the event representation that is at the core of this example. Specifically, it introduces the quantifier, event variable, and predications that make up the body of the final expression. What would be an event variable in FOL is captured by the equations unifying the *Verb* SEM VAR path with the appropriate arguments to the predicates in the body of the formula. Finally, it exposes the single missing argument (the entity being closed) through the $\langle Verb \text{ ARG0} \rangle$ equation.

Taking a step back, we can see that these equations serve the same basic functions as the λ-expressions in Section 18.2; they provide the content of the FOL formula being created, and they serve to expose and name the external arguments that will be filled in later at higher levels in the grammar.

These last few rules also display the division of labor that we've seen several times now; lexical rules introduce the bulk of the semantic content, and higher level grammatical rules assemble the pieces in the right way, rather than introducing content.

Of course, as was the case with the λ-based approach, things get quite a bit more complex when we look at expressions containing quantifiers. To see this, let's work through the following example.

(18.28) Every restaurant closed.

Again, the meaning representation for this expression should be the following:

$$\forall x\, Restaurant(x) \Rightarrow (\exists e\, Closing(e) \wedge Closed(e,x))$$

which is captured by the following feature structure.

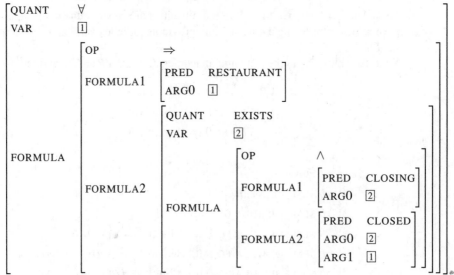

As we saw earlier with the λ-based approach, the outer structure for expressions like this comes largely from the subject noun phrase. Recall that schematically this semantic structure has the form $\forall x P(x) \Rightarrow Q(x)$, where the P expression is traditionally referred to as the *restrictor* and is provided by the head noun, and Q is referred to as the *nuclear scope* and comes from the verb phrase.

This structure gives rise to two distinct tasks for our semantic attachments: the semantics of the VP semantics must be unified with the nuclear scope of the subject noun phrase, and the variable representing that noun phrase must be assigned to the ARG1 role of the CLOSED predicate in the event structure. The following rules involved in the derivation of *Every restaurant* address these two tasks:

$NP \rightarrow Det\, Nominal$

$\langle\, NP\ \text{SEM}\rangle = \langle Det\ \text{SEM}\,\rangle$

$\langle\, NP\ \text{SEM VAR}\,\rangle = \langle\, NP\ \text{INDEXVAR}\,\rangle$

$\langle\, NP\ \text{SEM FORMULA FORMULA1}\,\rangle = \langle\, Nominal\ \text{SEM}\,\rangle$

$\langle\, NP\ \text{SEM FORMULA FORMULA2}\,\rangle = \langle\, NP\ \text{SCOPE}\,\rangle$

$$Nominal \rightarrow Noun$$
$$\langle\, Nominal\ \text{SEM}\,\rangle = \langle\, Noun\ \text{SEM}\,\rangle$$
$$\langle\, Nominal\ \text{INDEXVAR}\,\rangle = \langle\, Noun\ \text{INDEXVAR}\,\rangle$$

$$Noun \rightarrow restaurant$$
$$\langle\, Noun\ \text{SEM PRED}\,\rangle = \langle\, \text{RESTAURANT}\,\rangle$$
$$\langle\, Noun\ \text{INDEXVAR}\,\rangle = \langle\, Noun\ \text{SEM PRED}\,\rangle$$

$$Det \rightarrow every$$
$$\langle\, Det\ \text{SEM QUANT}\,\rangle = \forall$$
$$\langle\, Det\ \text{SEM FORMULA OP}\,\rangle = \Rightarrow$$

As one final exercise, let's walk through an example with a transitive verb phrase.

(18.29) Franco opened a restaurant.

This example has the following meaning representation.

$$\exists x\, Restaurant(x) \wedge \exists e\, Opening(e) \wedge Opener(e, Franco) \wedge Opened(e, x)$$

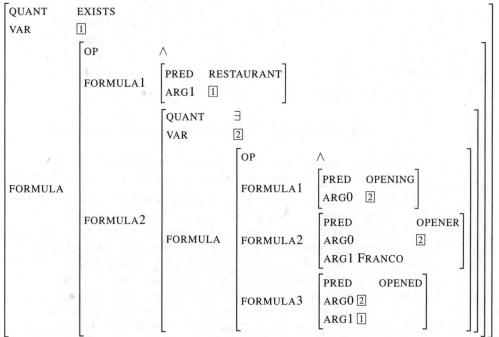

The only really new element that we need to address in this example is the following transitive *VP* rule.

$$VP \rightarrow Verb\ NP$$
$$\langle VP\ \text{SEM}\rangle = \langle Verb\ \text{SEM}\rangle$$
$$\langle NP\ \text{SCOPE}\rangle = \langle VP\ \text{SEM}\rangle$$
$$\langle Verb\ \text{ARG1}\rangle = \langle NP\ \text{INDEXVAR}\rangle$$

This rule has the two primary tasks that parallel those in our *S* rule: it has to fill the nuclear scope of the object *NP* with the semantics of the *VP*, and it has to insert the variable representing the object into the right role in the *VP*'s meaning representation.

One obvious problem with the approach we just described is that it fails to generate all the possible ambiguous representations arising from quantifier scope ambiguities. Fortunately, the approaches to underspecification described earlier in Section 18.3 can be adapted to the unification-based approach.

18.5   Integration of Semantics into the Earley Parser

In Section 18.1, we suggested a simple pipeline architecture for a semantic analyzer where the results of a complete syntactic parse are passed to a semantic analyzer. The motivation for this notion stems from the fact that the compositional approach requires the syntactic parse before it can proceed. It is, however, also possible to perform semantic analysis in parallel with syntactic processing. This is possible because in our compositional framework, the meaning representation for a constituent can be created as soon as all of its constituent parts are present. This section describes just such an approach to integrating semantic analysis into the Earley parser from Chapter 13.

The integration of semantic analysis into an Earley parser is straightforward and follows precisely the same lines as the integration of unification into the algorithm given in Chapter 15. Three modifications are required to the original algorithm:

1. The rules of the grammar are given a new field to contain their semantic attachments.
2. The states in the chart are given a new field to hold the meaning representation of the constituent.
3. The ENQUEUE function is altered so that when a complete state is entered into the chart, its semantics are computed and stored in the state's semantic field.

Figure 18.10 shows ENQUEUE modified to create meaning representations. When ENQUEUE is passed a complete state that can successfully unify its unification constraints, it calls APPLY-SEMANTICS to compute and store the meaning representation for this state. Note the importance of performing feature-structure unification prior to semantic analysis. This ensures that semantic analysis will be performed only on valid trees and that features needed for semantic analysis will be present.

The primary advantage of this integrated approach over the pipeline approach lies in the fact that APPLY-SEMANTICS can fail in a manner similar to the way that unification can fail. If a semantic ill-formedness is found in the meaning representation being created, the corresponding state can be blocked from entering the chart. In this way, semantic considerations can be brought to bear during syntactic processing. Chapter 19 describes in some detail the various ways by which this notion of ill-formedness can be realized.

Unfortunately, this also illustrates one of the primary disadvantages of integrating semantics directly into the parser—considerable effort may be spent on the semantic analysis of *orphan* constituents that do not in the end contribute to a successful parse.

```
procedure ENQUEUE(state, chart-entry)
    if INCOMPLETE?(state) then
        if state is not already in chart-entry then
            PUSH(state, chart-entry)
    else if UNIFY-STATE(state) succeeds then
        if APPLY-SEMANTICS(state) succeeds then
            if state is not already in chart-entry then
                PUSH(state, chart-entry)

procedure APPLY-SEMANTICS(state)
    meaning-rep ← APPLY(state.semantic-attachment, state)
    if meaning-rep does not equal failure then
        state.meaning-rep ← meaning-rep
```

Figure 18.10   The ENQUEUE function modified to handle semantics. If the state is complete and unification succeeds, then ENQUEUE calls APPLY-SEMANTICS to compute and store the meaning representation of completed states.

The question of whether the gains made by bringing semantics to bear early in the process outweigh the costs involved in performing extraneous semantic processing can only be answered on a case-by-case basis.

18.6   Idioms and Compositionality

> *Ce corps qui s'appelait et qui s'appelle encore le saint empire romain n'était en aucune manière ni saint, ni romain, ni empire.*
>
> *This body, which called itself and still calls itself the Holy Roman Empire, was neither Holy, nor Roman, nor an Empire.*
>
> Voltaire[2] (1756)

As innocuous as it seems, the principle of compositionality runs into trouble fairly quickly when real language is examined. There are many cases in which the meaning of a constituent is not based on the meaning of its parts, at least not in the straightforward compositional sense. Consider the following WSJ examples:

(18.30)   Coupons are just the tip of the iceberg.

(18.31)   The SEC's allegations are only the tip of the iceberg.

(18.32)   Coronary bypass surgery, hip replacement and intensive-care units are but the tip of the iceberg.

The phrase *the tip of the iceberg* in each of these examples clearly doesn't have much to do with tips or icebergs. Instead, it roughly means something like *the beginning*. The most straightforward way to handle idiomatic constructions like these is to

---

[2]   *Essai sur les moeurs et les esprit des nations.* Translation by Y. Sills, as quoted in Sills and Merton (1991).

introduce new grammar rules specifically designed to handle them. These idiomatic rules mix lexical items with grammatical constituents and introduce semantic content that is not derived from any of its parts. Consider the following rule as an example of this approach:

$$NP \rightarrow the\ tip\ of\ the\ iceberg$$
$$Beginning$$

The lower-case items on the right-hand side of this rule represent precisely the words in the input. Although, the constant *Beginning* should not be taken too seriously as a meaning representation for this idiom, it does illustrate the idea that the meaning of this idiom is not based on the meaning of any of its parts. Note that an Earley-style analyzer with this rule will produce two parses when this phrase is encountered: one representing the idiom and one representing the compositional meaning.

As with the rest of the grammar, it may take a few tries to get these rules right. Consider the following *iceberg* examples from the WSJ corpus:

(18.33) And that's but the tip of Mrs. Ford's iceberg.

(18.34) These comments describe only the tip of a 1,000-page iceberg.

(18.35) The 10 employees represent the merest tip of the iceberg.

The rule given above is clearly not general enough to handle these cases. These examples indicate that there is a vestigial syntactic structure to this idiom that permits some variation in the determiners used and also permits some adjectival modification of both the *iceberg* and the *tip*. A more promising rule would be something like the following:

$$NP \rightarrow TipNP\ of\ IcebergNP$$
$$Beginning$$

Here, the categories *TipNP* and *IcebergNP* can be given an internal nominal-like structure that permits some adjectival modification and some variation in the determiners while still restricting the heads of these noun phrases to the lexical items *tip* and *iceberg*. Note that this syntactic solution ignores the thorny issue that the modifiers *mere* and *1000-page* seem to indicate that both the *tip* and *iceberg* may in fact play some compositional role in the meaning of the idiom. We return to this topic in Chapter 19, when we take up the issue of metaphor.

To summarize, handling idioms requires at least the following changes to the general compositional framework:

- Allow the mixing of lexical items with traditional grammatical constituents.
- Allow the creation of additional idiom-specific constituents to handle the correct range of productivity of the idiom.
- Permit semantic attachments that introduce logical terms and predicates that are not related to any of the constituents of the rule.

This discussion is obviously only the tip of an enormous iceberg. Idioms are far more frequent and far more productive than is generally recognized and pose serious difficulties for many applications, including, as we discuss in Chapter 25, machine translation.

18.7   Summary

This chapter explores the notion of syntax-driven semantic analysis. Among the highlights of this chapter are the following topics:

- **Semantic analysis** is the process whereby meaning representations are created and assigned to linguistic inputs.
- **Semantic analyzers** that make use of static knowledge from the lexicon and grammar can create context-independent literal or conventional meanings.
- The **Principle of Compositionality** states that the meaning of a sentence can be composed from the meanings of its parts.
- In **syntax-driven semantic analysis**, the parts are the syntactic constituents of an input.
- Compositional creation of FOL formulas is possible with a few notational extensions, including λ-**expressions** and **complex terms**.
- Compositional creation of FOL formulas is also possible with the mechanisms provided by feature structures and unification.
- **Natural language quantifiers** introduce a kind of ambiguity that is difficult to handle compositionally.
- **Underspecified representations** can be used to effectively handle multiple interpretations arising from by scope ambiguities.
- **Idiomatic language** defies the principle of compositionality but can easily be handled by the adaptation of techniques used to design grammar rules and their semantic attachments.

Bibliographical and Historical Notes

As noted earlier, the principle of compositionality is traditionally attributed to Frege; Janssen (1997) discusses this attribution. Using the categorial grammar framework we describe in Chapter 12, Montague (1973) demonstrated that a compositional approach could be systematically applied to an interesting fragment of natural language. The rule-to-rule hypothesis was first articulated by Bach (1976). On the computational side of things, Woods's LUNAR system (Woods, 1977) was based on a pipelined syntax-first compositional analysis. Schubert and Pelletier (1982) developed an incremental rule-to-rule system based on Gazdar's GPSG approach (Gazdar, 1981, 1982; Gazdar et al., 1985). Main and Benson (1983) extended Montague's approach to the domain of question answering.

In one of the all-too-frequent cases of parallel development, researchers in programming languages developed essentially identical compositional techniques to aid in the design of compilers. Specifically, Knuth (1968) introduced the notion of attribute grammars that associate semantic structures with syntactic structures in a one-to-one correspondence. As a consequence, the style of semantic attachments used in this chapter will be familiar to users of the YACC-style (Johnson and Lesk, 1978) compiler tools.

Of necessity, a large number of important topics were not covered in this chapter. See Alshawi (1992) for the standard gap-threading approach to semantic interpretation in the presence of long-distance dependencies. ter Meulen (1995) presents a modern treatment of tense, aspect, and the representation of temporal information. Many limited-domain systems such as dialogue agents make use of an alternative approach to syntax-semantics integration called **semantic grammar** (Brown and Burton, 1975), related to other early models such as pragmatic grammars (Woods, 1977) and performance grammars (Robinson, 1975). All were centered around the notion of reshaping syntactic grammars to serve the needs of semantic processing. See Chapter 24 for details of this approach.

Semantic grammar

The store-and-retrieve approach to quantifier scope problems is due to Cooper (1983). Keller (1988) extended this approach with the introduction of nested stores to deal with a wider range of quantified noun phrases. The hole semantics approach to underspecified representations is due to Bos (1996, 2001, 2004). Blackburn and Bos (2005) provide a detailed description of hole semantics, including how it can be implemented in Prolog and integrated into a semantic analysis system. Other constraint-based approaches include Underspecified Discourse Representation Theory (Reyle, 1993), Minimal Recursion Semantics (MRS) (Copestake et al., 1995), and the Constraint Language for Lambda Structures (CLLS) (Egg et al., 2001). Player (2004) argues that these approaches are, for all practical purposes, notational variants.

Practical computational approaches to quantifier scoping can be found in Hobbs and Shieber (1987) and Alshawi (1992). VanLehn (1978) presents a set of human preferences for quantifier scoping. Higgins and Sadock (2003) use such preferences as features to train a classifier to predict the correct scope for quantifier ambiguities.

Over the years, a considerable amount of effort has been directed toward the interpretation of compound nominals. Linguistic research on this topic can be found in Lees (1970), Downing (1977), Levi (1978), and Ryder (1994); more computational approaches are described in Gershman (1977), Finin (1980), McDonald (1982), Pierre (1984), Arens et al. (1987), Wu (1992), Vanderwende (1994), and Lauer (1995).

The literature on idioms is long and extensive. Fillmore et al. (1988) describe a general grammatical framework called Construction Grammar that places idioms at the center of its underlying theory. Makkai (1972) presents an extensive linguistic analysis of many English idioms. Hundreds of idiom dictionaries for second-language learners are also available. On the computational side, Becker (1975) was among the first to suggest the use of phrasal rules in parsers. Wilensky and Arens (1980) were among the first to successfully make use of this notion in their PHRAN system. Zernik (1987) demonstrated a system that could learn such phrasal idioms in context. A collection of papers on computational approaches to idioms appeared in Fass et al. (1992).

We have neglected an entire branch of semantic analysis in which expectations arising from deep meaning representations drive the analysis process. Such systems avoid the direct representation and use of syntax, rarely making use of anything resembling a parse tree. Some of the earliest and most successful efforts along these lines were developed by Simmons (1973, 1978, 1983) and Wilks (1975a, 1975c). A series of similar approaches was developed by Roger Schank and his students (Riesbeck, 1975; Birnbaum and Selfridge, 1981; Riesbeck, 1986). In these approaches, the semantic analysis process is guided by detailed procedures associated with individual lexical items.

Finally, recent work has focused on the task of automatically learning the mapping from sentences to logical form, based on a training set of sentences labeled with their semantics (Zettlemoyer and Collins, 2005, 2007; Mooney, 2007; Wong and Mooney, 2007).

Exercises

18.1 Develop a set of grammar rules and semantic attachments to handle predicate adjectives such as the following:

1. Flight 308 from New York is expensive.
2. Murphy's restaurant is cheap.

18.2 Develop a set of grammar rules and semantic attachments to handle so-called *control verbs* as in the following:

1. Franco *decided* to leave.
2. Nicolas *told* Franco to go to Frasca.

The first of these is an example of subject control—*Franco* plays the role of the agent for both *decide* and *leave*. The second is an example of object control— there *Franco* is the person being told and the agent of the going event. The challenge in creating attachments for these rules is to properly incorporate the semantic representation of a single noun phrase into two roles.

18.3 None of the attachments given in this chapter provide temporal information. Augment a small number of the most basic rules to add temporal information along the lines sketched in Chapter 17. Use your rules to create meaning representations for the following examples:

1. Flight 299 departed at 9 o'clock.
2. Flight 208 will arrive at 3 o'clock.
3. Flight 1405 will arrive late.

18.4 As noted in Chapter 17, the present tense in English can be used to refer to either the present or the future. However, it can also be used to express habitual behavior, as in the following:

1. Flight 208 leaves at 3 o'clock.

This could be a simple statement about today's Flight 208, or alternatively it might state that this flight leaves at 3 o'clock every day. Create a FOL meaning representation along with appropriate semantic attachments for this habitual sense.

18.5 Implement an Earley-style semantic analyzer based on the discussion on page 604.

18.6 It has been claimed that it is not necessary to explicitly list the semantic attachment for most grammar rules. Instead, the semantic attachment for a rule should be inferable from the semantic types of the rule's constituents. For example, if a rule has two constituents, where one is a single-argument λ-expression and the other is a constant, then the semantic attachment must apply the λ-expression to the constant. Given the attachments presented in this chapter, does this *type-driven semantics* seem like a reasonable idea? Explain your answer.

18.7 Add a simple type-driven semantics mechanism to the Earley analyzer you implemented for Exercise 18.5.

18.8 Using a phrasal search on your favorite Web search engine, collect a small corpus of *the tip of the iceberg* examples. Be certain that you search for an appropriate range of examples (i.e., don't just search for "the tip of the iceberg"). Analyze these examples and come up with a set of grammar rules that correctly accounts for them.

18.9 Collect a similar corpus of examples for the idiom *miss the boat*. Analyze these examples and come up with a set of grammar rules that correctly accounts for them.

Chapter 19

Lexical Semantics

> *"When I use a word", Humpty Dumpty said in rather a scornful tone, "it means just what I choose it to mean – neither more nor less."*
>
> *Lewis Carroll*, Alice in Wonderland
>
> *How many legs does a dog have if you call its tail a leg?*
> *Four.*
> *Calling a tail a leg doesn't make it one.*
>
> Attributed to Abraham Lincoln

The previous two chapters focused on meaning representations for entire sentences. In those discussions, we made a simplifying assumption by representing *word meanings* as unanalyzed symbols like EAT or JOHN or RED. But representing the meaning of a word by capitalizing it is a pretty unsatisfactory model. In this chapter we introduce a richer model of the semantics of words, drawing on the linguistic study of word *Lexical semantics* meaning, a field called **lexical semantics**.

Before we try to define *word meaning* in the next section, we first need to be clear on what we mean by *word* since we have used the word *word* in many different ways in this book.

Lexeme We can use the word **lexeme** to mean a pairing of a particular form (orthographic *Lexicon* or phonological) with its meaning, and a **lexicon** is a finite list of lexemes. For the purposes of lexical semantics, particularly for dictionaries and thesauruses, we represent a *Lemma* lexeme by a **lemma**. A **lemma** or **citation form** is the grammatical form that is used *Citation form* to represent a lexeme; thus, *carpet* is the lemma for *carpets*. The lemma or citation form for *sing*, *sang*, *sung* is *sing*. In many languages the infinitive form is used as the lemma for the verb; thus in Spanish *dormir* "to sleep" is the lemma for verb forms like *duermes* "you sleep". The specific forms *sung* or *carpets* or *sing* or *duermes* are called *Wordform* **wordforms**.

Lemmatization The process of mapping from a wordform to a lemma is called **lemmatization**. Lemmatization is not always deterministic, since it may depend on the context. For example, the wordform *found* can map to the lemma *find* (meaning 'to locate') or the lemma *found* ('to create an institution'), as illustrated in the following WSJ examples:

(19.1) He has looked at 14 baseball and football stadiums and **found** that only one – private Dodger Stadium – brought more money into a city than it took out.

(19.2) Culturally speaking, this city has increasingly displayed its determination to **found** the sort of institutions that attract the esteem of Eastern urbanites.

In addition, lemmas are part-of-speech specific; thus, the wordform *tables* has two possible lemmas, the noun *table* and the verb *table*.

One way to do lemmatization is with the morphological parsing algorithms of Chapter 3. Recall that morphological parsing takes a surface form like *cats* and produces *cat +PL*. But a lemma is not necessarily the same as the stem from the morphological parse. For example, the morphological parse of the word *celebrations* might

From Chapter 19 of *Speech and Language Processing*, Second Edition. Daniel Jurafsky, James H. Martin.

produce the stem **celebrate** with the affixes *-ion* and *-s*, while the lemma for *celebrations* is the longer form **celebration**. In general, lemmas may be larger than morphological stems (e.g., *New York* or *throw up*). The intuition is that we want to have a different lemma whenever we need to have a completely different dictionary entry with its own meaning representation; we expect to have *celebrations* and *celebration* share an entry, since the difference in their meanings is mainly just grammatical, but not necessarily to share one with *celebrate*.

In the remainder of this chapter, when we refer to the meaning (or meanings) of a "word", we are generally referring to a lemma rather than a wordform.

Now that we have defined the locus of word meaning, we can proceed to different ways to represent this meaning. In the next section we introduce the idea of **word sense** as the part of a lexeme that represents word meaning. In subsequent sections we then describe ways of defining and representing these senses and introduce the lexical semantic aspects of the events defined in Chapter 17.

19.1   Word Senses

The meaning of a lemma can vary enormously given the context. Consider these two uses of the lemma *bank*, meaning something like "financial institution" and "sloping mound", respectively:

(19.3) Instead, a *bank* can hold the investments in a custodial account in the client's name.

(19.4) But as agriculture burgeons on the east *bank*, the river will shrink even more.

Word sense

We represent some of this contextual variation by saying that the lemma *bank* has two **senses**.[1] A **sense** (or **word sense**) is a discrete representation of one aspect of the meaning of a word. Loosely following lexicographic tradition, we represent each sense by placing a superscript on the orthographic form of the lemma as in **bank**[1] and **bank**[2].

The senses of a word might not have any particular relation between them; it may be almost coincidental that they share an orthographic form. For example, the *financial institution* and *sloping mound* senses of bank seem relatively unrelated. In such cases *Homonym* we say that the two senses are **homonyms**, and the relation between the senses is one *Homonymy* of **homonymy**. Thus **bank**[1] ("financial institution") and **bank**[2] ("sloping mound") are homonyms.

Sometimes, however, there is some semantic connection between the senses of a word. Consider the following WSJ "bank" example:

(19.5) While some *banks* furnish sperm only to married women, others are much less restrictive.

Although this is clearly not a use of the "sloping mound" meaning of *bank*, it just as clearly is not a reference to a promotional giveaway at a financial institution. Rather, *bank* has a whole range of uses related to repositories for various biological entities, as

---

[1] Confusingly, the word "lemma" is itself ambiguous; it is also sometimes used to mean these separate senses, rather than the citation form of the word. You should be prepared to see both uses in the literature.

in *blood bank*, *egg bank*, and *sperm bank*. So we could call this "biological repository" sense **bank³**. Now this new sense **bank³** has some sort of relation to **bank¹**; both **bank¹** and **bank³** are repositories for entities that can be deposited and taken out; in **bank¹** the entity is monetary, whereas in **bank³** the entity is biological.

Polysemy
When two senses are related semantically, we call the relationship between them **polysemy** rather than homonymy. In many cases of polysemy, the semantic relation between the senses is systematic and structured. For example, consider yet another sense of *bank*, exemplified in the following sentence:

(19.6) The bank is on the corner of Nassau and Witherspoon.

This sense, which we can call **bank⁴**, means something like "the building belonging to a financial institution". It turns out that these two kinds of senses (an organization and the building associated with an organization) occur together for many other words as well (*school*, *university*, *hospital*, etc.). Thus, there is a systematic relationship between senses that we might represent as

BUILDING ↔ ORGANIZATION

Metonymy
This particular subtype of polysemy relation is often called **metonymy**. Metonymy is the use of one aspect of a concept or entity to refer to other aspects of the entity or to the entity itself. Thus, we are performing metonymy when we use the phrase *the White House* to refer to the administration whose office is in the White House. Other common examples of metonymy include the relation between the following pairings of senses:

> Author (*Jane Austen wrote Emma*) ↔ Works of Author (*I really love Jane Austen*)
> Animal (*The chicken was domesticated in Asia*) ↔ Meat (*The chicken was overcooked*)
> Tree (*Plums have beautiful blossoms*) ↔ Fruit (*I ate a preserved plum yesterday*)

While it can be useful to distinguish polysemy from homonymy, there is no hard threshold for how related two senses must be to be considered polysemous. Thus, the difference is really one of degree. This fact can make it very difficult to decide how many senses a word has, that is, whether to make separate senses for closely related usages. There are various criteria for deciding that the differing uses of a word should be represented as distinct discrete senses. We might consider two senses discrete if they have independent truth conditions, different syntactic behavior, and independent sense relations, or if they exhibit antagonistic meanings.

Consider the following uses of the verb *serve* from the WSJ corpus:

(19.7) They rarely *serve* red meat, preferring to prepare seafood, poultry or game birds.

(19.8) He *served* as U.S. ambassador to Norway in 1976 and 1977.

(19.9) He might have *served* his time, come out and led an upstanding life.

The *serve* of *serving red meat* and that of *serving time* clearly have different truth conditions and presuppositions; the *serve* of *serve as ambassador* has the distinct subcategorization structure *serve as NP*. These heuristic suggests that these are probably three distinct senses of *serve*. One practical technique for determining if two senses are distinct is to conjoin two uses of a word in a single sentence; this kind of conjunction *Zeugma* of antagonistic readings is called **zeugma**. Consider the following ATIS examples:

(19.10) Which of those flights serve breakfast?

(19.11) Does Midwest Express serve Philadelphia?

(19.12) ?Does Midwest Express serve breakfast and Philadelphia?

We use (?) to mark those examples that are semantically ill-formed. The oddness of the invented third example (a case of zeugma) indicates there is no sensible way to make a single sense of *serve* work for both breakfast and Philadelphia. We can use this as evidence that *serve* has two different senses in this case.

Dictionaries tend to use many fine-grained senses so as to capture subtle meaning differences, a reasonable approach given that the traditional role of dictionaries is aiding word learners. For computational purposes, we often don't need these fine distinctions, so we may want to group or cluster the senses; we have already done this for some of the examples in this chapter.

We generally reserve the word **homonym** for two senses which share both a pronunciation and an orthography. A special case of multiple senses that causes problems for speech recognition and spelling correction is a homophone. **Homophones** are senses that are linked to lemmas with the same pronunciation but different spellings, such as *wood/would* or *to/two/too*. A related problem for speech synthesis are **homographs** (Chapter 8). **Homographs** are distinct senses linked to lemmas with the same orthographic form but different pronunciations, such as these homographs of *bass*:

Homophone

Homograph

(19.13) The expert angler from Dora, Mo., was fly-casting for **bass** rather than the traditional trout.

(19.14) The curtain rises to the sound of angry dogs baying and ominous **bass** chords sounding.

How can we define the meaning of a word sense? Can we just look in a dictionary? Consider the following fragments from the definitions of *right*, *left*, *red*, and *blood* from the *American Heritage Dictionary* (Morris, 1985).

> right *adj.* located nearer the right hand esp. being on the right when facing the same direction as the observer.
> left *adj.* located nearer to this side of the body than the right.
> red *n.* the color of blood or a ruby.
> blood *n.* the red liquid that circulates in the heart, arteries and veins of animals.

Note the circularity in these definitions. The definition of *right* makes two direct references to itself, and the entry for *left* contains an implicit self-reference in the phrase *this side of the body*, which presumably means the *left* side. The entries for *red* and *blood* avoid this kind of direct self-reference by instead referencing each other in their definitions. Such circularity is, of course, inherent in all dictionary definitions; these examples are just extreme cases. For humans, such entries are still useful since the user of the dictionary has sufficient grasp of these other terms.

For computational purposes, one approach to defining a sense is to make use of a similar approach to these dictionary definitions; defining a sense through its relationship with other senses. For example, the above definitions make it clear that *right* and *left* are similar kinds of lemmas that stand in some kind of alternation, or opposition, to one another. Similarly, we can glean that *red* is a color, that it can be applied to both *blood* and *rubies*, and that *blood* is a *liquid*. **Sense relations** of this sort are embodied in on-line databases like **WordNet**. Given a sufficiently large database of such relations, many applications are quite capable of performing sophisticated semantic tasks (even if they do not *really* know their right from their left).

A second computational approach to meaning representation is to create a small finite set of semantic primitives, atomic units of meaning, and then create each sense definition out of these primitives. This approach is especially common when defining aspects of the meaning of *events* such as *semantic roles*.

We explore both of these approaches to meaning in this chapter. In the next section we introduce various relations between senses, followed by a discussion of WordNet, a sense relation resource. We then introduce a number of meaning representation approaches based on semantic primitives such as semantic roles.

19.2   Relations Between Senses

This section explores some of the relations that hold among word senses, focusing on a few that have received significant computational investigation: **synonymy**, **antonymy**, and **hypernymy**, as well as a brief mention of other relations like **meronymy**.

19.2.1   Synonymy and Antonymy

Synonym

When two senses of two different words (lemmas) are identical, or nearly identical, we say the two senses are **synonyms**. Synonyms include such pairs as

couch/sofa   vomit/throw up   filbert/hazelnut   car/automobile

A more formal definition of synonymy (between words rather than senses) is that two words are synonymous if they are substitutable one for the other in any sentence without changing the truth conditions of the sentence. We often say in this case that

Propositional meaning

the two words have the same **propositional meaning**.

While substitutions between some pairs of words like *car/automobile* or *water/H_2O* are truth preserving, the words are still not identical in meaning. Indeed, probably no two words are absolutely identical in meaning, and if we define synonymy as identical meanings and connotations in all contexts, there are probably no absolute synonyms. Besides propositional meaning, many other facets of meaning that distinguish these words are important. For example, H_2O is used in scientific contexts and would be inappropriate in a hiking guide; this difference in genre is part of the meaning of the word. In practice, the word *synonym* is therefore commonly used to describe a relationship of approximate or rough synonymy.

Instead of talking about two *words* being synonyms, in this chapter we define synonymy (and other relations like hyponymy and meronymy) as a relation between senses rather than between words. We can see the usefulness of this by considering the words *big* and *large*. These may seem to be synonyms in the following ATIS sentences, since we could swap *big* and *large* in either sentence and retain the same meaning:

(19.15) How big is that plane?

(19.16) Would I be flying on a large or small plane?

But note the following WSJ sentence in which we cannot substitute *large* for *big*:

(19.17) Miss Nelson, for instance, became a kind of big sister to Benjamin.

(19.18) ?Miss Nelson, for instance, became a kind of large sister to Benjamin.

This is because the word *big* has a sense that means being older or grown up, while *large* lacks this sense. Thus, it is convenient to say that some senses of *big* and *large* are (nearly) synonymous while other ones are not.

Antonym Synonyms are words with identical or similar meanings. **Antonyms**, by contrast, are words with opposite meaning such as the following:

> *long/short big/little fast/slow cold/hot dark/light*
> *rise/fall   up/down in/out*

It is difficult to give a formal definition of antonymy. Two senses can be antonyms if they define a binary opposition or are at opposite ends of some scale. This is the case for *long/short*, *fast/slow*, or *big/little*, which are at opposite ends of the *length* or *size* scale. Another group of antonyms is **reversives**, which describe some sort of change or movement in opposite directions, such as *rise/fall* or *up/down*.

From one perspective, antonyms have very different meanings since they are opposite. From another perspective, they have very similar meanings since they share almost all aspects of their meaning except their position on a scale or their direction. Thus, automatically distinguishing synonyms from antonyms can be difficult.

19.2.2   Hyponymy

Hyponym One sense is a **hyponym** of another sense if the first sense is more specific, denoting a subclass of the other. For example, *car* is a hyponym of *vehicle*; *dog* is a hyponym of *animal*, and *mango* is a hyponym of *fruit*. Conversely, we say that *vehicle* is a **hypernym** of *car*, and *animal* is a hypernym of *dog*. It is unfortunate that the two words (hypernym and hyponym) are very similar and hence easily confused; for this reason, the word **superordinate** is often used instead of **hypernym**.

Hypernym

Superordinate

Superordinate	vehicle	fruit	furniture	mammal
Hyponym	car	mango	chair	dog

We can define hypernymy more formally by saying that the class denoted by the superordinate extensionally includes the class denoted by the hyponym. Thus, the class of animals includes as members all dogs, and the class of moving actions includes all walking actions. Hypernymy can also be defined in terms of entailment. Under this definition, a sense A is a hyponym of a sense B if everything that is A is also B, and hence being an A entails being a B, or $\forall x\ A(x) \Rightarrow B(x)$. Hyponymy is usually a transitive relation; if A is a hyponym of B and B is a hyponym of C, then A is a hyponym of C.

The concept of hyponymy is closely related to a number of other notions that play central roles in computer science, biology, and anthropology. As discussed in Chapter 17, an **ontology** usually refers to a set of distinct objects resulting from an analysis

Microworld
Taxonomy

of a single domain, or **microworld**. A **taxonomy** is a particular arrangement of the elements of an ontology into a tree-like class inclusion structure. Normally, there is a set of well-formedness constraints on taxonomies that go beyond their component class inclusion relations. For example, the lexemes *hound*, *mutt*, and *puppy* are all hyponyms of *dog*, as are *golden retriever* and *poodle*, but it would be odd to construct a taxonomy from all those pairs since the concepts motivating the relations are different in each case. Instead, we normally use the word **taxonomy** to talk about the hypernymy relation between *poodle* and *dog*; by this definition, **taxonomy** is a subtype of hypernymy.

19.2.3   Semantic Fields

So far we've seen the relations of synonymy, antonymy, hypernomy, and hyponymy.

Meronymy
Part-whole
Meronym
Holonym

Another common relation is **meronymy**, the **part-whole** relation. A *leg* is part of a *chair*; a *wheel* is part of a *car*. We say that *wheel* is a **meronym** of *car*, and *car* is a **holonym** of *wheel*.

Semantic field

But there is a more general way to think about sense relations and word meaning. Whereas the relations we've defined so far have been binary relations between two senses, a **semantic field** is a model of a more integrated, or holistic, relationship among entire sets of words from a single domain. Consider the following set of words:

> *reservation, flight, travel, buy, price, cost, fare, rates, meal, plane*

We could assert individual lexical relations of hyponymy, synonymy, and so on between many of the words in this list. The resulting set of relations does not, however, add up to a complete account of how these words are related. They are clearly all defined with respect to a coherent chunk of common-sense background information concerning air travel. Background knowledge of this kind has been studied under a

Frame
Model
Script

variety of frameworks and is known variously as a **frame** (Fillmore, 1985), **model** (Johnson-Laird, 1983), or **script** (Schank and Abelson, 1977) and plays a central role in a number of computational frameworks.

FrameNet

We discuss in Section 19.4.5 the **FrameNet** project (Baker et al., 1998), which is an attempt to provide a robust computational resource for this kind of frame knowledge. In the FrameNet representation, each of the words in the frame is defined with respect to the frame and shares aspects of meaning with other frame words.

19.3   WordNet: A Database of Lexical Relations

WordNet

The most commonly used resource for English sense relations is the **WordNet** lexical database (Fellbaum, 1998). WordNet consists of three separate databases, one each for nouns and verbs and a third for adjectives and adverbs; closed class words are not included. Each database consists of a set of lemmas, each one annotated with a set of senses. The WordNet 3.0 release has 117,097 nouns, 11,488 verbs, 22,141 adjectives, and 4,601 adverbs. The average noun has 1.23 senses, and the average verb has 2.16 senses. WordNet can be accessed on the Web or downloaded and accessed locally.

> The noun "bass" has 8 senses in WordNet.
> 1. bass^1 - (the lowest part of the musical range)
> 2. bass^2, bass part^1 - (the lowest part in polyphonic music)
> 3. bass^3, basso^1 - (an adult male singer with the lowest voice)
> 4. sea bass^1, bass^4 - (the lean flesh of a saltwater fish of the family Serranidae)
> 5. freshwater bass^1, bass^5 - (any of various North American freshwater fish with lean flesh (especially of the genus Micropterus))
> 6. bass^6, bass voice^1, basso^2 - (the lowest adult male singing voice)
> 7. bass^7 - (the member with the lowest range of a family of musical instruments)
> 8. bass^8 - (nontechnical name for any of numerous edible marine and freshwater spiny-finned fishes)
>
> The adjective "bass" has 1 sense in WordNet.
> 1. bass^1, deep^6 - (having or denoting a low vocal or instrumental range)
>   *"a deep voice"; "a bass voice is lower than a baritone voice"; "a bass clarinet"*

Figure 19.1   A portion of the WordNet 3.0 entry for the noun *bass*.

Gloss

Synset

A typical lemma entry for the noun and adjective *bass* are shown in Fig. 19.1. Note that there are eight senses for the noun and one for the adjective, each of which has a **gloss** (a dictionary-style definition), a list of synonyms for the sense (called a **synset**), and sometimes also usage examples (shown for the adjective sense). Unlike dictionaries, WordNet doesn't represent pronunciation, so doesn't distinguish the pronunciation [b ae s] in **bass^4**, **bass^5**, and **bass^8** from the other senses pronounced [b ey s].

The set of near-synonyms for a WordNet sense is called a **synset** (for **synonym set**); synsets are an important primitive in WordNet. The entry for *bass* includes synsets like *bass^1*, *deep^6*, or *bass^6*, *bass voice^1*, *basso^2*. We can think of a synset as representing a concept of the type we discussed in Chapter 17. Thus, instead of representing concepts in logical terms, WordNet represents them as lists of the word senses that can be used to express the concept. Here's another synset example:

chump^1, fool^2, gull^1, mark^9, patsy^1, fall guy^1, sucker^1, soft touch^1, mug^2

The gloss of this synset describes it as *a person who is gullible and easy to take advantage of.* Each of the lexical entries included in the synset can, therefore, be used to express this concept. Synsets like this one actually constitute the senses associated with WordNet entries, and hence it is synsets, not wordforms, lemmas, or individual senses, that participate in most of the lexical sense relations in WordNet.

Let's turn now to these lexical sense relations, some of which are illustrated in Fig. 19.2 and Fig. 19.3. WordNet hyponymy relations correspond to the notion of immediate hyponymy discussed on page 616. Each synset is related to its immediately more general and more specific synsets through direct hypernym and hyponym relations. These relations can be followed to produce longer chains of more general or more specific synsets. Figure 19.4 shows hypernym chains for **bass^3** and **bass^7**.

In this depiction of hyponymy, successively more general synsets are shown on successive indented lines. The first chain starts from the concept of a human bass singer. Its immediate superordinate is a synset corresponding to the generic concept

Relation	Also Called	Definition	Example
Hypernym	Superordinate	From concepts to superordinates	$breakfast^1 \rightarrow meal^1$
Hyponym	Subordinate	From concepts to subtypes	$meal^1 \rightarrow lunch^1$
Instance Hypernym	Instance	From instances to their concepts	$Austen^1 \rightarrow author^1$
Instance Hyponym	Has-Instance	From concepts to concept instances	$composer^1 \rightarrow Bach^1$
Member Meronym	Has-Member	From groups to their members	$faculty^2 \rightarrow professor^1$
Member Holonym	Member-Of	From members to their groups	$copilot^1 \rightarrow crew^1$
Part Meronym	Has-Part	From wholes to parts	$table^2 \rightarrow leg^3$
Part Holonym	Part-Of	From parts to wholes	$course^7 \rightarrow meal^1$
Substance Meronym		From substances to their subparts	$water^1 \rightarrow oxygen^1$
Substance Holonym		From parts of substances to wholes	$gin^1 \rightarrow martini^1$
Antonym		Semantic opposition between lemmas	$leader^1 \Longleftrightarrow follower^1$
Derivationally Related Form		Lemmas w/same morphological root	$destruction^1 \Longleftrightarrow destroy^1$

Figure 19.2   Noun relations in WordNet.

Relation	Definition	Example
Hypernym	From events to superordinate events	$fly^9 \rightarrow travel^5$
Troponym	From events to subordinate event (often via specific manner)	$walk^1 \rightarrow stroll^1$
Entails	From verbs (events) to the verbs (events) they entail	$snore^1 \rightarrow sleep^1$
Antonym	Semantic opposition between lemmas	$increase^1 \Longleftrightarrow decrease^1$
Derivationally Related Form	Lemmas with same morphological root	$destroy^1 \Longleftrightarrow destruction^1$

Figure 19.3   Verb relations in WordNet.

of a singer. Following this chain leads eventually to concepts such as *entertainer* and *person*. The second chain, which starts from musical instrument, has a completely different path leading eventually to such concepts as musical instrument, device, and physical object. Both paths do eventually join at the very abstract synset *whole, unit*, and then proceed together to *entity* which is the top (root) of the noun hierarchy (in WordNet this root is generally called the **unique beginner**).

Unique beginner

19.4   Event Participants

An important aspect of lexical meaning has to do with the semantics of events. When we discussed events in Chapter 17, we introduced the importance of predicate-argument structure for representing an event and the use of Davidsonian reification of events to represent each participant distinctly from the event itself. We now turn to representing the meaning of these *participants* or *arguments*. We introduce two kinds of semantic constraints on the arguments of event predicates: **semantic roles** and **selectional restrictions**. We begin with a particular model of semantic roles called **thematic roles**.

```
Sense 3
bass, basso --
(an adult male singer with the lowest voice)
=> singer, vocalist, vocalizer, vocaliser
    => musician, instrumentalist, player
        => performer, performing artist
            => entertainer
                => person, individual, someone...
                    => organism, being
                        => living thing, animate thing,
                            => whole, unit
                                => object, physical object
                                    => physical entity
                                        => entity
                    => causal agent, cause, causal agency
                        => physical entity
                            => entity

Sense 7
bass --
(the member with the lowest range of a family of
musical instruments)
=> musical instrument, instrument
    => device
        => instrumentality, instrumentation
            => artifact, artefact
                => whole, unit
                    => object, physical object
                        => physical entity
                            => entity
```

Figure 19.4   Hyponymy chains for two separate senses of the lemma *bass*. Note that the chains are completely distinct, only converging at the very abstract level *whole, unit*.

19.4.1   Thematic Roles

Consider how in Chapter 17 we represented the meaning of arguments for sentences like these:

(19.19) Sasha broke the window.

(19.20) Pat opened the door.

A neo-Davidsonian event representation of these two sentences would be

$$\exists e,x,y \, Breaking(e) \wedge Breaker(e, Sasha)$$
$$\wedge BrokenThing(e,y) \wedge Window(y)$$
$$\exists e,x,y \, Opening(e) \wedge Opener(e, Pat)$$
$$\wedge OpenedThing(e,y) \wedge Door(y)$$

In this representation, the roles of the subjects of the verbs *break* and *open* are
Deep roles   *Breaker* and *Opener* respectively. These **deep roles** are specific to each event; *Breaking* events have *Breakers*, *Opening* events have *Openers*, and so on.

Thematic Role	Definition
AGENT	The volitional causer of an event
EXPERIENCER	The experiencer of an event
FORCE	The non-volitional causer of the event
THEME	The participant most directly affected by an event
RESULT	The end product of an event
CONTENT	The proposition or content of a propositional event
INSTRUMENT	An instrument used in an event
BENEFICIARY	The beneficiary of an event
SOURCE	The origin of the object of a transfer event
GOAL	The destination of an object of a transfer event

Figure 19.5   Some commonly used thematic roles with their definitions.

Thematic Role	Example
AGENT	*The waiter* spilled the soup.
EXPERIENCER	*John* has a headache.
FORCE	*The wind* blows debris from the mall into our yards.
THEME	Only after Benjamin Franklin broke *the ice*...
RESULT	The French government has built a *regulation-size baseball diamond*...
CONTENT	Mona asked *"You met Mary Ann at a supermarket?"*
INSTRUMENT	He turned to poaching catfish, stunning them *with a shocking device*...
BENEFICIARY	Whenever Ann Callahan makes hotel reservations *for her boss*...
SOURCE	I flew in *from Boston*.
GOAL	I drove *to Portland*.

Figure 19.6   Some prototypical examples of various thematic roles.

If we are going to be able to answer questions, perform inferences, or do any further kinds of natural language understanding of these events, we'll need to know a little more about the semantics of these arguments. *Breakers* and *Openers* have something in common. They are both volitional actors, often animate, and they have direct causal responsibility for their events.

Thematic role

Agent

Thematic roles are one attempt to capture this semantic commonality between *Breakers* and *Eaters*. We say that the subjects of both these verbs are **agents**. Thus, AGENT is the thematic role that represents an abstract idea such as volitional causation. Similarly, the direct objects of both these verbs, the *BrokenThing* and *OpenedThing*, are both prototypically inanimate objects that are affected in some way by the action. The thematic role for these participants is **theme**.

Theme

Thematic roles are one of the oldest linguistic models, proposed first by the Indian grammarian Panini sometime between the 7th and 4th centuries BCE. Their modern formulation is due to Fillmore (1968) and Gruber (1965). Although there is no universally agreed-upon set of thematic roles, Figs. 19.5 and 19.6 list some thematic roles that have been used in various computational papers, together with rough definitions and examples.

633

19.4.2   Diathesis Alternations

The main reason computational systems use thematic roles, and semantic roles in general, is to act as a shallow meaning representation that can let us make simple inferences that aren't possible from the pure surface string of words, or even from the parse tree. For example, if a document says that *Company A acquired Company B*, we'd like to know that this answers the query *Was Company B acquired?* despite the fact that the two sentences have very different surface syntax. Similarly, this shallow semantics might act as a useful intermediate language in machine translation.

Thus, thematic roles help us generalize over different surface realizations of predicate arguments. For example, while the AGENT is often realized as the subject of the sentence, in other cases the THEME can be the subject. Consider these possible realizations of the thematic arguments of the verb *break*:

(19.21)   *John   broke the window.*
         AGENT   THEME

(19.22)   *John   broke the window with a rock.*
         AGENT   THEME   INSTRUMENT

(19.23)   *The rock   broke the window.*
     INSTRUMENT   THEME

(19.24)   *The window broke.*
     THEME

(19.25)   *The window was broken by John.*
     THEME   AGENT

These examples suggest that *break* has (at least) the possible arguments AGENT, THEME, and INSTRUMENT. The set of thematic role arguments taken by a verb is often called the **thematic grid**, θ-grid, or **case frame**. We can see that there are (among others) the following possibilities for the realization of these arguments of *break*:

Thematic grid
Case frame

- AGENT:Subject, THEME:Object
- AGENT:Subject, THEME:Object, INSTRUMENT:PP$_{with}$
- INSTRUMENT:Subject, THEME:Object
- THEME:Subject

It turns out that many verbs allow their thematic roles to be realized in various syntactic positions. For example, verbs like *give* can realize the THEME and GOAL arguments in two different ways:

(19.26)   a. *Doris gave the book to Cary.*
             AGENT   THEME   GOAL

    b. *Doris gave Cary the book.*
          AGENT   GOAL THEME

These multiple argument structure realizations (the fact that *break* can take AGENT, INSTRUMENT, or THEME as subject, and *give* can realize its THEME and GOAL in either order) are called **verb alternations** or **diathesis alternations**. The alternation we showed above for *give*, the **dative alternation**, seems to occur with particular semantic classes of verbs, including "verbs of future having" (*advance, allocate, offer, owe*),

Verb alternation
Diathesis
alternation
Dative alternation

"send verbs" (*forward*, *hand*, *mail*), "verbs of throwing" (*kick*, *pass*, *throw*), and so on. Levin (1993) is a reference book that lists for a large set of English verbs the semantic classes to which they belong and the various alternations in which they participate. These lists of verb classes have been incorporated into the online resource VerbNet (Kipper et al., 2000).

19.4.3   Problems with Thematic Roles

Representing meaning at the thematic role level seems like it should be useful in dealing with complications like diathesis alternations. But despite this potential benefit, it has proved quite difficult to come up with a standard set of roles, and equally difficult to produce a formal definition of roles like AGENT, THEME, or INSTRUMENT.

For example, researchers attempting to define role sets often find they need to fragment a role like AGENT or THEME into many specific roles. Levin and Rappaport Hovav (2005) summarize a number of such cases, such as the fact there seem to be at least two kinds of INSTRUMENTS, *intermediary* instruments that can appear as subjects and *enabling* instruments that cannot:

(19.27)   a. The cook opened the jar with the new gadget.

          b. The new gadget opened the jar.

(19.28)   a. Shelly ate the sliced banana with a fork.

          b. *The fork ate the sliced banana.

In addition to the fragmentation problem, there are cases in which we'd like to reason about and generalize across semantic roles, but the finite discrete lists of roles don't let us do this.

Finally, it has proved difficult to formally define the semantic roles. Consider the AGENT role; most cases of AGENTS are animate, volitional, sentient, causal, but any individual noun phrase might not exhibit all of these properties.

Generalized semantic role
Proto-agent

Proto-patient

These problems have led most research to alternative models of semantic roles. One such model is based on defining **generalized semantic roles** that abstract over the specific thematic roles. For example, PROTO-AGENT and PROTO-PATIENT are generalized roles that express roughly agent-like and roughly patient-like meanings. These roles are defined, not by necessary and sufficient conditions, but rather by a set of heuristic features that accompany more agent-like or more patient-like meanings. Thus, the more an argument displays agent-like properties (intentionality, volitionality, causality, etc.), the greater the likelihood that the argument can be labeled a PROTO-AGENT. The more patient-like the properties (undergoing change of state, causally affected by another participant, stationary relative to other participants, etc.), the greater the likelihood that the argument can be labeled a PROTO-PATIENT.

In addition to using proto-roles, many computational models avoid the problems with thematic roles by defining semantic roles that are specific to a particular verb or specific to a particular set of verbs or nouns.

In the next two sections we describe two commonly used lexical resources that make use of some of these alternative versions of semantic roles. **PropBank** uses both proto-roles and verb-specific semantic roles. **FrameNet** uses frame-specific semantic roles.

19.4.4   The Proposition Bank

PropBank   The **Proposition Bank**, generally referred to as **PropBank**, is a resource of sentences annotated with semantic roles. The English PropBank labels all the sentences in the Penn TreeBank; the Chinese PropBank labels sentences in the Penn Chinese TreeBank. Because of the difficulty of defining a universal set of thematic roles, the semantic roles in PropBank are defined with respect to an individual verb sense. Each sense of each verb thus has a specific set of roles, which are given only numbers rather than names: **Arg0**, **Arg1**, **Arg2**, and so on. In general, **Arg0** represents the PROTO-AGENT, and **Arg1**, the PROTO-PATIENT; the semantics of the other roles are specific to each verb sense. Thus, the **Arg2** of one verb is likely to have little in common with the **Arg2** of another verb.

Here are some slightly simplified PropBank entries for one sense each of the verbs *agree* and *fall*; the definitions for each role ("Other entity agreeing", "Extent, amount fallen") are informal glosses intended to be read by humans, rather than being formal definitions.

(19.29) **agree.01**
  Arg0: Agreer
  Arg1: Proposition
  Arg2: Other entity agreeing
  Ex1:   [$_{Arg0}$ The group] *agreed* [$_{Arg1}$ it wouldn't make an offer unless it had Georgia Gulf's consent].
  Ex2:   [$_{ArgM-TMP}$ Usually] [$_{Arg0}$ John] *agrees* [$_{Arg2}$ with Mary] [$_{Arg1}$ on everything].

(19.30) **fall.01**
  Arg1: Logical subject, patient, thing falling
  Arg2: Extent, amount fallen
  Arg3: start point
  Arg4: end point, end state of arg1
  Ex1:   [$_{Arg1}$ Sales] *fell* [$_{Arg4}$ to \$251.2 million] [$_{Arg3}$ from \$278.7 million].
  Ex2:   [$_{Arg1}$ The average junk bond] *fell* [$_{Arg2}$ by 4.2%].

Note that there is no Arg0 role for *fall*, because the normal subject of *fall* is a PROTO-PATIENT.

The PropBank semantic roles can be useful in recovering shallow semantic information about verbal arguments. Consider the verb *increase*:

(19.31) **increase.01** "go up incrementally"
  Arg0: causer of increase
  Arg1: thing increasing
  Arg2: amount increased by, EXT, or MNR
  Arg3: start point
  Arg4: end point

A PropBank semantic role labeling would allow us to infer the commonality in the event structures of the following three examples, that is, that in each case *Big Fruit*

Co. is the AGENT and *the price of bananas* is the THEME, despite the differing surface forms.

(19.32) [$_{Arg0}$ Big Fruit Co.] increased [$_{Arg1}$ the price of bananas].

(19.33) [$_{Arg1}$ The price of bananas] was increased again [$_{Arg0}$ by Big Fruit Co.]

(19.34) [$_{Arg1}$ The price of bananas] increased [$_{Arg2}$ 5%].

19.4.5   FrameNet

While making inferences about the semantic commonalities across different sentences with *increase* is useful, it would be even more useful if we could make such inferences in many more situations, across different verbs, and also between verbs and nouns.

For example, we'd like to extract the similarity among these three sentences:

(19.35) [$_{Arg1}$ The price of bananas] increased [$_{Arg2}$ 5%].

(19.36) [$_{Arg1}$ The price of bananas] rose [$_{Arg2}$ 5%].

(19.37) There has been a [$_{Arg2}$ 5%] rise [$_{Arg1}$ in the price of bananas].

Note that the second example uses the different verb *rise*, and the third example uses the noun rather than the verb *rise*. We'd like a system to recognize that *the price of bananas* is what went up, and that *5%* is the amount it went up, no matter whether the *5%* appears as the object of the verb *increased* or as a nominal modifier of the noun *rise*.

FrameNet

The **FrameNet** project is another semantic-role-labeling project that attempts to address just these kinds of problems (Baker et al., 1998; Lowe et al., 1997; Ruppenhofer et al., 2006). Whereas roles in the PropBank project are specific to an individual

Frame

verb, roles in the FrameNet project are specific to a **frame**. A **frame** is a script-like

Frame element

structure that instantiates a set of frame-specific semantic roles called **frame elements**. Each word evokes a frame and profiles some aspect of the frame and its elements. For example, the **change_position_on_a_scale** frame is defined as follows:

> This frame consists of words that indicate the change of an Item's position on a scale (the Attribute) from a starting point (Initial_value) to an end point (Final_value).

Core roles
Non-core roles

Some of the semantic roles (frame elements) in the frame, separated into **core roles** and **non-core roles**, are defined as follows (definitions are taken from the FrameNet Labelers Guide (Ruppenhofer et al., 2006)).

Core Roles	
ATTRIBUTE	The ATTRIBUTE is a scalar property that the ITEM possesses.
DIFFERENCE	The distance by which an ITEM changes its position on the scale.
FINAL_STATE	A description that presents the ITEM's state after the change in the ATTRIBUTE's value as an independent predication.
FINAL_VALUE	The position on the scale where the ITEM ends up.
INITIAL_STATE	A description that presents the ITEM's state before the change in the ATTRIBUTE's value as an independent predication.
INITIAL_VALUE	The initial position on the scale from which the ITEM moves away.
ITEM	The entity that has a position on the scale.
VALUE_RANGE	A portion of the scale, typically identified by its end points, along which the values of the ATTRIBUTE fluctuate.
Some Non-Core Roles	
DURATION	The length of time over which the change takes place.
SPEED	The rate of change of the VALUE.
GROUP	The GROUP in which an ITEM changes the value of an ATTRIBUTE in a specified way.

Here are some example sentences:

(19.38) [ITEM Oil] *rose* [ATTRIBUTE in price] [DIFFERENCE by 2%].

(19.39) [ITEM It] has *increased* [FINAL_STATE to having them 1 day a month].

(19.40) [ITEM Microsoft shares] *fell* [FINAL_VALUE to 7 5/8].

(19.41) [ITEM Colon cancer incidence] *fell* [DIFFERENCE by 50%] [GROUP among men].

(19.42) a steady *increase* [INITIAL_VALUE from 9.5] [FINAL_VALUE to 14.3] [ITEM in dividends]

(19.43) a [DIFFERENCE 5%] [ITEM dividend] *increase...*

Note from these example sentences that the frame includes target words like *rise*, *fall*, and *increase*. In fact, the complete frame consists of the following words:

VERBS:	dwindle	move	soar	escalation	shift
advance	edge	mushroom	swell	explosion	tumble
climb	explode	plummet	swing	fall	
decline	fall	reach	triple	fluctuation	**ADVERBS:**
decrease	fluctuate	rise	tumble	gain	increasingly
diminish	gain	rocket		growth	
dip	grow	shift	**NOUNS:**	hike	
double	increase	skyrocket	decline	increase	
drop	jump	slide	decrease	rise	

FrameNet also codes relationships between frames and frame elements. Frames can inherit from each other, and generalizations among frame elements in different frames can be captured by inheritance as well. Other relations between frames, like causation, are also represented. Thus, there is a **Cause_change_of_position_on_a_scale** frame that is linked to the **Change_of_position_on_a_scale** frame by the **cause** relation, but that adds an AGENT role and is used for causative examples such as the following:

(19.44) [$_\text{AGENT}$ They] *raised* [$_\text{ITEM}$ the price of their soda] [$_\text{DIFFERENCE}$ by 2%].

Together, these two frames would allow an understanding system to extract the common event semantics of all the verbal and nominal causative and non-causative usages.

Chapter 20 discusses automatic methods for extracting various kinds of semantic roles; indeed, one main goal of PropBank and FrameNet is to provide training data for such semantic-role-labeling algorithms.

19.4.6 Selectional Restrictions

Selectional restriction

Semantic roles gave us a way to express some of the semantics of an argument in its relation to the predicate. In this section we turn to another way to express semantic constraints on arguments. A **selectional restriction** is a kind of semantic type constraint that a verb imposes on the kind of concepts that are allowed to fill its argument roles. Consider the two meanings associated with the following example:

(19.45) I want to eat someplace that's close to ICSI.

There are two possible parses and semantic interpretations for this sentence. In the sensible interpretation, *eat* is intransitive and the phrase *someplace that's close to* ICSI is an adjunct that gives the location of the eating event. In the nonsensical *speaker-as-Godzilla* interpretation, *eat* is transitive and the phrase *someplace that's close to* ICSI is the direct object and the THEME of the eating, like the NP *Malaysian food* in the following sentences:

(19.46)   I want to eat Malaysian food.

How do we know that *someplace that's close to* ICSI isn't the direct object in this sentence? One useful cue is the semantic fact that the THEME of EATING events tends to be something that is *edible*. This restriction placed by the verb *eat* on the filler of its THEME argument is a selectional restriction.

Selectional restrictions are associated with senses, not entire lexemes. We can see this in the following examples of the lexeme *serve*:

(19.47)   Well, there was the time they served green-lipped mussels from New Zealand.

(19.48)   Which airlines serve Denver?

Example (19.47) illustrates the cooking sense of *serve*, which ordinarily restricts its THEME to be some kind foodstuff. Example (19.48) illustrates the *provides a commercial service to* sense of *serve*, which constrains its THEME to be some type of appropriate location. We show in Chapter 20 that the fact that selectional restrictions are associated with senses can be used as a cue to help in word sense disambiguation.

Selectional restrictions vary widely in their specificity. The verb *imagine*, for example, imposes strict requirements on its AGENT role (restricting it to humans and other animate entities) but places very few semantic requirements on its THEME role. A verb like *diagonalize*, on the other hand, places a very specific constraint on the filler of its THEME role: it has to be a matrix, while the arguments of the adjectives *odorless* are restricted to concepts that could possess an odor:

(19.49) In rehearsal, I often ask the musicians to *imagine* a tennis game.

(19.50) Radon is an *odorless* gas that can't be detected by human senses.

(19.51) To *diagonalize* a matrix is to find its eigenvalues.

These examples illustrate that the set of concepts we need to represent selectional restrictions (being a matrix, being able to possess an odor, etc) is quite open ended. This distinguishes selectional restrictions from other features for representing lexical knowledge, like parts-of-speech, which are quite limited in number.

Representing Selectional Restrictions

One way to capture the semantics of selectional restrictions is to use and extend the event representation of Chapter 17. Recall that the neo-Davidsonian representation of an event consists of a single variable that stands for the event, a predicate denoting the kind of event, and variables and relations for the event roles. Ignoring the issue of the λ-structures and using thematic roles rather than deep event roles, the semantic contribution of a verb like *eat* might look like the following:

$$\exists e,x,y \, Eating(e) \wedge Agent(e,x) \wedge Theme(e,y)$$

With this representation, all we know about y, the filler of the THEME role, is that it is associated with an *Eating* event through the *Theme* relation. To stipulate the selectional restriction that y must be something edible, we simply add a new term to that effect:

$$\exists e,x,y \, Eating(e) \wedge Agent(e,x) \wedge Theme(e,y) \wedge EdibleThing(y)$$

When a phrase like *ate a hamburger* is encountered, a semantic analyzer can form the following kind of representation:

$$\exists e,x,y \, Eating(e) \wedge Eater(e,x) \wedge Theme(e,y) \wedge EdibleThing(y) \wedge Hamburger(y)$$

This representation is perfectly reasonable since the membership of y in the category *Hamburger* is consistent with its membership in the category *EdibleThing*, assuming a reasonable set of facts in the knowledge base. Correspondingly, the representation for a phrase such as *ate a takeoff* would be ill-formed because membership in an event-like category such as *Takeoff* would be inconsistent with membership in the category *EdibleThing*.

While this approach adequately captures the semantics of selectional restrictions, there are two problems with its direct use. First, using FOL to perform the simple task of enforcing selectional restrictions is overkill. Other, far simpler, formalisms can do the job with far less computational cost. The second problem is that this approach presupposes a large, logical knowledge base of facts about the concepts that make up selectional restrictions. Unfortunately, although such common-sense knowledge bases are being developed, none currently have the kind of coverage necessary to the task.

A more practical approach is to state selectional restrictions in terms of WordNet synsets rather than as logical concepts. Each predicate simply specifies a WordNet synset as the selectional restriction on each of its arguments. A meaning representation is well-formed if the role filler word is a hyponym (subordinate) of this synset.

```
Sense 1
hamburger, beefburger --
(a fried cake of minced beef served on a bun)
=> sandwich
   => snack food
      => dish
         => nutriment, nourishment, nutrition...
            => food, nutrient
               => substance
                  => matter
                     => physical entity
                        => entity
```

Figure 19.7   Evidence from WordNet that hamburgers are edible.

For our *ate a hamburger* example, for instance, we could set the selectional restriction on the THEME role of the verb *eat* to the synset **food, nutrient**, glossed as *any substance that can be metabolized by an animal to give energy and build tissue*. Luckily, the chain of hypernyms for *hamburger* shown in Fig. 19.7 reveals that hamburgers are indeed food. Again, the filler of a role need not match the restriction synset exactly; it just needs to have the synset as one of its superordinates.

We can apply this approach to the THEME roles of the verbs *imagine*, *lift*, and *diagonalize*, discussed earlier. Let us restrict *imagine*'s THEME to the synset entity, *lift*'s THEME to physical entity, and *diagonalize* to matrix. This arrangement correctly permits *imagine a hamburger* and *lift a hamburger*, while also correctly ruling out *diagonalize a hamburger*.

Of course, WordNet is unlikely to have the exactly relevant synsets to specify selectional restrictions for all possible words of English; other taxonomies may also be used. In addition, it is possible to learn selectional restrictions automatically from corpora.

We return to selectional restrictions in Chapter 20 in which we introduce the extension to selectional preferences, whereby a predicate can place probabilistic preferences rather than strict deterministic constraints on its arguments.

19.5   Primitive Decomposition

Back at the beginning of the chapter, we said that one way of defining a word is to decompose its meaning into a set of primitive semantics elements or features. We saw one aspect of this method in our discussion of finite lists of thematic roles (agent, patient, instrument, etc.). We turn now to a brief discussion of how this kind of model, *Componential analysis* called **primitive decomposition** or **componential analysis**, could be applied to the meanings of all words. Wierzbicka (1992, 1996) shows that this approach dates back at least to continental philosophers like Descartes and Leibniz.

Consider trying to define words like *hen*, *rooster*, or *chick*. These words have something in common (they all describe chickens) and something different (their age *Semantic feature* and sex). This can be represented with **semantic features**, symbols that represent some sort of primitive meaning:

```
hen     +female, +chicken, +adult
rooster -female, +chicken, +adult
chick   +chicken, -adult
```

Various studies of decompositional semantics, especially in the computational literature, have focused on the meaning of verbs. Consider these examples of the verb *kill*:

(19.52) Jim killed his philodendron.

(19.53) Jim did something to cause his philodendron to become not alive.

There is a truth-conditional ('propositional semantics') perspective from which these two sentences have the same meaning. Assuming this equivalence, we could represent the meaning of *kill* as:

(19.54) KILL(x,y) $\Leftrightarrow$ CAUSE(x, BECOME(NOT(ALIVE(y))))

thus using semantic primitives like *do, cause, become not,* and *alive*.

Indeed, one such set of potential semantic primitives has been used to account for some of the verbal alternations discussed in Section 19.4.2 (Lakoff, 1965; Dowty, 1979). Consider the following examples.

(19.55) John opened the door. $\Rightarrow$ CAUSE(John(BECOME(OPEN(door))))

(19.56) The door opened. $\Rightarrow$ BECOME(OPEN(door))

(19.57) The door is open. $\Rightarrow$ OPEN(door)

The decompositional approach asserts that a single state-like predicate associated with *open* underlies all of these examples. The differences among the meanings of these examples arises from the combination of this single predicate with the primitives CAUSE and BECOME.

While this approach to primitive decomposition can explain the similarity between states and actions or causative and non-causative predicates, it still relies on having a large number of predicates like *open*. More radical approaches choose to break down these predicates as well. One such approach to verbal predicate decomposition is **conceptual dependency** (CD), a set of ten primitive predicates, shown in Fig. 19.8.

Below is an example sentence along with its CD representation. The verb *brought* is translated into the two primitives ATRANS and PTRANS to indicate that the waiter both physically conveyed the check to Mary and passed control of it to her. Note that CD also associates a fixed set of thematic roles with each primitive to represent the various participants in the action.

Conceptual dependency

(19.58) The waiter brought Mary the check.

$$\exists x,y \, Atrans(x) \wedge Actor(x,Waiter) \wedge Object(x,Check) \wedge To(x,Mary)$$
$$\wedge Ptrans(y) \wedge Actor(y,Waiter) \wedge Object(y,Check) \wedge To(y,Mary)$$

There are also sets of semantic primitives that cover more than just simple nouns and verbs. The following list comes from Wierzbicka (1996).

Primitive	Definition
ATRANS	The abstract transfer of possession or control from one entity to another
PTRANS	The physical transfer of an object from one location to another
MTRANS	The transfer of mental concepts between entities or within an entity
MBUILD	The creation of new information within an entity
PROPEL	The application of physical force to move an object
MOVE	The integral movement of a body part by an animal
INGEST	The taking in of a substance by an animal
EXPEL	The expulsion of something from an animal
SPEAK	The action of producing a sound
ATTEND	The action of focusing a sense organ

Figure 19.8   A set of conceptual dependency primitives.

substantives:	I, YOU, SOMEONE, SOMETHING, PEOPLE
mental predicates:	THINK, KNOW, WANT, FEEL, SEE, HEAR
speech:	SAY
determiners and quantifiers:	THIS, THE SAME, OTHER, ONE, TWO, MANY (MUCH), ALL, SOME, MORE
actions and events:	DO, HAPPEN
evaluators:	GOOD, BAD
descriptors:	BIG, SMALL
time:	WHEN, BEFORE, AFTER
space:	WHERE, UNDER, ABOVE,
partonomy and taxonomy:	PART (OF), KIND (OF)
movement, existence, life:	MOVE, THERE IS, LIVE
metapredicates:	NOT, CAN, VERY
interclausal linkers:	IF, BECAUSE, LIKE
space:	FAR, NEAR, SIDE, INSIDE, HERE
time:	A LONG TIME, A SHORT TIME, NOW
imagination and possibility:	IF... WOULD, CAN, MAYBE

Because of the difficulty of coming up with a set of primitives that can represent all possible kinds of meanings, most current computational linguistic work does not use semantic primitives. Instead, most computational work tends to use the lexical relations of Section 19.2 to define words.

19.6   Advanced: Metaphor

Metaphor   When we refer to and reason about a concept or domain in words and phrases whose meanings come from a completely different domain, we have used a **metaphor**. Metaphor is similar to **metonymy**, which we introduced as the use of one aspect of a concept or entity to refer to other aspects of the entity. In Section 19.1, we introduced metonymies like

(19.59) Author (*Jane Austen wrote Emma*) ↔ Works of Author (*I really love Jane Austen*).

in which two senses of a polysemous word are systematically related. In metaphor, by contrast, there is a systematic relation between two completely different domains of meaning.

Metaphor is pervasive. Consider the following WSJ sentence:

(19.60) That doesn't **scare** Digital, which has grown to be the world's second-largest computer maker by poaching customers of IBM's mid-range machines.

The verb *scare* means "to cause fear in", or "to cause to lose courage". For this sentence to make sense, it has to be the case that corporations can experience emotions like fear or courage as people do. Of course they don't, but we certainly speak of them and reason about them as if they do. We can therefore say that this use of *scare* is based on a metaphor that allows us to view a corporation as a person; we will refer to this as the CORPORATION AS PERSON metaphor.

This metaphor is neither novel nor specific to this use of *scare*. Instead, it is a fairly conventional way to think about companies and motivates the use of *resuscitate*, *hemorrhage*, and *mind* in the following WSJ examples:

(19.61) Fuqua Industries Inc. said Triton Group Ltd., a company it helped **resuscitate**, has begun acquiring Fuqua shares.

(19.62) And Ford was **hemorrhaging**; its losses would hit $1.54 billion in 1980.

(19.63) But if it changed its **mind**, however, it would do so for investment reasons, the filing said.

Each of these examples reflects an elaborated use of the basic CORPORATION AS PERSON metaphor. The first two examples extend it to use the notion of health to express a corporation's financial status, and the third example attributes a mind to a corporation to capture the notion of corporate strategy.

Conventional metaphor Metaphorical constructs such as CORPORATION AS PERSON are known as **conventional metaphors**. Lakoff and Johnson (1980) argue that many, if not most, of the metaphorical expressions that we encounter every day are motivated by a relatively small number of these simple conventional schemas.

19.7 Summary

This chapter has covered a wide range of issues concerning the meanings associated with lexical items. The following are among the highlights:

- **Lexical semantics** is the study of the meaning of words and the systematic meaning-related connections between words.
- A **word sense** is the locus of word meaning; definitions and meaning relations are defined at the level of the word sense rather than wordforms as a whole.
- **Homonymy** is the relation between unrelated senses that share a form, and **polysemy** is the relation between related senses that share a form.

- **Synonymy** holds between different words with the same meaning.
- **Hyponymy** relations hold between words that are in a class-inclusion relationship.
- **Semantic fields** are used to capture semantic connections among groups of lexemes drawn from a single domain.
- **WordNet** is a large database of lexical relations for English words.
- **Semantic roles** abstract from the specifics of deep semantic roles by generalizing over similar roles across classes of verbs.
- **Thematic roles** are a model of semantic roles based on a single finite list of roles. Other semantic role models include per-verb semantic role lists and **proto-agent/proto-patient**, both of which are implemented in **PropBank**, and per-frame role lists, implemented in **FrameNet**.
- Semantic **selectional restrictions** allow words (particularly predicates) to post constraints on the semantic properties of their argument words.
- **Primitive decomposition** is another way to represent the meaning of a word, in terms of finite sets of sublexical primitives.

Bibliographical and Historical Notes

Cruse (2004) is a useful introductory linguistic text on lexical semantics. Levin and Rappaport Hovav (2005) is a research survey covering argument realization and semantic roles. Lyons (1977) is another classic reference. Collections describing computational work on lexical semantics can be found in Pustejovsky and Bergler (1992), Saint-Dizier and Viegas (1995), and Klavans (1995).

The most comprehensive collection of work concerning WordNet can be found in Fellbaum (1998). Many efforts have been made to use existing dictionaries as lexical resources. One of the earliest was Amsler's (1980, 1981) use of the Merriam Webster dictionary. The machine-readable version of Longman's *Dictionary of Contemporary English* has also been used (Boguraev and Briscoe, 1989). See Pustejovsky (1995), Pustejovsky and Boguraev (1996), Martin (1986), and Copestake and Briscoe (1995), inter alia, for computational approaches to the representation of polysemy. Pustejovsky's theory of the **generative lexicon**, and in particular his theory of the **qualia structure** of words, is another way of accounting for the dynamic systematic polysemy of words in context.

Generative lexicon
Qualia structure

As we mentioned earlier, thematic roles are one of the oldest linguistic models, proposed first by the Indian grammarian Panini some time between the 7th and 4th centuries BCE. The modern formulation of thematic roles is due to Fillmore (1968) and Gruber (1965). Fillmore's work had a large and immediate impact on work in natural language processing—much early work in language understanding used some version of Fillmore's case roles (e.g., Simmons (1973, 1978, 1983)). Fillmore's extension of this work to the FrameNet project is described in Baker et al. (1998), Narayanan et al. (1999), and Baker et al. (2003).

Work on selectional restrictions as a way of characterizing semantic well-formedness began with Katz and Fodor (1963). McCawley (1968) was the first to point out that selectional restrictions could not be restricted to a finite list of semantic features but had to be drawn from a larger base of unrestricted world knowledge.

Lehrer (1974) is a classic text on semantic fields. More recent papers addressing this topic can be found in Lehrer and Kittay (1992).

The use of semantic primitives to define word meaning dates back to Leibniz; in linguistics, the focus on componential analysis in semantics was due to Hjelmslev (1969). See Nida (1975) for a comprehensive overview of work on componential analysis. Wierzbicka (1996) has long been a major advocate of the use of primitives in linguistic semantics; Wilks (1975a) has made similar arguments for the computational use of primitives in machine translation and natural language understanding. Another prominent effort has been Jackendoff's Conceptual Semantics work (1983, 1990), which has also been applied in machine translation (Dorr, 1993, 1992).

Computational approaches to the interpretation of metaphors include convention-based and reasoning-based approaches. Convention-based approaches encode specific knowledge about a relatively small core set of conventional metaphors. These representations are then used during understanding to replace one meaning with an appropriate metaphorical one (Norvig, 1987; Martin, 1990; Hayes and Bayer, 1991; Veale and Keane, 1992; Jones and McCoy, 1992; Narayanan, 1999). Reasoning-based approaches eschew representing metaphoric conventions, instead modeling figurative language processing through general reasoning ability, such as analogical reasoning, rather than as a specifically language-related phenomenon (Russell, 1976; Carbonell, 1982; Gentner, 1983; Fass, 1988, 1991, 1997).

An influential collection of papers on metaphor can be found in Ortony (1993). Lakoff and Johnson (1980) is the classic work on conceptual metaphor and metonymy. Russell (1976) presents one of the earliest computational approaches to metaphor. Additional early work can be found in DeJong and Waltz (1983), Wilks (1978), and Hobbs (1979b). More recent computational efforts to analyze metaphor can be found in Fass (1988, 1991, 1997), Martin (1990), Veale and Keane (1992), Iverson and Helmreich (1992), Chandler (1991), and Martin (2006). Martin (1996) presents a survey of computational approaches to metaphor and other types of figurative language. Gries and Stefanowitsch (2006) is a recent collection of papers on corpus-based approaches to metaphor.

Exercises

19.1 From a dictionary of your choice, collect three definitions of ordinary non-technical English words that you feel are flawed in some way. Explain the nature of the flaw and how it might be remedied.

19.2 Give a detailed account of similarities and differences among the following set of lexemes: *imitation, synthetic, artificial, fake,* and *simulated.*

19.3 Examine the entries for these lexemes in WordNet (or some dictionary of your choice). How well does it reflect your analysis?

19.4 The WordNet entry for the noun *bat* lists six distinct senses. Cluster these senses by using the definitions of homonymy and polysemy given in this chapter. For any senses that are polysemous, give an argument as to how the senses are related.

19.5 Assign the various verb arguments in the following WSJ examples to their appropriate thematic roles, using the set of roles shown in Fig. 19.6.

1. The intense heat buckled the highway about three feet.
2. He melted her reserve with a husky-voiced paean to her eyes.
3. But Mingo, a major Union Pacific shipping center in the 1890s, has melted away to little more than the grain elevator now.

19.6 Using WordNet, describe appropriate selectional restrictions on the verbs *drink*, *kiss*, and *write*.

19.7 Collect a small corpus of examples of the verbs *drink*, *kiss*, and *write*, and analyze how well your selectional restrictions worked.

19.8 Consider the following examples from McCawley (1968):

My neighbor is a father of three.

?My buxom neighbor is a father of three.

What does the ill-formedness of the second example imply about how constituents satisfy or violate selectional restrictions?

19.9 Find some articles about business, sports, or politics from your daily newspaper. Identify as many uses of conventional metaphors as you can in these articles. How many of the words used to express these metaphors have entries in either WordNet or your favorite dictionary that directly reflect the metaphor.

19.10 Consider the following example:

The stock exchange wouldn't talk publicly, but a spokesman said a news conference is set for today to introduce a new technology product.

Assuming that stock exchanges are not the kinds of things that can literally talk, give a sensible account for this phrase in terms of a metaphor or metonymy.

19.11 Choose an English verb that occurs in both FrameNet and PropBank. Compare the FrameNet and PropBank representations of the arguments of the verb.

Chapter 20

Computational Lexical Semantics

To get a single right meaning is better than a ship-load of pearls,
To resolve a single doubt is like the bottom falling off the bucket.
        Yuen Mei (1785) (translation by Arthur Waley)

The asphalt that Los Angeles is famous for occurs mainly on its freeways. But in the middle of the city is another patch of asphalt, the La Brea tar pits, and this asphalt preserves millions of fossil bones from the last of the Ice Ages of the Pleistocene Epoch. One of these fossils is the *Smilodon*, or sabre-toothed tiger, instantly recognizable by its long canines. Five million years ago or so, a completely different sabre-tooth tiger called *Thylacosmilus* lived in Argentina and other parts of South America. Thylacosmilus was a marsupial whereas Smilodon was a placental mammal, but Thylacosmilus had the same long upper canines and, like Smilodon, had a protective bone flange on the lower jaw. The similarity of these two mammals is one of many example of parallel or convergent evolution, in which particular contexts or environments lead to the evolution of very similar structures in different species (Gould, 1980).

The role of context is also important in the similarity of a less biological kind of organism: the word. Suppose we wanted to decide if two words have similar meanings. Not surprisingly, words with similar meanings often occur in similar contexts, whether in terms of corpora (having similar neighboring words or syntactic structures in sentences) or in terms of dictionaries and thesauruses (having similar definitions or being nearby in the thesaurus hierarchy). Thus, similarity of context turns out to be an important way to detect semantic similarity. Semantic similarity turns out to play an important role in a diverse set of applications including information retrieval, question answering, summarization and generation, text classification, automatic essay grading, and the detection of plagiarism.

Computational lexical semantics

In this chapter we introduce a series of topics related to computing with word meanings, or **computational lexical semantics**. Roughly in parallel with the sequence of topics in Chapter 19, we introduce computational tasks associated with word senses, relations among words, and the thematic structure of predicate-bearing words. We show the important role of context and similarity of sense in each of these.

Word sense disambiguation

We begin with **word sense disambiguation**, the task of examining word tokens in context and determining which sense of each word is being used. WSD is a task with a long history in computational linguistics, a non-trivial one given the somewhat elusive nature of many word senses. Nevertheless, there are robust algorithms that can achieve high levels of accuracy given certain reasonable assumptions. Many of these algorithms rely on contextual similarity to help choose the proper sense.

This leads us naturally to a consideration of the computation of **word similarity** and other relations between words, including the **hypernym**, **hyponym**, and **meronym** WordNet relations introduced in Chapter 19. We introduce methods based purely on corpus similarity and others based on structured resources such as WordNet.

Finally, we describe algorithms for **semantic role labeling**, also known as **case role** or **thematic role assignment**. These algorithms generally use features extracted from syntactic parses to assign semantic roles, such as AGENT, THEME, and INSTRUMENT, to the phrases in a sentence with respect to particular predicates.

20.1   Word Sense Disambiguation: Overview

Our discussion of compositional semantic analyzers in Chapter 18 pretty much ignored the issue of lexical ambiguity. It should be clear by now that this is an unreasonable approach. Without some means of selecting correct senses for the words in an input, the enormous amount of homonymy and polysemy in the lexicon would quickly overwhelm any approach in an avalanche of competing interpretations.

Word sense disambiguation
WSD

The task of selecting the correct sense for a word is called **word sense disambiguation**, or **WSD**. Disambiguating word senses has the potential to improve many natural language processing tasks. As we describe in Chapter 25, **machine translation** is one area in which word sense ambiguities can cause severe problems; others include **question answering**, **information retrieval**, and **text classification**. The way that WSD is exploited in these and other applications varies widely according to the particular needs of the application. The discussion presented here ignores these application-specific differences and focuses on WSD as as a stand-alone task.

In their most basic form, WSD algorithms take as input a word in context along with a fixed inventory of potential word senses and return as output the correct word sense for that use. Both the nature of the input and the inventory of senses depends on the task. For machine translation from English to Spanish, the sense tag inventory for an English word might be the set of different Spanish translations. If speech synthesis is our task, the inventory might be restricted to homographs with differing pronunciations such as *bass* and *bow*. If our task is automatic indexing of medical articles, the sense-tag inventory might be the set of MeSH (Medical Subject Headings) thesaurus entries. When we are evaluating WSD in isolation, we can use the set of senses from a dictionary/thesaurus resource like WordNet or LDOCE. Figure 20.1 shows an example for the word *bass*, which can refer to a musical instrument or a kind of fish.[1]

WordNet Sense	Spanish Translation	Roget Category	Target Word in Context
bass^4	lubina	FISH/INSECT	. . . fish as Pacific salmon and striped **bass** and. . .
bass^4	lubina	FISH/INSECT	. . . produce filets of smoked **bass** or sturgeon. . .
bass^7	bajo	MUSIC	. . . exciting jazz **bass** player since Ray Brown. . .
bass^7	bajo	MUSIC	. . . play **bass** because he doesn't have to solo. . .

Figure 20.1   Possible definitions for the inventory of sense tags for *bass*.

Lexical sample

It is useful to distinguish two variants of the generic WSD task. In the **lexical sample** task, a small pre-selected set of target words is chosen, along with an inventory

---

[1] The WordNet database includes eight senses; we have arbitrarily selected two for this example; we have also arbitrarily selected one of the many possible Spanish fishes that could translate English *sea bass*.

of senses for each word from some lexicon. Since the set of words and the set of senses are small, supervised machine learning approaches are often used to handle lexical sample tasks. For each word, a number of corpus instances (context sentences) can be selected and hand-labeled with the correct sense of the target word in each. Classifier systems can then be trained with these labeled examples. Unlabeled target words in context can then be labeled using such a trained classifier. Early work in word sense disambiguation focused solely on lexical sample tasks of this sort, building word-specific algorithms for disambiguating single words like *line*, *interest*, or *plant*.

All-words In contrast, in the **all-words** task, systems are given entire texts and a lexicon with an inventory of senses for each entry and are required to disambiguate every content word in the text. The all-words task is similar to part-of-speech tagging, except with a much larger set of tags since each lemma has its own set. A consequence of this larger set of tags is a serious data sparseness problem; it is unlikely that adequate training data for every word in the test set will be available. Moreover, given the number of polysemous words in reasonably sized lexicons, approaches based on training one classifier per term are unlikely to be practical.

In the following sections we explore the application of various machine learning paradigms to word sense disambiguation. We begin with supervised learning, followed by a section on how systems are standardly evaluated. We then turn to a variety of methods for dealing with the lack of sufficient data for fully supervised training, including dictionary-based approaches and bootstrapping techniques.

Finally, after we have introduced the necessary notions of distributional word similarity in Section 20.7, we return in Section 20.10 to the problem of unsupervised approaches to sense disambiguation.

20.2   Supervised Word Sense Disambiguation

If we have data that has been hand-labeled with correct word senses, we can use a **supervised learning** approach to the problem of sense disambiguation—extracting features from the text that are helpful in predicting particular senses and then training a classifier to assign the correct sense given these features. The output of training is thus a classifier system capable of assigning sense labels to unlabeled words in context.

For **lexical sample** tasks, there are various labeled corpora for individual words; these corpora consist of context sentences labeled with the correct sense for the target word. These include the *line-hard-serve* corpus containing 4,000 sense-tagged examples of *line* as a noun, *hard* as an adjective and *serve* as a verb (Leacock et al., 1993), and the *interest* corpus with 2,369 sense-tagged examples of *interest* as a noun (Bruce and Wiebe, 1994). The SENSEVAL project has also produced a number of such sense-labeled lexical sample corpora (SENSEVAL-1 with 34 words from the HECTOR lexicon and corpus (Kilgarriff and Rosenzweig, 2000; Atkins, 1993), SENSEVAL-2 and -3 with 73 and 57 target words, respectively (Palmer et al., 2001; Kilgarriff, 2001)).

Semantic concordance For training **all-word** disambiguation tasks we use a **semantic concordance**, a corpus in which each open-class word in each sentence is labeled with its word sense from a specific dictionary or thesaurus. One commonly used corpus is SemCor, a subset of the Brown Corpus consisting of over 234,000 words that were manually tagged with WordNet senses (Miller et al., 1993; Landes et al., 1998). In addition, sense-tagged corpora have been built for the SENSEVAL all-word tasks. The SENSEVAL-3 English all-words test data consisted of 2081 tagged content word tokens, from 5,000 total running words of English from the WSJ and Brown corpora (Palmer et al., 2001).

20.2.1   Feature Extraction for Supervised Learning

The first step in supervised training is to extract features that are predictive of word senses. As Ide and Véronis (1998b) point out, the insight that underlies all modern algorithms for word sense disambiguation was first articulated by Weaver (1955) in the context of machine translation:

> If one examines the words in a book, one at a time as through an opaque mask with a hole in it one word wide, then it is obviously impossible to determine, one at a time, the meaning of the words. [...] But if one lengthens the slit in the opaque mask, until one can see not only the central word in question but also say N words on either side, then if N is large enough one can unambiguously decide the meaning of the central word. [...] The practical question is : "What minimum value of N will, at least in a tolerable fraction of cases, lead to the correct choice of meaning for the central word?"

Feature vector

We first perform some processing on the sentence containing the window, typically including part-of-speech tagging, lemmatization or stemming, and, in some cases, syntactic parsing to reveal headwords and dependency relations. Context features relevant to the target word can then be extracted from this enriched input. A **feature vector** consisting of numeric or nominal values encodes this linguistic information as an input to most machine learning algorithms.

Collocation

Collocational features

Two classes of features are generally extracted from these neighboring contexts: collocational features and bag-of-words features. A **collocation** is a word or phrase in a position-specific relationship to a target word (i.e., exactly one word to the right, or exactly four words to the left, and so on). Thus, **collocational features** encode information about *specific* positions located to the left or right of the target word. Typical features extracted for these context words include the word itself, the root form of the word, and the word's part-of-speech. Such features are effective at encoding local lexical and grammatical information that can often accurately isolate a given sense.

As an example of this type of feature encoding, consider the situation in which we need to disambiguate the word *bass* in the following WSJ sentence:

(20.1) An electric guitar and **bass** player stand off to one side, not really part of the scene, just as a sort of nod to gringo expectations perhaps.

A collocational feature vector, extracted from a window of two words to the right and left of the target word, made up of the words themselves and their respective parts-of-speech, that is,

$$[w_{i-2}, \text{POS}_{i-2}, w_{i-1}, \text{POS}_{i-1}, w_{i+1}, \text{POS}_{i+1}, w_{i+2}, \text{POS}_{i+2}] \qquad (20.2)$$

would yield the following vector:

```
[guitar, NN, and, CC, player, NN, stand, VB]
```

Bag-of-words

The second type of feature consists of **bag-of-words** information about neighboring words. A **bag-of-words** means an unordered set of words, with their exact position ignored. The simplest bag-of-words approach represents the context of a target word by a vector of features, each binary feature indicating whether a vocabulary word *w* does or doesn't occur in the context. This vocabulary is typically pre-selected as some useful subset of words in a training corpus. In most WSD applications, the context region surrounding the target word is generally a small, symmetric, fixed-size window with the target word at the center. Bag-of-word features are effective at capturing the general topic of the discourse in which the target word has occurred. This, in turn, tends to identify senses of a word that are specific to certain domains. We generally don't use stopwords as features, and we may also limit the bag-of-words to consider only a small number of frequently used content words.

For example, a bag-of-words vector consisting of the 12 most frequent content words from a collection of *bass* sentences drawn from the WSJ corpus would have the following ordered word feature set:

[*fishing, big, sound, player, fly, rod, pound, double, runs, playing, guitar, band*]

Using these word features with a window size of 10, (20.1) would be represented by the following binary vector:

`[0,0,0,1,0,0,0,0,0,0,1,0]`

We revisit the bag-of-words technique in Chapter 23 where we show that it forms the basis for the **vector space model** of search in modern search engines.

Most approaches to sense disambiguation use both collocational and bag-of-words features, either by joining them into one long vector or by building a distinct classifier for each feature type and combining them in some manner.

20.2.2   Naive Bayes and Decision List Classifiers

Given training data together with the extracted features, any supervised machine learning paradigm can be used to train a sense classifier. We will restrict our discussion here to the naive Bayes and decision list approaches since they have been the focus of considerable work in word sense disambiguation and have not yet been introduced in previous chapters.

Naive Bayes classifier

The **naive Bayes classifier** approach to WSD is based on the premise that choosing the best sense $\hat{s}$ out of the set of possible senses S for a feature vector $\vec{f}$ amounts to choosing the most probable sense given that vector. In other words

$$\hat{s} = \underset{s \in S}{\operatorname{argmax}} P(s \mid \vec{f}) \qquad (20.3)$$

As is almost always the case, it would be difficult to collect reasonable statistics for this equation directly. To appreciate this, consider that a simple binary bag of words vector defined over a vocabulary of 20 words would have 2^{20} possible feature vectors. It's unlikely that any corpus to which we have access will provide coverage to adequately train this kind of feature vector. To get around this problem, we first reformulate our problem in the usual Bayesian manner as follows:

$$\hat{s} = \underset{s \in S}{\operatorname{argmax}} \frac{P(\vec{f} \mid s)P(s)}{P(\vec{f})} \tag{20.4}$$

Even this equation isn't helpful enough, since the available data that associates specific vectors $\vec{f}$ with each sense s is also too sparse. However, what is available in greater abundance in a tagged training set is information about individual feature-value pairs in the context of specific senses. Therefore, we can make the independence assumption that gives this method its name and that has served us well in part-of-speech tagging, speech recognition, and probabilistic parsing—**naively** assume that the features are independent of one another. Making the assumption that the features are **conditionally independent given the word sense** yields the following approximation for $P(\vec{f} \mid s)$:

$$P(\vec{f} \mid s) \approx \prod_{j=1}^{n} P(f_j \mid s) \tag{20.5}$$

In other words, we can estimate the probability of an entire vector given a sense by the product of the probabilities of its individual features given that sense. Since $P(\vec{f})$ is the same for all possible senses, it does not affect the final ranking of senses, leaving us with the following formulation of a **naive Bayes classifier for WSD**:

$$\hat{s} = \underset{s \in S}{\operatorname{argmax}} P(s) \prod_{j=1}^{n} P(f_j \mid s) \tag{20.6}$$

Given this equation, **training** a naive Bayes classifier consists of estimating each of these probabilities. Example (20.6) first requires an estimate for the prior probability of each sense $P(s)$. We get the maximum likelihood estimate of this probability from the sense-tagged training corpus by counting the number of times the sense s_i occurs and dividing by the total count of the target word w_j (i.e., the sum of the instances of each sense of the word). That is,

$$P(s_i) = \frac{\operatorname{count}(s_i, w_j)}{\operatorname{count}(w_j)} \tag{20.7}$$

We also need to know each of the individual feature probabilities $P(f_j \mid s)$. The maximum likelihood estimate for these would be

$$P(f_j \mid s) = \frac{\operatorname{count}(f_j, s)}{\operatorname{count}(s)} \tag{20.8}$$

Thus, if a collocational feature such as $[w_{i-2} = \text{guitar}]$ occurred 3 times for sense bass[1] and sense bass[1] itself occurred 60 times in training, the MLE is $P(f_j \mid s) = 0.05$. Binary bag-of-word features are treated in a similar manner; we simply count the number of times a given vocabulary item is present with each of the possible senses and divide by the count for each sense.

With the necessary estimates in place, we can assign senses to words in context by applying Eq. 20.6. More specifically, we take the target word in context, extract

Rule		Sense
fish within window	$\Rightarrow$	**bass**[1]
striped bass	$\Rightarrow$	**bass**[1]
guitar within window	$\Rightarrow$	**bass**[2]
bass player	$\Rightarrow$	**bass**[2]
piano within window	$\Rightarrow$	**bass**[2]
tenor within window	$\Rightarrow$	**bass**[2]
sea bass	$\Rightarrow$	**bass**[1]
play/V *bass*	$\Rightarrow$	**bass**[2]
river within window	$\Rightarrow$	**bass**[1]
violin within window	$\Rightarrow$	**bass**[2]
salmon within window	$\Rightarrow$	**bass**[1]
on bass	$\Rightarrow$	**bass**[2]
bass are	$\Rightarrow$	**bass**[1]

Figure 20.2   An abbreviated decision list for disambiguating the fish sense of *bass* from the music sense (Yarowsky, 1997).

the specified features, compute $P(s) \prod_{j=1}^{n} P(f_j \mid s)$ for each sense, and return the sense associated with the highest score. Note that in practice, the probabilities produced for even the highest scoring senses will be dangerously low because of the various multiplications involved; mapping everything to log-space and instead performing additions is the usual solution.

The use of a simple maximum likelihood estimator means that in testing, when a target word co-occurs with a word that it did not co-occur with in training, all of its senses will receive a probability of zero. Smoothing is therefore essential to the whole enterprise. Naive Bayes approaches to sense disambiguation generally use the simple Laplace (add-one or add-k) smoothing discussed in Chapter 4.

One problem with naive Bayes and some other classifiers is that it's hard for humans to examine their workings and understand their decisions. Decision lists and decision trees are somewhat more transparent approaches that lend themselves to in-

Decision list classifiers

spection. **Decision list classifiers** are equivalent to simple case statements in most programming languages. In a decision list classifier, a sequence of tests is applied to each target-word feature vector. Each test is indicative of a particular sense. If a test succeeds, then the sense associated with that test is returned. If the test fails, then the next test in the sequence is applied. This continues until the end of the list, where a default test simply returns the majority sense.

Figure 20.2 shows a portion of a decision list for the task of discriminating the fish sense of *bass* from the music sense. The first test says that if the word *fish* occurs anywhere within the input context, then **bass**[1] is the correct answer. If *fish* doesn't occur there, then each of the subsequent tests is consulted in turn until one returns true; as with case statements, a default test that returns true is included at the end of the list.

Learning a decision list classifier consists of generating and ordering individual tests according to the characteristics of the training data. A wide number of methods can be used to create such lists. In the approach used by Yarowsky (1994) for binary homonym discrimination, each individual feature-value pair constitutes a test. We can measure how much a feature indicates a particular sense by computing the probability of the sense given the feature. The ratio between the probabilities of the two senses tells us how discriminative a feature is between senses:

$$\left| \log \left(\frac{P(Sense_1 \; f_i)}{P(Sense_2 \; f_i)} \right) \right| \tag{20.9}$$

The decision list is then created from these tests by simply ordering the tests in the list according to the log-likelihood ratio. Each test is checked in order and returns the appropriate sense. This training method differs quite a bit from standard decision list learning algorithms. For the details and theoretical motivation for these approaches, see Rivest (1987) or Russell and Norvig (2002).

20.3 WSD Evaluation, Baselines, and Ceilings

Evaluating component technologies like WSD is always a complicated affair. In the long term, we're primarily interested in the extent to which they improve performance in some end-to-end application such as information retrieval, question answering or machine translation. Evaluating component NLP tasks embedded in end-to-end applications is called **extrinsic evaluation**, **task-based** evaluation, **end-to-end** evaluation, or **in vivo** evaluation. Only with extrinsic evaluation can we tell if a technology such as WSD is working in the sense of actually improving performance on some real task.

Extrinsic evaluation

In vivo

Extrinsic evaluations are much more difficult and time consuming to implement, however, since they require integration into complete working systems. Furthermore, an extrinsic evaluation may only tell us something about WSD in the context of the application and may not generalize to other applications.

For these reasons, WSD systems are typically developed and evaluated intrinsically. In **intrinsic** or **in vitro** evaluation we treat a WSD component as if it were a stand-alone system operating independently of any given application. In this style of evaluation, systems are evaluated either by exact-match **sense accuracy**—the percentage of words that are tagged identically with the hand-labeled sense tags in a test set—or with standard precision and recall measures if systems are permitted to pass on the labeling of some instances. In general, we evaluate by using held-out data from the same sense-tagged corpora that we used for training, such as the SemCor corpus discussed above or the various corpora produced by the SENSEVAL effort.

Intrinsic

In vitro

Sense accuracy

Many aspects of sense evaluation have been standardized by the SENSEVAL and SEMEVAL efforts (Palmer et al., 2006; Kilgarriff and Palmer, 2000). This framework provides a shared task with training and testing materials along with sense inventories for all-words and lexical sample tasks in a variety of languages.

Whichever WSD task we are performing, we ideally need two additional measures to assess how well we're doing: a baseline measure to tell us how well we're doing as compared to relatively simple approaches, and a ceiling to tell us how close we are to optimal performance.

Most frequent sense

The simplest baseline is to choose the **most frequent sense** for each word (Gale et al., 1992a) from the senses in a labeled corpus. For WordNet, this corresponds to the **take the first sense** heuristic, since senses in WordNet are generally ordered from most frequent to least frequent. WordNet sense frequencies come from the SemCor sense-tagged corpus described above.

Unfortunately, many WordNet senses do not occur in SemCor; these unseen senses are thus ordered arbitrarily after those that do. The four WordNet senses of the noun *plant*, for example, are shown below.

Freq	Synset	Gloss
338	plant[1], works, industrial plant	buildings for carrying on industrial labor
207	plant[2], flora, plant life	a living organism lacking the power of locomotion
2	plant[3]	something planted secretly for discovery by another
0	plant[4]	an actor situated in the audience whose acting is rehearsed but seems spontaneous to the audience

The most frequent sense baseline can be quite accurate, and is therefore often used as a default, to supply a word sense when a supervised algorithm has insufficient training data. A second commonly used baseline is the **Lesk algorithm**, discussed in the next section. Human inter-annotator agreement is generally considered as a ceiling, or upper bound, for sense disambiguation evaluations. Human agreement is measured by comparison of the annotations of two human annotators on the same data given the same tagging guidelines. The ceiling (inter-annotator agreement) for many all-words corpora using WordNet-style sense inventories seems to range from about 75% to 80% (Palmer et al., 2006). Agreement on more coarse-grained, often binary, sense inventories is closer to 90% (Gale et al., 1992a).

Although using hand-labeled test sets is the best current method for evaluation, labeling large amounts of data is still quite expensive. For supervised approaches, we need this data anyhow for training, so the effort to label large amounts of data seems justified. But for unsupervised algorithms like those we discuss in Section 20.10, we would like to have an evaluation method that avoided hand-labeling. The use of *Pseudowords* **pseudowords** is one such simplified evaluation method (Gale et al., 1992c; Schütze, 1992a). A pseudoword is an artificial word created by concatenation of two randomly chosen words (e.g., *banana* and *door* to create *banana-door*). Each occurrence of the two words in the test set is replaced by the new concatenation, creating a new "word" that is now ambiguous between the senses *banana* and *door*. The "correct sense" is defined by the original word, so we can apply our disambiguation algorithm and compute accuracy as usual. In general, pseudowords give an overly optimistic measure of performance since they are a bit easier to disambiguate than are average ambiguous words. This is because the different senses of real words tend to be similar, whereas pseudowords are generally not semantically similar, acting like homonymous but not polysemous words (Gaustad, 2001). Nakov and Hearst (2003) show that it is possible to improve the accuracy of pseudoword evaluation by a more careful choice of the pseudowords.

20.4   WSD: Dictionary and Thesaurus Methods

Supervised algorithms based on sense-labeled corpora are the best-performing algorithms for sense disambiguation. However, such labeled training data is expensive and limited and supervised approaches fail on words not in the training data. Thus this section and the next describe different ways to get indirect supervision from other sources. In this section, we describe methods for using a dictionary or thesaurus as an indirect kind of supervision; the next section describes bootstrapping approaches.

20.4.1   The Lesk Algorithm

Lesk algorithm

Simplified Lesk

By far the most well-studied dictionary-based algorithm for sense disambiguation is the **Lesk algorithm**, really a family of algorithms that choose the sense whose dictionary gloss or definition shares the most words with the target word's neighborhood. Figure 20.3 shows the simplest version of the algorithm, often called the **Simplified Lesk** algorithm (Kilgarriff and Rosenzweig, 2000).

---

function SIMPLIFIED LESK(*word, sentence*) **returns** best sense of *word*

   best-sense ← most frequent sense for *word*
   max-overlap ← 0
   context ← set of words in *sentence*
   for each *sense* **in** senses of *word* **do**
     signature ← set of words in the gloss and examples of *sense*
     overlap ← COMPUTEOVERLAP(*signature, context*)
     if *overlap* > *max-overlap* **then**
        max-overlap ← *overlap*
        best-sense ← *sense*
   end
   return(*best-sense*)

Figure 20.3   The Simplified Lesk algorithm. The COMPUTEOVERLAP function returns the number of words in common between two sets, ignoring function words or other words on a stop list. The original Lesk algorithm defines the *context* in a more complex way. The *Corpus Lesk* algorithm weights each overlapping word *w* by its $-\log P(w)$ and includes labeled training corpus data in the *signature*.

As an example of the Lesk algorithm at work, consider disambiguating the word *bank* in the following context:

(20.10) The **bank** can guarantee deposits will eventually cover future tuition costs because it invests in adjustable-rate mortgage securities.

given the following two WordNet senses:

bank[1]	Gloss:	a financial institution that accepts deposits and channels the money into lending activities
	Examples:	"he cashed a check at the bank", "that bank holds the mortgage on my home"
bank[2]	Gloss:	sloping land (especially the slope beside a body of water)
	Examples:	"they pulled the canoe up on the bank", "he sat on the bank of the river and watched the currents"

Sense **bank**[1] has two non-stopwords overlapping with the context in (20.10): *deposits* and *mortgage*, while sense bank[2] has zero words, so sense **bank**[1] is chosen.

There are many obvious extensions to Simplified Lesk. The original Lesk algorithm (Lesk, 1986) is slightly more indirect. Instead of comparing a target word's signature with the context words, the target signature is compared with the signatures of each of the context words. For example, consider Lesk's example of selecting the appropriate sense of *cone* in the phrase *pine cone* given the following definitions for *pine* and *cone*.

pine 1 kinds of evergreen tree with needle-shaped leaves
      2 waste away through sorrow or illness
cone 1 solid body which narrows to a point
      2 something of this shape whether solid or hollow
      3 fruit of certain evergreen trees

In this example, Lesk's method would select **cone**[3] as the correct sense since two of the words in its entry, *evergreen* and *tree*, overlap with words in the entry for *pine*, whereas neither of the other entries has any overlap with words in the definition of *pine*. In general Simplified Lesk seems to work better than original Lesk.

The primary problem with either the original or simplified approaches, however, is that the dictionary entries for the target words are short and may not provide enough chance of overlap with the context.[2] One remedy is to expand the list of words used in the classifier to include words related to, but not contained in, their individual sense definitions. But the best solution, if any sense-tagged corpus data like SemCor is available, is to add all the words in the labeled corpus sentences for a word sense into the signa-

Corpus Lesk   ture for that sense. This version of the algorithm, the **Corpus Lesk** algorithm, is the best-performing of all the Lesk variants (Kilgarriff and Rosenzweig, 2000; Vasilescu et al., 2004) and is used as a baseline in the SENSEVAL competitions. Instead of just counting up the overlapping words, the **Corpus Lesk** algorithm also applies a weight

Inverse document   to each overlapping word. The weight is the **inverse document frequency** or **IDF**, a
frequency   standard information-retrieval measure introduced in Chapter 23. IDF measures how
IDF   many different "documents" (in this case, glosses and examples) a word occurs in and is thus a way of discounting function words. Since function words like *the*, *of*, etc., occur in many documents, their IDF is very low, while the IDF of content words is high. Corpus Lesk thus uses IDF instead of a stop list.

Formally, the IDF for a word i can be defined as

$$\text{idf}_i = \log\left(\frac{Ndoc}{nd_i}\right) \qquad (20.11)$$

---

[2] Indeed, Lesk (1986) notes that the performance of his system seems to roughly correlate with the length of the dictionary entries.

where *Ndoc* is the total number of "documents" (glosses and examples) and nd_i is the number of these documents containing word i.

Finally, we can combine the Lesk and supervised approaches by adding new Lesk-like bag-of-words features. For example, the glosses and example sentences for the target sense in WordNet could be used to compute the supervised bag-of-words features in addition to the words in the SemCor context sentence for the sense (Yuret, 2004).

20.4.2   Selectional Restrictions and Selectional Preferences

The **selectional restrictions** defined in Chapter 19 were one of the earliest knowledge sources for sense disambiguation. For example, the verb *eat* might have a restriction that its THEME argument be [+FOOD]. Early systems used this idea to rule out senses that violated the selectional restrictions of neighboring words (Katz and Fodor, 1963; Hirst, 1987). Consider the following pair of WSJ examples of the word *dish*:

(20.12) "In our house, everybody has a career and none of them includes washing **dishes**," he says.

(20.13) In her tiny kitchen at home, Ms. Chen works efficiently, stir-frying several simple **dishes**, including braised pig's ears and chicken livers with green peppers.

These correspond to WordNet **dish**[1] (a piece of dishware normally used as a container for holding or serving food), with hypernyms like *artifact*, and **dish**[2] (a particular item of prepared food) with hypernyms like *food*.

The fact that we perceive no ambiguity in these examples can be attributed to the selectional restrictions imposed by *wash* and *stir-fry* on their THEME semantic roles. The restrictions imposed by *wash* (perhaps [+WASHABLE]) conflict with **dish**[2]. The restrictions on *stir-fry* ([+EDIBLE]) conflict with **dish**[1]. In early systems, the predicate strictly selected the correct sense of an ambiguous argument by eliminating the sense that fails to match one of its selectional restrictions. But such hard constraints have a number of problems. The main problem is that selectional restriction violations often occur in well-formed sentences, either because they are negated as in (20.14), or because selectional restrictions are overstated as in (20.15):

(20.14) But it fell apart in 1931, perhaps because people realized you can't **eat** gold for lunch if you're hungry.

(20.15) In his two championship trials, Mr. Kulkarni **ate** glass on an empty stomach, accompanied only by water and tea.

As Hirst (1987) observes, examples like these often result in the elimination of all senses, bringing semantic analysis to a halt. Modern models thus adopt the view of selectional restrictions as preferences, rather than rigid requirements. Although there have been many instantiations of this approach over the years (e.g., Wilks, 1975c, 1975b, 1978), we'll discuss a member of the popular probabilistic or information-theoretic family of approaches: Resnik's (1997) model of **selectional association**.

Selectional preference strength

Resnik first defines the **selectional preference strength** as the general amount of information that a predicate tells us about the semantic class of its arguments. For example, the verb *eat* tells us a lot about the semantic class of its direct objects, since they tend to be edible. The verb *be*, by contrast, tells us less about its direct objects. The selectional preference strength can be defined by the difference in information between two distributions: the distribution of expected semantic classes $P(c)$ (how likely is it that a direct object will fall into class c) and the distribution of expected semantic classes for the particular verb $P(c\ v)$ (how likely is it that the direct object of the specific verb v will fall into semantic class c). The greater the difference between these distributions, the more information the verb is giving us about possible objects. The difference between these two distributions can be quantified by **relative entropy**, or the **Kullback-Leibler divergence** (Kullback and Leibler, 1951). The Kullback-Leibler or KL divergence $D(P\ Q)$ expresses the difference between two probability distributions P and Q, and is discussed further when we discuss word similarity in Section 20.7.3.

Relative entropy
Kullback-Leibler
divergence

$$D(P\ Q) = \sum_x P(x)\log\frac{P(x)}{Q(x)} \tag{20.16}$$

The selectional preference $S_R(v)$ uses the KL divergence to express how much information, in bits, the verb v expresses about the possible semantic class of its argument.

$$
\begin{aligned}
S_R(v) &= D(P(c\ v)\ P(c)) \\
&= \sum_c P(c\ v)\log\frac{P(c\ v)}{P(c)}
\end{aligned}
\tag{20.17}
$$

Selectional association

Resnik then defines the **selectional association** of a particular class and verb as the relative contribution of that class to the general selectional preference of the verb:

$$A_R(v,c) = \frac{1}{S_R(p)}P(c\ v)\log\frac{P(c\ v)}{P(c)} \tag{20.18}$$

The selectional association is thus a probabilistic measure of the strength of association between a predicate and a class dominating the argument to the predicate. Resnik estimates the probabilities for these associations by parsing a corpus, counting all the times each predicate occurs with each argument word, and assuming that each word is a partial observation of all the WordNet concepts containing the word. The following table from Resnik (1996) shows some sample high and low selectional associations for verbs and some WordNet semantic classes of their direct objects.

Verb	Direct Object Semantic Class	Assoc	Direct Object Semantic Class	Assoc
read	WRITING	6.80	ACTIVITY	-.20
write	WRITING	7.26	COMMERCE	0
see	ENTITY	5.79	METHOD	-0.01

Resnik (1998) shows that these selectional associations can be used to perform a limited form of word sense disambiguation. Roughly speaking the algorithm selects as the correct sense for an argument the one that has the highest selectional association between one of its ancestor hypernyms and the predicate.

While we have presented only the Resnik model of selectional preferences, there are other more recent models that use probabilistic methods and relations other than just direct object; see the Historical Notes at the end of the chapter for a brief summary. In general, selectional restriction approaches perform as well as other unsupervised approaches at sense disambiguation, but not as well as Lesk or supervised approaches.

20.5   Minimally Supervised WSD: Bootstrapping

Bootstrapping

Yarowsky algorithm

One sense per collocation

Both the supervised approach and the dictionary-based approach to WSD require large hand-built resources: supervised training sets in one case, large dictionaries in the other. We can instead use **bootstrapping** algorithms, often called **semi-supervised learning** or **minimally supervised learning**, which need only a very small hand-labeled training set. The most widely emulated bootstrapping algorithm for WSD is the **Yarowsky algorithm** (Yarowsky, 1995).

The goal of the Yarowsky algorithm is to learn a classifier for a target word (in a lexical-sample task). The algorithm is given a small seedset Λ_0 of labeled instances of each sense and a much larger unlabeled corpus V_0. The algorithm first trains an initial decision-list classifier on the seedset Λ_0. It then uses this classifier to label the unlabeled corpus V_0. The algorithm then selects the examples in V_0 that it is most confident about, removes them, and adds them to the training set (call it now Λ_1). The algorithm then trains a new decision list classifier (a new set of rules) on Λ_1, and iterates by applying the classifier to the now-smaller unlabeled set V_1, extracting a new training set Λ_2, and so on. With each iteration of this process, the training corpus grows and the untagged corpus shrinks. The process is repeated until some sufficiently low error-rate on the training set is reached or until no further examples from the untagged corpus are above threshold.

The key to any bootstrapping approach lies in its ability to create a larger training set from a small set of seeds. This requires an accurate initial set of seeds and a good confidence metric for picking good new examples to add to the training set. The confidence metric used by Yarowsky (1995) is the measure described earlier in Section 20.2.2, the log-likelihood ratio of the decision list rule that classified the example.

One way to generate the initial seeds is to hand-label a small set of examples (Hearst, 1991). Instead of hand-labeling, we could also use a heuristic to automatically select accurate seeds. Yarowsky (1995) used the **one sense per collocation** heuristic, which relies on the intuition that certain words or phrases strongly associated with the target senses tend not to occur with the other sense. Yarowsky defines his seedset by choosing a single collocation for each sense. As an illustration of this technique, consider generating seed sentences for the fish and musical senses of *bass*. Without too much thought, we might come up with *fish* as a reasonable indicator of **bass**[1] and *play* as a reasonable indicator of **bass**[2]. Figure 20.5 shows a partial result of such a search for the strings "fish" and "play" in a corpus of *bass* examples drawn from the WSJ.

We can also suggest collocates automatically, for example, extracting words from machine-readable dictionary entries and selecting seeds using collocational statistics such as those described in Section 20.7 (Yarowsky, 1995).

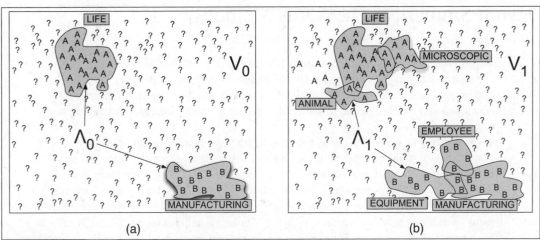

Figure 20.4 The Yarowsky algorithm disambiguating "plant" at two stages; "?" indicates an unlabeled observation, A and B are observations labeled as SENSE-A or SENSE-B. The initial stage (a) shows only seed sentences Λ_0 labeled by collocates ("life" and "manufacturing"). An intermediate stage is shown in (b) where more collocates have been discovered ("equipment", "microscopic", etc.) and more instances in V_0 have been moved into Λ_1, leaving a smaller unlabeled set V_1. Figure adapted from Yarowsky (1995).

We need more good teachers – right now, there are only a half a dozen who can **play** the free **bass** with ease.

An electric guitar and **bass play**er stand off to one side, not really part of the scene, just as a sort of nod to gringo expectations perhaps.

When the New Jersey Jazz Society, in a fund-raiser for the American Jazz Hall of Fame, honors this historic night next Saturday, Harry Goodman, Mr. Goodman's brother and **bass play**er at the original concert, will be in the audience with other family members.

The researchers said the worms spend part of their life cycle in such **fish** as Pacific salmon and striped **bass** and Pacific rockfish or snapper.

And it all started when **fish**ermen decided the striped **bass** in Lake Mead were too skinny.

Though still a far cry from the lake's record 52-pound **bass** of a decade ago, "you could fillet these **fish** again, and that made people very, very happy," Mr. Paulson says.

Figure 20.5 Samples of *bass* sentences extracted from the WSJ by using the simple correlates *play* and *fish*.

One sense per discourse

The original Yarowsky algorithm also makes use of a second heuristic, called **one sense per discourse**, based on the work of Gale et al. (1992b), who noticed that a particular word appearing multiple times in a text or discourse often appeared with the same sense. Yarowsky (1995), for example, showed in a corpus of 37,232 examples that every time the word *bass* occurred more than once in a discourse, it occurred in only the *fish* or only the *music* coarse-grained sense throughout the discourse. The validity of this heuristic depends on the granularity of the sense inventory and is not valid in every discourse situation; it seems to be true mostly for coarse-grained senses and particularly for cases of homonymy rather than polysemy (Krovetz, 1998). Nonetheless, it is still useful in a number of sense disambiguation situations.

20.6   Word Similarity: Thesaurus Methods

We turn now to the computation of various semantic relations that hold between words. We saw in Chapter 19 that such relations include synonymy, antonymy, hyponymy, hypernymy, and meronymy. Of these, the one that has been most computationally developed and has the greatest number of applications is the idea of word **synonymy** and **similarity**.

Synonymy is a binary relation between words; two words are either synonyms or not. For most computational purposes, we use instead a looser metric of **word similarity** or **semantic distance**. Two words are more similar if they share more features of meaning or are near-synonyms. Two words are less similar or have greater semantic distance, if they have fewer common meaning elements. Although we have described them as relations between words, synonymy, similarity, and distance are actually relations between word *senses*. For example, of the two senses of *bank*, we might say that the financial sense is similar to one of the senses of *fund* and the riparian sense is more similar to one of the senses of *slope*. In the next few sections of this chapter, we will compute these relations over both words and senses.

Word similarity
Semantic distance

The ability to compute word similarity is a useful part of many language understanding applications. In **information retrieval** or **question answering**, we might want to retrieve documents whose words have meanings similar to the query words. In **summarization**, **generation**, and **machine translation**, we need to know whether two words are similar to know if we can substitute one for the other in particular contexts. In **language modeling**, we can use semantic similarity to cluster words for class-based models. One interesting class of applications for word similarity is automatic grading of student responses. For example, algorithms for **automatic essay grading** use word similarity to determine if an essay is similar in meaning to a correct answer. We can also use word similarity as part of an algorithm to *take* an exam, such as a multiple-choice vocabulary test. Automatically taking exams is useful in test designs in order to see how easy or hard a particular multiple-choice question or exam is.

Two classes of algorithms can be used to measure word similarity. This section focuses on **thesaurus-based** algorithms, in which we measure the distance between two senses in an on-line thesaurus like WordNet or MeSH. The next section focuses on **distributional** algorithms, in which we estimate word similarity by finding words that have similar distributions in a corpus.

The thesaurus-based algorithms use the structure of the thesaurus to define word similarity. In principle, we could measure similarity by using any information available in a thesaurus (meronymy, glosses, etc.). In practice, however, thesaurus-based word similarity algorithms generally use only the hypernym/hyponym (*is-a* or subsumption) hierarchy. In WordNet, verbs and nouns are in separate hypernym hierarchies, so a thesaurus-based algorithm for WordNet can thus compute only noun-noun similarity, or verb-verb similarity; we can't compare nouns to verbs or do anything with adjectives or other parts of speech.

Word relatedness

Resnik (1995) and Budanitsky and Hirst (2001) draw the important distinction between **word similarity** and **word relatedness**. Two words are similar if they are near-synonyms or roughly substitutable in context. Word relatedness characterizes a larger set of potential relationships between words; antonyms, for example, have high relatedness but low similarity. The words *car* and *gasoline* are closely related but not similar, while *car* and *bicycle* are similar. Word similarity is thus a subcase of word relatedness. In general, the five algorithms we describe in this section do not attempt to distinguish between similarity and semantic relatedness; for convenience, we will call them *similarity* measures, although some would be more appropriately described as relatedness measures; we return to this question in Section 20.8.

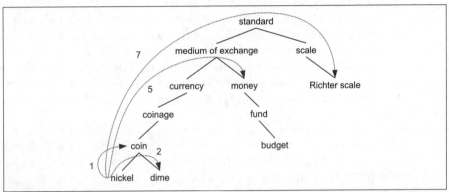

Figure 20.6   A fragment of the WordNet hypernym hierarchy, showing path lengths from *nickel* to *coin* (1), *dime* (2), *money* (5), and *Richter scale* (7).

The oldest and simplest thesaurus-based algorithms are based on the intuition that the shorter the **path** between two words or senses in the graph defined by the thesaurus hierarchy, the more similar they are. Thus, a word/sense is quite similar to its parents or its siblings and less similar to words that are far away in the network. We can make this notion operational by measuring the number of edges between the two concept nodes in the thesaurus graph. Figure 20.6 shows an intuition; the concept *dime* is most similar to *nickel* and *coin*, less similar to *money*, and even less similar to *Richter scale*. Formally, we specify path length as follows:

pathlen(c_1, c_2) = the number of edges in the shortest path in the thesaurus graph between the sense nodes c_1 and c_2

Path-based similarity can be defined as just the path length, often with a log transform (Leacock and Chodorow, 1998), resulting in the following common definition of **path-length based similarity**:

Path-length-based similarity

$$\mathrm{sim}_{\mathrm{path}}(c_1, c_2) = -\log \mathrm{pathlen}(c_1, c_2) \qquad (20.19)$$

For most applications, we don't have sense-tagged data, and thus we need our algorithm to give us the similarity between words rather than between senses or concepts. For any of the thesaurus-based algorithms, following Resnik (1995), we can approximate the correct similarity (which would require sense disambiguation) by just using the pair of senses for the two words that results in maximum sense similarity. Thus, based on sense similarity, we can define **word similarity** as follows:

Word similarity

$$\mathrm{wordsim}(w_1, w_2) = \max_{\substack{c_1 \in \mathrm{senses}(w_1) \\ c_2 \in \mathrm{senses}(w_2)}} \mathrm{sim}(c_1, c_2) \qquad (20.20)$$

The basic path-length algorithm makes the implicit assumption that each link in the network represents a uniform distance. In practice, this assumption is not appropriate. Some links (e.g., those that are deep in the WordNet hierarchy) often seem to represent an intuitively narrow distance, while other links (e.g., higher up in the WordNet hierarchy) represent an intuitively wider distance. For example, in Fig. 20.6, the distance from *nickel* to *money* (5) seems intuitively much shorter than the distance from *nickel* to an abstract word *standard*; the link between *medium of exchange* and *standard* seems wider than that between, say, *coin* and *coinage*.

It is possible to refine path-based algorithms with normalizations based on depth in the hierarchy (Wu and Palmer, 1994), but in general we'd like an approach that lets us independently represent the distance associated with each edge.

Information-content A second class of thesaurus-based similarity algorithms attempts to offer just such a fine-grained metric. These **information-content word-similarity** algorithms still rely on the structure of the thesaurus but also add probabilistic information derived from a corpus.

Using similar notions to those we introduced earlier to define soft selectional restrictions, let's first define $P(c)$, following Resnik (1995), as the probability that a randomly selected word in a corpus is an instance of concept c (i.e., a separate random variable, ranging over words, associated with each concept). This implies that $P(root) = 1$ since any word is subsumed by the root concept. Intuitively, the lower a concept in the hierarchy, the lower its probability. We train these probabilities by counting in a corpus; each word in the corpus counts as an occurrence of each concept that contains it. For example, in Fig. 20.6 above, an occurrence of the word *dime* would count toward the frequency of *coin*, *currency*, *standard*, etc. More formally, Resnik computes $P(c)$ as follows:

$$P(c) = \frac{\sum_{w \in \text{words}(c)} count(w)}{N} \tag{20.21}$$

where words(c) is the set of words subsumed by concept c, and N is the total number of words in the corpus that are also present in the thesaurus.

Figure 20.7, from Lin (1998b), shows a fragment of the WordNet concept hierarchy augmented with the probabilities $P(c)$.

We now need two additional definitions. First, following basic information theory, we define the information content (IC) of a concept c as

$$IC(c) = -\log P(c) \tag{20.22}$$

Lowest common subsumer Second, we define the **lowest common subsumer** or **LCS** of two concepts:

LCS

LCS(c_1, c_2) = the lowest common subsumer, that is, the lowest node in the hierarchy that subsumes (is a hypernym of) both c_1 and c_2

There are now a number of ways to use the information content of a node in a word similarity metric. The simplest way was first proposed by Resnik (1995). We think of the similarity between two words as related to their common information; the more two words have in common, the more similar they are. Resnik proposes to estimate the common amount of information by the **information content of the lowest common subsumer of the two nodes**. More formally, the **Resnik similarity** measure is

Resnik similarity

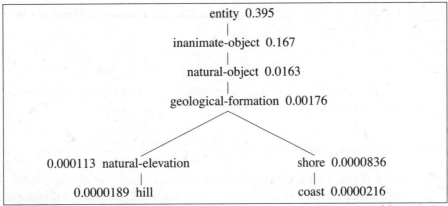

Figure 20.7   A fragment of the WordNet hierarchy, showing the probability $P(c)$ attached to each content, adapted from a figure from Lin (1998b).

$$\text{sim}_{\text{resnik}}(c_1, c_2) = -\log P(\text{LCS}(c_1, c_2)) \qquad (20.23)$$

Lin (1998b) extended the Resnik intuition by pointing out that a similarity metric between objects A and B needs to do more than measure the amount of information in common between A and B. For example, he additionally pointed out that the more **differences** between A and B, the less similar they are. In summary:

- **Commonality:** the more information A and B have in common, the more similar they are.
- **Difference:** the more differences between the information in A and B, the less similar they are.

Lin measures the commonality between A and B as the information content of the proposition that states the commonality between A and B:

$$\text{IC}(\text{common}(A,B)) \qquad (20.24)$$

He measures the difference between A and B as

$$\text{IC}(\text{description}(A,B)) - \text{IC}(\text{common}(A,B)) \qquad (20.25)$$

where description(A,B) describes A and B. Given a few additional assumptions about similarity, Lin proves the following theorem:

> Similarity Theorem: The similarity between A and B is measured by the ratio between the amount of information needed to state the commonality of A and B and the information needed to fully describe what A and B are.

$$\text{sim}_{\text{Lin}}(A,B) = \frac{\text{common}(A,B)}{\text{description}(A,B)} \qquad (20.26)$$

Applying this idea to the thesaurus domain, Lin shows (in a slight modification of Resnik's assumption) that the information in common between two concepts is twice the information in the lowest common subsumer $\text{LCS}(c_1, c_2)$. Adding in the above

Lin similarity

definitions of the information content of thesaurus concepts, the final **Lin similarity** function is

$$\text{sim}_{\text{Lin}}(c_1, c_2) = \frac{2 \ \log P(LCS(c_1, c_2))}{\log P(c_1) + \log P(c_2)} \tag{20.27}$$

For example, using sim_{Lin}, Lin (1998b) shows that the similarity between the concepts of *hill* and *coast* from Fig. 20.7 is

$$\text{sim}_{\text{Lin}}(\text{hill}, \text{coast}) = \frac{2 \ \log P(\text{geological-formation})}{\log P(\text{hill}) + \log P(\text{coast})} = 0.59 \tag{20.28}$$

Jiang-Conrath distance

A similar formula, **Jiang-Conrath distance** (Jiang and Conrath, 1997), although derived in a completely different way from Lin and expressed as a distance rather than similarity function, has been shown to work as well as or better than all the other thesaurus-based methods:

$$\text{dist}_{\text{JC}}(c_1, c_2) = 2 \ \log P(LCS(c_1, c_2)) - (\log P(c_1) + \log P(c_2)) \tag{20.29}$$

We can transform dist_{JC} into a similarity by taking the reciprocal.

Finally, we describe a **dictionary-based** method, an extension of the Lesk algorithm for word sense disambiguation described in Section 20.4.1. We call this a dictionary rather than a thesaurus method because it makes use of glosses, which are, in general, a property of dictionaries rather than thesauruses (although WordNet does have glosses). Like the Lesk algorithm, the intuition of this **extended gloss overlap**, or **Extended Lesk** measure (Banerjee and Pedersen, 2003) is that two concepts/senses in a thesaurus are similar if their glosses contain overlapping words. We'll begin by sketching an overlap function for two glosses. Consider these two concepts, with their glosses:

Extended gloss overlap
Extended Lesk

- *drawing paper:* paper that is specially prepared for use in drafting
- *decal:* the art of transferring designs from specially prepared paper to a wood or glass or metal surface.

For each *n*-word phrase that occurs in both glosses, Extended Lesk adds in a score of n^2 (the relation is non-linear because of the Zipfian relationship between lengths of phrases and their corpus frequencies; longer overlaps are rare, so they should be weighted more heavily). Here, the overlapping phrases are *paper* and *specially prepared*, for a total similarity score of $1^2 + 2^2 = 5$.

Given such an overlap function, when comparing two concepts (synsets), Extended Lesk not only looks for overlap between their glosses but also between the glosses of the senses that are hypernyms, hyponyms, meronyms, and other relations of the two concepts. For example, if we just considered hyponyms and defined gloss(hypo(A)) as the concatenation of all the glosses of all the hyponym senses of A, the total relatedness between two concepts A and B might be

$$\text{similarity}(A,B) = \text{overlap}(\text{gloss}(A), \text{gloss}(B))$$
$$+\text{overlap}(\text{gloss}(\text{hypo}(A)), \text{gloss}(\text{hypo}(B)))$$
$$+\text{overlap}(\text{gloss}(A), \text{gloss}(\text{hypo}(B)))$$
$$+\text{overlap}(\text{gloss}(\text{hypo}(A)), \text{gloss}(B))$$

Let RELS be the set of possible WordNet relations whose glosses we compare; assuming a basic overlap measure as sketched above, we can then define the **Extended Lesk** overlap measure as

$$\text{sim}_{\text{eLesk}}(c_1, c_2) = \sum_{r,q \in \text{RELS}} \text{overlap}(\text{gloss}(r(c_1)), \text{gloss}(q(c_2))) \qquad (20.30)$$

$$\text{sim}_{\text{path}}(c_1, c_2) = -\log \text{pathlen}(c_1, c_2)$$

$$\text{sim}_{\text{Resnik}}(c_1, c_2) = -\log P(\text{LCS}(c_1, c_2))$$

$$\text{sim}_{\text{Lin}}(c_1, c_2) = \frac{2 \ \log P(LCS(c_1, c_2))}{\log P(c_1) + \log P(c_2)}$$

$$\text{sim}_{\text{jc}}(c_1, c_2) = \frac{1}{2 \ \log P(\text{LCS}(c_1, c_2)) - (\log P(c_1) + \log P(c_2))}$$

$$\text{sim}_{\text{eLesk}}(c_1, c_2) = \sum_{r,q \in \text{RELS}} \text{overlap}(\text{gloss}(r(c_1)), \text{gloss}(q(c_2)))$$

Figure 20.8   Five thesaurus-based (and dictionary-based) similarity measures.

Figure 20.8 summarizes the five similarity measures we have described in this section. The publicly available `Wordnet::Similarity` package implementing all these and other thesaurus-based word similarity measures is described in Pedersen et al. (2004).

Evaluating Thesaurus-Based Similarity: Which of these similarity measures is best? Word similarity measures have been evaluated in two ways. One intrinsic method is to compute the correlation coefficient between word similarity scores from an algorithm and word similarity ratings assigned by humans; such human ratings have been obtained for 65 word pairs by Rubenstein and Goodenough (1965) and for 30 word pairs by Miller and Charles (1991). Another, more extrinsic, evaluation method is to embed the similarity measure in some end-application like detection of **malapropisms** (real-word spelling errors) (Budanitsky and Hirst, 2006; Hirst and Budanitsky, 2005), or other NLP applications, like word sense disambiguation (Patwardhan et al., 2003; McCarthy et al., 2004), and evaluate its impact on end-to-end performance. All of these evaluations suggest that all the above measures perform relatively well and that of these, Jiang-Conrath similarity and Extended Lesk similarity are two of the best approaches, depending on the application.

20.7   Word Similarity: Distributional Methods

The previous section showed how to compute similarity between any two senses in a thesaurus and, by extension, between any two words in the thesaurus hierarchy. But of course we don't have such thesauruses for every language. Even for languages for which we do have such resources, thesaurus-based methods have a number of limitations. The obvious limitation is that thesauruses often lack words, especially new or domain-specific words. In addition, thesaurus-based methods only work if rich hyponymy knowledge is present in the thesaurus. While we have this for nouns, hyponym information for verbs tends to be much sparser and doesn't exist at all for adjectives and adverbs. Finally, it is more difficult with thesaurus-based methods to compare words in different hierarchies, such as nouns with verbs.

For these reasons, methods that can automatically extract synonyms and other word relations from corpora have been developed. In this section we introduce such **distributional** methods, which can be applied directly to supply a word-relatedness measure for NLP tasks. Distributional methods can also be used for **automatic thesaurus generation** for automatically populating or augmenting on-line thesauruses like WordNet with new synonyms and, as we described in Section 20.8, with other relations like hyponymy and meronymy.

The intuition of distributional methods is that the meaning of a word is related to the distribution of words around it; in the famous dictum of Firth (1957), "You shall know a word by the company it keeps!". Consider the following example, modified by Lin (1998a) from (Nida, 1975, page 167):

(20.31)   A bottle of *tezgüino* is on the table.
   Everybody likes *tezgüino*.
   Tezgüino makes you drunk.
   We make *tezgüino* out of corn.

The contexts in which *tezgüino* occurs suggest that it might be some kind of fermented alcoholic drink made from corn. The distributional method tries to capture this intuition by representing features of the context of *tezgüino* that might overlap with features of similar words like *beer*, *liquor*, *tequila*, and so on. For example such features might be occurs before *drunk* or occurs after *bottle* or is the direct object of *likes*.

We can then represent a word w as a feature vector just as we saw with the bag-of-words features in Section 20.2. For example, suppose we had one binary feature f_i representing each of the N words in the lexicon v_i. The feature means w occurs in the neighborhood of word v_i, and hence takes the value 1 if w and v_i occur in some context window, and 0 otherwise. We could represent the meaning of word w as the feature vector

$$\vec{w} = (f_1, f_2, f_3, \quad , f_N)$$

If w=*tezgüino*, v_1=*bottle*, v_2=*drunk*, and v_3=*matrix*, the co-occurrence vector for w from the corpus above would be

$$\vec{w} = (1, 1, 0, \quad)$$

Given two words represented by such sparse feature vectors, we can apply a vector distance measure and say that the words are similar if the two vectors are close by this measure. Figure 20.9 shows an intuition about vector similarity for the four words *apricot*, *pineapple*, *digital*, and *information*. We would like a metric that based on the meanings of these four words shows *apricot* and *pineapple* to be similar, *digital* and *information*, to be similar, and the other four pairings to produce low similarity. For each word, Fig. 20.9 shows a short piece (eight dimensions) of the (binary) word co-occurrence vectors, computed from words that occur within a two-line context in the Brown corpus. Readers should convince themselves that the vectors for *apricot* and *pineapple* are indeed more similar than those of, say, *apricot* and *information*. For pedagogical purposes, we've shown the context words that are particularly good at discrimination. Note that since vocabularies are quite large (10,000–100,000 words) and most words don't occur near each other in any corpus, real vectors are quite sparse.

	arts	boil	data	function	large	sugar	summarized	water
apricot	0	1	0	0	1	1	0	1
pineapple	0	1	0	0	1	1	0	1
digital	0	0	1	1	1	0	1	0
information	0	0	1	1	1	0	1	0

Figure 20.9 Co-occurrence vectors for four words, computed from the Brown corpus, showing only eight of the (binary) dimensions (hand-picked for pedagogical purposes to show discrimination). Note that *large* occurs in all the contexts and *arts* occurs in none; a real vector would be extremely sparse.

Now that we have some intuitions, let's move on to examine the details of these measures. Specifying a distributional similarity measure requires that we specify three parameters: (1) how the co-occurrence terms are defined (i.e., what counts as a neighbor), (2) how these terms are weighted (binary? frequency? mutual information?), and (3) what vector distance metric we use (cosine? Euclidean distance?). Let's look at each of these requirements in the next three subsections.

20.7.1   Defining a Word's Co-Occurrence Vectors

In our example feature vector, we used the feature <u>w occurs in the neighborhood of word v_j</u>. That is, for a vocabulary size N, each word w had N features, specifying whether vocabulary element v_j occurred in the neighborhood. Neighborhoods range from a small window of words (as few as one or two words on either side) to very large windows of   500 words. In a minimal window, for example, we might have two features for each word v_j in the vocabulary, <u>word v_k occurs immediately before word w</u> and <u>word v_k occurs immediately after word w</u>.

To keep these contexts efficient, we often ignore frequent words that tend not to be very discriminative, for example, function words such as *a, am, the, of, 1, 2*.

Even with the removal of these stopwords, these co-occurrence vectors tend to be very large when used on very large corpora. Instead of using every word in the neighborhood, we could as Hindle (1990) suggested choose words that occur in some sort of **grammatical relation** or **dependency** to the target words. Hindle suggested that nouns bearing the same grammatical relation to the same verb might be similar.

For example, the words *tea*, *water*, and *beer* are all frequent direct objects of the verb *drink*. The words *senate*, *congress*, *panel*, and *legislature* all tend to be subjects of the verbs *consider*, *vote*, and *approve*.

Hindle's intuition follows from the early work of Harris (1968), who suggested the following:

> The meaning of entities, and the meaning of grammatical relations among them, is related to the restriction of combinations of these entities relative to other entities.

There have been a wide variety of realizations of Hindle's idea since then. In general, in these methods each sentence in a large corpus is parsed and a dependency parse is extracted. We saw in Chapter 12 lists of grammatical relations produced by dependency parsers, including noun-verb relations like subject, object, indirect object, and noun-noun relations like genitive, ncomp, and so on. A sentence like the following would result in the set of dependencies shown here.

(20.32) I discovered dried tangerines:

discover (subject I)   I (subj-of discover)
tangerine (obj-of discover)   tangerine (adj-mod dried)
dried (adj-mod-of tangerine)

Since each word can be in a variety of different dependency relations with other words, we'll need to augment the feature space. Each feature is now a pairing of a word and a relation, so instead of a vector of N features, we have a vector of $N \times R$ features, where R is the number of possible relations. Figure 20.10 shows a schematic example of such a vector, taken from Lin (1998a), for the word *cell*. As the value of each attribute we have shown the frequency of the feature co-occurring with *cell*; the next section discusses the use of what values and weights to use for each attribute.

	subj-of, absorb	*subj-of*, adapt	*subj-of*, behave	...	*pobj-of*, inside	*pobj-of*, into	...	*nmod-of*, abnormality	*nmod-of*, anemia	*nmod-of*, architecture	...	*obj-of*, attack	*obj-of*, call	*obj-of*, come from	*obj-of*, decorate	...	*nmod*, bacteria	*nmod*, body	*nmod*, bone marrow
cell	1	1	1		16	30		3	8	1		6	11	3	2		3	2	2

Figure 20.10 Co-occurrence vector for the word *cell*, from Lin (1998a), showing grammatical function (dependency) features. Values for each attribute are frequency counts from a 64-million word corpus, parsed by an early version of MINIPAR.

Since full parsing is expensive, it is common to use a chunker or shallow parser of the type defined in Section 13.5, with the goal of extracting only a smaller set of relations like subject, direct object, and prepositional object of a particular preposition (Curran, 2003).

20.7.2   Measuring Association with Context

Association

Now that we have a definition for the features or dimensions of a word's context vector, we are ready to discuss the values that should be associated with those features. These values are typically thought of as **weights** or measures of **association** between each target word w and a given feature f. In the example in Fig. 20.9, our association measure was a binary value for each feature, 1 if the relevant word had occurred in the context, 0 if not. In the example in Fig. 20.10, we used a richer association measure, the relative frequency with which the particular context feature had co-occurred with the target word.

Frequency or probability is certainly a better measure of association than just a binary value; features that occur often with a target word are more likely to be good indicators of the word's meaning. Let's define some terminology for implementing a probabilistic measure of association. For a target word w, each element of its co-occurrence vector is a feature f, consisting of a relation r and a related word w'; we can say $f = (r, w')$. For example, one of the features of the word *cell* in Fig. 20.10 is $f = (r, w') =$ (obj-of, *attack*). The probability of a feature f given a target word w is $P(f\ w)$, for which the maximum likelihood estimate is

$$P(f\ w) = \frac{\text{count}(f, w)}{\text{count}(w)} \tag{20.33}$$

Similarly, the maximum likelihood estimate for the joint probability $P(f, w)$ is

$$P(f, w) = \frac{\text{count}(f, w)}{\sum_{w'} \text{count}(w')} \tag{20.34}$$

$P(w)$ and $P(f)$ are computed similarly.

Thus, if we were to define simple probability as a measure of association, it would look as follows:

$$\text{assoc}_{\text{prob}}(w, f) = P(f\ w) \tag{20.35}$$

It turns out, however, that simple probability doesn't work as well as more sophisticated association schemes for word similarity.

Why isn't frequency or probability a good measure of association between a word and a context feature? Intuitively, if we want to know what kinds of contexts are shared by *apricot* and *pineapple* but not by *digital* and *information*, we're not going to get good discrimination from words like *the*, *it*, or *they*, which occur frequently with all sorts of words and aren't informative about any particular word. We'd like context words that are particularly informative about the target word. We, therefore, need a weighting or measure of association that asks how much more often than chance the feature co-occurs with the target word. As Curran (2003) points out, such a weighting is what we also want for finding good collocations, and so the measures of association used for weighting context words for semantic similarity are exactly the same measure used for finding a word's collocations.

One of the most important measures of association was first proposed by Church and Hanks (1989, 1990) and is based on the notion of mutual information. The **mutual**

Mutual information

information between two random variables X and Y is

$$I(X,Y) = \sum_x \sum_y P(x,y) \log_2 \frac{P(x,y)}{P(x)P(y)} \tag{20.36}$$

Pointwise mutual information

The **pointwise mutual information** (Fano, 1961)[3] is a measure of how often two events x and y occur, compared with what we would expect if they were independent:

$$I(x,y) = \log_2 \frac{P(x,y)}{P(x)P(y)} \tag{20.37}$$

We can apply this intuition to co-occurrence vectors by defining the pointwise mutual information association between a target word w and a feature f as

$$\text{assoc}_{\text{PMI}}(w,f) = \log_2 \frac{P(w,f)}{P(w)P(f)} \tag{20.38}$$

The intuition of the PMI measure is that the numerator tells us how often we observed the two words together (assuming we compute probability by using MLE as above). The denominator tells us how often we would **expect** the two words to co-occur assuming they each occurred independently, so their probabilities could just be multiplied. Thus, the ratio gives us an estimate of how much more the target and feature co-occur than we expect by chance.

Since f is itself composed of two variables r and w', there is a slight variant on this model, from Lin (1998a), that breaks down the expected value for $P(f)$ slightly differently; we'll call it the **Lin association measure** $\text{assoc}_{\text{Lin}}$, not to be confused with the WordNet measure sim_{Lin} that we discussed in the previous section:

Lin association measure

$$\text{assoc}_{\text{Lin}}(w,f) = \log_2 \frac{P(w,f)}{P(w)P(r\ w)P(w'\ w)} \tag{20.39}$$

For both $\text{assoc}_{\text{PMI}}$ and $\text{assoc}_{\text{Lin}}$, we generally use the feature f for a word w only if the assoc value is positive since negative PMI values (which imply things are co-occurring *less often* than we would expect by chance) tend to be unreliable unless the training corpora are enormous (Dagan et al., 1993; Lin, 1998a). In addition, when we are using the assoc-weighted features to compare two target words, we use only features that co-occur with both target words.

Figure 20.11 from Hindle (1990) shows the difference between raw frequency counts and PMI-style association for some direct objects of the verb *drink*.

One of the most successful association measures for word similarity attempts to capture the same intuition as mutual information, but uses the **t-test** statistic to measure how much more frequent the association is than chance. This measure was proposed for collocation detection by Manning and Schütze (1999, Chapter 5) and then applied to word similarity by Curran and Moens (2002) and Curran (2003).

T-test

The t-test statistic computes the difference between observed and expected means, normalized by the variance. The higher the value of t, the greater the likelihood that we can reject the null hypothesis that the observed and expected means are the same.

---

[3] Fano actually used the phrase *mutual information* to refer to what we now call *pointwise mutual information* and the phrase *expectation of the mutual information* for what we now call *mutual information*; the term *mutual information* is still often used to mean *pointwise mutual information*.

Object	Count	PMI Assoc	Object	Count	PMI Assoc
bunch beer	2	12.34	wine	2	9.34
tea	2	11.75	water	7	7.65
Pepsi	2	11.75	anything	3	5.15
champagne	4	11.75	much	3	5.15
liquid	2	10.53	it	3	1.25
beer	5	10.20	<SOME AMOUNT>	2	1.22

Figure 20.11   Objects of the verb *drink*, sorted by PMI, from Hindle (1990).

$$t = \frac{\bar{x} - \mu}{\sqrt{\frac{s^2}{N}}} \tag{20.40}$$

When applied to association between words, the null hypothesis is that the two words are independent, and hence $P(f,w) = P(f)P(w)$ correctly models the relationship between the two words. We want to know how different the actual MLE probability $P(f,w)$ is from this null hypothesis value, normalized by the variance. Note the similarity to the comparison with the product model in the PMI measure above. The variance s^2 can be approximated by the expected probability $P(f)P(w)$ (see Manning and Schütze (1999)). Ignoring N (since it is constant), the resulting t-test association measure from Curran (2003) is thus

$$\text{assoc}_{\text{t-test}}(w,f) = \frac{P(w,f) - P(w)P(f)}{\sqrt{P(f)P(w)}} \tag{20.41}$$

See the Historical Notes section for a summary of various other weighting factors that have been tested on word similarity.

20.7.3   Defining Similarity Between Two Vectors

From the previous sections we can now compute a co-occurrence vector for a target word, with each co-occurrence feature weighted by an association measure, giving us a distributional definition of the meaning of a target word.

To define similarity between two target words v and w, we need a measure for taking two such vectors and giving a measure of vector similarity. Perhaps the simplest two measures of vector distance are the Manhattan and Euclidean distance. Figure 20.12 shows a graphical intuition for Euclidean and Manhattan distance between *Manhattan distance* two 2-dimensional vectors $\vec{a}$ and $\vec{b}$. The **Manhattan distance**, also known as **Leven-** *Levenshtein distance* **shtein distance** or **L1 norm**, is *L1 norm*

$$\text{distance}_{\text{manhattan}}(\vec{x}, \vec{y}) = \sum_{i=1}^{N} x_i - y_i \tag{20.42}$$

L2 norm   The **Euclidean distance**, also called the **L2 norm**, was introduced in Chapter 9.

$$\text{distance}_{\text{euclidean}}(\vec{x}, \vec{y}) = \sqrt{\sum_{i=1}^{N} (x_i - y_i)^2} \tag{20.43}$$

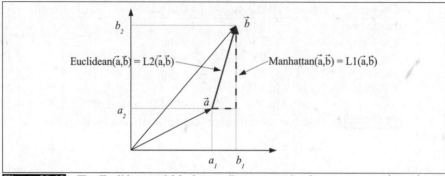

Figure 20.12   The Euclidean and Manhattan distance metrics for vectors $a = (a_1, a_2)$, and $b = (b_1, b_2)$, just to give the reader a graphical intuition about the idea of distance between vectors; these particular metrics are generally not used for word similarity. See Chapter 9 for more on distance metrics.

Although the Euclidean and Manhattan distance metrics provide a nice geometric intuition for vector similarity and distance, these measures are rarely used for word similarity. This is because both measures turn out to be especially sensitive to extreme values. Instead of these simple distance metrics, word similarity is based on closely related metrics from **information retrieval** and from **information theory**. The information retrieval methods seem to work better for word similarity, so we define a number of these in this section.

Let's begin with the intuition for a similarity metric in Fig. 20.9, in which the similarity between two binary vectors was just the number of features the two words had in common. If we assume a feature vector is a **binary vector**, we can define such a similarity metric by using the **dot product** or **inner product** operator from linear algebra, as follows:

Binary vector
Dot product
Inner product

$$\text{sim}_{\text{dot-product}}(\vec{v}, \vec{w}) = \vec{v} \cdot \vec{w} = \sum_{i=1}^{N} v_i \times w_i \tag{20.44}$$

In most cases, though, as we saw in the previous section, the values of our vector are not binary. Let's assume for the rest of this section that the entries in the co-occurrence vector are the **association** values between the target words and each of the features. In other words, let's define the vector for a target word $\vec{w}$ with N features $f_1..f_N$ as

$$\vec{w} = (\text{assoc}(w, f_1), \text{assoc}(w, f_2), \text{assoc}(w, f_3), \ldots, \text{assoc}(w, f_N)) \tag{20.45}$$

Now, to get the dot-product similarity between weighted values, we can apply $\text{sim}_{\text{dot-product}}$ to vectors with values defined as associations. This raw dot-product, however, has a problem as a similarity metric: it favors **long** vectors. The **vector length** is defined as

Vector length

$$|\vec{v}| = \sqrt{\sum_{i=1}^{N} v_i^2} \tag{20.46}$$

A vector can be longer because it has more non-zero values or because each dimension has a higher value. Both of these facts will increase the dot product. It turns out that both of these can occur as a by-product of word frequency. A vector from a frequent word will have more non-zero co-occurrence association values and will probably have higher values in each (even if we use association weights that control somewhat for frequency). The raw dot product thus favors frequent words.

We need to modify the dot product to normalize for the vector length. The simplest way is just to divide the dot product by the lengths of each of the two vectors. This **normalized dot product** turns out to be the same as the cosine of the angle between the two vectors. The **cosine** or normalized dot product similarity metric is thus

Normalized dot
product
Cosine

$$\text{sim}_{\text{cosine}}(\vec{v}, \vec{w}) = \frac{\vec{v} \; \vec{w}}{\vec{v} \; \vec{w}} = \frac{\sum_{i=1}^{N} v_i \; w_i}{\sqrt{\sum_{i=1}^{N} v_i^2} \sqrt{\sum_{i=1}^{N} w_i^2}} \qquad (20.47)$$

Because we have transformed the vectors to unit length, the cosine metric, unlike Euclidean or Manhattan distance, is no longer sensitive to long vectors from high-frequency words. The cosine value ranges from 1 for vectors pointing in the same direction, through 0 for vectors that are orthogonal (share no common terms), to -1 for vectors pointing in opposite directions, although in practice values tend to be positive.

Let's discuss two more similarity measures derived from information retrieval. The **Jaccard** (Jaccard, 1908, 1912) (also called **Tanimoto** or **min/max** (Dagan, 2000)) measure was originally designed for binary vectors. It was extended by Grefenstette (1994) to vectors of weighted associations as follows:

Jaccard
Tanimoto
Min/max

$$\text{sim}_{\text{Jaccard}}(\vec{v}, \vec{w}) = \frac{\sum_{i=1}^{N} \min(v_i, w_i)}{\sum_{i=1}^{N} \max(v_i, w_i)} \qquad (20.48)$$

The numerator of the Grefenstette/Jaccard function uses the min function, essentially computing the (weighted) number of overlapping features (since if either vector has a zero association value for an attribute, the result will be zero). The denominator can be viewed as a normalizing factor.

A like measure, the **Dice** measure, was similarly extended from binary vectors to vectors of weighted associations; one extension from Curran (2003) uses the Jaccard numerator but uses as the denominator normalization factor the total weighted value of non-zero entries in the two vectors.

Dice

$$\text{sim}_{\text{Dice}}(\vec{v}, \vec{w}) = \frac{2 \; \sum_{i=1}^{N} \min(v_i, w_i)}{\sum_{i=1}^{N} (v_i + w_i)} \qquad (20.49)$$

Finally, also based on the conditional probability-association measure $P(f \; w)$, is a family of information-theoretic distributional similarity measures (Pereira et al., 1993; Dagan et al., 1994, 1999; Lee, 1999). The intuition of these models is that two vectors, $\vec{v}$ and $\vec{w}$, are similar to the extent that their probability distributions $P(f \; w)$ and $P(f \; v)$ are similar. The basis of comparing two probability distributions P and Q is the **Kullback-Leibler divergence** or **KL divergence** or **relative entropy** (Kullback and Leibler, 1951):

KL divergence

$$\text{assoc}_{\text{prob}}(w,f) = P(f\,w) \tag{20.35}$$

$$\text{assoc}_{\text{PMI}}(w,f) = \log_2 \frac{P(w,f)}{P(w)P(f)} \tag{20.38}$$

$$\text{assoc}_{\text{Lin}}(w,f) = \log_2 \frac{P(w,f)}{P(w)P(r\,w)P(w'\,w)} \tag{20.39}$$

$$\text{assoc}_{\text{t-test}}(w,f) = \frac{P(w,f)-P(w)P(f)}{\sqrt{P(f)P(w)}} \tag{20.41}$$

$$\text{sim}_{\text{cosine}}(\vec{v},\vec{w}) = \frac{\vec{v}\,\vec{w}}{\vec{v}\,\vec{w}} = \frac{\sum_{i=1}^{N} v_i\,w_i}{\sqrt{\sum_{i=1}^{N} v_i^2}\sqrt{\sum_{i=1}^{N} w_i^2}} \tag{20.47}$$

$$\text{sim}_{\text{Jaccard}}(\vec{v},\vec{w}) = \frac{\sum_{i=1}^{N}\min(v_i,w_i)}{\sum_{i=1}^{N}\max(v_i,w_i)} \tag{20.48}$$

$$\text{sim}_{\text{Dice}}(\vec{v},\vec{w}) = \frac{2\sum_{i=1}^{N}\min(v_i,w_i)}{\sum_{i=1}^{N}(v_i+w_i)} \tag{20.49}$$

$$\text{sim}_{\text{JS}}(\vec{v}\,\vec{w}) = D(\vec{v}\,\tfrac{\vec{v}+\vec{w}}{2})+D(\vec{w}\,\tfrac{\vec{v}+\vec{w}}{2}) \tag{20.52}$$

Figure 20.13   Defining word similarity: measures of association between a target word w and a feature $f = (r,w')$ to another word w', and measures of vector similarity between word co-occurrence vectors $\vec{v}$ and $\vec{w}$.

$$D(P\,Q) = \sum_{x} P(x)\log\frac{P(x)}{Q(x)} \tag{20.50}$$

Unfortunately, the KL-divergence is undefined when $Q(x) = 0$ and $P(x) \neq 0$, which is a problem since these word-distribution vectors are generally quite sparse. One alternative (Lee, 1999) is to use the **Jenson-Shannon divergence**, which represents the divergence of each distribution from the mean of the two and doesn't have this problem with zeros.

Jenson-Shannon divergence

$$JS(P\,Q) = D(P\,\frac{P+Q}{2})+D(Q\,\frac{P+Q}{2}) \tag{20.51}$$

Rephrased in terms of vectors $\vec{v}$ and $\vec{w}$,

$$\text{sim}_{\text{JS}}(\vec{v}\,\vec{w}) = D(\vec{v}\,\frac{\vec{v}+\vec{w}}{2})+D(\vec{w}\,\frac{\vec{v}+\vec{w}}{2}) \tag{20.52}$$

Figure 20.13 summarizes the measures of association and of vector similarity that we have designed. See the Historical Notes section for a summary of other vector similarity measures.

Finally, let's look at some of the results of distributional word similarity. The following are the ten words most similar to the different parts of speech of *hope* and *brief*, derived with the online dependency-based similarity tool (Lin, 2007); this tool defines the co-occurrence vector by using all minipar grammatical relations, uses the $\text{assoc}_{\text{Lin}}$ measure of association, and uses a vector similarity metric from Lin (1998a).

- **hope (N):** optimism 0.141, chance 0.137, expectation 0.137, prospect 0.126, dream 0.119, desire 0.118, fear 0.116, effort 0.111, confidence 0.109, promise 0.108
- **hope (V):** would like 0.158, wish 0.140, plan 0.139, say 0.137, believe 0.135, think 0.133, agree 0.130, wonder 0.130, try 0.127, decide 0.125
- **brief (N):** legal brief 0.139, affidavit 0.103, filing 0.0983, petition 0.0865, document 0.0835, argument 0.0832, letter 0.0786, rebuttal 0.0778, memo 0.0768, article 0.0758
- **brief (A):** lengthy 0.256, hour-long 0.191, short 0.174, extended 0.163, frequent 0.163, recent 0.158, short-lived 0.155, prolonged 0.149, week-long 0.149, occasional 0.146

20.7.4   Evaluating Distributional Word Similarity

Distributional similarity can be evaluated in the same ways we evaluate thesaurus-based similarity: we can compare intrinsically to human similarity scores or we can evaluate it extrinsically as part of end-to-end applications. Besides word sense disambiguation and malapropism detection, similarity measures have been used as a part of systems for the grading of exams and essays (Landauer et al., 1997), or taking TOEFL multiple-choice exams (Landauer and Dumais, 1997; Turney et al., 2003).

Distributional algorithms are also often evaluated in a third intrinsic way: by comparison with a gold-standard thesaurus. We can compare directly with a single thesaurus (Grefenstette, 1994; Lin, 1998a), or we can use precision and recall measures against an ensemble of thesauruses (Curran and Moens, 2002). Let S be the set of words that are defined as similar in the thesaurus: being in the same synset or perhaps sharing the same hypernym or being in the hypernym-hyponym relation. Let S' be the set of words that are classified as similar by some algorithm. We can define precision and recall as

$$\text{precision} = \frac{S \cap S'}{S'} \quad \text{recall} = \frac{S \cap S'}{S} \qquad (20.53)$$

Curran (2003) evaluated a number of distributional algorithms by comparing with thesauruses and found that the Dice and Jaccard methods performed best as measures of vector similarity, and t-test performed best as a measure of association. Thus, the best metric weighted the associations with t-test, and then used either Dice or Jaccard to measure vector similarity.

20.8   Hyponymy and Other Word Relations

Similarity is only one kind of semantic relation between words. As we discussed in Chapter 19, WordNet and MeSH both include **hyponymy/hypernymy**, as do many thesauruses for other languages, such as CiLin for Chinese. WordNet also includes **antonymy**, **meronymy**, and other relations. Thus, if we want to know if two senses are related by one of these relations and the senses occur in WordNet or MeSH, we can just look them up. But since many words are not in these resources, it is important to be able to learn new hypernym and meronym relations automatically.

Much work on automatic learning of word relations is based on a key insight first articulated by Hearst (1992): that the presence of certain lexico-syntactic patterns can indicate a particular semantic relationship between two nouns. Consider the following sentence extracted by Hearst from the Groliers encyclopedia:

(20.54) Agar is a substance prepared from a mixture of red algae, such as Gelidium, for laboratory or industrial use.

Hearst points out that most human readers will not know what *Gelidium* is, but that they can readily infer that it is a kind of (a **hyponym** of) *red algae*, whatever that is. She suggests that the following **lexico-syntactic pattern**

$$NP_0 \text{ such as } NP_1 ,NP_2 \dots ,(and\ or)NP_i ,i \geq 1 \qquad (20.55)$$

implies the following semantics

$$\forall NP_i, i \geq 1, \text{hyponym}(NP_i, NP_0) \qquad (20.56)$$

allowing us to infer

$$\text{hyponym}(\text{Gelidium}, \text{red algae}) \qquad (20.57)$$

$NP ,NP *$, (and or) other NP_H	...temples, treasuries, and other important civic buildings.
NP_H such as NP, * (or and) NP	red algae such as Gelidium
such NP_H as NP, * (or and) NP	works by such authors as Herrick, Goldsmith, and Shakespeare
NP_H , including NP, * (or and) NP	All common-law countries, including Canada and England
NP_H , especially NP, * (or and) NP	...most European countries, especially France, England, and Spain

Figure 20.14   Hand-built lexico-syntactic patterns for finding hypernyms (Hearst, 1992, 1998).

Figure 20.14 shows five patterns Hearst (1992, 1998) suggested for inferring the hyponym relation; we've shown NP_H as the parent/hyponym. There are a number of other attempts to extract different WordNet relations with such patterns; see the Historical Notes section for more details.

Of course, the coverage of such pattern-based methods is limited by the number and accuracy of the available patterns. Unfortunately, once the obvious examples have been found, the process of creating patterns by hand becomes a difficult and slow process. Fortunately, we've already seen the solution to this kind of problem. We can find new patterns by **bootstrapping** methods that are common in information extraction (Riloff, 1996; Brin, 1998) and that are also key to the Yarowsky method described earlier in Section 20.5.

The key insight for the use of bootstrapping in relational pattern discovery is that with a large corpus we can expect words involved in a relation to show up with many different patterns that express that same relation. Therefore, in theory at least, we need only start with a small number of precise patterns to acquire a set of seed words involved in a given relation. These words can then be used to query a large corpus for sentences containing both terms in some kind of dependency relation; new patterns can then be extracted from these new sentences. The process can be repeated until the pattern set is large enough.

As an example of this process, consider the terms "red algae" and "Gelidium" discovered earlier with Hearst's simple pattern set. Among the results of a simple Google search with these as query terms is the following example:

(20.58) One example of a red algae is Gelidium.

Removing the seed words from such a sentence and replacing them with simple wildcards is the crudest kind of pattern generation. In this case, submitting the pattern "One example of a * is *" to Google currently yields nearly 500,000 hits, including the following example:

(20.59) One example of a boson is a photon.

We can also extract slightly more sophisticated patterns by parsing the extracted sentences and putting wildcards into the parse tree.

The key to the success of bootstrapping approaches is to avoid the *semantic drift* that tends to occur as part of repeated applications of bootstrapping. The further we get from the original set of seed words or patterns, the more likely it is that we'll come across patterns with meanings quite different from what we set out to discover. We describe methods for dealing with this drift when we discuss bootstrapping for information extraction in Chapter 22.

An alternative to bootstrapping is to use large lexical resources like WordNet as a source of training information, in which each WordNet hypernym/hyponym pair tells us something about what kinds of words are in this relation; and then train a classifier to help find new words that exhibit this relation.

This hyponym learning algorithm of Snow et al. (2005), for example, relies on WordNet to help learn large numbers of weak hyponym patterns and then combine them in a supervised classifier in five steps:

1. Collect all pairs of WordNet noun concepts c_i, c_j that are in the hypernym / hyponym relation.
2. For each noun pair, collect all sentences (in a 6-million-word corpus) in which both nouns occur.
3. Parse the sentences and automatically extract every possible Hearst-style lexico-syntactic pattern from the parse tree.
4. Use the large set of patterns as features in an logistic regression classifier.
5. Given a pair of nouns in the test set, extract features and use the classifier to determine whether the noun pair is related by the hypernym/hyponym relation.

Four of the new patterns automatically learned by this algorithm include

NP_H like NP	NP_H called NP
NP is a NP_H	NP, a NP_H (appositive):

Snow et al. (2005) then showed good hypernym detection performance by using each of these patterns as a weak feature combined by a logistic regression classifier.

Another way to use WordNet to help address the hypernym problem is to model the task as choosing the place to insert unknown words into an otherwise complete hierarchy. It is possible to do this without using lexico-syntactic patterns. For example, we can use a similarity classifier (using distributional information or morphological information) to find the words in the hierarchy that are most similar to an unknown word, using an approach like K-Nearest-Neighbors, and insert the new word there (Tseng, 2003). Or we can treat the task of hypernym labeling as a labeling task like named entity tagging. Ciaramita and Johnson (2003) take this approach, using as tags 26 *Supersenses*   **supersenses** from the 26 broad-category "lexicographer class" labels from WordNet (*person*, *location*, *event*, *quantity*, etc.). They extract features, such as surrounding part-of-speech tags, word bigram and trigram features, spelling, and morphological features, and apply a multiclass perceptron classifier.

Finding **meronyms** seems to be harder than finding hyponyms; here are some examples from Girju et al. (2003):

(20.60) The car's mail messenger is busy at work in the <PART>mail car</PART> as the <WHOLE>train</WHOLE> moves along.

(20.61) Through the open <PART>side door</PART> of the <WHOLE>car</WHOLE>, moving scenery can be seen.

Meronyms are hard to find because the lexico-syntactic patterns that characterize them are exceedingly ambiguous. For example, the two most common patterns indicating meronymy are the English genitive constructions [NP_1 of NP_2] and [NP_1's NP_2], which also express many other meanings such as *possession*; see Girju et al. (2003, 2006) for discussion and possible algorithms.

Thesaurus induction   Learning individual relations between words is an important component of the general task of **thesaurus induction**. In thesaurus induction, we combine our estimates of word similarity with our hypernym or other relations to build an entire ontology or thesaurus. For example, the two-step, thesaurus-induction algorithm of Caraballo (1999, 2001) first applies a bottom-up **clustering** algorithm to group semantically similar words into an unlabeled word hierarchy. Recall from Section 20.10 that in agglomerative clustering, we start by assigning each word its own cluster. The algorithm then forms new clusters in a bottom-up fashion by successively merging the two clusters that are most similar; we can use any metric for semantic similarity, such as one of the distributional metrics described in the previous section. In the second step, given the unlabeled hierarchy, the algorithm uses a pattern-based hyponym classifier to assign a hypernym label to each cluster of words. See the Historical Notes section for more recent work on thesaurus induction.

20.9   Semantic Role Labeling

Semantic role labeling   The final task we discuss in this chapter links word meanings with sentence meanings. This is the task of **semantic role labeling**, sometimes called **thematic role labeling**, **case role assignment**, or even **shallow semantic parsing**. Semantic role labeling is the task of automatically finding the **semantic roles** for each predicate in a sentence. More specifically, that means determining which constituents in a sentence are semantic arguments for a given predicate and then determining the appropriate role for each of those arguments. Semantic role labeling has the potential to improve performance in any language-understanding task, although to date its primary applications have been in question answering and information extraction.

Current approaches to semantic role labeling are based on supervised machine learning and hence require access to adequate amounts of training and testing materials. Over the last few years, both the FrameNet and PropBank resources discussed in Chapter 19 have played this role. That is, they have been used to specify what counts as a predicate, to define the set of roles used in the task, and to provide training and test data. The SENSEVAL-3 evaluation used FrameNet, and the CONLL evaluations in 2004 and 2005 were based on PropBank.

The following examples show the different representations from the two efforts. Recall that FrameNet (20.62) employs a large number of frame-specific frame elements as roles, and PropBank (20.63) makes use of a smaller number of numbered argument labels that can be interpreted as verb-specific labels.

(20.62) [You]   can't [blame] [the program] [for being unable to identify it]
         COGNIZER   TARGET   EVALUEE   REASON

(20.63) [The San Francisco Examiner] issued   [a special edition] [yesterday]
         ARG0   TARGET ARG1   ARGM-TMP

A simplified semantic-role-labeling algorithm is sketched in Fig. 20.15. Following the very earliest work on semantic role analysis (Simmons, 1973), most work on semantic role labeling begins by parsing the sentence. Publicly available broad-coverage parsers (such as Collins (1996) or Charniak (1997)) are typically used to assign a parse to the input string. Figure 20.16 shows a parse of (20.63) above. The resulting parse is then traversed to find all predicate-bearing words. For each of these predicates, the tree is again traversed to determine which role, if any, each constituent in the parse plays with respect to that predicate. The algorithm makes this judgment by first characterizing the constituent as a set of features with respect to the predicate. A classifier trained on an appropriate training set is then passed this feature set and makes the appropriate assignment.

---

function SEMANTICROLELABEL(*words*) **returns** labeled tree

    parse ← PARSE(*words*)
    for each *predicate* **in** *parse* **do**
        for each *node* **in** *parse* **do**
            featurevector ← EXTRACTFEATURES(*node, predicate, parse*)
            CLASSIFYNODE(*node, featurevector, parse*)

Figure 20.15   A generic semantic-role-labeling algorithm. The CLASSIFYNODE component can be a simple 1-of-*N* classifier that assigns a semantic role (or NONE for non-role constituents). CLASSIFYNODE can be trained on labeled data such as FrameNet or PropBank.

Let's look in more detail at the simple set of features suggested by Gildea and Jurafsky (2000, 2002), which have been incorporated into most role-labeling systems. We'll extract them for the first *NP* in Fig. 20.16, the *NP-SBJ* constituent *The San Francisco Examiner*.

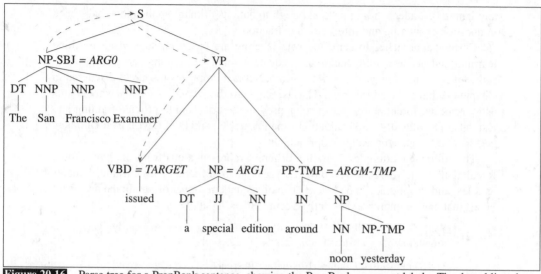

Figure 20.16 Parse tree for a PropBank sentence, showing the PropBank argument labels. The dotted line shows the **path** feature NP↑S↓VP↓VBD for ARG0, the NP-SBJ constituent *The San Francisco Examiner*.

- The governing **predicate**, in this case the verb *issued*. For PropBank, the predicates are always verbs; FrameNet also has noun and adjective predicates. The predicate is a crucial feature since both PropBank and FrameNet labels are defined only with respect to a particular predicate.

- The **phrase type** of the constituent, in this case, *NP* (or *NP-SBJ*). This is simply the name of the parse node that dominates this constituent in the parse tree. Some semantic roles tend to appear as *NPs*, others as *S* or *PP*, and so on.

- The **headword** of the constituent, *Examiner*. The headword of a constituent can be computed with standard head rules, such as those given in Chapter 12 in Fig. 12.13. Certain headwords (e.g., pronouns) place strong constraints on the possible semantic roles they are likely to fill.

- The **headword part of speech** of the constituent, *NNP*.

- The **path** in the parse tree from the constituent to the predicate. This path is marked by the dotted line in Fig. 20.16. Following (Gildea and Jurafsky, 2000), we can use a simple linear representation of the path, NP↑S↓VP↓VBD. ↑ and ↓ represent upward and downward movement in the tree, respectively. The path is very useful as a compact representation of many kinds of grammatical function relationships between the constituent and the predicate.

- The **voice** of the clause in which the constituent appears, in this case, **active** (as contrasted with **passive**). Passive sentences tend to have strongly different linkings of semantic roles to surface form than do active ones.

- The binary **linear position** of the constituent with respect to the predicate, either **before** or **after**.

- The **subcategorization** of the predicate. Recall from Chapter 12 that the subcategorization of a verb is the set of expected arguments that appear in the verb phrase. We can extract this information by using the phrase-structure rule that expands the immediate parent of the predicate; VP → NP PP for the predicate in Fig. 20.16.

Semantic-role-labeling systems often extract many other features, such as named entity tags (it is useful to know if a constituent is a LOCATION or PERSON, for example), more complex versions of the path features (the upward or downward halves, whether particular nodes occur in the path), the rightmost or leftmost words of the constituent, and so on.

We now have a set of observations like the following example, each with a vector of features; we have shown the features in the order described above (recall that most observations will have the value NONE rather than, for example, ARG0, since most constituents in the parse tree will not bear a semantic role):

ARG0: [issued, NP, Examiner, NNP, NP↑S↓VP↓VBD, active, before, VP → NP PP]

Just as we saw for word sense disambiguation, we can divide these observations into a training set and a test set, use the training examples in any supervised machine learning algorithm, and build a classifier. SVM and Maximum Entropy classifiers have yielded good results on this task on standard evaluations. Once trained, the classifier can be used on unlabeled sentences to propose a role for each constituent in the sentence. More precisely, an input sentence is parsed and a procedure similar to that described earlier for training is employed.

Instead of training a single-stage classifier, some role-labeling algorithms do classification in multiple stages for efficiency:

- **Pruning:** an elimination of some constituents from consideration as possible roles based on simple rules to speed up execution
- **Identification:** a binary classification of each node as an ARG to be labeled or a NONE
- **Classification:** a 1-of-N classification of all the constituents that were labeled as ARG by the previous stage

All semantic role labeling systems need to deal with a number of complications. Constituents in FrameNet and PropBank are required to be non-overlapping. Thus, if a system incorrectly labels two overlapping constituents as arguments, it needs to decide which of the two is correct. Additionally, the semantic roles of constituents are not independent; since PropBank does not allow multiple identical arguments, labeling one constituent as an ARG0 would greatly increase the probability of another constituent being labeled ARG1. Both of these problems can be addressed by the two-stage approaches based on lattice or N-best rescoring discussed in Chapter 9: having the classifier assign multiple labels to each constituent, each with a probability, and using a second global optimization pass to pick the best label sequence.

Instead of using parses as input, it is also possible to do semantic role labeling directly from raw (or part-of-speech tagged) text by applying the chunking techniques used for named entity extraction or partial parsing. Such techniques are particularly useful in domains such as bioinformatics where it is unlikely that syntactic parsers trained on typical newswire text will perform well.

Finally, semantic-role-labeling systems have generally been evaluated by requiring that each argument label must be assigned to the exactly correct word sequence or parse constituent. Precision, recall, and *F*-measure can then be computed. A simple rule-based system can be used as a baseline, for example, tagging the first NP before the predicate as ARG0 and the first NP after the predicate as ARG1 and switching these if the verb phrase is passive.

20.10   Advanced: Unsupervised Sense Disambiguation

Let's briefly return to the WSD task. It is expensive and difficult to build large corpora in which each word is labeled for its word sense. For this reason, unsupervised approaches to sense disambiguation are an exciting and important research area.

In unsupervised approaches, we don't use human-defined word senses. Instead, the set of "senses" of each word is created automatically from the instances of each word in the training set. Let's introduce a simplified version of the methods of Schütze (Schütze, 1992b, 1998) on unsupervised sense disambiguation. In Schütze's method, we first represent each instance of a word in the training set by distributional-context feature vectors that are a slight generalization of the feature vectors we defined in Section 20.7. (It is for this reason that we turned to unsupervised sense disambiguation only after introducing word similarity.)

As in Section 20.7, we will represent a word w as a vector based on frequencies of its neighboring words. For example, for a given target word (type) w, we might select 1000 words that occur most frequently within 25 words of any instance of w. These 1000 words become the dimension of the vector. Let's define f_i to mean the frequency with which word i occurs in the context of word w. We define the word vector $\vec{w}$ (for a given token (observation) of w) as

$$\vec{w} = (f_1, f_2, f_3, \quad , f_{1000})$$

So far this is just a version of the distributional context we saw in Section 20.7. We can also use a slightly more complex version of the distributional context. For example, Schütze defines the **context vector** of a word w not as this first-order vector, but instead by its **second order co-occurrence**. That is, we build the context vector for a word w by computing for each word x in the context of w, its word vector $\vec{x}$, and then taking the centroid (average) of the vectors $\vec{x}$.

Let's see how we use these context vectors (whether first-order or second-order) in unsupervised sense disambiguation of a word w. In training, we need only three steps:

1. For each token w_i of word w in a corpus, compute a context vector $\vec{c}$.
2. Use a **clustering algorithm** to **cluster** these word-token context vectors $\vec{c}$ into a predefined number of groups or clusters. Each cluster defines a sense of w.
3. Compute the **vector centroid** of each cluster. Each vector centroid $\vec{s}_j$ is a **sense vector** representing that sense of w.

Since this is an unsupervised algorithm, we don't have names for each of these "senses" of w; we just refer to the jth sense of w.

Now how do we disambiguate a particular token t of w? Again, we have three steps:

1. Compute a context vector $\vec{c}$ for t as discussed above.
2. Retrieve all sense vectors s_j for w.
3. Assign t to the sense represented by the sense vector s_j that is closest to t.

Agglomerative clustering

All we need is a clustering algorithm and a distance metric between vectors. Fortunately, clustering is a well-studied problem with a wide number of standard algorithms that can be applied to inputs structured as vectors of numerical values (Duda and Hart, 1973). A frequently used technique in language applications is known as **agglomerative clustering**. In this technique, each of the N training instances is initially assigned to its own cluster. New clusters are then formed in a bottom-up fashion by the successive merging of the two clusters that are most similar. This process continues until either a specified number of clusters is reached, or some global goodness measure among the clusters is achieved. In cases in which the number of training instances makes this method too expensive, random sampling can be used on the original training set (Cutting et al., 1992b) to achieve similar results.

How can we evaluate unsupervised sense disambiguation approaches? As usual, the best way is to do extrinsic or in vivo evaluation, in which the WSD algorithm is embedded in some end-to-end system. Intrinsic evaluation can also be useful, though, if we have some way to map the automatically derived sense classes into some hand-labeled gold-standard set so that we can compare a hand-labeled test set with a set labeled by our unsupervised classifier. One way of doing this mapping is to map each sense cluster to a predefined sense by choosing the sense that (in some training set) has the most word tokens overlapping with the cluster. Another is to consider all pairs of words in the test set, testing for each whether both the system and the hand-labeling put both members of the pair in the same cluster.

20.11   Summary

This chapter introduced three areas in the computation of word meaning:

- **Word-sense disambiguation** (**WSD**) is the task of determining the correct sense of a word in context. Supervised approaches make use of sentences in which individual words (**lexical sample task**) or all words (**all-words task**) are hand-labeled with senses from a resource like WordNet. Classifiers for supervised WSD include **naive Bayes**, **decision list**, and many others, trained on **collocational** and **bag-of-words** features that describe the surrounding words.

- An important baseline for WSD is the **most frequent sense**, equivalent, in Word-Net, to **take the first sense**.

- The **Lesk algorithm** chooses the sense whose dictionary definition shares the most words with the target word's neighborhood.

- **Word similarity** can be computed by measuring the **link distance** in a thesaurus, by measuring the **information content** in a thesaurus, by using **distributional similarity** in a corpus, or by usuing **information-theoretic methods**.

- Measures of association for distributional similarity include PMI, Lin, and *t*-test. Measures of vector similarity include cosine, Jaccard, Dice, and Jiang-Conrath.
- Lexical relations like **hyponymy** can be found via lexico-syntactic patterns.
- **Semantic role labeling** generally starts by parsing a sentence and then automatically tagging each parse tree node with a semantic role (or NONE).

Bibliographical and Historical Notes

Word sense disambiguation traces its roots to some of the earliest applications of digital computers. We saw above Warren Weaver's (1955) suggestion to disambiguate a word by looking at a small window around it, in the context of machine translation. Other notions first proposed in this early period include the use of a thesaurus for disambiguation (Masterman, 1957), supervised training of Bayesian models for disambiguation (Madhu and Lytel, 1965), and the use of clustering in word sense analysis (Sparck Jones, 1986).

An enormous amount of work on disambiguation has been conducted within the context of early AI-oriented natural language processing systems. While most natural language analysis systems of this type exhibited some form of lexical disambiguation capability, a number of these efforts made word sense disambiguation a larger focus of their work. Among the most influential efforts were the efforts of Quillian (1968) and Simmons (1973) with semantic networks, the work of Wilks with *Preference Semantics* (Wilks, 1975c, 1975b, 1975a), and the work of Small and Rieger (1982) and Riesbeck (1975) on word-based understanding systems. Hirst's ABSITY system (Hirst and Charniak, 1982; Hirst, 1987, 1988), which used a technique called marker passing based on semantic networks , represents the most advanced system of this type. As with these largely symbolic approaches, most connectionist approaches to word sense disambiguation have relied on small lexicons with hand-coded representations (Cottrell, 1985; Kawamoto, 1988).

Considerable work on sense disambiguation has been conducted in the areas of cognitive science and psycholinguistics. Appropriately enough, this work is generally described by a different name: lexical ambiguity resolution. Small et al. (1988) present a variety of papers from this perspective.

The earliest implementation of a robust empirical approach to sense disambiguation is due to Kelly and Stone (1975), who directed a team that hand-crafted a set of disambiguation rules for 1790 ambiguous English words. Lesk (1986) was the first to use a machine-readable dictionary for word sense disambiguation. Wilks et al. (1996) describe extensive explorations of the use of machine-readable dictionaries. The problem of dictionary senses being too fine-grained or lacking an appropriate organization has been addressed with models of clustering word senses (Dolan, 1994; Peters et al., 1998; Chen and Chang, 1998; Mihalcea and Moldovan, 2001; Agirre and de Lacalle, 2003; Chklovski and Mihalcea, 2003; Palmer et al., 2004; McCarthy, 2006; Navigli, 2006; Snow et al., 2007). Corpora with clustered word senses for training clustering

OntoNotes   algorithms include Palmer et al. (2006) and **OntoNotes** (Hovy et al., 2006).

Modern interest in supervised machine learning approaches to disambiguation began with Black (1988), who applied decision tree learning to the task. The need for large amounts of annotated text in these methods led to investigations into the use of bootstrapping methods (Hearst, 1991; Yarowsky, 1995). The problem of how to weight and combine disparate sources of evidence is explored in Ng and Lee (1996), McRoy (1992), and Stevenson and Wilks (2001).

Among the semi-supervised methods, more recent models of selectional preference include Li and Abe (1998), Ciaramita and Johnson (2000), McCarthy and Carroll (2003) and Light and Greiff (2002). Diab and Resnik (2002) give a semi-supervised algorithm for sense disambiguation based on aligned parallel corpora in two languages. For example, the fact that the French word *catastrophe* might be translated as English *disaster* in one instance and *tragedy* in another instance can be used to disambiguate the senses of the two English words (i.e., to choose senses of *disaster* and *tragedy* that are similar). Abney (2002, 2004) explores the mathematical foundations of the Yarowsky algorithm and its relation to co-training. The most-frequent-sense heuristic is an extremely powerful one but requires large amounts of supervised training data. McCarthy et al. (2004) propose an unsupervised way to automatically estimate the most frequent sense, based on the thesaurus similarity metrics defined in Section 20.6.

The earliest use of clustering in the study of word senses was by Sparck Jones (1986). Zernik (1991) successfully applied a standard information retrieval clustering algorithm to the problem and evaluated it according to improvements in retrieval performance. More extensive recent work on clustering can be found in Pedersen and Bruce (1997) and Schütze (1997, 1998).

A few algorithms have attempted to exploit the power of mutually disambiguating all the words in a sentence, either by multiple passes (Kelly and Stone, 1975) to take advantage of easily disambiguated words or by parallel search (Cowie et al., 1992; Véronis and Ide, 1990).

Recent work has focused on ways to use the Web for training data for word sense disambiguation, either unsupervised (Mihalcea and Moldovan, 1999) or labeled by volunteers.

Resnik (2006) describes potential applications of WSD. One recent application has been to improve machine translation (Chan et al., 2007; Carpuat and Wu, 2007).

Agirre and Edmonds (2006) is a comprehensive edited volume that summarizes the state of the art in WSD. Ide and Véronis (1998a) comprehensively review the history of word sense disambiguation up to 1998. Ng and Zelle (1997) provide a more focused review from a machine learning perspective. Wilks et al. (1996) describe dictionary and corpus experiments, along with detailed descriptions of very early work.

The models of distributional word similarity we discussed arose out of research in linguistics and psychology of the 1950s. The idea that meaning was related to distribution of words in context was widespread in linguistic theory of the 1950s; even before the well-known Firth (1957) and Harris (1968) dictums discussed earlier, Joos (1950) stated that

> the linguist's "meaning" of a morpheme. . . is by definition the set of conditional probabilities of its occurrence in context with all other morphemes.

The related idea that the meaning of a word could be modeled as a point in a Euclidean space and that the similarity of meaning between two words could be modeled as the distance between these points was proposed in psychology by Osgood et al. (1957). The application of these ideas in a computational framework was first made by Sparck Jones (1986) and became a core principle of information retrieval, from whence it came into broader use in speech and language processing.

There are a wide variety of other weightings and methods for word similarity. The largest class of methods not discussed in this chapter are the variants to and details of the **information-theoretic** methods like Jensen-Shannon divergence, KL-divergence and α-skew divergence that we briefly introduced (Pereira et al., 1993; Dagan et al., 1994, 1999; Lee, 1999, 2001); there are also other metrics from Hindle (1990) and Lin (1998a). Alternative paradigms include the **co-occurrence retrieval** model (Weeds, 2003; Weeds and Weir, 2005). Manning and Schütze (1999, Chapters 5 and 8) give collocation measures and other related similarity measures. A commonly used weight-

Weighted mutual information

ing is **weighted mutual information** (Fung and McKeown, 1997) in which the point-wise mutual information is weighted by the joint probability. In information retrieval, the **tf-idf** weight is widely used, as we discuss in Chapter 23. See Dagan (2000), Mohammad and Hirst (2005), Curran (2003), and Weeds (2003) for good summaries of distributional similarity.

Latent Semantic Indexing

LSA

An alternative vector space model of semantic similarity, **Latent Semantic Indexing** (LSI) or **Latent Semantic Analysis (LSA)**, uses **singular value decomposition** to reduce the dimensionality of the vector space with the intent of discovering higher-order regularities (Deerwester et al., 1990). We have already discussed Schütze (1992b) who developed another semantic similarity model based on singular value decomposition.

There is a wide variety of recent literature on other lexical relations and thesaurus induction. The use of distributional word similarity for thesaurus induction was explored systematically by Grefenstette (1994). Many distributional clustering algorithms have been applied to the task of discovering groupings of semantically similar words, including hard clustering (Brown et al., 1992), soft clustering (Pereira et al., 1993), as well as new algorithms like **Clustering By Committee** (CBC) (Lin and Pantel, 2002). For particular relations, Lin et al. (2003) applied hand-crafted patterns to find **antonyms**, with the goal of improving synonym detection. The distributional word similarity algorithms from Section 20.7 often incorrectly assign high similarity to antonyms. Lin et al. (2003) showed that words appearing in the patterns *from X to Y* or *either X or Y* tended to be antonyms. Girju et al. (2003, 2006) show improvements in **meronym** extraction by learning generalizations about the semantic superclasses of the two nouns. Chklovski and Pantel (2004) used hand-built patterns to extract fine-grained relations such as **strength** between verbs. Much recent work has focused on thesaurus induction by combining different relation extractors. Pantel and Ravichandran (2004), for example, extend Caraballo's algorithm for combining similarity and hyponymy information, while Snow et al. (2006) integrate multiple relation extractors to compute the most probable thesaurus structure. Recent work on similarity focuses on the use of the Web, for example relying on Wikipedia (Strube and Ponzetto, 2006; Gabrilovich and Markovitch, 2007). This Web-based work is also closely related to unsupervised information extraction; see Chapter 22 and references like Etzioni et al. (2005).

While not as old a field as word similarity or sense disambiguation, semantic role labeling has a long history in computational linguistics. The earliest work on semantic role labeling (Simmons, 1973) first parsed a sentence by means of an ATN parser. Each verb then had a set of rules specifying how the parse should be mapped to semantic roles. These rules mainly made reference to grammatical functions (subject, object, complement of specific prepositions) but also checked constituent internal features such as the animacy of head nouns.

Statistical work in the area revived in 2000 after the FrameNet and PropBank projects had created databases large enough and consistent enough to make training and testing possible. Many popular features used for role labeling are defined in Gildea and Jurafsky (2002), Chen and Rambow (2003), Surdeanu et al. (2003), Xue and Palmer (2004), Pradhan et al. (2003, 2005).

To avoid the need for huge labeled training sets, recent work has focused on unsupervised approaches for semantic role labeling (Swier and Stevenson, 2004).

The semantic-role-labeling work described above focuses on labeling each sentence token in a corpus with semantic roles. An alternative approach to semantic role labeling focuses on lexicon learning, using unsupervised learning on a corpus to learn the kinds of semantic classes a verb can belong to in terms of its possible semantic roles or argument alternation patterns (Stevenson and Merlo, 1999; Schulte im Walde, 2000; Merlo and Stevenson, 2001; Merlo et al., 2001; Grenager and Manning, 2006).

Exercises

20.1 Collect a small corpus of example sentences of varying lengths from any newspaper or magazine. Using WordNet or any standard dictionary, determine how many senses there are for each of the open-class words in each sentence. How many distinct combinations of senses are there for each sentence? How does this number seem to vary with sentence length?

20.2 Using WordNet or a standard reference dictionary, tag each open-class word in your corpus with its correct tag. Was choosing the correct sense always a straightforward task? Report on any difficulties you encountered.

20.3 Using the same corpus, isolate the words taking part in all the verb-subject and verb-object relations. How often does it appear to be the case that the words taking part in these relations could be disambiguated with only information about the words in the relation?

20.4 Between the words *eat* and *find*, which would you expect to be more effective in selectional restriction-based sense disambiguation? Why?

20.5 Using your favorite dictionary, simulate the original Lesk word overlap disambiguation algorithm described on page 647 on the phrase *Time flies like an arrow.* Assume that the words are to be disambiguated one at a time, from left to right, and that the results from earlier decisions are used later in the process.

20.6 Build an implementation of your solution to the previous exercise. Using Word-Net, implement the original Lesk word overlap disambiguation algorithm described on page 647 on the phrase *Time flies like an arrow*.

20.7 Implement and experiment with a decision-list sense disambiguation system. As a model, use the kinds of features shown in Fig. 20.2 on page 643. Use one of the publicly available decision-list packages like WEKA (or see Russell and Norvig (2002) for more details on implementing decision-list learning yourself). To facilitate evaluation of your system, you should obtain one of the freely available sense-tagged corpora.

20.8 Evaluate two or three of the similarity methods from the publicly available Word-net Similarity package (Pedersen et al., 2004). You might do this by hand-labeling some word pairs with similarity scores and seeing how well the algorithms approximate your hand labels.

20.9 Implement a distributional word similarity algorithm that can take different measures of association and different measures of vector similarity. Now evaluate two measures of association and two measures of vector similarity from Fig. 20.13 on page 666. Again, you might do this by hand-labeling some word pairs with similarity scores and seeing how well the algorithms approximate these labels.

Credits

Chapter 21

Computational Discourse

> Gracie: *Oh yeah...and then Mr. and Mrs. Jones were having matrimonial trouble, and my brother was hired to watch Mrs. Jones.*
> George: *Well, I imagine she was a very attractive woman.*
> Gracie: *She was, and my brother watched her day and night for six months.*
> George: *Well, what happened?*
> Gracie: *She finally got a divorce.*
> George: *Mrs. Jones?*
> Gracie: *No, my brother's wife.*
>
> George Burns and Gracie Allen in *The Salesgirl*

Orson Welles' movie *Citizen Kane* was groundbreaking in many ways, perhaps most notably in its structure. The story of the life of fictional media magnate Charles Foster Kane, the movie does not proceed in chronological order through Kane's life. Instead, the film begins with Kane's death (famously murmuring *"Rosebud"*) and is structured around flashbacks to his life inserted among scenes of a reporter investigating his death. The novel idea that the structure of a movie does not have to linearly follow the structure of the real timeline made apparent for 20th century cinematography the infinite possibilities and impact of different kinds of coherent narrative structures.

But coherent structure is not just a fact about movies or works of art. Up to this point of the book, we have focused primarily on language phenomena that operate at the word or sentence level. But just like movies, language does not normally consist of isolated, unrelated sentences, but instead of collocated, structured, **coherent** groups of
Discourse sentences. We refer to such a coherent structured group of sentences as a **discourse**.

The chapter you are now reading is an example of a discourse. It is in fact a dis-
Monologue course of a particular sort: a **monologue**. Monologues are characterized by a *speaker* (a term that we use to include writers, as it is here), and a *hearer* (which, analogously, includes readers). The communication flows in only one direction in a monologue, that is, from the speaker to the hearer.

After reading this chapter, you may have a conversation with a friend about it,
Dialogue which would consist of a much freer interchange. Such a discourse is called a **dialogue**, specifically a **human-human dialogue**. In this case, each participant periodically takes turns being a speaker and hearer. Unlike a typical monologue, dialogues generally consist of many different types of communicative acts: asking questions, giving answers, making corrections, and so forth.

You may also, for some purposes, such as booking an airline or train trip, have a conversation with a computer **conversational agent**. This use of **human-computer**
HCI **dialogue** for *human-computer interaction*, or **HCI**, has properties that distinguish it from normal human-human dialogue, in part due to the present-day limitations on the ability of computer systems to participate in free, unconstrained conversation.

From Chapter 21 of *Speech and Language Processing*, Second Edition. Daniel Jurafsky, James H. Martin.

While many discourse processing problems are common to these three forms of discourse, they differ in enough respects that different techniques have often been used to process them. This chapter focuses on techniques commonly applied to the interpretation of monologues; techniques for conversational agents and other dialogues are described in Chapter 24.

Language is rife with phenomena that operate at the discourse level. Consider the discourse shown in example (21.1).

(21.1)   The Tin Woodman went to the Emerald City to see the Wizard of Oz and ask for a heart. After he asked for it, the Woodman waited for the Wizard's response.

What do pronouns such as *he* and *it* denote? No doubt the reader had little trouble figuring out that *he* denotes the Tin Woodman and not the Wizard of Oz, and that *it* denotes the heart and not the Emerald City. Furthermore, it is clear to the reader that *the Wizard* is the same entity as *the Wizard of Oz*, and *the Woodman* is the same as *the Tin Woodman*.

But doing this disambiguation automatically is a difficult task. This goal of deciding what pronouns and other noun phrases refer to is called **coreference resolution**. Coreference resolution is important for **information extraction**, **summarization**, and for **conversational agents**. In fact, it turns out that just about any conceivable language processing application requires methods for determining the denotations of pronouns and related expressions.

There are other important discourse structures besides the relationships between pronouns and other nouns. Consider the task of **summarizing** the following passage:

(21.2)   First Union Corp is continuing to wrestle with severe problems. According to industry insiders at Paine Webber, their president, John R. Georgius, is planning to announce his retirement tomorrow.

We might want to extract a summary like the following:

(21.3)   First Union President John R. Georgius is planning to announce his retirement tomorrow.

To build such a summary, we need to know that the second sentence is the more important of the two, and that the first sentence is subordinate to it, just giving background information. Relationships of this sort between sentences in a discourse are called **coherence relations** and determining the coherence structures between discourse sentences is an important discourse task.

Since **coherence** is also a property of a good text, automatically detecting coherence relations is also useful for tasks like **automatic essay grading** that measure text quality. Automatic essay grading assigns a grade to short student essays by measuring the internal coherence of the essay as well as comparing its content to source material and hand-labeled, high-quality essays. Coherence is also used to evaluate the output quality of natural language generation systems.

Discourse structure and coreference are related in deep ways. Notice that in order to perform the summary above, a system must correctly identify *First Union Corp* as the denotation of *their* (as opposed to *Paine Webber*, for instance). Similarly, it turns out that determining the discourse structure can help in determining coreference.

Coherence

Let's conclude this introduction by discussing what it means for a text to be **coherent**. Assume that you have collected an arbitrary set of well-formed and independently interpretable utterances, for instance, by randomly selecting one sentence from each of the previous chapters of this book. Do you have a discourse? Almost certainly not. The reason is that these utterances, when juxtaposed, will not exhibit **coherence**. Consider, for example, the difference between passages (21.4) and (21.5).

Coherence

(21.4) John hid Bill's car keys. He was drunk.

(21.5) ?? John hid Bill's car keys. He likes spinach.

While most people find passage (21.4) to be rather unremarkable, they find passage (21.5) to be odd. Why is this so? Like passage (21.4), the sentences that make up passage (21.5) are well formed and readily interpretable. Something instead seems to be wrong with the fact that the sentences are juxtaposed. The hearer might ask, for instance, what hiding someone's car keys has to do with liking spinach. By asking this, the hearer is questioning the coherence of the passage.

Alternatively, the hearer might try to construct an explanation that makes it coherent, for instance, by conjecturing that perhaps someone offered John spinach in exchange for hiding Bill's car keys. In fact, if we consider a context in which we had known this already, the passage now sounds a lot better! Why is this? This conjecture allows the hearer to identify John's liking spinach as the cause of his hiding Bill's car keys, which would explain how the two sentences are connected. The very fact that hearers try to identify such connections is indicative of the need to establish coherence as part of discourse comprehension.

In passage (21.4) or in our new model of passage (21.5), the second sentence offers the reader an EXPLANATION or CAUSE for the first sentence. These examples show that a coherent discourse must have meaningful connections between its utterances, connections like EXPLANATION that are often called **coherence relations**. Coherence relations are introduced in Section 21.2.

Coherence relation

Let's introduce a second aspect of coherence by considering the following two texts from Grosz et al. (1995):

(21.6)   a. John went to his favorite music store to buy a piano.

         b. He had frequented the store for many years.

         c. He was excited that he could finally buy a piano.

         d. He arrived just as the store was closing for the day.

(21.7)   a. John went to his favorite music store to buy a piano.

         b. It was a store John had frequented for many years.

         c. He was excited that he could finally buy a piano.

         d. It was closing just as John arrived.

While these two texts differ only in how the two entities (John and the store) are realized in the sentences, the discourse in (21.6) is intuitively more coherent than the one in (21.7). As Grosz et al. (1995) point out, this is because the discourse in (21.6) is clearly about one individual, John, describing his actions and feelings. The discourse in (21.7), by contrast, focuses first on John, then the store, then back to John, then to the store again. It lacks the "aboutness" of the first discourse.

These examples show that for a discourse to be coherent, it must exhibit certain kinds of relationships with the entities it is about, introducing them and following them in a focused way. This kind of coherence can be called **entity-based coherence**. We introduce the **Centering** model of entity-based coherence in Section 21.6.2.

In the rest of the chapter we study aspects of both discourse structure and discourse entities. We begin in Section 21.1 with the simplest kind of discourse structure: simple **discourse segmentation** of a document into a linear sequence of multiparagraph passages. In Section 21.2, we then introduce more fine-grained discourse structure, the **coherence relation**, and give some algorithms for interpreting these relations. Finally, in Section 21.3, we turn to entities, describing methods for interpreting *referring expressions* such as pronouns.

21.1   Discourse Segmentation

The first kind of discourse task we examine is the extraction of a simplified version of the global or high-level structure of a text or discourse. Many genres of text are associated with particular conventional structures. Academic articles might be divided into sections like Abstract, Introduction, Methodology, Results, Conclusion. A newspaper story is often described as having an inverted pyramid structure, in which the opening

Lede

paragraphs (the **lede**) contains the most important information. Spoken patient reports are dictated by doctors in four sections following the standard SOAP format (Subjective, Objective, Assessment, Plan).

Automatically determining all of these types of structures for a large discourse is a difficult and unsolved problem. But some kinds of discourse structure detection algorithms exist. This section introduces one such algorithm for the simpler prob-

Discourse segmentation

lem of **discourse segmentation**: separating a document into a linear sequence of subtopics. Such segmentation algorithms are unable to find sophisticated hierarchical structure. Nonetheless, linear discourse segmentation can be important for **information retrieval**, for example, for automatically segmenting a TV news broadcast or a long news story into a sequence of stories so as to find a relevant story, for **text summarization** algorithms that need to make sure that different segments of the document are summarized correctly, or for **information extraction** algorithms that tend to extract information from inside a single discourse segment.

In the next two sections we introduce both an unsupervised and a supervised algorithm for discourse segmentation.

21.1.1   Unsupervised Discourse Segmentation

Let's consider the task of segmenting a text into multiple paragraph units that represent subtopics or passages of the original text. As we suggested above, this task is often

Linear segmentation

called **linear segmentation**, to distinguish it from the task of deriving more sophisticated hierarchical discourse structure. The goal of a segmenter, given raw text, might be to assign subtopic groupings such as the ones defined by Hearst (1997) for the following 21-paragraph science news article called "Stargazers" on the existence of life on earth and other planets (numbers indicate paragraphs):

1-3	Intro - the search for life in space
4–5	The moon's chemical composition
6-8	How early earth-moon proximity shaped the moon
9–12	How the moon helped life evolve on earth
13	Improbability of the earth-moon system
14–16	Binary/trinary star systems make life unlikely
17–18	The low probability of nonbinary/trinary systems
19–20	Properties of earth's sun that facilitate life
21	Summary

Cohesion

Lexical cohesion

An important class of unsupervised algorithms for the linear discourse segmentation task rely on the concept of **cohesion** (Halliday and Hasan, 1976). **Cohesion** is the use of certain linguistic devices to link or tie together textual units. **Lexical cohesion** is cohesion indicated by relations between words in the two units, such as use of an identical word, a synonym, or a hypernym. For example, the fact that the words *house*, *shingled*, and *I* occur in both of the two sentences in (21.8ab), is a cue that the two are tied together as a discourse:

(21.8)   Before winter **I** built a chimney, and **shingled** the sides of my **house**...
        I have thus a tight **shingled** and plastered **house**

In (21.9), lexical cohesion between the two sentences is indicated by the hypernym relation between *fruit* and the words *pears* and *apples*.

(21.9) Peel, core and slice **the pears and the apples**. Add **the fruit** to the skillet.

There are also non-lexical cohesion relations, such as the use of **anaphora**, shown here between *Woodhouses* and *them* (we define and discuss anaphora in detail in Section 21.6):

(21.10) **The Woodhouses** were first in consequence there. All looked up to **them**.

Cohesion chain

In addition to single examples of lexical cohesion between two words, we can have a **cohesion!chain**, in which cohesion is indicated by a whole sequence of related words:

(21.11) Peel, core and slice **the pears and the apples**. Add **the fruit** to the skillet.
        When **they** are soft...

Coherence and **cohesion** are often confused; let's review the difference. **Cohesion** refers to the way textual units are linked together. A cohesive relation is like a kind of glue grouping two units into a single unit. **Coherence** refers to the *meaning* relation between the two units. A coherence relation explains how the meaning of different textual units can combine to build a discourse meaning for the larger unit.

The intuition of the cohesion-based approach to segmentation is that sentences or paragraphs in a subtopic are cohesive with each other, but not with paragraphs in a neighboring subtopic. Thus, if we measured the cohesion between every neighboring sentence, we might expect a "dip" in cohesion at subtopic boundaries.

TextTiling

Let's look at one such cohesion-based approach, the **TextTiling** algorithm (Hearst, 1997). The algorithm has three steps: **tokenization**, **lexical score determination**, and

boundary identification. In the tokenization stage, each space-delimited word in the input is converted to lower case, words in a stop list of function words are thrown out, and the remaining words are morphologically stemmed. The stemmed words are grouped into pseudo-sentences of length $w = 20$ (equal-length pseudo-sentences are used rather than real sentences).

Now we look at each gap between pseudo-sentences and compute a **lexical cohesion score** across that gap. The cohesion score is defined as the average similarity of the words in the pseudo-sentences before the gap to the pseudo-sentences after the gap. We generally use a block of $k = 10$ pseudo-sentences on each side of the gap. To compute similarity, we create a word vector b from the block before the gap, and a vector a from the block after the gap, where the vectors are of length N (the total number of non-stopwords in the document) and the ith element of the word vector is the frequency of the word w_i. Now we can compute similarity by the cosine (= normalized dot product) measure defined in Eq. 20.47 from Chapter 20, rewritten here:

$$\text{sim}_{\text{cosine}}(\vec{b}, \vec{a}) = \frac{\vec{b} \; \vec{a}}{\vec{b} \; \vec{a}} = \frac{\sum_{i=1}^{N} b_i \; a_i}{\sqrt{\sum_{i=1}^{N} b_i^2} \sqrt{\sum_{i=1}^{N} a_i^2}} \qquad (21.12)$$

This similarity score (measuring how similar pseudo-sentences $i - k$ to i are to sentences $i+1$ to $i+k+1$) is computed for each gap i between pseudo-sentences. Let's look at the example in Fig. 21.1, where $k = 2$. Figure 21.1a shows a schematic view of four pseudo-sentences. Each 20-word pseudo-sentence might have multiple true sentences in it; we've shown each with two true sentences. The figure also indicates the computation of the dotproduct between successive pseudo-sentences. Thus, for example in the first pseudo-sentence, consisting of sentences 1 and 2, the word A occurs twice, B once, C twice, and so on. The dot product between the first two pseudo-sentences is 2 1+1 1+2 1+1 1+2 1 = 8. What is the cosine between these first two, assuming all words not shown have zero count?

Finally, we compute a **depth score** for each gap, measuring the depth of the "similarity valley" at the gap. The depth score is the distance from the peaks on both sides of the valley to the valley; in Fig. 21.1(b), this would be $(y_{a_1} - y_{a_2}) + (y_{a_3} - y_{a_2})$.

Boundaries are assigned at any valley that is deeper than a cutoff threshold (such as $\bar{s} - \sigma$, i.e., one standard deviation deeper than the mean valley depth).

Instead of using these depth score thresholds, more recent cohesion-based segmenters use **divisive clustering** (Choi, 2000; Choi et al., 2001); see the Historical Notes at the end of the chapter for more information.

21.1.2   Supervised Discourse Segmentation

We've now seen a method for segmenting discourses when no hand-labeled segment boundaries exist. For some kinds of discourse segmentation tasks, however, it is relatively easy to acquire boundary-labeled training data.

Consider the spoken discourse task of segmentation of broadcast news. To do summarization of radio or TV broadcasts, we first need to assign boundaries between news stories.   This is a simple discourse segmentation task, and training sets with hand-

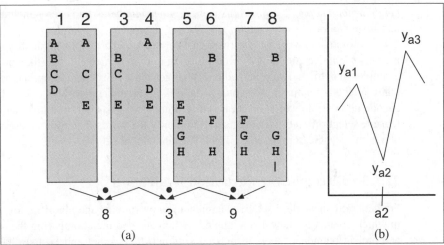

Figure 21.1   The TextTiling algorithm, showing (a) the dot-product computation of similarity between two sentences (1 and 2) and two following sentences (3 and 4); capital letters (A, B, C, etc.) indicate occurrences of words. (b) Shows the computation of the depth score of a valley. After Hearst (1997).

labeled news story boundaries exist. Similarly, for speech recognition of monologues like lectures or speeches, we often want to automatically break the text up into paragraphs. For the task of **paragraph segmentation**, it is trivial to find labeled training data from the Web (marked with <p>) or other sources.

Paragraph segmentation

Every kind of classifier has been used for this kind of supervised discourse segmentation. For example, we can use a binary classifier (SVM, decision tree) and make a yes-no boundary decision between any two sentences. We can also use a sequence classifier (HMM, CRF), making it easier to incorporate sequential constraints.

The features in supervised segmentation are generally a superset of those used in unsupervised classification. We can certainly use cohesion features such as word overlap, word cosine, LSA, lexical chains, coreference, and so on.

A key additional feature that is often used for supervised segmentation is the presence of **discourse markers** or **cue word**. A discourse marker is a word or phrase that functions to signal discourse structure. Discourse markers play an important role throughout this chapter. For the purpose of broadcast news segmentation, important discourse markers might include a phrase like *good evening, I'm* ⟨*PERSON*⟩, which tends to occur at the beginning of broadcasts, or the word *joining*, which tends to occur in the phrase *joining us now is* ⟨*PERSON*⟩, which often occurs at the beginning of specific segments. Similarly, the cue phrase *coming up* often appears at the end of segments (Reynar, 1999; Beeferman et al., 1999).

Discourse marker

Cue word

Discourse markers tend to be domain specific. For the task of segmenting newspaper articles from the *Wall Street Journal*, for example, the word *incorporated* is a useful feature, since *Wall Street Journal* articles often start by introducing a company with the full name *XYZ Incorporated*, but later using just *XYZ*. For the task of segmenting real estate ads, Manning (1998) used discourse cue features like '*is the following word a neighborhood name?'*, *'is previous word a phone number?'* and even punctuation cues like *'is the following word capitalized?'*

It is possible to write hand-written rules or regular expressions to identify discourse markers for a given domain. Such rules often refer to named entities (like the PERSON examples above), and so a named entity tagger must be run as a preprocessor. Automatic methods for finding discourse markers for segmentation also exist. They first encode all possible words or phrases as features to a classifier, and then some sort of **feature selection** on the training set to find only the words that are the best indicators of a boundary (Beeferman et al., 1999; Kawahara et al., 2004).

21.1.3   Discourse Segmentation Evaluation

We generally evaluate discourse segmentation by running the algorithm on a test set in which boundaries have been labeled by humans and then comparing the automatic and human boundary labels using the *WindowDiff* (Pevzner and Hearst, 2002) or P_k (Beeferman et al., 1999) metrics.

We generally don't use precision, recall, and F-measure for evaluating segmentation because they are not sensitive to near misses. If a segmentation algorithm is off by one sentence in assigning a boundary, standard F-measure gives it as bad a score as an algorithm that assigned boundaries nowhere near the correct locations. Both *WindowDiff* and P_k assign partial credit. We will present WindowDiff, since it is a more recent improvement to P_k.

WindowDiff compares a reference (human-labeled) segmentation with a hypothesis segmentation by sliding a probe, a moving window of length k, across the hypothesis segmentation. At each position in the hypothesis string, we compare the number of **reference** boundaries that fall within the probe (r_i) to the number of **hypothesized** boundaries that fall within the probe (h_i). The algorithm penalizes any hypothesis for which $r_i \neq h_i$, that is, for which $r_i - h_i \neq 0$. The window size k is set as half the average segment in the reference string. Figure 21.2 shows a schematic of the computation.

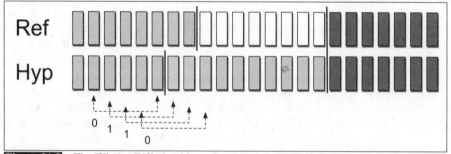

Figure 21.2   The WindowDiff algorithm, showing the moving window sliding over the hypothesis string, and the computation of $r_i - h_i$ at four positions. After Pevzner and Hearst (2002).

More formally, if $b(i, j)$ is the number of boundaries between positions i and j in a text, and N is the number of sentences in the text, then

$$\text{WindowDiff}(ref, hyp) = \frac{1}{N-k} \sum_{i=1}^{N-k} (\; b(ref_i, ref_{i+k}) - b(hyp_i, hyp_{i+k}) \;\neq 0) \;\; (21.13)$$

WindowDiff returns a value between 0 and 1, where 0 indicates that all boundaries are assigned correctly.

21.2 Text Coherence

The previous section showed that cohesive devices, like lexical repetition, can be used to find structure in a discourse. The existence of such devices alone, however, does not satisfy a stronger requirement that a discourse must meet, that of being *coherent*. We briefly introduced coherence in the introduction. In this section we offer more details on what it means for a text to be coherent, and we describe computational mechanisms for determining coherence. We focus on **coherence relations** and reserve **entity-based coherence** for Section 21.6.2.

Recall from the introduction the difference between passages (21.14) and (21.15).

(21.14) John hid Bill's car keys. He was drunk.

(21.15) ?? John hid Bill's car keys. He likes spinach.

Coherence relation

The reason (21.14) is more coherent is that the reader can form a connection between the two utterances, in which the second utterance provides a potential CAUSE or EXPLANATION for the first utterance. This link is harder to form for (21.15). The possible connections between utterances in a discourse can be specified as a set of **coherence relations**. A few such relations, proposed by Hobbs (1979a), are given below. The terms S_0 and S_1 represent the meanings of the two sentences being related.

Result: Infer that the state or event asserted by S_0 causes or could cause the state or event asserted by S_1.

(21.16) The Tin Woodman was caught in the rain. His joints rusted.

Explanation: Infer that the state or event asserted by S_1 causes or could cause the state or event asserted by S_0.

(21.17) John hid Bill's car keys. He was drunk.

Parallel: Infer $p(a_1, a_2, ...)$ from the assertion of S_0 and $p(b_1, b_2, ...)$ from the assertion of S_1, where a_i and b_i are similar, for all i.

(21.18) The Scarecrow wanted some brains. The Tin Woodman wanted a heart.

Elaboration: Infer the same proposition P from the assertions of S_0 and S_1.

(21.19) Dorothy was from Kansas. She lived in the midst of the great Kansas prairies.

Occasion: A change of state can be inferred from the assertion of S_0, whose final state can be inferred from S_1, or a change of state can be inferred from the assertion of S_1, whose initial state can be inferred from S_0.

(21.20) Dorothy picked up the oil-can. She oiled the Tin Woodman's joints.

We can also talk about the coherence of an entire discourse by considering the hierarchical structure between coherence relations. Consider passage 21.21.

(21.21) John went to the bank to deposit his paycheck. (S1)

He then took a train to Bill's car dealership. (S2)

He needed to buy a car. (S3)

The company he works for now isn't near any public transportation. (S4)

He also wanted to talk to Bill about their softball league. (S5)

Intuitively, the structure of (21.21) is not linear. The discourse is primarily about the sequence of events described in sentences S1 and S2, whereas sentences S3 and S5 are related most directly to S2, and S4 is related most directly to S3. The coherence relationships between these sentences result in the discourse structure shown in Fig. 21.3.

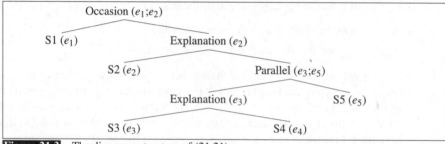

Figure 21.3   The discourse structure of (21.21).

Discourse segment   Each node in the tree represents a group of locally coherent clauses or sentences, called a **discourse segment**. Roughly speaking, one can think of discourse segments as being analogous to constituents in sentence syntax.

Now that we've seen examples of coherence, we can see more clearly how a coherence relation can play a role in summarization or information extraction. For example, discourses that are coherent by virtue of the Elaboration relation are often characterized by a summary sentence followed by one or more sentences adding detail to it, as in (21.19). Although there are two sentences describing events in this passage, the Elaboration relation tells us that the same event is being described in each. Automatic labeling of the Elaboration relation could thus tell an information extraction or summarization system to merge the information from the sentences and produce a single event description instead of two.

21.2.1   Rhetorical Structure Theory

Rhetorical Structure Theory
RST   Another theory of coherence relations that has received broad usage is **Rhetorical Structure Theory** (**RST**), a model of text organization that was originally proposed for the study of text generation (Mann and Thompson, 1987).

RST is based on a set of 23 *rhetorical relations* that can hold between spans of text within a discourse. Most relations hold between two text spans (often clauses or sentences), a **nucleus** and a **satellite**. The nucleus is the unit that is more central to the writer's purpose and that is interpretable independently; the satellite is less central and generally is only interpretable with respect to the nucleus.

Nucleus
Satellite

Evidence
Consider the **Evidence** relation, in which a satellite presents evidence for the proposition or situation expressed in the nucleus:

(21.22) Kevin must be here. His car is parked outside.

RST relations are traditionally represented graphically; the asymmetric Nucleus-Satellite relation is represented with an arrow from the satellite to the nucleus:

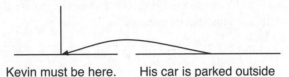

Kevin must be here.   His car is parked outside

In the original (Mann and Thompson, 1987) formulation, an RST relation is formally defined by a set of **constraints** on the nucleus and satellite, having to do with the goals and beliefs of the writer (W) and reader (R), and by the **effect** on the reader (R). The Evidence relation, for example, is defined as follows:

Relation Name:	Evidence
Constraints on N:	R might not believe N to a degree satisfactory to W
Constraints on S:	R believes S or will find it credible
Constraints on N+S:	R's comprehending S increases R's belief of N
Effects:	R's belief of N is increased

There are many different sets of rhetorical relations in RST and related theories and implementations. The RST TreeBank (Carlson et al., 2001), for example, defines 78 distinct relations, grouped into 16 classes. Here are some common RST relations, with definitions adapted from Carlson and Marcu (2001).

Elaboration: There are various kinds of elaboration relations; in each one, the satellite gives further information about the content of the nucleus:

[N The company wouldn't elaborate,] [S citing competitive reasons]

Attribution: The satellite gives the source of attribution for an instance of reported speech in the nucleus.

[S Analysts estimated,] [N that sales at U.S. stores declined in the quarter, too]

Contrast: This is a multinuclear relation, in which two or more nuclei contrast along some important dimension:

[N The priest was in a very bad temper,] [N but the lama was quite happy.]

List: In this multinuclear relation, a series of nuclei is given, without contrast or explicit comparison:

[N Billy Bones was the mate;] [N Long John, he was quartermaster]

Background: The satellite gives context for interpreting the nucleus:

[$_S$ T is the pointer to the root of a binary tree.] [$_N$ Initialize T.]

Just as we saw for the Hobbs coherence relations, RST relations can be hierarchically organized into an entire discourse tree. Figure 21.4 shows one from Marcu (2000a) for the text in (21.23) from the *Scientific American* magazine.

(21.23) With its distant orbit–50 percent farther from the sun than Earth–and slim atmospheric blanket, Mars experiences frigid weather conditions. Surface temperatures typically average about -60 degrees Celsius (-76 degrees Fahrenheit) at the equator and can dip to -123 degrees C near the poles. Only the midday sun at tropical latitudes is warm enough to thaw ice on occasion, but any liquid water formed in this way would evaporate almost instantly because of the low atmospheric pressure.

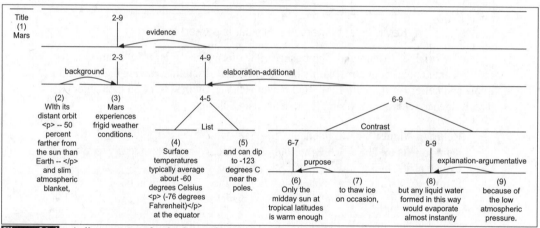

Figure 21.4   A discourse tree for the *Scientific American* text in (21.23), from Marcu (2000a). Note that asymmetric relations are represented with a curved arrow from the satellite to the nucleus.

See the Historical Notes at the end of the chapter for pointers to other theories of coherence relations and related corpora; see Chapter 23 for the application of RST and similar coherence relations to summarization.

21.2.2   Automatic Coherence Assignment

Given a sequence of sentences, how can we automatically determine the coherence relations between them? Whether we use RST, Hobbs, or one of the many other sets of relations, we call this task **coherence relation assignment**. If we extend this task from assigning a relation between two sentences to the larger goal of extracting a tree

Discourse parsing or graph representing an entire discourse, we often use the term **discourse parsing**.

Both of these tasks are quite difficult, and remain unsolved open research problems. Nonetheless, a variety of methods have been proposed, and in this section we describe shallow algorithms based on **cue phrases**. In the following section, we sketch a more sophisticated but less robust algorithm based on **abduction**.

A shallow cue-phrase-based algorithm for coherence extraction has three stages:

1. Identify the cue phrases in a text.

2. Segment the text into discourse segments, using cue phrases.

3. Classify the relationship between each consecutive discourse segment, using cue phrases.

Cue phrase

Discourse marker

We said earlier that a **cue phrase** (or **discourse marker** or **cue word**) is a word or phrase that functions to signal discourse structure, especially by linking together discourse segments. In Section 21.1 we mentioned cue phrases or features like *joining us now is* ⟨*PERSON*⟩ (for broadcast news segmentation) or *following word is the name of a neighborhood* (for real estate ad segmentation). For extracting coherence

Connective

relations, we rely on cue phrases called **connectives**, which are often conjunctions or adverbs, and which give us a cue to the coherence relations that hold between segments. For example, the connective *because* strongly suggests the EXPLANATION relation in (21.24).

(21.24) John hid Bill's car keys <u>because</u> he was drunk.

Other such cue phrases include *although*, *but*, *for example*, *yet*, *with*, and *and*. Discourse markers can be quite ambiguous between these **discourse** uses and non-discourse-related **sentential** uses. For example, the word *with* can be used as a cue

Sentential

phrase as in (21.25) or in a sentential use as in (21.26)[1]:

(21.25) **With** its distant orbit, Mars exhibits frigid weather conditions

(21.26) We can see Mars **with** an ordinary telescope.

Some simple disambiguation of the discourse versus sentential use of a cue phrase can be done with simple regular expressions, once we have sentence boundaries. For example, if the words *With* or *Yet* are capitalized and sentence-initial, they tend to be discourse markers. The words *because* or *where* tend to be discourse markers if preceded by a comma. More complete disambiguation requires the WSD techniques of Chapter 20 that use many other features. If speech is available, for example, discourse markers often bear different kinds of pitch accent than do sentential uses (Hirschberg and Litman, 1993).

The second step in determining the correct coherence relation is to segment the text into **discourse segments**. Discourse segments generally correspond to clauses or sentences, although sometimes they are smaller than clauses. Many algorithms approximate segmentation by using entire sentences, employing the sentence segmentation algorithm of Fig. 3.22 (page 71), or the algorithm of Section 8.1.1.

Often, however, a clause or clause-like unit is a more appropriate size for a discourse segment, as we see in the following examples from Sporleder and Lapata (2004):

(21.27) [We can't win] [but we must keep trying] (CONTRAST)

(21.28) [The ability to operate at these temperature is advantageous], [because the devices need less thermal insulation] (EXPLANATION)

One way to segment these clause-like units is to use hand-written segmentation rules based on individual cue phrases. For example, if the cue-phrase *Because* occurs sentence-initially and is eventually followed by a comma (as in (21.29)), it may begin

---

[1] In that case, perhaps it will be a cue instead for the semantic role INSTRUMENT.

a segment (terminated by the comma) that relates to the clause after the comma. If *because* occurs sentence-medially, it may divide the sentence into a previous and following discourse segment (as in (21.30)). These cases can be distinguished by handwritten rules based on punctuation and sentence boundaries.

(21.29)   [Because of the low atmospheric pressure,] [any liquid water would evaporate instantly]

(21.30)   [Any liquid water would evaporate instantly] [because of the low atmospheric pressure.]

If a syntactic parser is available, we can write more complex segmentation rules by making use of syntactic phrases.

The third step in coherence extraction is to automatically classify the relation between each pair of neighboring segments. We can again write rules for each discourse marker, just as we did for determining discourse segment boundaries. Thus, a rule could specify that a segment beginning with sentence-initial *Because* is a satellite in a CAUSE relationship with a nucleus segment that follows the comma.

In general, the rule-based approach to coherence extraction does not achieve extremely high accuracy. Partly this is because cue phrases are ambiguous; *because*, for example, can indicate both CAUSE and EVIDENCE, *but* can indicate CONTRAST, ANTITHESIS, and CONCESSION, and so on. We need features other than just the cue phrases themselves. But a deeper problem with the rule-based method is that many coherence relations are not signaled by cue phrases at all. In the RST corpus of Carlson et al. (2001), for example, Marcu and Echihabi (2002) found that only 61 of the 238 CONTRAST relations and only 79 of the 307 EXPLANATION-EVIDENCE relations were indicated by explicit cue phrases. Instead, many coherence relations are signaled by more implicit cues. For example, the following two sentences are in the CONTRAST relation, but there is no explicit *in contrast* or *but* connective beginning the second sentence:

(21.31)   The $6 billion that some 40 companies are looking to raise in the year ending March 31 compares with only $2.7 billion raised on the capital market in the previous fiscal year.

(21.32)   In fiscal 1984 before Mr. Gandhi came to power, only $810 million was raised.

How can we extract coherence relations between discourse segments if no cue phrases exist? There are certainly many implicit cues that we could use. Consider the following two discourse segments:

(21.33)   [I don't want a truck;] [I'd prefer a convertible.]

The CONTRAST relation between these segments is signaled by their syntactic parallelism, by the use of negation in the first segment, and by the lexical coordinate relation between *convertible* and *truck*. But many of these features are quite lexical, requiring a large number of parameters, which couldn't be trained on the small amount of labeled coherence relation data that currently exists.

This suggests the use of **bootstrapping** to automatically label a larger corpus with coherence relations that could then be used to train these more expensive features. We can do this by relying on discourse markers that are strong, unambiguous cues for particular relations. For example, *consequently* is an unambiguous signal for RESULT, *in other words* for SUMMARY, *for example* for ELABORATION, and *secondly* for CONTINUATION. We write regular expressions to extract pairs of discourse segments surrounding these cue phrases and then remove the cue phrases themselves. The resulting sentence pairs, without the cue phrases, are used as a supervised training set for these coherence relations.

Given this labeled training set, any supervised machine learning method can be used. Marcu and Echihabi (2002), for example, use a naive Bayes classifier based only on word-pair features (w_1, w_2), where the first word w_1 occurs in the first discourse segment, and the second w_2 occurs in the following segment. This feature captures lexical relations like *convertible/truck* above. Sporleder and Lascarides (2005) include other features, such as individual words, parts of speech, or stemmed words in the left and right discourse segment. They found, for example, that words like *other*, *still*, and *not* were chosen by feature selection as good cues for CONTRAST. Words like *so*, *indeed*, and *undoubtedly* were chosen as cues for RESULT.

21.3   Reference Resolution

> *and even Stigand, the patriotic archbishop of Canterbury, found it advisable–"'*
> *'Found WHAT?' said the Duck.*
> *'Found IT,' the Mouse replied rather crossly: 'of course you know what "it" means.'*
> *'I know what "it" means well enough, when I find a thing,' said the Duck: 'it's generally a frog or a worm. The question is, what did the archbishop find?'*
>
> Lewis Carroll, *Alice in Wonderland*

To interpret the sentences of any discourse, we need to know who or what entity is being talked about. Consider the following passage:

(21.34)   Victoria Chen, Chief Financial Officer of Megabucks Banking Corp since 2004, saw her pay jump 20%, to \$1.3 million, as the 37-year-old also became the Denver-based financial-services company's president. It has been ten years since she came to Megabucks from rival Lotsabucks.

In this passage, each of the underlined phrases is used by the speaker to denote one person named Victoria Chen. We refer to this use of linguistic expressions like *her* or *Victoria Chen* to denote an entity or individual as **reference**. In the next few sections of this chapter we study the problem of **reference resolution**. Reference resolution is the task of determining what entities are referred to by which linguistic expressions.

We first define some terminology. A natural language expression used to perform reference is called a **referring expression**, and the entity that is referred to is called the **referent**. Thus, *Victoria Chen* and *she* in (21.34) are referring expressions, and Victoria Chen is their referent. (To distinguish between referring expressions and their referents, we italicize the former.) As a convenient shorthand, we sometimes speak of a referring expression referring to a referent, for example, we might say that *she* refers

Reference
Reference resolution

Referring expression
Referent

to Victoria Chen. However, the reader should keep in mind that what we really mean is that the speaker is performing the act of referring to Victoria Chen by uttering *she*. Two

Corefer

referring expressions that are used to refer to the same entity are said to **corefer**; thus, *Victoria Chen* and *she* corefer in (21.34). There is also a term for a referring expression that licenses the use of another, in the way that the mention of *John* allows John to be

Antecedent
Anaphora
Anaphoric

subsequently referred to as *he*. We call *John* the **antecedent** of *he*. Reference to an entity that has been previously introduced into the discourse is called **anaphora**, and the referring expression used is said to be **anaphoric**. In passage (21.34), the pronouns *she* and *her* and the definite NP *the 37-year-old* are therefore anaphoric.

Natural languages provide speakers with a variety of ways to refer to entities. Say that your friend has a 1961 Ford Falcon automobile and you want to refer to it. De-

Discourse context

pending on the operative **discourse context**, you might say *it, this, that, this car, that car, the car, the Ford, the Falcon*, or *my friend's car*, among many other possibilities. However, you are not free to choose between any of these alternatives in any con-text. For instance, you cannot simply say *it* or *the Falcon* if the hearer has no prior knowledge of your friend's car, it has not been mentioned before, and it is not in the

Situational context

immediate surroundings of the discourse participants (i.e., the **situational context** of the discourse).

The reason for this is that each type of referring expression encodes different signals about the place that the speaker believes the referent occupies within the hearer's set of beliefs. A subset of these beliefs that has a special status forms the hearer's mental

Discourse model

model of the ongoing discourse, which we call a **discourse model** (Webber, 1978). The discourse model contains representations of the entities that have been referred to in the discourse and the relationships in which they participate. Thus, two components are required by a system to successfully interpret (or produce) referring expressions: a method for constructing a discourse model that evolves with the dynamically changing discourse it represents; and a method for mapping between the signals that various referring expressions encode and the hearer's set of beliefs. The latter includes this discourse model.

We will speak in terms of two fundamental operations to the discourse model. When a referent is first mentioned in a discourse, we say that a representation for it

Evoke

is **evoked** into the model. Upon subsequent mention, this representation is **accessed**

Access

from the model. The operations and relationships are illustrated in Fig. 21.5. As we show in Section 21.8, the discourse model plays an important role in how coreference algorithms are evaluated.

We are now ready to introduce two reference resolution tasks: **coreference reso-**

*Coreference
resolution*

lution and **pronominal anaphora resolution**. Coreference resolution is the task of finding referring expressions in a text that refer to the same entity, that is, finding ex-

Coreference chain

pressions that **corefer**. We call the set of coreferring expressions a **coreference chain**. For example, in processing (21.34), a coreference resolution algorithm would need to find four coreference chains:

1. *Victoria Chen, Chief Financial Officer of Megabucks Banking Corp since 1994, her, the 37-year-old, the Denver-based financial-services company's president, She*

2. *Megabucks Banking Corp, the Denver-based financial-services company, Megabucks*

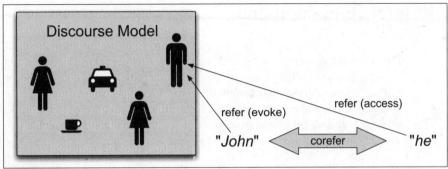

Figure 21.5   Reference operations and relationships with respect to the discourse model.

3.   *her pay*

4.   *Lotsabucks*

Pronominal
anaphora
resolution

Coreference resolution thus requires finding all referring expressions in a discourse and grouping them into coreference chains. By contrast, **pronominal anaphora resolution** is the task of finding the antecedent for a single pronoun; for example, given the pronoun *her*, our task is to decide that the antecedent of *her* is *Victoria Chen*. Thus pronominal anaphora resolution can be viewed as a subtask of coreference resolution.[2]

In the next section we introduce different kinds of reference phenomena. We then give various algorithms for reference resolution. Pronominal anaphora has received a lot of attention in speech and language processing, so we introduce three algorithms for pronoun processing: the **Hobbs** algorithm, a **Centering** algorithm, and a **log-linear** (MaxEnt) algorithm. We then give an algorithm for the more general coreference resolution task.

Each of these algorithms focuses on resolving reference to entities or individuals. It is important to note, however, that discourses do include reference to many other types of referents than entities. Consider the possibilities in (21.35), adapted from Webber (1991).

(21.35)   According to Doug, Sue just bought a 1961 Ford Falcon.

    a. But *that* turned out to be a lie.

    b. But *that* was false.

    c. *That* struck me as a funny way to describe the situation.

    d. *That* caused a financial problem for Sue.

The referent of *that* is a speech act (see Chapter 24) in (21.35a), a proposition in (21.35b), a manner of description in (21.35c), and an event in (21.35d). The field awaits the development of robust methods for interpreting these types of reference.

---

[2] Technically, however, some cases of anaphora are not cases of coreference; see van Deemter and Kibble (2000) for more discussion.

21.4 Reference Phenomena

The set of referential phenomena that natural languages provide is quite rich indeed. In this section, we briefly describe several basic reference phenomena, surveying five types of referring expression: *indefinite noun phrases, definite noun phrases, pronouns, demonstratives*, and *names*. We then summarize the way these referring expressions are used to encode **given** and **new** information, along the way introducing two types of referents that complicate the reference resolution problem: *inferrables* and *generics*.

21.4.1 Five Types of Referring Expressions

Indefinite Noun Phrases: Indefinite reference introduces into the discourse context entities that are new to the hearer. The most common form of indefinite reference is marked with the determiner *a* (or *an*), but it can also be marked by a quantifier such as *some* or even the determiner *this*:

(21.36)   a. Mrs. Martin was so very kind as to send Mrs. Goddard *a beautiful goose*.
　　　　b. He had gone round one day to bring her *some walnuts*.
　　　　c. I saw *this beautiful Ford Falcon* today.

· Such noun phrases evoke into the discourse model a representation for a new entity that satisfies the given description.

The indefinite determiner *a* does not indicate whether the entity is identifiable to the speaker, which in some cases leads to a *specific/non-specific* ambiguity. Example 21.36a has only the specific reading since the speaker has a particular goose in mind, the one Mrs. Martin sent. In (21.37), on the other hand, both readings are possible.

(21.37) I am going to the butcher's to buy a goose.

That is, the speaker may already have the goose picked out (specific) or may just be planning to pick one out that is to her liking (non-specific).

Definite Noun Phrases: Definite reference refers to an entity that is identifiable to the hearer. An entity can be identifiable to the hearer because it has been mentioned previously in the text and thus is already represented in the discourse model.

(21.38) It concerns a white stallion which I have sold to an officer. But the pedigree of *the white stallion* was not fully established.

Alternatively, an entity can be identifiable because it is contained in the hearer's set of beliefs about the world, or the uniqueness of the object is implied by the description itself, in which case it evokes a representation of the referent into the discourse model, as in (21.39):

(21.39) I read about it in the *New York Times*.

Pronouns: Another form of definite reference is pronominalization, illustrated in (21.40).

(21.40) Emma smiled and chatted as cheerfully as *she* could,

The constraints on using pronominal reference are stronger than those for full definite noun phrases, requiring that the referent have a high degree of activation or *Salience*   **salience** in the discourse model. Pronouns usually (but not always) refer to entities that were introduced no further than one or two sentences back in the ongoing discourse, whereas definite noun phrases can often refer further back. This is illustrated by the difference between (21.41d) and (21.41d').

(21.41)   a.   John went to Bob's party, and parked next to a classic Ford Falcon.

        b.   He went inside and talked to Bob for more than an hour.

        c.   Bob told him that he recently got engaged.

        d.   ?? He also said that he bought *it* yesterday.

        d.'   He also said that he bought *the Falcon* yesterday.

By the time the last sentence is reached, the Falcon no longer has the degree of salience required to allow for pronominal reference to it.

Cataphora   Pronouns can also participate in **cataphora**, in which they are mentioned before their referents are, as in (21.42).

(21.42) Even before *she* saw *it*, Dorothy had been thinking about the Emerald City every day.

Here, the pronouns *she* and *it* both occur *before* their referents are introduced.

Pronouns also appear in quantified contexts in which they are considered to be *Bound*   **bound**, as in (21.43).

(21.43) Every dancer brought *her* left arm forward.

Under the relevant reading, *her* does not refer to some woman in context, but instead behaves like a variable bound to the quantified expression *every dancer*. We are not concerned with the bound interpretation of pronouns in this chapter.

Demonstratives: Demonstrative pronouns, like *this* and *that*, behave somewhat differently than simple definite pronouns like *it*. They can appear either alone or as determiners, for instance, *this ingredient, that spice*. *This* and *that* differ in lexical meaning: *Proximal*   *this*, the **proximal demonstrative**, indicates literal or metaphorical closeness; *that*, the *Distal*   **distal demonstrative** indicating literal or metaphorical distance (further away in time). See the following example:

(21.44) I just bought a copy of Thoreau's *Walden*. I had bought one five years ago. *That one* had been very tattered; *this one* was in much better condition.

Note that *this NP* is ambiguous; in colloquial spoken English, it can be indefinite, as in (21.36), or definite, as in (21.44).

Names: Names are a common form of referring expression, including names of people, organizations, and locations, as we illustrate in the discussion of named entities in Section 22.1. Names can be used to refer to both new and old entities in the discourse:

(21.45)   a.   **Miss Woodhouse** certainly had not done him justice.

        b.   **International Business Machines** sought patent compensation from Amazon; **IBM** had previously sued other companies.

21.4.2   Information Status

Information status
Information structure

We noted above that the same referring expressions (such as many indefinite NPs) can be used to introduce new referents, and other expressions (such as many definite NPs or pronouns) can be used to refer anaphorically to old referents. This idea of studying the way different referential forms are used to provide new or old information is called **information status** or **information structure**.

Givenness hierarchy

A variety of theories express the relation between different types of referential form and the informativity or saliency of the referent in the discourse. For example, the **givenness hierarchy** (Gundel et al., 1993) is a scale representing six kinds of information status that different referring expression are used to signal.

The givenness hierarchy:

in focus >	activated >	familiar >	uniquely identifiable >	referential >	type identifiable
it	$\left\{ \begin{array}{l} that \\ this \\ this\ N \end{array} \right\}$	that N	the N	indef. *this* N	*a* N

Accessibility scale

The related **accessibility scale** of Ariel (2001) is based on the idea that referents that are more salient will be easier for the hearer to call to mind, and hence can be referred to with less linguistic material. By contrast, less salient entities will need a longer and more explicit referring expression to help the hearer recover the referent. The following shows a sample scale going from low to high accessibility:

> *Full name > long definite description > short definite description > last name > first name > distal demonstrative > proximate demonstrative > NP > stressed pronoun > unstressed pronoun*

Note that accessibility correlates with length, with less accessible NPs tending to be longer. Indeed, if we follow a coreference chain in a discourse, we often find longer NPs (e.g., long definition descriptions with relative clauses) early in the discourse and much shorter ones (for example pronouns) later in the discourse.

Another perspective, based on the work of (Prince, 1992), analyzes information status in terms of two crosscutting dichotomies: *hearer status* and *discourse status*. The *hearer status* of a referent expresses whether it is previously known to the hearer, or whether it is new. The *discourse status* expresses whether the referent has been previously mentioned in the discourse.

The relationship between referring expression form and information status can be complicated; we summarize below the use of three such complicating factors: **inferrables**, **generics**, and **non-referential forms**.

Inferrable
Bridging inference
Mediated

Inferrables: In some cases, a referring expression does not refer to an entity that has been explicitly evoked in the text, but instead to one that is inferentially related to an evoked entity. Such referents are called **inferrables**, **bridging inferences**, or **mediated** (Haviland and Clark, 1974; Prince, 1981; Nissim et al., 2004). Consider the expressions *a door* and *the engine* in (21.46).

(21.46) I almost bought a 1961 Ford Falcon today, but *a door* had a dent and *the engine* seemed noisy.

The indefinite noun phrase *a door* would normally introduce a new door into the discourse context, but in this case the hearer is to infer something more: that it is not just any door, but one of the doors of the Falcon. Similarly, the use of the definite noun phrase *the engine* normally presumes that an engine has been previously evoked or is otherwise uniquely identifiable. Here, no engine has been explicitly mentioned, but the hearer makes a **bridging inference** to infer that the referent is the engine of the previously mentioned Falcon.

Generics: Another kind of expression that does not refer back to an entity explicitly evoked in the text is *generic* reference. Consider (21.47).

(21.47) I'm interested in buying a Mac laptop. *They* are very stylish.

Here, *they* refers, not to a particular laptop (or even a particular set of laptops), but instead to the class of Mac laptops in general. Similarly, the pronoun *you* can be used generically in the following example:

(21.48) In March in Boulder *you* have to wear a jacket.

Non-referential uses: Finally, some non-referential forms bear a confusing superficial resemblance to referring expressions. For example, in addition to its referring usages, the word *it* can be used in **pleonastic** cases like *it is raining*, in idioms like *hit it off*, or in particular syntactic situations like **clefts** (21.49a) or **extraposition** (21.49b):

Pleonastic

Cleft

(21.49)   a. *It* was Frodo who carried the ring.

 b. *It* was good that Frodo carried the ring.

21.5   Features for Pronominal Anaphora Resolution

We now turn to the task of resolving pronominal reference. In general, this problem is formulated as follows. We are given a single pronoun (*he, him, she, her, it*, and sometimes *they/them*), together with the previous context. Our task is to find the antecedent of the pronoun in this context. We present three systems for this task; but first we summarize useful constraints on possible referents.

21.5.1   Features for Filtering Potential Referents

We begin with four relatively hard-and-fast morphosyntactic features that can be used to filter the set of possible referents: **number**, **person**, **gender**, and **binding theory** constraints.

Number Agreement: Referring expressions and their referents must agree in number; for English, this means distinguishing between *singular* and *plural* references. English *she/her/he/him/his/it* are singular, *we/us/they/them* are plural, and *you* is unspecified for number. Here are some illustrations of the constraints on number agreement:

John has a Ford Falcon. It is red.   * John has a Ford Falcon. They are red.
John has three Ford Falcons. They are red.   * John has three Ford Falcons. It is red.

We cannot always enforce a strict grammatical notion of number agreement, since sometimes semantically plural entities can be referred to by either *it* or *they*:

(21.50) IBM announced a new machine translation product yesterday. *They* have been working on it for 20 years.

Person Agreement: English distinguishes between three forms of person: first, second, and third. The antecedent of a pronoun must agree with the pronoun in number. In particular, a third person pronoun (*he, she, they, him, her, them, his, her, their*) must have a third person antecedent (one of the above or any other noun phrase).

Gender Agreement: Referents also must agree with the gender specified by the referring expression. English third-person pronouns distinguish between *male* (*he, him, his*), *female* (*she, her*), and *nonpersonal* (*it*) genders. Unlike the case in some languages, English male and female pronoun genders only apply to animate entities; with few exceptions, inanimate entities are always nonpersonal/neuter. Some examples:

(21.51) John has a Ford. He is attractive. (he=John, not the Ford)

(21.52) John has a Ford. It is attractive. (it=the Ford, not John)

Binding Theory Constraints: Reference relations may also be constrained by the syntactic relationships between a referential expression and a possible antecedent noun phrase when both occur in the same sentence. For instance, the pronouns in all of the following sentences are subject to the constraints indicated in brackets.

(21.53) John bought himself a new Ford. [himself=John]

(21.54) John bought him a new Ford. [him≠John]

(21.55) John said that Bill bought him a new Ford. [him≠Bill]

(21.56) John said that Bill bought himself a new Ford. [himself=Bill]

(21.57) He said that he bought John a new Ford. [He≠John; he≠John]

Reflexive

English pronouns such as *himself*, *herself*, and *themselves* are called **reflexives**. Oversimplifying the situation, a reflexive corefers with the subject of the most immediate clause that contains it (21.53), whereas a nonreflexive cannot corefer with this subject (21.54). That this rule applies only for the subject of the most immediate clause is shown by (21.55) and (21.56), in which the opposite reference pattern is manifest between the pronoun and the subject of the higher sentence. On the other hand, a full noun phrase like *John* cannot corefer with the subject of the most immediate clause or with a higher-level subject, as in (21.57).

Binding theory

These constraints are often called the **binding theory** (Chomsky, 1981), and quite complicated versions of these constraints have been proposed. A complete statement of the constraints requires reference to semantic and other factors and cannot be stated purely in terms of syntactic configuration. For the algorithms discussed in this chapter, we assume a simple syntactic account of restrictions on intrasentential coreference.

21.5.2   Preferences in Pronoun Interpretation

We next turn to features for predicting the referent of a pronoun that are less hard-and-fast: **recency**, **grammatical role**, **repeated mention**, **parallelism**, **verb semantics**, and **selectional restrictions**.

Recency: Entities introduced in recent utterances tend to be more salient than those introduced from utterances further back. Thus, in (21.58), the pronoun *it* is more likely to refer to Jim's map than the doctor's map.

(21.58) The doctor found an old map in the captain's chest. Jim found an even older map hidden on the shelf. It described an island.

Grammatical Role: Many theories specify a salience hierarchy of entities that is ordered by the grammatical position of the expressions that denote them. These typically treat entities mentioned in subject position as more salient than those in object position, which are in turn more salient than those mentioned in subsequent positions.

Passages such as (21.59) and (21.60) lend support for such a hierarchy. Although the first sentence in each case expresses roughly the same propositional content, the preferred referent for the pronoun *he* varies with the subject in each case—John in (21.59) and Bill in (21.60).

(21.59) Billy Bones went to the bar with Jim Hawkins. He called for a glass of rum.
[he = Billy]

(21.60) Jim Hawkins went to the bar with Billy Bones. He called for a glass of rum.
[he = Jim]

Repeated Mention: Some theories incorporate the idea that entities that have been focused on in the prior discourse are more likely to continue to be focused on in subsequent discourse, and hence references to them are more likely to be pronominalized. For instance, whereas the pronoun in (21.60) has Jim as its preferred interpretation, the pronoun in the final sentence of (21.61) may be more likely to refer to Billy Bones.

(21.61) Billy Bones had been thinking about a glass of rum ever since the pirate ship docked. He hobbled over to the Old Parrot bar. Jim Hawkins went with him. He called for a glass of rum. [he = Billy]

Parallelism: There are also strong preferences that appear to be induced by parallelism effects, as in (21.62).

(21.62) Long John Silver went with Jim to the Old Parrot. Billy Bones went with him to the Old Anchor Inn. [him = Jim]

The grammatical role hierarchy described above ranks Long John Silver as more salient than Jim and thus should be the preferred referent of *him*. Furthermore, there is no semantic reason that Long John Silver cannot be the referent. Nonetheless, *him* is instead understood to refer to Jim.

Verb Semantics: Certain verbs appear to place a semantically oriented emphasis on one of their argument positions, which can have the effect of biasing the manner in which subsequent pronouns are interpreted. Compare (21.63) and (21.64).

(21.63) John telephoned Bill. He lost the laptop.

(21.64) John criticized Bill. He lost the laptop.

These examples differ only in the verb used in the first sentence, yet the subject pronoun in (21.63) is typically resolved to John, whereas the pronoun in (21.64) is resolved to Bill. It has been argued that this effect results from the "implicit causality" of a verb:

the implicit cause of a "criticizing" event is considered to be its object, whereas the implicit cause of a "telephoning" event is considered to be its subject. This emphasis results in a higher degree of salience for the entity in this argument position.

Selectional Restrictions: Many other kinds of semantic knowledge can play a role in referent preference. For example, the selectional restrictions that a verb places on its arguments (see Chapter 19) can help eliminate referents, as in (21.65).

(21.65) John parked his car in the garage after driving it around for hours.

There are two possible referents for *it*, the car and the garage. The verb *drive*, however, requires that its direct object denote something that can be driven, such as a car, truck, or bus, but not a garage. Thus, the fact that the pronoun appears as the object of *drive* restricts the set of possible referents to the car. A system can implement selectional restrictions by storing a dictionary of probabilistic dependencies between the verb and the potential referent.

21.6   Three Algorithms for Anaphora Resolution

We now introduce three key algorithms for pronominal anaphora resolution: the **Hobbs** algorithm, a **Centering** algorithm, and a **log-linear** (or MaxEnt) algorithm.

21.6.1   Pronominal Anaphora Baseline: The Hobbs Algorithm

Hobbs algorithm   The **Hobbs algorithm** (the simpler of two algorithms presented originally in Hobbs (1978)) depends only on a syntactic parser plus a morphological gender and number checker. For this reason, the Hobbs algorithm is often used as a baseline for evaluating new pronominal anaphora resolution algorithms.

The input to the Hobbs algorithm is a pronoun to be resolved, together with a syntactic parse of the sentences up to and including the current sentence. The algorithm searches for an antecedent noun phrase in these trees. The intuition of the algorithm is to start with the target pronoun and walk up the parse tree to the root S. For each NP or S node that it finds, it does a breadth-first, left-to-right search of the node's children to the left of the target. As each candidate noun phrase is proposed, it is checked for gender, number, and person agreement with the pronoun. If no referent is found, the algorithm performs a left-to-right, breadth-first search on preceding sentences.

The Hobbs algorithm does not capture all the constraints and preferences on pronominalization described above. It does, however, approximate the *binding theory*, *recency*, and *grammatical role* preferences by the order in which the search is performed, and the *gender*, *person*, and *number* constraints by a final check.

An algorithm that searches parse trees must also specify a grammar, since the assumptions regarding the structure of syntactic trees will affect the results. A fragment for English that the algorithm uses is given in Fig. 21.6. The steps of the **Hobbs algorithm** are as follows:

1. Begin at the noun phrase (NP) node immediately dominating the pronoun.

$$S \rightarrow NP\ VP$$

$$NP \rightarrow \left\{ \begin{array}{l} (Det)\ \ Nominal \ \ \left(\left\{ \begin{array}{l} PP \\ Rel \end{array} \right\} \right)^* \\ pronoun \end{array} \right\}$$

$$Det \rightarrow \left\{ \begin{array}{l} determiner \\ NP\ \text{'}s \end{array} \right\}$$

$$PP \rightarrow preposition\ NP$$

$$Nominal \rightarrow noun\ (PP)^*$$

$$Rel \rightarrow wh\text{-}word\ S$$

$$VP \rightarrow verb\ NP\ (PP)^*$$

Figure 21.6   A grammar fragment for the Tree Search algorithm.

2. Go up the tree to the first NP or sentence (S) node encountered. Call this node X, and call the path used to reach it p.

3. Traverse all branches below node X to the left of path p in a left-to-right, breadth-first fashion. Propose as the antecedent any encountered NP node that has an NP or S node between it and X.

4. If node X is the highest S node in the sentence, traverse the surface parse trees of previous sentences in the text in order of recency, the most recent first; each tree is traversed in a left-to-right, breadth-first manner, and when an NP node is encountered, it is proposed as antecedent. If X is not the highest S node in the sentence, continue to step 5.

5. From node X, go up the tree to the first NP or S node encountered. Call this new node X, and call the path traversed to reach it p.

6. If X is an NP node and if the path p to X did not pass through the Nominal node that X immediately dominates, propose X as the antecedent.

7. Traverse all branches below node X to the *left* of path p in a left-to-right, breadth-first manner. Propose any NP node encountered as the antecedent.

8. If X is an S node, traverse all branches of node X to the *right* of path p in a left-to-right, breadth-first manner, but do not go below any NP or S node encountered. Propose any NP node encountered as the antecedent.

9. Go to Step 4.

Demonstrating that this algorithm yields the correct coreference assignments for an example sentence is left as Exercise 21.2.

Most parsers return number information (singular or plural), and person information is easily encoded by rule for the first- and second-person pronouns. But parsers for English rarely return gender information for common or proper nouns. Thus, the only additional requirement to implementing the Hobbs algorithm, besides a parser, is an algorithm for determining gender for each antecedent noun phrase.

One common way to assign gender to a noun phrase is to extract the head noun and then use WordNet (Chapter 19) to look at the hypernyms of the head noun. Ancestors like *person* or *living thing* indicate an animate noun. Ancestors like *female* indicate a female noun. A list of personal names associated with genders or patterns like `Mr.` can also be used (Cardie and Wagstaff, 1999).

More complex algorithms exist, such as that of Bergsma and Lin (2006); Bergsma and Lin also make freely available a large list of nouns and their (automatically extracted) genders.

21.6.2 A Centering Algorithm for Anaphora Resolution

Centering theory

The Hobbs algorithm does not use an explicit representation of a discourse model. By contrast, **Centering theory** (Grosz et al., 1995, henceforth GJW) is a family of models that have an explicit representation of a discourse model. This family incorporates an additional claim: that a single entity being "centered" on at any given point in the discourse is to be distinguished from all other entities that have been evoked. Centering theory has been applied to many problems in discourse, such as the computation of **entity-based coherence**; in this section we see its application to anaphora resolution.

Backward-looking center
Forward-looking center

Two main representations are tracked in the Centering theory discourse model. In what follows, take U_n and U_{n+1} to be two adjacent utterances. The **backward-looking center** of U_n, denoted as $C_b(U_n)$, represents the entity currently being focused on in the discourse after U_n is interpreted. The **forward-looking centers** of U_n, denoted as $C_f(U_n)$, form an ordered list containing the entities mentioned in U_n, all of which could serve as the C_b of the following utterance. In fact, $C_b(U_{n+1})$ is by definition the most highly ranked element of $C_f(U_n)$ mentioned in U_{n+1}. (The C_b of the first utterance in a discourse is undefined.) As for how the entities in the $C_f(U_n)$ are ordered, for simplicity's sake we can use the grammatical role hierarchy below.[3]

> subject > existential predicate nominal > object > indirect object or oblique
> > demarcated adverbial PP

As a shorthand, we call the highest-ranked forward-looking center C_p (for "preferred center").

We describe a centering-based algorithm for pronoun interpretation due to Brennan et al. (1987, henceforth BFP); see Walker et al. (1994) and the Historical Notes at the end of the chapter for other centering algorithms. In this algorithm, preferred referents of pronouns are computed from relations that hold between the forward- and backward-looking centers in adjacent sentences. The algorithm defines four intersentential relationships between a pair of utterances U_n and U_{n+1} that depend on the relationship between $C_b(U_{n+1})$, $C_b(U_n)$, and $C_p(U_{n+1})$; these are shown in Fig. 21.7.

	$C_b(U_{n+1}) = C_b(U_n)$ or undefined $C_b(U_n)$	$C_b(U_{n+1}) \neq C_b(U_n)$
$C_b(U_{n+1}) = C_p(U_{n+1})$	Continue	Smooth-Shift
$C_b(U_{n+1}) \neq C_p(U_{n+1})$	Retain	Rough-Shift

Figure 21.7 Transitions in the BFP algorithm.

---

[3] This is an extended form of the hierarchy used in Brennan et al. (1987), described below.

The following rules are used by the algorithm:

> **Rule 1:** If any element of $C_f(U_n)$ is realized by a pronoun in utterance U_{n+1}, then $C_b(U_{n+1})$ must be realized as a pronoun also.
>
> **Rule 2:** Transition states are ordered. Continue is preferred to Retain is preferred to Smooth-Shift is preferred to Rough-Shift.

Having defined these concepts and rules, the algorithm is defined as follows.

1. Generate possible C_b-C_f combinations for each possible set of reference assignments.
2. Filter by constraints, for example, syntactic coreference constraints, selectional restrictions, centering rules, and constraints.
3. Rank by transition orderings.

The pronominal referents that get assigned are those that yield the most preferred relation in Rule 2, assuming that Rule 1 and other coreference constraints (gender, number, syntactic, selectional restrictions) are not violated.

Let us step through (21.66) to illustrate the algorithm.

(21.66)   John saw a beautiful 1961 Ford Falcon at the used car dealership. (U_1)

He showed it to Bob. (U_2)

He bought it. (U_3)

Using the grammatical role hierarchy to order the C_f, for sentence U_1 we get:

$C_f(U_1)$:   John, Ford, dealership

$C_p(U_1)$: John

$C_b(U_1)$: undefined

Sentence U_2 contains two pronouns: *he*, which is compatible with John, and *it*, which is compatible with the Ford or the dealership. John is by definition $C_b(U_2)$ because he is the highest-ranked member of $C_f(U_1)$ mentioned in U_2 (since he is the only possible referent for *he*). We compare the resulting transitions for each possible referent of *it*. If we assume *it* refers to the Falcon, the assignments would be

$C_f(U_2)$:   John, Ford, Bob

$C_p(U_2)$: John

$C_b(U_2)$: John

Result: Continue   ($C_p(U_2)$=$C_b(U_2)$; $C_b(U_1)$ undefined)

If we assume *it* refers to the dealership, the assignments would be

$C_f(U_2)$:   John, dealership, Bob

$C_p(U_2)$: John

$C_b(U_2)$: John

Result: Continue   ($C_p(U_2)$=$C_b(U_2)$; $C_b(U_1)$ undefined)

Since both possibilities result in a Continue transition, the algorithm does not say which to accept. For the sake of illustration, we assume that ties are broken in terms of the ordering on the previous C_f list. Thus, we take *it* to refer to the Falcon instead of the dealership, leaving the current discourse model as represented in the first possibility above.

In sentence U_3, *he* is compatible with either John or Bob, whereas *it* is compatible with the Ford. If we assume *he* refers to John, then John is $C_b(U_3)$ and the assignments would be

$C_f(U_3)$:   John, Ford
$C_p(U_3)$: John
$C_b(U_3)$: John
Result: Continue $(C_p(U_3)=C_b(U_3)=C_b(U_2))$

If we assume *he* refers to Bob, then Bob is $C_b(U_3)$ and the assignments would be

$C_f(U_3)$:   Bob, Ford
$C_p(U_3)$: Bob
$C_b(U_3)$: Bob
Result: Smooth-Shift $(C_p(U_3)=C_b(U_3); C_b(U_3)\neq C_b(U_2))$

Since a Continue is preferred to a Smooth-Shift per Rule 2, John is correctly taken to be the referent.

The main salience factors that the centering algorithm implicitly incorporates include the grammatical role, recency, and repeated mention preferences. The manner in which the grammatical role hierarchy affects salience is indirect since it is the resulting transition type that determines the final reference assignments. In particular, a referent in a low-ranked grammatical role will be preferred to one in a more highly ranked role if the former leads to a more highly ranked transition. Thus, the centering algorithm may incorrectly resolve a pronoun to a low salience referent. For instance, in (21.67),

(21.67) Bob opened up a new dealership last week. John took a look at the Fords in his lot. He ended up buying one.

the centering algorithm will assign Bob as the referent of the subject pronoun *he* in the third sentence—since Bob is $C_b(U_2)$, this assignment results in a Continue relation, whereas assigning John results in a Smooth-Shift relation. On the other hand, the Hobbs algorithm will correctly assign John as the referent.

Like the Hobbs algorithm, the centering algorithm requires a full syntactic parse as well as morphological detectors for gender.

Centering theory is also a model of entity coherence and hence has implications for other discourse applications like summarization; see the Historical Notes at the end of the chapter for pointers.

21.6.3   A Log-Linear Model for Pronominal Anaphora Resolution

As our final model of pronominal anaphora resolution, we present a simple, supervised machine learning approach, in which we train a log-linear classifier on a corpus in which the antecedents are marked for each pronoun. Any supervised classifier can be used for this purpose; log-linear models are popular, but Naive Bayes and other classifiers have been used as well.

For training, the system relies on a hand-labeled corpus in which each pronoun has been linked by hand with the correct antecedent. The system needs to extract positive and negative examples of anaphoric relations. Positive examples occur directly in the training set. Negative examples are found by pairing each pronoun with some other noun phrase. Features (discussed in the next section) are extracted for each training observation, and a classifier is trained to predict *1* for the true pronoun-antecedent pairs, and *0* for the incorrect pronoun-antecedent pairs.

For testing, just as we saw with the Hobbs and Centering classifiers, the log-linear classifier takes as input a pronoun (*he, him, his, she, her, it, they, them, their*), together with the current and preceding sentences.

To deal with non-referential pronouns, we first filter out pleonastic pronouns (like the pleonastic *it is raining*), using hand-written rules based on frequent lexical patterns.

The classifier then extracts all potential antecedents by parsing the current and previous sentences, using either a full parser or a simple chunker. Next, each NP in the parse is considered a potential antecedent for each following pronoun. Each pronoun-potential antecedent pair is then presented to the classifier.

21.6.4   Features for Pronominal Anaphora Resolution

Some commonly used features for pronominal anaphora resolution between a pronoun Pro_i and a potential referent NP_j include the following:

- **Strict number [true or false]:** True if there is a strict match in number (e.g., singular pronoun with singular antecedent).
- **Compatible number [true or false]:** True if Pro_i and NP_j are merely compatible (e.g., singular pronoun Pro_i with antecedent NP_j of unknown number).
- **Strict gender [true or false]:** True if there is a strict match in gender (e.g., male pronoun Pro_i with male antecedent NP_j).
- **Compatible gender [true or false]:** True if Pro_i and NP_j are merely compatible (e.g., male pronoun Pro_i with antecedent NP_j of unknown gender).
- **Sentence distance [0, 1, 2, 3,...]:** The number of sentences between pronoun and potential antecedent.
- **Hobbs distance [0, 1, 2, 3,...]:** The number of noun groups that the Hobbs algorithm has to skip, starting backwards from the pronoun Pro_i, before the potential antecedent NP_j is found.
- **Grammatical role [subject, object, PP]:** The role taken by the potential antecedent—a syntactic subject, direct object, or an embedment in a PP.
- **Linguistic form [proper, definite, indefinite, pronoun]:** The form of the potential antecedent NP_j—a proper name, definite description, indefinite NP, or pronoun.

Figure 21.8 shows feature values for potential antecedents for the final *He* in U_3:

(21.68)   John saw a beautiful 1961 Ford Falcon at the used car dealership. (U_1)
He showed it to Bob. (U_2)
He bought it. (U_3)

	He (U_2)	it (U_2)	Bob (U_2)	John (U_1)
strict number	1	1	1	1
compatible number	1	1	1	1
strict gender	1	0	1	1
compatible gender	1	0	1	1
sentence distance	1	1	1	2
Hobbs distance	2	1	0	3
grammatical role	subject	object	PP	subject
linguistic form	pronoun	pronoun	proper	proper

Figure 21.8   Feature values in log-linear classifier, for various pronouns from (21.68).

The classifier will learn weights indicating which of these features are more likely to be good predictors of a successful antecedent (e.g., being nearby the pronoun, being in subject position, agreeing in gender and number). Thus, where the Hobbs and Centering algorithms rely on hand-built heuristics for antecedent selection, the machine learning classifiers learn the importance of these different features based on their co-occurrence in the training set.

21.7   Coreference Resolution

In the previous few sections, we concentrated on interpreting a particular subclass of the reference phenomena that we outlined in Section 21.4: the personal pronouns such as *he*, *she*, and *it*. But for the general coreference task we must decide whether any pair of noun phrases corefer. This means we must deal with the other types of referring expressions from Section 21.4, the most common of which are *definite noun phrases* and *names*. Let's return to our coreference example, repeated below:

(21.69) Victoria Chen, <u>Chief Financial Officer of Megabucks Banking Corp</u> since 2004, saw <u>her</u> pay jump 20%, to $1.3 million, as <u>the 37-year-old</u> also became <u>the Denver-based financial-services company's president</u>. It has been ten years since <u>she</u> came to Megabucks from rival Lotsabucks.

Recall that we need to extract four coreference chains from this data:

1. *Victoria Chen, Chief Financial Officer of Megabucks Banking Corp since 1994, her, the 37-year-old, the Denver-based financial-services company's president, She*

2. *Megabucks Banking Corp, the Denver-based financial-services company, Megabucks*

3. *her pay*

4. *Lotsabucks*

As before, we have to deal with pronominal anaphora (figuring out that *her* refers to *Victoria Chen*). And we still need to filter out non-referential pronouns like the pleonastic *It* in *It has been ten years*), as we did for pronominal anaphora.

But for full NP coreference we also need to deal with definite noun phrases, to figure out that *the 37-year-old* is coreferent with *Victoria Chen*, and that *the Denver-*

based financial-services company is the same as *Megabucks*. And we need to deal with names, to realize that *Megabucks* is the same as *Megabucks Banking Corp*.

An algorithm for coreference resolution can use the same log-linear classifier architecture we saw for pronominal anaphora. Thus, we'll build a binary classifier that is given an anaphor and a potential antecedent and returns true (the two are coreferential) or false (the two are not coreferential). We'll use this classifier in the resolution algorithm as follows. We process a document from left to right. For each NP_j we encounter, we search backwards through the document, examining each previous NP. For each such potential antecedent NP_i, we run our classifier, and if it returns true, we successfully co-index NP_i and NP_j. The process for each NP_j terminates when we either find a successful antecedent NP_i or reach the beginning of the document. We then move on to the next anaphor NP_j.

To train our binary coreference classifier, just as for pronoun resolution, we'll need a labeled training set in which each anaphor NP_i has been linked by hand with the correct antecedent. To build a classifier, we'll need both positive and negative training examples of coreference relations. A positive example for NP_i is the noun phrase NP_j that is marked as co-indexed. We get negative examples by pairing the anaphor NP_j with the intervening NPs NP_{i+1}, NP_{i+2} that occur between the true antecedent NP_i and the anaphor NP_j.

Next, features are extracted for each training observation, and a classifier is trained to predict whether an (NP_j, NP_i) pair corefer. Which features should we use in the binary coreference classifier? We can use all the features we used for anaphora resolution: number, gender, syntactic position, and so on. But we will also need to add new features to deal with phenomena that are specific to names and definite noun phrases. For example, we'll want a feature representing the fact that *Megabucks* and *Megabucks Banking Corp* share the word *Megabucks* or that *Megabucks Banking Corp* and *the Denver-based financial-services company* both end in words (*Corp* and *company*), indicating a corporate organization.

Here are some commonly used features for coreference between an anaphor NP_i and a potential antecedent NP_j (in addition to the features for pronominal anaphora resolution listed on page 709).

- **Anaphor edit distance [0,1,2,....,]:** The character **minimum edit distance** from the potential antecedent to the anaphor. Recall from Chapter 3 that the character minimum edit distance is the minimum number of character editing operations (insertions, substitutions, deletions) necessary to turn one string into another. More formally,

$$100 \quad \frac{m-(s+i+d)}{m}$$

given the antecedent length m, and the number of substitutions s, insertions i, and deletions d.

- **Antecedent edit distance [0,1,2,....,]:** The **minimum edit distance** from the anaphor to the antecedent. Given the anaphor length n,

$$100 \quad \frac{n-(s+i+d)}{n}$$

- **Alias [true or false]:** A multipart feature proposed by Soon et al. (2001) that requires a **named entity tagger**. Returns true if NP_i and NP_j are both named entities of the same type, and NP_i is an **alias** of NP_j. The meaning of **alias** depends on the types; two dates are aliases of each other if they refer to the same date. For type PERSON, prefixes like *Dr.* or *Chairman* are stripped off and the NPs are then checked to see if they are identical. For type ORGANIZATION, the alias function checks for acronyms (e.g., *IBM* for *International Business Machines Corp*).

- **Appositive [true or false]:** True if the anaphor is in the syntactic apposition relation to the antecedent. For example, the NP *Chief Financial Officer of Megabucks Banking Corp* is in apposition to the NP *Victoria Chen*. These can be detected by a parser, or more shallowly by a search for commas and a requirement that neither NP have a verb and that one of them be a name.

- **Linguistic form [proper, definite, indefinite, pronoun]:** The form of the potential anaphor NP_j—a proper name, definite description, indefinite NP, or a pronoun.

21.8   Evaluation of Coreference Resolution

B-CUBED

One class of algorithms for evaluating coreference are **model-theoretic coreference evaluations** such as the **B-CUBED** algorithm (Bagga and Baldwin, 1998), an extension of the earlier Vilain et al. (1995) evaluation algorithm for MUC-6 (Sundheim, 1995a). Model-theoretic algorithms like B-CUBED are based on a human-labeled gold standard for coreference between referring expressions. We can represent this gold standard information as a set of equivalence classes of referring expressions. An equivalence class is the transitive closure of a coreference chain.

For example, we represent the fact that referring expressions A and B corefer by putting A and B in one class. We represent the fact that A, B, and C corefer by having a class with A, B, and C. For each entity e, the **reference chain** or **true chain** is the correct or true coreference chain an entity occurs in, while the **hypothesis chain** is the chain/class assigned to the entity by a coreference algorithm.

What the B-CUBED algorithm computes is the precision and recall of entities in the **hypothesis** chains against entities in the **reference** chains. For each entity, we compute a precision and recall, and then we take a weighted sum over all N entities in the document to compute a precision and recall for the entire task.

$$\text{Precision} = \sum_{i=1}^{N} w_i \frac{\textit{\# of correct elements in hypothesis chain containing entity}_i}{\textit{\# of elements in hypothesis chain containing entity}_i}$$

$$\text{Recall} = \sum_{i=1}^{N} w_i \frac{\textit{\# of correct elements in hypothesis chain containing entity}_i}{\textit{\# of elements in reference chain containing entity}_i}$$

The weight w_i for each entity can be set to different values to produce different versions of the algorithm.

21.9   Advanced: Inference-Based Coherence Resolution

The algorithms we have seen in this chapter for the resolution of coherence and coreference have relied solely on shallow information like cue phrases and other lexical and simple syntactic cues. But many problems in resolution seem to require much more sophisticated kinds of knowledge. Consider the following example of coreference, adapted from Winograd (1972b):

(21.70) The city council denied the demonstrators a permit because

> a. they feared violence.
> b. they advocated violence.

Determining the correct antecedent for the pronoun *they* requires understanding first that the second clause is intended as an **Explanation** of the first clause, and also that city councils are perhaps more likely than demonstrators to fear violence and that demonstrators might be more likely to advocate violence. A more advanced method for coherence resolution might assign this Explanation relation and in doing so help us figure out the referents of both pronouns.

We might perform this kind of more sophisticated coherence resolution by relying on the semantic constraints that are associated with each coherence relation, assuming a parser that could assign reasonable semantics to each clause.

Applying these constraints requires a method for performing inference. Perhaps the most familiar type of inference is **deduction**; recall from Section 17.3 that the central rule of deduction is modus ponens:

Deduction

$$\alpha \Rightarrow \beta$$
$$\frac{\alpha}{\beta}$$

An example of modus ponens is the following:

> All Falcons are fast.
> John's car is an Falcon.
> ─────────────────
> John's car is fast.

Sound inference

Deduction is a form of **sound inference**: if the premises are true, then the conclusion must be true.

However, much of language understanding is based on inferences that are not sound. While the ability to draw unsound inferences allows a greater range of inferences to be made, it can also lead to false interpretations and misunderstandings.

Abduction

A method for such inference is logical **abduction** (Peirce, 1955). The central rule of abductive inference is

$$\alpha \Rightarrow \beta$$
$$\frac{\beta}{\alpha}$$

Whereas deduction runs an implication relation forward, abduction runs it backwards, reasoning from an effect to a potential cause. An example of abduction is the following:

All Falcons are fast.
John's car is fast.
_____
John's car is an Falcon.

Obviously, this may be an incorrect inference: John's car may be made by another manufacturer yet still be fast.

In general, a given effect β may have many potential causes α_i. We generally don't want to merely reason from a fact to a *possible* explanation of it; instead, we want to identify the *best* explanation of it. To do this, we need a method for comparing the quality of alternative abductive proofs. This comparison can be done with probabilistic models (Charniak and Goldman, 1988; Charniak and Shimony, 1990) or with heuristic strategies (Charniak and McDermott, 1985, Chapter 10), such as preferring the explanation with the smallest number of assumptions or the most specific explanation. We will illustrate a third approach to abductive interpretation, from Hobbs et al. (1993), which applies a more general cost-based strategy that combines features of the probabilistic and heuristic approaches. To simplify the discussion, however, we will largely ignore the cost component of the system, keeping in mind that one is nonetheless necessary.

Hobbs et al. (1993) apply their method to a broad range of problems in language interpretation; here, we focus on its use in establishing discourse coherence, in which world and domain knowledge are used to determine the most plausible coherence relation holding between utterances. Let us step through the analysis that leads to establishing the coherence of (21.4). First, we need axioms about coherence relations themselves. Axiom 21.71 states that a possible coherence relation is the Explanation relation; other relations would have analogous axioms.

$$\forall e_i, e_j \; Explanation(e_i, e_j) \Rightarrow CoherenceRel(e_i, e_j) \qquad (21.71)$$

The variables e_i and e_j represent the events (or states) denoted by the two utterances being related. In this axiom and those given below, quantifiers always scope over everything to their right. This axiom tells us that, given that we need to establish a coherence relation between two events, one possibility is to abductively assume that the relation is Explanation.

The Explanation relation requires that the second utterance express the cause of the effect that the first sentence expresses. We can state this as axiom 21.72.

$$\forall e_i, e_j \; cause(e_j, e_i) \Rightarrow Explanation(e_i, e_j) \qquad (21.72)$$

In addition to axioms about coherence relations, we also need axioms representing general knowledge about the world. The first axiom we use says that if someone is drunk, then others will not want that person to drive, and that the former causes the latter (for convenience, the state of not wanting is denoted by the *diswant* predicate).

$$\forall x, y, e_i \; drunk(e_i, x) \Rightarrow \qquad\qquad\qquad\qquad (21.73)$$
$$\exists e_j, e_k \; diswant(e_j, y, e_k) \wedge drive(e_k, x) \wedge cause(e_i, e_j)$$

Before we move on, a few notes are in order concerning this axiom and the others we present. First, axiom 21.73 is stated with universal quantifiers to bind several of the variables, which essentially says that in all cases in which someone is drunk, all people do not want that person to drive. Although we might hope that this is generally the case, such a statement is nonetheless too strong. The way in which the Hobbs et al. system handles this is by including an additional relation, called an *etc* predicate, in the antecedent of such axioms. An *etc* predicate represents all the other properties that must be true for the axiom to apply, but that are too vague to state explicitly. These predicates therefore cannot be proven; they can only be assumed at a corresponding cost. Because rules with high assumption costs will be dispreferred to ones with low costs, the likelihood that the rule applies can be encoded in terms of this cost. Since we have chosen to simplify our discussion by ignoring costs, we similarly ignore the use of *etc* predicates.

Second, each predicate has what may look like an "extra" variable in the first argument position; for instance, the *drive* predicate has two arguments instead of one. This variable is used to reify the relationship denoted by the predicate so that it can be referred to from argument places in other predicates. For instance, reifying the *drive* predicate with the variable e_k allows us to express the idea of not wanting someone to drive by referring to it in the final argument of the *diswant* predicate.

Picking up where we left off, the second world-knowledge axiom we use says that if someone does not want someone else to drive, then they do not want this person to have his car keys, since car keys enable someone to drive.

$$\forall x, y, e_j, e_k \, diswant(e_j, y, e_k) \land drive(e_k, x) \Rightarrow \qquad (21.74)$$
$$\exists z, e_l, e_m \, diswant(e_l, y, e_m) \land have(e_m, x, z)$$
$$\land carkeys(z, x) \land cause(e_j, e_l)$$

The third axiom says that if someone doesn't want someone else to have something, he might hide it from him.

$$\forall x, y, z, e_l, e_m \, diswant(e_l, y, e_m) \land have(e_m, x, z) \Rightarrow \qquad (21.75)$$
$$\exists e_n \, hide(e_n, y, x, z) \land cause(e_l, e_n)$$

The final axiom says simply that causality is transitive, that is, if e_i causes e_j and e_j causes e_k, then e_i causes e_k.

$$\forall e_i, e_j, e_k \, cause(e_i, e_j) \land cause(e_j, e_k) \Rightarrow cause(e_i, e_k) \qquad (21.76)$$

Finally, we have the content of the utterances themselves, that is, that John hid Bill's car keys (from Bill),

$$hide(e_1, John, Bill, ck) \land carkeys(ck, Bill) \qquad (21.77)$$

and that someone described by the pronoun "he" was drunk; we represent the pronoun with the free variable *he*.

$$drunk(e_2, he) \qquad (21.78)$$

We can now see how reasoning with the content of the utterances along with the aforementioned axioms allows the coherence of (21.4) to be established under the Explanation relation. The derivation is summarized in Fig. 21.9; the sentence interpretations are shown in boxes. We start by assuming there is a coherence relation, and using axiom 21.71, hypothesize that this relation is Explanation,

$$Explanation(e_1, e_2) \tag{21.79}$$

which, by axiom 21.72, means we hypothesize that

$$cause(e_2, e_1) \tag{21.80}$$

holds. By axiom 21.76, we can hypothesize that an intermediate cause e_3,

$$cause(e_2, e_3) \wedge cause(e_3, e_1) \tag{21.81}$$

and we can repeat this again by expanding the first conjunct of (21.81) to have an intermediate cause e_4.

$$cause(e_2, e_4) \wedge cause(e_4, e_3) \tag{21.82}$$

We can take the *hide* predicate from the interpretation of the first sentence in (21.77) and the second *cause* predicate in (21.81), and, using axiom 21.75, hypothesize that John did not want Bill to have his car keys:

$$diswant(e_3, John, e_5) \wedge have(e_5, Bill, ck) \tag{21.83}$$

From this, the *carkeys* predicate from (21.77) and the second *cause* predicate from (21.82), we can use axiom 21.74 to hypothesize that John does not want Bill to drive:

$$diswant(e_4, John, e_6) \wedge drive(e_6, Bill) \tag{21.84}$$

From this, axiom 21.73, and the second *cause* predicate from (21.82), we can hypothesize that Bill was drunk:

$$drunk(e_2, Bill) \tag{21.85}$$

But now we can "prove" this fact from the interpretation of the second sentence if we assume that the variable *he* is bound to Bill. Thus, the establishment of coherence has gone through; we have identified a chain between the sentence interpretations—one that includes unprovable assumptions about axiom choice and pronoun assignment— that results in $cause(e_2, e_1)$, as required for establishing the Explanation relationship.

This derivation illustrates a powerful property of coherence establishment, namely, its ability to cause the hearer to infer information about the situation described by the discourse that the speaker has left unsaid. In this case, the derivation required the assumption that John hid Bill's keys because he did not want him to drive (presumably out of fear of him having an accident or getting stopped by the police), as opposed to some other explanation, such as playing a practical joke on him. This cause is not stated anywhere in (21.4); it arises only from the inference process triggered by the need to establish coherence. In this sense, the meaning of a discourse is greater than the sum of the meanings of its parts. That is, a discourse typically communicates far more information than is contained in the interpretations of the individual sentences that comprise it.

We now return to (21.5), repeated below as (21.87), which was notable in that it lacks the coherence displayed by (21.4), repeated below as (21.86).

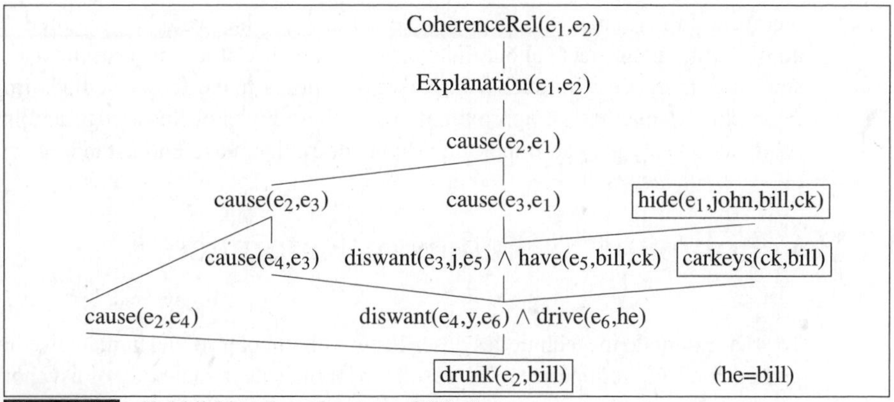

Figure 21.9   Establishing the coherence of (21.4).

(21.86) John hid Bill's car keys. He was drunk.

(21.87) ?? John hid Bill's car keys. He likes spinach.

We can now see why this is: there is no analogous chain of inference capable of linking the two utterance representations, in particular, there is no causal axiom analogous to (21.73) that says that liking spinach might cause someone to not want you to drive. Without additional information that can support such a chain of inference (such as the aforementioned scenario in which someone promised John spinach in exchange for hiding Bill's car keys), the coherence of the passage cannot be established.

Because abduction is a form of unsound inference, it must be possible to subsequently retract the assumptions made during abductive reasoning, that is, abductive *Defeasible*   inferences are **defeasible**. For instance, if (21.86) were followed by (21.88),

(21.88) Bill's car isn't here anyway; John was just playing a practical joke on him.

the system would have to retract the original chain of inference connecting the two clauses in (21.86) and replace it with one utilizing the fact that the hiding event was part of a practical joke.

In a more general knowledge base designed to support a broad range of inferences, we would want axioms that are more general than those we used to establish the coherence of (21.86). For instance, consider axiom 21.74, which says that if you do not want someone to drive, then you do not want them to have their car keys. A more general form of the axiom would say that if you do not want someone to perform an action and an object enables them to perform that action, then you do not want them to have the object. The fact that car keys enable someone to drive would then be encoded separately, along with many other similar facts. Likewise, axiom 21.73 says that if someone is drunk, you don't want them to drive. We might replace this with an axiom that says that if someone does not want something to happen, then they don't want something that will likely cause it to happen. Again, the facts that people typically don't want other people to get into car accidents and that drunk driving causes accidents would be encoded separately.

While it is important to have computational models that shed light on the coherence establishment problem, large barriers remain for widely employing this and similar methods. In particular, the large number of axioms that would be required to encode all of the necessary facts about the world and the lack of a robust mechanism for constraining inference with such a large set of axioms make these methods impractical in practice. Nonetheless, approximations to these kinds of knowledge and inferential rules can already play an important role in natural language understanding systems.

21.10   Psycholinguistic Studies of Reference

To what extent do the techniques described in this chapter model human discourse comprehension? We summarize a few results from the substantial body of psycholinguistic research; for reasons of space, we focus here solely on anaphora resolution.

A significant amount of work has been concerned with the extent to which people use the preferences described in Section 21.5 to interpret pronouns, the results of which are often contradictory. Clark and Sengal (1979) studied the effects that sentence recency plays in pronoun interpretation, using a set of **reading-time experiments**. After receiving and acknowledging a three-sentence context to read, human subjects were given a target sentence containing a pronoun. The subjects pressed a button when they felt that they understood the target sentence. Clark and Sengal found that the reading time was significantly faster when the referent for the pronoun was evoked from the most recent clause in the context than when it was evoked from two or three clauses back. On the other hand, there was no significant difference between referents evoked from two clauses and three clauses back, leading them to claim that "the last clause processed grants the entities it mentions a privileged place in working memory".

Reading-time experiments

Crawley et al. (1990) compared the preference for pronouns to be assigned to the (referents evoked by the) subject of the previous sentence with the preference for grammatical role parallelism. They found that in two task environments—a **question answering task** that revealed how the human subjects interpreted the pronoun and a **referent naming task** in which the subjects identified the referent of the pronoun directly— the human subjects resolved pronouns to the subject of the previous sentence more often than the object. However, Smyth (1994), using data that met more stringent requirements for assessing parallelism, found that subjects overwhelmingly followed the parallelism preference in a referent-naming task. The experiment supplied weaker support for the preference for subject referents over object referents, which Smyth posited as a default strategy when sentences are not sufficiently parallel.

Referent naming task

Caramazza et al. (1977) studied the effect of the "implicit causality" of verbs on pronoun resolution. They categorized verbs in terms of having subject bias or object bias by using a **sentence completion task**. Subjects were given sentence fragments such as (21.89).

Sentence completion task

(21.89) John telephoned Bill because he

The subjects completed the sentences, which identified to the experimenters what referent for the pronoun they favored. Verbs for which a large percentage of human subjects indicated a grammatical subject or object preference were categorized as having that bias. A sentence pair was then constructed for each biased verb: a "congruent" sentence in which the semantics supported the pronoun assignment suggested by the verb's bias and an "incongruent" sentence in which the semantics supported the opposite prediction. For example, (21.90) is congruent for the subject-bias verb "telephoned" since the semantics of the second clause support assigning the subject *John* as the antecedent of *he*, whereas sentence (21.91) is incongruent since the semantics support assigning the object *Bill*.

(21.90) John telephoned Bill because he wanted some information.

(21.91) John telephoned Bill because he withheld some information.

In a referent-naming task, Caramazza et al. found that naming times were faster for the congruent sentences than for the incongruent ones. Perhaps surprisingly, this was even true for cases in which the two people mentioned in the first clause were of different genders, thus rendering the reference unambiguous.

Matthews and Chodorow (1988) analyzed the problem of intrasentential reference and the predictions of syntactically based search strategies. In a question-answering task, they found that subjects exhibited slower comprehension times for sentences in which a pronoun antecedent occupied an early, syntactically deep position than for sentences in which the antecedent occupied a late, syntactically shallow position. This result is consistent with the search process used in Hobbs's tree search algorithm.

There has also been psycholinguistic work concerned with testing the principles of Centering theory. In a set of reading-time experiments, Gordon et al. (1993) found that reading times were slower when the current backward-looking center was referred to with a full noun phrase instead of a pronoun, even though the pronouns were ambiguous and the proper names were not. This effect—which they called a **repeated name** *Repeated name* **penalty**—was found only for referents in subject position, suggesting that the C_b is *penalty* preferentially realized as a subject. Brennan (1995) analyzed how choice of linguistic form correlates with centering principles. She ran a set of experiments in which a human subject watched a basketball game and had to describe it to a second person. She found that the human subjects tended to refer to an entity by a full noun phrase in subject position before subsequently pronominalizing it, even if the referent had already been introduced in object position.

21.11   Summary

In this chapter, we saw that many of the problems that natural language processing systems face operate between sentences, that is, at the *discourse* level. Here is a summary of some of the main points we discussed:

- Discourses, like sentences, have hierarchical structure. In the simplest kind of structure detection, we assume a simpler linear structure, and we segment a discourse on topic or other boundaries. The main cues for this are **lexical cohesion** and discourse markers/cue phrases.

- Discourses are not arbitrary collections of sentences; they must be *coherent*. Among the factors that make a discourse coherent are coherence relations between the sentences and entity-based coherence.

- Various sets of **coherence relations** and rhetorical relations have been proposed. Algorithms for detecting these coherence relations can use surface-based cues (cue phrases, syntactic information).

- Discourse interpretation requires that one build an evolving representation of discourse state, called a *discourse model*, that contains representations of the entities that have been referred to and the relationships in which they participate.

- Natural languages offer many ways to refer to entities. Each form of reference sends its own signals to hearers about how it should be processed with respect to their discourse model and set of beliefs about the world.

- Pronominal reference can be used for referents that have an adequate degree of *salience* in the discourse model. A variety of lexical, syntactic, semantic, and discourse factors appear to affect salience.

- The Hobbs, Centering, and log-linear models for pronominal anaphora offer different ways of drawing on and combining various of these constraints.

- The full NP coreference task also has to deal with names and definite NPs. String edit distance is a useful features for these.

- Advanced algorithms for establishing coherence apply constraints imposed by one or more coherence relations, often leading to the inference of additional information left unsaid by the speaker. The unsound rule of logical *abduction* can be used for performing such inference.

Bibliographical and Historical Notes

Building on the foundations set by early systems for natural language understanding (Woods et al., 1972; Winograd, 1972b; Woods, 1978), much of the fundamental work in computational approaches to discourse was performed in the late 70s. Webber's (1978, 1983) work provided fundamental insights into how entities are represented in the discourse model and the ways in which they can license subsequent reference. Many of the examples she provided continue to challenge theories of reference to this day. Grosz (1977a) addressed the focus of attention that conversational participants maintain as the discourse unfolds. She defined two levels of focus; entities relevant to the entire discourse were said to be in *global* focus, whereas entities that are locally in focus (i.e., most central to a particular utterance) were said to be in *immediate* focus. Sidner (1979, 1983) described a method for tracking (immediate) discourse foci and their use in resolving pronouns and demonstrative noun phrases. She made a distinction between the current discourse focus and potential foci, which are the predecessors to the backward- and forward-looking centers of Centering theory, respectively.

The roots of the centering approach originate from papers by Joshi and Kuhn (1979) and Joshi and Weinstein (1981), who addressed the relationship between immediate focus and the inferences required to integrate the current utterance into the discourse model. Grosz et al. (1983) integrated this work with the prior work of Sidner and Grosz. This led to a manuscript on centering which, while widely circulated since 1986, remained unpublished until Grosz et al. (1995). A series of papers on centering based on this manuscript/paper were subsequently published (Kameyama, 1986; Brennan et al., 1987; Di Eugenio, 1990; Walker et al., 1994; Di Eugenio, 1996; Strube and Hahn, 1996; Kehler, 1997a, inter alia). A collection of later centering papers appears in Walker et al. (1998); see Poesio et al. (2004) for more recent work. We have focused in this chapter on Centering and anaphora resolution; for the application of Centering to entity-based coherence, see Karamanis (2003, 2007), Barzilay and Lapata (2008), and related papers discussed in Chapter 23.

Studies of *information status* have a long history in linguistics (Chafe, 1976; Prince, 1981; Ariel, 1990; Prince, 1992; Gundel et al., 1993; Lambrecht, 1994, inter alia).

Beginning with Hobbs's (1978) tree-search algorithm, researchers have pursued syntax-based methods for identifying reference robustly in naturally occurring text. An early system for a weighted combination of different syntactic and other features was Lappin and Leass (1994). Kennedy and Boguraev (1996) describe a similar system that does not rely on a full syntactic parser, but merely a mechanism for identifying noun phrases and labeling their grammatical roles. Both approaches use Alshawi's (1987) framework for integrating salience factors. An algorithm that uses this framework for resolving references in a multimodal (i.e., speech and gesture) human-computer interface is described in Huls et al. (1995). A discussion of a variety of approaches to reference in operational systems can be found in Mitkov and Boguraev (1997).

Methods for reference resolution based on supervised learning were proposed quite early (Connolly et al., 1994; Aone and Bennett, 1995; McCarthy and Lehnert, 1995; Kehler, 1997b; Ge et al., 1998, inter alia). More recently, both supervised and unsupervised approaches have received a lot of research attention, focused both on anaphora resolution (Kehler et al., 2004; Bergsma and Lin, 2006) and full NP coreference (Cardie and Wagstaff, 1999; Ng and Cardie, 2002b; Ng, 2005). For definite NP reference, there are general algorithms (Poesio and Vieira, 1998; Vieira and Poesio, 2000), as well as specific algorithms that focus on deciding whether a particular definite NP is anaphoric or not (Bean and Riloff, 1999, 2004; Ng and Cardie, 2002a; Ng, 2004). The use of global optimization is an important recent focus (Denis and Baldridge, 2007; Haghighi and Klein, 2007). See Mitkov (2002) for an excellent comprehensive overview of anaphora resolution and Branco et al. (2002) for a collection of papers.

The idea of using cohesion for linear discourse segmentation was implicit in the groundbreaking work of (Halliday and Hasan, 1976) but was first explicitly implemented by Morris and Hirst (1991) and quickly picked up by many other researchers, including (Kozima, 1993; Reynar, 1994; Hearst, 1994, 1997; Reynar, 1999; Kan et al., 1998; Choi, 2000; Choi et al., 2001; Brants et al., 2002; Bestgen, 2006). Power et al. (2003) study discourse structure, and Filippova and Strube (2006), Sporleder and Lapata (2004, 2006) focus on paragraph segmentation.

The use of cue phrases in segmentation has been widely studied, including work on many textual genres as well as speech (Passonneau and Litman, 1993; Hirschberg and Litman, 1993; Manning, 1998; Kawahara et al., 2004).

Many researchers have posited sets of coherence relations that can hold between utterances in a discourse (Halliday and Hasan, 1976; Hobbs, 1979a; Longacre, 1983; Mann and Thompson, 1987; Polanyi, 1988; Hobbs, 1990; Sanders et al., 1992; Carlson et al., 2001, 2002; Asher and Lascarides, 2003; Baldridge et al., 2007, inter alia). A compendium of over 350 relations that have been proposed in the literature can be found in Hovy (1990).

There are a wide variety of approaches to coherence extraction. The cue-phrase-based model described in Section 21.2.2 is due to Daniel Marcu and colleagues (Marcu, 2000b, 2000a; Carlson et al., 2001, 2002). The Linguistic Discourse Model (Polanyi, 1988; Scha and Polanyi, 1988; Polanyi et al., 2004a, 2004b) is a framework in which discourse syntax is more heavily emphasized; in this approach, a discourse parse tree is built, clause-by-clause, in direct analogy with how a sentence parse tree is built, constituent-by-constituent. Corston-Oliver (1998) also explores syntactic and parser-based features. A more recent line of work has applied a version of the tree-adjoining grammar formalism to discourse parsing (Webber et al., 1999; Webber, 2004). This model has also been used to annotate the Penn Discourse Treebank (Miltsakaki et al., 2004b, 2004a). See Asher and Lascarides (2003) and Baldridge et al. (2007) on seg-*SDRT* mented discourse representation structure (**SDRT**). Wolf and Gibson (2005) argue that coherence structure includes crossed bracketings, which make it impossible to represent as a tree, and propose a graph representation instead.

In addition to determining discourse structure and meaning, theories of discourse coherence have been used in algorithms for interpreting discourse-level linguistic phenomena, including pronoun resolution (Hobbs, 1979a; Kehler, 2000), verb phrase ellipsis and gapping (Prüst, 1992; Asher, 1993; Kehler, 1993, 1994a), and tense interpretation (Lascarides and Asher, 1993; Kehler, 1994b, 2000). An extensive investigation into the relationship between coherence relations and discourse connectives can be found in Knott and Dale (1994).

Exercises

21.1 Early work in syntactic theory attempted to characterize rules for pronominalization through purely syntactic means. One such early rule interprets a pronoun by deleting it from the syntactic structure of the sentence that contains it and replacing it with the syntactic representation of the antecedent noun phrase. Explain why the following sentences (called "Bach-Peters" sentences) are problematic for such an analysis:

(21.92) The man who deserves it gets the prize he wants.

(21.93) The pilot who shot at it hit the MIG that chased him.

What other types of reference discussed on pages 698–701 are problematic for this type of analysis?

21.2 Draw syntactic trees for Example 21.66 on page 707 and apply Hobbs's tree-search algorithm to it, showing each step in the search.

21.3 Hobbs (1977) cites the following examples from his corpus as being problematic for his tree-search algorithm:

(21.94)   The positions of pillars in one hall were marked by river boulders and a shaped convex cushion of bronze that had served as <u>their</u> footings.

(21.95) They were at once assigned an important place among the scanty remains which record the physical developments of the human race from the time of <u>its</u> first appearance in Asia.

(21.96) Sites at which the coarse grey pottery of the Shang period has been discovered do not extend far beyond the southernmost reach of the Yellow River, or westward beyond <u>its</u> junction with the Wei.

(21.97) The thin, hard, black-burnished pottery, made in shapes of angular profile, which archaeologists consider as the clearest hallmark of the Lung Shan culture, developed in the east. The site from which <u>it</u> takes its name is in Shantung. <u>It</u> is traced to the north-east as far as Liao-ning province.

(21.98) He had the duty of performing the national sacrifices to heaven and earth: his role as source of honours and material rewards for services rendered by feudal lords and ministers is commemorated in thousands of inscriptions made by the recipients on bronze vessels which were eventually deposited in <u>their</u> graves.

In each case, identify the correct referent of the underlined pronoun and the one that the algorithm will identify incorrectly. Discuss any factors that come into play in determining the correct referent in each case, and the types of information that might be necessary to account for them.

21.4 Implement the Hobbs algorithm. Test it on a sample of the Penn TreeBank. You will need to modify the algorithm to deal with differences between the Hobbs and TreeBank grammars.

21.5 Consider the following passage, from Brennan et al. (1987):

(21.99) Brennan drives an Alfa Romeo.
She drives too fast.
Friedman races her on weekends.
She goes to Laguna Seca.

Identify the referent that the BFP algorithm finds for the pronoun in the final sentence. Do you agree with this choice, or do you find the example ambiguous? Discuss why introducing a new noun phrase in subject position with a pronominalized reference in object position might lead to an ambiguity for a subject pronoun in the next sentence. What preferences are competing here?

21.6 Consider passages (21.100a-b), adapted from Winograd (1972b).

(21.100) The city council denied the demonstrators a permit because

a. they feared violence.
b. they advocated violence.

What are the correct interpretations for the pronouns in each case? Sketch an analysis of each in the interpretation as abduction framework, in which these reference assignments are made as a by-product of establishing the Explanation relation.

21.7 Select an editorial column from your favorite newspaper, and determine the discourse structure for a 10–20 sentence portion. What problems did you encounter? Were you helped by superficial cues the speaker included (e.g., discourse connectives) in any places?

Credit

Figs. 21.1 and 21.2 (© the authors; thanks to the Association of Computational Linguistics, the *Journal of Computational Linguistics* and its editor Robert Dale, and to Marti Hearst)

Chapter 22

Information Extraction

> *I am the very model of a modern Major-General,*
> *I've information vegetable, animal, and mineral,*
> *I know the kings of England, and I quote the fights historical*
> *From Marathon to Waterloo, in order categorical...*
> Gilbert and Sullivan, *Pirates of Penzance*

Imagine that you are an analyst with an investment firm that tracks airline stocks. You're given the task of determining the relationship (if any) between airline announcements of fare increases and the behavior of their stocks the next day. Historical data about stock prices is easy to come by, but what about the information about airline announcements? To do a good job on this task, you would need to know at least the name of the airline, the nature of the proposed fare hike, the dates of the announcement, and possibly the response of other airlines. Fortunately, this information resides in archives of news articles reporting on airline's actions, as in the following recent example.

> Citing high fuel prices, United Airlines said Friday it has increased fares by $6 per round trip on flights to some cities also served by lower-cost carriers. American Airlines, a unit of AMR Corp., immediately matched the move, spokesman Tim Wagner said. United, a unit of UAL Corp., said the increase took effect Thursday and applies to most routes where it competes against discount carriers, such as Chicago to Dallas and Denver to San Francisco.

Of course, distilling information like names, dates, and amounts from naturally occurring text is a non-trivial task. This chapter presents a series of techniques that extract limited kinds of semantic content from text. This process of **information extraction** (IE), also called **text analytics**, turns the unstructured information embedded in texts into structured data. More concretely, information extraction is an effective way to populate the contents of a relational database. Once the information is encoded formally, we can apply all the capabilities provided by database systems, statistical analysis packages, and other forms of decision support systems to address the problems we're trying to solve.

Information extraction
Text analytics

As we proceed through this chapter, we show that robust solutions to IE problems are actually clever combinations of techniques we've seen earlier in the book. In particular, the finite-state methods described in Chapters 2 and 3, the probabilistic models introduced in Chapters 4 through 6, and the syntactic chunking methods from Chapter 13 form the core of most current approaches to information extraction. Before diving into the details of how these techniques are applied, we quickly introduce the major problems in IE and describe how they can be approached.

The first step in most IE tasks is to detect and classify all the proper names mentioned in a text—a task generally referred to as **named entity recognition** (NER). Not surprisingly, what constitutes a proper name and the particular scheme used to classify

Named entity recognition

them is application specific. Generic NER systems tend to focus on finding the names of people, places, and organizations that are mentioned in ordinary news texts; practical applications have also been built to detect everything from the names of genes and proteins (Settles, 2005) to the names of college courses (McCallum, 2005).

Named entity mentions

Our introductory example contains 13 instances of proper names, which we'll refer to as **named entity mentions**, that can be classified as organizations, people, places, times, or amounts.

Having located all of the mentions of named entities in a text, it is useful to link, or cluster, these mentions into sets that correspond to the entities behind the mentions. This is the task of **reference resolution**, which we introduced in Chapter 21, and is also an important component in IE. In our sample text, we would like to know that the *United Airlines* mention in the first sentence and the *United* mention in the third sentence refer to the same real-world entity. This general reference resolution problem also includes anaphora resolution as a sub-problem, in this case, determining that the two uses of *it* refer to *United Airlines* and *United*, respectively.

Relation detection and classification

The task of **relation detection and classification** is to find and classify semantic relations among the entities discovered in a given text. In most practical settings, the focus of relation detection is on small fixed sets of binary relations. Generic relations that appear in standard system evaluations include family, employment, part-whole, membership, and geospatial relations. The relation detection and classification task is the one that most closely corresponds to the problem of populating a relational database. Relation detection among entities is also closely related to the problem of discovering semantic relations among words, introduced in Chapter 20.

Our sample text contains three explicit mentions of generic relations: *United* is a part of *UAL*, *American Airlines* is a part of *AMR*, and *Tim Wagner* is an employee of *American Airlines*. Domain-specific relations from the airline industry would include the fact that *United* serves *Chicago, Dallas, Denver*, and *San Francisco*.

Event detection and classification

In addition to knowing about the entities in a text and their relation to one another, we might like to find and classify the events in which the entities are participating; this is the problem of **event detection and classification**. In our sample text, the key events are the fare increases by *United* and *American*. In addition, several events report these main events, as indicated by the two uses of *said* and the use of *cite*. As with entity recognition, event detection brings with it the problem of reference resolution; we need to figure out which of the many event mentions in a text refer to the same event. In our running example, the events referred to as *the move* and *the increase* in the second and third sentences are the same as the *increase* in the first sentence.

Temporal expression recognition Temporal analysis

The problem of figuring out when the events in a text happened and how they relate to each other in time raises the twin problems of **temporal expression recognition** and **temporal analysis**. Temporal expression detection tells us that our sample text contains the temporal expressions *Friday* and *Thursday*. Temporal expressions include date expressions such as days of the week, months, holidays, etc., as well as relative expressions including phrases like *two days from now* or *next year*. They also include expressions for clock times such as *3:30 P.M.* or *noon*.

The overall problem of **temporal analysis** is to map temporal expressions onto specific calendar dates or times of day and then to use those times to situate events in time. It includes the following subtasks:

- Fixing the temporal expressions with respect to an anchoring date or time, typically the dateline of the story in the case of news stories;
- Associating temporal expressions with the events in the text;
- Arranging the events into a complete and coherent timeline.

In our sample text, the temporal expressions *Friday* and *Thursday* should be anchored with respect to the dateline associated with the article itself. We also know that *Friday* refers to the time of United's announcement, and *Thursday* refers to the time that the fare increase went into effect (i.e., the Thursday immediately preceding the Friday). Finally, we can use this information to produce a timeline in which United's announcement follows the fare increase and American's announcement follows both of those events. Temporal analysis of this kind is useful in nearly any NLP application that deals with meaning, including question answering, summarization, and dialogue systems.

Template filling   Finally, many texts describe stereotypical situations that recur with some frequency in the domain of interest. The task of **template filling** is to find documents that evoke such situations and then fill the slots in templates with appropriate material. These slot-fillers may consist of text segments extracted directly from the text, or they may consist of concepts that have been inferred from text elements through some additional processing (times, amounts, entities from an ontology, etc.).

Our airline text is an example of this kind of stereotypical situation since airlines are often attempting to raise fares and then waiting to see if competitors follow along. In this situation, we can identify *United* as a lead airline that initially raised its fares, $6 as the amount by which fares are being raised, *Thursday* as the effective date for the fare increase, and *American* as an airline that followed along. A filled template from our original airline story might look like the following.

FARE-RAISE ATTEMPT:	LEAD AIRLINE:	UNITED AIRLINES
	AMOUNT:	$6
	EFFECTIVE DATE:	2006-10-26
	FOLLOWER:	AMERICAN AIRLINES

The following sections review current approaches to each of these problems in the context of generic news text. Section 22.5 then describes how many of these problems arise in the context of processing biology texts.

22.1   Named Entity Recognition

Named entity   The starting point for most information extraction applications is the detection and classification of the named entities in a text. By **named entity**, we simply mean anything that can be referred to with a proper name. This process of **named entity recognition** refers to the combined task of finding spans of text that constitute proper names and then classifying the entities being referred to according to their type.

Type	Tag	Sample Categories
People	PER	Individuals, fictional characters, small groups
Organization	ORG	Companies, agencies, political parties, religious groups, sports teams
Location	LOC	Physical extents, mountains, lakes, seas
Geo-Political Entity	GPE	Countries, states, provinces, counties
Facility	FAC	Bridges, buildings, airports
Vehicles	VEH	Planes, trains, and automobiles

Figure 22.1 A list of generic named entity types with the kinds of entities they refer to.

Type	Example
People	*Turing* is often considered to be the father of modern computer science.
Organization	The *IPCC* said it is likely that future tropical cyclones will become more intense.
Location	The *Mt. Sanitas* loop hike begins at the base of *Sunshine Canyon*.
Geo-Political Entity	*Palo Alto* is looking at raising the fees for parking in the University Avenue district.
Facility	Drivers were advised to consider either the *Tappan Zee Bridge* or the *Lincoln Tunnel*.
Vehicles	The updated *Mini Cooper* retains its charm and agility.

Figure 22.2 Named entity types with examples.

Generic news-oriented NER systems focus on the detection of things like people, places, and organizations. Figures 22.1 and 22.2 list typical named entity types with examples of each. Specialized applications may be concerned with many other types of entities, including commercial products, weapons, works of art, or as we show in Section 22.5, proteins, genes and other biological entities. What these applications all share is a concern with proper names, the characteristic ways that such names are signaled in a given language or genre, and a fixed set of categories of entities from a domain of interest.

By the way that names are signaled, we simply mean that names are denoted in a way that sets them apart from ordinary text. For example, if we're dealing with standard English text, then two adjacent capitalized words in the middle of a text are likely to constitute a name. Further, if they are preceded by a *Dr.* or followed by an *MD*, then it is likely that we're dealing with a person. In contrast, if they are preceded by *arrived in* or followed by *NY* then we're probably dealing with a location. Note that these signals include facts about the proper names as well as their surrounding contexts.

The notion of a named entity is commonly extended to include things that aren't entities per se, but nevertheless have practical importance and do have characteristic signatures that signal their presence; examples include dates, times, named events, *Temporal expressions* and other kinds of **temporal expressions**, as well as measurements, counts, prices, and *Numerical expressions* other kinds of **numerical expressions**. We consider some of these later in Section 22.3.

Let's revisit the sample text introduced earlier with the named entities marked (with TIME and MONEY used to mark the temporal and monetary expressions).

Citing high fuel prices, [$_{ORG}$ United Airlines] said [$_{TIME}$ Friday] it has increased fares by [$_{MONEY}$ $6] per round trip on flights to some cities also served by lower-cost carriers. [$_{ORG}$ American Airlines], a unit of [$_{ORG}$ AMR Corp.], immediately matched the move, spokesman [$_{PERS}$ Tim Wagner] said. [$_{ORG}$ United], a unit of

Name	Possible Categories
Washington	Person, Location, Political Entity, Organization, Facility
Downing St.	Location, Organization
IRA	Person, Organization, Monetary Instrument
Louis Vuitton	Person, Organization, Commercial Product

Figure 22.3   Common categorical ambiguities associated with various proper names.

[$_{PERS}$ Washington] was born into slavery on the farm of James Burroughs.
[$_{ORG}$ Washington] went up 2 games to 1 in the four-game series.
Blair arrived in [$_{LOC}$ Washington] for what may well be his last state visit.
In June, [$_{GPE}$ Washington] passed a primary seatbelt law.
The [$_{FAC}$ Washington] had proved to be a leaky ship, every passage I made...

Figure 22.4   Examples of type ambiguities in the use of the name *Washington*.

[$_{ORG}$ UAL Corp.], said the increase took effect [$_{TIME}$ Thursday] and applies to most routes where it competes against discount carriers, such as [$_{LOC}$ Chicago] to [$_{LOC}$ Dallas] and [$_{LOC}$ Denver] to [$_{LOC}$ San Francisco].

As shown, this text contains 13 mentions of named entities including 5 organizations, 4 locations, 2 times, 1 person, and 1 mention of money. The 5 organizational mentions correspond to 4 unique organizations, since *United* and *United Airlines* are distinct mentions that refer to the same entity.

22.1.1   Ambiguity in Named Entity Recognition

Named entity recognition systems face two types of ambiguity. The first arises from the fact the same name can refer to different entities of the same type. For example, *JFK* can refer to the former president or his son. This is basically a reference resolution problem; approaches to resolving this kind of ambiguity are discussed in Chapter 21.

The second source of ambiguity arises from the fact that identical named entity mentions can refer to entities of completely different types. For example, in addition to people, *JFK* might refer to the airport in New York or to any number of schools, bridges, and streets around the United States. Some examples of this kind of cross-type confusion are given in Figures 22.3 and 22.4.

Notice that some of the ambiguities shown in Fig. 22.3 are completely coincidental. There is no relationship between the financial and organizational uses of the name *IRA*—they simply arose coincidentally as acronyms from different sources (*Individual Retirement Account* and *International Reading Association*). On the other hand, the organizational uses of *Washington* and *Downing St.* are examples of a LOCATION-FOR-ORGANIZATION **metonymy**, as discussed in Chapter 19.

22.1.2   NER as Sequence Labeling

The standard way to approach the problem of named entity recognition is as a word-by-word sequence labeling task, for which the assigned tags capture both the boundary and the type of any detected named entities. Viewed in this light, named entity recognition looks very much like the problem of syntactic base-phrase chunking. In fact, the dominant approach to NER is based on the same statistical sequence-labeling techniques introduced in Chapter 5 for part of speech tagging and in Chapter 13 for syntactic chunking.

In the sequence-labeling approach to NER, classifiers are trained to label the tokens in a text with tags that indicate the presence of particular kinds of named entities. This approach makes use of the same style of IOB encoding employed for syntactic chunking. Recall that in this scheme an I is used to label tokens *inside* a chunk, B is used to mark the beginning of a chunk, and O labels tokens outside any chunk of interest. Consider the following sentence from our running example.

(22.1) [$_{ORG}$ American Airlines], a unit of [$_{ORG}$ AMR Corp.], immediately matched
        the move, spokesman [$_{PERS}$ Tim Wagner] said.

This bracketing notation provides us with the extent and the type of the named entities in this text. Figure 22.5 shows a standard word-by-word IOB-style tagging that captures the same information. As with syntactic chunking, the tagset for such an encoding consists of 2 tags for each entity type being recognized, plus 1 for the O tag outside any entity, or $(2 \quad N) + 1$ tags.

Having encoded our training data with IOB tags, the next step is to select a set of features to associate with each input example (i.e., each of the tokens to be labeled in Fig. 22.5). These features should be plausible predictors of the class label and should be easily and reliably extractable from the source text. Recall that such features can be based not only on characteristics of the token to be classified but also on the text in a surrounding window.

Figure 22.6 lists standard features employed in state-of-the-art named entity recognition systems. We've seen many of these features before in the context of part-of-speech tagging and syntactic base-phrase chunking. Several, however, are particularly important in the context of NER. The **shape feature** feature includes the usual upper case, lower case, and capitalized forms, as well as more elaborate patterns designed to capture expressions that make use of numbers (*A9*), punctuation (*Yahoo!*), and atypical case alternations (*eBay*). It turns out that this feature by itself accounts for a considerable part of the success of NER systems for English news text. And as we show in Section 22.5, shape features are also par-

Shape feature

Words	Label
American	B$_{ORG}$
Airlines	I$_{ORG}$
,	O
a	O
unit	O
of	O
AMR	B$_{ORG}$
Corp.	I$_{ORG}$
,	O
immediately	O
matched	O
the	O
move	O
,	O
spokesman	O
Tim	B$_{PERS}$
Wagner	I$_{PERS}$
said	O
.	O

Figure 22.5   IOB encoding.

ticularly important in recognizing names of proteins and genes in biological texts. Figure 22.7 describes some commonly employed shape feature values.

The **presence in a named entity list** feature can be quite predictive. Extensive lists of names for all manner of things are available from both publicly available and commercial sources. Lists of place names, called **gazetteers**, contain millions of entries for all manner of locations along with detailed geographical, geologic, and political

Gazetteers

Feature	Explanation
Lexical items	The token to be labeled
Stemmed lexical items	Stemmed version of the target token
Shape	The orthographic pattern of the target word
Character affixes	Character-level affixes of the target and surrounding words
Part of speech	Part of speech of the word
Syntactic chunk labels	Base-phrase chunk label
Gazetteer or name list	Presence of the word in one or more named entity lists
Predictive token(s)	Presence of predictive words in surrounding text
Bag of words/Bag of N-grams	Words and/or *N*-grams occurring in the surrounding context

Figure 22.6   Features commonly used in training named entity recognition systems.

Shape	Example
Lower	cummings
Capitalized	Washington
All caps	IRA
Mixed case	eBay
Capitalized character with period	H.
Ends in digit	A9
Contains hyphen	H-P

Figure 22.7   Selected shape features.

information.[1] The United States Census Bureau provides extensive lists of first names and surnames derived from its decadal census in the U.S.[2] Similar lists of corporations, commercial products, and all manner of things biological and mineral are also available from a variety of sources.

This feature is typically implemented as a binary vector with a bit for each available kind of name list. Unfortunately, such lists can be difficult to create and maintain, and their usefulness varies considerably depending on the named entity class. It appears that gazetteers can be quite effective, while extensive lists of persons and organizations are not nearly as beneficial (Mikheev et al., 1999).

Finally, features based on the presence of **predictive words and N-grams** in the context window can also be informative. When they are present, preceding and following titles, honorifics, and other markers such as *Rev.*, *MD*, and *Inc.* can accurately indicate the class of an entity. Unlike name lists and gazetteers, these lists are relatively short and stable over time and are therefore easy to develop and maintain.

The relative usefulness of any of these features or combination of features depends to a great extent on the application, genre, media, language, and text encoding. For example, shape features, which are critical for English newswire texts, are of little use with materials transcribed from spoken text by automatic speech recognition, materials gleaned from informally edited sources such as blogs and discussion forums, and for character-based languages like Chinese where case information isn't available. The set of features given in Fig. 22.6 should therefore be thought of as only a starting point for any given application.

---

[1] www.geonames.org

[2] www.census.gov

Features				Label
American	NNP	B_{NP}	cap	B_{ORG}
Airlines	NNPS	I_{NP}	cap	I_{ORG}
,		PUNC	O	punc	O
a	DT	B_{NP}	lower	O
unit	NN	I_{NP}	lower	O
of	IN	B_{PP}	lower	O
AMR	NNP	B_{NP}	upper	B_{ORG}
Corp.	NNP	I_{NP}	cap_punc	I_{ORG}
,	PUNC	O	punc	O
immediately	RB	B_{ADVP}	lower	O
matched	VBD	B_{VP}	lower	O
the	DT	B_{NP}	lower	O
move	NN	I_{NP}	lower	O
,	PUNC	O	punc	O
spokesman	NN	B_{NP}	lower	O
Tim	NNP	I_{NP}	cap	B_{PER}
Wagner	NNP	I_{NP}	cap	I_{PER}
said	VBD	B_{VP}	lower	O
.	PUNC	O	punc	O

Figure 22.8   Simple word-by-word feature encoding for NER.

Once an adequate set of features has been developed, they are extracted from a representative training set and encoded in a form appropriate to train a machine learning-based sequence classifier. A standard way of encoding these features is to simply augment our earlier IOB scheme with more columns. Figure 22.8 illustrates the result of adding part-of-speech tags, syntactic base-phrase chunk tags, and shape information to our earlier example.

Given such a training set, a sequential classifier can be trained to label new sentences. As with part-of-speech tagging and syntactic chunking, this problem can be cast either as Markov-style optimization using HMMs or MEMMs, as described in Chapter 6, or as a multiway classification task deployed as a sliding-window labeler, as described in Chapter 13. Figure 22.9 illustrates the operation of such a sequence labeler at the point where the token *Corp.* is next to be labeled. If we assume a context window that includes the two preceding and following words, then the features available to the classifier are those shown in the boxed area. Figure 22.10 summarizes the overall sequence labeling approach to creating a NER system.

22.1.3   Evaluation of Named Entity Recognition

The familiar metrics of **recall**, **precision**, and F_1 **measure** introduced in Chapter 13 are used to evaluate NER systems. Remember that recall is the ratio of the number of correctly labeled responses to the total that should have been labeled; precision is the ratio of the number of correctly labeled responses to the total labeled. The F-measure (van Rijsbergen, 1975) provides a way to combine these two measures into a single

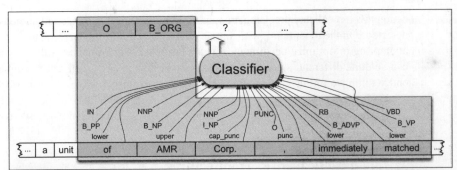

Figure 22.9 Named entity recognition as sequence labeling. The features available to the classifier during training and classification are those in the boxed area.

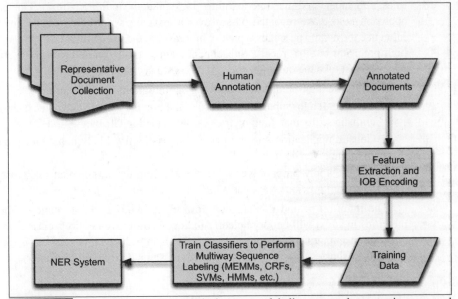

Figure 22.10 Basic steps in the statistical sequence labeling approach to creating a named entity recognition system.

metric. The *F*-measure is defined as

$$F_\beta = \frac{(\beta^2 + 1)PR}{\beta^2 P + R} \tag{22.2}$$

The β parameter differentially weights the importance of recall and precision, based perhaps on the needs of an application. Values of $\beta > 1$ favor recall, and values of $\beta < 1$ favor precision. When $\beta = 1$, precision and recall are equally balanced; this is sometimes called $F_{\beta=1}$ or just F_1:

$$F_1 = \frac{2PR}{P + R} \tag{22.3}$$

As with syntactic chunking, it is important to distinguish the metrics used to measure performance at the application level from those used during training. At the application level, recall and precision are measured with respect to the actual named entities detected. On the other hand, with an IOB encoding scheme, the learning algorithms are attempting to optimize performance at the tag level. Performance at these two levels can be quite different; since the vast majority of tags in any given text are outside any entity, simply emitting an O tag for every token gives fairly high tag-level performance.

High-performing systems at recent standardized evaluations achieve entity level F-measures around .92 for PERSONS and LOCATIONS, and around .84 for ORGANIZA-TIONS (Tjong Kim Sang and De Meulder, 2003).

22.1.4   Practical NER Architectures

Commercial approaches to NER are often based on pragmatic combinations of lists, rules, and supervised machine learning (Jackson and Moulinier, 2002). One common approach is to make repeated passes over a text, allowing the results of one pass to influence the next. The stages typically first involve the use of rules that have extremely high precision but low recall. Subsequent stages employ more error-prone statistical methods that take the output of the first pass into account.

1. First, use high-precision rules to tag unambiguous entity mentions.
2. Then, search for substring matches of the previously detected names, using prob-abilistic string matching metrics (as described in Chapter 19).
3. Consult application-specific name lists to identify likely name entity mentions from the given domain.
4. Finally, apply probabilistic sequence labeling techniques that make use of the tags from previous stages as additional features.

The intuition behind this staged approach is twofold. First, some of the entity mentions in a text will be more clearly indicative of a given entity's class than others. Second, once an unambiguous entity mention is introduced into a text, it is likely that subsequent shortened versions will refer to the same entity (and thus the same type of entity).

22.2   Relation Detection and Classification

Next on our list of tasks is to discern the relationships that exist among the entities detected in a text. To see what this means, let's return to our sample airline text with all the entities marked.

> Citing high fuel prices, [$_{ORG}$ United Airlines] said [$_{TIME}$ Friday] it has increased fares by [$_{MONEY}$ $6] per round trip on flights to some cities also served by lower-cost carriers. [$_{ORG}$ American Airlines], a unit of [$_{ORG}$ AMR Corp.], immediately matched the move, spokesman [$_{PERS}$ Tim Wagner] said. [$_{ORG}$ United], a unit of [$_{ORG}$ UAL Corp.], said the increase took effect [$_{TIME}$ Thursday] and applies to most routes where it competes against discount carriers, such as [$_{LOC}$ Chicago] to [$_{LOC}$ Dallas] and [$_{LOC}$ Denver] to [$_{LOC}$ San Francisco].

This text stipulates a set of relations among the named entities mentioned within it. We know, for example, that *Tim Wagner* is a spokesman for *American Airlines*,

Relations		Examples	Types
Affiliations			
	Personal	*married to, mother of*	PER → PER
	Organizational	*spokesman for, president of*	PER → ORG
	Artifactual	*owns, invented, produces*	(PER ORG) → ART
Geospatial			
	Proximity	*near, on outskirts*	LOC → LOC
	Directional	*southeast of*	LOC → LOC
Part-Of			
	Organizational	*a unit of, parent of*	ORG → ORG
	Political	*annexed, acquired*	GPE → GPE

Figure 22.11   Semantic relations with examples and the named entity types they involve.

that *United* is a unit of *UAL Corp.*, and that *American* is a unit of *AMR*. These are all binary relations that can be seen as instances of more generic relations such as **part-of** or **employs** that occur with fairly high frequency in news-style texts. Figure 22.11 lists generic relations of the kind used in recent standardized evaluations.[3] A more domain-specific relation that might be extracted includes the notion of an airline route. For example, from this text we can conclude that United has routes to Chicago, Dallas, Denver, and San Francisco.

These relations correspond nicely to the model-theoretic notions we introduced in Chapter 17 to ground the meanings of the logical forms. That is, a relation consists of set of ordered tuples over elements of a domain. In most standard information-extraction applications, the domain elements correspond to the named entities that occur in the text, to the underlying entities that result from co-reference resolution, or to entities selected from a domain ontology. Figure 22.12 shows a model-based view of the set of entities and relations that can be extracted from our running example. Notice how this model-theoretic view subsumes the NER task as well; named entity recognition corresponds to the identification of a class of unary relations.

22.2.1   Supervised Learning Approaches to Relation Analysis

Supervised machine learning approaches to relation detection and classification follow a scheme that should be familiar by now. Texts are annotated with relations chosen from a small fixed set by human analysts. These annotated texts are then used to train systems to reproduce similar annotations on unseen texts. Such annotations indicate the text spans of the two arguments, the roles played by each argument, and the type of the relation involved.

The most straightforward approach breaks the problem down into two subtasks: detecting when a relation is present between two entities and then classifying any detected relations. In the first stage, a classifier is trained to make a binary decision as to whether a given pair of named entities participate in a relation. Positive examples are extracted directly from the annotated corpus, and negative examples are generated from within-sentence entity pairs that are not annotated with a relation.

---

3   http://www.nist.gov/speech/tests/ace/

Domain	$\mathscr{D} = a,b,c,d,e,f,g,h,i$
United, UAL, American Airlines, AMR	a,b,c,d
Tim Wagner	e
Chicago, Dallas, Denver, and San Francisco	f,g,h,i
Classes	
United, UAL, American, and AMR are organizations	$Org = a,b,c,d$
Tim Wagner is a person	$Pers = e$
Chicago, Dallas, Denver, and San Francisco are places	$Loc = f,g,h,i$
Relations	
United is a unit of UAL	$PartOf = \langle a,b \rangle, \langle c,d \rangle$
American is a unit of AMR	
Tim Wagner works for American Airlines	$OrgAff = \langle c,e \rangle$
United serves Chicago, Dallas, Denver, and San Francisco	$Serves = \langle a,f \rangle, \langle a,g \rangle, \langle a,h \rangle, \langle a,i \rangle$

Figure 22.12   A model-based view of the relations and entities in our sample text.

---

function FINDRELATIONS(*words*) **returns** *relations*

    relations ← *nil*
    entities ← FINDENTITIES(*words*)
    forall entity pairs $\langle e1, e2 \rangle$ **in** *entities* **do**
        if RELATED?(*e1,e2*)
            relations ← *relations*+CLASSIFYRELATION(*e1,e2*)

Figure 22.13   Finding and classifying the relations among entities in a text.

In the second phase, a classifier is trained to label the relations that exist between candidate entity pairs. As discussed in Chapter 6, techniques such as decision trees, naive Bayes, or MaxEnt handle multiclass labeling directly. Binary approaches based on the discovery of separating hyperplanes, such as SVMs, solve multiclass problems by employing a one-versus-all training paradigm. In this approach, sets of classifiers are trained such that each classifier is trained on one label as the positive class and all the other labels as the negative class. Final classification is performed by passing each instance to be labeled to all of the classifiers and then choosing the label from the classifier with the most confidence or returning a rank ordering over the positively responding classifiers. Figure 22.13 illustrates the basic approach for finding and classifying relations among the named entities within a discourse unit.

As with named entity recognition, the most important step in this process is to identify surface features that will be useful for relation classification (Zhou et al., 2005). The first sources of information to consider are **features of the named entities** themselves.

- Named entity types of the two candidate arguments
- Concatenation of the two entity types
- Headwords of the arguments
- Bag-of-words from each of the arguments

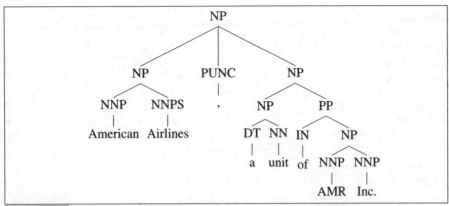

Figure 22.14   An appositive construction expressing an **a-part-of** relation.

The next set of features is derived from **the words in the text** being examined. It is useful to think of these features as being extracted from three locations: the text between the two candidate arguments, a fixed window before the first argument, and a fixed window after the second argument. Given these locations, the following word-based features have proven to be useful.

- The bag-of-words and bag-of-bigrams between the entities
- Stemmed versions of the same
- Words and stems immediately preceding and following the entities
- Distance in words between the arguments
- Number of entities between the arguments

Finally, **the syntactic structure** of a sentence can signal many of the relationships among any entities contained within it. The following features can be derived from various levels of syntactic analysis, including base-phrase chunking, dependency parsing, and full constituent parsing.

- Presence of particular constructions in a constituent structure
- Chunk base-phrase paths
- Bags of chunk heads
- Dependency-tree paths
- Constituent-tree paths
- Tree distance between the arguments

One method of exploiting parse trees is to create detectors that signal the presence of particular syntactic constructions and then associate binary features with those detectors. As an example of this, consider the subtree shown in Fig. 22.14 that dominates the named entities *American* and *AMR Inc.* The *NP* construction that dominates these two entities is called an appositive construction and is often associated with both **part-of** and **a-kind-of** relations in English. A binary feature indicating the presence of this construction can be useful in detecting these relations.

This method of feature extraction relies on a certain amount of a priori linguistic analysis to identify those syntactic constructions that may be useful predictors of cer-

Entity-based features	
Entity$_1$ type	ORG
Entity$_1$ head	*airlines*
Entity$_2$ type	PERS
Entity$_2$ head	*Wagner*
Concatenated types	ORGPERS

Word-based features	
Between-entity bag of words	*a, unit, of, AMR, Inc., immediately, matched, the, move, spokesman*
Word(s) before Entity$_1$	NONE
Word(s) after Entity$_2$	*said*

Syntactic features	
Constituent path	$NP \uparrow NP \uparrow S \uparrow S \downarrow NP$
Base syntactic chunk path	$NP \rightarrow NP \rightarrow PP \rightarrow NP \rightarrow VP \rightarrow NP \rightarrow NP$
Typed-dependency path	$Airlines \leftarrow_{subj} matched \leftarrow_{comp} said \rightarrow_{subj} Wagner$

Figure 22.15   Sample of features extracted during classification of the <American Airlines, Tim Wagner> tuple.

tain classes. An alternative method is to automatically encode certain aspects of tree structures as feature values and allow the machine learning algorithms to determine which values are informative for which classes. One simple and effective way to do this involves the use of **syntactic paths** through trees. Consider again the tree discussed earlier that dominates *American Airlines* and *AMR Inc*. The syntactic relationship between these arguments can be characterized by the path traversed through the tree in getting from one to the other:

$NP \uparrow NP \downarrow NP \downarrow PP \downarrow NP$

Similar path features defined over syntactic dependency trees as well as flat base-phrase chunk structures have been shown to be useful for relation detection and classification (Culotta and Sorensen, 2004; Bunescu and Mooney, 2005). Recall that syntactic path features featured prominently in Chapter 20 in the context of semantic role labeling.

Figure 22.15 illustrates some of the features that would be extracted during the classification of the relationship between *American Airlines* and *Tim Wagner* from our example text.

22.2.2   Lightly Supervised Approaches to Relation Analysis

The supervised machine learning approach just described assumes that we have ready access to a large collection of previously annotated material with which to train classifiers. Unfortunately, this assumption is impractical in many real-world settings. A simple approach to extracting relational information without large amounts of annotated material is to use regular expression patterns to match text segments that are likely to contain expressions of the relations in which we are interested.

Consider the problem of building a table containing all the hub cities that various airlines utilize. Assuming we have access to a search engine that permits some form of phrasal search with wildcards, we might try something like the following as a query:

```
/ * has a hub at * /
```

Given access to a reasonable amount of material of the right kind, such a search would yield a fair number of correct answers. A recent Google search with this pattern yielded the following relevant sentences among the return set.

(22.4) Milwaukee-based Midwest has a hub at KCI.

(22.5) Delta has a hub at LaGuardia.

(22.6) Bulgaria Air has a hub at Sofia Airport, as does Hemus Air.

(22.7) American Airlines has a hub at the San Juan airport.

Of course, patterns such as this can fail in the two ways we discussed all the way back in Chapter 2: by finding some things they shouldn't and by failing to find things they should. As an example of the first kind of error, consider the following sentences that were also included in the earlier return set.

(22.8) airline j has a hub at airport k

(22.9) The catheter has a hub at the proximal end

(22.10) A star topology often has a hub at its center.

We can address these errors by making our proposed pattern more specific. In this case, replacing the unrestricted wildcard operator with a named entity class restriction would rule out these examples:

```
/[ORG] has a hub at [LOC]/
```

The second problem is that we can't know if we've found all the hubs for all airlines, since we've limited ourselves to this one rather specific pattern. Consider the following close calls missed by our first pattern.

(22.11) No frills rival easyJet, which has established a hub at Liverpool...

(22.12) Ryanair also has a continental hub at Charleroi airport (Belgium).

These examples are missed because they contain minor variations that cause the original pattern to fail. There are two ways to address this problem. The first is to generalize our pattern to capture expressions like these that contain the information we are seeking. We can accomplish this by relaxing the pattern to allow matches that skip parts of the candidate text. Of course, this approach is likely to introduce more of the false positives that we tried to eliminate by making our pattern more specific in the first place.

Bootstrapping

Seed patterns

The second, more promising, solution is to expand our set of specific high-precision patterns. Given a large and diverse document collection, an expanded set of patterns should be able to capture more of the information we're looking for. One way to acquire these additional patterns is to simply have human analysts familiar with the domain come up with more patterns and hope to get better coverage. A more interesting automatic alternative is to induce new patterns by **bootstrapping** from the initial search results from a small set of **seed patterns**.

To see how this works, let's assume that we've discovered that Ryanair has a hub at Charleroi. We can use this fact to discover new patterns by finding other mentions of this relation in our corpus. The simplest way to do this is to search for the terms *Ryanair*, *Charleroi* and *hub* in some proximity. The following are among the results from a recent search in Google News.

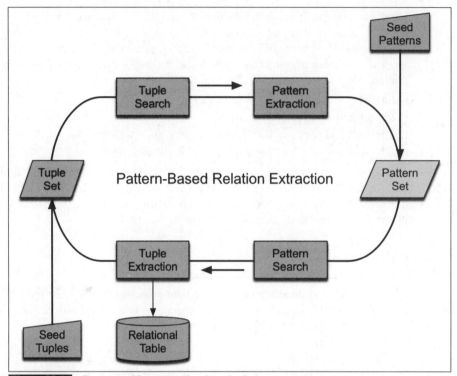

Figure 22.16   Pattern and bootstrapping-based relation extraction.

(22.13) Budget airline Ryanair, which uses Charleroi as a hub, scrapped all weekend
flights out of the airport.

(22.14) All flights in and out of Ryanair's Belgian hub at Charleroi airport were
grounded on Friday...

(22.15) A spokesman at Charleroi, a main hub for Ryanair, estimated that 8000
passengers had already been affected.

From these results, we can extract patterns such as the following that look for relevant named entities of various types in the right places.

```
/ [ORG], which uses [LOC] as a hub /
/ [ORG]'s hub at [LOC] /
/ [LOC] a main hub for [ORG] /
```

These new patterns can then be used to search for additional tuples.

Figure 22.16 illustrates the overall bootstrapping approach. This figure shows that
the dual nature of patterns and seeds permits the process to start with either a small
set of **seed tuples** or a set of **seed patterns**. This style of bootstrapping- and pattern-
based relation extraction is closely related to the techniques discussed in Chapter 20
for extracting hyponym- and meronym-based lexical relations.

There are, of course, a fair number of technical details to be worked out to actually
implement such an approach. The following are among some of the key problems.

- Representing the search patterns

- Assessing the accuracy and coverage of discovered patterns
- Assessing the reliability of the discovered tuples

Patterns are typically represented in a way that captures the following four factors.

- Context before the first entity mention
- Context between the entity mentions
- Context following the second mention
- The order of the arguments in the pattern

Contexts are either captured as regular expression patterns or as vectors of features similar to those described earlier for machine learning-based approaches. In either case, they can be defined over character strings, word-level tokens, or syntactic and semantic structures. In general, regular expression approaches tend to be quite specific, yielding high-precision results; feature-based approaches, on the other hand, are more capable of ignoring potentially inconsequential elements of contexts.

Semantic drift

Our next problem is how to assess the reliability of newly discovered patterns and tuples. Recall that we don't, in general, have access to annotated materials giving us the right answers. We therefore must rely on the accuracy of the initial seed sets of patterns and/or tuples for gold-standard evaluation, and we must ensure that we don't permit any significant **semantic drift** to occur as we're learning new patterns and tuples. Semantic drift occurs when an erroneous pattern leads to the introduction of erroneous tuples, which can, in turn, lead to the creation of problematic patterns.

Consider the following example:

(22.16) Sydney has a ferry hub at Circular Quay.

If accepted as a positive example, this expression could lead to the introduction of the tuple $\langle Sydney, CircularQuay \rangle$. Patterns based on this tuple could propagate further errors into the database.

Two factors need to be balanced in assessing a proposed new pattern: the pattern's performance with respect to the current set of tuples and the pattern's productivity in terms of the number of matches it produces in the document collection. More formally, given a document collection $\mathscr{D}$, a current set of tuples T, and a proposed pattern p, we need to track three factors:

- *hits*: the set of tuples in T that p matches while looking in $\mathscr{D}$
- *misses*: The set of tuples in T that p misses while looking at $\mathscr{D}$
- *finds*: The total set of tuples that p finds in $\mathscr{D}$

The following equation balances these considerations (Riloff and Jones, 1999).

$$Conf_{RlogF}(p) = \frac{hits_p}{hits_p + misses_p} \; log(finds_p) \qquad (22.17)$$

It is useful to be able to treat this metric as a probability, so we'll need to normalize it. A simple way to do this is to track the range of confidences in a development set and divide by some previously observed maximum confidence (Agichtein and Gravano, 2000).

We can assess the confidence in a proposed new tuple by combining the evidence supporting it from all the patterns P' that match that tuple in $\mathscr{D}$ (Agichtein and Gravano,

2000). One way to combine such evidence is the **noisy-or** technique. Assume that a given tuple is supported by a subset of the patterns in P, each with its own confidence assessed as above. In the noisy-or model, we make two basic assumptions. First, that for a proposed tuple to be false, *all* of its supporting patterns must have been in error, and second, that the sources of their individual failures are all independent. If we loosely treat our confidence measures as probabilities, then the probability of any individual pattern p failing is $1 - Conf(p)$; the probability of all of the supporting patterns for a tuple being wrong is the product of their individual failure probabilities, leaving us with the following equation for our confidence in a new tuple.

$$Conf(t) = 1 - \prod_{p \in P'} 1 - Conf(p) \qquad (22.18)$$

The independence assumptions associated with the noisy-or model are exceedingly strong indeed. If the failure modes of the patterns are not independent, then the method will overestimate the confidence for the tuple. This overestimate is typically compensated for by setting a very high threshold for the acceptance of new tuples.

Given these measures, we can dynamically assess our confidence in both new tuples and patterns as the bootstrapping process iterates. Setting conservative thresholds for the acceptance of new patterns and tuples should help prevent the system from drifting from the targeted relation.

Although no standardized evaluations for this style of relation extraction are publicly available, the technique has gained acceptance as a practical way to quickly populate relational tables from open source materials, most commonly from the Web (Etzioni et al., 2005).

22.2.3   Evaluation of Relation Analysis Systems

There are two separate methods for evaluating relation detection systems. In the first, the focus is on how well systems can find and classify all the relation mentions in a given text. In this approach, labeled and unlabeled recall, precision, and F-measure are used to evaluate systems against a test collection with human-annotated, gold-standard relations. Labeled precision and recall require the system to classify the relation correctly, whereas unlabeled methods simply measure a system's ability to detect entities that are related.

The second approach focuses on the tuples to be extracted from a body of text rather than on the relation mentions. In this method, systems need not detect every mention of a relation to be scored correctly. Instead, the final evaluation is based on the set of tuples occupying the database when the system is finished. That is, we want to know if the system can discover that Ryanair has a hub at Charleroi; we don't really care how many times it discovers it.

This method has typically been used to evaluate unsupervised methods of the kind discussed in the last section. In these evaluations, human analysts simply examine the set of tuples produced by the system. Precision is simply the fraction of correct tuples out of all the tuples produced as judged by the human experts.

Recall remains a problem in this approach. It is obviously too costly to search by hand for all the relations that could have been extracted from a potentially large collection such as the Web. One solution is to compute recall at various levels of precision, as described in Chapter 23 (Etzioni et al., 2005). Of course, this isn't true recall, since we're measuring against the number of correct tuples discovered rather than the number of tuples that are theoretically extractable from the text.

Another possibility is to evaluate recall on problems for which large resources containing comprehensive lists of correct answers are available. Examples include gazetteers for facts about locations, the Internet Movie Database (IMDB) for facts about movies, or Amazon for facts about books. The problem with this approach is that it measures recall against a database that may be far more comprehensive than the text collections used by the relation extraction system.

22.3   Temporal and Event Processing

Our focus thus far has been on extracting information about entities and their relations to one another. However, in most texts, entities are introduced in the course of describing the events in which they take part. Finding and analyzing the events in a text, and determining how they relate to each other in time are crucial to extracting a more complete picture of the contents of a text. Such temporal information is particularly important in applications such as question answering and summarization.

In question answering, whether or not a system detects a correct answer may depend on temporal relations extracted from both the question and the potential answer text. As an example of this, consider the following sample question and potential answer text.

When did airlines as a group last raise fares?

> Last week, Delta boosted thousands of fares by $10 per round trip, and most big network rivals immediately matched the increase. ("Dateline" 7/2/2007).

This snippet does provide an answer to the question, but extracting it requires temporal reasoning to anchor the phrase *last week*, to link that time to the *boosting* event, and finally to link the time of the *matching* event to that.

The following sections introduce approaches to recognizing temporal expressions, figuring out the times that those expressions refer to, detecting events, and associating times with those events.

22.3.1   Temporal Expression Recognition

Absolute temporal expressions

Relative temporal expressions
Durations

Temporal expressions are those that refer to absolute points in time, relative times, durations, and sets of these. **Absolute temporal expressions** are those that can be mapped directly to calendar dates, times of day, or both. **Relative temporal expressions** map to particular times through some other reference point (as in *a week from last Tuesday*). Finally, **durations** denote spans of time at varying levels of granularity (seconds, minutes, days, weeks, centuries etc.). Figure 22.17 lists some sample temporal expressions in each of these categories.

Absolute	Relative	Durations
April 24, 1916	yesterday	four hours
The summer of '77	next semester	three weeks
10:15 AM	two weeks from yesterday	six days
The 3rd quarter of 2006	last quarter	the last three quarters

Figure 22.17   Examples of absolute, relational and durational temporal expressions.

Category	Examples
Noun	*morning, noon, night, winter, dusk, dawn*
Proper Noun	*January, Monday, Ides, Easter, Rosh Hashana, Ramadan, Tet*
Adjective	*recent, past, annual, former*
Adverb	*hourly, daily, monthly, yearly*

Figure 22.18   Examples of temporal lexical triggers.

Lexical triggers   Syntactically, temporal expressions are syntactic constructions that have temporal **lexical triggers** as their heads. In the annotation scheme in widest use, lexical triggers can be nouns, proper nouns, adjectives, and adverbs; full temporal expression consist of their phrasal projections: noun phrases, adjective phrases, and adverbial phrases. Figure 22.18 provides examples of lexical triggers from these categories.

The annotation scheme in widest use is derived from the TIDES standard (Ferro et al., 2005). The approach presented here is based on the TimeML effort (Pustejovsky et al., 2005). TimeML provides an XML tag, TIMEX3, along with various attributes to that tag, for annotating temporal expressions. The following example illustrates the basic use of this scheme (ignoring the additional attributes, which we discuss in Section 22.3.2).

> A fare increase initiated <TIMEX3>last week </TIMEX3> by UAL Corp's United Airlines was matched by competitors over <TIMEX3>the weekend </TIMEX3>, marking the second successful fare increase in <TIMEX3>two weeks</TIMEX2>.

The temporal expression recognition task consists of finding the start and end of all of the text spans that correspond to such temporal expressions. Although there are myriad ways to compose time expressions in English, the set of temporal trigger terms is, for all practical purposes, static and the set of constructions used to generate temporal phrases is quite conventionalized. These facts suggest that any of the major approaches to finding and classifying text spans that we've already studied should be successful. The following three approaches have all been successfully employed in recent evaluations:

- Rule-based systems based on partial parsing or chunking
- Statistical sequence classifiers based on standard token-by-token IOB encoding
- Constituent-based classification as used in semantic role labeling

Rule-based approaches to temporal expression recognition use cascades of automata to recognize patterns at increasing levels of complexity. Since temporal expressions are limited to a fixed set of standard syntactic categories, most of these systems make use of pattern-based methods for recognizing syntactic chunks. That is, tokens are first part-of-speech tagged, and then larger and larger chunks are recognized from the results from previous stages. The only difference from the usual partial parsing approaches is the fact that temporal expressions must contain temporal lexical triggers. Patterns must, therefore, contain either specific trigger words (e.g., *February*) or patterns representing classes (e.g., *MONTH*). Figure 22.19 illustrates this approach with a small representative fragment from a rule-based system written in Perl.

Sequence-labeling approaches follow the same scheme introduced in Chapter 13 for syntactic chunking. The three tags I, O, and B are used to mark tokens that are either inside, outside or at the beginning of a temporal expression, as delimited by TIMEX3 tags. Our current example would be labeled as follows in this scheme.

A fare increase initiated last week by UAL Corp's...
O   O   O   O   B   I   O   O

As expected, features are extracted from the context surrounding a token to be tagged, and a statistical sequence labeler is trained with those features. As with syntactic chunking and named entity recognition, any of the usual statistical sequence methods can be applied. Figure 22.20 lists the standard features used in the machine-learning-based approach to temporal tagging.

Constituent-based approaches to temporal expression recognition combine aspects of both chunking and token-by-token labeling. In this approach, a complete constituent parse is produced by automatic means. The nodes in the resulting tree are then classified, one by one, according to whether or not they contain a temporal expression. This task is accomplished by training a binary classifier with annotated training data, using many of the same features employed in IOB-style training. This approach separates the classification problem from the segmentation problem by assigning the segmentation problem to the syntactic parser. The motivation for this choice was mentioned earlier; in currently available training materials, temporal expressions are limited to syntactic constituents from one of a fixed set of syntactic categories. Therefore, it makes sense to allow a syntactic parser to solve the segmentation part of the problem.

In standard evaluations, temporal expression recognizers are evaluated with the usual recall, precision, and *F*-measures. In recent evaluations, both rule-based and statistical systems achieve about the same level of performance, with the best systems reaching an *F*-measure of around .87 on strict, exact-match criteria. On a looser criterion based on overlap with gold-standard temporal expressions, the best systems reach an *F*-measure of .94.[4]

The major difficulties for all of these approaches are achieving reasonable coverage, correctly identifying the extent of temporal expressions, and dealing with expressions that trigger false positives. The problem of false positives arises from the use of temporal trigger words as parts of proper names. For example, all of the following examples are likely to cause false positives for either rule-based or statistical taggers.

(22.19) *1984* tells the story of Winston Smith and his degradation by the totalitarian state in which he lives.

(22.20) Edge is set to join Bono onstage to perform U2's classic *Sunday* Bloody *Sunday*.

---

4 http://www.nist.gov/speech/tests/ace/

```
# yesterday/today/tomorrow
$string =~ s/(($OT+(early|earlier|later?)$CT+\s+)?(($OT+the$CT+\s+)?$OT+day$CT+\s+
$OT+(before|after)$CT+\s+)?$OT+$TERelDayExpr$CT+(\s+$OT+(morning|afternoon|
evening|night)$CT+)?)/<TIMEX2 TYPE=\"DATE\">$1<\/TIMEX2>/gio;

$string =~ s/($OT+\w+$CT+\s+)
<TIMEX2 TYPE=\"DATE\"[^>]*>($OT+(Today|Tonight)$CT+)<\/TIMEX2>/$1$2/gso;

# this/that (morning/afternoon/evening/night)
$string =~ s/(($OT+(early|earlier|later?)$CT+\s+)?$OT+(this|that|every|the$CT+\s+
$OT+(next|previous|following))$CT+\s*$OT+(morning|afternoon|evening|night)
$CT+(\s+$OT+thereafter$CT+)?)/<TIMEX2 TYPE=\"DATE\">$1<\/TIMEX2>/gosi;
```

Figure 22.19   Fragment of Perl code from MITRE's TempEx temporal tagging system.

Feature	Explanation
Token	The target token to be labeled
Tokens in window	Bag of tokens in the window around a target
Shape	Character shape features
POS	Parts of speech of target and window words
Chunk tags	Base-phrase chunk tag for target and words in a window
Lexical triggers	Presence in a list of temporal terms

Figure 22.20   Typical features used to train IOB-style temporal expression taggers.

```
<TIMEX3 id=t1 type="DATE" value="2007-07-02" functionInDocument="CREATION_TIME">
July 2, 2007 </TIMEX3>  A fare increase initiated <TIMEX3 id="t2" type="DATE"
value="2007-W26"  anchorTimeID="t1">last week</TIMEX3> by UAL Corp's United  Airlines
was matched by competitors over <TIMEX3 id="t3" type="DURATION" value="P1WE"
anchorTimeID="t1"> the weekend </TIMEX3>, marking the second successful fare increase
in <TIMEX3 id="t4" type="DURATION" value="P2W" anchorTimeID="t1"> two weeks </TIMEX3>.
```

Figure 22.21   TimeML markup including normalized values for temporal expressions.

(22.21) Black *September* tried to detonate three car bombs in New York City in
March 1973.

22.3.2   Temporal Normalization

Temporal normalization

The task of recognizing temporal expressions is typically followed by the task of normalization. **Temporal normalization** refers to the process of mapping a temporal expression to either a specific point in time or to a duration. Points in time correspond to calendar dates, to times of day, or both. Durations primarily consist of lengths of time but may also include information concerning the start and end points of a duration when that information is available.

Normalized representations of temporal expressions are captured with the VALUE attribute from the ISO 8601 standard for encoding temporal values (ISO8601, 2004). To illustrate some aspects of this scheme, let's return to our earlier example, reproduced in Fig. 22.21 with the value attributes added in.

The dateline, or document date, for this text was *July 2, 2007*. The ISO representation for this kind of expression is YYYY-MM-DD, or in this case, 2007-07-02. The encodings for the temporal expressions in our sample text all follow from this date, and are shown here as values for the VALUE attribute. Let's consider each of these temporal expressions in turn.

Unit	Pattern	Sample Value
Fully specified dates	YYYY-MM-DD	1991-09-28
Weeks	YYYY-nnW	2007-27W
Weekends	PnWE	P1WE
24-hour clock times	HH:MM:SS	11:13:45
Dates and times	YYYY-MM-DDTHH:MM:SS	1991-09-28T11:00:00
Financial quarters	Qn	1999-Q3

Figure 22.22   Sample ISO patterns for representing various times and durations.

The first temporal expression in the text proper refers to a particular week of the year. In the ISO standard, weeks are numbered from 01 to 53, with the first week of the year being the one that has the first Thursday of the year. These weeks are represented with the template YYYY-Wnn. The ISO week for our document date is week 27; thus the value for *last week* is represented as "2007-W26".

The next temporal expression is *the weekend*. ISO weeks begin on Monday; thus, weekends occur at the end of a week and are fully contained within a single week. Weekends are treated as durations, so the value of the VALUE attribute has to be a length. Durations are represented according to the pattern P*nx*, where *n* is an integer denoting the length and *x* represents the unit, as in P3Y for *three years* or P2D for *two days*. In this example, one weekend is captured as P1WE. In this case, there is also sufficient information to anchor this particular weekend as part of a particular week. Such information is encoded in the ANCHORTIMEID attribute. Finally, the phrase *two weeks* also denotes a duration captured as P2W.

There is a lot more to both the ISO 8601 standard and the various temporal annotation standards—far too much to cover here. Figure 22.22 describes some of the basic ways that other times and durations are represented. Consult ISO8601 (2004), Ferro et al. (2005), and Pustejovsky et al. (2005) for more details.

Most current approaches to temporal normalization employ rule-based methods that associate semantic analysis procedures with patterns matching particular temporal expressions. This is a domain-specific instantiation of the compositional rule-to-rule approach introduced in Chapter 18. In this approach, the meaning of a constituent is computed from the meaning of its parts, and the method used to perform this computation is specific to the constituent being created. The only difference here is that the semantic composition rules involve simple temporal arithmetic rather than λ-calculus attachments.

To normalize temporal expressions, we'll need rules for four kinds of expressions.

- Fully qualified temporal expressions
- Absolute temporal expressions
- Relative temporal expressions
- Durations

Fully qualified date expressions

Fully qualified date expressions contain a year, month, and day in some conventional form. The units in the expression must be detected and then placed in the correct place in the corresponding ISO pattern. The following pattern normalizes the fully qualified temporal expression used in expressions like *April 24, 1916*.

$$FQTE \rightarrow Month\,Date\,,\,Year \qquad Year.val\,-\,Month.val\,-\,Date.val$$

In this rule, the non-terminals *Month*, *Date*, and *Year* represent constituents that have already been recognized and assigned semantic values, accessed through the *.val* notation. The value of this *FQE* constituent can, in turn, be accessed as *FQTE.val* during further processing.

Fully qualified temporal expressions are fairly rare in real texts. Most temporal expressions in news articles are incomplete and are only implicitly anchored, often with respect to the dateline of the article, which we refer to as the document's **temporal anchor**. The values of relatively simple temporal expressions such as *today*, *yesterday*, or *tomorrow* can all be computed with respect to this temporal anchor. The semantic procedure for *today* simply assigns the anchor, and the attachments for *tomorrow* and *yesterday* add a day and subtract a day from the anchor, respectively. Of course, given the cyclic nature of our representations for months, weeks, days, and times of day, our temporal arithmetic procedures must use modulo arithmetic appropriate to the time unit being used.

Temporal anchor

Unfortunately, even simple expressions such as *the weekend* or *Wednesday* introduce a fair amount of complexity. In our current example, *the weekend* clearly refers to the weekend of the week that immediately precedes the document date. But this won't always be the case, as is illustrated in the following example.

(22.22) Random security checks that began yesterday at Sky Harbor will continue at least through the weekend.

In this case, the expression *the weekend* refers to the weekend of the week that the anchoring date is part of (i.e., the coming weekend). The information that signals this meaning comes from the tense of *continue*, the verb governing *the weekend*.

Relative temporal expressions are handled with temporal arithmetic similar to that used for *today* and *yesterday*. To illustrate this, consider the expression *last week* from our example. From the document date, we can determine that the ISO week for the article is week 27, so *last week* is simply 1 minus the current week.

Again, even simple constructions such as this can be ambiguous in English. The resolution of expressions involving *next* and *last* must take into account the distance from the anchoring date to the nearest unit in question. For example, a phrase such as *next Friday* can refer either to the immediately next Friday or to the Friday following that. The determining factor has to do with the proximity to the reference time. The closer the document date is to a Friday, the more likely it is that the phrase *next Friday* will skip the nearest one. Such ambiguities are handled by encoding language and domain-specific heuristics into the temporal attachments.

The need to associate highly idiosyncratic temporal procedures with particular temporal constructions accounts for the widespread use of rule-based methods in temporal expression recognition. Even when high-performance statistical methods are used for temporal recognition, rule-based patterns are still required for normalization. Although the construction of these patterns can be tedious and filled with exceptions, it appears that sets of patterns that provide good coverage in newswire domains can be created fairly quickly (Ahn et al., 2005).

Feature	Explanation
Character affixes	Character-level prefixes and suffixes of target word
Nominalization suffix	Character level suffixes for nominalizations (e.g., *-tion*)
Part of speech	Part of speech of the target word
Light verb	Binary feature indicating that the target is governed by a light verb
Subject syntactic category	Syntactic category of the subject of the sentence
Morphological stem	Stemmed version of the target word
Verb root	Root form of the verb basis for a nominalization
WordNet hypernyms	Hypernym set for the target

Figure 22.23   Features commonly used in both rule-based and statistical approaches to event detection.

Finally, many temporal expressions are anchored to events mentioned in a text and not directly to other temporal expressions. Consider the following example:

(22.23) One week after the storm, JetBlue issued its customer bill of rights.

To determine when JetBlue issued its customer bill of rights we need to determine the time of *the storm* event, and then we need to modify that time by the temporal expression *one week after*. We return to this issue when we take up event detection in the next section.

22.3.3   Event Detection and Analysis

Event detection and classification

The task of **event detection and classification** is to identify mentions of events in texts and then assign those events to a variety of classes. For the purposes of this task, an event mention is any expression denoting an event or state that can be assigned to a particular point, or interval, in time. The following markup of the sample text on page 744 shows all the events in this text.

> [*EVENT* Citing] high fuel prices, United Airlines [*EVENT* said] Friday it has [*EVENT* increased] fares by $6 per round trip on flights to some cities also served by lower-cost carriers. American Airlines, a unit of AMR Corp., immediately [*EVENT* matched] [*EVENT* the move], spokesman Tim Wagner [*EVENT* said]. United, a unit of UAL Corp., [*EVENT* said] [*EVENT* the increase] took effect Thursday and [*EVENT* applies] to most routes where it [*EVENT* competes] against discount carriers, such as Chicago to Dallas and Denver to San Francisco.

In English, most event mentions correspond to verbs, and most verbs introduce events. However, as we can see from our example, this is not always the case. Events can be introduced by noun phrases, as in *the move* and *the increase*, and some verbs fail to introduce events, as in the phrasal verb *took effect*, which refers to when the event began rather than to the event itself. Similarly, light verbs such as *make*, *take*, and *have* often fail to denote events. In these cases, the verb is simply providing a syntactic structure for the arguments to an event expressed by the direct object as in *took a flight*.

Both rule-based and statistical machine learning approaches have been applied to the problem of event detection. Both approaches make use of surface information such as parts of speech information, presence of particular lexical items, and verb tense information. Figure 22.23 illustrates the key features used in current event detection and classification systems.

With both the events and the temporal expressions in a text having been detected, the next logical task is to use this information to fit the events into a complete timeline. Such a timeline would be useful for applications such as question answering and summarization. This ambitious task is the subject of considerable current research but is beyond the capabilities of current systems.

A somewhat simpler, but still useful, task is to impose a partial ordering on the events and temporal expressions mentioned in a text. Such an ordering can provide many of the same benefits as a true timeline. An example of such a partial ordering is the determination that the fare increase by *American Airlines* came *after* the fare increase by *United* in our sample text. Determining such an ordering can be viewed as a binary relation detection and classification task similar to those described earlier in Section 22.2.

Current approaches to this problem attempt to identify a subset of Allen's 13 temporal relations discussed earlier in Chapter 17 and shown here in Fig. 22.24. Recent evaluation efforts have focused on detecting the *before*, *after*, and *during* relations among the temporal expressions, document date, and event mentions in a text (Verhagen et al., 2007). Most of the top-performing systems employ statistical classifiers of the kind discussed earlier in Section 22.2, trained on the TimeBank corpus (Pustejovsky et al., 2003b).

22.3.4   TimeBank

As we've seen with other tasks, it's tremendously useful to have access to text annotated with the types and relations in which we're interested. Such resources facilitate both corpus-based linguistic research as well as the training of systems to perform automatic *TimeBank*   tagging. The **TimeBank** corpus consists of text annotated with much of the information we've been discussing throughout this section (Pustejovsky et al., 2003b). The current release (TimeBank 1.2) of the corpus consists of 183 news articles selected from a variety of sources, including the Penn TreeBank and PropBank collections.

Each article in the TimeBank corpus has had the temporal expressions and event mentions in them explicitly annotated in the TimeML annotation (Pustejovsky et al., 2003a). In addition to temporal expressions and events, the TimeML annotation provides temporal links between events and temporal expressions that specify the nature of the relation between them. Consider the following sample sentence and its corresponding markup shown in Fig. 22.25, selected from one of the TimeBank documents.

(22.24) Delta Air Lines soared 33% to a record in the fiscal first quarter, bucking the industry trend toward declining profits.

As annotated, this text includes three events and two temporal expressions. The events are all in the occurrence class and are given unique identifiers for use in further annotations. The temporal expressions include the creation time of the article, which serves as the document time, and a single temporal expression within the text.

In addition to these annotations, TimeBank provides four links that capture the temporal relations between the events and times in the text. The following are the within-sentence temporal relations annotated for this example.

- Soaring$_{e1}$ is **included** in the fiscal first quarter$_{t58}$

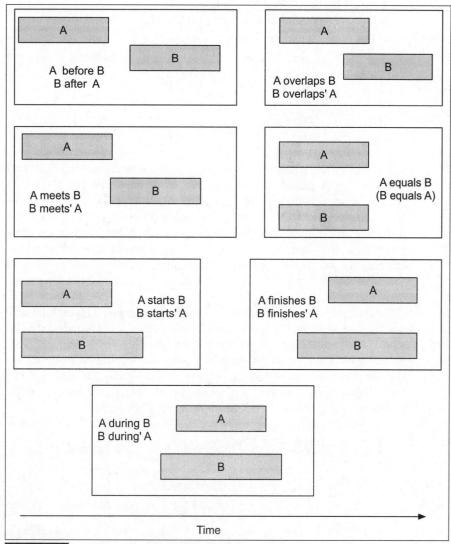

Figure 22.24   Allen's 13 possible temporal relations.

```
<TIMEX3 tid="t57" type="DATE" value="1989-10-26"  functionInDocument="CREATION_TIME">
10/26/89   </TIMEX3>

Delta Air Lines earnings <EVENT eid="e1" class="OCCURRENCE"> soared </EVENT> 33% to a
record in  <TIMEX3 tid="t58" type="DATE" value="1989-Q1" anchorTimeID="t57"> the
fiscal first quarter </TIMEX3>, <EVENT eid="e3"  class="OCCURRENCE">bucking</EVENT>
the industry trend toward <EVENT eid="e4" class="OCCURRENCE">declining</EVENT>
profits.
```

Figure 22.25   Example from the TimeBank corpus.

- Soaring$_{e1}$ is **before** 1989-10-26$_{t57}$
- Soaring$_{e1}$ is **simultaneous** with the bucking$_{e3}$
- Declining$_{e4}$ **includes** soaring$_{e1}$

The set of 13 temporal relations used in TimeBank are based on Allen's (1984) relations, introduced in Fig. 22.24.

22.4   Template Filling

Scripts

Many texts contain reports of events, and possibly sequences of events, that often correspond to fairly common, stereotypical situations in the world. These abstract situations can be characterized as **scripts**, in that they consist of prototypical sequences of sub-events, participants, roles, and props (Schank and Abelson, 1977). The use of explicit representations of such scripts in language processing can assist in many of the IE tasks we've been discussing. In particular, the strong expectations provided by these scripts can facilitate the proper classification of entities, the assignment of entities into roles and relations, and most critically, the drawing of inferences that fill in things that have been left unsaid.

Templates

Template filling

In their simplest form, such scripts can be represented as **templates** consisting of fixed sets of **slots** that take as values **slot-fillers** belonging to particular classes. The task of **template filling** is to find documents that invoke particular scripts and then fill the slots in the associated templates with fillers extracted from the text. These slot-fillers may consist of text segments extracted directly from the text, or they may consist of concepts that have been inferred from text elements through some additional processing (times, amounts, entities from an ontology, etc.).

A filled template from our original airline story might look like the following.

FARE-RAISE ATTEMPT:	LEAD AIRLINE:	UNITED AIRLINES
	AMOUNT:	$6
	EFFECTIVE DATE:	2006-10-26
	FOLLOWER:	AMERICAN AIRLINES

As is often the case, the slot-fillers in this example all correspond to detectable named entities of various kinds (organizations, amounts, and times). This suggests that template-filling applications should rely on tags provided by named entity recognition, temporal expression, and coreference algorithms to identify candidate slot-fillers.

The next section describes a straightforward approach to filling slots that employs sequence-labeling techniques. Section 22.4.2 then describes a system based on the use of cascades of finite-state transducers and designed to address a considerably more complex template-filling task.

22.4.1   Statistical Approaches to Template-Filling

A surprisingly effective approach to template filling casts it as a statistical sequence labeling problem. In this approach, systems are trained to label sequences of tokens as potential fillers for particular slots. There are two ways to instantiate this approach: the first is to train separate sequence classifiers for each slot and then send the entire text through each labeler; the other is to train one large classifier (usually an HMM) that assigns labels for each of the slots to be recognized. We focus on the former approach here and take up the single-large-classifier approach in Chapter 24.

Under the one classifier per slot approach, slots are filled with the text segments identified by each slot's corresponding classifier. As with the other IE tasks described earlier in this chapter, all manner of statistical sequence classifiers have been applied to this problem, all using the usual set of features: tokens, shapes of tokens, part-of-speech tags, syntactic chunk tags, and named entity tags.

There is the possibility in this approach that multiple non-identical text segments will be labeled with the same slot label. This situation can arise in two ways: from competing segments that refer to the same entity but use different referring expressions, or from competing segments that represent truly distinct hypotheses. In our sample text, we might expect the segments *United, United Airlines* to be labeled as the LEAD AIRLINE. These are not incompatible choices and the reference resolution techniques introduced in Chapter 21 can provide a path to a solution.

Truly competing hypotheses arise when a text contains multiple entities of the expected type for a given slot. In our example, *United Airlines* and *American Airlines* are both airlines and both could be tagged as LEAD AIRLINE on the basis of their similarity to exemplars in the training data. In general, most systems simply choose the hypothesis with the highest confidence. Of course, the implementation of this confidence heuristic depends on the style of sequence classifier being employed. Markov-based approaches simply select the segment with the highest-probability labeling (Freitag and McCallum, 1999).

A variety of annotated collections have been used to evaluate this style of approach to template filling, including sets of job announcements, conference calls for papers, restaurant guides, and biological texts. A frequently employed collection is the CMU Seminar Announcement Corpus,[5] a collection of 485 seminar announcements retrieved from the Web with slots annotated for the SPEAKER, LOCATION, START TIME, and END TIME. State-of-the-art F-measures on this dataset range from around .98 for the start and end time slots, to as high as .77 for the speaker slot (Roth and Yih, 2001; Peshkin and Pfefer, 2003).

As impressive as these results are, they are due as much to the constrained nature of the task as to the techniques they have been employed. Three strong task constraints have contributed to this success. First, in most evaluations all the documents in the collection are all relevant and homogeneous, that is they are known to contain the slots of interest. Second, the documents are all relatively small, providing little room for distractor segments that might incorrectly fill slots. And finally, the target output consists solely of a small set of slots which are to be filled with snippets from the text itself.

---

[5]   http://www.isi.edu/info-agents/RISE/

TIE-UP-1:
RELATIONSHIP: TIE-UP
ENTITIES: "Bridgestone Sports Co."
                       "a local concern"
                       "a Japanese trading house"
JOINTVENTURECOMPANY   "Bridgestone Sports Taiwan Co."
ACTIVITY   ACTIVITY-1
AMOUNT   NT$20000000

ACTIVITY-1:
COMPANY   "Bridgestone Sports Taiwan Co."
PRODUCT   "iron and "metal wood" clubs"
STARTDATE   DURING: January 1990

Figure 22.26   The templates produced by the FASTUS (Hobbs et al., 1997) information-extraction engine given the input text on page 754.

22.4.2   Finite-State Template-Filling Systems

The tasks introduced in the *Message Understanding Conferences* (MUC) (Sundheim, 1993), a series of U.S. government-organized, information-extraction evaluations, represent a considerably more complex template-filling problem. Consider the following sentences selected from the MUC-5 materials from Grishman and Sundheim (1995).

> Bridgestone Sports Co. said Friday it has set up a joint venture in Taiwan with a local concern and a Japanese trading house to produce golf clubs to be shipped to Japan.
>
> The joint venture, Bridgestone Sports Taiwan Co., capitalized at 20 million new Taiwan dollars, will start production in January 1990 with production of 20,000 iron and "metal wood" clubs a month.

The MUC-5 evaluation task required systems to produce hierarchically linked templates describing the participants in the joint venture, the resulting company, and its intended activity, ownership and capitalization. Figure 22.26 shows the resulting structure produced by the FASTUS system (Hobbs et al., 1997). Note how the filler of the ACTIVITY slot of the TIE-UP template is itself a template with slots to be filled.

The FASTUS system produces the template given above, based on a cascade of transducers in which each level of linguistic processing extracts some information from the text, which is passed on to the next higher level, as shown in Fig. 22.27.

Most systems base most of these levels on finite-automata, although in practice most complete systems are not technically finite-state because the individual automata are augmented with feature registers (as in FASTUS), because they are used only as preprocessing steps for full parsers (e.g., Gaizauskas et al., 1995; Weischedel, 1995), or because they are combined with other components according to statistical methods (Fisher et al., 1995).

Let's sketch the FASTUS implementation of each of these levels, following Hobbs et al. (1997) and Appelt et al. (1995). After tokenization, the second level recognizes multiwords like *set up* and *joint venture* and names like *Bridgestone Sports Co.* The

No.	Step	Description
1	Tokens:	Transfer an input stream of characters into a token sequence.
2	Complex Words:	Recognize multiword phrases, numbers, and proper names.
3	Basic phrases:	Segment sentences into noun groups, verb groups, and particles.
4	Complex phrases:	Identify complex noun groups and complex verb groups.
5	Semantic Patterns:	Identify semantic entities and events and insert into templates.
6	Merging:	Merge references to the same entity or event from different parts of the text.

Figure 22.27   Levels of processing in FASTUS (Hobbs et al., 1997). Each level extracts a specific type of information which is then passed on to the next higher level.

named entity recognizer is a transducer, composed of a large set of specific mappings designed to handle the usual set of named entities.

The following are typical rules for modeling names of performing organizations like *San Francisco Symphony Orchestra* and *Canadian Opera Company*. While the rules are written in a context-free syntax, they are not recursive and therefore can be automatically compiled into finite-state transducers.

Performer-Org   → (pre-location) Performer-Noun+ Perf-Org-Suffix
pre-location   → locname nationality
locname   → city region
Perf-Org-Suffix → orchestra, company
Performer-Noun   → symphony, opera
nationality   → Canadian, American, Mexican
city   → San Francisco, London

The second stage also might transduce sequences like *forty two* into the appropriate numeric value (recall the discussion of this problem in Chapter 8).

The third FASTUS stage implements chunking and produces a sequence of basic syntactic chunks, such as noun groups, verb groups, and so on, using finite-state rules of the sort discussed in Chapter 13. The output of the FASTUS basic phrase identifier is shown in Figure 22.28; note the use of some domain-specific basic phrases like *Company* and *Location*.

Chapter 13 described how these basic phrases can be combined into more complex noun groups and verb groups. Stage 4 of FASTUS accomplishes this by dealing with conjunction and with the attachment of measure phrases as in the following:

20,000 iron and "metal wood" clubs a month,

and prepositional phrases:

production of 20,000 iron and "metal wood" clubs a month,

The output of Stage 4 is a list of complex noun groups and verb groups. Stage 5 takes this list, ignores all input that has not been chunked into a complex group, recognizes entities and events in the complex groups, and inserts the recognized objects

Phrase Type	Phrase
Company	Bridgestone Sports Co.
Verb Group	said
Noun Group	Friday
Noun Group	it
Verb Group	had set up
Noun Group	a joint venture
Preposition	in
Location	Taiwan
Preposition	with
Noun Group	a local concern
Conjunction	and
Noun Group	a Japanese trading house
Verb Group	to produce
Noun Group	golf clubs
Verb Group	to be shipped
Preposition	to
Location	Japan

Figure 22.28   The output of Stage 2 of the FASTUS basic-phrase extractor, which uses finite-state rules of the sort described by Appelt and Israel (1997).

	Template/Slot	Value
1	RELATIONSHIP:	TIE-UP
	ENTITIES:	"Bridgestone Sports Co."
		"a local concern"
		"a Japanese trading house"
2	ACTIVITY:	PRODUCTION
	PRODUCT:	"golf clubs"
3	RELATIONSHIP:	TIE-UP
	JOINTVENTURECOMPANY:	"Bridgestone Sports Taiwan Co."
	AMOUNT:	NT$20000000
4	ACTIVITY:	PRODUCTION
	COMPANY:	"Bridgestone Sports Taiwan Co."
	STARTDATE:	DURING: January 1990
5	ACTIVITY:	PRODUCTION
	PRODUCT:	"iron and "metal wood" clubs"

Figure 22.29   The five partial templates produced by Stage 5 of the FASTUS system. These templates will be merged by the Stage 6 merging algorithm to produce the final template shown in Fig. 22.26 on page 754.

into the appropriate slots in templates. The recognition of entities and events is done by hand-coded finite-state automata whose transitions are based on particular complex-phrase types annotated by particular headwords or particular features like *company*, *currency*, or *date*.

As an example, the first sentence of the news story above realizes the semantic patterns based on the following two regular expressions (where NG indicates Noun-

Group and VG Verb-Group):

- NG(Company/ies) VG(Set-up) NG(Joint-Venture) with NG(Company/ies)
- VG(Produce) NG(Product)

The second sentence realizes the second pattern above as well as the following two patterns:

- NG(Company) VG-Passive(Capitalized) at NG(Currency)
- NG(Company) VG(Start) NG(Activity) in/on NG(Date)

The result of processing these two sentences is the set of five draft templates shown in Fig. 22.29. These five templates must then be merged into the single hierarchical structure shown in Fig. 22.26. The merging algorithm decides whether two activity or relationship structures are sufficiently consistent that they might be describing the same events, and merges them if so. The merging algorithm must also perform reference resolution, as described in Chapter 21.

22.5   Advanced: Biomedical Information Extraction

Information extraction from biomedical journal articles has become an important application area in recent years. The motivation for this work comes primarily from biologists, who find themselves faced with an enormous increase in the number of publications in their field since the advent of modern genomics—so many that keeping up with the relevant literature is nearly impossible for many scientists. Figure 22.30 amply demonstrates the severity of the problem faced by these scientists. Clearly, applications that can automate the extraction and aggregation of useful information from such sources would be a boon to researchers.

A growing application area for information extraction in the biomedical domain is as an aid to the construction of large databases of genomic and related information. Without the availability of information-extraction-based curator assistance tools, many manual database construction efforts will not be complete for decades—a time-span much too long to be useful (Baumgartner, Jr. et al., 2007).

A good example of this kind of application is the MuteXt system. This system targets two named entity types—mutations in proteins and two very specific types of proteins called *G-coupled protein receptors and nuclear hormone receptors*. MuteXt was used to build a database that drew information from 2,008 documents; building it by hand would have been an enormously time-consuming and expensive undertaking. Mutations in G-coupled protein receptors are associated with a range of diseases that includes diabetes, ocular albinism, and retinitis pigmentosa, so even this simple text mining system has a clear application to the relief of human suffering.

Biologists and bioinformaticians have recently come up with even more innovative uses for text-mining systems, in which the output is never intended for viewing by humans but rather is used as part of the analysis of high-throughput assays—experimental

---

*This section was largely written by Kevin Bretonnel Cohen.

771

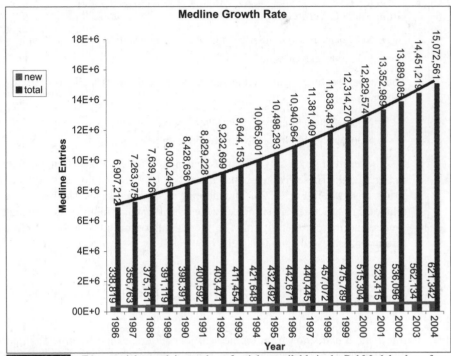

Figure 22.30   Exponential growth in number of articles available in the PubMed database from 1986 to 2004 (Data from Cohen and Hunter (2004)).

methods that produce masses of data points that would have been unimaginable just twenty years ago—and as part of techniques for using data in genomic data repositories. Ng (2006) provides a review and an insightful analysis of work in this vein.

22.5.1   Biological Named Entity Recognition

Information extraction in the biological realm is characterized by a much wider range of relevant types of entities than the PERSON, ORGANIZATION, and LOCATION semantic classes that characterize work that is focused on news-style texts. Figure 22.31 and the following example illustrate just a small subset of the variety of semantic classes of named entities that have been the target of NER systems in the biomedical domain.

> [$_{TISSUE}$ Plasma] [$_{GP}$ BNP] concentrations were higher in both the [$_{POPULATION}$ judo] and [$_{POPULATION}$ marathon groups] than in [$_{POPULATION}$ controls], and positively correlated with [$_{ANAT}$ LV] mass as well as with deceleration time.

Nearly all of the techniques described in Section 22.1 have been applied to the biomedical NER problem, with a particular focus on the problem of recognizing gene and protein names. This task is particularly difficult due to the wide range of forms that gene names can take: *white, insulin, BRCA1, ether a go-go,* and *breast cancer associated 1* are all the names of genes. The choice of algorithm for gene name recognition seems to be less important than the choice of features; typical feature sets include word-shape and contextual features, as discussed earlier; additionally, knowledge-based fea-

Semantic class	Examples
Cell lines	*T98G, HeLa cell, Chinese hamster ovary cells, CHO cells*
Cell types	*primary T lymphocytes, natural killer cells, NK cells*
Chemicals	*citric acid, 1,2-diiodopentane, C*
Drugs	*cyclosporin A, CDDP*
Genes/proteins	*white, HSP60, protein kinase C, L23A*
Malignancies	*carcinoma, breast neoplasms*
Medical/clinical concepts	*amyotrophic lateral sclerosis*
Mouse strains	*LAFT, AKR*
Mutations	*C10T, Ala64 → Gly*
Populations	*judo group*

Figure 22.31   A sample of the semantic classes of named entities that have been recognized in biomedical NLP. Note the surface similarities between many of the examples.

tures, such as using the count of Google hits for a sequence like *BRCA1 gene* to decide whether or not a token of the string *BRCA1* is a reference to a gene, are sometimes incorporated into statistical systems.

Surprisingly, the use of huge publicly available lists of gene names has not generally contributed to the performance of a gene/protein NER system (Yeh et al., 2005) and in fact may actually degrade it (Baumgartner, Jr. et al., 2006). It is not uncommon for gene names to be many tokens long (e.g., *breast cancer associated 1*). Gene name length has a demonstrable effect on NER system performance (Kinoshita et al., 2005; Yeh et al., 2005), and any technique for correctly finding the boundaries of multi-token names seems to increase performance. Use of the abbreviation-definition-detection algorithm (Schwartz and Hearst, 2003) is common for this purpose since many such names appear as abbreviation or symbol definitions at some point in a publication. Base-noun-group chunkers can also be useful in this regard, as can a surprisingly small number of heuristic rules (Kinoshita et al., 2005).

22.5.2 Gene Normalization

Gene normalization

Having identified all the mentions of biological entities in a text, the next step is to map them to unique identifiers in databases or ontologies. This task has been most heavily studied for genes, where it is known as **gene normalization**. Some of the complexities of the problem come from high degrees of variability in the realization of the names of specific entities in naturally occurring text; the nature of the problem was first delineated by Cohen et al. (2002). In that work, a standard discovery procedure from descriptive linguistics was used to determine what sorts of variability in gene names can be ignored and what sorts must not be ignored. More recently, Morgan et al. (2007) have shown how linguistic characteristics of community-specific, gene-naming conventions affect the complexity of this task when the normalization of genes from varying species is attempted. Gene normalization can be considered a type of word sense disambiguation task, midway between a targetted WSD task and an all-words WSD task.

An important thread of work on this problem involves mapping named entities to biomedical ontologies, especially the Gene Ontology (Ashburner et al., 2000). This has proved considerably more challenging; terms in the Gene Ontology tend to be long, to have many possible lexical and syntactic forms, and to sometimes require significant amounts of inference.

22.5.3   Biological Roles and Relations

Finding and normalizing all the mentions of biological entities in a text is a preliminary step to determining the roles played by entities in the text. Two ways to do this have been the focus of recent research: discover and classify the expressed binary relations between the entities in a text; identify and classify the roles played by entities with respect to the central events in the text. These two tasks correspond roughly to the tasks of classifying the relationship between pairs of entities, as described in Section 22.2, and to the semantic role labeling task introduced in Chapter 20.

Consider the following example texts that express binary relations between entities:

(22.25) These results suggest that con A-induced [$_{DISEASE}$ hepatitis] was ameliorated by pretreatment with [$_{TREATMENT}$ TJ-135].

(22.26) [$_{DISEASE}$ Malignant mesodermal mixed tumor of the uterus] following [$_{TREATMENT}$ irradiation]

Each of these examples asserts a relationship between a *disease* and a *treatment*. In the first example, the relationship can be classified as that of *curing*. In the second example, the disease is a *result* of the mentioned treatment. Rosario and Hearst (2004) present a system for the classification of seven kinds of disease-treatment relations. In this work, a series of HMM-based generative models and a discriminative neural network model were successfully applied.

More generally, a wide range of rule-based and statistical approaches has been applied to binary relation recognition problems such as this. Examples of other widely studied biomedical relation recognition problems include genes and their biological functions (Blaschke et al., 2005), genes and drugs (Rindflesch et al., 2000), genes and mutations (Rebholz-Schuhmann et al., 2004), and protein-protein interactions (Rosario and Hearst, 2005).

Now consider the following example that corresponds to a semantic role-labeling style of problem.

(22.27) [$_{THEME}$ Full-length cPLA2] was [$_{TARGET}$ phosphorylated] stoichiometrically by [$_{AGENT}$ p42 mitogen-activated protein (MAP) kinase] in vitro... and the major site of phosphorylation was identified by amino acid sequencing as [$_{SITE}$ Ser505]

The *phosphorylation* event that lies at the core of this text has three semantic roles associated with it: the causal AGENT of the event, the THEME or entity being phosphorylated, and the location, or SITE, of the event. The problem is to identify the constituents in the input that play these roles and assign them the correct role labels. Note that this example contains a further complication in that the second event mention *phosphorylation* must be identified as coreferring with the first *phosphorylated* in order to capture the SITE role correctly.

Much of the difficulty with semantic role labeling in the biomedical domain stems from the preponderance of nominalizations in these texts. Nominalizations like *phos-

phorylation typically offer fewer syntactic cues to signal their arguments than their verbal equivalents, making the identification task more difficult. A further complication is that different semantic roles arguments often occur as parts of the same, or dominating, nominal constituents. Consider the following examples

(22.28) Serum stimulation of fibroblasts in floating matrices does not result in [$_{TARGET}$ [$_{ARG1}$ ERK] translocation] to the [$_{ARG3}$ nucleus] and there was decreased serum activation of upstream members of the ERK signaling pathway, MEK and Raf,

(22.29) The translocation of RelA/p65 was investigated using Western blotting and immunocytochemistry. The COX-2 inhibitor SC236 worked directly through suppressing [$_{TARGET}$ [$_{ARG3}$ nuclear] translocation] of [$_{ARG1}$ RelA/p65].

(22.30) Following UV treatment, Mcl-1 protein synthesis is blocked, the existing pool of Mcl-1 protein is rapidly degraded by the proteasome, and [$_{ARG1}$ [$_{ARG2}$ cytosolic] Bcl-xL] [$_{TARGET}$ translocates] to the [$_{ARG3}$ mitochondria]

Each of these examples contains arguments that are bundled into constituents with other arguments or with the target predicate itself. For instance, in the second example the constituent *nuclear translocation* signals both the TARGET and the ARG3 role.

Both rule-based and statistical approaches have been applied to these semantic role-like problems. As with relation finding and NER, the choice of algorithm is less important than the choice of features, many of which are derived from accurate syntactic analyses. However, since no large treebanks are available for biological texts, we are left with the option using off-the-shelf parsers trained on generic newswire texts. Of course, the errors introduced in this process may negate whatever power we can derive from syntactic features. Therefore, an important area of research revolves around the adaptation of generic syntactic tools to this domain (Blitzer et al., 2006).

Relational and event-extraction applications in this domain often have extremely limited foci. The motivation for this limitation is that even systems with narrow scope can contribute to the productivity of working bioscientists. An extreme example of this is the RLIMS-P system discussed earlier. It tackles only the verb *phosphorylate* and the associated nominalization *phosphorylization*. Nevertheless, this system was successfully used to produce a large on-line database that is in widespread use by the research community.

As the targets of biomedical information extraction applications have become more ambitious, the range of BioNLP application types has become correspondingly broad. Computational lexical semantics and semantic role labeling (Verspoor et al., 2003; Wattarujeekrit et al., 2004; Ogren et al., 2004; Kogan et al., 2005; Cohen and Hunter, 2006), summarization (Lu et al., 2006), and question answering are all active research topics in the biomedical domain. Shared tasks like BioCreative continue to be a source of large data sets for named entity recognition, question answering, relation extraction, and document classification (Hirschman and Blaschke, 2006), as well as a venue for head-to-head assessment of the benefits of various approaches to information-extraction tasks.

22.6   Summary

This chapter has explored a series of techniques for extracting limited forms of semantic content from texts. Most techniques can be characterized as problems in detection followed by classification.

- **Named entities** can be recognized and classified by **statistical sequence labeling** techniques.

- **Relations among entities** can be detected and classified by supervised learning methods when annotated training data is available; lightly supervised **bootstrapping** methods can be used when small numbers of **seed tuples** or **seed patterns** are available.

- Reasoning about time can be facilitated by detection and normalization of **temporal expressions** through a combination of statistical learning and rule-based methods.

- Rule-based and statistical methods can be used to detect, classify, and order **events** in time. The **TimeBank corpus** can facilitate the training and evaluation of temporal analysis systems.

- **Template-filling** applications can recognize stereotypical situations in texts and assign elements from the text to roles represented as **fixed sets of slots**.

- Information extraction techniques have proved to be particularly effective in processing texts from the **biological domain**.

Bibliographical and Historical Notes

The earliest work on information extraction addressed the template-filling task and was performed in the context of the Frump system (DeJong, 1982). Later work was stimulated by the U.S. government-sponsored MUC conferences (Sundheim, 1991, 1992, 1993, 1995b). Chinchor et al. (1993) describe the evaluation techniques used in the MUC-3 and MUC-4 conferences. Hobbs (1997) partially credits the inspiration for FASTUS to the success of the University of Massachusetts CIRCUS system (Lehnert et al., 1991) in MUC-3. Another system that did well in MUC-3 was the SCISOR system based loosely on cascades and semantic expectations (Jacobs and Rau, 1990).

Due to the difficulty of reusing or porting systems from one domain to another, attention shifted to the problem of automatic knowledge acquisition for these systems. The earliest supervised learning approaches to IE are described in Cardie (1993), Cardie (1994), Riloff (1993), Soderland et al. (1995), Huffman (1996), and Freitag (1998).

These early learning efforts focused on automating the knowledge acquisition process for mostly finite-state rule-based systems. Their success, and the earlier success of HMM-based methods for automatic speech recognition, led to the development of statistical systems based on sequence labeling. Early efforts applying HMMs to IE problems include the work of Bikel et al. (1997, 1999) and Freitag and McCallum (1999). Subsequent efforts demonstrated the effectiveness of a range of statistical methods including MEMMs (McCallum et al., 2000), CRFs (Lafferty et al., 2001), and SVMs (Sassano and Utsuro, 2000; McNamee and Mayfield, 2002).

Progress in this area continues to be stimulated by formal evaluations with shared benchmark datasets. The MUC evaluations of the mid-1990s were succeeded by the Automatic Content Extraction (ACE) program evaluations held periodically from 2000 to 2007.[6] These evaluations focused on the tasks of named entity recognition, relation detection, and temporal expression detection and normalization. Other IE evaluations include the 2002 and 2003 CoNLL shared tasks on language-independent named entity recognition (Tjong Kim Sang, 2002; Tjong Kim Sang and De Meulder, 2003) and the 2007 SemEval tasks on temporal analysis (Verhagen et al., 2007; Bethard and Martin, 2007) and people search (Artiles et al., 2007; Chen and Martin, 2007).

The scope of information extraction continues to expand to meet the ever-increasing needs of applications for novel kinds of information. Some of the emerging IE tasks that we haven't discussed include the classification of gender (Koppel et al., 2002), moods (Mishne and de Rijke, 2006), sentiment, affect, and opinions (Qu et al., 2005). *User-generated content* / *Social media* Much of this work involves **user-generated content** in the context of **social media** such as blogs, discussion forums, newsgroups and the like. Research results in this domain have been the focus of a number of recent workshops and conferences (Nicolov et al., 2006; Nicolov and Glance, 2007).

Exercises

22.1 Develop a set of regular expressions to recognize the character shape features described in Fig. 22.7.

22.2 Using a statistical sequence modeling toolkit of your choosing, develop and evaluate an NER system.

22.3 The IOB labeling scheme given in this chapter isn't the only possible one. For example, an E tag might be added to mark the end of entities, or the B tag can be reserved only for those situations where an ambiguity exists between adjacent entities. Propose a new set of IOB tags for use with your NER system. Experiment with it and compare its performance with the scheme presented in this chapter.

22.4 Names of works of art (books, movies, video games, etc.) are quite different from the kinds of named entities we've discussed in this chapter. Collect a list of names of works of art from a particular category from a Web-based source (e.g., gutenberg.org, amazon.com, imdb.com, etc.). Analyze your list and give examples of ways that the names in it are likely to be problematic for the techniques described in this chapter.

---

6 www.nist.gov/speech/tests/ace/

22.5 Develop an NER system specific to the category of names that you collected in the last exercise. Evaluate your system on a collection of text likely to contain instances of these named entities.

22.6 Acronym expansion, the process of associating a phrase with an acronym, can be accomplished by a simple form of relational analysis. Develop a system based on the relation analysis approaches described in this chapter to populate a database of acronym expansions. If you focus on English **Three Letter Acronyms** (TLAs) you can evaluate your system's performance by comparing it to Wikipedia's TLA page.

22.7 A useful functionality in newer email and calendar applications is the ability to associate temporal expressions connected with events in email (doctor's appointments, meeting planning, party invitations, etc.) with specific calendar entries. Collect a corpus of email containing temporal expressions related to event planning. How do these expressions compare to the kinds of expressions commonly found in news text that we've been discussing in this chapter?

22.8 Develop and evaluate a recognition system capable of recognizing temporal expressions of the kind appearing in your email corpus.

22.9 Design a system capable of normalizing these expressions to the degree required to insert them into a standard calendaring application.

22.10 Acquire the CMU seminar announcement corpus and develop a template-filling system by using any of the techniques mentioned in Section 22.4. Analyze how well your system performs as compared with state-of-the-art results on this corpus.

22.11 Given your corpus, develop an approach to annotating the relevant slots in your corpus so that it can serve as a training corpus. Your approach should involve some hand-annotation but should not be based solely on it.

22.12 Retrain your system and analyze how well it functions on your new domain.

22.13 Species identification is a critical issue for biomedical information extraction applications such as document routing and classification. But it is especially crucial for realistic versions of the gene normalization problem.
Build a species identification system that works on the document level, using the machine learning or rule-based method of your choice. Use the BioCreative gene normalization data (`biocreative.sourceforge.net`) as gold-standard data.

22.14 Build, or borrow, a named entity recognition system that targets mentions of genes and gene products in texts. As development data, use the BioCreative gene mention corpus (`biocreative.sourceforge.net`).

22.15 Build a gene normalization system that maps the output of your gene mention recognition system to the appropriate database entry. Use the BioCreative gene normalization data as your development and test data. Be sure you don't give your system access to the species identification in the metadata.

Chapter 23

Question Answering and Summarization

"Alright", said Deep Thought. "The Answer to the Great Question..."
"Yes!"
"Of Life The Universe and Everything...", said Deep Thought.
"Yes!"
"Is..."
"Yes...!!!...?"
"Forty-two", said Deep Thought, with infinite majesty and calm...
Douglas Adams, *The Hitchhiker's Guide to the Galaxy*

I read *War and Peace*...It's about Russia...
Woody Allen, *Without Feathers*

Because so much text information is available generally on the Web or in specialized collections such as PubMed or even on the hard drives of our laptops, the single most important use of language processing these days is to help us query and extract meaning from these large repositories. If we have a structured idea of what we are looking for, we can use the information-extraction algorithms from the previous chapter. But many times we have an information need that is best expressed more informally in words or sentences, and we want to find either a specific answer fact, a specific document, or something in between.

In this chapter we introduce the tasks of **question answering (QA)** and **summarization**, tasks that produce specific phrases, sentences, or short passages, often in response to a user's need for information expressed in a natural language query. In studying these topics, we also cover highlights from the field of **information retrieval (IR)**, the task of returning documents that are relevant to a particular natural language query. IR is a complete field in its own right, and we only give a brief introduction to it here, but one that is essential for an understanding of QA and summarization.

We focus on a central idea behind all of these subfields, the idea of meeting a user's information needs by **extracting** passages directly from documents or from document collections like the Web.

Information retrieval is an extremely broad field, encompassing a wide range of topics pertaining to the storage, analysis, and retrieval of all manner of media, including text, photographs, audio, and video (Baeza-Yates and Ribeiro-Neto, 1999). Our concern in this chapter is solely with the storage and retrieval of text documents in response to users' word-based queries for information. In Section 23.1 we present the **vector space model**, some variant of which is used in most current systems, including most Web search engines.

Rather than make the user read through an entire document, we'd often prefer to give a single, concise, short answer. Researchers have been trying to automate this

From Chapter 23 of *Speech and Language Processing*, Second Edition. Daniel Jurafsky, James H. Martin.

process of **question answering** since the earliest days of computational linguistics (Simmons, 1965).

The simplest form of question answering is dealing with **factoid questions**. As the name implies, the answers to factoid questions are simple facts that can be found in short text strings. The following are canonical examples of this kind of question.

(23.1) Who founded Virgin Airlines?

(23.2) What is the average age of the onset of autism?

(23.3) Where is Apple Computer based?

Each of these questions can be answered directly with a text string that contains the name of a person, a temporal expression, or a location, respectively. Factoid questions, therefore, are questions whose answers can be found in short spans of text and correspond to a specific, easily characterized, category, often a named entity of the kind we discussed in Chapter 22. These answers may be found on the Web, or alternatively, within some smaller text collection. For example, a system might answer questions about a company's product line by searching for answers in documents on a particular corporate website or internal set of documents. Effective techniques for answering these kinds of questions are described in Section 23.2.

Sometimes we are seeking information whose scope is greater than a single factoid but less than an entire document. In such cases, we might need a **summary** of a document or set of documents. The goal of **text summarization** is to produce an abridged version of a text that contains the important or relevant information. For example, we might want to generate an **abstract** of a scientific article, a **summary** of email threads, *Snippet*   a **headline** for a news article, or a short **snippet** that Web search engines return to the user to describe each retrieved document. For example, Fig. 23.1 shows some sample snippets from Google summarizing the first four documents returned from the query *German Expressionism Brücke*.

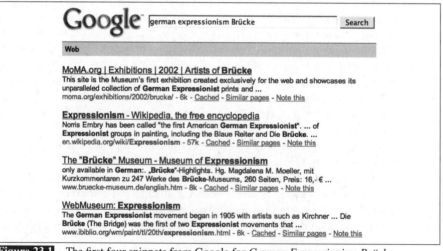

Figure 23.1   The first four snippets from Google for *German Expressionism Brücke*.

To produce these various kinds of summaries, we introduce algorithms for summarizing single documents and those for producing summaries of multiple documents by combining information from different textual sources.

Finally, we turn to a field that tries to go beyond factoid question answering by borrowing techniques from summarization to try to answer more complex questions like the following:

(23.4)   Who is Celia Cruz?

(23.5)   What is a Hajj?

(23.6)   In children with an acute febrile illness, what is the efficacy of single-medication therapy with acetaminophen or ibuprofen in reducing fever?

Answers to questions such as these do not consist of simple named entity strings. Rather they involve potentially lengthy coherent texts that knit together an array of associated facts to produce a biography, a complete definition, a summary of current events, or a comparison of clinical results on particular medical interventions. In addition to the complexity and style differences in these answers, the facts that go into such answers may be context, user, and time dependent.

Complex question Current methods answer these kinds of **complex questions** by piecing together relevant text segments that come from summarizing longer documents. For example, we might construct an answer from text segments extracted from a corporate report, a set of medical research journal articles, a set of relevant news articles, or Web pages. This idea of summarizing text in response to a user query is called **query-based summa-**
Query-based
summarization **rization** or **focused summarization**, and is explored in Section 23.6.

Finally, we reserve for Chapter 24 all discussion of the role that questions play in extended dialogues; this chapter focuses only on responding to a single query.

23.1   Information Retrieval

Information
retrieval
IR
Information retrieval (IR) is a growing field that encompasses a wide range of topics related to the storage and retrieval of all manner of media. The focus of this section is on the storage of text documents and their subsequent retrieval in response to users' requests for information. In this section our goal is just to give a sufficient overview of IR techniques to lay a foundation for the following sections on question answering and summarization. Readers with more interest specifically in information retrieval should see the Historical Notes section at the end of the chapter.

Most current IR systems are based on a kind of extreme version of compositional semantics in which the meaning of a document resides solely in the set of words it contains. To revisit the Mad Hatter's quote from the beginning of Chapter 19, in these systems *I see what I eat* and *I eat what I see* mean precisely the same thing. The ordering and constituency of the words that make up the sentences that make up documents play no role in determining their meaning. Because they ignore syntactic information, *Bag-of-words* these approaches are often referred to as **bag-of-words** models.

Before moving on, we need to introduce some new terminology. In information
Document retrieval, a **document** refers generically to the unit of text indexed in the system and available for retrieval. Depending on the application, a document can refer to anything

from common artifacts like newspaper articles or encyclopedia entries to smaller units
such as paragraphs and sentences. In Web-based applications, document can refer to
a Web page, a part of a page, or an entire website. A **collection** refers to a set of
documents being used to satisfy user requests. A **term** refers to a lexical item that
occurs in a collection, but it may also include phrases. Finally, a **query** represents a
user's information need expressed as a set of terms.

Collection
Term
Query

The specific information retrieval task that we will consider in detail is known as **ad
hoc retrieval**. In this task, it is assumed that an unaided user poses a query to a retrieval
system, which then returns a possibly ordered set of potentially useful documents. The
high-level architecture is shown in Fig. 23.2.

Ad hoc retrieval

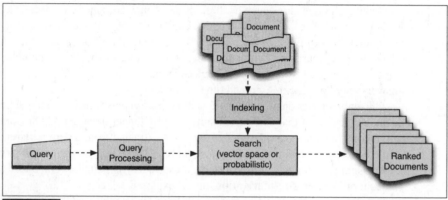

Figure 23.2   The architecture of an ad hoc IR system.

23.1.1   The Vector Space Model

Vector space model

In the **vector space model** of information retrieval, documents and queries are represented as vectors of features representing the terms (words) that occur within the
collection (Salton, 1971).

Term weight

The value of each feature is called the **term weight** and is usually a function of the
term's frequency in the document, along with other factors.

For example, in a fried chicken recipe we found on the Web, the four terms *chicken*,
fried, *oil*, and *pepper* occur with term frequencies 8, 2, 7, and 4, respectively. So if we
just used simple term frequency as our weights and assuming we pretended only these
four words occurred in the collection and we put the features in the above order, the
vector for this document (call it j) would be

$$\vec{d}_j = (8, 2, 7, 4)$$

More generally, we represent a vector for a document d_j as

$$\vec{d}_j = (w_{1,j}, w_{2,j}, w_{3,j}, \quad , w_{n,j})$$

where $\vec{d}_j$ denotes a particular document and the vector contains a weight feature for
each of the N terms that occur in the collection as a whole; $w_{2,j}$ thus refers to the
weight that term 2 has in document j.

We can also represent a query in the same way. For example, a query q for *fried chicken* would have the representation:

$$\vec{q} = (1,1,0,0)$$

More generally,

$$\vec{q} = (w_{1,q}, w_{2,q}, w_{3,q}, \quad , w_{n,q})$$

Note that N, the number of dimensions in the vector, is the total number of terms in the whole collection. This can be hundreds of thousands of words, even if (as is often done) we don't consider some function words in the set of possible terms. But of course, a query or even a long document can't contain very many of these hundreds of thousands of terms. Thus, most of the values of the query and document vectors will be zero. In practice, we don't actually store all the zeros (we use hashes and other sparse representations).

Now consider a different document, a recipe for poached chicken; here the counts are

$$\vec{d}_k = (6,0,0,0)$$

Intuitively we'd like the query q *fried chicken* to match document d_j (the fried chicken recipe) rather than document d_k (the poached chicken recipe). A brief glance at the feature suggests that this might be the case; both the query and the fried chicken recipe have the words *fried* and *chicken*, while the poached chicken recipe is missing the word *fried*.

It is useful to view the features used to represent documents and queries in this model as dimensions in a multidimensional space, where the feature weights serve to locate documents in that space. A user's query translated into a vector denotes a point in that space. Documents that are located close to the query can then be judged as being more relevant than documents that are farther away.

Figure 23.3 graphically illustrates a plot of the first two dimensions (*chicken* and *fried*) for all three vectors. Note that if we measure the similarity between vectors by the angle between the vectors, the query is more similar to d_j than to d_k, because the angle between the query and d_j is smaller.

Cosine   In vector-based information retrieval we standardly use the **cosine** metric that we introduced in Chapter 20 rather than the actual angle. We measure the distance between two documents by the **cosine** of the angle between their vectors. When two documents are identical, they will receive a cosine of 1; when they are orthogonal (share no common terms) they will receive a cosine of 0. The equation for cosine is

$$sim(\vec{q}, \vec{d}_j) = \frac{\sum_{i=1}^{N} w_{i,q} \quad w_{i,j}}{\sqrt{\sum_{i=1}^{N} w_{i,q}^2} \quad \sqrt{\sum_{i=1}^{N} w_{i,j}^2}} \tag{23.7}$$

Recall from Chapter 20 that another way to think of the cosine is as the **normalized dot product**. That is, the cosine is the dot product between the two vectors divided by the lengths of each of the two vectors. This is because the numerator of the cosine is *Dot product*   the **dot product**:

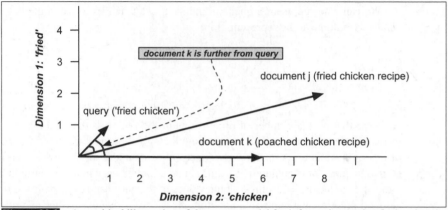

Figure 23.3   A graphical illustration of the vector model for information retrieval, showing the first two dimensions (*fried* and *chicken*) and assuming that we use raw frequency in the document as the feature weights.

$$\text{dot-product}(\vec{x}, \vec{y}) = \vec{x} \cdot \vec{y} = \sum_{i=1}^{N} x_i \cdot y_i \tag{23.8}$$

Vector length

while the denominator of the cosine contains terms for the lengths of the two vectors; recall that **vector length** is defined as

$$|\vec{x}| = \sqrt{\sum_{i=1}^{N} x_i^2} \tag{23.9}$$

This characterization of documents and queries as vectors provides all the basic parts for an ad hoc retrieval system. A document-retrieval system can simply accept a user's query, create a vector representation for it, compare it against the vectors representing all known documents, and sort the results. The result is a list of documents rank-ordered by their similarity to the query.

A further note on representation: the characterization of documents as vectors of term weights allows us to view the document collection as a whole as a (sparse) matrix of weights, where $w_{i,j}$ represents the weight of term i in document j. This weight

Term-by-document matrix

matrix is typically called a **term-by-document matrix** . Under this view, the columns of the matrix represent the documents in the collection, and the rows represent the terms. The term-by-document matrix for the two recipe documents above (again using only the raw term frequency counts as the term weights) would be

$$A = \begin{pmatrix} 8 & 6 \\ 2 & 0 \\ 7 & 0 \\ 4 & 0 \end{pmatrix}$$

23.1.2   Term Weighting

In the examples above, we assumed that the term weights were set as the simple frequency counts of the terms in the documents. This is a simplification of what we do in practice. The method used to assign terms weights in the document and query vectors has an enormous impact on the effectiveness of a retrieval system. Two factors have proved to be critical in deriving effective term weights. We have already seen the first, the term frequency, in its simplest form—the raw frequency of a term within a document (Luhn, 1957). This factor reflects the intuition that terms that occur frequently within a document may reflect its meaning more strongly than terms that occur less frequently and should thus have higher weights.

The second factor is used to give a higher weight to words that occur only in a few documents. Terms that are limited to a few documents are useful for discriminating those documents from the rest of the collection; terms that occur frequently across the entire collection aren't as helpful. The **inverse document frequency** or **IDF** term weight (Sparck Jones, 1972) is one way of assigning higher weights to these more discriminative words. IDF is defined using the fraction N/n_i, where N is the total number of documents in the collection, and n_i is the number of documents in which term i occurs. The fewer documents in which a term occurs, the higher this weight. The lowest weight of 1 is assigned to terms that occur in all the documents. Because of the large number of documents in many collections, this measure is usually squashed with a log function. The resulting definition for inverse document frequency (IDF) is thus

Inverse document frequency
IDF

$$\text{idf}_i = \log\left(\frac{N}{n_i}\right) \tag{23.10}$$

tf-idf
Combining term frequency with IDF results in a scheme known as **tf-idf** weighting:

$$w_{i,j} = \text{tf}_{i,j} \quad \text{idf}_i \tag{23.11}$$

In tf-idf weighting, the weight of term i in the vector for document j is the product of its overall frequency in j with the log of its inverse document frequency in the collection (sometimes the term frequency is logged as well). Tf-idf thus prefers words that are frequent in the current document j but rare overall in the collection. Let's repeat the cosine formula for query-document comparison with tf-idf weights added. We'll modify the formula slightly, since as we noted earlier, most values for any query or document vector will be zero. This means that in practice we don't compute the cosine by iterating over all the (mostly zero) dimensions. Instead, we only compute over the words that are present, as suggested by the following equation for the **tf-idf weighted cosine** between a query q and a document d:

$$sim(\vec{q}, \vec{d}) = \frac{\displaystyle\sum_{w \in q, d} \textit{tf}_{w,q} \textit{tf}_{w,d} (\textit{idf}_w)^2}{\sqrt{\displaystyle\sum_{q_i \in q} (\textit{tf}_{q_i,q} \textit{idf}_{q_i})^2} \sqrt{\displaystyle\sum_{d_i \in d} (\textit{tf}_{d_i,d} \textit{idf}_{d_i})^2}} \tag{23.12}$$

With some minor variations, this tf-idf weighting scheme is used to assign term weights to documents in nearly all vector-space-retrieval models. The tf-idf scheme is also used in many other aspects of language processing; we show it again when we introduce **summarization** on page 794.

785

23.1.3   Term Selection and Creation

Thus far, we have been assuming that it is precisely the words that occur in a collection that are used to index the documents in the collection. Two common variations on this assumption involve the use of **stemming** and a **stop list**.

Stemming   **Stemming**, as we discussed in Chapter 3, is the process of collapsing together the morphological variants of a word. For example, without stemming, the terms *process*, *processing*, and *processed* will be treated as distinct items with separate term frequencies in a term-by-document matrix; with stemming, they will be conflated to the single term *process* with a single summed frequency count. The major advantage to using stemming is that it allows a particular query term to match documents containing any of the morphological variants of the term. The Porter stemmer (Porter, 1980) described in Chapter 3 is frequently used for retrieval from collections of English documents.

A problem with this approach is that it throws away useful distinctions. For example, consider the use of the Porter stemmer on documents and queries containing the words *stocks* and *stockings*. In this case, the Porter stemmer reduces these surface forms to the single term *stock*. Of course, the result is that queries concerning *stock prices* will return documents about *stockings*, and queries about *stockings* will find documents about *stocks*. Additionally we probably don't want to stem, for example, the word *Illustrator* to *illustrate*, since the capitalized form *Illustrator* tends to refer to the software package. Most modern Web search engines therefore need to use more sophisticated methods for stemming.

Stop list   A second common technique involves the use of stop lists, which address the issue of what words should be allowed into the index. A **stop list** is simply a list of high-frequency words that are eliminated from the representation of both documents and queries. Two motivations are normally given for this strategy: high-frequency, closed-class terms are seen as carrying little semantic weight and are thus unlikely to help with retrieval; eliminating them can save considerable space in the inverted index files used to map from terms to the documents that contain them. The downside of using a stop list is that it makes it difficult to search for phrases that contain words in the stop list. For example, a common stop list presented in Frakes and Baeza-Yates (1992) would reduce the phrase *to be or not to be* to the phrase *not*.

23.1.4   Evaluation of Information-Retrieval Systems

The basic tools used to measure the performance of ranked retrieval systems are the **precision** and **recall** measures we employed in earlier settings. Here we assume that the returned items can be divided into two categories: those that are relevant to our purposes and those that are not. Therefore, precision is the fraction of the returned documents that are relevant, and recall is the fraction of all possible relevant documents that are contained in the return set. More formally, let's assume that we have been given a total of T ranked documents in response to a given information request, that a subset of these documents, R, consists of relevant documents, and that a disjoint subset, N, consists of the remaining irrelevant documents. Finally, let's assume that U documents in the collection as a whole are relevant to this particular request. Given all this, we can define our precision and recall measures to be:

$$Precision = \frac{R}{T} \qquad (23.13)$$

$$Recall = \frac{R}{U} \qquad (23.14)$$

Unfortunately, these metrics are not quite sufficient to measure the performance of a system that *ranks* the documents it returns. That is, if we are comparing the performance of two ranked retrieval systems, we require a metric that will prefer the one that ranks the relevant documents higher. Simple precision and recall as defined above are not dependent on rank in any way; we need to adapt them to capture how well a system does at putting relevant documents higher in the ranking. The two standard methods in information retrieval for accomplishing this are based on plotting precision/recall curves and on averaging precision measures in various ways.

Rank	Judgment	$Precision_{Rank}$	$Recall_{Rank}$
1	R	1.0	.11
2	N	.50	.11
3	R	.66	.22
4	N	.50	.22
5	R	.60	.33
6	R	.66	.44
7	N	.57	.44
8	R	.63	.55
9	N	.55	.55
10	N	.50	.55
11	R	.55	.66
12	N	.50	.66
13	N	.46	.66
14	N	.43	.66
15	R	.47	.77
16	N	.44	.77
17	N	.44	.77
18	R	.44	.88
19	N	.42	.88
20	N	.40	.88
21	N	.38	.88
22	N	.36	.88
23	N	.35	.88
24	N	.33	.88
25	R	.36	1.0

Figure 23.4   Rank-specific precision and recall values calculated as we proceed down through a set of ranked documents.

Let's consider each of these methods in turn using the data given in the table in Fig. 23.4. This table lists rank-specific precision and recall values calculated as we proceed down through a set of ranked items. That is, the precision numbers are the fraction of relevant documents seen at a given rank, and recall is the fraction of relevant documents found at the same rank. The recall measures in this example are based on this query having nine relevant documents in the collection as a whole. Note that recall is non-decreasing as we proceed; when relevant items are encountered, recall increases and when non-relevant documents are found it remains unchanged. Precision on the other hand, hops up and down, increasing when relevant documents are found, and decreasing otherwise.

One common way to get a handle on this kind of data is to plot precision against recall on a single graph, using data gathered from across a set of queries. To do this, we need a way to average the recall and precision values across a set of queries. The standard way is to plot averaged precision values at 11 fixed levels of recall (0 to 100, in steps of 10). Of course, as is illustrated by Fig. 23.4, we're not likely to have datapoints at these exact levels for all (or any) of the queries in our evaluation set, but we can use *Interpolated precision* **interpolated precision** values for the 11 recall values from the data points we do have. We can accomplish this by choosing the maximum precision value achieved at any level of recall at or above the one we're calculating. In other words,

$$IntPrecision(r) = \max_{i>=r} Precision(i) \qquad (23.15)$$

Note that this interpolation scheme not only provides us with the means to average performance over a set of queries, but it also provides a sensible way to smooth over the irregular precision values in the original data. This particular smoothing method is designed to give systems the benefit of the doubt by assigning the maximum precision value achieved at higher levels of recall from the one being measured. The interpolated data points for our earlier example are listed in Fig. 23.5 and plotted in Fig. 23.6.

Interpolated Precision	Recall
1.0	0.0
1.0	.10
.66	.20
.66	.30
.66	.40
.63	.50
.55	.60
.47	.70
.44	.80
.36	.90
.36	1.0

Figure 23.5   Interpolated data points from Fig. 23.4.

Given curves such as that in Fig. 23.6 we can compare two systems or approaches by comparing their curves. Clearly, curves that are higher in precision across all recall values are preferred. However, these curves can also provide insight into the overall behavior of a system. Systems that are higher in precision toward the left may favor precision over recall, while systems that are more geared towards recall will be higher at higher levels of recall (to the right).

Mean average precision A second popular way to evaluate ranked retrieval systems is known as **mean average precision** (MAP). In this approach, we again descend through the ranked list of items and note the precision only at those points where a relevant item has been

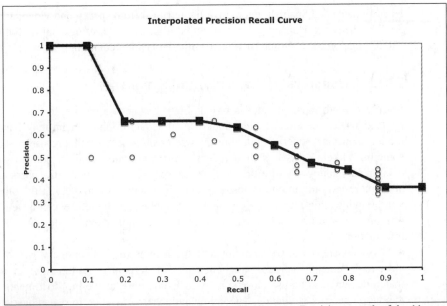

Figure 23.6   An 11 point interpolated precision-recall curve. Precision at each of the 11 standard recall levels is interpolated for each query from the maximum at any higher level of recall. The original measured precision recall points are also shown.

encountered. For a single query, we average these individual precision measurements over the return set up to some fixed cutoff. More formally, if we assume that R_r is the set of relevant documents at or above r, then the average precision for a single query is

$$\frac{1}{R_r} \sum_{d \in R_r} Precision_r(d) \qquad (23.16)$$

where $Precision_r(d)$ is the precision measured at the rank at which document d was found. For an ensemble of queries, we then average over these averages, to get our final MAP measure. Applying this technique to the data in Fig. 23.5 yields a MAP measure of 0.6 for this single retrieval.

MAP has the advantage of providing a single crisp metric that can be used to compare competing systems or approaches. Note that MAP will tend to favor systems that provide relevant documents at high ranks. Of course, this isn't really a problem since that is a big part of what we're looking for in a retrieval system. But since the measure essentially ignores recall, it can favor those systems that are tuned to return small sets of documents in which they are highly confident, at the expense of systems that attempt to be more comprehensive by trying to attain higher levels of recall.

The U.S. government-sponsored TREC (Text REtrieval Conference) evaluations, run annually since 1992, provide a rigorous testbed for the evaluation of a variety of information-retrieval tasks and techniques. TREC provides large document sets for both training and testing, along with a uniform scoring system. Training materials consist of sets of documents accompanied by sets of queries (called topics in TREC) and relevance judgments. TREC subtasks over the years have included question answering,

IR in Chinese and Spanish, interactive IR, retrieval from speech and video, and others. See Voorhees and Harman (2005). Details of all of the meetings can be found at the TREC page on the National Institute of Standards and Technology website.

23.1.5   Homonymy, Polysemy, and Synonymy

Since the vector space model is based solely on the use of simple terms, it is useful to consider the effect that various lexical semantic phenomena may have on the model. Consider a query containing the word *canine*, a word that has senses meaning something like *tooth* and *dog*. A query containing *canine* will be judged similar to documents making use of either of these senses. However, given that users are probably interested only in one of these senses, the documents containing the other sense will be judged non-relevant. Homonymy and polysemy, therefore, can have the effect of *reducing precision* by leading a system to return documents irrelevant to the user's information need.

Now consider a query consisting of the lexeme *dog*. This query will be judged close to documents that make frequent use of the term *dog*, but the system may fail to match documents that use close synonyms like *canine*, as well as documents that use hyponyms such as *Malamute*. Synonymy and hyponymy, therefore, can have the effect of *reducing recall* by causing the retrieval system to miss relevant documents.

Note that it is misleading to state flatly that polysemy reduces precision, and synonymy reduces recall since, as we discuss on page 774, both measures are relative to a fixed cutoff. As a result, every non-relevant document that rises above the cutoff because of polysemy takes up a slot in the fixed-size return set and may thus push a relevant document below threshold, thereby reducing recall. Similarly, when a document is missed because of synonymy, a slot is opened in the return set for a non-relevant document, potentially reducing precision as well.

These issues lead naturally to the question of whether word sense disambiguation can help in information retrieval. The current evidence on this point is mixed, with some experiments reporting a gain when disambiguation-like techniques are used (Schütze and Pedersen, 1995), and others reporting either no gain, or a degradation in performance (Krovetz and Croft, 1992; Sanderson, 1994; Voorhees, 1998).

23.1.6   Ways to Improve User Queries

One of the most effective ways to improve retrieval performance is to find a way to improve user queries. The techniques presented in this section have been shown to varying degrees to be effective at this task.

Relevance feedback

The most effective way to improve retrieval performance in the vector space model is the use of **relevance feedback** (Rocchio, 1971). In this method, a user presents a query to the system and is presented with a small set of retrieved documents. The user is then asked to specify which of these documents appears relevant to their need. The original query is then reformulated according to the distribution of terms in the relevant and non-relevant documents that the user examined. This reformulated query is then passed to the system as a *new* query, with the new results being shown to the user. Typically, a significant improvement is seen after a single iteration of this technique.

The formal basis for the implementation of this technique falls out directly from some of the basic geometric intuitions of the vector model. In particular, we would like to *push* the vector representing the user's original query toward the documents that have been found to be relevant and away from the documents judged not relevant. We can do this by adding an averaged vector representing the relevant documents to the original query and subtracting an averaged vector representing the non-relevant documents.

More formally, let's assume that $\vec{q}_i$ represents the user's original query, R is the number of relevant documents returned from the original query, S is the number of non-relevant documents, and $\vec{r}$ and $\vec{s}$ denote documents in the relevant and non-relevant sets, respectively. In addition, assume that β and γ range from 0 to 1 and that $\beta + \gamma = 1$. Given these assumptions, the following represents a standard relevance feedback update formula:

$$\vec{q}_{i+1} = \vec{q}_i + \frac{\beta}{R} \sum_{j=1}^{R} \vec{r}_j - \frac{\gamma}{S} \sum_{k=1}^{S} \vec{s}_k$$

The factors β and γ in this formula represent parameters that can be adjusted experimentally. Intuitively, β represents how far the new vector should be pushed toward the relevant documents, and γ represents how far it should be pushed away from the non-relevant ones. Salton and Buckley (1990) report good results with $\beta = .75$ and $\gamma = .25$.

Evaluating systems that use relevance feedback is rather tricky. An enormous improvement is often seen in the documents retrieved by the first reformulated query. This should not be too surprising, since it includes the documents that the user told the system were relevant on the first round. The preferred way to avoid this inflation is to compute recall and precision measures only for what is called the **residual collection**, the original collection without any of the documents shown to the user on any previous round. This technique usually has the effect of driving the system's raw performance below that achieved with the first query since the most highly relevant documents have now been eliminated. Nevertheless, this is an effective technique to use when comparing distinct relevance-feedback mechanisms.

Residual collection

An alternative approach to query improvement focuses on terms that make up the query vector. In **query expansion**, the user's original query is expanded by the addition of terms that are synonymous with or related to the original terms. Query expansion is thus a technique for improving recall, perhaps at the expense of precision. For example, the query *Steve Jobs* could be expanded by adding terms like *Apple* or *Macintosh*.

Query expansion

The terms to be added to the query are taken from a **thesaurus**. It is possible to use a hand-built resource like WordNet or UMLS as the thesaurus for query expansion when the domain is appropriate. But often these thesauruses are not suitable for the collection, and instead, we do **thesaurus generation**, automatically generating a thesaurus from documents in the collection. We can do this by clustering the words in the collection, a method known as **term clustering**. Recall from our characterization of the term-by-document matrix that the columns in the matrix represent the documents and the rows represent the terms. Thus, in thesaurus generation, the rows can be clustered to form sets of synonyms, which can then be added to the user's original query to improve its recall. The distance metric for clustering can be simple cosine or any of

Thesaurus

Thesaurus generation

Term clustering

the other distributional methods for word relatedness discussed in Chapter 20.

The thesaurus can be generated once from the document collection as a whole (Crouch and Yang, 1992), or sets of synonym-like terms can be generated dynamically from the returned set for the original query (Attar and Fraenkel, 1977). Note that this second approach entails far more effort since in effect a small thesaurus is generated for the documents returned for every query rather than once for the entire collection.

23.2   Factoid Question Answering

In many situations a user wants a particular piece of information rather than an entire document or document set. We use the term **question answering** for the task of returning a particular piece of information to the user in response to a question. We call the task **factoid question answering** if the information is a simple fact, and particularly if this fact has to do with a **named entity** like a person, organization, or location.

The task of a factoid question-answering system is thus to answer questions by finding, either from the Web or some other collection of documents, short text segments that are likely to contain answers to questions, reformatting them, and presenting them to the user. Figure 23.7 shows some sample factoid questions and their answers.

Question	Answer
Where is the Louvre Museum located?	in Paris, France
What's the abbreviation for limited partnership?	L.P.
What are the names of Odin's ravens?	Huginn and Muninn
What currency is used in China?	the yuan
What kind of nuts are used in marzipan?	almonds
What instrument does Max Roach play?	drums
What's the official language of Algeria?	Arabic
What is the telephone number for the University of Colorado, Boulder?	(303)492-1411
How many pounds are there in a stone?	14

Figure 23.7   Some sample factoid questions and their answers.

Since factoid question answering is based on information-retrieval techniques to find these segments, it is subject to the same difficulties as information retrieval. That is, the fundamental problem in factoid question answering is the gap between the way that questions are posed and the way that answers are expressed in a text. Consider the following question/answer pair from the TREC question-answering task:

User Question: What company sells the most greeting cards?
Potential Document Answer: Hallmark remains the largest maker of greeting cards.

Here the user uses the verbal phrase *sells the most* while the document segment uses a nominal *the largest maker*. The solution to the possible mismatches between question and answer form lies in the ability to robustly process *both* questions and candidate answer texts in such a way that a measure of similarity between the question and putative answers can be performed. As we show, this process involves many of the techniques that we have introduced in earlier chapters, including limited forms of morphological analysis, part-of-speech tagging, syntactic parsing, semantic role labeling, named-entity recognition, and information retrieval.

Because it is impractical to employ relatively expensive NLP techniques like parsing or role labeling on vast amounts of textual data, question-answering systems generally use information-retrieval methods to first retrieve a smallish number of potential documents. The most expensive techniques are then used in a second pass on these smaller numbers of candidate relevant texts.

Figure 23.8 shows the three phases of a modern factoid question-answering system: question processing, passage retrieval and ranking, and answer processing.

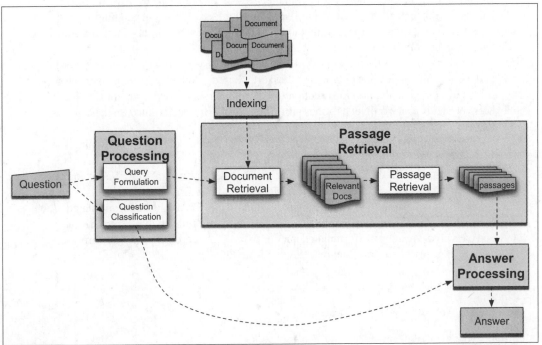

Figure 23.8 Question answering has three stages: question processing, passage retrieval, and answer processing.

23.2.1 Question Processing

The goal of the question-processing phase is to extract two things from the question: a keyword **query** suitable as input to an IR system and an **answer type**, a specification of the kind of entity that would constitute a reasonable answer to the question.

Query Formulation

The process of **query formulation** is similar to the processing done on other IR queries. Our goal is to create from the question a list of keywords that form an IR query.

Exactly what query to form depends on the question-answering application. If question answering is applied to the Web, we might simply create a keyword from every word in the question, letting the Web search engine automatically remove any stopwords. Often, we leave out the question word (*where*, *when*, etc.). Alternatively, keywords can be formed from only the terms found in the noun phrases in the question, applying stopword lists to ignore function words and high-frequency, low-content verbs.

When question answering is applied to smaller sets of documents, for example, to answer questions about corporate information pages, we still use an IR engine to search our documents for us. But for this smaller set of documents, we generally need to apply query expansion. On the Web the answer to a question might appear in many different forms, so if we search with words from the question we'll probably find an answer written in the same form. In smaller sets of corporate pages, by contrast, an answer might appear only once, and the exact wording might look nothing like the question. Thus, query expansion methods can add query terms in hopes of matching the particular form of the answer as it appears.

Thus, we might add to the query all morphological variants of the content words in the question, as well as applying the thesaurus-based or other query expansion algorithms discussed in the previous section to get a larger set of keywords for the query. Many systems use WordNet as a thesaurus; others rely on special-purpose thesauruses that are specifically hand-built for question answering.

Query reformulation

Another query formulation approach that is sometimes used for questioning the Web is to apply a set of **query reformulation** rules to the query. The rules rephrase the question to make it look like a substring of possible declarative answers. For example, the question *"when was the laser invented?"* would be reformulated as *the laser was invented*; the question *"where is the Valley of the Kings?"* might be reformulated as *"the Valley of the Kings is located in"*. We can apply multiple such rules to the query and pass all the resulting reformulated queries to the Web search engine. Here are some sample hand-written reformulation rules from Lin (2007):

(23.17) *wh-word* did A *verb* B $\rightarrow$ ... A *verb*+ed B

(23.18) Where is A $\rightarrow$ A is located in

Question Classification

Answer type

Question classification

The second task in question processing is to classify the question by its expected **answer type**. For example, a question like *"Who founded Virgin Airlines"* expects an answer of type PERSON. A question like *"What Canadian city has the largest population?"* expects an answer of type CITY. This task is called **question classification** or **answer type recognition**. If we know the answer type for a question, we can avoid looking at every sentence or noun phrase in the entire suite of documents for the answer, instead focusing on, for example, just people or cities. Knowing an answer type is also important for presenting the answer. A DEFINITION question like *"What is a prism"* might use a simple answer template like *"A prism is... "*, whereas an answer to a BIOGRAPHY question like *"Who is Zhou Enlai?"* might use a biography-specific template, perhaps beginning with the person's nationality and proceeding to date of birth and other biographical information.

As some of the above examples suggest, we might draw the set of possible answer types for a question classifier from a set of named entities like PERSON, LOCATION, and ORGANIZATION described in Chapter 22. Usually, however, a somewhat richer set of answer types is used. These richer tagsets are often hierarchical, so we usually *Answer type* call them an **answer type taxonomy** or a **question ontology**. Such taxonomies can *taxonomy* be built semi-automatically and dynamically, for example, from WordNet (Harabagiu *Question ontology* et al., 2000; Pasca, 2003), or they can be designed by hand.

Figure 23.9 shows one such hand-built ontology, the hierarchical Li and Roth (2005) tagset. In this tagset, each question can be labeled with a coarse-grained tag like HUMAN or a fine-grained tag like HUMAN:DESCRIPTION, HUMAN:GROUP, HU-MAN:IND, and so on. Similar tags are used in other systems; the HUMAN:DESCRIPTION type is often called a BIOGRAPHY question because the answer is required to give a brief biography of the person rather than just a name.

Question classifiers can be built by hand-writing rules, by supervised machine learning, or with some combination. The Webclopedia QA Typology, for example, contains 276 hand-written rules associated with the approximately 180 answer types in the typology (Hovy et al., 2002). A regular expression rule for detecting an answer type like BIOGRAPHY (which assumes the question has been named-entity-tagged) might be

(23.19)   who is was are were PERSON

Most modern question classifiers, however, are based on supervised machine learning techniques. These classifiers are trained on databases of questions that have been hand-labeled with an answer type such as the corpus of Li and Roth (2002). Typical features used for classification include the words in the questions, the part-of-speech of each word, and named entities in the questions.

Often, a single word in the question gives extra information about the answer type, and its identity is used as a feature. This word is sometimes called the question **head-word**, or the **answer type word**, and may be defined as the headword of the first NP after the question's *wh-word*; headwords are indicated in boldface in the following examples:

(23.20)   Which **city** in China has the largest number of foreign financial companies?

(23.21)   What is the state **flower** of California?

Finally, it often helps to use semantic information about the words in the questions. The WordNet synset ID of the word can be used as a feature, as can the IDs of the hypernym and hyponyms of each word in the question.

In general, question classification accuracies are relatively high on easy question types like PERSON, LOCATION, and TIME questions; detecting REASON and DESCRIP-TION questions can be much harder.

23.2.2   Passage Retrieval

The query that was created in the question-processing phase is next used to query an information-retrieval system, either a general IR engine over a proprietary set of indexed documents or a Web search engine. The result of this document retrieval stage is a set of documents.

Tag	Example
ABBREVIATION	
abb	What's the abbreviation for limited partnership?
exp	What does the "c" stand for in the equation E=mc2?
DESCRIPTION	
definition	What are tannins?
description	What are the words to the Canadian National anthem?
manner	How can you get rust stains out of clothing?
reason	What caused the Titanic to sink ?
ENTITY	
animal	What are the names of Odin's ravens?
body	What part of your body contains the corpus callosum?
color	What colors make up a rainbow ?
creative	In what book can I find the story of Aladdin?
currency	What currency is used in China?
disease/medicine	What does Salk vaccine prevent?
event	What war involved the battle of Chapultepec?
food	What kind of nuts are used in marzipan?
instrument	What instrument does Max Roach play?
lang	What's the official language of Algeria?
letter	What letter appears on the cold-water tap in Spain?
other	What is the name of King Arthur's sword?
plant	What are some fragrant white climbing roses?
product	What is the fastest computer?
religion	What religion has the most members?
sport	What was the name of the ball game played by the Mayans?
substance	What fuel do airplanes use?
symbol	What is the chemical symbol for nitrogen?
technique	What is the best way to remove wallpaper?
term	How do you say " Grandma " in Irish?
vehicle	What was the name of Captain Bligh's ship?
word	What's the singular of dice?
HUMAN	
description	Who was Confucius?
group	What are the major companies that are part of Dow Jones?
ind	Who was the first Russian astronaut to do a spacewalk?
title	What was Queen Victoria's title regarding India?
LOCATION	
city	What's the oldest capital city in the Americas?
country	What country borders the most others?
mountain	What is the highest peak in Africa?
other	What river runs through Liverpool?
state	What states do not have state income tax?
NUMERIC	
code	What is the telephone number for the University of Colorado?
count	About how many soldiers died in World War II?
date	What is the date of Boxing Day?
distance	How long was Mao's 1930s Long March?
money	How much did a McDonald's hamburger cost in 1963?
order	Where does Shanghai rank among world cities in population?
other	What is the population of Mexico?
period	What was the average life expectancy during the Stone Age?
percent	What fraction of a beaver's life is spent swimming?
speed	What is the speed of the Mississippi River?
temp	How fast must a spacecraft travel to escape Earth's gravity?
size	What is the size of Argentina?
weight	How many pounds are there in a stone?

Figure 23.9   Question typology from Li and Roth (2002, 2005). Example sentences are from their corpus of 5500 labeled questions. A question can be labeled either with a coarse-grained tag like HUMAN or NUMERIC or with a fine-grained tag like HUMAN:DESCRIPTION, HUMAN:GROUP, HUMAN:IND, and so on.

Although the set of documents is generally ranked by relevance, the top-ranked document is probably not the answer to the question. This is because documents are not an appropriate unit to rank with respect to the goals of a question-answering system. A highly relevant and large document that does not prominently answer a question is not an ideal candidate for further processing.

Therefore, the next stage is to extract a set of potential answer passages from the retrieved set of documents. The definition of a passage is necessarily system dependent, but the typical units include sections, paragraphs, and sentences. For example, we might run a paragraph segmentation algorithm of the type discussed in Chapter 21 on all the returned documents and treat each paragraph as a segment.

Passage retrieval   We next perform **passage retrieval**. In this stage, we first filter out passages in the returned documents that don't contain potential answers and then rank the rest according to how likely they are to contain an answer to the question. The first step in this process is to run a named entity or answer type classification on the retrieved passages. The answer type that we determined from the question tells us the possible answer types (extended named entities) we expect to see in the answer. We can therefore filter out documents that don't contain any entities of the right type.

The remaining passages are then ranked; either by hand-crafted rules or by supervised training with machine learning techniques. In either case, the ranking is based on a relatively small set of features that can be easily and efficiently extracted from a potentially large number of answer passages. The following are among the more common features.

- The number of **named entities** of the right type in the passage
- The number of **question keywords** in the passage
- The longest exact sequence of question keywords that occurs in the passage
- The rank of the document from which the passage was extracted
- The **proximity** of the keywords from the original query to each other
  For each passage identify the shortest span that covers the keywords contained in that passage. Prefer smaller spans that include more keywords (Pasca, 2003; Monz, 2004).
- The *N*-**gram overlap** between the passage and the question
  Count the *N*-grams in the question and the *N*-grams in the answer passages. Prefer the passages with higher *N*-gram overlap with the question (Brill et al., 2002).

For question answering from the Web, instead of extracting passages from all returned documents, we can rely on the Web search to do passage extraction for us. We do this by using **snippets** produced by the Web search engine as the returned passages. For example, Fig. 23.10 shows snippets for the first five documents returned from Google for the query *When was movable type metal printing invented in Korea?*

23.2.3   Answer Processing

The final stage of question answering is to extract a specific answer from the passage so as to be able to present the user with an answer like *300 million* to the question *"What is the current population of the United States"*.

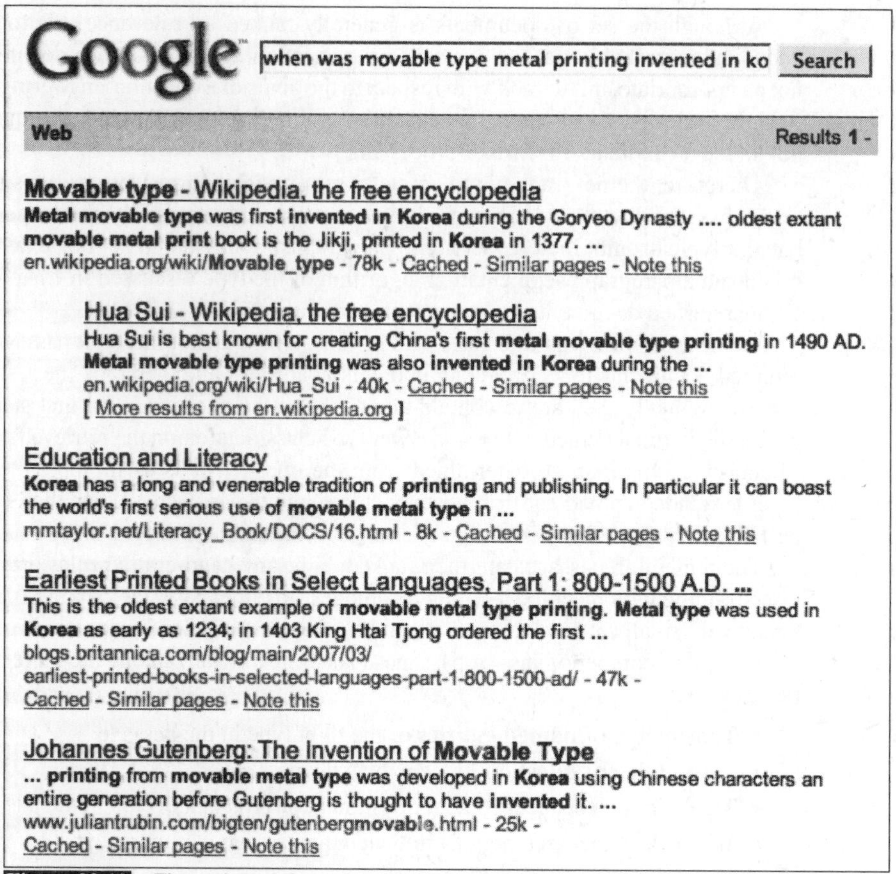

Figure 23.10   Five snippets from Google in response to the query *When was movable type metal printing invented in Korea?*

Two classes of algorithms have been applied to the answer-extraction task, one based on **answer-type pattern extraction** and one based on *N*-gram tiling.

In the **pattern-extraction** methods for answer processing, we use information about the expected answer type together with regular expression patterns. For example, for questions with a HUMAN answer type, we run the answer type or named entity tagger on the candidate passage or sentence and return whatever entity is labeled with type HUMAN. Thus, in the following examples, the underlined named entities are extracted from the candidate answer passages as the answer to the HUMAN and DISTANCE-QUANTITY questions:

"Who is the prime minister of India"
Manmohan Singh, Prime Minister of India, had told left leaders that the deal would not be renegotiated.

"How tall is Mt. Everest?"
The official height of Mount Everest is 29035 feet

Unfortunately, the answers to some questions, such as DEFINITION questions, don't tend to be of a particular named entity type. For some questions, then, instead of using answer types, we use hand-written regular expression patterns to help extract the answer. These patterns are also useful in cases in which a passage contains multiple examples of the same named entity type. Figure 23.11 shows some patterns from Pasca (2003) for the question phrase (QP) and answer phrase (AP) of definition questions.

Pattern	Question	Answer
<AP> such as <QP>	What is autism?	", developmental disorders such as autism"
<QP>, a <AP>	What is a caldera?	"the Long Valley caldera, a volcanic crater 19 miles long"

Figure 23.11   Some answer-extraction patterns for definition questions (Pasca, 2003).

The patterns are specific to each question type and can either be written by hand or learned automatically.

The automatic pattern learning methods of Ravichandran and Hovy (2002) and Echihabi et al. (2005), for example, make use of the pattern-based methods for relation extraction we introduced in Chapters 20 and 22 (Brin, 1998; Agichtein and Gravano, 2000). The goal of the pattern learning is to learn a relation between a particular answer type, such as YEAR-OF-BIRTH, and a particular aspect of the question, in this case, the name of the person whose birth year we want. We are thus trying to learn patterns that are good cues for a relation between two phrases (PERSON-NAME/YEAR-OF-BIRTH, or TERM-TO-BE-DEFINED/DEFINITION, etc). This task is thus similar to the task of learning hyponym/hyponym relations between WordNet synsets introduced in Chapter 20 and to learning ACE relations between words from Chapter 22. Here is a sketch of the algorithm as applied to question-answer relation extraction:

1. For a given relation between two terms (i.e., person-name→year-of-birth), we start with a hand-built list of correct pairs (e.g., "gandhi:1869", "mozart:1756").

2. Now query the Web with instances of these pairs (e.g., "gandhi" and "1869", etc.), and examine the top returned documents.

3. Break each document into sentences, and keep only sentences containing both terms (e.g., PERSON-NAME and BIRTH-YEAR).

4. Extract a regular expression pattern representing the words and punctuation that occur between and around the two terms.

5. Keep all patterns that are sufficiently high precision.

In Chapters 20 and 22 we discussed various ways to measure accuracy of the patterns. A method used in question-answer pattern matching is to keep patterns that are **high precision**. We measure precision by performing a query with only the question terms, but not the answer terms (i.e., query with just "gandhi" or "mozart"). We then run the resulting patterns on the sentences from the document and extract a birth date. Since we know the correct birth date, we can compute the percentage of times this pattern produced a correct birthdate. This percentage is the precision of the pattern.

For the YEAR-OF-BIRTH answer type, this method learns patterns like the following:

```
<NAME> (<BD>-<DD>),
<NAME> was born on <BD>
```

These two methods, named entity detection and question-answer pattern extraction, are still not sufficient for answer extraction. Not every relation is signaled by unambiguous surrounding words or punctuation, and multiple instances of the same named-entity type often occur in the answer passages. The most successful answer-extraction method is thus to combine all these methods, using them together with other information as features in a classifier that ranks candidate answers. We extract potential answers by using named entities or patterns or even just by looking at every sentence returned from passage retrieval and rank them using a classifier with features like the following.

Answer type match: True if the candidate answer contains a phrase with the correct answer type.

Pattern match: The identity of a pattern that matches the candidate answer.

Number of matched question keywords: How many question keywords are contained in the candidate answer.

Keyword distance: The distance between the candidate answer and query keywords (measured in average number of words or as the number of keywords that occur in the same syntactic phrase as the candidate answer).

Novelty factor: True if at least one word in the candidate answer is novel, that is, not in the query.

Apposition features: True if the candidate answer is an appositive to a phrase containing many question terms. Can be approximated by the number of question terms separated from the candidate answer through at most three words and one comma (Pasca, 2003).

Punctuation location: True if the candidate answer is immediately followed by a comma, period, quotation marks, semicolon, or exclamation mark.

Sequences of question terms: The length of the longest sequence of question terms that occurs in the candidate answer.

N-gram tiling

N-gram mining

N-gram filtering

An alternative approach to answer extraction, used solely in Web search, is based on **N-gram tiling**, sometimes called the **redundancy-based approach** (Brill et al., 2002; Lin, 2007). This simplified method begins with the snippets returned from the Web search engine, produced by a reformulated query. In the first step, **N-gram mining**, every unigram, bigram, and trigram occurring in the snippet is extracted and weighted. The weight is a function of the number of snippets in which the N-gram occurred, and the weight of the query reformulation pattern that returned it. In the **N-gram filtering** step, N-grams are scored by how well they match the predicted answer type. These scores are computed by hand-written filters built for each answer type. Finally, an N-gram tiling algorithm concatenates overlapping N-gram fragments into longer answers. A standard greedy method is to start with the highest-scoring candidate and try to tile each other candidate with this candidate. The best-scoring concatenation is added to the set of candidates, the lower-scoring candidate is removed, and the process continues until a single answer is built.

For any of these answer-extraction methods, the exact answer phrase can just be presented to the user by itself. In practice, however, users are rarely satisfied with an unadorned number or noun as an answer; they prefer to see the answer accompanied by enough passage information to substantiate the answer. Thus, we often give the user an entire passage with the exact answer inside it highlighted or boldfaced.

23.2.4   Evaluation of Factoid Answers

A wide variety of techniques have been employed to evaluate question-answering systems. By far the most influential evaluation framework has been provided by the TREC Q/A track first introduced in 1999.

The primary measure used in TREC is an **intrinsic** or **in vitro** evaluation metric known as **mean reciprocal rank**, or **MRR**. As with the ad hoc information retrieval task described in Section 23.1, MRR assumes a test set of questions that have been human-labeled with correct answers. MRR also assumes that systems are returning a short **ranked** list of answers or passages containing answers. Each question is then scored according to the reciprocal of the **rank** of the first correct answer. For example if the system returned five answers but the first three are wrong and hence the highest-ranked correct answer is ranked fourth, the reciprocal rank score for that question would be $\frac{1}{4}$. Questions with return sets that do not contain any correct answers are assigned a zero. The score of a system is then the average of the score for each question in the set. More formally, for an evaluation of a system returning M ranked answers for test set consisting of N questions, the MRR is defined as

Mean reciprocal rank
MRR

$$\text{MRR} = \frac{\sum_{i=1}^{N} \frac{1}{rank_i}}{N} \qquad (23.22)$$

23.3   Summarization

The algorithms we have described so far in this chapter present the user an entire document (information retrieval) or a short factoid answer phrase (factoid question answering). But sometimes the user wants something that lies in between these extremes: something like a **summary** of a document or set of documents.

Text summarization

Text summarization is *the process of distilling the most important information from a text to produce an abridged version for a particular task and user* (definition adapted from Mani and Maybury (1999)). Important kinds of summaries that are the focus of current research include the following:

- **outlines** of any document
- **abstracts** of a scientific article
- **headlines** of a news article
- **snippets** summarizing a Web page on a search engine results page
- **action items or other summaries** of a (spoken) business meeting
- **summaries** of email threads

- **compressed sentences** for producing simplified or compressed text
- **answers** to complex questions, constructed by summarizing multiple documents

These kinds of summarization goals are often characterized by their position on two dimensions:

- **single-document** versus **multiple-document** summarization
- **generic** summarization versus **query-focused** summarization

Single-document summarization

In **single-document summarization** we are given a single document and produce a summary. Single-document summarization is thus used in situations like producing a headline or an outline, for which the final goal is to characterize the content of a single document.

Multiple-document summarization

In **multiple-document summarization**, the input is a group of documents, and our goal is to produce a condensation of the content of the entire group. We might use multiple-document summarization when we are summarizing a series of news stories on the same event or when we have Web content on the same topic that we'd like to synthesize and condense.

Generic summary

A **generic summary** is one in which we don't consider a particular user or a particular information need; the summary simply gives the important information in the document(s). By contrast, in **query-focused summarization**, also called **focused summarization**, **topic-based summarization**, and **user-focused summarization**, the summary is produced in response to a user query. We can think of query-focused summarization as a kind of longer, non-factoid answer to a user question.

Query-focused summarization

In the remainder of this section we briefly review the architecture of automatic text summarization systems; the following sections then give details.

Extract

One crucial architectural dimension for text summarizers is whether they are producing an **abstract** or an **extract**. The simplest kind of summary, an **extract**, is formed by the combination of phrases or sentences selected (extracted) from the document to be summarized. By contrast, an **abstract** uses different words to describe the contents of the document. We'll illustrate the difference between an extract and an abstract by using the well-known Gettysburg address, a famous speech by Abraham Lincoln, shown in Fig. 23.12.[1] Figure 23.13 shows an extractive summary from the speech followed by an abstract of the speech.

Abstract

Most current text summarizers are extractive, since extraction is much easier than abstracting; the transition to more sophisticated abstractive summarization is a key goal of recent research.

Text summarization systems and, as it turns out, **natural language generation** systems as well, are generally described by their solutions to the following three problems.

1. **Content Selection:** What information to select from the document(s) we are summarizing. We usually make the simplifying assumption that the granularity of extraction is the sentence or clause. Content selection thus mainly consists of choosing which sentences or clauses to extract into the summary.

2. **Information Ordering:** How to order and structure the extracted units.

---

[1] In general, one probably wouldn't need a summary of such a short speech, but a short text makes it easier to see how the extract maps to the original for pedagogical purposes. For an amusing alternative application of modern technology to the Gettysburg Address, see Norvig (2005).

Fourscore and seven years ago our fathers brought forth on this continent a new nation, conceived in liberty, and dedicated to the proposition that all men are created equal. Now we are engaged in a great civil war, testing whether that nation, or any nation so conceived and so dedicated, can long endure. We are met on a great battle-field of that war. We have come to dedicate a portion of that field as a final resting-place for those who here gave their lives that this nation might live. It is altogether fitting and proper that we should do this. But, in a larger sense, we cannot dedicate...we cannot consecrate...we cannot hallow... this ground. The brave men, living and dead, who struggled here, have consecrated it far above our poor power to add or detract. The world will little note nor long remember what we say here, but it can never forget what they did here. It is for us, the living, rather, to be dedicated here to the unfinished work which they who fought here have thus far so nobly advanced. It is rather for us to be here dedicated to the great task remaining before us...that from these honored dead we take increased devotion to that cause for which they gave the last full measure of devotion; that we here highly resolve that these dead shall not have died in vain; that this nation, under God, shall have a new birth of freedom; and that government of the people, by the people, for the people, shall not perish from the earth.

Figure 23.12   The Gettysburg Address. Abraham Lincoln, 1863.

Extract from the Gettysburg Address:

Four score and seven years ago our fathers brought forth upon this continent a new nation, conceived in liberty, and dedicated to the proposition that all men are created equal. Now we are engaged in a great civil war, testing whether that nation can long endure. We are met on a great battle-field of that war. We have come to dedicate a portion of that field. But the brave men, living and dead, who struggled here, have consecrated it far above our poor power to add or detract. From these honored dead we take increased devotion to that cause for which they gave the last full measure of devotion — that government of the people, by the people, for the people, shall not perish from the earth.

Abstract of the Gettysburg Address:

This speech by Abraham Lincoln commemorates soldiers who laid down their lives in the Battle of Gettysburg. It reminds the troops that it is the future of freedom in America that they are fighting for.

Figure 23.13   An extract versus an abstract from the Gettysburg Address (abstract from Mani (2001)).

3. **Sentence Realization:** What kind of cleanup to perform on the extracted units so they are fluent in their new context.

In the next sections we show these components in three summarization tasks: **single-document** summarization, **multiple-document** summarization, and **query-focused summarization**.

23.4   Single-Document Summarization

Let's first consider the task of building an extractive summary for a single document. Assuming that the units being extracted are at the level of the sentence, the three summarization stages for this task are as follows.

1. **Content Selection:** Choose sentences to extract from the document.
2. **Information Ordering:** Choose an order in which to place these sentences in the summary.
3. **Sentence Realization:** Clean up the sentences, for example, by removing non-essential phrases from each sentence, by fusing multiple sentences into a single sentence, or by fixing problems in coherence.

Figure 23.14 illustrates the basic architecture underlying this approach.

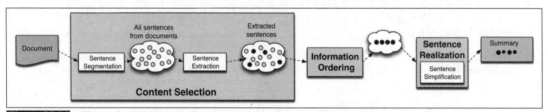

Figure 23.14   The basic architecture of a generic single-document summarizer.

We'll first describe basic summarization techniques with only one of these components: *content selection*. Indeed, many single-document summarizers have no information-ordering component, simply ordering the extracted sentences in the order they appeared in the original document. In addition, we'll assume for now that sentences are not combined or cleaned up after they are extracted, although we'll briefly mention later how this is done.

23.4.1   Unsupervised Content Selection

Content selection   The **content selection** task of extracting sentences is often treated as a classification task. The goal of the classifier is to label each sentence in a document with a binary label: *important* versus *unimportant* (or *extract worthy* versus *not extract worthy*). We begin with some unsupervised algorithms for sentence classification and then turn to supervised algorithms in the next section.

The simplest unsupervised algorithm, based on an intuition that dates back to the early summarizer of (Luhn, 1958), selects sentences that have more **salient** or **informative** words. Sentences that contain more informative words tend to be more extract worthy. Saliency is usually defined by computing the **topic signature**, a set of **salient** or **signature terms**, each of whose saliency scores is greater than some threshold θ.

Topic signature
Signature terms

Saliency could be measured in terms of simple word frequency, but frequency has the problem that a word might have a high probability in English in general but not be particularly topical to a particular document. Therefore, weighting schemes like **tf-idf** or **log-likelihood ratio** are more often used.

Recall from page 771 that the tf-idf scheme gives a high weight to words that appear frequently in the current document but rarely in the overall document collection, suggesting that the word is particularly relevant to this document. For each term i that occurs in the sentence to be evaluated, we compute its count in the current document j $tf_{i,j}$ and multiply by the inverse document frequency over the whole collection idf_i:

$$weight(w_i) = tf_{i,j} \quad idf_i \tag{23.23}$$

Log-likelihood ratio

A better-performing method for finding informative words is the **log-likelihood ratio** (LLR). The LLR for a word, generally called $\lambda(w)$, is the ratio between the probability of observing w both in the input and in the background corpus assuming equal probabilities in both corpora, and the probability of observing w in both assuming different probabilities for w in the input and the background corpus. See Dunning (1993), Moore (2004), and Manning and Schütze (1999) for details on log-likelihood and how it is calculated.

It turns out for the log-likelihood ratio that the quantity $-2\log(\lambda)$ is asymptotically well approximated by the χ^2 distribution, which means that a word appears in the input significantly more often than in the background corpus (at $\alpha = 0.001$) if $-2log(\lambda) > 10.8$. Lin and Hovy (2000) suggested that this made the log-likelihood ratio particularly appropriate for selecting a topic signature for summarization. Thus, the word weight with the log-likelihood ratio is generally defined as follows:

$$weight(w_i) = \begin{cases} 1 & \text{if } -2\log(\lambda(w_i)) > 10 \\ 0 & \text{otherwise.} \end{cases} \tag{23.24}$$

Equation 23.24 is used to set a weight of 1 or 0 for each word in the sentence. The score for a sentence s_i is then the average weight of its non-stop words:

$$weight(s_i) = \sum_{w \in s_i} \frac{weight(w)}{w \; w \in s_i} \tag{23.25}$$

The summarization algorithm computes this weight for every sentence, and then ranks all sentences by their score. The extracted summary consists of the top ranked sentences.

The family of algorithms that this thresholded LLR algorithm belongs to is called **centroid-based summarization** because we can view the set of signature terms as a pseudo-sentence that is the "centroid" of all the sentences in the document and we are looking for sentences that are as close as possible to this centroid sentence.

Centrality

A common alternative to the log-likelihood ratio/centroid method is to use a different model of sentence **centrality**. These other centrality-based methods resemble the centroid method described above, in that their goal is to rank the input sentences in terms of how central they are in representing the information present in the document. But rather than just ranking sentences by whether they contain salient words, centrality-based methods compute distances between each candidate sentence and each other sentence and choose sentences that are on average closer to other sentences. To compute centrality, we can represent each sentence as a bag-of-words vector of length N, as described in Chapter 20. For each pair of sentences x and y, we compute the tf-idf weighted cosine as described in Eq. 23.12 on page 771.

Each of the k sentences in the input is then assigned a centrality score that is its average cosine with all other sentences:

$$centrality(x) = \frac{1}{K} \sum_y \textit{tf-idf-cosine}(x, y) \qquad (23.26)$$

Sentences are ranked by this centrality score, and the sentence that has the highest average cosine across all pairs, that is, is most like other sentences, is chosen as the most "representative" or "topical" of all the sentences in the input.

It is also possible to extend this centrality score to use more complex graph-based measures of centrality like PageRank (Erkan and Radev, 2004).

23.4.2   Unsupervised Summarization Based on Rhetorical Parsing

The sentence-extraction algorithm we introduced above for content extraction relied solely on a single shallow feature, word saliency, ignoring possible higher-level cues such as discourse information. In this section we briefly summarize a way to get more sophisticated discourse knowledge into the summarization task.

The summarization algorithm we describe makes use of coherence relations such as the RST (Rhetorical Structure Theory) relations described in Chapter 21. Recall that RST relations are often expressed in terms of a satellite and a nucleus; nucleus sentences are more likely to be appropriate for a summary. For example, consider the following two paragraphs taken from the *Scientific American* magazine text that we introduced in Section 21.2.1:

> With its distant orbit – 50 percent farther from the sun than Earth – and slim atmospheric blanket, Mars experiences frigid weather conditions. Surface temperatures typically average about −70 degrees Fahrenheit at the equator, and can dip to −123 degrees C near the poles.
>
> Only the midday sun at tropical latitudes is warm enough to thaw ice on occasion, but any liquid water formed in this way would evaporate almost instantly because of the low atmospheric pressure. Although the atmosphere holds a small amount of water, and water-ice clouds sometimes develop, most Martian weather involves blowing dust or carbon dioxide.

The first two discourse units in this passage are related by the RST JUSTIFICATION relation, with the first discourse unit justifying the second unit, as shown in Fig. 23.15. The second unit (*"Mars experiences frigid weather conditions"*) is thus the nucleus and captures better what this part of the document is about.

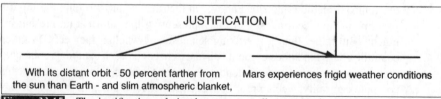

Figure 23.15   The justification relation between two discourse units, a satellite (on the left) and a nucleus (on the right).

We can use this intuition for summarization by first applying a discourse parser of the type discussed in Chapter 21 to compute the coherence relations between each discourse unit. Once a sentence has been parsed into a coherence relation graph or parse tree, we can use the intuition that the nuclear units are important for summarization by recursively extracting the salient units of a text.

Consider the coherence parse tree in Fig. 23.16. The salience of each node in the tree can be defined recursively as follows:

- Base case: The salient unit of a leaf node is the leaf node itself.
- Recursive case: The salient units of an intermediate node are the union of the salient units of its immediate *nuclear* children.

By this definition, discourse unit (2) is the most salient unit of the entire text (since the root node spanning units 1–8 has the node spanning units 1–6 as its nucleus, and unit 2 is the nucleus of the node spanning units 1–6).

If we rank each discourse unit by the height of the nodes of which it is the nucleus, we can assign a partial ordering of salience to units; the algorithm of Marcu (1995) assigns the following partial ordering to this discourse:

$$2 > 8 > 3 > 1,4,5,7 > 6 \tag{23.27}$$

See Marcu (1995, 2000b) for the details of exactly how this partial order is computed, and Teufel and Moens (2002) for another method for using rhetorical structure in summarization.

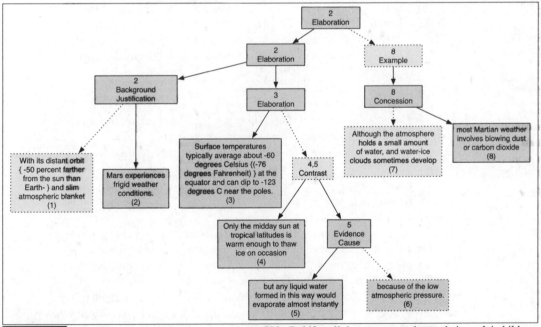

Figure 23.16   The discourse tree for the text on page 792. Boldface links connect nodes to their nuclei children; dotted lines to the satellite children. After Marcu (2000a).

23.4.3 Supervised Content Selection

While the use of topic signatures for unsupervised content selection is an extremely effective method, a topic signature is only a single cue for finding extract-worthy sentences. Many other cues exist, including the alternative saliency methods discussed above like centrality and PageRank methods, as well as other cues like the position of the sentence in the document (sentences at the very beginning or end of the document tend to be more important), the length of each sentence, and so on. We'd like a method that can weigh and combine all of these cues.

The most principled method for weighing and combining evidence is supervised machine learning. For supervised machine learning, we need a training set of documents paired with human-created summary extracts, such as the Ziff-Davis corpus (Marcu, 1999). Since these are *extracts*, each sentence in the summary is, by definition, taken from the document. That means we can assign a label to every sentence in the document; **1** if it appears in the extract, **0** if it doesn't. To build our classifier, then, we just need to choose features to extract that are predictive of being a good sentence to appear in a summary. Some of the features commonly used in sentence classification are shown in Fig. 23.17.

position	The position of the sentence in the document. For example, Hovy and Lin (1999) found that the single most extract-worthy sentence in most newspaper articles is the title sentence. In the Ziff-Davis corpus they examined, the next most informative was the first sentence of paragraph 2 (P1S1), followed by the first sentence of paragraph 3 (P3S1); thus the list of ordinal sentence positions starting from the most informative was: T1, P2S1, P3S1, P4S1, P1S1, P2S2,... Position, like almost all summarization features, is heavily genre dependent. In *Wall Street Journal articles*, they found the most important information appeared in the following sentences: T1, P1S1, P1S2,...
cue phrases	Sentences containing phrases like *in summary*, *in conclusion*, or *this paper* are more likely to be extract worthy. These cue phrases are very dependent on the genre. For example, in British House of Lords legal summaries, the phrase *it seems to me that* is a useful cue phrase (Hachey and Grover, 2005).
word informativeness	Sentences that contain more terms from the **topic signature**, as described in the previous section, are more extract worthy.
sentence length	Very short sentences are rarely appropriate for extracting. We usually capture this fact by using a binary feature based on a cutoff (true if the sentence has more than, say, five words).
cohesion	Recall from Chapter 21 that a **lexical chain** is a series of related words that occurs throughout a discourse. Sentences that contain more terms from a lexical chain are often extract worthy because they are indicative of a continuing topic (Barzilay and Elhadad, 1997). This kind of cohesion can also be computed by graph-based methods (Mani and Bloedorn, 1999). The PageRank graph-based measures of sentence centrality discussed above can also be viewed as a coherence metric (Erkan and Radev, 2004).

Figure 23.17 Some features commonly used in supervised classifiers for determining whether a document sentence should be extracted into a summary.

Each sentence in our training document thus has a label (0 if the sentence is not in the training summary for that document, 1 if it is) and a set of extracted feature values like those in Fig. 23.17. We can then train our classifier to estimate these labels for unseen data; for example, a probabilistic classifier like naive Bayes or MaxEnt would be computing the probability that a particular sentence s is extract worthy given a set of features $f_1...f_n$; we can then just extract any sentences for which this probability is greater than 0.5:

$$P(\text{extract-worthy}(s)\ f_1, f_2, f_3, ..., f_n) \qquad (23.28)$$

There is one problem with the algorithm as we've described it: it requires that we have for each document a training summary that consists solely of extracted sentences. If we could weaken this restriction, we could apply the algorithm to a much wider variety of summary-document pairs, such as conference papers or journal articles and their abstracts. Luckily, it turns out that when humans write summaries, even with the goal of writing abstractive summaries, they very often use phrases and sentences from the document to compose the summary. But they don't use *only* extracted sentences; they often combine two sentences into one, change some of the words in the sentences, or write completely new abstractive sentences. Here is an example of an extracted sentence from a human summary that, although modified in the final human summary, was clearly a document sentence that should be labeled as extract worthy:

(23.29) **Human summary**: This paper identifies the desirable features of an ideal multisensor gas monitor and lists the different models currently available.

(23.30) **Original document sentence**: The present part lists the desirable features and the different models of portable, multisensor gas monitors currently available.

Thus, an important preliminary stage is to *align* each training document with its summary, with the goal of finding which sentences in the document were (completely or mostly) included in the summary. A simple algorithm for **alignment** is to find the source document and abstract sentences with the longest common subsequences of non-stopwords; alternatively, minimum edit distance can be computed or more sophisticated knowledge sources, such as WordNet, can be used. Recent work has focused on more complex alignment algorithms such as the use of HMMs (Jing, 2002; Daumé III and Marcu, 2005, inter alia).

Alignment

Given such alignment algorithms, supervised methods for content selection can make use of parallel corpora of documents and human abstractive summaries, such as academic papers with their abstracts (Teufel and Moens, 2002).

23.4.4   Sentence Simplification

Sentence compression
Sentence simplification

Once a set of sentences has been extracted and ordered, the final step is **sentence realization**. One component of sentence realization is **sentence compression** or **sentence simplification**. The following examples, taken by Jing (2000) from a human summary, show that the human summarizer chose to eliminate some of the adjective modifiers and subordinate clauses when expressing the extracted sentence in the summary.

(23.31) **Original sentence:** ~~When it arrives sometime new year in new TV sets,~~ the V-chip will give parents a ~~new and potentially revolutionary~~ device to block out programs they don't want their children to see.

(23.32) **Simplified sentence by humans:** The V-chip will give parents a device to block out programs they don't want their children to see.

The simplest algorithms for sentence simplification use rules to select parts of the sentence to prune or keep, often by running a parser or partial parser over the sentences. Some representative rules from Zajic et al. (2007), Conroy et al. (2006), and Vanderwende et al. (2007) remove the following:

appositives	Rajam, ~~28, an artist who was living at the time in Philadelphia,~~ found the inspiration in the back of city magazines.
attribution clauses	Rebels agreed to talks with government officials, ~~international observers said Tuesday.~~
PPs without named entities	The commercial fishing restrictions in Washington will not be lifted [SBAR unless the salmon population 329 increases [PP ~~to a sustainable number~~]
initial adverbials	"For example", "On the other hand", "As a matter of fact", "At this point"

More sophisticated models of sentence compression are based on supervised machine learning, in which a parallel corpus of documents together with their human summaries is used to compute the probability that particular words or parse nodes will be pruned. See the Historical Notes section at the end of the chapter for pointers to this extensive recent literature.

23.5   Multi-Document Summarization

Multi-document summarization

When we apply summarization techniques to groups of documents rather than to a single document, we call the goal **multi-document summarization**. Multi-document summarization is particularly appropriate for Web-based applications, for example, for building summaries of a particular event in the news by combining information from different news stories, or finding answers to complex questions by including components from extracted from multiple documents.

While multi-document summarization is far from a solved problem, even the current technology can be useful for information-finding tasks. McKeown et al. (2005), for example, gave documents to human participants along with a human summary and an automatically generated summary or no summary, and had the participants perform time-restricted, fact-gathering tasks. The participants had to answer three related questions about an event in the news; subjects who read the automatic summaries gave higher-quality answers to the questions.

Multi-document summarization algorithms are based on the same three steps we've seen before. In most cases, we start with a cluster of documents that we'd like to summarize; we must then perform **content selection**, **information ordering**, and **sentence realization**, as described in the next three sections and sketched in Fig. 23.18.

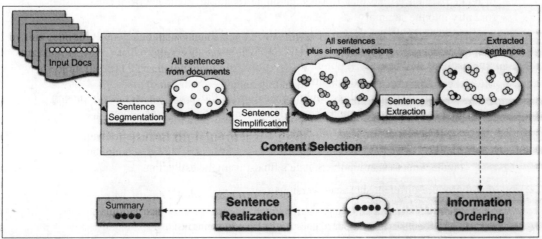

Figure 23.18   The basic architecture of a multi-document summarizer.

23.5.1   Content Selection in Multi-Document Summarization

In single-document summarization we used both supervised and unsupervised methods for content selection. For multiple-document summarization, supervised training sets are less available, and we focus more on unsupervised methods.

The major difference between the tasks of single-document and multiple-document summarization is the greater amount of **redundancy** when we start with multiple documents. A group of documents can have significant overlap in words, phrases, and concepts, in addition to information that might be unique to each article. While we want each sentence in the summary to be about the topic, we don't want the summary to consist of a set of identical sentences.

For this reason, algorithms for multi-document summarization focus on ways to avoid redundancy when selecting sentences for the summary. When adding a new sentence to a list of extracted sentences, we need some way to make sure the sentence doesn't overlap too much with the already extracted sentences.

A simple method of avoiding redundancy is to explicitly include a redundancy factor in the scoring for choosing a sentence to extract. The redundancy factor is based on the similarity between a candidate sentence and the sentences that have already been extracted into the summary; a sentence is penalized if it is too similar to the summary. For example, the **MMR** or **Maximal Marginal Relevance** scoring system (Carbonell and Goldstein, 1998; Goldstein et al., 2000) includes the following penalty term for representing the similarity between a sentence s and the set of sentences already extracted for the summary *Summary*, where λ is a weight that can be tuned and Sim is some similarity function:

MMR
Maximal
Marginal
Relevance

811

$$\text{MMR penalization factor}(s) = \lambda max_{s_i \in Summary} \text{Sim}(s, s_i) \qquad (23.33)$$

An alternative to this MMR-based method is to instead apply a clustering algorithm to all the sentences in the documents to be summarized to produce a number of clusters of related sentences and then to select a single (centroid) sentence from each cluster for entry into the summary.

By adding MMR or clustering methods for avoiding redundancy, we can also do sentence simplification or compression at the content-selection stage rather than at the sentence-realization stage. A common way to fit simplification into the architecture is to run various sentence simplification rules (Section 23.4.4) on each sentence in the input corpus. The result will be multiple versions of the input sentence, each version with different amounts of simplification. For example, the following sentence

> Former Democratic National Committee finance director Richard Sullivan
> faced more pointed questioning from Republicans during his second day
> on the witness stand in the Senate's fund-raising investigation.

might produce different shortened versions:

- Richard Sullivan faced pointed questioning.
- Richard Sullivan faced pointed questioning from Republicans.
- Richard Sullivan faced pointed questioning from Republicans during day on stand in Senate fund-raising investigation.
- Richard Sullivan faced pointed questioning from Republicans in Senate fund-raising investigation.

This expanded corpus is now used as the input to content extraction. Redundancy methods such as clustering or MMR will choose only the (optimally long) single version of each original sentence.

23.5.2   Information Ordering in Multi-Document Summarization

The second stage of an extractive summarizer is the ordering or structuring of information, when we must decide how to concatenate the extracted sentences into a coherent order. Recall that in single-document summarization, we can just use the original article ordering for these sentences. This isn't appropriate for most multiple-document applications, although we can certainly apply it if many or all of the extracted sentences happen to come from a single article.

Chronological ordering

For sentences extracted from news stories, one technique is to use the dates associated with the story, a strategy known as **chronological ordering**. It turns out that pure chronological ordering can produce summaries that lack cohesion; this problem can be addressed by the ordering of slightly larger chunks of sentences rather than single sentences; see Barzilay et al. (2002).

Perhaps the most important factor for information ordering, however, is **coherence**. Recall from Chapter 21 the various devices that contribute to the coherence of a discourse. One is having sensible coherence relations between the sentences; thus, we could prefer orderings in summaries that result in sensible coherence relations between the sentences. Another aspect of coherence has to do with cohesion and lexical chains; we could, for example, prefer orderings that have more local cohesion. A final aspect of coherence is coreference; a coherence discourse is one in which entities are mentioned in coherent patterns. We could prefer orderings with coherent entity-mention patterns.

All of these kinds of coherence have been used for information ordering. For example, we can use *lexical cohesion* as an ordering heuristic by ordering each sentence next to sentences containing similar words. We can do this by defining the standard tf-idf cosine distance between each pair of sentences and choosing the overall ordering that minimizes the average distance between neighboring sentences (Conroy et al., 2006), or we can build models of predictable word sequences across sentences (Soricut and Marcu, 2006).

Coreference-based coherence algorithms have also made use of the intuitions of **Centering**. Recall that the Centering algorithm was based on the idea that each discourse segment has a salient entity, the *focus*. Centering theory proposed that certain syntactic realizations of the focus (i.e., as subject or object) and certain transitions between these realizations (e.g., if the same entity is the subject of adjacent sentences) created a more coherent discourse. Thus, we can prefer orderings in which the transition between entity mentions is a preferred one.

Entity grid

For example, in the entity-based information approach of Barzilay and Lapata (2005, 2008), a training set of summaries is parsed and labeled for coreference. The resulting sequence of entity realizations can be automatically extracted and represented into an **entity grid**. Figure 23.19 shows a simplified version of a parsed summary and the extracted grid. A probabilistic model of particular entity transitions (i.e., $S, O, X, -$) can then be trained from the entity grid. For example, the transitions X, O, S, S for the headword *Microsoft* exemplify the fact that new entities in a discourse are often introduced first in oblique or object position and then only later appear in subject position. See Barzilay and Lapata (2008) for details.

A general way to view all of these methods is as assigning a coherence score to a sequence of sentences through a local coherence score between pairs or sequences of sentences; a single general transition score between sentences could then combine lexical coherence and entity-based coherence. Once we have such a scoring function, choosing an ordering that optimizes all these local pairwise distances is known to be quite difficult. The task of finding the optimal ordering of a set of sentences given a set of pairwise distances between the sentences is equivalent to very hard problems like Cyclic Ordering and the Traveling Salesman Problem.[2] Sentence ordering is thus equivalent to the difficult class of problems known as **NP-complete**. While these problems are difficult to solve exactly, a number of good approximation methods for solving NP-complete problems have been applied to the information ordering task. See Althaus et al. (2004), Knight (1999a), Cohen et al. (1999), and Brew (1992) for the relevant proofs and approximation techniques.

In the models described above, the information-ordering task is completely separate from content extraction. An alternative approach is to learn the two tasks jointly, resulting in a model that both selects sentences and orders them. For example, in the HMM model of Barzilay and Lee (2004), the hidden states correspond to document

---

2   The Traveling Salesman Problem: given a set of cities and the pairwise distances between them, find the shortest path that visits each city exactly once and then returns to the start city.

		Department	Trial	Microsoft	Markets	Products	Brands	Case	Netscape	Software	Tactics
1	[The Justice Department]$_S$ is conducting an [anti-trust trial]$_O$ against [Microsoft Corp.]$_X$										
2	[Microsoft]$_O$ is accused of trying to forcefully buy into [markets]$_X$ where [its own products]$_S$ are not competitive enough to unseat [established brands]$_O$										
3	[The case]$_S$ resolves around [evidence]$_O$ of [Microsoft]$_S$ aggressively pressuring [Netscape]$_O$ into merging [browser software]$_O$										
4	[Microsoft]$_S$ claims [its tactics]$_S$ are commonplace and good economically.										
1		S	O	X	-	-	-	-	-	-	-
2		-	-	O	X	S	O	-	-	-	-
3		-	-	S	O	-	-	S	O	O	-
4		-	-	S	-	-	-	-	-	-	O

Figure 23.19   A summary (showing entities in subject (S), object (O), or oblique (X) position), and the entity grid that is extracted from it. Adapted from Barzilay and Lapata (2005).

content topics and the observations to sentences. For example for newspaper articles on earthquakes, the hidden states (topics) might be *strength of earthquake*, *location*, *rescue efforts*, and *casualties*. Barzilay and Lee apply clustering and HMM induction to induce these hidden states and the transitions between them. For example, here are three sentences from the *location* cluster they induce:

(23.34) The Athens seismological institute said the temblor's epicenter was located 380 kilometers (238 miles) south of the capital.

(23.35) Seismologists in Pakistan's Northwest Frontier Province said the temblor's epicenter was about 250 kilometers (155 miles) north of the provincial capital Peshawar.

(23.36) The temblor was centered 60 kilometers (35 miles) northwest of the provincial capital of Kunming, about 2,200 kilometers (1,300 miles) southwest of Beijing, a bureau seismologist said.

The learned structure of the HMM then implicitly represents information-ordering facts like *mention "casualties" prior to "rescue" efforts* through the HMM transition probabilities.

In summary, we've seen information ordering based on **chronological order**, based on **coherence**, and an ordering that is learned automatically from the data. In the next section on query-focused summarization, we introduce a final method in which information ordering can be specified according to an ordering template that is predefined for different query types.

Sentence Realization

While discourse coherence can be factored in during sentence ordering, the resulting sentences may still have coherence problems. For example, as we saw in Chapter 21, when a referent appears multiple times in a coreference chain in a discourse, the longer or more descriptive noun phrases occur before shorter, reduced, or pronominal forms. But the ordering we choose for the extracted sentences may not respect this coherence preference.

For example, the boldfaced names in the original summary in Fig. 23.20 appear in an incoherent order; the full name **U.S. President George W. Bush** occurs only after the shortened form **Bush** has been introduced.

One possible way to address this problem in the sentence-realization stage is to apply a coreference resolution algorithm to the output, extracting names and applying some simple cleanup rewrite rules like the following:

(23.37) Use the **full name** at the first mention, and just the **last name** at subsequent mentions.

(23.38) Use a **modified** form for the first mention, but remove appositives or premodifiers from any subsequent mentions.

The rewritten summary in Fig. 23.20 shows how such rules would apply; in general, such methods would depend on high-accuracy coreference resolution.

Original summary:

Presidential advisers do not blame **O'Neill**, but they've long recognized that a shakeup of the economic team would help indicate **Bush** was doing everything he could to improve matters. **U.S. President George W. Bush** pushed out **Treasury Secretary Paul O'Neill** and top economic adviser Lawrence Lindsey on Friday, launching the first shakeup of his administration to tackle the ailing economy before the 2004 election campaign.

Rewritten summary:

Presidential advisers do not blame **Treasury Secretary Paul O'Neill**, but they've long recognized that a shakeup of the economic team would help indicate **U.S. President George W. Bush** was doing everything he could to improve matters. **Bush** pushed out **O'Neill** and White House economic adviser Lawrence Lindsey on Friday, launching the first shakeup of his administration to tackle the ailing economy before the 2004 election campaign.

Figure 23.20   Rewriting references, from Nenkova and McKeown (2003).

Sentence fusion

Recent research has also focused on a finer granularity for realization than the extracted sentence by using **sentence fusion** algorithms to combine phrases from different sentences. The sentence fusion algorithm of Barzilay and McKeown (2005) parses each sentence, uses multiple-sequence alignment of the parses to find areas of common information, builds a fusion lattice with overlapping information, and creates a new fused sentence by linearizing a string of words from the lattice.

23.6   Focused Summarization and Question Answering

As noted at the beginning of this chapter, most interesting questions are not factoid questions. User needs require longer, more informative answers than a single phrase can provide. For example, while a DEFINITION question might be answered by a short phrase like "*Autism is* **a developmental disorder**" or "*A caldera is* **a volcanic crater**", a user might want more information, as in the following definition of *water spinach*:

> *Water spinach* (ipomoea aquatica) is a semi-aquatic leafy green plant characterized by long hollow stems and spear-shaped or heart-shaped leaves which is widely grown throughout Asia as a leaf vegetable. The leaves and stems are often eaten stir-fried as greens with salt or salty sauces, or in soups. Other common names include *morning glory vegetable, kangkong*

(Malay), *rau muong* (Vietnamese), *ong choi* (Cantonese), and *kong xin cai* (Mandarin). It is not related to spinach, but is closely related to sweet potato and convolvulus.

Complex questions can also be asked in domains like medicine, such as this question about a particular drug intervention:

(23.39) In children with an acute febrile illness, what is the efficacy of single-medication therapy with acetaminophen or ibuprofen in reducing fever?

For this medical question, we'd like to be able to extract an answer of the following type, perhaps giving the document ID(s) that the extract came from and some estimate of our confidence in the result:

> Ibuprofen provided greater temperature decrement and longer duration of antipyresis than acetaminophen when the two drugs were administered in approximately equal doses. (PubMedID: 1621668, Evidence Strength: A)

Questions can be even more complex, such as this one from the Document Understanding Conference annual summarization competition:

(23.40) Where have poachers endangered wildlife, what wildlife has been endangered and what steps have been taken to prevent poaching?

Where a factoid answer might be found in a single phrase in a single document or Web page, these kinds of complex questions are likely to require much longer answers that are synthesized from many documents or pages.

For this reason, summarization techniques are often used to build answers to these kinds of complex questions. But unlike the summarization algorithms introduced above, the summaries produced for complex question answering must be relevant to some user question. When a document is summarized for the purpose of answering some user query or information need, we call the goal **query-focused summarization** or sometimes just **focused summarization**. (The terms **topic-based summarization** and **user-focused summarization** are also used.) A query-focused summary is thus really a kind of longer, non-factoid answer to a user question or information need.

Query-focused summarization

One kind of query-focused summary is a **snippet**, the kind that Web search engines like Google return to the user to describe each retrieved document. Snippets are query-focused summaries of a single document. But since for complex queries we will want to aggregate information from multiple documents, we'll need to summarize multiple documents.

Snippet

Indeed, the simplest way to do query-focused summarization is to slightly modify the algorithms for multiple document summarization that we introduced in the previous section to make use of the query. For example, when ranking sentences from all the returned documents in the content-selection phase, we can require that any extracted sentence must contain at least one word overlapping with the query. Or we can just add the cosine distance from the query as one of the relevance features in sentence extraction. We can characterize such a method of query-focused summarization as a bottom-up, domain-independent method.

An alternative way to do query-focused summarization is to make additional use of top-down or information-extraction techniques, building specific content-selection algorithms for different types of complex questions. Thus, we could specifically build a query-focused summarizer for the kinds of advanced questions introduced above, like definition questions, biography questions, and certain medical questions. In each case, we use our top-down expectations for what makes a good definition, biography, or medical answer to guide what kinds of sentences we extract.

Genus
Species

For example, a **definition** of a term often includes information about the term's **genus** and **species**. The genus is the hypernym or superordinate of the word; thus, a sentence like *The Hajj is a type of ritual* is a genus sentence. The species gives important additional properties of the term that differentiate the term from other hyponyms of the genus; an example is *"The annual hajj begins in the twelfth month of the Islamic year"*. Other kinds of information that can occur in a definition include **synonyms**, **etymology**, **subtypes**, and so on.

To build extractive answers for definition questions, we'll need to make sure we extract sentences with the genus information, the species information, and other generally informative sentences. Similarly, a good **biography** of a person contains information such as the person's **birth/death**, **fame factor**, **education**, **nationality** and so on; we'll need to extract sentences with each of these kinds of information. A medical answer that summarizes the results of a study on applying a drug to a medical problem would need to contain information like the **problem** (the medical condition), the **intervention** (the drug or procedure), and the **outcome** (the result of the study). Figure 23.21 shows some example predicates for definition, biography, and medical intervention questions.

Definition	
genus	The Hajj is a type of ritual
species	the annual hajj begins in the twelfth month of the Islamic year
synonym	The Hajj, or Pilgrimage to Mecca, is the central duty of Islam
subtype	Qiran, Tamattu', and Ifrad are three different types of Hajj
Biography	
dates	was assassinated on April 4, 1968
nationality	was born in Atlanta, Georgia
education	entered Boston University as a doctoral student
Drug efficacy	
population	37 otherwise healthy children aged 2 to 12 years
problem	acute, intercurrent, febrile illness
intervention	acetaminophen (10 mg/kg)
outcome	ibuprofen provided greater temperature decrement and longer duration of antipyresis than acetaminophen when the two drugs were administered in approximately equal doses

Figure 23.21 Examples of some different types of information that must be extracted in order to produce answers to certain kinds of complex questions.

In each case, we use the **information-extraction** methods of Chapter 22 to find specific sentences for genus and species (for definitions), or dates, nationality, and education (for biographies), or problems, interventions, and outcomes (for medical questions). We can then use standard domain-independent, content-selection algorithms to find other good sentences to add on to these.

A typical architecture consists of the four steps shown in Fig. 23.22 from the definition-extraction system of Blair-Goldensohn et al. (2004). The input is a definition question T, the number N of documents to retrieve, and the length L of the answer (in sentences).

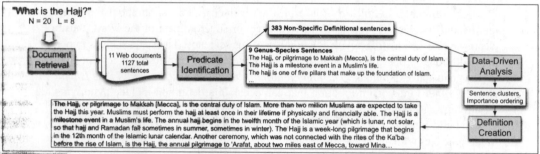

Figure 23.22 Architecture of a query-focused summarizer for definition questions (Blair-Goldensohn et al., 2004).

The first step in any IE-based, complex question-answering system is information retrieval. In this case, a handwritten set of patterns is used to extract the term to be defined from the query T (*Hajj*) and to generate a series of queries that are sent to an IR engine. Similarly, in a biography system it would be the name that would be extracted and passed to the IR engine. The returned documents are broken up into sentences.

In the second stage, we apply classifiers to label each sentence with an appropriate set of classes for the domain. For definition questions, Blair-Goldensohn et al. (2004) used a set of four classes: **genus**, **species**, **other definitional**, or **other**. The third class, **other definitional**, is used to select other sentences that might be added into the summary. These classifiers can be based on any of the information extraction techniques introduced in Chapter 22, including hand-written rules or supervised machine learning.

In the third stage, we can use the methods described in the section on generic (non-query-focused), multiple-document summarization content selection to add additional sentences to our answer that might not fall into a specific information-extraction type. For example, for definition questions, all the sentences that are classified as *other definitional* are examined and a set of relevant sentences is selected from them. This selection can be done by the centroid method, in which we form a tf-idf vector for each sentence, find the centroid of all the vectors, and then choose the K sentences closest to the centroid. Alternatively, we can use a method for avoiding redundancy, like clustering the vectors and choosing the best sentence from each cluster.

Because query-focused summarizers of this type are domain specific, we can use domain-specific methods such as fixed hand-built templates for information ordering as well. For biography questions we might use a template like the following:

(23.41) <NAME> is <WHY FAMOUS>. She was born on <BIRTHDATE> in <BIRTHLOCATION>. She <EDUCATION>. <DESCRIPTIVE SENTENCE>. <DESCRIPTIVE SENTENCE>.

The various sentences or phrases selected in the content selection phase can then be fit into this template. These templates can also be somewhat more abstract. For example, for definitions, we could place a genus-species sentence first, followed by remaining sentences ordered by their saliency scores.

23.7   Summarization Evaluation

As is true for other speech and language processing areas like machine translation, there are a wide variety of evaluation metrics for summarization, metrics requiring human annotation as well as completely automatic metrics.[3]

As we have seen for other tasks, we can evaluate a system by **extrinsic** (task-based) or **intrinsic** (task-independent) methods. We described a kind of extrinsic evaluation of multi-document summarization in Section 23.5, in which subjects were asked to perform time-restricted, fact-gathering tasks and were given full documents together with either no summaries, human summaries, or automatically generated summaries to read. The subjects had to answer three related questions about an event in the news. For query-focused, single-document summarization (like the task of generating Web **snippets**), we can measure how different summarization algorithms affect human performance at the task of deciding if a document is relevant/not-relevant to a query by looking solely at the summary.

ROUGE   The most commonly used intrinsic summarization evaluation metric is an automatic method called **ROUGE, Recall-Oriented Understudy for Gisting Evaluation** (Lin and Hovy, 2003; Lin, 2004). ROUGE is inspired by the BLEU metric used for evaluating machine translation output and, like BLEU, automatically scores a machine-generated candidate summary by measuring the amount of N-gram overlap between the candidate and human-generated summaries (the references).

BLEU is computed by averaging the number of overlapping N-grams of different length between the hypothesis and reference translations. In ROUGE, by contrast, the
ROUGE-1   length of the N-gram is fixed; **ROUGE-1** uses unigram overlap, and **ROUGE-2** uses
ROUGE-2   bigram overlap. We'll define ROUGE-2; the definitions of all the other ROUGE-N metrics follow naturally. ROUGE-2 is a measure of the bigram recall between the candidate summary and the set of human reference summaries:

$$ROUGE2 = \frac{\displaystyle\sum_{S \in \textit{ReferenceSummaries}} \sum_{bigram \in S} \text{Count}_{\text{match}}(bigram)}{\displaystyle\sum_{S \in \textit{ReferenceSummaries}} \sum_{bigram \in S} \text{Count}(bigram)} \qquad (23.42)$$

The function $\text{Count}_{\text{match}}(bigram)$ returns the maximum number of bigrams that co-occur in the candidate summary and the set of reference summaries. ROUGE-1 is the same but counts unigrams instead of bigrams.

---

[3] We focus here on evaluation of entire summarization algorithms and ignore evaluation of subcomponents such as information ordering, although see, for example, Lapata (2006) on the use of Kendall's τ, a metric of rank correlation, for information ordering.

Note that ROUGE is a recall-oriented measure, whereas BLEU is a precision-oriented measure. This is because the denominator of (23.42) is the total sum of the number of bigrams in the reference summaries. By contrast, in BLEU the denominator is the total sum of the number of N-grams in the candidates. Thus, ROUGE is measuring something like how many of the human reference summary bigrams are covered by the candidate summary, whereas BLEU is measuring something like how many of the candidate translation bigrams occurred in the human reference translations.

ROUGE-L
ROUGE-S
ROUGE-SU
Skip bigram

Variants of ROUGE include **ROUGE-L**, which measures the **longest common subsequence** between the reference and candidate summaries, and **ROUGE-S** and **ROUGE-SU**, which measure the number of **skip bigrams** between the reference and candidate summaries. A skip bigram is a pair of words in their sentence order, but allowing for any number of other words to appear between the pair.

While ROUGE is the most commonly applied automatic baseline, it is not as applicable to summarization as similar metrics like BLEU are to machine translation. This is because human summarizers seem to disagree strongly about which sentences to include in a summary, making even the overlap of humans with each other very low.

Pyramid Method

This difference in which sentences humans choose to extract has motivated human evaluation methods that attempt to focus more on meaning. One metric, the **Pyramid Method**, is a way of measuring how many units of meaning are shared between the candidate and reference summaries. The Pyramid Method also weights the units of meaning by importance; units of meaning that occur in more of the human summaries are weighted more highly. The units of meaning are called **Summary Content Units** (SCU), which are sub-sentential semantic units that roughly correspond to propositions or coherent pieces of propositions.

Summary Content Units

In the Pyramid Method, humans label the Summary Content Units in each reference and candidate summary, and then an overlap measure is computed.

Let's see an example from Nenkova et al. (2007) of how two SCUs are labeled in sentences from six human abstracts. We'll first show sentences from the human summaries indexed by a letter (corresponding to one of the six human summaries) and a number (the position of the sentence in the human summary):

A1. The industrial espionage case involving GM and VW began with the hiring of Jose Ignacio Lopez, an employee of GM subsidiary Adam Opel, by VW as a production director.

B3. However, he left GM for VW under circumstances, which along with ensuing events, were described by a German judge as "potentially the biggest-ever case of industrial espionage".

C6. He left GM for VW *in March 1993*.

D6. The issue stems from the alleged recruitment of GM's eccentric and visionary Basque-born procurement chief Jose Ignacio Lopez de Arriortura and seven of Lopez's business colleagues.

E1. *On March 16, 1993*, with Japanese car import quotas to Europe expiring in two years, renowned cost-cutter, Agnacio Lopez De Arriortura, left his job as head of purchasing at General Motor's Opel, Germany, to become Volkswagen's Purchasing and Production director.

F3. *In March 1993*, Lopez and seven other GM executives moved to VW overnight.

The annotators first identify similar sentences, like those above, and then label SCUs. The underlined and italicized spans of words in the above sentences result in the following two SCUs, each one with a weight corresponding to the number of summaries in which it appears (six for the first SCU, and three for the second):

> **SCU1** (w=6): *Lopez left GM for VW*
> *A1*. the hiring of Jose Ignacio Lopez, an employee of GM . . . by VW
> *B3*. he left GM for VW
> *C6*. He left GM for VW
> *D6*. recruitment of GMs . . . Jose Ignacio Lopez
> *E1*. Agnacio Lopez De Arriortura, left his job . . . at General Motors Opel
> . . . to become Volkswagens . . . director
> *F3*. Lopez . . . GM . . . moved to VW
>
> **SCU2** (w=3) *Lopez changes employers in March 1993*
> *C6*. in March, 1993
> *E1*. On March 16, 1993
> *F3*. In March 1993

Once the annotation is done, the informativeness of a given summary can be measured as the ratio of the sum of the weights of its SCUs to the weight of an optimal summary with the same number of SCUs. See the Historical Notes section at the end of the chapter for more details and pointers to the literature.

Random sentence baseline
Leading sentence baseline

The standard baselines for evaluating summaries are the **random sentences** baseline and the **leading sentences** baseline. Assuming we are evaluating summaries of length N sentences, the random baseline just chooses N random sentences, and the leading baseline chooses the first N sentences. The leading sentences method is quite a strong baseline and many proposed summarization algorithms fail to beat it.

23.8   Summary

- The dominant models of information retrieval represent the meanings of documents and queries as bags of words.
- The **vector space model** views documents and queries as vectors in a large multidimensional space. The similarity between documents and queries or other documents can be measured by the cosine of the angle between the vectors.
- The main components of a factoid question-answering system are the **question classification** module to determine the named entity type of the answer, a **passage retrieval** module to identify relevant passages, and an answer processing module to extract and format the final answer.
- Factoid question answers can be evaluated with **mean reciprocal rank** (**MRR**).
- Summarization can be **abstractive** or **extractive**; most current algorithms are extractive.
- Three components of **summarization algorithms** are **content selection**, **information ordering**, and **sentence realization**.

- Current single-document summarization algorithms focus mainly on **sentence extraction**, relying on features like **position** in the discourse, **word informativeness**, **cue phrases**, and **sentence length**.
- Multiple-document summarization algorithms often perform **sentence simplification** on document sentences.
- **Redundancy avoidance** is important in multiple-document summarization; it is often implemented by the addition of a redundancy penalty term like **MMR** into sentence extraction.
- **Information-ordering** algorithms in multi-document summarization are often based on maintaining **coherence**.
- **Query-focused summarization** can be done by slight modifications to **generic summarization** algorithms or by using information-extraction methods.

Bibliographical and Historical Notes

Luhn (1957) is generally credited with first advancing the notion of fully automatic indexing of documents based on their contents. Over the years, Salton's SMART project (Salton, 1971) at Cornell developed or evaluated many of the most important notions in information retrieval, including the vector model, term weighting schemes, relevance feedback, and the use of cosine as a similarity metric. The notion of using inverse document frequency in term weighting is due to Sparck Jones (1972). The original notion of relevance feedback is due to Rocchio (1971).

Probabilistic IR An alternative to the vector model that we have not covered is the **probabilistic model** originally shown to be effective by Robinson and Sparck Jones (1976). See Crestani et al. (1998) and Chapter 11 of Manning et al. (2008) on probabilistic models in information retrieval.

Manning et al. (2008) is a comprehensive modern text on information retrieval. Good but slightly older texts include Baeza-Yates and Ribeiro-Neto (1999) and Frakes and Baeza-Yates (1992); older classic texts include Salton and McGill (1983) and van Rijsbergen (1975). Many of the classic papers in the field can be found in Sparck Jones and Willett (1997). Current work is published in the annual proceedings of the ACM Special Interest Group on Information Retrieval (SIGIR). The U.S. National Institute of Standards and Technology (NIST) has run an annual evaluation project for text information retrieval and extraction called the Text REtrieval Conference (TREC) since the early 1990s; the conference proceedings from TREC contain results from these standardized evaluations. The primary journals in the field are the *Journal of the American Society of Information Sciences*, *ACM Transactions on Information Systems*, *Information Processing and Management*, and *Information Retrieval*.

Question answering was one of the earliest tasks for NLP systems in the 1960s and 1970s (Green et al., 1961; Simmons, 1965; Woods et al., 1972; Lehnert, 1977), but the field lay dormant for a few decades until the need for querying the Web brought the task back into focus. The TREC QA track began in 1999, and a wide variety of factoid and non-factoid systems have been competing in annual evaluations since then.

In addition to the references in this chapter, see Strzalkowski and Harabagiu (2006) for a collection of recent research papers.

Research on text summarization began with the work of Luhn (1958) on extractive methods for the automatic generation of abstracts, focusing on surface features like term frequency, and the later work of Edmunson (1969) incorporating positional features as well. Term-based features were also used in the early application of automatic summarization at Chemical Abstracts Service (Pollock and Zamora, 1975). The 1970s and 1980s saw a number of approaches grounded in AI methodology such as scripts (DeJong, 1982), semantic networks (Reimer and Hahn, 1988), or combinations of AI and statistical methods (Rau et al., 1989).

The work of Kupiec et al. (1995) on training a sentence classifier with supervised machine learning led to many statistical methods for sentence extraction. Around the turn of the century, the growth of the Web led naturally to interest in multi-document summarization and query-focused summarization.

There have been a wide variety of algorithms for the main components of summarizers. The simple, unsupervised, log-linear content-selection algorithm we describe is simplified from the **SumBasic** algorithm of Nenkova and Vanderwende (2005), Vanderwende et al. (2007), and the **centroid** algorithm of Radev et al. (2000) and Radev et al. (2001). A number of algorithms for information ordering have used entity coherence, including Kibble and Power (2000), Lapata (2003), Karamanis and Manurung (2002), Karamanis (2003), Barzilay and Lapata (2005), and Barzilay and Lapata (2008). Algorithms for combining multiple cues for coherence and searching for the optimal ordering include Althaus et al. (2004), based on linear programming, the genetic algorithms of Mellish et al. (1998) and Karamanis and Manurung (2002), and the Soricut and Marcu (2006) algorithm, which uses A^* search based on IDL expressions. Karamanis (2007) showed that adding coherence based on rhetorical relations to entity coherence didn't improve sentence ordering. See Lapata (2006, 2003), Karamanis et al. (2004), and Karamanis (2006) on methods for evaluating information ordering.

Sentence compression is an especially active area of research. Early algorithms focused on the use of syntactic knowledge for eliminating less important words or phrases (Grefenstette, 1998; Mani et al., 1999; Jing, 2000). Recent research has focused on using supervised machine learning, in which a parallel corpus of documents together with their human summaries is used to compute the probability that particular words or parse nodes will be pruned. Methods include the use of maximum entropy (Riezler et al., 2003), the noisy channel model and synchronous context-free grammars (Galley and McKeown, 2007; Knight and Marcu, 2000; Turner and Charniak, 2005; Daumé III and Marcu, 2002), Integer Linear Programming (Clarke and Lapata, 2007), and large-margin learning (McDonald, 2006). These methods rely on various features, especially including syntactic or parse knowledge (Jing, 2000; Dorr et al., 2003; Siddharthan et al., 2004; Galley and McKeown, 2007; Zajic et al., 2007; Conroy et al., 2006; Vanderwende et al., 2007), but also including coherence information (Clarke and Lapata, 2007). Alternative recent methods are able to function without these kinds of parallel document/summary corpora (Hori and Furui, 2004; Turner and Charniak, 2005; Clarke and Lapata, 2006).

See Daumé III and Marcu (2006) for a recent Bayesian model of query-focused summarization.

For more information on summarization evaluation, see Nenkova et al. (2007), Passonneau et al. (2005), and Passonneau (2006) for details on the Pyramid Method, van Halteren and Teufel (2003) and Teufel and van Halteren (2004) on related semantic-coverage evaluation methods, and Lin and Demner-Fushman (2005) on the link between evaluations for summarization and question answering. A NIST program starting in 2001, the Document Understanding Conference (DUC), has sponsored an annual evaluation of summarization algorithms. These have included single-document, multiple-document, and query-focused summarization; proceedings from the annual workshop are available online.

Mani and Maybury (1999) is the definitive collection of classic papers on summarization. Sparck Jones (2007) is a good recent survey, and Mani (2001) is the standard textbook.

Paraphrase detection   The task of **paraphrase detection** is an important task related to improving recall in question answering and avoiding redundancy in summarization, and it is also relevant for tasks like textual entailment. See Lin and Pantel (2001), Barzilay and Lee (2003), Pang et al. (2003), Dolan et al. (2004), Quirk et al. (2004) for representative papers on techniques for detecting paraphrases.

Text categorization   Another task related to information retrieval and summarization is the **text categorization** task, which is to assign a new document to one of a pre-existing set of document classes. The standard approach is to use supervised machine learning to train classifiers on a set of documents that have been labeled with the correct class. A *Spam detection*   most important application of text categorization is for **spam detection**.

Exercises

23.1   Pose the following queries to your favorite Web search engine.

> Who did the Vice President kill?
> Who killed the former Treasury Secretary?

Do an error-analysis on the returned snippets and pages. What are the sources of the errors? How might these errors be addressed by a more intelligent question-answering system?

23.2   Do some error analysis on Web-based question answering. Choose 10 questions and type them all into two different search engines. Analyze the errors. For example, what kinds of questions could neither system answer? Which kinds of questions did one work better on? Was there a type of question that could be answered just from the snippets?

23.3   Read Brill et al. (2002). Implement a simple version of the AskMSR system.

23.4   Apply the system you developed for the last question to a small, closed, set of Web pages of interest. For example, you could use the set of pages that describe the undergraduate degree and course requirements at a university. How does the restriction to a small collection affect the performance of the system?

Credits

Fig. 23.16 (© the authors; thanks to the Association of Computational Linguistics, the *Journal of Computational Linguistics* and its editor Robert Dale, and to Daniel Marcu)

Fig. 23.19 (© the authors; thanks to the Association of Computational Linguistics, the *Journal of Computational Linguistics* and its editor Robert Dale, and to Regina Barzilay)

Chapter 24

Dialogue and Conversational Agents

> C: *I want you to tell me the names of the fellows on the St. Louis team.*
> A: *I'm telling you. Who's on first, What's on second, I Don't Know is on third.*
> C: *You know the fellows' names?*
> A: *Yes.*
> C: *Well, then, who's playing first?*
> A: *Yes.*
> C: *I mean the fellow's name on first.*
> A: *Who.*
> C: *The guy on first base.*
> A: *Who is on first.*
> C: *Well what are you askin' me for?*
> A: *I'm not asking you – I'm telling you. Who is on first.*
> Who's on First – Bud Abbott and Lou Costello's version of an old burlesque standard.

The literature of the fantastic abounds in inanimate objects magically endowed with sentience and the gift of speech. From Ovid's statue of Pygmalion to Mary Shelley's Frankenstein, there is something deeply touching about creating something and then having a chat with it. Legend has it that after finishing his sculpture of *Moses*, Michelangelo thought it so lifelike that he tapped it on the knee and commanded it to speak. Perhaps this shouldn't be surprising. Language is the mark of humanity and *Conversation* sentience, and **conversation** or **dialogue** is the most fundamental and specially privi- *Dialogue* leged arena of language. It is the first kind of language we learn as children, and for most of us, it is the kind of language we most commonly indulge in, whether we are ordering curry for lunch or buying spinach, participating in business meetings or talking with our families, booking airline flights or complaining about the weather.

This chapter introduces the fundamental structures and algorithms in **conversational agents**. Conversational agents most often communicate through speech rather than text, and so they are also known as **spoken dialogue systems**, or **spoken language systems**. These programs communicate with users in spoken natural language to make travel arrangements, answer questions about weather or sports, route telephone calls, act as a general telephone assistant, or perform even more sophisticated tasks.

Many of these tasks involve telephony and also involve mobile situations in which a large screen and keyboard may not be available (Cohen and Oviatt, 1994). Applications relating to travel are thus very common. Indeed, travel planning and management have been a key concern of dialogue systems since the early influential GUS system for planning airline travel (Bobrow et al., 1977). More recently, a number of spoken language systems for booking airline flights were built under the Air Traffic Information System (ATIS) (Hemphill et al., 1990) and Communicator (Walker et al., 2002) programs. We will use this travel domain as an example throughout the chapter (as we used it to discuss grammar rules for parsing ATIS sentences in Chapter 12). Figure 24.1 shows a sample dialogue from the Communicator system of Xu and Rudnicky (2000).

S1:	Hello. You've reached the [Communicator]. Tell me your full name
U2:	*hi i'd like to fly to seattle tuesday morning*
S3:	Traveling to Seattle on Tuesday, August eleventh in the morning. Your full name?
U4:	*[John Doe]*
S5:	Hello, [John], I'm glad to hear from you again. You can now ask me for help.
S6:	OK. Let's see I have a United flight departing Pittsburgh at ten forty five a.m. arriving into Seattle at one fifty seven p.m. Is that OK?
U7:	*Yes*
S8:	Will you return to Pittsburgh from Seattle?
U9:	*no i will go to Los Angeles*
S10:	Traveling to Los Angeles. on what date
U11:	*Sorry can we go back to talk about the previous leg again*
S12:	For the first leg, you are on a United flight 1446 departing Pittsburgh at ten forty five A.M. tomorrow, arriving in Seattle at one fifty seven P.M. Do you want to take that?
U13:	*actually i want to leave on wednesday*
S14:	a flight on wednesday.
S15:	I have a flight departing Pittsburgh at ten forty five a.m., arrives Seattle at one fifty seven p.m. Is that OK?
U16:	*Yes*

Figure 24.1   The travel domain: A fragment from a successful conversation between a user (U) and the Communicator system (S) of Xu and Rudnicky (2000).

Another promising domain is automatic call routing. A call routing system directs incoming calls in a telephone call center, transferring the call to the appropriate human. Call routing dialogue systems generally begin by asking the user open-ended questions like *How may I help you?* (Gorin et al., 1997) or *How may I direct your call?* (Chu-Carroll and Carpenter, 1999). Figure 24.2 shows sample conversations from the AT&T How May I Help You (HMIHY) system (Gorin et al., 1997).

S:	How may I help you?
U:	*can you tell me how much it is to tokyo?*
S:	You want to know the cost of a call?
U:	*yes that's right*
S:	Please hold on for rate information.
S:	How may I help you?
U:	*what's the area code for chicago?*
S:	You want an area code.
U:	*(silence)*
S:	The area code for Chicago is 312.

Figure 24.2   The call routing domain: Two conversations between a user (U) and the AT&T How May I Help You (HMIHY) system (S) (Gorin et al., 1997).

A somewhat different domain, which is very far from the telephony area, is automatic tutoring systems. Figure 24.3 shows part of a dialogue from the ITSPOKE dialogue system (Litman and Silliman, 2004), which uses the Why2-Atlas text-based tutoring system as its tutoring backend (VanLehn et al., 2002).

S: I didn't understand. What force acts on all objects within close proximity to earth?
U: *uh the force of gravity*
S: Fine. Besides the Earth's gravitational force, are there any other forces acting on the person, keys, and elevator after the release?
U: *no*
S: Yep. Thus, keep in mind that after the release, the only force on the person, keys, and elevator is the force of gravity. If gravity is the only force acting on an object, will it be moving or staying still?
U: *it will be moving*
S: Fine. Not only are the person, keys, and elevator moving, they have only gravitational forces on them. When an object is falling and has only gravitational force on it, it is said to be in what?
U: *freefall*

Figure 24.3   The tutoring domain: Part of an conversation between a student user (U) and the ITSPOKE system (S) of Litman and Silliman (2004).

Section 24.1 starts out with a summary of facts about human conversation, including the idea of turns and utterances, speech acts, grounding, dialogue structure, and conversational implicature. The next few sections introduce the components of spoken language systems and some evaluation metrics. We then turn in Section 24.5 and Section 24.6 to the more sophisticated information-state architecture and Markov decision process models of conversational agents, and we conclude with some advanced topics like the BDI (belief-desire-intention) paradigm.

24.1   Properties of Human Conversations

Conversation between humans is an intricate and complex joint activity. Because of the limitations of our current technologies, conversations between humans and machines are vastly simpler and more constrained than these human conversations. Nonetheless, before we attempt to design a conversational agent to converse with humans, it is crucial to understand something about how humans converse with each other.

In this section we discuss some properties of human-human conversation that distinguish it from the kinds of (text-based) discourses we have seen so far. The main difference is that conversation is a kind of **joint activity** between two (or more) interlocutors. This basic fact has a number of ramifications; conversations are built up out of consecutive **turns**, each turn consists of **joint action** of the speaker and hearer, and the hearer makes special inferences called **conversational implicatures** about the speaker's intended meaning.

24.1.1   Turns and Turn-Taking

Turn-taking

Dialogue is characterized by **turn-taking**; Speaker A says something, then speaker B, then speaker A, and so on. If having a turn (or "taking the floor") is a resource to be allocated, what is the process by which turns are allocated? How do speakers know when it is the proper time to contribute their turn?

It turns out that conversation and language itself are structured in such a way as to deal efficiently with this resource allocation problem. One source of evidence for this is the timing of the utterances in normal human conversations. Although speakers can overlap each other while talking, it turns out that on average the total amount of overlap is remarkably small; perhaps less than 5% (Levinson, 1983). Furthermore, the amount of time between turns is generally less than a few hundred milliseconds, which is quite short given that it takes hundreds of milliseconds for a speaker to plan the motor routines for an utterance. Thus, speakers must begin planning the exact moment to start their next utterance before the previous speaker has finished talking. For this to be possible, natural conversation must be set up in such a way that (most of the time) people can quickly figure out **who** should talk next and exactly **when** they should talk. This kind of turn-taking behavior is generally studied in the field of
Conversation analysis **Conversation analysis (CA)**. In a key conversation-analytic paper, Sacks et al. (1974) argued that turn-taking behavior, at least in American English, is governed by a set of turn-taking rules. These rules apply at a **transition-relevance place**, or **TRP**: places where the structure of the language allows speaker shift to occur. Here is a version of the turn-taking rules simplified from Sacks et al. (1974):

(24.1) **Turn-taking rule.** At each TRP of each turn:

    a. If during this turn the current speaker has selected A as the next speaker then A must speak next.

    b. If the current speaker does not select the next speaker, any other speaker may take the next turn.

    c. If no one else takes the next turn, the current speaker may take it.

There are a number of important implications of rule (24.1) for dialogue modeling. First, (24.1a) implies that there are some utterances by which the speaker specifically selects who the next speaker will be. The most obvious of these are questions, in which the speaker selects another speaker to answer the question. Two-part structures
Adjacency pair like QUESTION-ANSWER are called **adjacency pairs** (Schegloff, 1968) or **dialogic**
Dialogic pair **pair** (Harris, 2005). Other adjacency pairs include GREETING followed by GREETING, COMPLIMENT followed by DOWNPLAYER, REQUEST followed by GRANT. We will show that these pairs and the dialogue expectations they set up will play an important role in dialogue modeling.

Subrule (24.1a) also has an implication for the interpretation of silence. While silence can occur after any turn, silence in between the two parts of an adjacency pair
Significant silence is **significant silence**. For example, Levinson (1983) notes this example from Atkinson and Drew (1979); pause lengths are marked in parentheses (in seconds):

(24.2) A: Is there something bothering you or not?
        (1.0)
    A: Yes or no?
        (1.5)
    A: Eh?
    B: No.

Since A has just asked B a question, the silence is interpreted as a refusal to respond,
Dispreferred or perhaps a **dispreferred** response (a response, like saying "no" to a request, which is

stigmatized). By contrast, silence in other places, for example, a lapse after a speaker finishes a turn, is not generally interpretable in this way. These facts are relevant for user interface design in spoken dialogue systems; users are disturbed by the pauses in dialogue systems caused by slow speech recognizers (Yankelovich et al., 1995).

Utterance

Another implication of (24.1) is that transitions between speakers don't occur just anywhere; the **transition-relevance places** where they tend to occur are generally at **utterance** boundaries. Recall from Chapter 12 that spoken utterances differ from written sentences in a number of ways. They tend to be shorter, they are more likely to be single clauses or even just single words, their subjects are usually pronouns rather than full lexical noun phrases, and they include filled pauses and repairs. A hearer must take all this (and other cues like prosody) into account to know where to begin talking.

24.1.2   Language as Action: Speech Acts

The previous section showed that conversation consists of a sequence of turns, each of which consists of one or more utterance. A key insight into conversation is due to Wittgenstein (1953) but was worked out more fully by Austin (1962): an utterance in a dialogue is a kind of **action** being performed by the speaker.

Performative

The idea that an utterance is a kind of action is particularly clear in **performative** sentences like the following:

(24.3) I name this ship the *Titanic*.

(24.4) I second that motion.

(24.5) I bet you five dollars it will snow tomorrow.

Speech act

When uttered by the proper authority, for example, (24.3) has the effect of changing the state of the world (causing the ship to have the name *Titanic*) just as any action can change the state of the world. Verbs like *name* or *second* that perform this kind of action are called performative verbs, and Austin called these kinds of actions **speech acts**. What makes Austin's work so far-reaching is that speech acts are not confined to this small class of performative verbs. Austin's claim is that the utterance of any sentence in a real speech situation constitutes three kinds of acts:

Locutionary act:	the utterance of a sentence with a particular meaning
Illocutionary act:	the act of asking, answering, promising, etc., in uttering a sentence
Perlocutionary act:	the (often intentional) production of certain effects upon the feelings, thoughts, or actions of the addressee in uttering a sentence

Illocutionary force

For example, Austin explains that the utterance of (24.6) might have the **illocutionary force** of protesting and the perlocutionary effect of stopping the addressee from doing something or annoying the addressee.

(24.6) You can't do that.

The term **speech act** is generally used to describe illocutionary acts rather than either of the other two types of acts. Searle (1975b), in modifying a taxonomy of Austin's, suggests that all speech acts can be classified into one of five major classes:

Assertives:	committing the speaker to something's being the case (*suggesting, putting forward, swearing, boasting, concluding*)
Directives:	attempts by the speaker to get the addressee to do something (*asking, ordering, requesting, inviting, advising, begging*)
Commissives:	committing the speaker to some future course of action (*promising, planning, vowing, betting, opposing*)
Expressives:	expressing the psychological state of the speaker about a state of affairs (*thanking, apologizing, welcoming, deploring*)
Declarations:	bringing about a different state of the world by the utterance (including many of the performative examples above; *I resign, You're fired*)

24.1.3   Language as Joint Action: Grounding

The previous section suggested that each turn or utterance could be viewed as an action by a speaker. But dialogue is not a series of unrelated independent acts. Instead, dialogue is a collective act performed by the speaker and the hearer. One implication of joint action is that, unlike in monologue, the speaker and hearer must constantly establish **common ground** (Stalnaker, 1978), the set of things that are mutually believed by both speakers. The need to achieve common ground means that the hearer must **ground** the speaker's utterances, making it clear that the hearer has understood the speaker's meaning and intention.

Common ground

Grounding

As Clark (1996) points out, people need closure or grounding for non-linguistic actions as well. For example, why does a well-designed elevator button light up when it's pressed? Because this indicates to the elevator traveler that she has successfully called the elevator. Clark phrases this need for closure as follows, after Norman (1988):

> **Principle of closure.** Agents performing an action require evidence, sufficient for current purposes, that they have succeeded in performing it.

Grounding is also important when the hearer needs to indicate that the speaker has *not* succeeded in performing an action. If the hearer has problems in understanding, she must indicate these problems to the speaker, again so that mutual understanding can eventually be achieved.

How is closure achieved? Clark and Schaefer (1989) introduce the idea that each joint linguistic act or **contribution** has two phases, called **presentation** and **acceptance**. In the first phase, a speaker presents the hearer with an utterance, performing a sort of speech act. In the acceptance phase, the hearer has to ground the utterance, indicating to the speaker whether understanding was achieved.

Contribution

What methods can the hearer (call her B) use to ground the speaker A's utterance? Clark and Schaefer (1989) discuss five main types of methods, ordered from weakest to strongest:

Continued attention:	B shows she is continuing to attend and therefore remains satisfied with A's presentation.
Next contribution:	B starts in on the next relevant contribution.
Acknowledgment:	B nods or says a continuer like *uh-huh*, *yeah*, or the like, or an **assessment** like *that's great*.
Demonstration:	B demonstrates all or part of what she has understood A to mean, for example, by **reformulating** (paraphrasing) A's utterance or by **collaborative completion** of A's utterance.
Display:	B displays verbatim all or part of A's presentation.

Let's look for examples of grounding in a conversation between a human travel agent and a human client in Fig. 24.4. We return to this dialogue throughout the chapter to inform our design of a machine travel-dialogue agent.

C_1:	...I need to travel in May.
A_1:	And, what day in May did you want to travel?
C_2:	OK uh I need to be there for a meeting that's from the 12th to the 15th.
A_2:	And you're flying into what city?
C_3:	Seattle.
A_3:	And what time would you like to leave Pittsburgh?
C_4:	Uh hmm I don't think there's many options for non-stop.
A_4:	Right. There's three non-stops today.
C_5:	What are they?
A_5:	The first one departs PGH at 10:00am arrives Seattle at 12:05 their time. The second flight departs PGH at 5:55pm, arrives Seattle at 8pm. And the last flight departs PGH at 8:15pm arrives Seattle at 10:28pm.
C_6:	OK I'll take the 5ish flight on the night before on the 11th.
A_6:	On the 11th? OK. Departing at 5:55pm arrives Seattle at 8pm, U.S. Air flight 115.
C_7:	OK.

Figure 24.4   Part of a conversation between a travel agent (A) and client (C).

Utterance A_1, in which the agent repeats *in May*, repeated below in boldface, shows the strongest form of grounding, in which the hearer displays understanding by repeating verbatim part of the speaker's words:

C_1:	...I need to travel **in May**.
A_1:	And, what day **in May** did you want to travel?

This particular fragment doesn't have an example of an *acknowledgment*, but there's an example in another fragment:

C:	He wants to fly from Boston to Baltimore
A:	**Uh huh**

Continuer

Backchannel

The word *uh-huh* here is a **continuer**, also often called an **acknowledgment token** or a **backchannel**. A continuer is a (short) optional utterance that acknowledges the content of the utterance of the other and that doesn't require an acknowledgment by the other (Yngve, 1970; Jefferson, 1984; Schegloff, 1982; Ward and Tsukahara, 2000).

In Clark and Schaefer's third method, the speaker starts in on a relevant next contribution. We see a number of examples of this in the dialogue in Fig. 24.4, for example, where the speaker asks a question and the hearer answers it. We mentioned these **adjacency pairs** above; other examples include PROPOSAL followed by ACCEPTANCE or REJECTION, APOLOGY followed by ACCEPTANCE/REJECTION, SUMMONS followed by ANSWER, and so on.

In a more subtle act of grounding, the speaker can combine this method with the previous one. For example, notice that whenever the client answers a question, the agent begins the next question with *And*. The *And* indicates to the client that the agent has successfully understood the answer to the last question:

> And, what day in May did you want to travel?
> ...
> And you're flying into what city?
> ...
> And what time would you like to leave Pittsburgh?

As we show in Section 24.5, the notions of grounding and contributions can be combined with speech acts to give a more sophisticated model of joint action in conversation; these more sophisticated models are called **dialogue acts**.

Grounding is just as crucial in human-machine conversation as it is in human conversation. The examples below, from Cohen et al. (2004), suggest how unnatural it sounds when a machine doesn't ground properly. The use of *Okay* makes (24.7) a much more natural response than (24.8) to ground a user's rejection:

(24.7)   System: Did you want to review some more of your personal profile?
          Caller: No.
          System: *Okay,* what's next?

(24.8)   System: Did you want to review some more of your personal profile?
          Caller: No.
          System: What's next?

Indeed, this kind of lack of grounding can cause errors. Stifelman et al. (1993) and Yankelovich et al. (1995) found that humans become confused when a conversational system doesn't give explicit acknowledgments.

24.1.4   Conversational Structure

We have already seen how conversation is structured by adjacency pairs and contributions. Here we briefly discuss one aspect of the **overall organization** of a conversation: conversational openings. The openings of telephone conversations, for example, tend to have a 4-part structure (Clark, 1994; Schegloff, 1968, 1979):

Stage 1: Enter a conversation, with summons-response adjacency pair

Stage 2: Identify speakers

Stage 3: Establish joint willingness to converse

Stage 4: Raise the first topic, usually done by the caller.

These four stages appear in the opening of this short task-oriented conversation from Clark (1994).

Stage	Speaker and Utterance
1	A_1: (rings B's telephone)
1,2	B_1: Benjamin Holloway
2	A_1: this is Professor Dwight's secretary, from Polymania College
2,3	B_1: ooh yes –
4	A_1: uh:m . about the: lexicology *seminar*
4	B_1: *yes*

It is common for the person who answers the phone to speak first (since the caller's ring functions as the first part of the adjacency pair) but for the caller to bring up the first topic, as the caller did above concerning the "lexicology seminar". This fact that the caller usually brings up the first topic causes confusion when the answerer brings up the first topic instead; here's an example of this from the British directory enquiry service from Clark (1994).

Customer: (rings)
Operator: Directory Enquiries, for which town please?
Customer: Could you give me the phone number of um: Mrs. um: Smithson?
Operator: Yes, which town is this at please?
Customer: Huddleston.
Operator: Yes. And the name again?
Customer: Mrs. Smithson.

In the conversation above, the operator brings up the topic (*for which town please?*) in her first sentence, confusing the caller, who ignores this topic and brings up her own. This fact that callers expect to bring up the topic explains why conversational agents for call routing or directory information often use open prompts like *How may I help you?* or *How may I direct your call?* rather than a directive prompt like *For which town please?* Open prompts allow callers to state their own topic, reducing recognition errors caused by customer confusion.

Conversation has many other kinds of structure, including the intricate nature of conversational closings and the wide use of presequences. We discuss structure based on **coherence** in Section 24.7.

24.1.5   Conversational Implicature

We have seen that conversation is a kind of joint activity, in which speakers produce turns according to a systematic framework, and that the contributions made by these turns include a presentation phase of performing a kind of action and an acceptance phase of grounding the previous actions of the interlocutor. So far we have only talked about what might be called the "infrastructure" of conversation. But we have so far said nothing about the actual information that gets communicated from speaker to hearer in dialogue.

While Chapter 17 showed how we can compute meanings from sentences, it turns out that in conversation, the meaning of a contribution is often quite a bit extended from the compositional meaning that might be assigned from the words alone. This is because inference plays a crucial role in conversation. The interpretation of an utterance relies on more than just the literal meaning of the sentences. Consider the client's response C_2 from the sample conversation in Fig. 24.4, repeated here:

A_1: And, what day in May did you want to travel?

C_2: OK uh I need to be there for a meeting that's from the 12th to the 15th.

Notice that the client does not in fact answer the question. The client merely states that he has a meeting at a certain time. The semantics for this sentence produced by a semantic interpreter will simply mention this meeting. What is it that licenses the agent to infer that the client is mentioning this meeting so as to inform the agent of the travel dates?

Now consider another utterance from the sample conversation, this one by the agent:

A_4: …There's three non-stops today.

Now this statement would still be true if there were seven non-stops today, since if there are seven of something, there are by definition also three. But what the agent means here is that there are three **and not more than three** non-stops today. How is the client to infer that the agent means **only three** non-stops?

These two cases have something in common; in both cases the speaker seems to expect the hearer to draw certain inferences; in other words, the speaker is communicating more information than seems to be present in the uttered words. These kind of examples were pointed out by Grice (1975, 1978) as part of his theory of **conversational implicature**. **Implicature** means a particular class of licensed inferences. Grice proposed that what enables hearers to draw these inferences is that conversation is guided by a set of **maxims**, general heuristics that play a guiding role in the interpretation of conversational utterances. He proposed the following four maxims:

Implicature

Maxim

Quantity
- **Maxim of Quantity:** Be exactly as informative as is required.

  1. Make your contribution as informative as is required (for the current purposes of the exchange).
  2. Do not make your contribution more informative than is required.

Quality
- **Maxim of Quality:** Try to make your contribution one that is true:

  1. Do not say what you believe to be false.
  2. Do not say that for which you lack adequate evidence.

Relevance
- **Maxim of Relevance:** Be relevant.

Manner
- **Maxim of Manner:** Be perspicuous.

  1. Avoid obscurity of expression.
  2. Avoid ambiguity.
  3. Be brief (avoid unnecessary prolixity).
  4. Be orderly.

It is the Maxim of Quantity (specifically Quantity 1) that allows the hearer to know that *three non-stops* did not mean *seven non-stops*. This is because the hearer assumes the speaker is following the maxims, and thus if seven non-stops were meant, the speaker would have said seven non-stops ("as informative as is required"). The Maxim of Relevance is what allows the agent to know that the client wants to travel by the 12th. The agent assumes the client is following the maxims, and hence would only have mentioned the meeting if it was relevant at this point in the dialogue. The most natural inference that would make the meeting relevant is the inference that the client meant the agent to understand that his departure time was before the meeting time.

24.2   Basic Dialogue Systems

We've now seen a bit about how human dialogue works, although as we show, not every aspect of human-human conversation is modeled in human-machine conversation. Let's therefore turn to the spoken dialogue systems used in commercial applications.

Figure 24.5 shows a typical architecture for a dialogue system. It has six components. The speech recognition and understanding components extract meaning from the input, and the generation and TTS components map from meaning to speech. The dialogue manager controls the whole process, along with a task manager that has knowledge about the task domain (such as air travel). We go through each of these components in the next sections. Then we explore more sophisticated research systems in following sections.

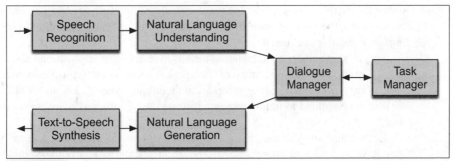

Figure 24.5   Simplified architecture of the components of a conversational agent.

24.2.1   ASR Component

The ASR (automatic speech recognition) component takes audio input, generally from a telephone, but also from a PDA or desktop microphone, and returns a transcribed string of words, as discussed in Chapter 9.

Various aspects of the ASR system may be optimized specifically for use in conversational agents. For example, the large-vocabulary speech recognizers we discussed in Chapter 9 for dictation or transcription focused on transcribing any sentence on any topic using any English word. But for domain-dependent dialogue systems, it is of little use to be able to transcribe such a wide variety of sentences. The sentences that the speech recognizer needs to be able to transcribe are just those that can be understood by the natural language understanding component. For this reason, commercial dialogue systems generally use non-probabilistic language models based on finite-state grammars. These grammars are generally hand-written and specify all possible responses that the system understands. We give an example of such a hand-written grammar for a VoiceXML system in Section 24.3. Such grammar-based language models can also be compiled automatically from, for example, unification grammars used for natural language understanding (Rayner et al., 2006).

Because what the user says to the system is related to what the system has just said, language models in conversational agent are usually *dialogue-state dependent*. For example, if the system has just asked the user "What city are you departing from?", the ASR language model can be constrained to consist only of city names or perhaps sentences of the form 'I want to (leave depart) from [CITYNAME]'. These dialogue-state-specific language models often consist of hand-written finite-state (or even context-free) grammars as discussed above, one for each dialogue state.

In some systems, the understanding component is more powerful, and the set of sentences the system can understand is larger. In such cases, instead of a finite-state grammar, we can use an N-gram language model whose probabilities are similarly conditioned on the dialogue state.

Whether we use a finite-state, context-free, or an N-gram language model, we call such a dialogue-state-dependent language model a **restrictive grammar**. When the system wants to constrain the user to respond to the system's last utterance, it can use a restrictive grammar. When the system wants to allow the user more options, it might mix this state-specific language model with a more general language model. As we show, the choice between these strategies can be tuned according to how much *initiative* the user is allowed.

Restrictive grammar

Speech recognition in dialogue, as well as in many other applications like dictation, has the property that the identity of the speaker remains constant across many utterances. This means that speaker-adaptation techniques like MLLR and VTLN (Chapter 9) can be applied to improve recognition as the system gets more speech from the user.

Embedding an ASR engine in a dialogue system also requires that an ASR engine have real-time response since users are unwilling to accept long pauses before responses. Dialogue systems also generally require that an ASR system return a **confidence** value for a sentence, which can then be used, for example, for deciding whether to ask the user to confirm a response.

24.2.2   NLU Component

The NLU (natural language understanding) component of dialogue systems must produce a semantic representation that is appropriate for the dialogue task. Many speech-based dialogue systems, since as far back as the GUS system (Bobrow et al., 1977), are based on the frame-and-slot semantics discussed in Chapter 22. A travel system, for example, which has the goal of helping a user find an appropriate flight, would have a frame with slots for information about the flight; thus, a sentence like *Show me morning flights from Boston to San Francisco on Tuesday* might correspond to the following filled-out frame (from Miller et al. (1994)):

```
SHOW:
FLIGHTS:
   ORIGIN:
      CITY:   Boston
      DATE:
         DAY-OF-WEEK:   Tuesday
      TIME:
         PART-OF-DAY:   morning
   DEST:
      CITY:   San Francisco
```

How does the NLU component generate this semantic representation? Some dialogue systems use general-purpose unification grammars with semantic attachments, such as the those introduced in Chapter 18. A parser produces a sentence meaning from which the slot-fillers are extracted. Other dialogue systems rely on simpler domain-specific semantic analyzers, such as **semantic grammars**. A semantic grammar is a CFG in which the rule left-hand sides correspond to the semantic entities being expressed, as in the following fragment:

SHOW	→	show me i want can i see ...
DEPART_TIME_RANGE	→	(after around before) HOUR
		morning afternoon evening
HOUR	→	one two three four... twelve (AMPM)
FLIGHTS	→	(a) flight flights
AMPM	→	am pm
ORIGIN	→	from CITY
DESTINATION	→	to CITY
CITY	→	Boston San Francisco Denver Washington

These **grammars take** the form of context-free grammars or recursive transition networks (Issar and Ward, 1993; Ward and Issar, 1994), and hence can be parsed by any standard CFG parsing algorithm, such as the CKY or Earley algorithms introduced in Chapter 13. The result of the CFG or RTN parse is a hierarchical labeling of the input string with semantic node labels:

```
SHOW      FLIGHTS      ORIGIN  DESTINATION      DEPART_DATE  DEPART_TIME
                               to CITY
Show me   flights  from boston  to san francisco  on tuesday   morning
```

Since semantic grammar nodes like ORIGIN correspond to the slots in the frame, the slot-fillers can be read almost directly off the resulting parse above. It remains only to put the fillers into some sort of canonical form (e.g., as discussed in Chapter 22, dates can be normalized into a DD:MM:YY form, times into 24-hour time, etc.).

The semantic grammar approach is very widely used but is unable to deal with ambiguity and requires hand-written grammars that can be expensive and slow to create.

Ambiguity can be addressed by adding probabilities to the grammar; one such probabilistic semantic grammar system is the TINA system (Seneff, 1995) shown in Fig. 24.6; note the mix of syntactic and semantic node names. The grammar rules in TINA are written by hand, but parse tree node probabilities are trained by a modified version of the PCFG method described in Chapter 14.

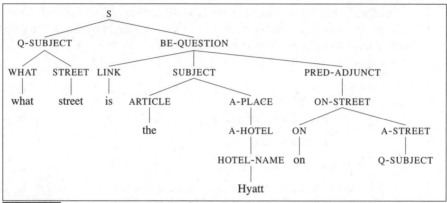

Figure 24.6   A parse of a sentence in the TINA semantic grammar (Seneff, 1995).

An alternative to semantic grammars that is probabilistic and also avoids hand-coding of grammars is the semantic HMM model of Pieraccini et al. (1991). The hidden states of this HMM are semantic slot labels, and the observed words are the fillers of the slots. Figure 24.7 shows how a sequence of hidden states, corresponding to slot names, could be decoded from (or could generate) a sequence of observed words. Note that the model includes a hidden state called DUMMY, which generates words that do not fill any slots in the frame.

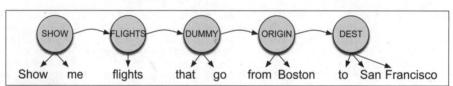

Figure 24.7   The Pieraccini et al. (1991) HMM model of semantics for filling slots in frame-based dialogue systems. Each hidden state can generate a sequence of words; such a model, in which a single hidden state can correspond to multiple observations, is technically called a **semi-HMM**.

The goal of the HMM model is to compute the labeling of semantic roles $C = c_1, c_2, ..., c_i$ (C for "cases" or "concepts") that has the highest probability $P(C\ W)$ given some words $W = w_1, w_2, ..., w_n$. As usual, we use Bayes Rule as follows:

$$
\begin{aligned}
\underset{C}{\operatorname{argmax}} P(C\ W) &= \underset{C}{\operatorname{argmax}} \frac{P(W\ C)P(C)}{P(W)} \\
&= \underset{C}{\operatorname{argmax}} P(W\ C)P(C) \\
&= \prod_{i=2}^{N} P(w_i\ w_{i-1}...w_1, C)P(w_1\ C) \prod_{i=2}^{M} P(c_i\ c_{i-1}...c_1) \quad (24.9)
\end{aligned}
$$

The Pieraccini et al. (1991) model makes a simplification that the concepts (the hidden states) are generated by a Markov process (a concept M-gram model), and that the observation probabilities for each state are generated by a state-dependent (concept-dependent) word N-gram word model:

$$P(w_i \mid w_{i-1},...,w_1,C) = P(w_i \mid w_{i-1},...,w_{i-N+1},c_i) \qquad (24.10)$$
$$P(c_i \mid c_{i-1},...,c_1) = P(c_i \mid c_{i-1},...,c_{i-M+1}) \qquad (24.11)$$

With this simplifying assumption, the final HMM model equations are

$$\operatorname*{argmax}_{C} P(C \mid W) = \prod_{i=2}^{N} P(w_i \mid w_{i-1}...w_{i-N+1},c_i) \prod_{i=2}^{M} P(c_i \mid c_{i-1}...c_{i-M+1}) \ (24.12)$$

These probabilities can be trained on a labeled training corpus, in which each sentence is hand-labeled with the concepts/slot-names associated with each string of words. The best sequence of concepts for a sentence and the alignment of concepts to word sequences can be computed by the standard Viterbi decoding algorithm.

In summary, the resulting HMM model is a generative model with two components. The $P(C)$ component represents the choice of what meaning to express; it assigns a prior over sequences of semantic slots, computed by a concept N-gram. $P(W \mid C)$ represents the choice of what words to use to express that meaning: the likelihood of a particular string of words being generated from a given slot. It is computed by a word N-gram conditioned on the semantic slot. This model extends similar models for **named entity** detection in Chapter 22 and for statistical template filling (Section 22.4.1) by imposing more ordering constraints. HMM models like this, in which each hidden

Semi-HMM   state corresponds to multiple output observations, are called **semi-HMMs**. In a classic HMM, by contrast, each hidden state corresponds to a single output observation.

Many other kinds of statistical models have been proposed for the semantic understanding component of dialogue systems. These include the hidden understanding model (HUM), which adds hierarchical structure to the HMM to combine the advantages of the semantic grammar and semantic HMM approaches (Miller et al., 1994, 1996, 2000), or the decision list method of Rayner and Hockey (2003).

24.2.3   Generation and TTS Components

The generation component of a conversational agent chooses the concepts to express to the user, plans how to express these concepts in words, and assigns any necessary prosody to the words. Then, as described in Chapter 8, the TTS component takes these words and their prosodic annotations and synthesizes a waveform.

The generation task can be separated into two tasks: *what to say* and *how to say it*. The **content planner** module addresses the first task, decides what content to express to the user, whether to ask a question, present an answer, and so on. The content-planning component of dialogue systems is generally merged with the dialogue manager; we return to it below.

The **language generation** module addresses the second task, choosing the syntactic structures and words needed to express the meaning. Language generation modules are implemented in one of two ways. In the simplest and most common method, all or most of the words in the sentence to be uttered to the user are prespecified by the dialogue designer. This method is known as template-based generation, and the sentences created by these templates are often called **prompts**. While most of the words in the template are fixed, templates can include some variables that are filled in by the generator, as in the following:

> What time do you want to leave CITY-ORIG?
> **Will you return to CITY-ORIG from CITY-DEST?**

A second method for language generation relies on techniques from the field **natural language generation**. Here the dialogue manager builds a representation of the meaning of the utterance to be expressed and passes this meaning representation to a full generator. Such generators generally have three components, a sentence planner, surface realizer, and prosody assigner. A sketch of this architecture is shown in Fig. 24.8. See Reiter and Dale (2000) for further information on natural language generation systems and their use in dialogue.

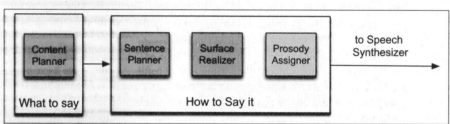

Figure 24.8 Architecture of a natural language generation system for a dialogue system, after Walker and Rambow (2002).

In the hand-designed prompts that are common in current systems, a number of important conversational and discourse constraints must be implemented. Like any discourse, a conversation needs to be coherent. For example, as Cohen et al. (2004) show, the use of discourse markers and pronouns in the hand-built system prompts makes the dialogue in (24.14) more natural than the dialogue in (24.13):

(24.13)   Please say the data.

     ...

     Please say the start time.

     ...

     Please say the duration.

     ...

     Please say the subject.

(24.14)   First, tell me the date.

     ...

     Next, I'll need the time it starts.

     ...

     Thanks. <pause> Now, how long is it supposed to last?

     ...

     Last of all, I just need a brief description...

Another important case of discourse coherence occurs when particular prompts may need to repeatedly be said to the user. In these cases, it is standard in dialogue systems to use **tapered prompts**, prompts that get incrementally shorter. The following example from Cohen et al. (2004) shows a series of (hand-designed) tapered prompts:

(24.15) System: Now, what's the first company to add to your watch list?
        Caller: Cisco
        System: What's the next company name? (Or, you can say, "Finished.")
        Caller: IBM
        System: Tell me the next company name, or say, "Finished."
        Caller: Intel
        System: Next one?
        Caller: America Online.
        System: Next?
        Caller: ...

Other constraints on generation are more specific to spoken dialogue and refer to facts about human memory and attentional processes. For example, when humans are prompted to give a particular response, it taxes their memory less if the suggested response is the last thing they hear. Thus, as Cohen et al. (2004) point out, the prompt "To hear the list again, say 'Repeat list'" is easier for users than "Say 'Repeat list' to hear the list again."

Similarly, presentation of long lists of query results (e.g., flights or movies) can tax users. Thus, most dialogue systems have content-planning rules to deal with this. In the Mercury system for travel planning (Seneff, 2002), for example, a rule specifies that if there are more than three flights to describe to the user, the system will just list the available airlines and describe explicitly only the earliest flight.

24.2.4   Dialogue Manager

The final component of a dialogue system is the dialogue manager, which controls the architecture and structure of the dialogue. The dialogue manager takes input from the ASR/NLU components, maintains some sort of state, interfaces with the task manager, and passes output to the NLG/TTS modules.

We saw a trivial dialogue manager in Chapter 2's ELIZA, whose architecture was a simple read-substitute-print loop. The system read in a sentence, applied a series of text transformations to the sentence, and then printed it. No state was kept; the transformation rules were only aware of the current input sentence. In addition to its ability to interact with a task manager, a modern dialogue manager is very different than ELIZA's manager both in the amount of state that the manager keeps about the conversation and in the ability of the manager to model structures of dialogue above the level of a single response.

Four kinds of dialogue management architectures are most common. The simplest and most commercially developed architectures, finite-state and frame-based, are discussed in this section. Later sections discuss the more powerful information-state dialogue managers, including a probabilistic version of information-state managers based on Markov decision processes, and finally the more classic plan-based architectures.

The simplest dialogue manager architecture is a finite-state manager. For example, imagine a trivial airline travel system whose job was to ask the user for a departure city, a destination city, a time, and one-way or round-trip. Figure 24.9 shows a sample dialogue manager for such a system. The states of the FSA correspond to questions that the dialogue manager asks the user, and the arcs correspond to actions to take depend-

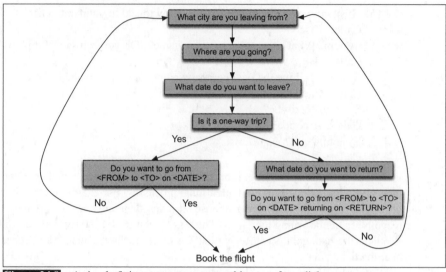

Figure 24.9   A simple finite-state automaton architecture for a dialogue manager.

ing on what the user responds. This system completely controls the conversation with the user. It asks the user a series of questions, ignoring (or misinterpreting) anything that is not a direct answer to the question and then going on to the next question.

System initiative
Single initiative
Initiative

Systems that control the conversation in this way are called **system-initiative** or **single-initiative** systems. We say that the speaker in control of the conversation has the **initiative**; in normal human-human dialogue, initiative shifts back and forth between the participants (Walker and Whittaker, 1990).[1] The limited single-initiative finite-state dialogue manager architecture has the advantage that the system always knows what question the user is answering. This means the system can prepare the speech recognition engine with a specific language model tuned to answers for this question. Knowing what the user is going to be talking about also makes the task of the natural language understanding engine easier. Most finite-state systems also allow

Universal

universal commands that can be said anywhere in the dialogue; every dialogue state recognizes the universal commands in addition to the answer to the question that the system just asked. Common universals include **help**, which gives the user a (possibly state-specific) help message, **start over** (or **main menu**), which returns the user to some specified main start state, and some sort of command to correct the system's understanding of the user's last statement (San-Segundo et al., 2001). System-initiative, finite-state dialogue managers with universals may be sufficient for simple tasks such as entering a credit card number, or a name and password, on the phone.

Pure system-initiative, finite-state dialogue manager architectures are probably too restricted, however, even for the relatively uncomplicated task of a spoken dialogue travel agent system. The problem is that pure system-initiative systems require that the

---

[1] Single-initiative systems can also be controlled by the user, in which case they are called **user-initiative** systems. Pure user-initiative systems are generally used for stateless database querying systems, where the user asks single questions of the system, which the system converts into SQL database queries and returns the results from some database.

user answer exactly the question that the system asked. But this can make a dialogue awkward and annoying. Users often need to be able to say something that is not exactly the answer to a single question from the system. For example, in a travel-planning situation, users often want to express their travel goals with complex sentences that may answer more than one question at a time, as in Communicator example 24.16 repeated from Fig. 24.1 or ATIS example 24.17.

(24.16) Hi I'd like to fly to Seattle Tuesday morning

(24.17) I want a flight from Milwaukee to Orlando one way leaving after five p.m. on Wednesday.

A finite-state dialogue system, as typically implemented, can't handle these kinds of utterances since it requires that the user answer each question as it is asked. Of course, it is theoretically possible to create a finite-state architecture that has a separate state for each possible subset of questions that the user's statement could be answering, but this would require a vast explosion in the number of states, making such an architecture difficult to conceptualize.

Therefore, most systems avoid the pure system-initiative, finite-state approach and use an architecture that allows **mixed initiative**, in which conversational initiative can shift between the system and user at various points in the dialogue.

One common mixed-initiative dialogue architecture relies on the structure of the frame itself to guide the dialogue. These **frame-based** or **form-based** dialogue managers asks the user questions to fill slots in the frame, but allow the user to guide the dialogue by giving information that fills other slots in the frame. Each slot may be associated with a question to ask the user, of the following type:

Slot	Question
ORIGIN CITY	"From what city are you leaving?"
DESTINATION CITY	"Where are you going?"
DEPARTURE TIME	"When would you like to leave?"
ARRIVAL TIME	"When do you want to arrive?"

A frame-based dialogue manager thus needs to ask questions of the user, filling any slot that the user specifies, until it has enough information to perform a database query and then return the result to the user. If the user happens to answer two or three questions at a time, the system has to fill in these slots and then remember not to ask the user the associated questions for the slots. Not every slot need have an associated question, since the dialogue designer may not want the user deluged with questions. Nonetheless, the system must be able to fill these slots if the user happens to specify them. This kind of form-filling dialogue manager thus does away with the strict constraints that the finite-state manager imposes on the order in which the user can specify information.

While some domains may be representable with a single frame, others, like the travel domain, seem to require the ability to deal with multiple frames. In order to handle possible user questions, we might need frames with general route information (for questions like *Which airlines fly from Boston to San Francisco?*), information about airfare practices (for questions like *Do I have to stay a specific number of days to get a decent airfare?*) or about car or hotel reservations. Since users may switch from frame

The margin notes:
Mixed initiative
Frame-based
Form-based

to frame, the system must be able to disambiguate which slot of which frame a given input is supposed to fill and then switch dialogue control to that frame.

Because of this need to dynamically switch control, frame-based systems are often implemented as **production rule** systems. Different types of inputs cause different productions to fire, each of which can flexibly fill in different frames. The production rules can then switch control according to factors such as the user's input and some simple dialogue history like the last question that the system asked. The Mercury flight reservation system (Seneff and Polifroni, 2000; Seneff, 2002) uses a large "dialogue control table" to store 200–350 rules, rules covering requests for help, rules to determine if the user is referring to a flight in a list ("I'll take that nine a.m. flight"), and rules to decide which flights to describe to the user first.

Now that we've seen the frame-based architecture, let's return to our discussion of conversational initiative. It's possible in the same agent to allow system-initiative, user-initiative, and mixed-initiative interactions. We said earlier that initiative refers to who has control of the conversation at any point. The phrase **mixed initiative** is generally used in two ways. It can mean that the system or the user could arbitrarily take or give up the initiative in various ways (Walker and Whittaker, 1990; Chu-Carroll and Brown, 1997). This kind of mixed initiative is difficult to achieve in current dialogue systems. In form-based dialogue systems, the term mixed initiative is used for a more limited kind of shift, operationalized according to a combination of prompt type (open versus directive) and the type of grammar used in the ASR. An **open prompt** is one in which the system allows users to respond roughly however they please, as in

Open prompt

> How may I help you?

Directive prompt

A **directive prompt** is one that explicitly instructs users how to respond:

> Say *yes* if you accept the call; otherwise, say *no*.

A **restrictive** grammar (Section 24.2.1) is a language model that strongly constrains the ASR system, only recognizing proper responses to a given prompt.

We can combine these as in Fig. 24.10 to define initiative as used in form-based dialogue systems, following Singh et al. (2002) and others.

| | Prompt Type | |
Grammar	Open	Directive
Restrictive	*Doesn't make sense*	System Initiative
Non-Restrictive	User Initiative	Mixed Initiative

Figure 24.10   Operational definition of initiative, following Singh et al. (2002).

Here, a system-initiative interaction uses a directive prompt and a restrictive grammar; the user is told how to respond, and the ASR system is constrained to recognize only the responses that are prompted for. In user initiative, the user is given an open prompt, and the grammar must recognize any kind of response, since the user could say anything. Finally, in a mixed-initiative interaction, the system gives the user a directive prompt with particular suggestions for response, but the non-restrictive grammar allows the user to respond outside the scope of the prompt.

Defining initiative as a property of the prompt and grammar type in this way allows systems to dynamically change their initiative type for different users and interactions.

Novice users, or users with high speech recognition error, might be better served by more system-initiative interaction. Expert users, or those who happen to speak more recognizably, might do well with mixed- or user-initiative interactions. We show in Section 24.6 how machine learning techniques can be used to choose initiative.

24.2.5   Dealing with Errors: Confirmation and Rejection

In a dialogue system, mishearings are a particularly important class of problems because speech recognition has such a high error rate. It is therefore important for dialogue systems to make sure that they have achieved the correct interpretation of the user's input. This is generally done by two methods: **confirming** understandings with the user and **rejecting** utterances that the system is likely to have misunderstood.

Explicit confirmation

Various strategies can be employed for confirmation with the user. A system using the **explicit confirmation** strategy asks the user a direct question to confirm the system's understanding. Here are two examples of explicit confirmations from travel-planning systems. The (boldface) confirmation questions are both yes-no questions, one using a single sentence, the other presenting a declarative sentence followed by a tag question (a short question phrase like "right?" or "isn't it?").

S:	Which city do you want to leave from?
U:	Baltimore.
S:	**Do you want to leave from Baltimore?**
U:	Yes.
U:	I'd like to fly from Denver Colorado to New York City on September twenty first in the morning on United Airlines
S:	**Let's see then. I have you going from Denver Colorado to New York on September twenty first. Is that correct?**
U:	Yes

Implicit confirmation

A system using the **implicit confirmation** strategy, rather than asking a direct question, uses the *demonstration* or *display* grounding strategies described above, confirming to the user by repeating back what the system understood the user to have said.

U:	I want to travel to Berlin
S:	**When do you want to travel to Berlin?**
U2:	Hi I'd like to fly to Seattle Tuesday Morning
A3:	**Traveling to Seattle on Tuesday, August eleventh in the morning.** Your full name?

Explicit and implicit confirmation have complementary strengths. Explicit confirmation makes it easier for users to correct the system's misrecognitions since a user can just answer "no" to the confirmation question. But explicit confirmation is awkward and increases the length of the conversation (Danieli and Gerbino, 1995; Walker et al., 1998). The explicit confirmation dialogue fragments above sound non-natural and definitely non-human; implicit confirmation is much more conversationally natural.

Rejection

Confirmation is just one kind of conversational action by which a system can express lack of understanding. Another option is **rejection**. An ASR system rejects an ut-

Progressive prompting

terance by giving the user a prompt like *I'm sorry, I didn't understand that.* Sometimes utterances are rejected multiple times. This might mean that the user is using language that the system is unable to follow. Thus, when an utterance is rejected, systems often follow a strategy of **progressive prompting** or **escalating detail** (Yankelovich et al., 1995; Weinschenk and Barker, 2000), as in this example from Cohen et al. (2004):

> System: When would you like to leave?
> Caller: Well, um, I need to be in New York in time for the first World Series game.
> System: <reject>. Sorry, I didn't get that. Please say the month and day you'd like to leave.
> Caller: I wanna go on October fifteenth.

In this example, instead of just repeating "When would you like to leave?", the rejection prompt gives the caller more guidance about how to formulate an utterance the system will understand. These *you-can-say* help messages are important in helping improve systems' understanding performance (Bohus and Rudnicky, 2005). If the caller's utterance gets rejected yet again, the prompt can reflect this ("I *still* didn't get that"), and give the caller even more guidance.

Rapid reprompting

An alternative strategy for error handling is **rapid reprompting**, in which the system rejects an utterance just by saying "I'm sorry?" or "What was that?" Only if the caller's utterance is rejected a second time does the system start applying progressive prompting. Cohen et al. (2004) summarize experiments showing that users greatly prefer rapid reprompting as a first-level error prompt.

24.3   VoiceXML

VoiceXML

vxml

VoiceXML is the Voice Extensible Markup Language, an XML-based dialogue design language released by the W3C, and the most commonly used of the various speech markup languages (such as SALT). The goal of VoiceXML (or **vxml**) is to create simple audio dialogues of the type we have been describing, making use of ASR and TTS and dealing with very simple mixed-initiative in a frame-based architecture. While VoiceXML is more common in the commercial rather than academic setting, it is a good way to get a hands-on grasp of dialogue system design issues.

A VoiceXML document contains a set of dialogues, each of which can be a *form* or a *menu*. We will limit ourselves to introducing forms; see `http://www.voicexml.org/` for more information on VoiceXML in general. The VoiceXML document in Fig. 24.11 defines a form with a single field named "transporttype". The field has an attached prompt, *Please choose airline, hotel, or rental car*, which can be passed to the TTS system. It also has a grammar (language model) that is passed to the speech recognition engine to specify which words the recognizer is allowed to recognize. In the example in Fig. 24.11, the grammar consists of a disjunction of the three words *airline*, *hotel*, and *rental car*.

A `<form>` generally consists of a sequence of `<field>`s, together with a few other commands. Each field has a name (`transporttype` is the name of the field

```
<form>
  <field name="transporttype">
    <prompt>
       Please choose airline, hotel, or rental car.
    </prompt>
    <grammar type="application/x=nuance-gsl">
      [airline hotel "rental car"]
    </grammar>
  </field>
  <block>
    <prompt>
     You have chosen <value expr="transporttype">.
    </prompt>
  </block>
</form>
```

Figure 24.11   A minimal VoiceXML script for a form with a single field. User is prompted, and the response is then repeated back.

in Fig. 24.11), which is also the name of the variable where the user's response will be stored. The prompt associated with the field is specified with the `<prompt>` command. The grammar associated with the field is specified with the `<grammar>` command. VoiceXML supports various ways of specifying a grammar, including XML Speech Grammar, ABNF, and commercial standards, like Nuance GSL. We use the Nuance GSL format in the following examples.

The VoiceXML interpreter walks through a form in document order, repeatedly selecting each item in the form. If there are multiple fields, the interpreter visits each one in order. The interpretation order can be changed in various ways, as we show later. The example in Fig. 24.12 shows a form with three fields, for specifying the origin, destination, and flight date of an airline flight.

The prologue of the example shows two global defaults for error handling. If the user doesn't answer after a prompt (i.e., silence exceeds a timeout threshold), the VoiceXML interpreter will play the `<noinput>` prompt. If the user says something that doesn't match the grammar for that field, the VoiceXML interpreter will play the `<nomatch>` prompt. After any failure of this type, it is normal to repeat the question that failed to get a response. Since these routines can be called from any field the exact prompt will be different every time. VoiceXML thus provides a `<reprompt\>` command, which repeats the prompt for whatever field caused the error.

The three fields of this form show another feature of VoiceXML, the `<filled>` tag. The `<filled>` tag for a field is executed by the interpreter as soon as the field has been filled by the user. Here, this feature is used to confirm the user's input.

The last field, `departdate`, shows another feature of VoiceXML, the `type` attribute. VoiceXML 2.0 specifies seven built-in grammar types: `boolean`, `currency`, `date`, `digits`, `number`, `phone`, and `time`. Since the type of this field is `date`, a data-specific language model (grammar) will automatically be passed to the speech recognizer, so we don't need to specify the grammar here explicitly.

Figure 24.13 gives a final example, which shows mixed initiative. In a mixed-initiative dialogue, users can choose not to answer the question that was asked by the system. For example, they might answer a different question or use a long sentence to fill in multiple slots at once. This means that the VoiceXML interpreter can no longer just evaluate each field of the form in order; it needs to skip fields whose values are

```
<noinput>
I'm sorry, I didn't hear you.  <reprompt/>
</noinput>

<nomatch>
I'm sorry, I didn't understand that.  <reprompt/>
</nomatch>

<form>
  <block>     Welcome to the air travel consultant.  </block>
  <field name="origin">
     <prompt>    Which city do you want to leave from?  </prompt>
     <grammar type="application/x=nuance-gsl">
       [(san francisco) denver (new york) barcelona]
     </grammar>
     <filled>
        <prompt>  OK, from <value expr="origin">  </prompt>
     </filled>
  </field>
  <field name="destination">
     <prompt>  And which city do you want to go to?   </prompt>
     <grammar type="application/x=nuance-gsl">
       [(san francisco) denver (new york) barcelona]
     </grammar>
     <filled>
        <prompt>   OK, to <value expr="destination">   </prompt>
     </filled>
  </field>
  <field name="departdate" type="date">
     <prompt>  And what date do you want to leave?  </prompt>
     <filled>
        <prompt>   OK, on <value expr="departdate">   </prompt>
     </filled>
  </field>
  <block>
     <prompt> OK, I have you are departing from  <value expr="origin">
            to <value expr="destination"> on <value expr="departdate">
     </prompt>
     send the info to book a flight...
  </block>
</form>
```

Figure 24.12   A VoiceXML script for a form with three fields, which confirms each field and handles the noinput and nomatch situations.

set. This is done by a *guard condition*, a test that keeps a field from being visited. The default guard condition for a field tests to see if the field's form item variable has a value, and if it does have a value the field is not interpreted.

Figure 24.13 also shows a much more complex use of a grammar. This grammar is a CFG grammar with two rewrite rules, named Flight and City. The Nuance GSL grammar formalism uses parentheses () to mean concatenation and square brackets [] to mean disjunction. Thus, a rule like (24.18) means that Wantsentence can be expanded as i want to fly or i want to go, and Airports can be expanded as san francisco or denver.

(24.18) Wantsentence (i want to [fly go])
         Airports [(san francisco) denver]

Grammar rules can refer to other grammar rules recursively, and so in the grammar in Fig. 24.13 we see the grammar for Flight referring to the rule for City.

VoiceXML grammars take the form of CFG grammars with optional semantic attachments. The semantic attachments are generally either a text string (such as "denver, colorado") or a slot and a filler. We can see an example of the for-

```
<noinput>    I'm sorry, I didn't hear you.  <reprompt/>  </noinput>

<nomatch> I'm sorry, I didn't understand that.  <reprompt/> </nomatch>

<form>
   <grammar type="application/x=nuance-gsl">
    <![ CDATA[
    Flight (  ?[
              (i [wanna (want to)] [fly go])
              (i'd like to [fly go])
              ([(i wanna)(i'd like a)] flight)
           ]
           [
            ( [from leaving departing] City:x) {<origin $x>}
            ( [(?going to)(arriving in)] City:x) {<destination $x>}
            ( [from leaving departing] City:x
              [(?going to)(arriving in)] City:y) {<origin $x> <destination $y>}
           ]
           ?please
       )
       City [ [(san francisco) (s f o)] {return( "san francisco, california")}
             [(denver) (d e n)] {return( "denver, colorado")}
             [(seattle) (s t x)] {return( "seattle, washington")}
       ]
       ]]> </grammar>

   <initial name="init">
      <prompt> Welcome to the consultant. What are your travel plans?  </prompt>
   </initial>

   <field name="origin">
      <prompt> Which city do you want to leave from?  </prompt>
      <filled>
         <prompt> OK, from <value expr="origin"> </prompt>
      </filled>
   </field>
   <field name="destination">
      <prompt> And which city do you want to go to?  </prompt>
      <filled>
         <prompt> OK, to <value expr="destination"> </prompt>
      </filled>
   </field>
   <block>
      <prompt> OK, I have you are departing from  <value expr="origin">
               to  <value expr="destination">.  </prompt>
      send the info to book a flight...
   </block>
</form>
```

Figure 24.13   A mixed-initiative VoiceXML dialogue. The grammar allows sentences that specify the origin or destination cities or both. The user can respond to the initial prompt by specifying origin city, destination city, or both.

mer in the semantic attachments for the `City` rule (the `return` statements at the end of each line), which pass up the city and state name. The semantic attachments for the `Flight` rule show the latter case, in which the slot (`<origin>` or `<destination>` or both) is filled with the value passed up in the variable x from the `City` rule.

Because Fig. 24.13 is a mixed-initiative grammar, the grammar has to be applicable to any of the fields. This is done by making the expansion for `Flight` a disjunction; note that it allows the user to specify only the origin city, the destination city, or both.

24.4   Dialogue System Design and Evaluation

The user plays a more important role in dialogue systems than in most other areas of speech and language processing. In this section we focus on the role of the user in both designing and evaluating dialogue systems.

24.4.1   Designing Dialogue Systems

VUI

How does a dialogue system developer choose dialogue strategies, prompts, error messages, and so on? This process is often called **VUI (Voice User Interface)** design. The **user-centered design** principles of Gould and Lewis (1985) are as follows:

1. Study the user and task: Understand the potential users and the nature of the task by interviews with users, investigation of similar systems, and study of related human-human dialogues.

Wizard-of-Oz

2. Build simulations and prototypes: In **Wizard-of-Oz systems** (WOZ) or PNAMBIC (Pay No Attention to the Man BehInd the Curtain) systems, the users interact with what they think is a software system but is in fact a human operator ("wizard") behind some disguising interface software (e.g., Gould et al., 1983; Good et al., 1984; Fraser and Gilbert, 1991).[2] A WOZ system can be used to test out an architecture before implementation; only the interface software and databases need to be in place. The wizard's linguistic output can be disguised by a text-to-speech system or by text-only interactions. It is difficult for the wizard to exactly simulate the errors, limitations, or time constraints of a real system; results of WOZ studies are thus somewhat idealized, but still can provide a useful first idea of the domain issues.

3. Iteratively test the design on users: An iterative design cycle with embedded user testing is essential in system design (Nielsen, 1992; Cole et al., 1994, 1997; Yankelovich et al., 1995; Landauer, 1995). For example, Stifelman et al. (1993) built a system that originally required the user to press a key to interrupt the system. They

Barge-in

found in user testing that users instead tried to interrupt the system (**barge-in**), suggesting a redesign of the system to recognize overlapped speech. The iterative method is also important for designing prompts that cause the user to respond in normative ways, such as the use in particular situations of constrained forms (Oviatt et al., 1993) or **directive prompts** rather than open prompts (Kamm, 1994). Simulations can also be used at this stage; user simulations that interact with a dialogue system can help test the interface for brittleness or errors (Chung, 2004).

See Cohen et al. (2004) and Harris (2005) for more on conversational interface design.

24.4.2   Evaluating Dialogue Systems

We said above that user testing and evaluation is crucial in dialogue system design. Computing a *user satisfaction rating* can be done by having users interact with a dialogue system to perform a task and then having them complete a questionnaire

---

[2] The name comes from the children's book *The Wizard of Oz* (Baum, 1900), in which the Wizard turned out to be just a simulation controlled by a man behind a curtain.

TTS Performance	Was the system easy to understand ?
ASR Performance	Did the system understand what you said?
Task Ease	Was it easy to find the message/flight/train you wanted?
Interaction Pace	Was the pace of interaction with the system appropriate?
User Expertise	Did you know what you could say at each point?
System Response	How often was the system sluggish and slow to reply to you?
Expected Behavior	Did the system work the way you expected it to?
Future Use	Do you think you'd use the system in the future?

Figure 24.14   User satisfaction survey, adapted from Walker et al. (2001).

(Shriberg et al., 1992; Polifroni et al., 1992; Stifelman et al., 1993; Yankelovich et al., 1995; Möller, 2002). For example, Fig. 24.14 shows multiple-choice questions of the sort used by Walker et al. (2001); responses are mapped into the range of 1 to 5, and then averaged over all questions to get a total user satisfaction rating.

It is often economically infeasible to run complete user satisfaction studies after every change in a system. For this reason, it is often useful to have performance evaluation heuristics that correlate well with human satisfaction. A number of such factors and heuristics have been studied. One method that has been used to classify these factors is based on the idea that an optimal dialogue system is one that allows users to accomplish their goals (maximizing task success) with the least problems (minimizing costs). We can then study metrics that correlate with these two criteria.

Task completion success: Task success can be measured by evaluating the correctness of the total solution. For a frame-based architecture, this might be the percentage of slots that were filled with the correct values or the percentage of subtasks that were completed (Polifroni et al., 1992). Since different dialogue systems may be applied to different tasks, it is hard to compare them on this metric, so Walker et al. (1997) suggested using the Kappa coefficient, κ, to compute a completion score that is normalized for chance agreement and that better enables cross-system comparison.

Efficiency cost: Efficiency costs are measures of the system's efficiency at helping users. This can be measured by the total elapsed time for the dialogue in seconds, the number of total turns or of system turns, or the total number of queries (Polifroni et al., 1992). Other metrics include the number of system non-responses and the "turn correction ratio": the number of system or user turns that were used solely to correct errors divided by the total number of turns (Danieli and Gerbino, 1995; Hirschman and Pao, 1993).

Quality cost: Quality cost measures other aspects of the interactions that affect users' perception of the system. One such measure is the number of times the ASR system failed to return any sentence, or the number of ASR rejection prompts. Similar metrics include the number of times the user had to barge-in (interrupt the system), or the number of time-out prompts played when the user didn't respond quickly enough. Other quality metrics focus on how well the system understood and responded to the user. This can include the inappropriateness (verbose or ambiguous) of the system's questions, answers, and error messages (Zue et al., 1989) or the correctness of each question, answer, or error message (Zue et al., 1989; Polifroni et al., 1992). An important quality cost is **concept accuracy** or **concept error rate**, which measures the

Concept accuracy

853

percentage of semantic concepts that the NLU component returns correctly. Systems with frame-based architectures can measure this by counting the percentage of slots that are filled with the correct meaning. For example, if the sentence "I want to arrive in Austin at 5:00" is misrecognized to have the semantics "DEST-CITY: Boston, Time: 5:00" the concept accuracy would be 50% (one of two slots is wrong).

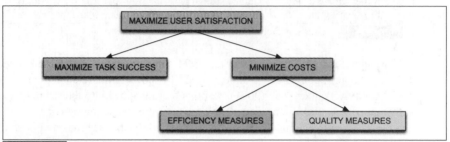

Figure 24.15   PARADISE's structure of objectives for spoken dialogue performance. After Walker et al. (1997).

How should these success and cost metrics be combined and weighted? One approach is the PARADISE algorithm (PARAdigm for DIalogue System Evaluation), which applies multiple regression to this problem. The algorithm first assigns each dialogue a user satisfaction rating from questionnaires like the one in Fig. 24.14. A set of cost and success factors like those above is then treated as a set of independent factors; multiple regression is used to train a weight for each factor, measuring its importance in accounting for user satisfaction. Figure 24.15 shows the particular model of performance that the PARADISE experiments have assumed. Each box is related to a set of factors that we summarized on the previous page. The resulting metric can be used to compare quite different dialogue strategies; evaluations using methods like PARADISE have suggested that task completion and concept accuracy may be the most important predictors of user satisfaction; see Walker et al. (1997, 2001, 2002).

A wide variety of other evaluation metrics and taxonomies have been proposed for describing the quality of spoken dialogue systems (Fraser, 1992; Möller, 2002, 2004; Delgado and Araki, 2005, inter alia).

24.5   Information-State and Dialogue Acts

The basic frame-based dialogue systems we have introduced so far are only capable of limited domain-specific conversations. This is because the semantic interpretation and generation processes in frame-based dialogue systems are based only on what is needed to fill slots. To be usable for more than just form-filling applications, a conversational agent needs to be able to do things like decide when the user has asked a question, made a proposal, or rejected a suggestion, and needs to be able to ground a user's utterance, ask clarification questions, and suggest plans. This suggests that a conversational agent needs sophisticated models of interpretation and generation in terms of speech acts and grounding and a more sophisticated representation of the dialogue context than just a list of slots.

Information-state

In this section we sketch a more advanced architecture for dialogue management that allows for these more sophisticated components. This model is generally called the **information-state** architecture (Traum and Larsson, 2003, 2000), although we use the term loosely to include architectures such as those in Allen et al. (2001). A probabilistic architecture that can be seen as an extension of the information-state approach, the **Markov decision process** model, is described in the next section. The term **information-state architecture** is really a cover term for a number of quite different efforts toward more sophisticated agents; we'll assume here a structure consisting of five components:

- The information state (the "discourse context" or "mental model")
- A dialogue act interpreter (or "interpretation engine")
- A dialogue act generator (or "generation engine")
- A set of update rules that update the information state as dialogue acts are interpreted and includes rules to generate dialogue acts
- A control structure to select which update rules to apply

The term **information state** is intentionally abstract and might include things like the discourse context and the common ground of the two speakers, the beliefs or intentions of the speakers, user models, and so on. Crucially, information state is intended to be a more complex notion than the static states in a finite-state dialogue manager; the current state includes the values of many variables, the discourse context, and other elements that are not easily modeled by a state number in a finite network.

Dialogue acts are an extension of speech acts that integrate ideas from grounding theory and will be defined more fully in the next subsection. The interpretation engine takes speech as input and figures out sentential semantics and an appropriate dialogue act. The dialogue act generator takes dialogue acts and sentential semantics as input and produces text/speech as output.

Finally, the update rules modify the information state with information from the dialogue acts. These update rules are a generalization of the production rules used in frame-based dialogue systems described above (e.g., Seneff and Polifroni, 2000). A subset of update rules, called **selection rules**, are used to generate dialogue acts. For example, an update rule might say that when the interpretation engine recognizes an assertion, it must update the information state with the assertion's information, and with a new obligation to perform a grounding act. When a question is recognized, an update rule might specify the need to answer the question. We can refer to the combination of the update rules and control structure as the Behavioral Agent (Allen et al., 2001), as suggested in Fig. 24.16.

While the intuition of the information-state model is quite simple, the details can be quite complex. The information state might involve rich discourse models such as Discourse Representation Theory or sophisticated models of the user's belief, desire, and intention (which we return to in Section 24.7). Instead of describing a particular implementation here, we focus in the next few sections on the dialogue act interpretation and generation engines and a probabilistic information-state architecture via Markov decision processes.

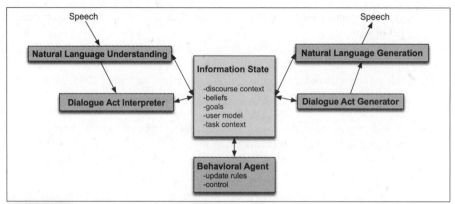

Figure 24.16 A version of the information-state approach to dialogue architecture.

24.5.1   Using Dialogue Acts

Dialogue act
Conversational
move

As we implied above, the speech acts as originally defined by Austin don't model key features of conversation such as grounding, contributions, adjacency pairs, and so on. To capture these conversational phenomena, we use an extension of speech acts called **dialogue acts** (Bunt, 1994) (or **dialogue moves** or **conversational moves** (Power, 1979; Carletta et al., 1997b)). A dialogue act extends speech acts with internal structure related specifically to these other conversational functions (Allen and Core, 1997; Bunt, 2000).

A wide variety of dialogue act tagsets have been proposed. Figure 24.17 shows a domain-specific tagset for the Verbmobil two-party scheduling domain, in which speakers were asked to plan a meeting at some future date. Notice that it has domain-specific tags, such as SUGGEST, used for the proposal of a particular date to meet, and ACCEPT and REJECT, used for acceptance or rejection of a proposal for a date. Thus this tagset has elements both from the presentation and acceptance phases of the Clark contributions discussed on page 816.

There are a number of more general and domain-independent dialogue act tagsets. In the DAMSL (Dialogue Act Markup in Several Layers) architecture inspired by the work of Clark and Schaefer (1989), Allwood et al. (1992), and (Allwood, 1995), each utterance is tagged for two types of functions, **forward-looking functions** like speech act functions, and **backward-looking** functions, like grounding and answering, which "look back" to the interlocutor's previous utterance (Allen and Core, 1997; Walker et al., 1996; Carletta et al., 1997a; Core et al., 1999).

Conversation act

Traum and Hinkelman (1992) proposed that the core speech acts and grounding acts that constitute dialogue acts could fit into an even richer hierarchy of **conversation acts**. Figure 24.18 shows the four levels of act types they propose, with the two middle levels corresponding to DAMSL dialogue acts (grounding and core speech acts). The two new levels include turn-taking acts and a type of coherence relations called *argumentation* relations.

The acts form a hierarchy, in that performance of an act at a higher level (e.g., a core speech act) entails performance of a lower-level act (taking a turn). We show the use

Tag	Example
THANK	*Thanks*
GREET	*Hello Dan*
INTRODUCE	*It's me again*
BYE	*Allright bye*
REQUEST-COMMENT	*How does that look?*
SUGGEST	*from thirteenth through seventeenth June*
REJECT	*No Friday I'm booked all day*
ACCEPT	*Saturday sounds fine*
REQUEST-SUGGEST	*What is a good day of the week for you?*
INIT	*I wanted to make an appointment with you*
GIVE_REASON	*Because I have meetings all afternoon*
FEEDBACK	*Okay*
DELIBERATE	*Let me check my calendar here*
CONFIRM	*Okay, that would be wonderful*
CLARIFY	*Okay, do you mean Tuesday the 23rd?*
DIGRESS	*[we could meet for lunch] and eat lots of ice cream*
MOTIVATE	*We should go to visit our subsidiary in Munich*
GARBAGE	*Oops, I-*

Figure 24.17   The 18 high-level dialogue acts used in Verbmobil-1, abstracted over a total of 43 more specific dialogue acts. Examples are from Jekat et al. (1995).

Act Type	Sample Acts
turn-taking	take-turn, keep-turn, release-turn, assign-turn
grounding	acknowledge, repair, continue
core speech acts	inform, wh-question, accept, request, offer
argumentation	elaborate, summarize, question-answer, clarify

Figure 24.18   Conversation act types, from Traum and Hinkelman (1992).

of conversational acts in generation later on in this section and return to the question of coherence and dialogue structure in Section 24.7.

24.5.2   Interpreting Dialogue Acts

How can we interpret a dialogue act, deciding whether a given input is a QUESTION, a STATEMENT, a SUGGEST (directive), or an ACKNOWLEDGMENT? Perhaps we can just rely on surface syntax? We saw in Chapter 12 that yes-no questions in English have **aux-inversion** (the auxiliary verb precedes the subject), statements have declarative syntax (no aux-inversion), and commands have no syntactic subject:

(24.19)   YES-NO QUESTION   Will breakfast be served on USAir 1557?
          STATEMENT   I don't care about lunch.
          COMMAND   Show me flights from Milwaukee to Orlando.

Alas, as is clear from Abbott and Costello's famous *Who's on First* routine at the beginning of the chapter, the mapping from surface form to illocutionary act is complex. For example, the following ATIS utterance looks like a YES-NO QUESTION meaning something like *Are you capable of giving me a list of...?*:

(24.20) Can you give me a list of the flights from Atlanta to Boston?

In fact, however, this person was not interested in whether the system was *capable* of giving a list; this utterance was a polite form of a REQUEST, meaning something more like *Please give me a list of....* Thus, what looks on the surface like a QUESTION can really be a REQUEST.

Similarly, what looks on the surface like a STATEMENT can really be a QUESTION. The very common CHECK question (Carletta et al., 1997b; Labov and Fanshel, 1977), asks an interlocutor to confirm something that she has privileged knowledge about. CHECKS have declarative surface form:

A	OPEN-OPTION	I was wanting to make some arrangements for a trip that I'm going to be taking uh to LA uh beginning of the week after next.
B	HOLD	OK uh let me pull up your profile and I'll be right with you here. [pause]
B	CHECK	**And you said you wanted to travel next week?**
A	ACCEPT	Uh yes.

Indirect speech act

Utterances that use a surface statement to ask a question or a surface question to issue a request are called **indirect speech acts**.

To resolve these dialogue act ambiguities, we can model dialogue act interpretation as a supervised classification task, with dialogue act labels as hidden classes to be detected. We train classifiers on a corpus in which each utterance is hand-labeled for dialogue acts. The features used for dialogue act interpretation derive from the conversational context and from the act's **microgrammar** (Goodwin, 1996) (its characteristic lexical, grammatical, prosodic, and conversational properties):

Microgrammar

1. **Words and grammar:** *Please* or *would you* is a good cue for a REQUEST, *are you* for YES-NO QUESTIONS, detected by **dialogue-specific N-gram** grammars.

2. **Prosody:** Rising pitch is a good cue for a YES-NO QUESTION, while declarative utterances (like STATEMENTS) have **final lowering**: a drop in F0 at the end of the utterance. Loudness or stress can help distinguish the *yeah* that is an AGREEMENT from the *yeah* that is a BACKCHANNEL. We can extract acoustic correlates of prosodic features like F0, duration, and energy.

Final lowering

3. **Conversational structure:** A *yeah* following a proposal is probably an AGREEMENT; a *yeah* after an INFORM is likely a BACKCHANNEL. Drawing on the idea of adjacency pairs (Schegloff, 1968; Sacks et al., 1974), we can model conversational structure as a bigram of dialogue acts.

Formally, our goal is to find the dialogue act d^* that has the highest posterior probability $P(d|o)$ given the observation of a sentence:

$$
\begin{aligned}
d^* &= \operatorname*{argmax}_d P(d|o) \\
&= \operatorname*{argmax}_d \frac{P(d)P(o|d)}{P(o)} \\
&= \operatorname*{argmax}_d P(d)P(o|d) \quad\quad (24.21)
\end{aligned}
$$

Making some simplifying assumptions (that the prosody of the sentence f and the word sequence W are independent and that the prior of a dialogue act can be modeled by the conditional given the previous dialogue act), we can estimate the observation likelihood for a dialogue act d as in (24.22):

$$P(o\ d) \ = \ P(f\ d)P(W\ d) \tag{24.22}$$

$$d^* \ = \ \underset{d}{\mathrm{argmax}}\, P(d\ d_{t-1})P(f\ d)P(W\ d) \tag{24.23}$$

where

$$P(W\ d) \ = \ \prod_{i=2}^{N} P(w_i\ w_{i-1}...w_{i-N+1}, d) \tag{24.24}$$

Training the prosodic predictor to compute $P(f\ d)$ has often been done with a decision tree. Shriberg et al. (1998), for example, built a CART tree to distinguish the four dialogue acts STATEMENT (S), YES-NO QUESTION (QY), DECLARATIVE-QUESTION like CHECK (QD), and WH-QUESTION (QW) based on acoustic features such as the slope of F0 at the end of the utterance, the average energy at different places in the utterance, and various normalized duration measures. Figure 24.19 shows the decision tree that gives the posterior probability $P(d\ f)$ of a dialogue act d type given a set of acoustic features f. Note that the difference between S and QY toward the right of the tree is based on the feature `norm_f0_diff` (normalized difference between mean F0 of end and penultimate regions), and the difference between QW and QD at the bottom left is based on `utt_grad`, which measures F0 slope across the whole utterance.

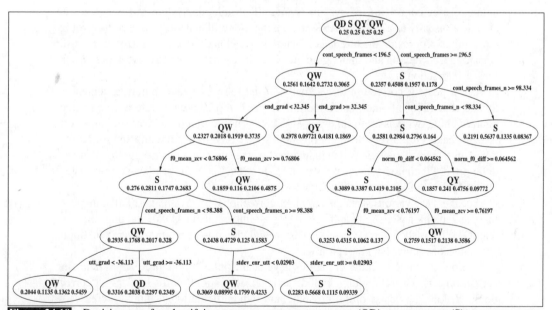

Figure 24.19   Decision tree for classifying DECLARATIVE QUESTIONS (QD), STATEMENT (S), YES-NO QUESTIONS (QY), and WH-QUESTIONS (QW), after Shriberg et al. (1998). Each node in the tree shows four probabilities, one for each of the four dialogue acts in the order QD, S, QY, QW; the most likely of the four is shown as the label for the node. Note that questions are shorter than statements (cont_speech_frames), that QYs rise at the end (end_grad), and that QDs rise throughout the utterance (utt_grad).

Since decision trees produce a posterior probability $P(d f)$, and equation (24.23) requires a likelihood $P(f d)$, we need to massage the output of the decision tree by Bayesian inversion (dividing by the prior $P(d_i)$ to turn it into a likelihood); we saw this same process with the use of SVMs and MLPs instead of Gaussian classifiers in speech recognition in Section 10.4.2. After all our simplifying assumptions, the resulting equation for choosing a dialogue act tag would be

$$
\begin{aligned}
d^* &= \underset{d}{\operatorname{argmax}} P(d)P(f d)P(W d) \\
&= \underset{d}{\operatorname{argmax}} P(d d_{t-1}) \frac{P(d f)}{P(d)} \prod_{i=2}^{N} P(w_i w_{i-1}...w_{i-N+1},d)
\end{aligned}
\tag{24.25}
$$

24.5.3   Detecting Correction Acts

In addition to general-purpose dialogue act interpretation, we may want to build special-purpose detectors for particular acts. Let's consider one such detector, for the recognition of user **correction** of system errors. If a dialogue system misrecognizes an utterance (usually as a result of ASR errors), the user will generally correct the error by repeating or rephrasing the utterance. Dialogue systems need to recognize that the user is making a correction and then figure out what the user is trying to correct, perhaps by further interaction.

Correction

Unfortunately, corrections are actually *harder* to recognize than normal sentences. Swerts et al. (2000) found that corrections in the TOOT dialogue system were misrecognized about twice as often (in terms of WER) as non-corrections. One reason for this is that speakers use a very different prosodic style called **hyperarticulation** for corrections. In hyperarticulated speech, some part of the utterance has exaggerated energy, duration, or F0 contours, such as *I said BAL-TI-MORE, not Boston* (Wade et al., 1992; Oviatt et al., 1998; Levow, 1998; Hirschberg et al., 2001).

Hyperarticulation

Speakers use various strategies to make corrections; Swerts et al. (2000) categorize these as repetition (REP), paraphrase (PAR), adding content (ADD), and omitting content (OMIT), as shown in Fig. 24.20. They found that most corrections were repetitions and omissions rather than paraphrases.

Various machine learning classifiers have been applied to the problem of detecting correction acts. Useful features include lexical information (words like "no", "correction", "I don't", swear words), prosodic and hyperarticulation features (increases in F0 range, pause duration, and word duration, generally normalized by the values for previous sentences), features indicating utterance length, ASR features (confidence, language model probability), and various dialogue features (Levow, 1998; Hirschberg et al., 2001; Bulyko et al., 2005).

In addition to correction detection, a conversational agent also needs appropriate control or update rules in the dialogue manager (Bulyko et al., 2005).

	Turn	Corr Type
S	On which day of the week do you want to leave?	
S	Sorry, I didn't hear anything from you. Please tell me your departure date	
U	*Um tomorrow*	NA
S	You can say the departure date. For example, you can say "today" or "tomorrow". Or you can say "Monday", "Tuesday", "Wednesday"...	
U	*Tomorrow*	REP
S	You can say the departure date. For example, you can say "today" or "tomorrow". Or you can say "Monday", "Tuesday", "Wednesday"...	
U	*Saturday*	PAR
S	Do you want to leave on Saturday?	
U	Yes	
S	What time do you want to leave?	
U	Eight o'clock A M	
S	Do you want to leave around ten oclock p-m	
U	*Eight o'clock*	OMIT
S	Do you want to leave around ten oclock p-m	
U	*No*	OMIT
S	What time do you want to leave?	
U	*Eight o'clock A M*	ADD

Figure 24.20   Dialogue fragment from the TOOT system labeled for correction type, from Swerts et al. (2000).

Cue	Turn-taking acts signaled
um	KEEP-TURN, TAKE-TURN, RELEASE-TURN
<lipsmack>, <click>, so, uh	KEEP-TURN, TAKE-TURN
you know, isn't that so	ASSIGN-TURN

Figure 24.21   Language used to perform turn-taking acts, from Stent (2002).

24.5.4   Generating Dialogue Acts: Confirmation and Rejection

Deciding which dialogue acts to generate has received much less attention than dialogue act interpretation. Stent (2002) is one recent model of dialogue act generation in the TRIPS system (Allen et al., 2001), based on Conversation Acts (page 841) and the BDI model described in Section 24.7. Stent uses a set of update rules for content planning. One such rule says that if a user has just released the turn, the system can perform a TAKE-TURN act. Another rule says that if the system has a problem-solving need to summarize some information for the user, then it should use the ASSERT conversation act with that information as the semantic content. The content is then mapped into words by the standard techniques of natural language generation systems (see, e.g., Reiter and Dale (2000)). After an utterance is generated, the information state (discourse context) is updated with its words, syntactic structure, semantic form, and semantic and conversation act structure. We sketch in Section 24.7 some of the issues in modeling and planning that make generation a tough, ongoing research effort.

Stent showed that a crucial issue in dialogue generation that doesn't occur in monologue text generation is turn-taking acts. Figure 24.21 shows some examples of the turn-taking function of various linguistic forms, from her labeling of conversation acts in the Monroe corpus.

A focus of much work on dialogue act generation is the task of generating the **confirmation** and **rejection** acts discussed in Section 24.2.5. Because this task is often solved by probabilistic methods, we'll begin this discussion here but continue it in the following section.

For example, while early dialogue systems tended to fix the choice of **explicit** versus **implicit** confirmation, recent systems treat confirmation as a dialogue act generation task, in which the confirmation strategy is adaptive, changing from sentence to sentence.

Various factors can be included in the information state and then used as features to a classifier in making this decision. For example, the **confidence** that the ASR system assigns to an utterance can be used by explicitly confirming low-confidence sentences (Bouwman et al., 1999; San-Segundo et al., 2001; Litman et al., 1999; Litman and Pan, 2002). Recall from page 340 that confidence is a metric that the speech recognizer can assign to its transcription of a sentence to indicate how confident it is in that transcription. Confidence is often computed from the acoustic log-likelihood of the utterance (greater probability means higher confidence), but prosodic features can also be used in confidence prediction. For example, utterances with large F0 excursions or longer durations, or those preceded by longer pauses, are likely to be misrecognized (Litman et al., 2000).

Another common feature in confirmation is the **cost** of making an error. For example, explicit confirmation is common before a flight is actually booked or money in an account is moved (Kamm, 1994; Cohen et al., 2004).

A system can also choose to **reject** an utterance when the ASR confidence is so low or the best interpretation is so semantically ill formed that the system can be relatively sure that the user's input was not recognized at all. Systems thus might have a three-tiered level of confidence; below a certain confidence threshold, an utterance is rejected. Above the threshold, it is explicitly confirmed. If the confidence is even higher, the utterance is implicitly confirmed.

Instead of rejecting or confirming entire utterances, it would be nice to be able to clarify only the parts of the utterance that the system didn't understand. If a system can assign confidence at a more fine-grained level than the utterance, it can clarify such *Clarification* individual elements with **clarification subdialogues**.

Much of the recent work on generating dialogue acts has been within the Markov decision process framework, which we therefore turn to next.

24.6   Markov Decision Process Architecture

One of the fundamental insights of the information-state approach to dialogue architecture is that the choice of conversational actions is dynamically dependent on the current information state. The previous section discussed how dialogue systems could change confirmation and rejection strategies according to context. For example, if the ASR or NLU confidence is low, we might choose to do explicit confirmation. If confidence is high, we might chose implicit confirmation or even decide not to confirm at all. Using a dynamic strategy lets us choose the action that maximizes dialogue success while

*Markov decision
process*

minimizing costs. This idea of changing the actions of a dialogue system based on optimizing some kinds of rewards or costs is the fundamental intuition behind modeling dialogue as a **Markov decision process**. This model extends the information-state model by adding a probabilistic way of deciding on the proper actions given the current state.

MDP

A Markov decision process or **MDP** is characterized by a set of **states** S an agent can be in, a set of **actions** A the agent can take, and a **reward** $r(a,s)$ that the agent receives for taking an action in a state. Given these factors, we can compute a **policy** π that specifies which action a the agent should take when in a given state s so as to receive the best reward. To understand each of these components, we need to look at a tutorial example in which the state space is extremely reduced. Thus, we return to the simple frame-and-slot world, looking at a pedagogical MDP implementation taken from Levin et al. (2000). Their tutorial example is a "Day-and-Month" dialogue system, whose goal is to get correct values of day and month for a two-slot frame through the shortest possible interaction with the user.

In principle, a state of an MDP could include any possible information about the dialogue, such as the complete dialogue history so far. Using such a rich model of state would make the number of possible states extraordinarily large. So a model of state is usually chosen that encodes a much more limited set of information, such as the values of the slots in the current frame, the most recent question asked to the user, the user's most recent answer, the ASR confidence, and so on. For the Day-and-Month example, let's represent the state of the system as the values of the two slots *day* and *month*. There are 411 states (366 states with a day and month (counting leap year), 12 states with a month but no day ($d = 0$, $m = 1, 2, ..., 12$), 31 states with a day but no month ($m = 0$, $d = 1, 2, ..., 31$), and a special initial state s_i and final state s_f.

Actions of an MDP dialogue system might include generating particular speech acts, or performing a database query to find out information. For the Day-and-Month example, Levin et al. (2000) propose the following actions:

- a_d: a question asking for the day
- a_m: a question asking for the month
- $a_d m$: a question asking for both the day and the month
- a_f: a final action submitting the form and terminating the dialogue

Since the goal of the system is to get the correct answer with the shortest interaction, one possible reward function for the system would integrate three terms:

$$R = -(w_i n_i + w_e n_e + w_f n_f) \qquad (24.26)$$

The term n_i is the number of interactions with the user, n_e is the number of errors, n_f is the number of slots that are filled (0, 1, or 2), and the ws are weights.

Finally, a dialogue policy π specifies which actions to apply in which state. Consider two possible policies: (1) asking for day and month separately, and (2) asking for them together. These might generate the two dialogues shown in Fig. 24.22.

In policy 1, the action specified for the no-date/no-month state is to ask for a day, and the action specified for any of the 31 states where we have a day but not a month is to ask for a month. In policy 2, the action specified for the no-date/no-month state is to ask an open-ended question (*Which date*) to get both a day and a month. The two

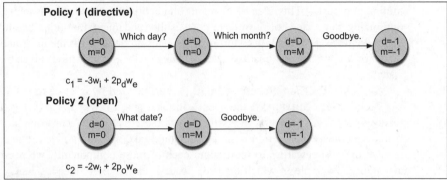

Figure 24.22 Two policies for getting a month and a day. After Levin et al. (2000).

policies have different advantages; an open prompt can lead to shorter dialogues but is likely to cause more errors, whereas a directive prompt is slower but less error-prone. Thus, the optimal policy depends on the values of the weights w and also on the error rates of the ASR component. Let's call p_d the probability of the recognizer making an error interpreting a month or a day value after a directive prompt. The (presumably higher) probability of error interpreting a month or day value after an open prompt we'll call p_o. The reward for the first dialogue in Fig. 24.22 is thus -3 $w_i + 2$ p_d w_e. The reward for the second dialogue in Fig. 24.22 is -2 $w_i + 2$ p_o w_e. The directive prompt policy, policy 1, is thus better than policy 2 when the improved error rate justifies the longer interaction, that is, when $p_d - p_o > \frac{w_i}{2w_e}$.

In the example we've seen so far, there were only two possible actions, and hence only a tiny number of possible policies. In general, the number of possible actions, states, and policies is quite large, and so the problem of finding the optimal policy π^* is much harder.

Markov decision theory together with classical reinforcement learning gives us a way to think about this problem. First, generalizing from Fig. 24.22, we can think of any particular dialogue as a trajectory in state space:

$$s_1 \xrightarrow{a1,r1} s_2 \xrightarrow{a2,r2} s_3 \xrightarrow{a3,r3} \qquad (24.27)$$

The best policy π^* is the one with the greatest expected reward over all trajectories. What is the expected reward for a given state sequence? The most common way to as-

Discounted reward

sign utilities or rewards to sequences is to use **discounted rewards**. Here we compute the expected cumulative reward Q of a sequence as a discounted sum of the utilities of the individual states:

$$Q([s_0, a_0, s_1, a_1, s_2, a_2 \quad]) = R(s_0, a_0) + \gamma R(s_1, a_1) + \gamma^2 R(s_2, a_2) + \quad, \qquad (24.28)$$

The discount factor γ is a number between 0 and 1. This makes the agent care more about current rewards than future rewards; the more future a reward, the more discounted its value.

Given this model, it is possible to show that the expected cumulative reward $Q(s, a)$ for taking a particular action from a particular state is the following recursive equation

Bellman equation

called the **Bellman equation**:

$$Q(s,a) = R(s,a) + \gamma \sum_{s'} P(s' \mid s,a) \max_{a'} Q(s',a') \tag{24.29}$$

What the Bellman equation says is that the expected cumulative reward for a given state/action pair is the immediate reward for the current state plus the expected discounted utility of all possible next states s', weighted by the probability of moving to that state s', and assuming that once there we take the optimal action a'.

Equation 24.29 makes use of two parameters. We need a model of $P(s' \mid s,a)$, that is, how likely a given state/action pair (s,a) is to lead to a new state s'. And we also need a good estimate of $R(s,a)$. If we had lots of labeled training data, we could simply compute both of these from labeled counts. For example, with labeled dialogues, to estimate $P(s' \mid s,a)$ we could simply count how many times we were in a given state s, and out of that how many times we took action a to get to state s'. Similarly, if we had a hand-labeled reward for each dialogue, we could build a model of $R(s,a)$.

Value iteration   Given these parameters, it turns out that there is an iterative algorithm for solving the Bellman equation and determining proper Q values, the **value iteration** algorithm (Sutton and Barto, 1998; Bellman, 1957). We don't present this here, but see Chapter 17 of Russell and Norvig (2002) for the details of the algorithm as well as further information on Markov decision processes.

How do we get enough labeled training data to set these parameters? This is especially worrisome since in real problems the number of states s is extremely large. Two methods have been applied in the past. The first is to carefully hand-tune the states and policies so that only a very small number of states and policies need to be set automatically. In this case, we can build a dialogue system that explores the state space by generating random conversations. Probabilities can then be set from this corpus of conversations. The second method is to build a simulated user. The user interacts with the system millions of times, and the system learns the state transition and reward probabilities from this corpus.

The first approach, using real users to set parameters in a small state space, was taken by Singh et al. (2002). They used reinforcement learning to make a small set of optimal policy decisions. Their NJFun system learned to choose actions that varied the initiative (system, user, or mixed) and the confirmation strategy (explicit or none). The state of the system was specified by values of seven features including which slot in the frame was being worked on (1–4), what the ASR confidence value (0–5) was, how many times a current slot question had been asked, whether a restrictive or non-restrictive grammar was used, and so on. The result of using only seven features with a small number of attributes resulted in a small state space (62 states). Each state had only two possible actions (system versus user initiative when asking questions, explicit versus no confirmation when receiving answers). They ran the system with real users, creating 311 conversations. Each conversation had a simple binary reward function; 1 if the user completed the task (finding specified museums, theater, winetasting in the New Jersey area), 0 if the user did not. The system successfully learned a good dialogue policy (roughly, start with user initiative, then back off to either mixed or system initiative when re-asking for an attribute; confirm only at lower confidence values; both initiative and confirmation policies, however, are different for different attributes). They showed, from various objective measures, that their policy actually was more successful than many hand-designed policies reported in the literature.

The simulated user strategy was taken by Levin et al. (2000) in their MDP model with reinforcement learning in the ATIS task. Their simulated user was a generative stochastic model that given the system's current state and actions, produced a frame-slot representation of a user response. The parameters of the simulated user were estimated from a corpus of ATIS dialogues. The simulated user then interacted with the system for tens of thousands of conversations, leading to an optimal dialogue policy.

While the MDP architecture offers a powerful new way of modeling dialogue behavior, it relies on the problematic assumption that the system actually knows what state it is in. This is, of course, not true in a number of ways; the system never knows the true internal state of the user, and even the state in the dialogue may be obscured by speech recognition errors. Recent attempts to relax this assumption have relied on partially observable Markov decision processes, or POMDPs (sometimes pronounced 'pom-deepeez'). In a POMDP, we model the user output as an observed signal generated from yet another hidden variable. Both MDPs and POMDPs, however, have problems due to computational complexity and due to their reliance on simulations that don't reflect true user behavior; see the end of the chapter for references.

24.7   Advanced: Plan-Based Dialogue Agents

One of the earliest models of conversational agent behavior, and also one of the most sophisticated, is based on the use of AI planning techniques. For example, the TRIPS agent (Allen et al., 2001) simulates helping with emergency management, planning where and how to supply ambulances or personnel in a simulated emergency situation. The same planning algorithms that reason how to get an ambulance from point A to point B can be applied to conversation as well. Since communication and conversation are just special cases of rational action in the world, these actions can be planned like any other. So an agent seeking to find out some information can come up with the plan of asking the interlocutor for the information. An agent hearing an utterance can interpret a speech act by running the planner "in reverse", using inference rules to infer from what the interlocutor said what the plan might have been.

Using plans to generate and interpret sentences in this way require that the planner have good models of its **beliefs**, **desires**, and **intentions** (BDI), as well as those *BDI* of the interlocutor. Plan-based models of dialogue are thus often referred to as **BDI** models. BDI models of dialogue were first introduced by Allen, Cohen, Perrault, and their colleagues in a number of influential papers showing how speech acts could be generated (Cohen and Perrault, 1979) and interpreted (Perrault and Allen, 1980; Allen and Perrault, 1980). At the same time, Wilensky (1983) introduced plan-based models of understanding as part of the task of interpreting stories. In another related line of research, Grosz and her colleagues showed how using similar notions of intention and plans allowed ideas of discourse structure and coherence to be applied to dialogue.

24.7.1   Plan-Inferential Interpretation and Production

Let's first sketch the ideas of plan-based comprehension and production. How might a plan-based agent act as the human travel agent to understand sentence C_2 in the dialogue repeated below?

C_1: I need to travel in May.

A_1: And, what day in May did you want to travel?

C_2: OK uh I need to be there for a meeting that's from the 12th to the 15th.

The Gricean principle of Relevance can be used to infer that the client's meeting is relevant to the flight booking. The system may know that one precondition for having a meeting (at least before Web conferencing) is being at the place where the meeting is held. One way of being at a place is flying there, and booking a flight is a precondition for flying there. The system can follow this chain of inference, abducing that the user wants to fly on a date before the 12th.

Next, consider how our plan-based agent could act as the human travel agent to produce sentence A_1 in the dialogue above. The planning agent would reason that to help a client book a flight, it must know enough information about the flight to book it. It reasons that knowing the month (May) is insufficient information to specify a departure or return date. The simplest way to find out the needed date information is to ask the client.

In the rest of this section, we'll flesh out the sketchy outlines of planning for understanding and generation by using Perrault and Allen's formal definitions of belief and desire in the predicate calculus. Reasoning about belief is done with a number of axiom schemas inspired by Hintikka (1969). We'll represent "S believes the proposition P" as the two-place predicate $B(S,P)$, with axiom schemas such as $B(A,P) \wedge B(A,Q) \Rightarrow B(A,P \wedge Q)$. Knowledge is defined as "true belief"; S *knows that* P will be represented as $KNOW(S,P)$, defined as $KNOW(S,P) \equiv P \wedge B(S,P)$.

The theory of desire relies on the predicate WANT. If an agent S wants P to be true, we say $WANT(S,P)$, or $W(S,P)$ for short. P can be a state or the execution of some action. Thus, if ACT is the name of an action, $W(S,\mathrm{ACT}(H))$ means that S wants H to do ACT. The logic of WANT relies on its own set of axiom schemas just like the logic of belief.

Action schema   The BDI models also require an axiomatization of actions and planning; the simplest of these is based on a set of **action schema**s based in turn on the simple AI planning model STRIPS (Fikes and Nilsson, 1971). Each action schema has a set of parameters with *constraints* about the type of each variable and three parts:

- *Preconditions:* conditions that must already be true to perform the action.

- *Effects:* conditions that become true as a result of performing the action.

- *Body:* a set of partially ordered goal states that must be achieved in performing the action.

In the travel domain, for example, the action of agent A booking flight $F1$ for client C might have the following simplified definition:

BOOK-FLIGHT(A,C,F):

Constraints:	Agent(A) $\wedge$ Flight(F) $\wedge$ Client(C)
Precondition:	Know(A,depart-date(F)) $\wedge$ Know(A,depart-time(F))
	$\wedge$ Know(A,origin(F)) $\wedge$ Know(A,flight-type(F))
	$\wedge$ Know(A,destination(F)) $\wedge$ Has-Seats(F) $\wedge$
	W(C,(BOOK(A,C,F))) $\wedge \ldots$
Effect:	Flight-Booked(A,C,F)
Body:	Make-Reservation(A,F,C)

This same kind of STRIPS action specification can be used for speech acts. IN-FORM is the speech act of informing the hearer of some proposition, based on Grice's (1957) idea that a speaker informs the hearer of something merely by causing the hearer to believe that the speaker wants them to know something:

INFORM(S,H,P):

Constraints:	Speaker(S) $\wedge$ Hearer(H) $\wedge$ Proposition(P)
Precondition:	Know(S,P) $\wedge$ W(S, INFORM(S, H, P))
Effect:	Know(H,P)
Body:	B(H,W(S,Know(H,P)))

REQUEST is the directive speech act for requesting the hearer to perform some action:

REQUEST(S,H,ACT):

Constraints:	Speaker(S) $\wedge$ Hearer(H) $\wedge$ ACT(A) $\wedge$ H is agent of ACT
Precondition:	W(S,ACT(H))
Effect:	W(H,ACT(H))
Body:	B(H,W(S,ACT(H)))

Let's now see how a plan-based dialogue system might interpret the sentence:

C_2: I need to be there for a meeting that's from the 12th to the 15th.

We'll assume the system has the BOOK-FLIGHT plan mentioned above. In addition, we'll need knowledge about meetings and getting to them, in the form of the MEETING, FLY-TO, and TAKE-FLIGHT plans, sketched broadly below:

MEETING(P,L,T1,T2):

Constraints:	Person(P) $\wedge$ Location (L) $\wedge$ Time (T1) $\wedge$ Time (T2) $\wedge$ Time (TA)
Precondition:	At (P, L, TA)
	Before (TA, T1)
Body:	...

FLY-TO(P, L, T):

Constraints:	Person(P) $\wedge$ Location (L) $\wedge$ Time (T)
Effect:	At (P, L, T)
Body:	TAKE-FLIGHT(P, L, T)

TAKE-FLIGHT(P, L, T):

Constraints:	Person(P) $\wedge$ Location (L) $\wedge$ Time (T) $\wedge$ Flight (F) $\wedge$ Agent (A)
Precondition:	BOOK-FLIGHT (A, P, F)
	Destination-Time(F) = T
	Destination-Location(F) = L
Body:	...

Now let's assume that an NLU module returns a meaning of the client's utterance that (among other things) includes the following semantic content:

MEETING (P, ?L, T1, T2)

Constraints: P = Client $\wedge$ T1 = May 12 $\wedge$ T2 = May 15

Our plan-based system now has two plans established, one MEETING plan from this utterance, and one BOOK-FLIGHT plan from the previous utterance. The system implicitly uses the Gricean Relevance intuition to try to connect them. Since BOOK-FLIGHT is a precondition for TAKE-FLIGHT, the system may hypothesize (infer) that the user is planning a TAKE-FLIGHT. Since TAKE-FLIGHT is in the body of FLY-TO, the system further infers a FLY-TO plan. Finally, since the effect of FLY-TO is a precondition of the MEETING, the system can unify each of the people, locations, and times of all of these plans. The result will be that the system knows that the client wants to arrive at the destination before May 12th.

Let's turn to the details of our second example:

C_1: I need to travel in May.

A_1: And, what day in May did you want to travel?

How does a plan-based agent know to ask question A_1? This knowledge comes from the BOOK-FLIGHT plan, whose preconditions were that the agent know a variety of flight parameters, including the departure date and time, origin and destination cities, and so forth. Utterance C_1 contains the origin city and partial information about the departure date; the agent has to request the rest. A plan-based agent would use an action schema like REQUEST-INFO to represent a plan for asking information questions (simplified from Cohen and Perrault (1979)):

REQUEST-INFO(A,C,I):

Constraints:	Agent(A) $\wedge$ Client(C)
Precondition:	Know(C,I)
Effect:	Know(A,I)
Body:	B(C,W(A,Know(A,I)))

Because the effects of REQUEST-INFO match each precondition of BOOK-FLIGHT, the agent can use REQUEST-INFO to acquire the missing information.

24.7.2   The Intentional Structure of Dialogue

In Section 21.2 we introduced the idea that the segments of a discourse are related by **coherence relations** like **Explanation** or **Elaboration** which describe the **informational** relation between discourse segments. The BDI approach to utterance interpretation gives rise to another view of coherence that is particularly relevant for dialogue,

Intentional structure

the **intentional** approach (Grosz and Sidner, 1986). According to this approach, what makes a dialogue coherent is its **intentional structure**, the plan-based intentions of the speaker underlying each utterance.

Discourse purpose

Discourse segment purpose

These intentions are instantiated in the model by assuming that each discourse has an underlying purpose called the **discourse purpose** (DP), held by the person who initiates it. Each discourse segment within the discourse has a corresponding purpose, a **discourse segment purpose** (DSP), which has a role in achieving the overall DP. Possible DPs/DSPs include intending that some other agent intend to perform some physical task, or that some agent believe some fact.

As opposed to the larger sets of coherence relations used in informational accounts of coherence, only two such relations are proposed by Grosz and Sidner: **dominance** and **satisfaction-precedence**. DSP_1 dominates DSP_2 if satisfying DSP_2 is intended to provide part of the satisfaction of DSP_1. DSP_1 satisfaction-precedes DSP_2 if DSP_1 must be satisfied before DSP_2.

C_1:	I need to travel in May.
A_1:	And, what day in May did you want to travel?
C_2:	OK uh I need to be there for a meeting that's from the 12th to the 15th.
A_2:	And you're flying into what city?
C_3:	Seattle.
A_3:	And what time would you like to leave Pittsburgh?
C_4:	Uh hmm I don't think there's many options for non-stop.
A_4:	Right. There's three non-stops today.
C_5:	What are they?
A_5:	The first one departs PGH at 10:00am arrives Seattle at 12:05 their time. The second flight departs PGH at 5:55pm, arrives Seattle at 8pm. And the last flight departs PGH at 8:15pm arrives Seattle at 10:28pm.
C_6:	OK I'll take the 5ish flight on the night before on the 11th.
A_6:	On the 11th? OK. Departing at 5:55pm arrives Seattle at 8pm, U.S. Air flight 115.
C_7:	OK.

Figure 24.23   A fragment from a telephone conversation between a client (C) and a travel agent (A) (repeated from Fig. 24.4).

Consider the dialogue between a client (C) and a travel agent (A) that we saw earlier, repeated here in Fig. 24.23. Collaboratively, the caller and agent successfully identify a flight that suits the caller's needs. Achieving this joint goal requires that a top-level discourse intention be satisfied, listed as I1 below, in addition to several intermediate intentions that contributed to the satisfaction of I1, listed as I2–I5:

I1: (Intend C (Intend A (A find a flight for C)))

I2: (Intend A (Intend C (Tell C A departure date)))

I3: (Intend A (Intend C (Tell C A destination city)))

I4: (Intend A (Intend C (Tell C A departure time)))

I5: (Intend C (Intend A (A find a nonstop flight for C)))

Intentions I2–I5 are all subordinate to intention I1, because they were all adopted to meet preconditions for achieving intention I1. This is reflected in the dominance relationships below:

I1 dominates I2 $\wedge$ I1 dominates I3 $\wedge$ I1 dominates I4 $\wedge$ I1 dominates I5

Furthermore, intentions I2 and I3 needed to be satisfied before intention I5, since the agent needed to know the departure date and destination in order to start listing nonstop flights. This is reflected in the satisfaction-precedence relationships below:

I2 satisfaction-precedes I5 $\wedge$ I3 satisfaction-precedes I5

The dominance relations give rise to the discourse structure depicted in Fig. 24.24. Each discourse segment is numbered in correspondence with the intention number that serves as its DP/DSP.

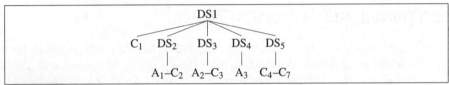

Figure 24.24   Discourse structure of the flight reservation dialogue.

Intentions and their relationships give rise to a coherent discourse based on their role in the overall *plan* that the caller is inferred to have. We assume that the caller and agent have the plan BOOK-FLIGHT described on page 852. This plan requires that the agent know the departure time and date and so on. As we discussed above, the agent can use the REQUEST-INFO action scheme from page 853 to ask the user for this information.

Subdialogue   Subsidiary discourse segments are also called **subdialogues**; DS2 and DS3 in particular are **information-sharing** (Chu-Carroll and Carberry, 1998), **knowledge-precondition** subdialogues (Lochbaum et al., 1990; Lochbaum, 1998), since they are initiated by the agent to help satisfy preconditions of a higher-level goal.

Algorithms for inferring intentional structure in dialogue work similarly to algorithms for inferring dialogue acts, either employing the BDI model (e.g., Litman, 1985; Grosz and Sidner, 1986; Litman and Allen, 1987; Carberry, 1990; Passonneau and Litman, 1993; Chu-Carroll and Carberry, 1998), or machine learning architectures based on cue phrases (Reichman, 1985; Grosz and Sidner, 1986; Hirschberg and Litman, 1993), prosody (Hirschberg and Pierrehumbert, 1986; Grosz and Hirschberg, 1992; Pierrehumbert and Hirschberg, 1990; Hirschberg and Nakatani, 1996), and other cues.

24.8   Summary

Conversational agents are a crucial speech and language processing application that are already widely used commercially. Research on these agents relies crucially on an understanding of human dialogue or conversational practices.

- Dialogue systems generally have five components: speech recognition, natural language understanding, dialogue management, natural language generation, and speech synthesis. They may also have a task manager specific to the task domain.

- Common dialogue architectures include finite-state and frame-based as well as advanced systems such as information-state, Markov decision processes, and **BDI (belief-desire-intention)** models.

- Turn-taking, grounding, conversational structure, and initiative are crucial human dialogue phenomena that must also be dealt with in conversational agents.

- In dialogue, speaking is a kind of action; these acts are referred to as speech acts or **dialogue acts**. Models exist for generating and interpreting these acts.

Bibliographical and Historical Notes

Early work on speech and language processing had very little emphasis on the study of dialogue. The dialogue manager for the simulation of the paranoid agent PARRY (Colby et al., 1971), was a little more complex. Like ELIZA, it was based on a production system, but where ELIZA's rules were based only on the words in the user's previous sentence, PARRY's rules also rely on global variables indicating its emotional state. Furthermore, PARRY's output sometimes makes use of script-like sequences of statements when the conversation turns to its delusions. For example, if PARRY's **anger** variable is high, he will choose from a set of "hostile" outputs. If the input mentions his delusion topic, he will increase the value of his **fear** variable and then begin to express the sequence of statements related to his delusion.

The appearance of more sophisticated dialogue managers awaited the better understanding of human-human dialogue. Studies of the properties of human-human dialogue began to accumulate in the 1970s and 1980s. The conversation analysis community (Sacks et al., 1974; Jefferson, 1984; Schegloff, 1982) began to study the interactional properties of conversation. Grosz's (1977b) dissertation significantly influenced the computational study of dialogue with its introduction of the study of dialogue structure, with its finding that "task-oriented dialogues have a structure that closely parallels the structure of the task being performed" (p. 27), which led to her work on intentional and attentional structure with Sidner. Lochbaum et al. (2000) is a good recent summary of the role of intentional structure in dialogue. The BDI model integrating earlier AI planning work (Fikes and Nilsson, 1971) with speech-act theory (Austin, 1962; Gordon and Lakoff, 1971; Searle, 1975a) was first worked out by Cohen and Perrault (1979) showing how speech acts could be generated, and Perrault and Allen (1980) and Allen and Perrault (1980) applying the approach to speech-act interpretation. Simultaneous work on a plan-based model of understanding was developed by Wilensky (1983) in the Schankian tradition.

Probabilistic models of dialogue act interpretation were informed by linguistic work that focused on the discourse meaning of prosody (Sag and Liberman, 1975; Pierrehumbert, 1980), by conversation analysis work on microgrammar (e.g., Goodwin, 1996), by work such as Hinkelman and Allen (1989), who showed how lexical and phrasal cues could be integrated into the BDI model. The models were then worked out at a number of speech and dialogue labs in the 1990s (Waibel, 1988; Daly and Zue, 1992; Kompe et al., 1993; Nagata and Morimoto, 1994; Woszczyna and Waibel, 1994; Reithinger et al., 1996; Kita et al., 1996; Warnke et al., 1997; Chu-Carroll, 1998; Taylor et al., 1998; Stolcke et al., 2000).

Modern dialogue systems drew on research at many different labs in the 1980s and 1990s. Models of dialogue as collaborative behavior introduced in this period included the ideas of common ground (Clark and Marshall, 1981), reference as a collaborative process (Clark and Wilkes-Gibbs, 1986), **joint intention** (Levesque et al., 1990), and **shared plans** (Grosz and Sidner, 1980). Related to this area is the study of **initiative** in dialogue, studying how dialogue control shifts between participants (Walker and Whittaker, 1990; Smith and Gordon, 1997; Chu-Carroll and Brown, 1997).

A wide body of dialogue research came out of AT&T and Bell Laboratories around the turn of the century, including much of the early work on MDP dialogue systems as well as fundamental work on cue phrases, prosody, and rejection and confirmation. Work on dialogue acts and dialogue moves drew from a number of sources: HCRC's Map Task (Carletta et al., 1997b); the work of James Allen and his colleagues and students, for example, Hinkelman and Allen (1989), showing how lexical and phrasal cues could be integrated into the BDI model of speech acts; Traum (2000) and Traum and Hinkelman (1992); and Sadek (1991).

Much recent academic work in dialogue focuses on multimodal applications (Johnston et al., 2007; Niekrasz and Purver, 2006, inter alia), on the information-state model (Traum and Larsson, 2003, 2000) or on reinforcement learning architectures including POMDPs (Roy et al., 2000; Young, 2002; Lemon et al., 2006; Williams and Young, 2005, 2000). Work in progress on MDPs and POMDPs focuses on computational complexity (they currently can only be run on quite small domains with limited numbers of slots) and on making simulations more reflective of true user behavior. Alternative algorithms include SMDPs (Cuayáhuitl et al., 2007). See Russell and Norvig (2002) and Sutton and Barto (1998) for a general introduction to reinforcement learning.

Clarissa Recent years have seen the widespread commercial use of dialogue systems, often based on VoiceXML. Some more sophisticated systems have also seen deployment. For example, **Clarissa**, the first spoken dialogue system used in space, is a speech-enabled procedure navigator that was used by astronauts on the International Space Station (Rayner et al., 2003; Rayner and Hockey, 2004). Much research focuses on more mundane in-vehicle applications in cars (e.g., Weng et al., 2006). Among the important technical challenges in embedding these dialogue systems in real applications are good

End-pointing techniques for **end-pointing** (deciding if the speaker is done talking) (Ferrer et al., 2003) and for noise robustness.

Good surveys on dialogue systems include Harris (2005), Cohen et al. (2004), McTear (2002, 2004), Sadek and De Mori (1998), Delgado and Araki (2005), and the dialogue chapter in Allen (1995).

Exercises

24.1 List the dialogue act misinterpretations in the *Who's on First* routine at the beginning of the chapter.

24.2 Write a finite-state automaton for a dialogue manager for checking your bank balance and withdrawing money at an automated teller machine.

24.3 Dispreferred responses (e.g., turning down a request) are usually signaled by surface cues such as significant silence. Try to notice the next time you or someone else utters a dispreferred response, and write down the utterance. What are some other cues in the response that a system might use to detect a dispreferred response? Consider non-verbal cues like eye gaze and body gestures.

24.4 When asked a question to which they aren't sure they know the answer, people display their lack of confidence by cues that resemble other dispreferred responses. Try to notice some unsure answers to questions. What are some of the cues? If you have trouble doing this, read Smith and Clark (1993) and listen specifically for the cues they mention.

24.5 Build a VoiceXML dialogue system for giving the current time around the world. The system should ask the user for a city and a time format (24 hour, etc) and should return the current time, properly dealing with time zones.

24.6 Implement a small air-travel help system based on text input. Your system should get constraints from users about a particular flight that they want to take, expressed in natural language, and display possible flights on a screen. Make simplifying assumptions. You may build in a simple flight database or you may use a flight information system on the Web as your backend.

24.7 Augment your previous system to work with speech input through VoiceXML. (Or alternatively, describe the user interface changes you would have to make for it to work via speech over the phone.) What were the major differences?

24.8 Design a simple dialogue system for checking your email over the telephone. Implement in VoiceXML.

24.9 Test your email-reading system on some potential users. Choose some of the metrics described in Section 24.4.2 and evaluate your system.

Credits

Figs. 24.8, 24.14, and 24.15 (© the authors; thanks to the Association of Computational Linguistics, the *Journal of Computational Linguistics* and its editor Robert Dale, and to Marilyn Walker)

Fig. 24.22 (© IEEE and the authors; we thank Esther Levin)

Chapter 25

Machine Translation

The process of translating comprises in its essence the whole
secret of human understanding and social communication...
Attributed to Hans-Georg Gadamer

What is translation? On a platter / A poet's pale and glaring head,
A parrot's screech, a monkey's chatter, / And profanation of the dead.
Nabokov, *On Translating Eugene Onegin*

Proper words in proper places
Jonathan Swift

Machine translation
MT

This chapter introduces techniques for **machine translation** (**MT**), the use of computers to automate translation from one language to another. Translation, in its full generality, is a difficult, fascinating, and intensely human endeavor, as rich as any other area of human creativity. Consider the following passage from the end of Chapter 45 of the 18th-century novel *The Story of the Stone*, also called *Dream of the Red Chamber*, by Cao Xue Qin (Cao, 1792), together with the Mandarin phonetics:

黛玉自在枕上感念宝钗。。。又听见窗外竹梢焦叶之上，
雨声淅沥，清寒透幕，不觉又滴下泪来 。

dai yu zi zai zhen shang gan nian bao chai... you ting jian chuang wai zhu shao xiang ye
zhe shang, yu sheng xi li, qing han tou mu, bu jue you di xia lei lai.

Figure 25.1 shows the English translation of this passage by David Hawkes, in sentences labeled E_1–E_4. For ease of reading, instead of giving the Chinese, we show the English glosses of each Chinese word IN SMALL CAPS. Words in white boxes are words that only appear in one of the two languages. We show **alignment** lines between words or phrases that roughly correspond in the two languages.

Consider some of the issues involved in this translation. First, the English and Chinese texts are very different structurally and lexically. The four English sentences (notice the periods) correspond to one long Chinese sentence. The word order of the two texts is very different, as we can see by the many crossed alignment lines in Fig. 25.1. The English has many more words than the Chinese, as we can see by the large number of English words in white. Many of these differences are caused by structural differences between the two languages. For example, because Chinese rarely marks verbal aspect or tense, the English translation has additional words like *as*, *turned to*, and *had begun*, and Hawkes had to decide to translate Chinese *tou* as *penetrated*, rather than say *was penetrating* or *had penetrated*. Chinese has fewer articles than English, explaining the large number of white *the*s. Chinese also uses far fewer pronouns than English, so Hawkes had to insert *she* and *her* in many places into the English translation.

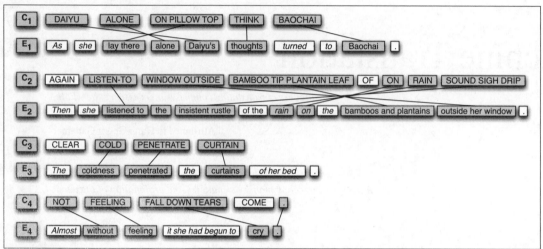

Figure 25.1   A Chinese passage from *Dream of the Red Chamber*, with the Chinese words represented by English glosses IN SMALL CAPS. Alignment lines are drawn between "Chinese" words and their English translations. Words in white boxes only appear in one of the languages.

Stylistic and cultural differences are another source of difficulty. Unlike English names, Chinese names are made up of regular content words with meanings. Hawkes chose to use transliterations (*Daiyu*) for the names of the main characters but to translate names of servants by their meanings (Aroma, Skybright). To clarify for English readers unfamiliar with Chinese bed-curtains, Hawkes translated *ma* ("curtain") as *curtains of her bed*. The phrase *bamboo tip plantain leaf*, although elegant in Chinese, where such four-character phrases are a hallmark of literate prose, would be awkward if translated word-for-word into English, and so Hawkes used simply *bamboos and plantains*.

Translation of this sort requires a deep and rich understanding of the source language and the input text and a poetic and creative command of the target language. The problem of automatically performing high-quality literary translation between languages as different as Chinese to English is thus far too hard to automate completely.

However, even non-literary translations between such similar languages as English and French can be difficult. Here is an English sentence from the Hansards corpus of Canadian parliamentary proceedings, with its French translation:

> **English**: Following a two-year transitional period, the new Foodstuffs Ordinance for Mineral Water came into effect on April 1, 1988. Specifically, it contains more stringent requirements regarding quality consistency and purity guarantees.
>
> **French:** La nouvelle ordonnance fèdèrale sur les denrées alimentaires concernant entre autres les eaux minérales, entrée en vigueur le 1er avril 1988 aprés une période transitoire de deux ans. exige surtout une plus grande constance dans la qualité et une garantie de la pureté.
>
> **French gloss:** THE NEW ORDINANCE FEDERAL ON THE STUFF FOOD CONCERNING AMONG OTHERS THE WATERS MINERAL CAME INTO EFFECT THE 1ST APRIL 1988 AFTER A PERIOD TRANSITORY OF TWO YEARS REQUIRES ABOVE ALL A LARGER CONSISTENCY IN THE QUALITY AND A GUARANTEE OF THE PURITY.

Despite the strong structural and vocabulary overlaps between English and French, such translation, like literary translation, still has to deal with differences in word order (e.g., the location of the *following a two-year transitional period* phrase) and in structure (e.g., English uses the noun *requirements* while the French uses the verb *exige* 'REQUIRE').

Nonetheless, such translations are much easier, and a number of non-literary translation tasks can be addressed with current computational models of machine translation, including (1) tasks for which a **rough translation** is adequate, (2) tasks for which a human **post-editor** is used, and (3) tasks limited to small **sublanguage** domains in which **fully automatic, high-quality translation** (**FAHQT**) is still achievable.

FAHQT

Information acquisition on the Web is the kind of task for which a rough translation is useful. Suppose this morning you saw some lovely *plátanos* (plantains, a kind of banana) at the local Caribbean grocery store and you want to know how to cook them. You go to the Web, and find the following recipe.

Platano en Naranja   Para 6 personas
3 Plátanos maduros   2 cucharadas de mantequilla derretida
1 taza de jugo (zumo) de naranja   5 cucharadas de azúcar morena o blanc
1/8 cucharadita de nuez moscada en polvo 1 cucharada de ralladura de naranja
 1 cucharada de canela en polvo (opcional)

Pelar los plátanos, cortarlos por la mitad y, luego, a lo largo. Engrasar una fuente o pirex con margarina. Colocar los plátanos y bañarlos con la mantequilla derretida. En un recipiente hondo, mezclar el jugo (zumo) de naranja con el azúcar, jengibre, nuez moscada y ralladura de naranja. Verter sobre los plátanos y hornear a 325 ° F. Los primeros 15 minutos, dejar los pátanos cubiertos, hornear 10 o 15 minutos más destapando los plátanos

---

An MT engine (we ran this through Google in early 2008) produces the following translation:

Platano in Orange   For 6 people
3 ripe bananas   2 tablespoon butter, melted
1 cup of juice (juice) orange   5 tablespoons brown sugar or white
1/8 teaspoon nutmeg powder 1 tablespoon orange zest
 1 tablespoon cinnamon (optional)

Peel bananas, cut them in half and then along. Grease a source or pirex with margarine. Put bananas and bañarlos with melted butter. In a deep bowl, mix the juice (juice) orange with the sugar, ginger, nutmeg and orange zest. Pour over bananas and bake at 325° F. The first 15 minutes, leave covered bananas, bake 10 to 15 minutes more uncovering bananas.

While there are still lots of confusions in this translation (is it for bananas or plantains? What exactly is the pot you should use? What is *bañarlos*?) it's probably enough, perhaps after you look up one or two words, to get a basic idea of something to try in the kitchen with your new purchase!

An MT system can also be used to speed up the human translation process by producing a draft translation that is fixed up in a **post-editing** phase by a human translator. Strictly speaking, systems used in this way are doing **computer-aided human translation** (CAHT or CAT) rather than (fully automatic) machine translation. This use of MT is effective especially for high-volume jobs requiring quick turnaround, such as the translation of software manuals for **localization**.

Post-editing

Computer-aided human translation

Localization

Weather forecasting is an example of a **sublanguage** domain that can be modeled completely enough to use raw MT output without post-editing. Weather forecasts consist of phrases like *Cloudy with a chance of showers today and Thursday*, or *Outlook for Friday: Sunny*. This domain has a limited vocabulary and only a few basic phrase types. Ambiguity is rare, and the senses of ambiguous words are easily disambiguated. Other domains that are sublanguage-like include software manuals, air travel queries, appointment scheduling, restaurant recommendation, and recipes.

Applications for machine translation can also be characterized by the number and direction of the translations. Localization tasks like translations of computer manuals require one-to-many translation (from English into many languages). One-to-many translation is also needed for non-English speakers around the world to access Web information in English. Conversely, many-to-one translation (into English) is relevant for anglophone readers who need the gist of Web content written in other languages. Many-to-many translation is relevant for environments like the European Union, where 23 official languages (at the time of this writing) need to be intertranslated.

Before we turn to MT systems, we begin in Section 25.1 by summarizing key differences among languages. The three classic models for doing MT— the **direct**, **transfer**, and **interlingua** approaches—are then presented in Section 25.2. We then investigate in detail modern **statistical MT** in Sections 25.3–25.8, finishing in Section 25.9 with a discussion of **evaluation**.

25.1   Why Machine Translation Is Hard

Translation divergence
We began this chapter with some of the issues that made it hard to translate *The Story of the Stone* from Chinese to English. In this section we look in more detail about what makes translation difficult. We discuss what makes languages similar or different, including **systematic** differences that we can model in a general way and **idiosyncratic** and lexical differences that must be dealt with one by one. These differences between languages are referred to as **translation divergences** and an understanding of what causes them will help us in building models that overcome the differences (Dorr, 1994).

25.1.1   Typology

Universal
When you accidentally pick up a radio program in some foreign language it seems like chaos, completely unlike the familiar languages of your everyday life. But there are patterns in this chaos, and indeed, some aspects of human language seem to be **universal**, holding true for every language. Many universals arise from the functional role of language as a communicative system by humans. Every language, for example, seems to have words for referring to people, for talking about women, men, and children, eating and drinking, for being polite or not. Other universals are more subtle; for example, every language seems to have nouns and verbs (Chapter 5).

Typology
Even when languages differ, the differences often have systematic structure. The study of these systematic cross-linguistic similarities and differences is called **typology** (Croft, 1990; Comrie, 1989). This section sketches some typological facts.

Isolating

Polysynthetic

Agglutinative

Fusion

Morphologically, languages are often characterized along two dimensions of variation. The first is the number of morphemes per word, ranging from **isolating** languages like Vietnamese and Cantonese, in which each word generally has one morpheme, to **polysynthetic** languages like Siberian Yupik ("Eskimo"), in which a single word may have very many morphemes, corresponding to a whole sentence in English. The second dimension is the degree to which morphemes are segmentable, ranging from **agglutinative** languages like Turkish (discussed in Chapter 3), in which morphemes have relatively clean boundaries, to **fusion** languages like Russian, in which a single affix may conflate multiple morphemes, like *-om* in the word *stolom* (table-SG-INSTR-DECL1), which fuses the distinct morphological categories instrumental, singular, and first declension.

SVO

SOV

VSO

Syntactically, languages are saliently different in the basic word order of verbs, subjects, and objects in simple declarative clauses. German, French, English, and Mandarin, for example, are all **SVO** (**subject-verb-object**) languages, meaning that the verb tends to come between the subject and object. Hindi and Japanese, by contrast, are **SOV** languages, meaning that the verb tends to come at the end of basic clauses, and Irish, Arabic, and Biblical Hebrew are **VSO** languages. Two languages that share their basic word-order type often have other similarities. For example, **SVO** languages generally have **prepositions**, whereas **SOV** languages generally have **postpositions**.

For example, in the following SVO English sentence, the verb *adores* is followed by its argument VP *listening to music*, the verb *listening* is followed by its argument PP *to music*, and the preposition *to* is followed by its argument *music*. By contrast, in the Japanese example that follows, each of these orderings is reversed; both verbs are *preceded* by their arguments, and the postposition follows its argument.

(25.1) English: *He adores listening to music*

Japanese: *kare ha ongaku wo kiku   no ga daisuki desu*
          he   music to listening   adores

Head-marking

Another important dimension of typological variation has to do with **argument structure** and **linking** of predicates with their arguments, such as the difference between **head-marking** and **dependent-marking** languages (Nichols, 1986). Head-marking languages tend to mark the relation between the head and its dependents on the head. Dependent-marking languages tend to mark the relation on the non-head. Head-marking Hungarian, for example, marks the possessive relation with an affix (A) on the head noun (H), and English marks it on the (non-head) possessor:

(25.2) English: *the man-[A]'s [H]house*
       Hungarian: *az ember [H]ház-[A]a*
                  the man   house-his

Typological variation in linking can also relate to how the conceptual properties of an event are mapped onto specific words. Talmy (1985, 1991) noted that languages can be characterized by whether direction of motion and manner of motion are marked on the verb or on the "satellites": particles, prepositional phrases, or adverbial phrases. For example, a bottle floating out of a cave would be described in English with the direction marked on the particle *out*, while in Spanish the direction would be marked on the verb:

(25.3)   English: *The bottle floated out.*

Spanish: La   botella salió   flotando.
The bottle   exited floating.

Verb-framed

Verb-framed languages mark the direction of motion on the verb (leaving the satellites to mark the manner of motion), like Spanish *acercarse* 'approach', *alcan-*

Satellite-framed

zar 'reach', *entrar* 'enter', *salir* 'exit'. **Satellite-framed** languages mark the direction of motion on the satellite (leaving the verb to mark the manner of motion), like English *crawl out*, *float off*, *jump down*, *run after*. Languages like Japanese, Tamil, and the many languages in the Romance, Semitic, and Mayan languages families, are verb-framed; Chinese as well as non-Romance Indo-European languages like English, Swedish, Russian, Hindi, and Farsi are satellite framed (Talmy, 1991; Slobin, 1996).

Finally, languages vary along a typological dimension related to the things they can omit. Many languages require that we use an explicit pronoun when talking about a referent that is given in the discourse. In other languages, however, we can sometimes omit pronouns altogether, as the following example from Spanish shows, using the Ø-notation introduced in Chapter 21:

(25.4)   [El jefe]$_i$ dio con un libro. Ø$_i$ Mostró a un descifrador ambulante.
[The boss] came upon a book. [He] showed it to a wandering decoder.

Pro-drop

Languages that can omit pronouns are called **pro-drop** languages. Even among the pro-drop languages, there are marked differences in frequencies of omission. Japanese and Chinese, for example, tend to omit far more than does Spanish. We refer to this

Referential density

dimension as **referential density**; languages that tend to use more pronouns are more referentially dense than those that use more zeros. Referentially sparse languages, like Chinese or Japanese, that require the hearer to do more inferential work to recover

Cold language

antecedents are called **cold** languages. Languages that are more explicit and make it

Hot language

easier for the hearer are called **hot** languages. The terms *hot* and *cold* are borrowed from Marshall McLuhan's (1964) distinction between hot media like movies, which fill in many details for the viewer, versus cold media like comics, which require the reader to do more inferential work to fill out the representation (Bickel, 2003).

Typological differences between languages can cause problems for translation. Obviously, translating from SVO languages like English to SOV languages like Japanese requires huge structural reorderings, since all the constituents are at different places in the sentence. Translating from a satellite-framed to a verb-framed language or from a head-marking to a dependent-marking language requires changes to sentence structure and constraints on word choice. Languages with extensive pro-drop, like Chinese or Japanese, cause huge problems for translation into non-pro-drop languages like English since each zero has to be identified and the anaphor recovered.

25.1.2   Other Structural Divergences

Many structural divergences between languages are based on typological differences. Others are simply idiosyncratic differences characteristic of particular languages or language pairs. For example, in English the unmarked order in a noun phrase has adjectives precede nouns, but in French and Spanish adjectives generally follow nouns.[1]

	Spanish	*bruja verde*	**French**	*maison bleue*
(25.5)		witch green		house blue
	English	"green witch"		"blue house"

Chinese relative clauses are structured differently from English relative clauses, making it hard to translate long Chinese sentences.

Language-specific constructions abound. English, for example, has an idiosyncratic syntactic construction involving the word *there* that is often used to introduce a new scene in a story, as in *there burst into the room three men with guns*. To give an idea of how trivial, yet crucial, these differences can be, think of dates. Dates not only appear in various formats—typically DD/MM/YY in British English, MM/DD/YY in American English, and YYMMDD in Japanese—but the calendars themselves may also differ. Dates in Japanese, for example, are often relative to the start of the current Emperor's reign rather than to the start of the Christian Era.

25.1.3   Lexical Divergences

Lexical divergences also cause huge difficulties in translation. We saw in Chapter 20, for example, that the English source-language word *bass* could appear in Spanish as the fish *lubina* or the instrument *bajo*. Thus translation often requires solving exactly the same problems as word sense disambiguation, and the two fields are closely linked.

In English the word *bass* is homonymous; the two senses of the word are not closely related semantically, and so it is natural that we would have to disambiguate in order to translate. Even in cases of polysemy, however, we often have to disambiguate if the target language doesn't have the exact same kind of polysemy. The English word *know*, for example, is polysemous; it can refer to knowing of a fact or proposition (*I know that snow is white*) or familiarity with a person or location (*I know Jon Stewart*). It turns out that translating these different senses requires distinct French verbs, including the verbs *connaître* and *savoir*. *Savoir* is generally used with sentential complements to indicate knowledge or mental representation of a fact or proposition, or verbal complements to indicate knowledge of how to do something (e.g., WordNet 3.0 senses #1, #2, #3). *Connaître* is generally used with NP complements to indicate familiarity or acquaintance with people, entities, or locations (e.g., WordNet 3.0 senses #4, #7). Similar distinctions occur in German, Chinese, and many other languages:

(25.6) **English:** I know he just bought a book.

(25.7) **French:** Je sais qu'il vient d'acheter un livre.

(25.8) **English:** I know John.

(25.9) **French:** Je connais Jean.

The *savoir*/*connaître* distinction corresponds to different groups of WordNet senses. Sometimes, however, a target language will make a distinction that is not even recognized in fine-grained dictionaries. German, for example, uses two distinct words for

---

[1] As always, there are exceptions to this generalization, such as *galore* in English and *gros* in French; furthermore in French some adjectives can appear before the noun with a different meaning; *route mauvaise* "bad road, badly paved road" versus *mauvaise route* "wrong road" (Waugh, 1976).

what in English would be called a *wall*: *Wand* for walls inside a building, and *Mauer* for walls outside a building. Similarly, where English uses the word *brother* for any male sibling, both Japanese and Chinese have distinct words for *older brother* and *younger brother* (Chinese *gege* and *didi*, respectively).

In addition to these distinctions, lexical divergences can be grammatical. For example, a word may translate best to a different part of speech in the target language. Many English sentences involving the verb *like* must be translated into German as the adverbial *gern*; thus *she likes to sing* maps to *sie singt gerne* (SHE SINGS LIKINGLY).

In translation, we can think of sense disambiguation as a kind of **specification**; we have to make a vague word like *know* or *bass* more specific in the target language. This kind of specification is also quite common with grammatical differences. Sometimes one language places more grammatical constraints on word choice than another. French and Spanish, for example, mark gender on adjectives, so an English translation into French requires specifying adjective gender. English distinguishes gender in pronouns, where Mandarin does not; thus, translating a third-person singular pronoun *tā* from Mandarin to English (*he*, *she*, or *it*) requires deciding who the original referent was. In Japanese, because there is no single word for *is*, the translator must choose between *iru* or *aru*, according to whether or not the subject is animate.

The way that languages differ in lexically dividing up conceptual space may be more complex than this one-to-many translation problem, leading to many-to-many mappings. For example, Fig. 25.2 summarizes some of the complexities discussed by Hutchins and Somers (1992) in relating English *leg, foot*, and *paw*, to the French *Lexical gap* — *jambe, pied, patte*, etc. Further, one language may have a **lexical gap**, where no word or phrase, short of an explanatory footnote, can express the meaning of a word in the other language. For example, Japanese does not have a word for *privacy*, and English does not have a word for Japanese *oyakoko* or Chinese *xiáo* (we make do with the awkward phrase *filial piety* for both).

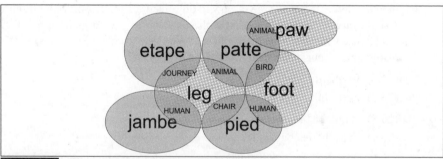

Figure 25.2   The complex overlap between English *leg*, *foot*, etc., and various French translations like *patte* discussed by Hutchins and Somers (1992).

25.2   Classical MT and the Vauquois Triangle

The next few sections introduce the classical pre-statistical architectures for machine translation. Real systems tend to involve combinations of elements from these three architectures; thus, each is best thought of as a point in an algorithmic design space rather than as an actual algorithm.

In **direct** translation, we proceed word-by-word through the source-language text, translating each word as we go. Direct translation uses a large bilingual dictionary, each of whose entries is a small program with the job of translating one word. In **transfer** approaches, we first parse the input text and then apply rules to transform the source-language parse into a target language parse. We then generate the target language sentence from the parse tree. In **interlingua** approaches, we analyze the source language text into some abstract meaning representation, called an **interlingua**. We then generate into the target language from this interlingual representation.

Vauquois triangle   A common way to visualize these three approaches is with the **Vauquois triangle** shown in Fig. 25.3. The triangle shows the increasing depth of analysis required (on both the analysis and generation end) as we move from the direct approach through transfer approaches to interlingual approaches. In addition, it shows the decreasing amount of transfer knowledge needed as we move up the triangle, from huge amounts of transfer at the direct level (almost all knowledge is transfer knowledge for each word) through transfer (transfer rules only for parse trees or thematic roles) through interlingua (no specific transfer knowledge).

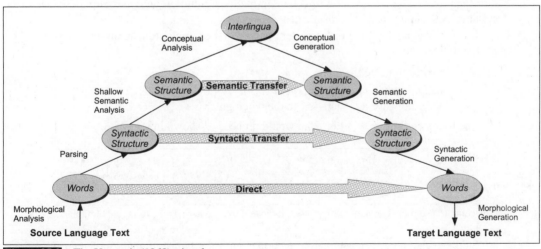

Figure 25.3   The Vauquois (1968) triangle.

In the next sections we show how these algorithms address some of the four translation examples shown in Fig. 25.4.

English	Mary didn't slap the green witch
⇒ Spanish	*Maria no dió una bofetada a la bruja verde*
	Mary not gave a slap to the witch green
English	The green witch is at home this week
⇒ German	*Diese Woche ist die grüne Hexe zu Hause.*
	this week is the green witch at house
English	He adores listening to music
⇒ Japanese	*kare ha ongaku wo kiku no ga daisuki desu*
	he music to listening adores
Chinese	*cheng long dao xiang gang qu*
	Jackie Chan to Hong Kong go
⇒ English	Jackie Chan went to Hong Kong

Figure 25.4   Example sentences used throughout the chapter.

25.2.1   Direct Translation

Direct translation   In **direct translation**, we proceed word-by-word through the source-language text, translating each word as we go. We make use of no intermediate structures, except for shallow morphological analysis; each source word is directly mapped onto some target word. Direct translation is thus based on a large bilingual dictionary; each entry in the dictionary can be viewed as a small program whose job is to translate one word. After the words are translated, simple reordering rules can apply, for example, for moving adjectives after nouns when translating from English to French.

The guiding intuition of the direct approach is that we translate by incrementally **transforming** the source-language text into a target-language text. While the pure direct approach is no longer used, this transformational intuition underlies all modern systems, both statistical and non-statistical.

Let's look at a simplified direct system on our first example, translating from English into Spanish:

(25.10)   Mary didn't slap the green witch

Maria no dió una bofetada a la bruja verde
Mary not gave a slap to the witch green

The four steps outlined in Fig. 25.5 would proceed as shown in Fig. 25.6.

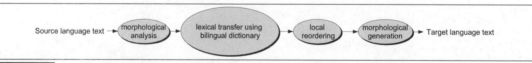

Figure 25.5   Direct machine translation. The major component, indicated by size here, is the bilingual dictionary.

Step 2 presumes that the bilingual dictionary has the phrase *dar una bofetada a* as the Spanish translation of English *slap*. The local reordering step 3 would need to switch the adjective-noun ordering from *green witch* to *bruja verde*. And some combination of ordering rules and the dictionary would deal with the negation and past tense in English *didn't*. These dictionary entries can be quite complex; a sample dictionary entry from an early direct English-Russian system is shown in Fig. 25.7.

Input:	Mary didn't slap the green witch
After 1: Morphology	Mary DO-PAST not slap the green witch
After 2: Lexical Transfer	Maria PAST no dar una bofetada a la verde bruja
After 3: Local reordering	Maria no dar PAST una bofetada a la bruja verde
After 4: Morphology	Maria no dió una bofetada a la bruja verde

Figure 25.6   An example of processing in a direct system.

---

function DIRECT_TRANSLATE_MUCH/MANY(word) **returns** Russian translation

if preceding word is *how* **return** *skol'ko*
else if preceding word is *as* **return** *stol'ko zhe*
else if word is *much*
  if preceding word is *very* **return** nil
  else if following word is a noun **return** *mnogo*
else /* word is many */
  if preceding word is a preposition and following word is a noun **return** *mnogii*
  else return *mnogo*

Figure 25.7   A procedure for translating *much* and *many* into Russian, adapted from Hutchins' (1986, pg. 133) discussion of Panov (1960). Note the similarity to decision list algorithms for word sense disambiguation.

While the direct approach can deal with our simple Spanish example and can handle single-word reorderings, it has no parsing component or indeed any knowledge about phrasing or grammatical structure in the source or target language. It thus cannot reliably handle longer-distance reorderings or those involving phrases or larger structures. This can happen even in languages very similar to English, like German, where adverbs like *heute* ("today") occur in different places and the subject (e.g., *die grüne Hexe*) can occur after the main verb, as shown in Fig. 25.8.

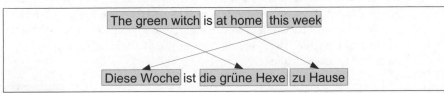

Figure 25.8   Complex reorderings necessary when translating from English to German. German often puts adverbs in initial position that English would more naturally put later. German tensed verbs often occur in second position in the sentence, causing the subject and verb to be inverted.

Similar kinds of reorderings happen between Chinese (where goal PPs often occur pre-verbally) and English (where goal PPs must occur post-verbally), as shown in Fig. 25.9.

Finally, even more complex reorderings occur when we translate from SVO to SOV languages, as we see in the English-Japanese example from Yamada and Knight (2002):

(25.11) He adores listening to music
    kare ha ongaku wo kiku   no ga daisuki desu
    he   music to listening   adores

Chinese goal PPs often occur pre-verbally, unlike in English.

These three examples suggest that the direct approach is too focused on individual words and that in order to deal with real examples we need to add phrasal and structural knowledge into our MT models. We flesh out this intuition in the next section.

25.2.2 Transfer

As Section 25.1 illustrated, languages differ systematically in structural ways. One strategy for doing MT is to translate by a process of overcoming these differences, altering the structure of the input to make it conform to the rules of the target language. *Contrastive knowledge* This can be done by applying **contrastive knowledge**, that is, knowledge about the differences between the two languages. Systems that use this strategy are said to be *Transfer model* based on the **transfer model**.

The transfer model presupposes a parse of the source language and is followed by a generation phase to actually create the output sentence. Thus, on this model, MT involves three phases: **analysis**, **transfer**, and **generation**, where transfer bridges the gap between the output of the source-language parser and the input to the target-language generator.

It is worth noting that a parse for MT may differ from parses required for other purposes. For example, suppose we need to translate *John saw the girl with the binoculars* into French. The parser does not need to bother to figure out where the prepositional phrase attaches, because both possibilities lead to the same French sentence.

Once we have parsed the source language, we'll need rules for **syntactic transfer** and **lexical transfer**. The syntactic transfer rules will tell us how to modify the source parse tree to resemble the target parse tree.

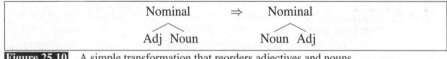

A simple transformation that reorders adjectives and nouns.

Figure 25.10 gives an intuition for simple cases like adjective-noun reordering; we transform one parse tree, suitable for describing an English phrase, into another parse tree, suitable for describing a Spanish sentence. These **syntactic transformations** are *Syntactic transformations* operations that map from one tree structure to another.

The transfer approach and this rule can be applied to our example *Mary did not slap the green witch*. Besides this transformation rule, we'll need to assume that the morphological processing figures out that *didn't* is composed of *do-PAST* plus *not*, and that the parser attaches the PAST feature onto the VP. Lexical transfer, through lookup in the bilingual dictionary, will then remove *do*, change *not* to *no*, and turn *slap* into the phrase *dar una bofetada a*, with a slight rearrangement of the parse tree, as suggested in Fig. 25.11.

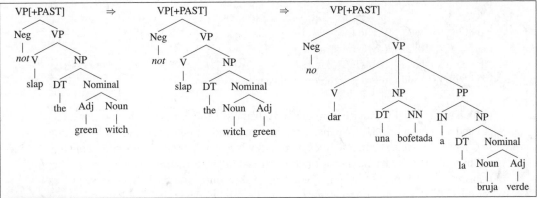

Figure 25.11   A further sketch of the transfer approach.

For translating from SVO languages like English to SOV languages like Japanese, we'll need even more complex transformations, for moving the verb to the end, changing prepositions into postpositions, and so on. An example of the result of such rules is shown in Fig. 25.12. An informal sketch of some transfer rules is shown in Fig. 25.13.

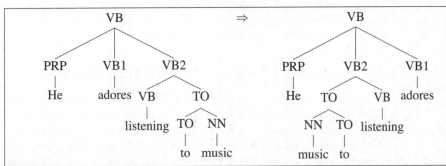

Figure 25.12   The result of Yamada and Knight's (2001) syntactic transformations from English order (SVO) to Japanese order (SOV) for the sentence *He adores listening to music* (*kare ha ongaku wo kiku no ga daisuki desu*). This transform would require rules for moving verbs after their NP and VP complements, and changing prepositions to postpositions.

Figure 25.13 also shows that transfer systems can be based on richer structures than just pure syntactic parses. For example, a transfer-based system for translating Chinese to English might have rules to deal with the fact shown in Fig. 25.9 that in Chinese PPs that fill the semantic role GOAL (like *to the store* in *I went to the store*) tend to appear before the verb, while in English these goal PPs must appear after the verb. For a transformation to be built to deal with this and related PP ordering differences, the parse of the Chinese must include thematic structure, so as to distinguish BENEFACTIVE PPs (which must occur before the verb) from DIRECTION and LOCATIVE PPs

	English to Spanish:		
1.	NP → Adjective$_1$ Noun$_2$	⇒	NP → Noun$_2$ Adjective$_1$
	Chinese to English:		
2.	VP → PP[+Goal] V	⇒	VP → V PP[+Goal]
	English to Japanese:		
3.	VP → V NP	⇒	VP → NP V
4.	PP → P NP	⇒	PP → NP P
5.	NP → NP$_1$ Rel. Clause$_2$	⇒	NP → Rel. Clause$_2$ NP$_1$

Figure 25.13   An informal description of some transformations.

(which preferentially occur before the verb) from RECIPIENT PPs (which occur after) (Li and Thompson, 1981). We discussed how to do this kind of semantic role labeling in Chapter 20. Using semantic roles in this way is generally called **semantic transfer**.

Semantic transfer

In addition to syntactic transformations, transfer-based systems need to have lexical transfer rules. Lexical transfer is generally based on a bilingual dictionary, just as for direct MT. The dictionary itself can also be used to deal with problems of lexical ambiguity. For example, the English word *home* has many possible translations in German, including *nach Hause* (in the sense of *going home*), *Heim* (in the sense of a *home game*), *Heimat* (in the sense of *homeland*, *home country*, or *spiritual home*), and *zu Hause* (in the sense of being *at home*). In this case, the phrase *at home* is very likely to be translated *zu Hause*, so the bilingual dictionary can list this translation idiomatically.

Many cases of lexical transfer are too complex to handle with a phrasal dictionary. In these cases, transfer systems can do disambiguation during the source-language analysis by applying the sense disambiguation techniques of Chapter 20.

25.2.3   Combined Direct and Transfer Approaches in Classic MT

Although the transfer metaphor offers the ability to deal with more complex source language phenomena than the direct approach, it turns out the simple SVO → SOV rules we've described above are not sufficient. In practice, we need messy rules that combine rich lexical knowledge of both languages with syntactic and semantic features. We briefly saw an example of such a rule for changing *slap* to *dar una bofetada a*.

For this reason, commercial MT systems tend to be combinations of the direct and transfer approaches, using rich bilingual dictionaries but also using taggers and parsers. The Systran system, for example, as described in Hutchins and Somers (1992), Senellart et al. (2001), has three components.

First is a shallow **analysis** stage, including

- Morphological analysis and part-of-speech tagging
- Chunking of NPs, PPs, and larger phrases
- Shallow dependency parsing (subjects, passives, head modifiers)

Next is a **transfer** phase, including

- Translation of idioms
- Word sense disambiguation

- Assignment of prepositions according to governing verbs

Finally is the **synthesis** stage, including

- Lexical translation with a rich bilingual dictionary to do lexical translation
- Reorderings
- Morphological generation

Thus, like the direct system, the Systran system relies for much of its processing on the bilingual dictionary, which has lexical, syntactic, and semantic knowledge. Also like a direct system, Systran does reordering in a post-processing step. But like a transfer system, the Systran system informs many of its steps by syntactic and shallow semantic processing of the source language.

25.2.4   The Interlingua Idea: Using Meaning

One problem with the transfer model is that it requires a distinct set of transfer rules for each pair of languages. This is clearly suboptimal for translation systems employed in many-to-many multilingual environments like the European Union.

This suggests a different perspective on the nature of translation. Instead of directly transforming the words of the source-language sentence into the target language, the interlingua intuition is to treat translation as a process of extracting the meaning of the input and then expressing that meaning in the target language. If this could be done, an MT system could do without contrastive knowledge, merely relying on the same syntactic and semantic rules used by a standard interpreter and generator for the language. The amount of knowledge needed would then be proportional to the number of languages the system handles, rather than to the square of that number.

Interlingua   This scheme presupposes the existence of a meaning representation, or **interlingua**, in a language-independent canonical form, like the semantic representations we saw in Chapter 17. The idea is for the interlingua to represent all sentences that mean the "same" thing in the same way, regardless of the language they happen to be in. This model translates by performing a deep semantic analysis on the input from language X into the interlingual representation and generating from the interlingua to language Y.

What kind of representation scheme can we use as an interlingua? First order logic or a variant such as minimal recursion semantics is one possibility. Semantic decomposition into some kind of atomic semantic primitives is another. We will illustrate a third common approach, a simple event-based representation, in which events are linked to their arguments through a small fixed set of thematic roles. Whether we use logic or other representations of events, we'll need to specify temporal and aspectual properties of the events, and we'll also need to represent non-eventive relationships between entities, such as the *has-color* relation between *green* and *witch*. Figure 25.14 shows a possible interlingual representation for *Mary did not slap the green witch* as a unification-style feature structure.

We can create these interlingual representation from the source-language text by using the **semantic analyzer** techniques of Chapters 18 and 20. A semantic role labeler can discover the AGENT relation between *Mary* and the *slap* event, or the THEME relation between the *witch* and the *slap* event. We would also need to disambiguate the noun-modifier relation to recognize that the relationship between *green* and *witch*

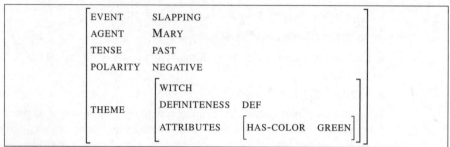

$$\begin{bmatrix} \text{EVENT} & \text{SLAPPING} \\ \text{AGENT} & \text{MARY} \\ \text{TENSE} & \text{PAST} \\ \text{POLARITY} & \text{NEGATIVE} \\ \text{THEME} & \begin{bmatrix} \text{WITCH} \\ \text{DEFINITENESS} & \text{DEF} \\ \text{ATTRIBUTES} & [\text{HAS-COLOR} \quad \text{GREEN}] \end{bmatrix} \end{bmatrix}$$

Figure 25.14   Interlingual representation of *Mary did not slap the green witch.*

is the *has-color* relation, and we'll need to discover that this event has negative polarity (from the word *didn't*). The interlingua thus requires more analysis work than the transfer model, which required only syntactic parsing (or at most, shallow thematic role labeling). But generation can now proceed directly from the interlingua with no need for syntactic transformations.

In addition to doing without syntactic transformations, the interlingual system does without lexical transfer rules. Recall our earlier problem of whether to translate *know* into French as *savoir* or *connaître*. Most of the processing involved in making this decision is not specific to the goal of translating into French; German, Spanish, and Chinese all make similar distinctions, and furthermore, the disambiguation of *know* into concepts such as HAVE-A-PROPOSITION-IN-MEMORY and BE-ACQUAINTED-WITH-ENTITY is also important for other NLU applications that require word senses. Thus, by using such concepts in an interlingua, a larger part of the translation process can be done with general language processing techniques and modules, and the processing specific to the English-to-French translation task can be eliminated or at least reduced, as suggested in Fig. 25.3.

The interlingual model has its own problems. For example, for translation from Japanese to Chinese, the universal interlingua must include concepts such as ELDER-BROTHER and YOUNGER-BROTHER. Using these same concepts, translating from German-to-English would then require large amounts of unnecessary disambiguation. Furthermore, doing the extra work involved by the interlingua commitment requires exhaustive analysis of the semantics of the domain and formalization into an ontology. Generally, this is only possible in relatively simple domains based on a database model, as in the air travel, hotel reservation, or restaurant recommendation domains, where the database definition determines the possible entities and relations. For these reasons, interlingual systems are generally only used in sublanguage domains.

25.3   Statistical MT

The three classic architectures for MT (direct, transfer, and interlingua) all provide answers to the questions of what representations to use and what steps to perform to translate. But there is another way to approach the problem of translation: to focus on the result, not the process. Taking this perspective, let's consider what it means for a sentence to be a translation of some other sentence.

This is an issue to which philosophers of translation have given a lot of thought. The consensus seems to be, sadly, that it is impossible for a sentence in one language to be a translation of a sentence in an other, strictly speaking. For example, one cannot really translate Hebrew *adonai roi* ("the Lord is my shepherd") into the language of a culture that has no sheep. On one hand, we can write something that is clear in the target language, at some cost in fidelity to the original, something like *the Lord will look after me*. On the other hand, we can be faithful to the original, at the cost of producing something obscure to the target-language readers, perhaps like *the Lord is for me like somebody who looks after animals with cotton-like hair*. As another example, if we translate the Japanese phrase *fukaku hansei shite orimasu*, as *we apologize*, we are not being faithful to the meaning of the original, but if we produce *we are deeply reflecting (on our past behavior, and what we did wrong, and how to avoid the problem next time)*, then our output is unclear or awkward. Problems such as these arise not only for culture-specific concepts, but whenever one language uses a metaphor, a construction, a word, or a tense without an exact parallel in the other language.

So, true translation, which is both faithful to the source language and natural as an utterance in the target language, is sometimes impossible. If you are going to go ahead and produce a translation anyway, you have to compromise. This is exactly what translators do in practice: they produce translations that do tolerably well on both criteria.

This provides us with a hint for how to do MT. We can model the goal of translation as the production of an output that maximizes some value function that represents the importance of both faithfulness and fluency. Statistical MT is the name for a class of approaches that do just this by building probabilistic models of faithfulness and fluency and then combining these models to choose the most probable translation. If we chose the product of faithfulness and fluency as our quality metric, we could model the translation from a source-language sentence S to a target-language sentence $\hat{T}$ as

$$\text{best-translation } \hat{T} = \text{argmax}_T \text{ faithfulness(T,S) fluency(T)}$$

This intuitive equation clearly resembles the Bayesian **noisy channel model** we've seen in Chapter 5 for spelling and Chapter 9 for speech. Let's make the analogy perfect and formalize the noisy channel model for statistical machine translation.

First of all, for the rest of this chapter, we'll assume we are translating from a foreign language sentence $F = f_1, f_2, ..., f_m$ to English. For some examples we'll use French as the foreign language, and for others Spanish. But in each case we are translating **into English** (although of course the statistical model also works for translating out of English). In a probabilistic model, the best English sentence $\hat{E} = e_1, e_2, ..., e_l$ is the one whose probability $P(E\,F)$ is the highest. As is usual in the noisy channel model, we can rewrite this with Bayes' rule:

$$
\begin{aligned}
\hat{E} &= \text{argmax}_E P(E\,F) \\
&= \text{argmax}_E \frac{P(F\,E)P(E)}{P(F)} \\
&= \text{argmax}_E P(F\,E)P(E)
\end{aligned}
\tag{25.12}
$$

We can ignore the denominator $P(F)$ inside the argmax since we are choosing the best English sentence for a fixed foreign sentence F, and hence $P(F)$ is a constant. The resulting noisy channel equation shows that we need two components: a **translation model** $P(F\ E)$ and a **language model** $P(E)$.

Translation model
Language model

$$\hat{E} = \underset{E\in\text{English}}{\text{argmax}}\quad \overbrace{P(F\ E)}^{\text{translation model}}\quad \overbrace{P(E)}^{\text{language model}} \tag{25.13}$$

Notice that applying the noisy channel model to machine translation requires that we think of things backwards, as shown in Fig. 25.15. We pretend that the foreign (source-language) input F we must translate is a corrupted version of some English (target-language) sentence E, and that our task is then to discover this hidden (target-language) sentence E that generated our observation sentence F.

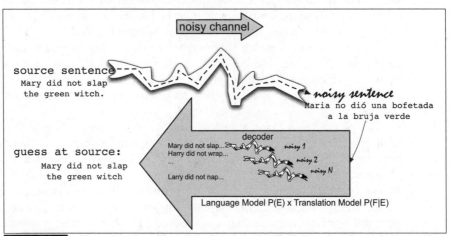

Figure 25.15   The noisy channel model of statistical MT. To translate Spanish (source language) to English (target language), we instead think of "sources" and "targets" backwards. We build a model of the generation process from an English sentence through a channel to a Spanish sentence. Now given a Spanish sentence to translate, we pretend it is the output of an English sentence going through the noisy channel, and search for the best possible "source" English sentence.

The noisy channel model of statistical MT thus requires three components to translate from a French sentence F to an English sentence E:

- A **language model** to compute $P(E)$
- A **translation model** to compute $P(F\ E)$
- A **decoder**, which is given F and produces the most probable E

Of these three components, we have already introduced the language model $P(E)$ in Chapter 4. Statistical MT systems are based on the same N-gram language models as speech recognition and other applications. The language model component is monolingual, so acquiring training data is relatively easy.

The next few sections therefore concentrate on the other two components: the translation model and the decoding algorithm.

25.4 $P(F\ E)$: The Phrase-Based Translation Model

The job of the translation model, given an English sentence E and a foreign sentence F, is to assign a probability that E generates F. While we can estimate these probabilities by thinking about how each individual word is translated, modern statistical MT is based on the intuition that a better way to compute these probabilities is by considering the behavior of **phrases**. As we see in Fig. 25.16, repeated from page 869, entire *Phrase-based* phrases often need to be translated and moved as a unit. The intuition of **phrase-based** statistical MT is to use phrases (sequences of words) as well as single words as the fundamental units of translation.

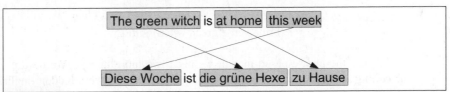

Figure 25.16   Phrasal reorderings necessary when generating German from English; repeated from Fig. 25.8.

There are a wide variety of phrase-based models; in this section we sketch the model of Koehn et al. (2003). We use a Spanish example, seeing how the phrase-based model computes the probability P(*Maria no dió una bofetada a la bruja verde Mary did not slap the green witch*).

The generative story of phrase-based translation has three steps. First, we group the English source words into phrases $\bar{e}_1, \bar{e}_2...\bar{e}_I$. Next, we translate each English phrase $\bar{e}_i$ into a Spanish phrase $\bar{f}_i$. Finally, we (optionally) reorder each of the Spanish phrases.

The probability model for phrase-based translation relies on a **translation probability** and a **distortion probability**. The factor $\phi(\bar{f}_i\ \bar{e}_i)$ is the translation probability of generating Spanish phrase $\bar{f}_i$ from English phrase $\bar{e}_i$. The reordering of the Spanish phrases is done by the **distortion** probability d. Distortion in statistical machine trans- *Distortion* lation refers to a word having a different ("distorted") position in the Spanish sentence than it had in the English sentence; it is thus a measure of the **distance** between the positions of a phrase in the two languages. The distortion probability in phrase-based MT means the probability of two consecutive English phrases being separated in Spanish by a span (of Spanish words) of a particular length. More formally, the distortion is parameterized by $d(a_i - b_{i-1})$, where a_i is the start position of the foreign (Spanish) phrase generated by the ith English phrase $\bar{e}_i$, and b_{i-1} is the end position of the foreign (Spanish) phrase generated by the $i-1$th English phrase $\bar{e}_{i-1}$. We can use a simple distortion probability, in which we simply raise some small constant α to the distortion: $d(a_i - b_{i-1}) = \alpha^{a_i-b_{i-1}-1}$. This distortion model penalizes large distortions by giving lower and lower probability the larger the distortion.

The final translation model for phrase-based MT is

$$P(F\ E) = \prod_{i=1}^{I} \phi(\bar{f}_i, \bar{e}_i)d(a_i - b_{i-1}) \tag{25.14}$$

Let's consider the following particular set of phrases for our example sentences:[2]

Position	1	2	3		4	5
English	Mary	did not	slap		the	green witch
Spanish	Maria	no	dió una bofetada	a la	bruja verde

Since each phrase follows directly in order (nothing moves around in this example, unlike the German example in (25.16)), the distortions are all 1 and the probability $P(F\ E)$ can be computed as

$$
\begin{aligned}
P(F\ E) = \ & P(\text{Maria, Mary}) \quad d(1) \quad P(\text{no did not}) \quad d(1) \\
& P(\text{dió una bofetada slap}) \quad d(1) \quad P(\text{a la the}) \quad d(1) \\
& P(\text{bruja verde green witch}) \quad d(1) \quad\quad\quad\quad\quad (25.15)
\end{aligned}
$$

To use the phrase-based model, we need two more things. We need a model of **decoding** so that we can go from a surface Spanish string to a hidden English string. And we need a model of **training**, so that we can learn parameters. We introduce the decoding algorithm in Section 25.8. Let's turn first to training.

How do we learn the simple phrase-based translation probability model in (25.14)? The main set of parameters that needs to be trained is the set of phrase translation probabilities $\phi(\bar{f}_i, \bar{e}_i)$.

These parameters, as well as the distortion constant α, could be set if only we had a large bilingual training set, in which each Spanish sentence was paired with an English sentence and if, furthermore, we knew exactly which phrase in the Spanish sentence was translated by which phrase in the English sentence. We call such a mapping a *Phrase alignment* **phrase alignment**.

The table of phrases above showed an implicit alignment of the phrases for this sentence, for example, *green witch* aligned with *bruja verde*. If we had a large training set with each pair of sentences labeled with such a phrase alignment, we could just count the number of times each phrase-pair occurred, and normalize to get probabilities:

$$
\phi(\bar{f}, \bar{e}) = \frac{\text{count}(\bar{f}, \bar{e})}{\sum_{\bar{f}} \text{count}(\bar{f}, \bar{e})} \quad\quad\quad (25.16)
$$

Phrase-translation table We could store each phrase pair $(\bar{f}, \bar{e})$, together with its probability $\phi(\bar{f}, \bar{e})$, in a large **phrase-translation table**.

Alas, we don't have large, hand-labeled, phrase-aligned training sets. But it turns out that we can extract phrases from another kind of alignment called a **word align-** *Word alignment* **ment**. A word alignment is different from a phrase alignment because it shows exactly which Spanish word aligns to which English word inside each phrase. We can visualize a word alignment in various ways. Figures 25.17 and 25.18 show a graphical model and an alignment matrix, respectively, for a word alignment.

---

[2] Exactly which phrases we use depends on which phrases are discovered in the training process, as described in Section 25.7; thus, for example, if we don't see the phrase *green witch* in our training data, we would have to translate *green* and *witch* independently.

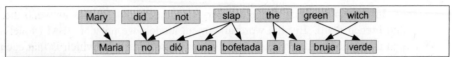

Figure 25.17   A graphical model representation of a word alignment between the English and Spanish sentences. We later show how to extract phrases.

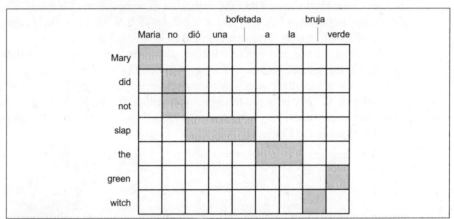

Figure 25.18   An alignment matrix representation of a word alignment between the English and Spanish sentences. We later show how to extract phrases.

The next section introduces a few algorithms for deriving word alignments. We then show in Section 25.7 how we can extract a phrase table from word alignments, and finally, in Section 25.8 how the phrase table can be used in decoding.

25.5   Alignment in MT

Word alignment   All statistical translation models are based on the idea of **word alignment**. A word alignment is a mapping between the source words and the target words in a set of parallel sentences.

Figure 25.19 illustrates an alignment between the English sentence *And the program has been implemented* and the French sentence *Le programme a été mis en application*. For now, we assume that we already know which sentences in the English text alignwith which sentences in the French text.

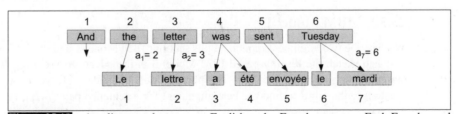

Figure 25.19   An alignment between an English and a French sentence. Each French word aligns to a single English word.

897

In principle, we can have arbitrary alignment relationships between the English and French word. But the word alignment models we present (IBM Models 1 and 3 and the HMM model) make a more stringent requirement, which is that each French word comes from exactly one English word; this is consistent with Fig. 25.19. One advantage of this assumption is that we can represent an alignment by giving the index number of the English word that the French word comes from. We can thus represent the alignment shown in Fig. 25.19 as $A = 2,3,4,4,5,6,6$. This is a likely alignment. A most unlikely alignment, by contrast, might be $A = 3,3,3,3,3,3,3$.

We will make one addition to this basic alignment idea, which is to allow the appearance in the foreign sentence of words that don't align to any word in the English sentence. We model these words by assuming the existence of a NULL English word e_0 at position 0. Words in the foreign sentence that are not in the English sentence, *Spurious word* called **spurious words**, may be generated by e_0. Figure 25.20 shows the alignment of spurious Spanish *a* to English NULL.[3]

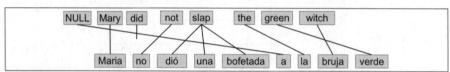

Figure 25.20   The alignment of the **spurious** Spanish word *a* to the English NULL word e_0.

While the simplified model of alignment above disallows many-to-one or many-to-many alignments, we will discuss more powerful translation models that allow such alignments. Here are two such sample alignments; in Fig. 25.21 we see an alignment that is many-to-one; each French word does not align to a single English word, although each English word does align to a single French word.

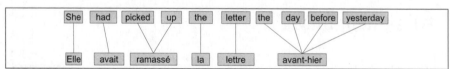

Figure 25.21   An alignment between an English and a French sentence, in which each French word does not align to a single English word, but each English word aligns to one French word.

Figure 25.22 shows an even more complex example, in which multiple English words *don't have any money* jointly align to the French words *sont démunis*. Such **phrasal alignments** are necessary for phrasal MT, but it turns out they can't be directly generated by the IBM Model 1, Model 3, or HMM word alignment algorithms.

25.5.1   IBM Model 1

We describe two alignment models in this section: IBM Model 1 and the HMM model (we also sketch the fertility-based IBM Model 3 in the advanced section). Both are **statistical alignment** algorithms. For phrase-based statistical MT, we use the alignment algorithms just to find the best alignment for a sentence pair (F, E), in order to

---

[3]   While this particular *a* might instead be aligned to English *slap*, there are many cases of spurious words that have no other possible alignment site.

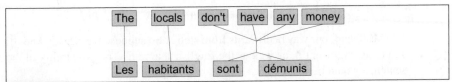

Figure 25.22   An alignment between an English and a French sentence, in which there is a many-to-many alignment between English and French words.

help extract a set of phrases. But we can also use these word alignment algorithms as a translation model $P(F,E)$ as well. As we show, the relationship between alignment and translation can be expressed as follows:

$$P(F \mid E) \; = \; \sum_A P(F, A \mid E)$$

We start with IBM Model 1, so called because it is the first and simplest of five models proposed by IBM researchers in a seminal paper (Brown et al., 1993).

Here's the general IBM Model 1 generative story for how we generate a Spanish sentence from an English sentence $E = e_1, e_2, ..., e_I$ of length I:

1. Choose a length J for the Spanish sentence, henceforth $F = f_1, f_2, ..., f_J$.
2. Now choose an alignment $A = a_1, a_2, ..., a_J$ between the English and Spanish sentences.
3. Now for each position j in the Spanish sentence, choose a Spanish word f_j by translating the English word that is aligned to it.

Figure 25.23 illustrates this generative process.

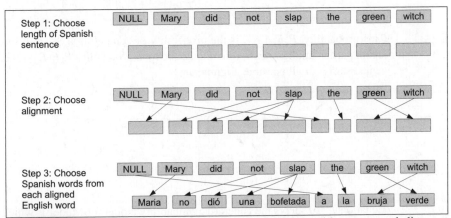

Figure 25.23   The three steps of IBM Model 1 generating a Spanish sentence and alignment from an English sentence.

Let's see how this generative story assigns a probability $P(F \mid E)$ of generating the Spanish sentence F from the English sentence E. We'll use this terminology:

- e_{a_j} is the English word that is aligned to the Spanish word f_j

- $t(f_x\ e_y)$ is the probability of translating e_y by f_x (i.e., $P(f_x\ e_y)$)

We'll work our way backwards from step 3. So suppose we already knew the length J and the alignment A, as well as the English source E. The probability of the Spanish sentence would be

$$P(F\ E,A) = \prod_{j=1}^{J} t(f_j\ e_{a_j}) \tag{25.17}$$

Now let's formalize steps 1 and 2 of the generative story. This is the probability $P(A\ E)$ of an alignment A (of length J) given the English sentence E. IBM Model 1 makes the (very) simplifying assumption that each alignment is equally likely. How many possible alignments are there between an English sentence of length I and a Spanish sentence of length J? Again assuming that each Spanish word must come from one of the I English words (or the 1 NULL word), there are $(I+1)^J$ possible alignments. Model 1 also assumes that the probability of choosing length J is some small constant ϵ. The combined probability of choosing a length J and then choosing any particular one of the $(I+1)^J$ possible alignments is

$$P(A\ E) = \frac{\epsilon}{(I+1)^J} \tag{25.18}$$

We can combine these probabilities as follows:

$$
\begin{aligned}
P(F,A\ E) &= P(F\ E,A)\quad P(A\ E) \\[2mm]
&= \frac{\epsilon}{(I+1)^J} \prod_{j=1}^{J} t(f_j\ e_{a_j})
\end{aligned}
\tag{25.19}
$$

This probability, $P(F,A\ E)$, is the probability of generating a Spanish sentence F through a particular alignment. To compute the total probability $P(F\ E)$ of generating F, we just sum over all possible alignments:

$$
\begin{aligned}
P(F\ E) &= \sum_A P(F,A\ E) \\[2mm]
&= \sum_A \frac{\epsilon}{(I+1)^J} \prod_{j=1}^{J} t(f_j\ e_{a_j})
\end{aligned}
\tag{25.20}
$$

Equation 25.20 shows the generative probability model for Model 1, which assigns a probability to each possible Spanish sentence F.

To find the best alignment between a pair of sentences F and E, we need a way to **decode** using this probabilistic model. It turns out there is a very simple polynomial algorithm for computing the best (Viterbi) alignment with Model 1 because the best alignment for each word is independent of the decision about best alignments of the surrounding words:

$$\hat{A} = \operatorname*{argmax}_{A} P(F, A\ E)$$

$$= \operatorname*{argmax}_{A} \frac{\epsilon}{(I+1)^J} \prod_{j=1}^{J} t(f_j\ e_{a_j})$$

$$= \operatorname*{argmax}_{a_j} t(f_j\ e_{a_j}) \qquad 1 < j < J \qquad (25.21)$$

Training for Model 1 is done by the EM algorithm, which we cover in Section 25.6.

25.5.2   HMM Alignment

Now that we've seen Model 1, it should be clear that it makes some really appalling simplifying assumptions. One of the most egregious is the assumption that all alignments are equally likely. One way in which this is a bad assumption is that alignments tend to preserve **locality**; neighboring words in English are often aligned with neighboring words in Spanish. If we look back at the Spanish/English alignment in Fig. 25.17, for example, we can see this locality in the neighboring alignments. The HMM alignment model captures this kind of locality by conditioning each alignment decision on previous decisions. Let's see how this works.

The HMM alignment model is based on the familiar HMM model we've now seen in many chapters. As with IBM Model 1, we are trying to compute $P(F, A\ E)$. The HMM model is based on a restructuring of this probability, using the chain rule as follows:

$$P(f_1^J, a_1^J\ e_1^I) = P(J\ e_1^I)\ \prod_{j=1}^{J} P(f_j, a_j\ f_1^{j-1}, a_1^{j-1}, e_1^I)$$

$$= P(J\ e_1^I)\ \prod_{j-1}^{J} P(a_j\ f_1^{j-1}, a_1^{j-1}, e_1^I)\ \ P(f_j\ f_1^{j-1}, a_1^{j}, e_1^I) \ (25.22)$$

Through this restructuring, we can think of $P(F, A\ E)$ as being computable from probabilities of the following three types: a length probability $P(J\ e_1^I)$, an alignment probabilityi $P(a_j\ f_1^{j-1}, a_1^{j-1}, e_1^I)$, and a lexicon probability $P(f_j\ f_1^{j-1}, a_1^{j}, e_1^I)$.

We next make some standard Markov simplifying assumptions. We assume that the probability of a particular alignment a_j for Spanish word j depends only on the previous aligned position a_{j-1}. We also assume that the probability of a Spanish word f_j depends only on the aligned English word e_{a_j} at position a_j:

$$P(a_j\ f_1^{j-1}, a_1^{j-1}, e_1^I) = P(a_j\ a_{j-1}, I) \qquad (25.23)$$

$$P(f_j\ f_1^{j-1}, a_1^{j}, e_1^I) = P(f_j\ e_{a_j}) \qquad (25.24)$$

Finally, we assume that the length probability can be approximated just as $P(J\ I)$.

Thus, the probabilistic model for HMM alignment is

$$P(f_1^J, a_1^J \, e_1^I) \;=\; P(J \, I) \; \prod_{j=1}^{J} P(a_j \, a_{j-1}, I) P(f_j \, e_{a_j}) \tag{25.25}$$

To get the total probability of the Spanish sentence $P(f_1^J \, e_1^I)$, we need to sum over all alignments:

$$P(f_1^J \, e_1^I) \;=\; P(J \, I) \; \sum_A \prod_{j=1}^{J} P(a_j \, a_{j-1}, I) P(f_j \, e_{a_j}) \tag{25.26}$$

As we suggested at the beginning of the section, we've conditioned the alignment probability $P(a_j \, a_{j-1}, I)$ on the previous aligned word, to capture the locality of alignments. Let's rephrase this probability for a moment as $P(i \, i', I)$, where i stands for the absolute positions in the English sentence of consecutive aligned states in the Spanish sentence. We'd like to make these probabilities dependent not on the absolute word *Jump width* positions i and i', but rather on the **jump width** between words; the jump width is the distance between their positions $i' - i$. This is because our goal is to capture the fact that *'the English words that generate neighboring Spanish words are likely to be nearby'*. We thus don't want to be keeping separate probabilities for each absolute word position like $P(7 \, 6, 15)$ and $P(8 \, 7, 15)$. Instead, we compute alignment probabilities by using a non-negative function of the jump width:

$$P(i \, i', I) = \frac{c(i - i')}{\sum_{i''=1}^{I} c(i'' - i')} \tag{25.27}$$

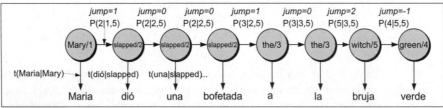

Figure 25.24   The HMM alignment model generating from *Mary slappped the green witch*, showing the alignment and lexicon components of the probability $P(F, A \, E)$ for this particular alignment.

Figure 25.24 illustrates how the HMM model gives the probability of a particular alignment of a simplified version of our English-Spanish sentences *Maria dió una bofetada a la bruja verde*. The probability $P(F, A \, E)$ for this alignment is the following product:

$$\begin{aligned}
P(F, A \, E) \;=\;\; & P(J \, I) \quad P(Maria \, Mary) \quad P(2 \, 1, 5) \quad t(di\acute{o} \; slapped) \\
& P(2 \, 2, 5) \quad T(una \; slapped) \quad P(2 \, 2, 5) \quad \dots
\end{aligned} \tag{25.28}$$

There are also more sophisticated augmentations to the basic HMM alignment model. These include adding NULL words in the English source to align with Spanish words that don't align with English words or conditioning the alignment on $C(e_{a_{j-1}})$, the word class of the preceding target word: $P(a_j \, a_{j-1}, I, C(e_{a_{j-1}}))$ (Och and Ney, 2003; Toutanova et al., 2002).

The main advantage of the HMM alignment model is that there are well-understood algorithms for decoding and training. For decoding, we can use the Viterbi algorithm of Chapters 5 and 6 to find the best (Viterbi) alignment for a sentence pair (F,E). For training, we can use the Baum-Welch algorithm of Chapters 6 and 9 as summarized in the next section.

25.6   Training Alignment Models

Parallel corpus
Bitext

All statistical translation models are trained with a large **parallel corpus**. A **parallel corpus**, **parallel text**, or **bitext** is a text that is available in two languages. For example, the proceedings of the Canadian Parliament are kept in both French and English. Each

Hansards
Hong Kong Hansards

sentence spoken in Parliament is translated, producing a volume with running text in both languages. These volumes are called **Hansards**, after the publisher of the British parliamentary proceedings. Similarly, the **Hong Kong Hansards** corpus contains the proceedings of the Hong Kong SAR Legislative Council in both English and Chinese. Both of these corpora contain tens of millions to hundreds of millions of words. Other parallel corpora have been made available by the United Nations. It is possible to make parallel corpora out of literary translations, but this is less common for MT purposes, partly because it is difficult to acquire the legal rights to fiction, but mainly because, as we saw at the beginning of the chapter, translating fiction is very difficult and translations are not very literal. Thus, statistical systems tend to be trained on very literal translations such as Hansards.

Sentence segmentation
Sentence alignment

The first step in training is to segment the corpus into sentences. This task is called **sentence segmentation** or **sentence alignment**. The simplest methods align sentences purely according to their length in words or characters, without looking at the contents of the words in the sentences. The intuition is that if we see a long sentence in roughly the same position in each language of the parallel text, we might suspect that these sentences are translations. This intuition can be implemented by a dynamic programming algorithm. More sophisticated algorithms also make use of information about word alignments. Sentence-alignment algorithms are run on a parallel corpus before MT models are trained. Sentences that don't align to anything are thrown out, and the remaining aligned sentences can be used as a training set. See the end of the chapter for pointers to more details on sentence segmentation.

Once we have done sentence alignment, the input to our training algorithm is a corpus consisting of S sentence pairs $(F_s, E_s) : s = 1 \ldots S$. For each sentence pair (F_s, E_s) the goal is to learn an alignment $A = a_1^J$ and the component probabilities (t for Model 1, and the lexicon and alignment probabilities for the HMM model).

25.6.1   EM for Training Alignment Models

If each sentence pair (F_s, E_s) were already hand-labeled with a perfect alignment, learning the Model 1 or HMM parameters would be trivial. For example, to get a maximum likelihood estimate in Model 1 for the translation probability $t(verde, green)$, we would just count the number of times *green* is aligned to *verde*, and normalize by the total count of *green*.

But of course we don't know the alignments in advance; all we have are the **probabilities** of each alignment. Recall that Eq. 25.19 showed that if we already had good estimates for the Model 1 t parameter, we could use this to compute probabilities $P(F, A E)$ for alignments. Given $P(F, A E)$, we can generate the probability of an alignment just by normalizing

$$P(A E, F) = \frac{P(A, F E)}{\sum_A P(A, F E)}$$

So, if we had a rough estimate of the Model 1 t parameters, we could compute the probability for each alignment. Then instead of estimating the t probabilities from the (unknown) perfect alignment, we would estimate them from each possible alignment and combine these estimates weighted by the probability of each alignment. For example for two possible alignments, one of probability .9 and one of probability .1, we would estimate the t parameters separately from the two alignments and mix these two estimates with weights of .9 and .1.

Thus, if we already had Model 1 parameters, we could **re-estimate** these parameters by using the original parameters to compute the probability of each possible alignment, and then using the weighted sum of alignments for re-estimation. This idea of iteratively improving our estimates of probabilities is a special case of the **EM algorithm** that we introduced in Chapter 6 and that we saw again for speech recognition in Chapter 9. Recall that we use the EM algorithm when we have a variable that we can't optimize directly because it is **hidden**. In this case, the hidden variable is the alignment. But we can use the EM algorithm to estimate the parameters, compute alignments from these estimates, use the alignments to re-estimate the parameters, and so on!

Let's walk through an example inspired by Knight (1999b), using a simplified version of Model 1, in which we ignore the NULL word and we consider only a subset of the alignments (ignoring alignments for which an English word aligns with no Spanish word). Hence we compute the simplified probability $P(A, F E)$ as follows:

$$P(A, F E) = \prod_{j=1}^{J} t(f_j e_{a_j}) \tag{25.29}$$

The goal of this example is just to give an intuition of EM applied to this task; the actual details of Model 1 training would be somewhat different.

The intuition of EM training is that in the E-step, we compute **expected counts** for the t parameter based on summing over the hidden variable (the alignment), while in the M-step, we compute the maximum likelihood estimate of the t probability from these counts.

Let's see a few stages of EM training of this parameter on a corpus of two sentences:

$$\begin{array}{cc} \text{green} & \text{house} \\ \text{casa} & \text{verde} \end{array} \qquad \begin{array}{cc} \text{the} & \text{house} \\ \text{la} & \text{casa} \end{array}$$

The vocabularies for the two languages are $E =$ green, house, the and $S =$ casa, la, verde . We start with uniform probabilities:

t(casa green) $= \frac{1}{3}$	t(verde green) $= \frac{1}{3}$	t(la green) $= \frac{1}{3}$
t(casa house) $= \frac{1}{3}$	t(verde house) $= \frac{1}{3}$	t(la house) $= \frac{1}{3}$
t(casa the) $= \frac{1}{3}$	t(verde the) $= \frac{1}{3}$	t(la the) $= \frac{1}{3}$

Now let's walk through the steps of EM:

E-step 1:   Compute the expected counts $E[\text{count}(t(f\ e))]$ for all word pairs (f_j, e_{a_j}).

E-step 1a: We first need to compute $P(a, f\ e)$ by multiplying all the t probabilities, following Eq. 25.29.

green house	green house	the house	the house
| |	casa verde (crossed)	| |	la casa (crossed)
casa verde	casa verde	la casa	la casa
$P(a, f\ e) = t(\text{casa,green})$	$P(a, f\ e) = t(\text{verde,green})$	$P(a, f\ e) = t(\text{la,the})$	$P(a, f\ e) = t(\text{casa,the})$
$t(\text{verde,house})$	$t(\text{casa,house})$	$t(\text{casa,house})$	$t(\text{la,house})$
$= \frac{1}{3}\ \frac{1}{3} = \frac{1}{9}$	$= \frac{1}{3}\ \frac{1}{3} = \frac{1}{9}$	$= \frac{1}{3}\ \frac{1}{3} = \frac{1}{9}$	$= \frac{1}{3}\ \frac{1}{3} = \frac{1}{9}$

E-step 1b: Normalize $P(a, f\ e)$ to get $P(a\ e, f)$, using the following:

$$P(a\ e, f) = \frac{P(a, f\ e)}{\sum_a P(a, f\ e)}$$

The resulting values of $P(a\ f, e)$ for each alignment are as follows:

green house	green house	the house	the house
casa verde	casa verde (crossed)	la casa	la casa (crossed)
$P(a\ f,e) = \frac{1/9}{2/9} = \frac{1}{2}$	$P(a\ f,e) = \frac{1/9}{2/9} = \frac{1}{2}$	$P(a\ f,e) = \frac{1/9}{2/9} = \frac{1}{2}$	$P(a\ f,e) = \frac{1/9}{2/9} = \frac{1}{2}$

E-step 1c: Compute expected (fractional) counts, by weighting each count by $P(a\ e, f)$.

tcount(casa green) $= \frac{1}{2}$	tcount(verde green) $= \frac{1}{2}$	tcount(la green) $= 0$	total(green) $= 1$
tcount(casa house) $= \frac{1}{2} + \frac{1}{2}$	tcount(verde house) $= \frac{1}{2}$	tcount(la house) $= \frac{1}{2}$	total(house) $= 2$
tcount(casa the) $= \frac{1}{2}$	tcount(verde the) $= 0$	tcount(la the) $= \frac{1}{2}$	total(the) $= 1$

M-step 1:   Compute the MLE probability parameters by normalizing the tcounts to sum to 1.

t(casa green) $= \frac{1/2}{1} = \frac{1}{2}$	t(verde green) $= \frac{1/2}{1} = \frac{1}{2}$	t(la green) $= \frac{0}{1} = 0$
t(casa house) $= \frac{1}{2} = \frac{1}{2}$	t(verde house) $= \frac{1/2}{2} = \frac{1}{4}$	t(la house) $= \frac{1/2}{2} = \frac{1}{4}$
t(casa the) $= \frac{1/2}{1} = \frac{1}{2}$	t(verde the) $= \frac{0}{1} = 0$	t(la the) $= \frac{1/2}{1} = \frac{1}{2}$

Note that each of the correct translations has increased in probability from the initial assignment; for example, the translation *casa* for *house* has increased in probability from $\frac{1}{3}$ to $\frac{1}{2}$.

E-step 2a: We recompute $P(a, f\ e)$, again by multiplying the t probabilities, following Eq. 25.29.

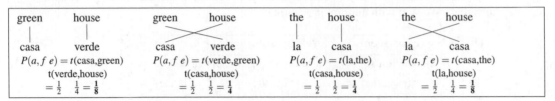

Note that the two correct alignments are now higher in probability than the two incorrect alignments. Performing the second and further round of E-steps and M-steps is left as Exercise 25.6 for the reader.

We have shown that we can use EM to learn the parameters for a simplified version of Model 1. Our intuitive algorithm, however, requires that we enumerate all possible alignments. For a long sentence, enumerating every possible alignment would be very inefficient. Luckily, in practice, a very efficient version of EM for Model 1 efficiently and implicitly sums over all alignments.

We also use EM, in the form of the Baum-Welch algorithm, for learning the parameters of the HMM model.

25.7   Symmetrizing Alignments for Phrase-Based MT

The reason we needed Model 1 or HMM alignments was to build word alignments on the training set so that we could extract aligned pairs of phrases.

Unfortunately, HMM (or Model 1) alignments are insufficient for extracting pairings of Spanish phrases with English phrases. This is because in the HMM model, each Spanish word must be generated from a single English word; we cannot generate a Spanish phrase from multiple English words. The HMM model thus cannot align a multiword phrase in the source language with a multiword phrase in the target language.

Symmetrizing

We can, however, extend the HMM model to produce phrase-to-phrase alignments for a pair of sentences (F, E), by a method called **symmetrizing**. First, we train two separate HMM aligners, an English-to-Spanish aligner and a Spanish-to-English aligner. We then align (F, E) by using both aligners. We can then combine these alignments in clever ways to get an alignment that maps phrases to phrases.

Intersection

To combine the alignments, we start by taking the **intersection** of the two alignments, as shown in Fig. 25.25. The intersection will contain only places where the two alignments agree, hence the high-precision aligned words. We can also separately compute the **union** of these two alignments. The union will have lots of less accurately aligned words. We can then build a classifier to select words from the union, which we incrementally add back in to this minimal intersective alignment.

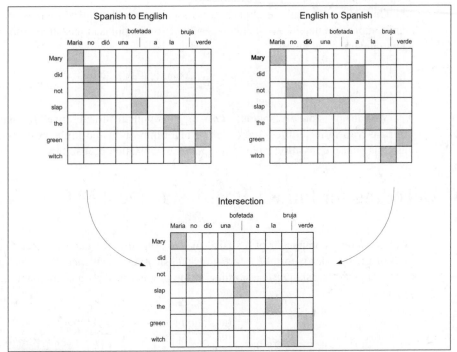

Figure 25.25 Intersection of English-to-Spanish and Spanish-to-English alignments to produce a high-precision alignment. Alignment can then be expanded with points from both alignments to produce an alignment like that shown in Fig. 25.26. After Koehn (2003b).

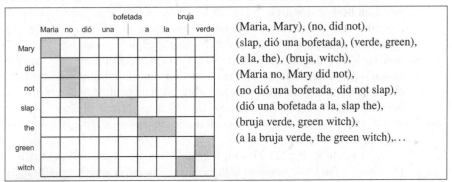

(Maria, Mary), (no, did not),
(slap, dió una bofetada), (verde, green),
(a la, the), (bruja, witch),
(Maria no, Mary did not),
(no dió una bofetada, did not slap),
(dió una bofetada a la, slap the),
(bruja verde, green witch),
(a la bruja verde, the green witch),...

Figure 25.26 A better phrasal alignment for the *green witch* sentence, computed by starting with the intersection alignment in Fig. 25.25 and adding points from the union alignment, using the algorithm of Och and Ney (2003). On the right, some of the phrases consistent with this alignment, after Koehn (2003b).

Figure 25.26 shows an example of the resulting word alignment. Note that it does allow many-to-one alignments in both directions. We can now harvest all phrase pairs that are consistent with this word alignment. A consistent phrase pair is one in which all the words are aligned only with each other and not to any external words. Figure 25.26 also shows some phrases consistent with the alignment.

Once we collect all the aligned phrases pairs from the entire training corpus, we can compute the maximum likelihood estimate for the phrase translation probability of a particular pair as follows:

$$\phi(\bar{f}, \bar{e}) = \frac{\text{count}(\bar{f}, \bar{e})}{\sum_{\bar{f}} \text{count}(\bar{f}, \bar{e})} \tag{25.30}$$

Phrase-translation table

We can now store each phrase $(\bar{f}, \bar{e})$, together with its probability $\phi(\bar{f}, \bar{e})$, in a large **phrase-translation table**. The decoding algorithm discussed in the next section can use this phrase translation table to compute the translation probability.

25.8   Decoding for Phrase-Based Statistical MT

The remaining component of a statistical MT system is the decoder. Recall that the job of the decoder is to take a foreign (Spanish) source sentence F and produce the best (English) translation E according to the product of the translation and language models:

$$\hat{E} = \underset{E \in \text{English}}{\text{argmax}} \quad \overbrace{P(F\ E)}^{\text{translation model}} \quad \overbrace{P(E)}^{\text{language model}} \tag{25.31}$$

Finding the sentence that maximizes the translation and language model probabilities is a **search** problem, and decoding is thus a kind of search. Decoders in MT are based on **best-first search**, a kind of **heuristic** or **informed search**; these are search algorithms that are informed by knowledge from the problem domain. Best-first search algorithms select a node n in the search space to explore, based on an evaluation function $f(r)$. MT decoders are variants of a specific kind of best-first search called **A*** search. A* search was first implemented for machine translation by IBM (Brown et al., 1995), based on IBM's earlier work on A* search for speech recognition (Jelinek, 1969). As we discussed in Section 10.2, for historical reasons A* search and

Stack decoding

its variants are commonly called **stack decoding** in speech recognition and sometimes also in machine translation.

Let's begin in Fig. 25.27 with a generic version of stack decoding for machine translation. The basic intuition is to maintain a **priority queue** (traditionally referred to as a **stack**) with all the partial translation hypotheses, together with their scores.

Let's now describe stack decoding in more detail. While the original IBM statistical decoding algorithms were for word-based MT, we will describe the application to phrase-based decoding in the publicly available MT decoder **Pharaoh** (Koehn, 2004). To limit the search space in decoding, we don't want to search through the space of all English sentences; we want to consider only the ones that are possible translations for F. To help reduce the search space, we want to consider only sentences that include words or phrases that are possible translations of words or phrases in the Spanish sentence F. We do this by searching the **phrase-translation table**, described in the previous section, for all possible English translations for all possible phrases in F.

```
function STACK DECODING(source sentence) returns target sentence

initialize stack with a null hypothesis
loop do
    pop best hypothesis h off of stack
    if h is a complete sentence, return h
    for each possible expansion h' of h
        assign a score to h'
        push h' onto stack
```

Figure 25.27   Generic version of stack or A* decoding for machine translation. A hypothesis is expanded by choosing a single word or phrase to translate. We show a more fleshed-out version of the algorithm in Fig. 25.30.

A sample lattice of possible translation options is shown in Fig. 25.28, drawn from Koehn (2003a, 2004). Each of these options consists of a Spanish word or phrase, the English translation, and the phrase translation probability ϕ. We'll need to search through combinations of these to find the best translation string.

Maria	no	dió	una	bofetada	a	la	bruja	verde
Mary	not	give	a	slap	to	the	witch	green
	did not			a slap	to		green witch	
	no		slap		to the			
	did not give				to			
					the			
			slap		the witch			

Figure 25.28   The lattice of possible English translations for words and phrases in a particular sentence F, taken from the entire aligned training set. After Koehn (2003a).

Now let's walk informally through the stack-decoding example in Fig. 25.29, producing an English translation of *Mary dió una bofetada a la bruja verde* left to right. For now we'll assume that there is a single stack and no pruning.

We start with the null hypothesis as the initial **search state**, in which we have selected no Spanish words and produced no English translation words. We now **expand** this hypothesis by choosing each possible source word or phrase that could generate an English sentence-initial phrase. Figure 25.29a shows this first ply of the search. For example, the top state represents the hypothesis that the English sentence starts with *Mary* and that the Spanish word *Maria* has been covered (the asterisk for the first word is marked with an M). Each state is also associated with a cost, discussed below. Another state at this ply represents the hypothesis that the English translation starts with the word *No*, and that Spanish *no* has been covered. This turns out to be the lowest-cost node on the queue, so we pop it off the queue and push all its expansions back on the queue. Now the state *Mary* is the lowest cost, so we expand it; *Mary did not* is now the lowest cost translation so far, so it will be the next to be expanded. We

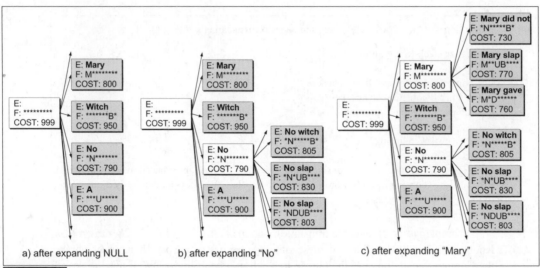

a) after expanding NULL   b) after expanding "No"   c) after expanding "Mary"

Figure 25.29 Three stages in stack decoding of *Maria no dió una bofetada a la bruja verde* (simplified by assuming a single stack and no pruning). The nodes in gray, on the fringe of the search space, are all on the stack, and are **open** nodes still involved in the search. Nodes in white are **closed** nodes that have been popped off the stack.

can then continue to expand the search space until we have states (hypotheses) that cover the entire Spanish sentence; we can just read off an English translation from this state.

We mentioned that each state is associated with a cost that, as we show below, is used to guide the search, The cost combines the **current cost** with an estimate of the **future cost**. The **current cost** is the total probability of the phrases that have been translated so far in the hypothesis, that is, the product of the translation, distortion, and language model probabilities. For the set of partially translated phrases $S = (F, E)$, this probability would be

$$\text{cost}(E, F) = \prod_{i \in S} \phi(\bar{f}_i, \bar{e}_i) d(a_i - b_{i-1}) P(E) \tag{25.32}$$

The **future cost** is our estimate of the cost of translating the *remaining* words in the Spanish sentence. By combining these two factors, the state cost gives an estimate of the total probability of the search path for the eventual complete translation sentence E passing through the current node. A search algorithm based only on the current cost would tend to select translations that had a few high-probability words at the beginning, at the expense of translations with a higher overall probability.[4] For the future cost, it turns out to be far too expensive to compute the true minimum probability for all possible translations. Instead, we approximate this cost by ignoring the distortion cost and just finding the sequence of English phrases that has the minimum product of the language model and translation model costs, which can be easily computed by the Viterbi algorithm.

---

[4] We saw this same kind of cost function for A* search in speech recognition, where we used the A* evaluation function: $f^*(p) = g(p) + h^*(p)$.

Beam search pruning

This sketch of the decoding process suggests that we search the entire state space of possible English translations. But we can't possibly afford to expand the entire search space, because there are far too many states; unlike the case in speech recognition, the need for distortion in MT means there is (at least) a distinct hypothesis for every possible ordering of the English words![5]

For this reason MT decoders, like decoders for speech recognition, all require some sort of pruning. Pharaoh and similar decoders use a version of **beam search pruning**, just as we saw in decoding for speech recognition and probabilistic parsing. Recall that in beam search pruning, at every iteration we keep only the most promising states and prune unlikely (high-cost) states (those "outside the search beam"). We could modify the search sequence depicted in Fig. 25.29, by pruning all bad (high-cost) states at every ply of the search and expanding only the best state. In fact, in Pharaoh, instead of expanding only the best state, we expand all states within the beam; thus, Pharaoh is technically **beam search** rather than **best-first search** or A* search.

More formally, at each ply of the search we keep around a stack (priority queue) of states. The stack fits only n entries. At every ply of the search, we expand all the states on the stack, push them onto the stack, order them by cost, keep the best n entries, and delete the rest.

We need one final modification. While in speech we just used one stack for stack decoding, in MT we use multiple stacks because we can't easily compare the cost of hypotheses that translate different numbers of foreign words. So we use m stacks, where stack s_m includes all hypotheses that cover m foreign words. When we expand a hypothesis by choosing a phrase to translate, we insert the new state into the correct stack for the number of foreign words covered. Then we use beam search inside each of these stacks, and keep only n hypotheses for each of the m stacks. The final multistack version of beam search stack decoding is shown in Fig. 25.30.

---

function BEAM SEARCH STACK DECODER(source sentence) **returns** target sentence

initialize hypothesisStack[0..nf]
push initial null hypothesis on hypothesisStack[0]
for $i \leftarrow 0$ to *nf-1*
  for each *hyp* in *hypothesisStack[i]*
    for each *new_hyp* that can be derived from *hyp*
      nf_new_hyp ← number of foreign words covered by *new_hyp*
      add *new_hyp* to hypothesisStack[nf_new_hyp]
      prune hypothesisStack[nf_new_hyp]
find best hypothesis *best_hyp* in hypothesisStack[nf]
return best path that leads to *best_hyp* via backtrace

Figure 25.30   Pharaoh beam search multistack decoding algorithm, adapted from (Koehn, 2003a). For efficiency, most decoders don't store the entire foreign and English sentence in each state, requiring that we backtrace to find the state path from the initial to the final state so that we can generate the entire English target sentence.

---

[5] Indeed, as Knight (1999a) shows, decoding even in IBM Model 1 with a bigram language model is equivalent to the difficult class of problems known as **NP-complete**.

A number of additional issues in decoding must be dealt with. All decoders attempt to limit somewhat the exponential explosion in the search space by **recombining hypotheses**. We saw hypothesis recombination in the **Exact *N*-Best** algorithm of Section 10.1. In MT, we can merge any two hypotheses that are sufficiently similar (cover the same foreign words, have the same last-two English words, and have the same end of the last foreign phrase covered).

In addition, it turns out that decoders for phrasal MT optimize a slightly different function than the one we presented in Eq. 25.31. In practice, it turns out that we need to add another factor, which serves to penalize sentences that are too short. Thus the decoder is actually choosing the sentence that maximizes

$$\hat{E} = \operatorname*{argmax}_{E \in \text{English}} \overbrace{P(F \mid E)}^{\text{translation model}} \overbrace{P(E)}^{\text{language model}} \overbrace{\omega^{\text{length}(E)}}^{\text{short sentence penalty}} \tag{25.33}$$

This final equation is extremely similar to the use of the word insertion penalty in speech recognition in Eq. 9.49.

25.9   MT Evaluation

Evaluating the quality of a translation is an extremely subjective task, and disagreements about methodology are rampant. Nevertheless, evaluation is essential, and research on evaluation methodology has played an important role from the earliest days of MT (Miller and Beebe-Center, 1958). Broadly speaking, translations are evaluated along two dimensions, corresponding to the **fidelity** and **fluency** discussed in Section 25.3.

25.9.1   Using Human Raters

The most accurate evaluations use human raters to evaluate each translation along each dimension. For example, along the dimension of **fluency**, we can ask how intelligible, how clear, how readable, or how natural the MT output (the target translated text) is. There are two broad ways to use human raters to answer these questions. One method is to give the raters a scale, for example, from 1 (totally unintelligible) to 5 (totally intelligible) and ask them to rate each sentence or paragraph of the MT output. We can use distinct scales for any of the aspects of fluency, such as **clarity**, **naturalness**, or **style**. The second class of methods relies less on the conscious decisions of the participants. For example, we can measure the time it takes for the raters to read each output sentence or paragraph. Clearer or more fluent sentences should be faster or easier to read. We can also measure fluency with the **cloze** task (Taylor, 1953, 1957). The cloze task is a metric often used in psychological studies of reading. The rater sees an output sentence with a word replaced by a space (for example, every 8th word might be deleted). Raters have to guess the identity of the missing word. Accuracy at the cloze task, that is, the average success of raters at guessing the missing words, generally correlates with how intelligible or natural the MT output is.

A similar variety of metrics can be used to judge the second dimension, **fidelity**. Two common aspects of fidelity that are measured are **adequacy** and **informativeness**.

Adequacy

The **adequacy** of a translation is judged by whether it contains the information that existed in the original. We measure adequacy by using raters to assign scores on a scale. If we have bilingual raters, we can give them the source sentence and a proposed target sentence, and rate, perhaps on a 5-point scale, how much of the information in the source was preserved in the target. If we only have monolingual raters but we have a good human translation of the source text, we can give the monolingual raters the human reference translation and a target machine translation and again rate how

Informativeness

much information is preserved. The **informativeness** of a translation is a task-based evaluation of whether the information in the MT output is sufficient to perform some task. For example we can give raters multiple-choice questions about the content of the material in the source sentence or text. The raters answer these questions based only on the MT output. The percentage of correct answers is an informativeness score.

Another set of metrics attempt to judge the overall quality of a translation, combining fluency and fidelity. For example, the typical evaluation metric for MT output to be

Edit cost
Post-editing

post-edited is the **edit cost** of **post-editing** the MT output into a good translation. For example, we can measure the number of words, the amount of time, or the number of keystrokes required for a human to correct the output to an acceptable level.

25.9.2   Automatic Evaluation: BLEU

While humans produce the best evaluations of machine translation output, running a human evaluation can be time consuming, taking days or even weeks. It is useful to have an automatic metric that can be run relatively frequently to quickly evaluate potential system improvements. To have such convenience, we would be willing for the metric to be much worse than human evaluation, as long as there was some correlation with human judgments.

In fact, there are a number of such heuristic methods, such as **BLEU**, **NIST**, **TER**, **Precision and Recall**, and **METEOR** (see the Historical Notes section). The intuition of these metrics derives from Miller and Beebe-Center (1958), who pointed out that a good MT output is one that is very similar to a human translation.

In the field of automatic speech recognition, we define "very similar" by the word error rate, which is the minimum edit distance to a human transcript. But in translation, we don't rely on a single human translation, because a source sentence could be legitimately translated in many ways. A very good MT output might look like one human translation, but very unlike another one. For this reason, MT metrics generally require that we have multiple human translations of each sentence in a test set. This may seem time consuming, but the hope is that we can reuse this translated test set over and over again to evaluate new ideas.

Now, given an MT output sentence in a test set, we compute the translation closeness between the MT output and the human sentences. An MT output is ranked as better if on average it is closer to the human translations. The metrics differ on what counts as "translation closeness".

For the rest of this section, let's walk through one of these metrics, the **BLEU** metric, following closely the original presentation in Papineni et al. (2002). In BLEU we rank each MT output by a weighted average of the number of *N*-gram overlaps with the human translations.

Figure 25.31 shows an intuition from two candidate translations of a Chinese source sentence (Papineni et al., 2002), shown with three reference human translations of the source sentence. Note that Candidate 1 shares many more words (shown in gray boxes) with the reference translations than does Candidate 2.

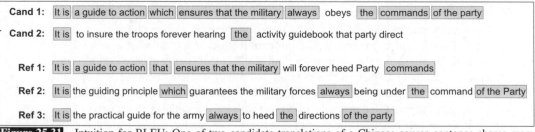

Figure 25.31 Intuition for BLEU: One of two candidate translations of a Chinese source sentence shares more words with the reference human translations.

Let's look at how the BLEU score is computed, starting with just unigrams. BLEU is based on precision. A basic unigram precision metric would be a count of the number of words in the candidate translation (MT output) that occur in some reference translation divided by the total number of words in the candidate translation. If a candidate translation had 10 words and 6 of them occurred in at least one of the reference translations, we would have a precision of $6/10 = 0.6$. Alas, there is a flaw in using simple precision: it rewards candidates that have extra repeated words. Figure 25.32 shows an example of a pathological candidate sentence composed of multiple instances of the single word *the*. Since each of the 7 (identical) words in the candidate occurs in one of the reference translations, the unigram precision would be 7/7!

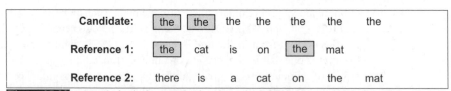

Figure 25.32 A pathological example showing why BLEU uses a modified precision metric. Unigram precision would be unreasonably high (7/7). Modified unigram precision is appropriately low (2/7).

Modified N-gram precision

To avoid this problem, BLEU uses a **modified *N*-gram precision** metric. We first count the maximum number of times a word is used in any single reference translation. The count of each *candidate* word is then clipped by this maximum *reference* count. Thus, the modified unigram precision in the example in Fig. 25.32 would be 2/7, since Reference 1 has a maximum of 2 *thes*. Going back to Chinese example in Fig. 25.31, Candidate 1 has a modified unigram precision of 17/18, and Candidate 2 has one of 8/14. We compute the modified precision similarly for higher order *N*-grams as well.

The modified bigram precision for Candidate 1 is 10/17, and for Candidate 2 is 1/13. Readers should check these numbers for themselves on Fig. 25.31.

To compute a score over the whole test set, BLEU first computes the N-gram matches for each sentence and sums the clipped counts over all the candidate sentences, then divides by the total number of candidate N-grams in the test set. The modified precision score is thus

$$p_n = \frac{\sum\limits_{C \in \text{ } Candidates} \sum\limits_{n\text{-}gram \in C} \text{Count}_{\text{clip}}(n\text{-}gram)}{\sum\limits_{C' \in \text{ } Candidates} \sum\limits_{n\text{-}gram' \in C'} \text{Count}(n\text{-}gram')} \tag{25.34}$$

BLEU uses unigrams, bigrams, trigrams, and often quadrigrams; it combines these modified N-gram precisions by taking their geometric mean.

In addition, BLEU penalizes candidate translations that are too short. Consider the candidate translation *of the*, compared with References 1–3 in Fig. 25.31 above. Because this candidate is so short and all its words appear in some translation, its modified unigram precision is inflated to 2/2. Normally, we deal with these problems by combining precision with *recall*. But as we discussed above, we can't use recall over multiple human translations, since recall would require (incorrectly) that a good translation must contain lots of N-grams from *every* translation. Instead, BLEU includes a brevity penalty over the whole corpus. Let c be the total length of the candidate translation corpus. We compute the **effective reference length** r for that corpus by summing, for each candidate sentence, the lengths of the best matches. The brevity penalty is then an exponential in r/c. In summary:

$$BP = \begin{cases} 1 & \text{if } c > r \\ e^{(1-r/c)} & \text{if } c \leq r \end{cases}$$

$$\text{BLEU} = BP \; \exp\left(\frac{1}{N}\sum_{n=1}^{N} \log p_n\right) \tag{25.35}$$

While automatic metrics like BLEU (or NIST, METEOR, etc) have been useful in quickly evaluating potential system improvements and they match human judgments in many cases, they have certain limitations that are important to consider. First, many of them focus only on local information. Consider slightly moving a phrase in Fig. 25.31 to produce a candidate like *Ensures that the military it is a guide to action which always obeys the commands of the party*. This sentence would have an identical BLEU score to Candidate 1, although a human rater would give it a lower score.

Furthermore, the automatic metrics probably do poorly at comparing systems that have radically different architectures. Thus, BLEU, for example, is known to perform poorly (i.e., not agree with human judgments of translation quality) when evaluating the output of commercial systems like Systran against N-gram-based statistical systems, or even when evaluating human-aided translation against machine translation (Callison-Burch et al., 2006). We can conclude that automatic metrics are most appropriate when evaluating incremental changes to a single system or comparing systems with very similar architectures.

25.10   Advanced: Syntactic Models for MT

The earliest statistical MT systems (like IBM Models 1, 2, and 3) were based on words as the elementary units. The phrase-based systems that we described in earlier sections improved on these word-based systems by using larger units, thus capturing larger contexts and providing a more natural unit for representing language divergences.

Recent work in MT has focused on ways to move even further up the Vauquois hierarchy, from simple phrases to larger and hierarchical syntactic structures.

It turns out that it doesn't work just to constrain each phrase to match the syntactic boundaries assigned by traditional parsers (Yamada and Knight, 2001). Instead, modern approaches attempt to assign a parallel syntactic tree structure to a pair of sentences in different languages, with the goal of translating the sentences by applying reordering operations on the trees. The mathematical model for these parallel structures is known
Transduction grammar as a **transduction grammar**. These transduction grammars can be viewed as an explicit implementation of the **syntactic transfer** systems that we introduced on page 871, but based on a modern statistical foundation.

Synchronous grammar A transduction grammar (also called a **synchronous grammar**) describes a structurally correlated pair of languages. From a generative perspective, we can view a transduction grammar as generating pairs of aligned sentences in two languages. Formally, a transduction grammar is a generalization of the finite-state transducers we saw in Chapter 3. A number of transduction grammars and formalisms are used for MT, most of which are generalizations of context-free grammars to the two-language situation. Let's consider one of the most widely used such models for MT, the **inversion**
Inversion transduction grammar **transduction grammar** (ITG).

In an ITG grammar, each non-terminal generates two separate strings. There are three types of these rules. A lexical rule like

$$N \rightarrow witch/bruja$$

generates the word *witch* on one stream and *bruja* on the second stream. A non-terminal rule in square brackets, like

$$S \rightarrow [NP\ VP]$$

generates two separate streams, each of *NP   VP*. A non-terminal in angle brackets, like

$$Nominal \rightarrow \langle Adj\ N \rangle$$

generates two separate streams, with *different orderings*: *Adj N* in one stream, and *N Adj* in the other stream.

Figure 25.33 shows a sample grammar with some simple rules. Note that each lexical rule derives distinct English and Spanish word strings, that rules in square brackets ([]) generate two identical non-terminal right-hand sides, and that the one rule in angle brackets (⟨⟩) generates different orderings in Spanish from English. An ITG parse tree is thus a single joint structure that spans the two observed sentences:

(25.36)   (a) [_S [_{NP} Mary] [_{VP} didn't [_{VP} slap [_{PP} [_{NP} the [_{Nom} green witch]]]]]]

(b) [_S [_{NP} María] [_{VP} no [_{VP} dió una bofetada [_{PP} a [_{NP} la [_{Nom} bruja verde]]]]]]

$$
\begin{array}{rl}
S & \rightarrow \ [NP\ VP] \\
NP & \rightarrow \ [Det\ Nominal] \qquad Maria/María \\
Nominal & \rightarrow \ \langle Adj\ Noun \rangle \\
VP & \rightarrow \ [V\ PP] \qquad [Negation\ VP] \\
Negation & \rightarrow \ didn't/no \\
V & \rightarrow \ slap/dió\ una\ bofetada \\
PP & \rightarrow \ [P\ NP] \\
P & \rightarrow \ \epsilon/a \qquad from/de \\
Det & \rightarrow \ the/la \quad \cdot the/le \\
Adj & \rightarrow \ green/verde \\
N & \rightarrow \ witch/bruja
\end{array}
$$

Figure 25.33   A mini Inversion Transduction Grammar for the *green witch* sentence.

Each non-terminal in the parse derives two strings, one for each language. Thus, we could visualize the two sentences in a single parse, where the angle brackets mean that the order of the *Adj N* constituents *green witch* and *bruja verde* are generated in opposite order in the two languages:

[S [NP Mary/María] [VP didn't/no [VP slap/dió una bofetada [PP ε/a [NP the/la ⟨Nom witch/bruja green/verde⟩]]]]]

Related kinds of synchronous grammars include synchronous context-free grammars (Chiang, 2005), multitext grammars (Melamed, 2003), lexicalized ITGs (Melamed, 2003; Zhang and Gildea, 2005), and synchronous tree-adjoining and tree-insertion grammars (Shieber and Schabes, 1992; Shieber, 1994b; Nesson et al., 2006). The synchronous CFG system of Chiang (2005), for example, learns hierarchical pairs of rules that capture the fact that Chinese relative clauses appear to the left of their head, while English relative clauses appear to the right of their head:

<① de ②,   the ② that ①>

Other models for translation align parallel parse trees (Wu, 2000; Yamada and Knight, 2001; Eisner, 2003; Melamed, 2003; Galley et al., 2004; Quirk et al., 2005; Wu and Fung, 2005).

25.11   Advanced: IBM Model 3 and Fertility

The seminal IBM paper that began work on statistical MT proposed five models for MT. We saw IBM's Model 1 in Section 25.5.1. Models 3, 4, and 5 all use the important concept of **fertility**. We introduce Model 3 in this section; our description here is influenced by Kevin Knight's nice tutorial (Knight, 1999b). Model 3 has a more complex generative model than Model 1. The generative model from an English sentence $E = e_1, e_2, ..., e_I$ has five steps.

Fertility

1. For each English word e_i, we choose a **fertility** ϕ_i.[6] The fertility is the number of (zero or more) Spanish words that will be generated from e_i and depends only on e_i.

Spurious word

2. We also need to generate Spanish words from the NULL English word. Recall that we defined these earlier as **spurious words**. Instead of having a fertility for NULL, we generate spurious words differently. Every time we generate an English word, we consider (with some probability) generating a spurious word (from NULL).

3. We now know how many Spanish words to generate from each English word. So now for each of these Spanish potential words, generate it by translating its aligned English word. As with Model 1, the translation will be based only on the English word. Spurious Spanish words will be generated by translating the NULL word into Spanish.

4. Move all the non-spurious words into their final positions in the Spanish sentence.

5. Insert the spurious Spanish words in the remaining open positions in the Spanish sentence.

Figure 25.34 illustrates the Model 3 generative process.

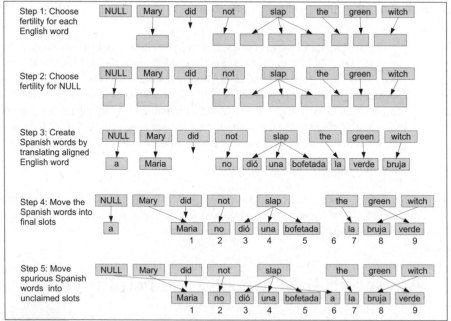

Figure 25.34 The five steps of IBM Model 3 for generating a Spanish sentence and alignment from an English sentence.

n
t
d
p1

Model 3 has more parameters than Model 1. The most important are the **n**, **t**, **d**, and **p1** probabilities. The fertility probability ϕ_i of a word e_i is represented by the

---

[6] This ϕ is not related to the ϕ that was used in phrase-based translation.

parameter n. So we use $n(1\ green)$ to represent the probability that English *green* will produce one Spanish word, $n(2\ green)$ is the probability that English *green* will produce two Spanish words, $n(0\ did)$ is the probability that English *did* will produce no Spanish words, and so on. Like IBM Model 1, Model 3 has a translation probability $t(f_j\ e_i)$. Next, the probability that expresses the word position that English words end

Distortion

up in the Spanish sentence is the **distortion** probability, which is conditioned on the English and Spanish sentence lengths. The distortion probability $d(1,3,6,7)$ expresses the probability that the English word e_1 will align to Spanish word f_3, given that the English sentence has length 6, and the Spanish sentence is of length 7.

As we suggested above, Model 3 does not use fertility probabilities like $n(1\ NULL)$, or $n(3\ NULL)$ to decide how many spurious foreign words to generate from English NULL. Instead, each time Model 3 generates a real word, it generates a spurious word for the target sentence with probability p_1. This way, longer source sentences will naturally generate more spurious words. Figure 25.35 shows a slightly more detailed version of the five steps of the Model 3 generative story using these parameters.

---

1. **for each** English word e_i, $1 < i < I$, we choose a fertility ϕ_i with probability $n(\phi_i\ e_i)$
2. Using these fertilities and p_1, determine ϕ_0, the number of spurious Spanish words, and hence m.
3. **for each** i, $0 < i < I$
    for each k, $1 < k < \phi_i$
      Choose a Spanish word τ_{ik} with probability $t(\tau_{ik}, e_i)$
4. **for each** i, $1 < i < I$
    for each k, $1 < k < \phi_i$
      Choose a target Spanish position π_{ik} with probability $d(\pi_{ik}, i, I, J)$
5. **for each** k, $1 < k < \phi_0$
    Choose a target Spanish position π_{0k} from one of the available Spanish slots, for a total probability of $\frac{1}{\phi_0!}$

Figure 25.35   The Model 3 generative story for generating a Spanish sentence from an English sentence. Remember that we are not translating from English to Spanish; this is just the generative component of the noisy channel model. Adapted from Knight (1999b).

Switching for a moment to the task of French to English translation, Fig. 25.36 shows some of the t and ϕ parameters learned for French-English translation from Brown et al. (1993). Note that *the* in general translates to a French article like *le*, but sometimes it has a fertility of 0, indicating that English uses an article where French does not. Conversely, note that *farmers* prefers a fertility of 2, and the most likely translations are *agriculteurs* and *les*, indicating that here French tends to use an article where English does not.

Now that we have seen the generative story for Model 3, let's build the equation for the probability assigned by the model. The model needs to assign a probability $P(F\ E)$ of generating the Spanish sentence F from the English sentence E. As we did with Model 1, we'll start by showing how the model gives the probability $P(F, A\ E)$, the probability of generating sentence F with a particular alignment A. Then we'll sum over all alignments to get the total $P(F\ E)$.

	the				*farmers*				*not*		
f	$t(f\,e)$	ϕ	$n(\phi\,e)$	f	$t(f\,e)$	ϕ	$n(\phi\,e)$	f	$t(f\,e)$	ϕ	$n(\phi\,e)$
le	0.497	1	0.746	agriculteurs	0.442	2	0.731	ne	0.497	2	0.735
la	0.207	0	0.254	les	0.418	1	0.228	pas	0.442	0	0.154
les	0.155			cultivateurs	0.046	0	0.039	non	0.029	1	0.107
l'	0.086			producteurs	0.021			rien	0.011		
ce	0.018										
cette	0.011										

Figure 25.36 Examples of Model 3 parameters from the Brown et al. (1993) French-English translation system, for three English words. Note that both *farmers* and *not* are likely to have fertilities of 2.

To compute $P(F,A\,E)$, we need to multiply the main three factors n, t, and d, for generating words, translating them into Spanish, and moving them around. So a first pass at $P(F,A\,E)$ would be

$$\prod_{i=1}^{I} n(\phi_i\,e_i) \quad \prod_{j=1}^{J} t(f_j\,e_{a_j}) \quad \prod_{j=1}^{J} d(j\,a_j,I,J) \tag{25.37}$$

But (25.37) isn't sufficient as it stands; we need to add factors for generating spurious words, for inserting them into the available slots, and for representing the number of ways (permutations) a word can align with multiple words. Equation 25.38 gives the true final equation for IBM Model 3 in Knight's modification of the original formula. We don't give the details of these additional factors, but encourage the interested reader to see the original presentation in Brown et al. (1993) and the very clear explanation of the equation in Knight (1999b).

$$P(F,A\,E) = \overbrace{\binom{J-\phi_0}{\phi_0} p_0^{J-2\phi_0} p_1^{\phi_0}}^{\text{generate spurious}} \quad \overbrace{\frac{1}{\phi_0!}}^{\text{insert spurious}} \quad \overbrace{\prod_{i=0}^{I} \phi_i!}^{\text{multi-align permutations}}$$

$$\prod_{i=1}^{I} n(\phi_i\,e_i) \quad \prod_{j=1}^{J} t(f_j\,e_{a_j}) \quad \prod_{j:a_j\neq 0}^{J} d(j\,a_j,I,J) \tag{25.38}$$

Once again, to get the total probability of the Spanish sentence we sum over all possible alignments:

$$P(F\,E) = \sum_{A} P(F,A\,E)$$

We can also make it more explicit exactly how we sum over alignments (and also emphasize the incredibly large number of possible alignments) by expressing this formula as follows, where we specify an alignment by specifying the aligned English a_j for each of the J words in the foreign sentence:

$$P(F\,E) = \sum_{a_1=0}^{J} \sum_{a_2=0}^{J} \quad \sum_{a_J=0}^{I} P(F,A\,E)$$

25.11.1   Training for Model 3

Given a parallel corpus, training the translation model for IBM Model 3 means setting values for the n, d, t, and p_1 parameters.

As we noted for Model 1 and HMM models, if the training-corpus were hand-labeled with perfect alignments, getting maximum likelihood estimates would be simple. Consider the probability $n(0\ did)$ that a word like *did* would have a zero fertility. We could estimate this from an aligned corpus just by counting the number of times *did* aligned to nothing and normalize by the total count of *did*. We can do similar things for the t translation probabilities. To train the distortion probability $d(1,3,6,7)$, we similarly count the number of times in the corpus that English word e_1 maps to Spanish word f_3 in English sentences of length 6 that are aligned to Spanish sentences of length 7. Let's call this counting function dcount. We again need a normalization factor:

$$d(1,3,6,7) = \frac{\text{dcount}(1,3,6,7)}{\sum_{i=1}^{I} \text{dcount}(i,3,6,7)} \qquad (25.39)$$

Finally, we need to estimate p_1. Again, we look at all the aligned sentences in the corpus; let's assume that the Spanish sentences contain a total of N words. From the alignments for each sentence, we determine that a total of S Spanish words are spurious, that is, aligned to English NULL. Thus, $N - S$ of the words in the Spanish sentences were generated by real English words. After S of these $N - S$ Spanish words, we generate a spurious word. The probability p_1 is thus $S/(N - S)$.

Of course, we don't have hand-alignments for Model 3. We need to use EM to learn the alignments and the probability model simultaneously. With Model 1 and the HMM model, there were efficient ways to do training without explicitly summing over all alignments. Unfortunately, this is not true for Model 3; we actually would need to compute all possible alignments. For a real pair of sentences, with 20 English words and 20 Spanish words, and allowing NULL and allowing fertilities, there are a very large number of possible alignments (determining the exact number of possible alignments is left as Exercise 25.7). Instead, we approximate by considering only the best few alignments. To find the best alignments without looking at all alignments, we can use an iterative or bootstrapping approach. In the first step, we train the simpler IBM Model 1 or 2 as discussed above. We then use these Model 2 parameters to evaluate $P(A\ E,F)$, giving a way to find the best alignments to bootstrap Model 3. See Brown et al. (1993) and Knight (1999b) for details.

25.12   Advanced: Log-Linear Models for MT

While statistical MT was first based on the noisy channel model, much recent work combines the language and translation models through a log-linear model in which we directly search for the sentence with the highest posterior probability:

$$\hat{E} = \underset{E}{\operatorname{argmax}} P(E\ F) \qquad (25.40)$$

We do this by modeling $P(E|F)$ through a set of M feature functions $h_m(E,F)$, each of which has a parameter λ_m. The translation probability is then

$$P(E|F) = \frac{\exp[\sum_{m=1}^{M} \lambda_m h_m(E,F)]}{\sum_{E'} \exp[\sum_{m=1}^{M} \lambda_m h_m(E',F)]} \tag{25.41}$$

The best sentence is thus

$$
\begin{aligned}
\hat{E} &= \operatorname*{argmax}_{E} P(E|F) \\
&= \operatorname*{argmax}_{E} \exp[\sum_{m=1}^{M} \lambda_m h_m(E,F)]
\end{aligned}
\tag{25.42}
$$

In practice, the noisy channel model factors (the language model $P(E)$ and translation model $P(F|E)$) are still the most important feature functions in the log-linear model, but the architecture has the advantage of allowing for arbitrary other features as well; a common set of features would include the following:

- Language model $P(E)$.
- Translation model $P(F|E)$.
- *Reverse translation model* **Reverse translation model** $P(E|F)$.
- Lexicalized versions of both translation models.
- *Word penalty* **Word penalty**.
- *Phrase penalty* **Phrase penalty**.
- *Unknown-word penalty* **Unknown-word penalty**.

See Foster (2000), Och and Ney (2002, 2004) for more details.

Log-linear models for MT could be trained with the standard maximum mutual information criterion. In practice, however, log-linear models are instead trained to directly optimize evaluation metrics like BLEU in a method known as **Minimum Error Rate Training**, or **MERT** (Och, 2003; Chou et al., 1993).

25.13   Summary

Machine translation is an exciting field that has both theoretical and practical interest, and recent theoretical advances have enabled commercial deployment on the Web.

- Languages have many **divergences**, both structural and lexical, that make translation difficult.
- The field of **typology** investigates some of these differences; languages can be classified by their position along typological dimensions like SVO/VSO/etc.
- Three paradigms for **classic MT** include the **direct**, **transfer**, and **interlingua** approaches.
- Statistical MT is based on combining a **translation model** and a **language model** in the noisy channel model.

- **Phrase-based MT** is the main paradigm for statistical machine translation, based on a bilingual **phrase table**.
- Models such as the **IBM Model 1**, **HMM**, and **IBM Model 3** models, are important for generating the alignments from which phrase tables can be extracted.
- These **alignment models** can also be used in MT decoding.
- **Stack decoding** with **beam search pruning** can be used for decoding in phrase-based MT.
- Automatic Evaluation metrics for MT include **BLEU**, **TER**, **METEOR**, and **precision and recall**.
- Modern statistical MT systems are **log-linear models** trained with **MERT**.

Bibliographical and Historical Notes

Work on models of the process and goals of translation goes back at least to Saint Jerome in the fourth century (Kelley, 1979). The development of logical languages, free of the imperfections of human languages, for reasoning correctly and for communicating truths and thereby also for translation, has been pursued at least since the 1600s (Hutchins, 1986).

By the late 1940s, scant years after the birth of the electronic computer, the idea of MT was raised seriously (Weaver, 1955). In 1954, the first public demonstration of an MT system prototype (Dostert, 1955) led to great excitement in the press (Hutchins, 1997). The next decade saw a great flowering of ideas, prefiguring most subsequent developments. But this work was ahead of its time—implementations were limited by, for example, the fact that pending the development of disks there was no good way to store dictionary information.

As high-quality MT proved elusive (Bar-Hillel, 1960), there grew a consensus on the need for better evaluation and more basic research in the new fields of formal and computational linguistics. This consensus culminated in the famous ALPAC (Automatic Language Processing Advisory Committee) report of 1966 (Pierce et al., 1966) that led in the mid 1960s to a dramatic cut in funding for MT. As MT research lost academic respectability, the Association for Machine Translation and Computational Linguistics dropped MT from its name. Some MT developers, however, persevered, such as Systran, developed initially by Peter Toma, which has been continuously improved over 40 years. Another early MT system was Météo, which translated weather forecasts from English to French; incidentally, its original implementation (1976) used "Q-systems", an early unification model.

The late 1970s saw the birth of another wave of academic interest in MT. One strand attempted to apply meaning-based techniques developed for story understanding and knowledge engineering (Carbonell et al., 1981). There were wide discussions of interlingual ideas through the late 1980s and early 1990s (Tsujii, 1986; Nirenburg et al., 1992; Ward, 1994; Carbonell et al., 1992). Meanwhile, MT usage was increasing, fueled by globalization, government policies requiring the translation of all documents into multiple official languages, and the proliferation of word processors and then personal computers.

Modern statistical methods began to be applied in the early 1990s, enabled by the development of large bilingual corpora and the growth of the Web. Early on, a number of researchers showed that it was possible to extract pairs of aligned sentences from bilingual corpora (Kay and Röscheisen, 1988, 1993; Warwick and Russell, 1990; Brown et al., 1991; Gale and Church, 1991, 1993). The earliest algorithms made use of the words of the sentence as part of the alignment model; others relied solely on other cues like sentence length in words or characters.

At the same time, the IBM group, drawing directly on algorithms for speech recognition (many of which had themselves been developed originally at IBM!) proposed the *Candide* **Candide** system, based on the IBM statistical models we have described (Brown et al., 1990, 1993). These papers described the probabilistic model and the parameter estimation procedure. The decoding algorithm was never published, but it was described in a patent filing (Brown et al., 1995). The IBM work had a huge impact on the research community, and by the turn of this century, much or most academic research on machine translation was statistical. Progress was made hugely easier by the development *EGYPT* of publicly available toolkits, particularly tools extended from the **EGYPT** toolkit developed by the Statistical Machine Translation team during the summer 1999 research workshop at the Center for Language and Speech Processing at the Johns Hopkins *GIZA++* University. These include the **GIZA++** aligner, developed by Franz Josef Och by extending the GIZA toolkit (Och and Ney, 2003), which implements IBM models 1–5 as well as the HMM alignment model.

Most early implementations focused on IBM Model 3, but very quickly researchers moved to phrase-based models. While the earliest phrase-based translation model was IBM Model 4 (Brown et al., 1993), modern models derive from Och's (1998) work on **alignment templates**. Key phrase-based translation models include Marcu and Wong (2002), Zens et al. (2002), Venugopal et al. (2003), Koehn et al. (2003), Tillmann (2003) Och and Ney (2004), Deng and Byrne (2005), and Kumar and Byrne (2005).

Other work on MT decoding includes the A^* decoders of Wang and Waibel (1997) and Germann et al. (2001), and the polynomial-time decoder for binary-branching stochastic transduction grammar of Wu (1996).

Moses The most recent open-source MT toolkit is the phrase-based **Moses** system (Koehn et al., 2006; Koehn and Hoang, 2007; Zens and Ney, 2007). Moses developed out of the *Pharaoh* **Pharaoh** publicly available phrase-based stack decoder, developed by Philipp Koehn (Koehn, 2004, 2003b), which extended both the A^* decoders of (Och et al., 2001) and Brown et al. (1995) and the EGYPT tools discussed above. Commercial statistical MT systems like Google's were widely commercially deployed by 2007.

Modern research continues on sentence and word alignment as well; more recent algorithms include Moore (2002, 2005), Fraser and Marcu (2005), Callison-Burch et al. (2005), Liu et al. (2005).

Research on evaluation of machine translation began quite early. Miller and Beebe-Center (1958) proposed a number of methods drawing on work in psycholinguistics. These included the use of cloze and Shannon tasks to measure intelligibility as well as a metric of edit distance from a human translation, the intuition that underlies all modern automatic evaluation metrics like BLEU. The ALPAC report included an early evaluation study conducted by John Carroll that was extremely influential (Pierce et al., 1966, Appendix 10). Carroll proposed distinct measures for fidelity and intelligibility, and had raters score them subjectively on 9-point scales. More recent work on evaluation has focused on coming up with automatic metrics, include the work on BLEU discussed in Section 25.9.2 (Papineni et al., 2002), as well as related measures like **NIST** (Doddington, 2002), **TER (Translation Error Rate)** (Snover et al., 2006), **Precision and Recall** (Turian et al., 2003), and **METEOR** (Banerjee and Lavie, 2005). Statistical significance for these metrics is often computed by methods such as approximate randomization (Noreen, 1989; Riezler and Maxwell III, 2005).

Good surveys of the early history of MT are Hutchins (1986) and (1997). The textbook by Hutchins and Somers (1992) has a wealth of examples of language phenomena and summaries of historically significant MT systems. Nirenburg et al. (2002) is a comprehensive collection of classic readings in MT. Knight (1999b) is an excellent tutorial introduction to statistical MT.

Academic papers on machine translation appear in standard NLP journals and conferences, as well as in the journal *Machine Translation* and in the proceedings of various conferences, including MT Summit, organized by the International Association for Machine Translation, the individual conferences of its three regional divisions (Association for MT in the Americas – AMTA, European Association for MT – EAMT, and Asia-Pacific Association for MT – AAMT), and the Conference on Theoretical and Methodological Issues in Machine Translation (TMI).

Exercises

25.1 Select at random a paragraph of Chapter 12 that describes a fact about English syntax. a) Describe and illustrate how your favorite foreign language differs in this respect. b) Explain how an MT system could deal with this difference.

25.2 Choose a foreign language novel in a language you know. Copy down the shortest sentence on the first page. Now look up the rendition of that sentence in an English translation of the novel. a) For both original and translation, draw parse trees. b) For both original and translation, draw dependency structures. c) Draw a case structure representation of the meaning that the original and translation share. d) What does this exercise suggest to you regarding intermediate representations for MT?

25.3 Version 1 (for native English speakers): Consider the following sentence:

> These lies are like their father that begets them; gross as a mountain, open, palpable.　　　　　　　　　　　　　　　　　　Henry IV, Part 1, act 2, scene 2

Translate this sentence into some dialect of modern vernacular English, such as the style of a *New York Times* editorial, an *Economist* opinion piece, or your favorite television talk-show host.

Version 2 (for native speakers of other languages): Translate the following sentence into your native language.

One night my friend Tom, who had just moved into a new apartment, saw a cockroach scurrying about in the kitchen.

For either version, now:

a) Describe how you did the translation: What steps did you perform? In what order did you do them? Which steps took the most time? b) Could you write a program that would translate by the same methods that you did? Why or why not? c) What aspects were hardest for you? Would they be hard for an MT system? d) What aspects would be hardest for an MT system? Are they hard for people too? e) Which models are best for describing various aspects of your process (direct, transfer, interlingua, or statistical)? f) Now compare your translation with those produced by friends or classmates. What is different? Why were the translations different?

25.4 Type a sentence into any MT system and see what it outputs. a) List the problems with the translation. b) Rank these problems in order of severity. c) For the two most severe problems, suggest the probable root cause.

25.5 Build a very simple, direct MT system for translating from some language you know at least somewhat into English (or into a language in which you are relatively fluent), as follows. a) First, find some good test sentences in the source language. Reserve half of these as a development test set, and half as an unseen test set. Next, acquire a bilingual dictionary for these two languages (for many languages, limited dictionaries can be found on the Web that will be sufficient for this exercise). Your program should translate each word by looking up its translation in your dictionary. You may need to implement some stemming or simple morphological analysis. b) Next, examine your output, and do a preliminary error analysis on the development test set. What are the major sources of error? c) Write some general rules for correcting the translation mistakes. You will probably want to run a part-of-speech tagger on the English output, if you have one. d) Then see how well your system runs on the test set.

25.6 Continue the calculations for the EM example on page 887, performing the second and third round of E-steps and M-steps.

25.7 (Derived from Knight (1999b)) How many possible Model 3 alignments are there between a 20-word English sentence and a 20-word Spanish sentence, allowing for NULL and fertilities?

Credits

Fig. 25.35 (© the authors; thanks to the Association of Computational Linguistics, the *Journal of Computational Linguistics* and its editor Robert Dale, and to Kevin Knight)

Figs. 25.25, 25.26, and 25.28 (© the authors; thanks to the Association of Computational Linguistics, the *Journal of Computational Linguistics* and its editor Robert Dale, and to Philipp Koehn)

Index

Page references followed by "f" indicate illustrated figures or photographs; followed by "t" indicates a table.